# HAESE & HARRIS PUBLICATIONS

Specialists in mathematics publishing

# Mathematics
## for the international student
## Mathematical Studies SL
### second edition

Mal Coad

Glen Whiffen

Marjut Mäenpää

Mark Humphries

James

Michael

Sandra

for use
IB Diploma
Programme

# MATHEMATICS FOR THE INTERNATIONAL STUDENT
## Mathematical Studies SL second edition

Mal Coad            B.Ec., Dip.T.
Glen Whiffen        B.Sc., B.Ed.
Marjut Mäenpää      B.Sc., Dip.Ed.
Mark Humphries      B.Sc.(Hons.)
James Foley         B.Ma.Comp.Sc.(Hons.)
Michael Haese       B.Sc.(Hons.), Ph.D.
Sandra Haese        B.Sc.

Haese & Harris Publications
3 Frank Collopy Court, Adelaide Airport, SA 5950, AUSTRALIA
Telephone: +61 8 8355 9444, Fax: + 61 8 8355 9471
Email: info@haeseandharris.com.au
Web: www.haeseandharris.com.au

National Library of Australia Card Number & ISBN 978-1-921500-13-8

© Haese & Harris Publications 2010

Published by Raksar Nominees Pty Ltd.
3 Frank Collopy Court, Adelaide Airport, SA 5950, AUSTRALIA

| | |
|---|---|
| First Edition | 2004 |
| *Reprinted* | 2005 three times *(with minor corrections)*, 2006, 2007, 2008 twice, 2009 |
| Second Edition | 2010 |
| *Reprinted* | 2011 |

Cartoon artwork by John Martin. Artwork by Piotr Poturaj and David Purton.
Cover design by Piotr Poturaj.
Computer software by David Purton, Thomas Jansson and Troy Cruickshank.

Typeset in Australia by Susan Haese and Charlotte Sabel (Raksar Nominees).

Typeset in Times Roman $10\frac{1}{2}/11\frac{1}{2}$.

The textbook and its accompanying CD have been developed independently of the International Baccalaureate Organization (IBO). The textbook and CD are in no way connected with, or endorsed by, the IBO.

# FOREWORD

**Mathematics for the International Student: Mathematical Studies SL** has been written for use with the two-year Mathematical Studies SL course, which is one of the courses of study in the IB Diploma Programme. It is not our intention to define the course. Teachers are encouraged to use other resources. We have developed this book independently of the International Baccalaureate Organization (IBO) in consultation with many experienced teachers of IB Mathematics. The text is not endorsed by the IBO.

The second edition builds on the strength of the first edition. The main difference in this second edition is the inclusion of more questions in the book and the addition of **◄꜀) Self Tutor** on the CD. Extra questions have been included throughout, and a new final chapter with 200 exam-style questions has been added. A clear distinction is made between core (examinable) and extension material and syllabus references are given for each chapter.

Comprehensive graphics calculator instructions are given for Casio fx-9860G, TI-84 Plus and TI-$n$spire in an introductory chapter (see p. 15) and, occasionally, where additional help may be needed, more detailed instructions are available as printable pages on the CD. The extensive use of graphics calculators and computer packages throughout the book enables students to realise the importance, application and appropriate use of technology. No single aspect of technology has been favoured. It is as important that students work with a pen and paper as it is that they use their calculator or graphics calculator, or use a spreadsheet or graphing package on computer.

This package is language rich and technology rich. The combination of textbook and interactive Student CD will foster the mathematical development of students in a stimulating way. Frequent use of the interactive features on the CD is certain to nurture a much deeper understanding and appreciation of mathematical concepts. The CD also offers **◄꜀) Self Tutor** for every worked example. **◄꜀) Self Tutor** is accessed via the CD – click anywhere on any worked example to hear a teacher's voice explain each step in that worked example. This is ideal for catch-up and revision, or for motivated students who want to do some independent study outside school hours.

The interactive features of the CD allow immediate access to our own specially designed geometry software, graphing software and more. Teachers are provided with a quick and easy way to demonstrate concepts, and students can discover for themselves and revisit when necessary.

It is not our intention that each chapter be worked through in full. Time constraints will not allow for this. Teachers must select exercises carefully, according to the abilities and prior knowledge of their students, to make the most efficient use of time and give as thorough coverage of work as possible. Investigations throughout the book will add to the discovery aspect of the course and enhance student understanding and learning.

In this changing world of mathematics education, we believe that the contextual approach shown in this book, with the associated use of technology, will enhance the students' understanding, knowledge and appreciation of mathematics, and its universal application.

We welcome your feedback.    Email:   *info@haeseandharris.com.au*
                              Web:     *www.haeseandharris.com.au*

MC   GAW   EMM   MAH

JMF   PMH   SHH

# ACKNOWLEDGEMENTS

The authors and publishers would like to thank all those teachers who offered advice and encouragement on both the first and second editions of this book. Many of them read the page proofs and offered constructive comments and suggestions. These teachers include: Cameron Hall, Fran O'Connor, Glenn Smith, Anne Walker, Ian Hilditch, Phil Moore, Julie Wilson, Kestie Nelligan, Carolyn Farr. To anyone we may have missed, we offer our apologies.

The publishers wish to make it clear that acknowledging these individuals does not imply any endorsement of this book by any of them, and all responsibility for the content rests with the authors and publishers.

# USING THE INTERACTIVE STUDENT CD

The interactive CD is ideal for independent study.

Students can revisit concepts taught in class and undertake their own revision and practice. The CD also has the text of the book, allowing students to leave the textbook at school and keep the CD at home.

By clicking on the relevant icon, a range of interactive features can be accessed:

INTERACTIVE LINK

- **◄) Self Tutor**
- Graphics calculator instructions
- Interactive links to spreadsheets, graphing and geometry software, computer demonstrations and simulations

**Graphics calculator instructions**: where additional help may be needed, detailed instructions are available on the CD, as printable pages. Click on the relevant icon for TI-*n*spire, TI-84 Plus or Casio fx-9860G.

**SELF TUTOR** is an exciting feature of this book.

The **◄) Self Tutor** icon on each worked example denotes an active link on the CD.

Simply 'click' on the **◄) Self Tutor** (or anywhere in the example box) to access the worked example, with a teacher's voice explaining each step necessary to reach the answer.

Play any line as often as you like. See how the basic processes come alive using movement and colour on the screen.

Ideal for students who have missed lessons or need extra help.

---

### Example 8         Self Tutor

Construct a truth table for the compound proposition $(p \vee q) \wedge r$.

To find $(p \vee q) \wedge r$, we must first find $p \vee q$. We then find the conjunction of $p \vee q$ and $r$.

| $p$ | $q$ | $r$ | $p \vee q$ | $(p \vee q) \wedge r$ |
|---|---|---|---|---|
| T | T | T | T | T |
| T | T | F | T | F |
| T | F | T | T | T |
| T | F | F | T | F |
| F | T | T | T | T |
| F | T | F | T | F |
| F | F | T | F | F |
| F | F | F | F | F |

See **Chapter 17, Logic**, p. 542

# TABLE OF CONTENTS

# SYMBOLS AND NOTATION USED IN THIS BOOK

| | | | |
|---|---|---|---|
| $\mathbb{N}$ | the set of positive integers and zero, $\{0, 1, 2, 3, ......\}$ | $\equiv$ | identity or is equivalent to |
| $\mathbb{Z}$ | the set of integers, $\{0, \pm 1, \pm 2, \pm 3, ......\}$ | $\approx$ | is approximately equal to |
| $\mathbb{Z}^+$ | the set of positive integers, $\{1, 2, 3, ......\}$ | $>$ | is greater than |
| $\mathbb{Q}$ | the set of rational numbers | $\geq$ or $\geqslant$ | is greater than or equal to |
| $\mathbb{Q}^+$ | the set of positive rational numbers, $\{x \mid x > 0, \ x \in \mathbb{Q}\}$ | $<$ | is less than |
| $\mathbb{R}$ | the set of real numbers | $\leq$ or $\leqslant$ | is less than or equal to |
| $\mathbb{R}^+$ | the set of positive real numbers, $\{x \mid x > 0, \ x \in \mathbb{R}\}$ | $u_n$ | the $n$th term of a sequence or series |
| $\{x_1, x_2, ....\}$ | the set with elements $x_1, x_2, ....$ | $d$ | the common difference of an arithmetic sequence |
| $n(A)$ | the number of elements in set $A$ | $r$ | the common ratio of a geometric sequence |
| $\{x \mid ....\}$ | the set of all $x$ such that | $S_n$ | the sum of the first $n$ terms of a sequence, $u_1 + u_2 + .... + u_n$ |
| $\in$ | is an element of | $\displaystyle\sum_{i=1}^{n} u_i$ | $u_1 + u_2 + .... + u_n$ |
| $\notin$ | is not an element of | | |
| $\varnothing$ | the empty (null) set | $f : A \rightarrow B$ | $f$ is a function under which each element of set $A$ has an image in set $B$ |
| $U$ | the universal set | $f : x \mapsto y$ | $f$ is a function which maps $x$ onto $y$ |
| $\cup$ | union | $f(x)$ | the image of $x$ under the function $f$ |
| $\cap$ | intersection | $\displaystyle\lim_{x \to a} f(x)$ | the limit of $f(x)$ as $x$ tends to $a$ |
| $\subset$ | is a proper subset of | | |
| $\subseteq$ | is a subset of | $\dfrac{dy}{dx}$ | the derivative of $y$ with respect to $x$ |
| $A'$ | the complement of the set $A$ | $f'(x)$ | the derivative of $f(x)$ with respect to $x$ |
| $p \Rightarrow q$ | implication 'if $p$ then $q$' | $\dfrac{d^2 y}{dx^2}$ | the second derivative of $y$ with respect to $x$ |
| $p \Leftrightarrow q$ | equivalence '$p$ is equivalent to $q$' | $f''(x)$ | the second derivative of $f(x)$ with respect to $x$ |
| $p \wedge q$ | conjunction '$p$ and $q$' | | |
| $p \vee q$ | disjunction '$p$ or $q$' | sin, cos, tan | the circular functions |
| $p \underline{\vee} q$ | exclusive disjunction '$p$ or $q$ but not both' | $A(x, y)$ | the point A in the plane with Cartesian coordinates $x$ and $y$ |
| $\neg p$ | negation 'not $p$' | AB | the line through A and B, the line segment with end points A and B, or the length from A to B. |
| $a^{\frac{1}{n}}, \sqrt[n]{a}$ | $a$ to the power of $\frac{1}{n}$, $n$th root of $a$ (if $a \geqslant 0$ then $\sqrt[n]{a} \geqslant 0$) | | |
| $a^{\frac{1}{2}}, \sqrt{a}$ | $a$ to the power $\frac{1}{2}$, square root of $a$ (if $a \geqslant 0$ then $\sqrt{a} \geqslant 0$) | $\widehat{A}$ | the angle at A |
| | | $C\widehat{A}B$ | the angle between CA and AB |
| $|x|$ | the modulus or absolute value of $x$ $|x| = \begin{cases} x & \text{for } x \geqslant 0 \quad x \in \mathbb{R} \\ -x & \text{for } x < 0 \quad x \in \mathbb{R} \end{cases}$ | $\triangle ABC$ | the triangle whose vertices are A, B and C |

| | |
|---|---|
| $\parallel$ | is parallel to |
| $\perp$ | is perpendicular to |
| $P(A)$ | probability of event $A$ |
| $P(A')$ | probability of the event 'not $A$' |
| $P(A \mid B)$ | probability of the event $A$ given $B$ |
| $x_1, x_2, ....$ | observations of a variable |
| $f_1, f_2, ....$ | frequencies with which the observations $x_1, x_2, x_3, .....$ occur |
| $\mu$ | population mean |
| $\sigma$ | population standard deviation |
| $\overline{x}$ | sample mean |
| $s_n$ | standard deviation of the sample |
| $r$ | Pearson's product-moment correlation coefficient |
| $s_{xy}$ | covariance of $X$ and $Y$ |
| $\chi^2_{crit}$ | critical value of the chi-squared distribution |
| $\chi^2_{calc}$ | calculated chi-squared value |
| $f_o$ | observed frequency of a variable |
| $f_e$ | expected frequency of a variable |

# USEFUL FORMULAE

## STATISTICS

**Mean**
$$\bar{x} = \frac{\sum fx}{n} \quad \text{where} \quad n = \sum f$$

**Standard deviation**
$$s_n = \sqrt{\frac{\sum f(x - \bar{x})^2}{n}} \quad \text{where} \quad n = \sum f$$

**Pearson's product-moment correlation coefficient**
$$r = \frac{s_{xy}}{s_x s_y} \quad \text{where} \quad s_x = \sqrt{\frac{\sum (x - \bar{x})^2}{n}},$$
$$s_y = \sqrt{\frac{\sum (y - \bar{y})^2}{n}} \quad \text{and} \quad s_{xy} \text{ is the covariance.}$$

**Equation of regression line for $y$ on $x$**
$$y - \bar{y} = \frac{s_{xy}}{s_x^2}(x - \bar{x})$$

**The $\chi^2$ test statistic**
$$\chi_{calc}^2 = \sum \frac{(f_e - f_o)^2}{f_e} \quad \text{where } f_o \text{ are the observed frequencies, } f_e \text{ are the expected frequencies.}$$

## GEOMETRY

**Equation of a straight line**
$$y = mx + c \quad \text{or} \quad ax + by + d = 0$$

**Gradient formula**
$$m = \frac{y_2 - y_1}{x_2 - x_1}$$

**Equation of axis of symmetry**
$$x = \frac{-b}{2a}$$

**Distance between two points $(x_1, y_2)$ and $(x_2, y_2)$**
$$d = \sqrt{(x_1 - x_2)^2 + (y_1 - y_2)^2}$$

**Coordinates of the midpoint of a line segment with endpoints $(x_1, y_2)$ and $(x_2, y_2)$**
$$\left( \frac{x_1 + x_2}{2}, \frac{y_1 + y_2}{2} \right)$$

## ALGEBRA

**Solution of a quadratic equation**

If $ax^2 + bx + c = 0$, $a \neq 0$

then $x = \dfrac{-b \pm \sqrt{b^2 - 4ac}}{2a}$

## TRIGONOMETRY

**Sine rule**
$$\frac{a}{\sin A} = \frac{b}{\sin B} = \frac{c}{\sin C}$$

**Cosine rule**
$$a^2 = b^2 + c^2 - 2bc\cos A$$

$$\cos A = \frac{b^2 + c^2 - a^2}{2bc}$$

**Area of a triangle**  $A = \frac{1}{2}ab\sin C$  where $a$ and $b$ are adjacent sides, $C$ is the included angle.

## PLANE AND SOLID FIGURES

**Area of a parallelogram**  $A = (b \times h)$, where $b$ is the base, $h$ is the height

**Area of a triangle**  $A = \frac{1}{2}(b \times h)$, where $b$ is the base, $h$ is the height

**Area of a trapezium**  $A = \frac{1}{2}(a+b)h$, where $a$ and $b$ are the parallel sides, $h$ is the height

**Area of a circle**  $A = \pi r^2$, where $r$ is the radius

**Circumference of a circle**  $C = 2\pi r$, where $r$ is the radius

**Volume of a pyramid**  $V = \frac{1}{3}(\text{area of base} \times \text{vertical height})$

**Volume of a cuboid**  $V = l \times w \times h$, where $l$ is the length, $w$ is the width, $h$ is the height

**Volume of a cylinder**  $V = \pi r^2 h$, where $r$ is the radius, $h$ is the height

**Area of the curved surface of a cylinder**  $A = 2\pi r h$, where $r$ is the radius, $h$ is the height

**Volume of a sphere**  $V = \frac{4}{3}\pi r^3$, where $r$ is the radius

**Surface area of a sphere**  $A = 4\pi r^2$, where $r$ is the radius

**Volume of a cone**  $V = \frac{1}{3}\pi r^2 h$, where $r$ is the radius, $h$ is the height

**Area of the curved surface of a cone**  $\pi r l$, where $r$ is the radius, $l$ is the slant height

# FINITE SEQUENCES

**The $n$th term of an arithmetic sequence**
$$u_n = u_1 + (n-1)d$$

**The sum of $n$ terms of an arithmetic sequence**
$$S_n = \frac{n}{2}(2u_1 + (n-1)d) = \frac{n}{2}(u_1 + u_n)$$

**The $n$th term of a geometric sequence**
$$u_n = u_1 r^{n-1}$$

**The sum of $n$ terms of a geometric sequence**
$$S_n = \frac{u_1(r^n - 1)}{r - 1} = \frac{u_1(1 - r^n)}{1 - r}, \quad r \neq 1$$

# PROBABILITY

**Probability of an event A**
$$P(A) = \frac{n(A)}{n(U)}$$

**Complementary events**
$$P(A') = 1 - P(A)$$

**Combined events**
$$P(A \cup B) = P(A) + P(B) - P(A \cap B)$$

**Mutually exclusive events**
$$P(A \cup B) = P(A) + P(B)$$

**Independent events**
$$P(A \cap B) = P(A) \times P(B)$$

**Conditional probability**
$$P(A \mid B) = \frac{P(A \cap B)}{P(B)}$$

# FINANCIAL MATHEMATICS

**Simple Interest**
$$I = \frac{Crn}{100},$$ where $C$ is the capital,
$r\%$ is the interest rate,
$n$ is the number of time periods,
$I$ is the interest

**Compound Interest**
$$I = C \times \left(1 + \frac{r}{100k}\right)^{kn} - C,$$

where $C$ is the capital,
$r\%$ is the interest rate per annum,
$k$ is the number of compounds per year,
$n$ is the number of years,
$I$ is the interest

## DIFFERENTIAL CALCULUS

**Derivative of $f(x)$**

If $y = f(x)$

then $\dfrac{dy}{dx} = f'(x) = \lim\limits_{h \to 0} \left( \dfrac{f(x+h) - f(x)}{h} \right)$

**Derivative of $ax^n$**

If $f(x) = ax^n$ then $f'(x) = nax^{n-1}$

**Derivative of a polynomial**

If $f(x) = ax^n + bx^{n-1} + \ldots$

then $f'(x) = nax^{n-1} + (n-1)bx^{n-2} + \ldots$

# Graphics calculator instructions

**A**    Casio fx-9860G
**B**    Texas Instruments TI-84 Plus
**C**    Texas Instruments TI-$n$spire

In this course it is assumed that you have a **graphics calculator**. If you learn how to operate your calculator successfully, you should experience little difficulty with future arithmetic calculations.

There are many different brands (and types) of calculators. Different calculators do not have exactly the same keys. It is therefore important that you have an instruction booklet for your calculator, and use it whenever you need to.

However, to help get you started, we have included here some basic instructions for the **Casio fx-9860G**, the **Texas Instruments TI-84 plus** and the **Texas Instruments TI-*n*spire** calculators. Note that instructions given may need to be modified slightly for other models.

The instructions have been divided into three sections, one for each of the calculator models.

# A                                        CASIO FX-9860G

## BASIC FUNCTIONS

### GROUPING SYMBOLS (BRACKETS)

The Casio has bracket keys that look like $\boxed{(\,}$ and $\boxed{)\,}$ .

Brackets are regularly used in mathematics to indicate an expression which needs to be evaluated before other operations are carried out.

For example, to evaluate $2 \times (4 + 1)$ we type   2 $\boxed{\times}$ $\boxed{(\,}$ 4 $\boxed{+}$ 1 $\boxed{)\,}$ $\boxed{\text{EXE}}$ .

We also use brackets to make sure the calculator understands the expression we are typing in.

For example, to evaluate $\frac{2}{4+1}$ we type   2 $\boxed{\div}$ $\boxed{(\,}$ 4 $\boxed{+}$ 1 $\boxed{)\,}$ $\boxed{\text{EXE}}$ .

If we typed   2 $\boxed{\div}$ 4 $\boxed{+}$ 1 $\boxed{\text{EXE}}$   the calculator would think we meant $\frac{2}{4} + 1$.

In general, it is a good idea to place brackets around any complicated expressions which need to be evaluated separately.

### POWER KEYS

The Casio has a power key that looks like $\boxed{\wedge}$ . We type the base first, press the power key, then enter the index or exponent.

For example, to evaluate $25^3$ we type   25 $\boxed{\wedge}$ 3 $\boxed{\text{EXE}}$ .

Numbers can be squared on the Casio using the special key $\boxed{x^2}$ .

For example, to evaluate $25^2$ we type   25 $\boxed{x^2}$ $\boxed{\text{EXE}}$ .

## ROOTS

To enter roots on the Casio we need to use the secondary function key $\boxed{\text{SHIFT}}$ .

We enter square roots by pressing $\boxed{\text{SHIFT}}$ $\boxed{x^2}$ .

For example, to evaluate $\sqrt{36}$ we press $\boxed{\text{SHIFT}}$ $\boxed{x^2}$ 36 $\boxed{\text{EXE}}$ .

If there is a more complicated expression under the square root sign you should enter it in brackets.

For example, to evaluate $\sqrt{18 \div 2}$ we press $\boxed{\text{SHIFT}}$ $\boxed{x^2}$ $\boxed{(}$ 18 $\boxed{\div}$ 2 $\boxed{)}$ $\boxed{\text{EXE}}$ .

Cube roots are entered by pressing $\boxed{\text{SHIFT}}$ $\boxed{(}$ .

For example, to evaluate $\sqrt[3]{8}$ we press $\boxed{\text{SHIFT}}$ $\boxed{(}$ 8 $\boxed{\text{EXE}}$ .

Higher roots are entered by pressing $\boxed{\text{SHIFT}}$ $\boxed{\wedge}$ .

For example, to evaluate $\sqrt[4]{81}$ we press 4 $\boxed{\text{SHIFT}}$ $\boxed{\wedge}$ 81 $\boxed{\text{EXE}}$ .

## INVERSE TRIGONOMETRIC FUNCTIONS

The inverse trigonometric functions $\sin^{-1}$, $\cos^{-1}$ and $\tan^{-1}$ are the secondary functions of $\boxed{\text{sin}}$ , $\boxed{\text{cos}}$ and $\boxed{\text{tan}}$ respectively. They are accessed by using the secondary function key $\boxed{\text{SHIFT}}$ .

For example, if $\cos x = \frac{3}{5}$, then $x = \cos^{-1}\left(\frac{3}{5}\right)$.

To calculate this, press $\boxed{\text{SHIFT}}$ $\boxed{\text{cos}}$ $\boxed{(}$ 3 $\boxed{\div}$ 5 $\boxed{)}$ $\boxed{\text{EXE}}$ .

## SCIENTIFIC NOTATION

If a number is too large or too small to be displayed neatly on the screen, it will be expressed in scientific notation, which is the form $a \times 10^k$ where $1 \leqslant a < 10$ and $k$ is an integer.

To evaluate $2300^3$, press 2300 $\boxed{\wedge}$ 3 $\boxed{\text{EXE}}$ . The answer displayed is 1.2167E+10, which means $1.2167 \times 10^{10}$.

To evaluate $\frac{3}{20\,000}$, press 3 $\boxed{\div}$ 20000 $\boxed{\text{EXE}}$ . The answer displayed is 1.5E−04, which means $1.5 \times 10^{-4}$.

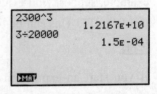

You can enter values in scientific notation using the $\boxed{\text{EXP}}$ key. For example, to evaluate $\frac{2.6 \times 10^{14}}{13}$, press 2.6 $\boxed{\text{EXP}}$ 14 $\boxed{\div}$ 13 $\boxed{\text{EXE}}$ . The answer is $2 \times 10^{13}$.

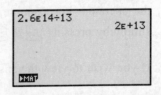

## SECONDARY FUNCTION AND ALPHA KEYS

The **shift function** of each key is displayed in yellow above the key. It is accessed by pressing the SHIFT key followed by the key corresponding to the desired shift function.

For example, to calculate $\sqrt{36}$, press SHIFT $x^2$ ($\sqrt{\ }$) 36 EXE .

The **alpha function** of each key is displayed in red above the key. It is accessed by pressing the ALPHA key followed by the key corresponding to the desired letter. The main purpose of the alpha keys is to store values which can be recalled later.

## MEMORY

Utilising the memory features of your calculator allows you to recall calculations you have performed previously. This not only saves time, but also enables you to maintain accuracy in your calculations.

### SPECIFIC STORAGE TO MEMORY

Values can be stored into the variable letters A, B, ...., Z. Storing a value in memory is useful if you need that value multiple times.

Suppose we wish to store the number 15.4829 for use in a number of calculations. To store this number in variable A, type in the number then press → ALPHA X,θ,T (A) EXE .

```
15.4829→A
              15.4829
A+10
              25.4829
A^3
          3711.563767
▶MAT
```

We can now add 10 to this value by pressing ALPHA X,θ,T + 10 EXE , or cube this value by pressing ALPHA X,θ,T ∧ 3 EXE .

### ANS VARIABLE

The variable **Ans** holds the most recent evaluated expression, and can be used in calculations by pressing SHIFT (−) . For example, suppose you evaluate $3 \times 4$, and then wish to subtract this from 17. This can be done by pressing 17 − SHIFT (−) EXE .

```
3×4
               12
17-Ans
                5
▶MAT
```

If you start an expression with an operator such as + , − , etc, the previous answer **Ans** is automatically inserted ahead of the operator. For example, the previous answer can be halved simply by pressing ÷ 2 EXE .

```
3×4
               12
17-Ans
                5
Ans÷2
              2.5
▶MAT
```

If you wish to view the answer in fractional form, press F↔D .

### RECALLING PREVIOUS EXPRESSIONS

Pressing the left cursor key allows you to edit the most recently evaluated expression, and is useful if you wish to repeat a calculation with a minor change, or if you have made an error in typing.

Suppose you have evaluated $100 + \sqrt{132}$. If you now want to evaluate $100 + \sqrt{142}$, instead of retyping the command, it can be recalled by pressing the left cursor key. Move the cursor between the 3 and the 2, then press DEL 4 to remove the 3 and change it to a 4. Press EXE to re-evaluate the expression.

## LISTS

Lists enable us to store sets of data, which we can then analyse and compare.

### CREATING A LIST

Selecting **STAT** from the Main Menu takes you to the **list editor** screen.

To enter the data {2, 5, 1, 6, 0, 8} into **List 1**, start by moving the cursor to the first entry of **List 1**. Press 2 EXE 5 EXE .... and so on until all the data is entered.

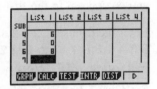

### DELETING LIST DATA

To delete a list of data from the list editor screen, move the cursor to anywhere on the list you wish to delete, then press    F6 (▷) F4 (**DEL-A**) F1 (**Yes**).

### REFERENCING LISTS

Lists can be referenced using the List function, which is accessed by pressing SHIFT 1.

For example, if you want to add 2 to each element of **List 1** and display the results in **List 2**, move the cursor to the heading of **List 2** and press    SHIFT 1 (**List**) 1 + 2 EXE .

Casio models without the List function can do this by pressing    OPTN F1 (**LIST**) F1 (**List**) 1 + 2 EXE .

## STATISTICS

Your graphics calculator is a useful tool for analysing data and creating statistical graphs.

We will first produce descriptive statistics and graphs for the data set:
$$5\ 2\ 3\ 3\ 6\ \ 4\ 5\ 3\ 7\ 5\ \ 7\ 1\ 8\ 9\ 5.$$

Enter the data into **List 1**. To obtain the descriptive statistics, press F6 (▷) until the **GRPH** icon is in the bottom left corner of the screen, then press F2 (**CALC**) F1 (**1 VAR**).

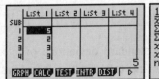

To obtain a boxplot of the data, press EXIT EXIT F1 (GRPH) F6 (SET), and set up **StatGraph 1** as shown. Press EXIT F1 (GPH1) to draw the boxplot.

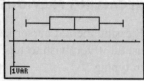

To obtain a vertical bar chart of the data, press EXIT F6 (SET) F2 (GPH 2), and set up **StatGraph 2** as shown. Press EXIT F2 (GPH 2) to draw the bar chart (set Start to 0, and Width to 1).

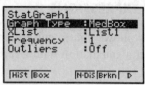

We will now enter a second set of data, and compare it to the first.

Enter the data set   9 6 2 3 5 5 7 5 6 7 6 3 4 4 5 8 4   into **List 2**, then press F6 (SET) F2 (GPH2) and set up **StatGraph 2** to draw a boxplot of this data set as shown. Press EXIT F4 (SEL), and turn on both **StatGraph 1** and **StatGraph 2**. Press F6 (DRAW) to draw the side-by-side boxplots.

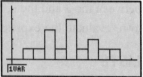

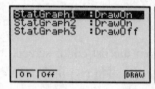

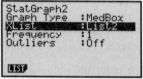

## STATISTICS FROM GROUPED DATA

To obtain descriptive statistics for the data in the table alongside, enter the data values into **List 1**, and the frequency values into **List 2**.

| Data | Frequency |
|------|-----------|
| 2 | 3 |
| 3 | 4 |
| 4 | 8 |
| 5 | 5 |

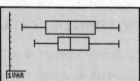

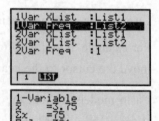

Press F2 (CALC) F6 (SET), and change the **1 Var Freq** variable to **List 2**. Press EXIT F1 (1Var) to view the statistics.

## TWO VARIABLE STATISTICS

Consider the data

| $x$ | 1 | 2 | 3 | 4 | 5 | 6 | 7 |
|-----|---|---|---|---|---|---|---|
| $y$ | 5 | 8 | 10 | 13 | 16 | 18 | 20 |

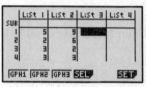

To find $s_x$ and $s_y$, the standard deviations of $x$ and $y$, enter the $x$ values into **List 1** and the $y$ values into **List 2** using the instructions on page **19**.

Press $\boxed{\text{F2}}$ (**CALC**) $\boxed{\text{F2}}$ (**2VAR**) to obtain the two variable statistics. $s_x$ is given by $x\sigma_n = 2$. Use the $\boxed{\blacktriangledown}$ key to scroll down to find $s_y$, which is given by $y\sigma_n \approx 5.08$.

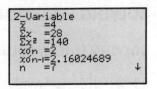

## FINDING $r$ AND THE LINE OF BEST FIT

We can use our graphics calculator to find the line of best fit connecting two variables. We can also find the values of Pearson's correlation coefficient $r$ and the coefficient of determination $r^2$, which measure the strength of the linear correlation between the two variables.

We will examine the relationship between the variables $x$ and $y$ for the previous data.

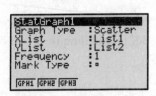

Enter the $x$ values into **List 1** and the $y$ values into **List 2**.

To produce a scatter diagram, press $\boxed{\text{F1}}$ (**GRPH**) $\boxed{\text{F6}}$ (**SET**), and set up **StatGraph 1** as shown. Press $\boxed{\text{EXIT}}$ $\boxed{\text{F1}}$ (**GPH 1**) to draw the scatter diagram.

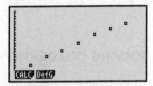

To find the line of best fit, press $\boxed{\text{F1}}$ (**CALC**) $\boxed{\text{F2}}$ (**X**).

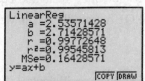

We can see that the line of best fit is $y \approx 2.54x + 2.71$, and that $r \approx 0.998$, indicating a very strong positive correlation between $x$ and $y$.

Press $\boxed{\text{F6}}$ (**DRAW**) to view the line of best fit.

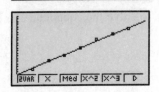

## CALCULATING $\chi^2$

To calculate $\chi^2$ for the data alongside, select **STAT** from the Main Menu, then press $\boxed{\text{F3}}$ (**TEST**) $\boxed{\text{F3}}$ (**CHI**).

|       | $A_1$ | $A_2$ |
| ----- | ----- | ----- |
| $B_1$ | 21    | 28    |
| $B_2$ | 13    | 24    |

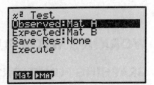

Press $\boxed{\text{F2}}$ ($\boxed{\blacktriangleright}$ **MAT**), then enter the values of the table into matrix **A**, using the instructions given on page **24**.

Press $\boxed{\text{EXIT}}$ twice to return to the $\chi^2$ **Test** screen, highlight **Execute**, then press $\boxed{\text{EXE}}$ .

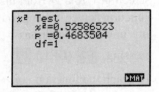

So, $\chi^2 \approx 0.526$. The $p$-value and the degrees of freedom are also given. The expected values are stored in matrix **B**.

# SOLVING EQUATIONS

## SOLVING LINEAR EQUATIONS

To solve the linear equation $3.2x - 4.2 = 7.4$, select **EQUA** from the Main Menu, then press F3 (**SOLV**).

Enter the equation by pressing 3.2 X,θ,T — 4.2 SHIFT . (=) 7.4 EXE .

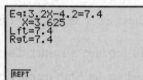

Highlight **X=** with the cursor and press F6 (**SOLV**) to solve the equation. So, the solution is $x = 3.625$.

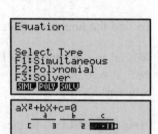

## SOLVING QUADRATIC EQUATIONS

To solve the quadratic equation $3x^2 + 2x - 11 = 0$, select **EQUA** from the Main Menu. Press F2 (**POLY**) then F1 (**2**).

Enter the coefficients 3, 2 and −11 and then press F1 (**SOLV**) to solve the equation.

So, the solutions are $x \approx -2.28$ or $1.61$.

# WORKING WITH FUNCTIONS

## GRAPHING FUNCTIONS

Selecting **GRAPH** from the Main Menu takes you to the Graph Function screen, where you can store functions to graph. Delete any unwanted functions by scrolling down to the function and pressing F2 (**DEL**) F1 (**Yes**).

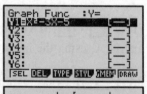

To graph the function $y = x^2 - 3x - 5$, move the cursor to **Y1** and press X,θ,T $x^2$ — 3 X,θ,T — 5 EXE . This stores the function into **Y1**. Press F6 (**DRAW**) to draw a graph of the function.

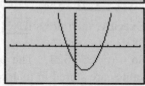

To view a table of values for the function, press $\boxed{\text{MENU}}$ and select **TABLE**. The function is stored in **Y1**, but not selected. Press $\boxed{\text{F1}}$ (**SEL**) to select the function, and $\boxed{\text{F6}}$ (**TABL**) to view the table. You can adjust the table settings by pressing $\boxed{\text{EXIT}}$ and then $\boxed{\text{F5}}$ (**SET**) from the Table Function screen.

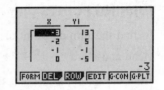

## ADJUSTING THE VIEWING WINDOW

When graphing functions it is important that you are able to view all the important features of the graph. As a general rule it is best to start with a large viewing window to make sure all the features of the graph are visible. You can then make the window smaller if necessary.

The viewing window can be adjusted by pressing $\boxed{\text{SHIFT}}$ $\boxed{\text{F3}}$ (**V-Window**). You can manually set the minimum and maximum values of the $x$ and $y$ axes, or press $\boxed{\text{F3}}$ (**STD**) to obtain the standard viewing window $-10 \leqslant x \leqslant 10$, $-10 \leqslant y \leqslant 10$.

## FINDING POINTS OF INTERSECTION

It is often useful to find the points of intersection of two graphs, for instance, when you are trying to solve simultaneous equations.

We can solve $y = 11 - 3x$ and $y = \dfrac{12 - x}{2}$ simultaneously by finding the point of intersection of these two lines. Select **GRAPH** from the Main Menu, then store $11 - 3x$ into **Y1** and $\dfrac{12 - x}{2}$ into **Y2**. Press $\boxed{\text{F6}}$ (**DRAW**) to draw a graph of the functions.

To find their point of intersection, press $\boxed{\text{F5}}$ (**G-Solv**) $\boxed{\text{F5}}$ (**ISCT**). The solution $x = 2$, $y = 5$ is given.

If there is more than one point of intersection, the remaining points of intersection can be found by pressing $\boxed{\blacktriangleright}$ .

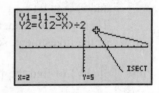

## FINDING $x$-INTERCEPTS

In the special case when you wish to solve an equation of the form $f(x) = 0$, this can be done by graphing $y = f(x)$ and then finding when this graph cuts the $x$-axis.

To solve $x^3 - 3x^2 + x + 1 = 0$, select **GRAPH** from the Main Menu and store $x^3 - 3x^2 + x + 1$ into **Y1**. Press $\boxed{\text{F6}}$ (**DRAW**) to draw the graph.

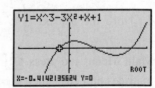

To find where this function cuts the $x$-axis, press $\boxed{\text{F5}}$ (**G-Solv**) $\boxed{\text{F1}}$ (**ROOT**). The first solution $x \approx -0.414$ is given.

Press $\boxed{\blacktriangleright}$ to find the remaining solutions $x = 1$ and $x \approx 2.41$ .

## TURNING POINTS

To find the turning point or vertex of $y = -x^2 + 2x + 3$, select **GRAPH** from the Main Menu and store $-x^2 + 2x + 3$ into **Y1**. Press F6 (**DRAW**) to draw the graph.

From the graph, it is clear that the vertex is a maximum, so to find the vertex press F5 (**G-Solv**) F2 (**MAX**). The vertex is $(1, 4)$.

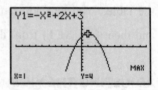

## FINDING THE TANGENT TO A FUNCTION

To find the equation of the tangent to $y = x^2$ when $x = 2$, we first press SHIFT MENU (**SET UP**), and change the **Derivative** setting to **On**. Draw the graph of $y = x^2$, then press SHIFT F4 (**Sketch**) F2 (**Tang**).

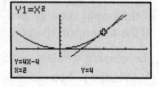

Press 2 EXE EXE to draw the tangent at $x = 2$.

The tangent has gradient 4, and equation $y = 4x - 4$.

## FINANCIAL MATHEMATICS

Suppose we invest \$5000 at 7.2% p.a. compounded annually. To find the value of the investment after 10 years, select **TVM** from the Main Menu and press F2 (**CMPD**) to display the compound interest screen.

Set up the screen as shown:

**Note:** All money being invested is considered as outgoings and is entered as a negative value.
There are no payments into the account during the term of the investment, so **PMT** is set to 0.

Press F5 (**FV**) to find the future value.

So, the investment amounts to \$10 021.16.

## MATRICES

### STORING MATRICES

To store the matrix $\begin{pmatrix} 2 & 3 \\ 1 & 4 \\ 5 & 0 \end{pmatrix}$, select **RUN·MAT** from the

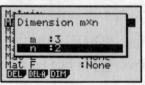

Main Menu, and press F1 (**▶MAT**). This is where you define matrices and enter their elements.

To define the matrix as matrix **A**, make sure **Mat A** is highlighted, and press F3 (**DIM**) 3 EXE 2 EXE EXE . This indicates that the matrix has 3 rows and 2 columns.

Enter the elements of the matrix, pressing $\boxed{\text{EXE}}$ after each entry. Press $\boxed{\text{EXIT}}$ twice to return to the home screen when you are done.

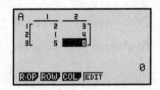

##  TEXAS INSTRUMENTS TI-84 PLUS

## BASIC FUNCTIONS

### GROUPING SYMBOLS (BRACKETS)

The TI-84 Plus has bracket keys that look like $\boxed{(}$ and $\boxed{)}$.

Brackets are regularly used in mathematics to indicate an expression which needs to be evaluated before other operations are carried out.

For example, to evaluate $2 \times (4+1)$ we type $\;2\;\boxed{\times}\;\boxed{(}\;4\;\boxed{+}\;1\;\boxed{)}\;\boxed{\text{ENTER}}$.

We also use brackets to make sure the calculator understands the expression we are typing in.

For example, to evaluate $\frac{2}{4+1}$ we type $\;2\;\boxed{\div}\;\boxed{(}\;4\;\boxed{+}\;1\;\boxed{)}\;\boxed{\text{ENTER}}$.

If we typed $\;2\;\boxed{\div}\;4\;\boxed{+}\;1\;\boxed{\text{ENTER}}\;$ the calculator would think we meant $\frac{2}{4}+1$.

In general, it is a good idea to place brackets around any complicated expressions which need to be evaluated separately.

### POWER KEYS

The TI-84 Plus has a power key that looks like $\boxed{\wedge}$. We type the base first, press the power key, then enter the index or exponent.

For example, to evaluate $25^3$ we type $\;25\;\boxed{\wedge}\;3\;\boxed{\text{ENTER}}$.

Numbers can be squared on the TI-84 Plus using the special key $\boxed{x^2}$.

For example, to evaluate $25^2$ we type $\;25\;\boxed{x^2}\;\boxed{\text{ENTER}}$.

### ROOTS

To enter roots on the TI-84 Plus we need to use the secondary function key $\boxed{\text{2nd}}$.

We enter square roots by pressing $\;\boxed{\text{2nd}}\;\boxed{x^2}$.

For example, to evaluate $\sqrt{36}$ we press $\;\boxed{\text{2nd}}\;\boxed{x^2}\;36\;\boxed{)}\;\boxed{\text{ENTER}}$.

The end bracket is used to tell the calculator we have finished entering terms under the square root sign.

Cube roots are entered by pressing $\boxed{\text{MATH}}$ **4:** $\sqrt[3]{\phantom{x}}$ ( .

To evaluate $\sqrt[3]{8}$ we press $\boxed{\text{MATH}}$ **4** : 8 $\boxed{)}$ $\boxed{\text{ENTER}}$ .

Higher roots are entered by pressing $\boxed{\text{MATH}}$ **5:** $\sqrt[x]{\phantom{x}}$ .

To evaluate $\sqrt[4]{81}$ we press 4 $\boxed{\text{MATH}}$ **5** : 81 $\boxed{\text{ENTER}}$ .

## INVERSE TRIGONOMETRIC FUNCTIONS

The inverse trigonometric functions $\sin^{-1}$, $\cos^{-1}$ and $\tan^{-1}$ are the secondary functions of $\boxed{\text{SIN}}$ , $\boxed{\text{COS}}$ and $\boxed{\text{TAN}}$ respectively. They are accessed by using the secondary function key $\boxed{\text{2nd}}$ .

For example, if $\cos x = \frac{3}{5}$, then $x = \cos^{-1}\left(\frac{3}{5}\right)$.

To calculate this, press $\boxed{\text{2nd}}$ $\boxed{\text{COS}}$ 3 $\boxed{\div}$ 5 $\boxed{)}$ $\boxed{\text{ENTER}}$ .

## SCIENTIFIC NOTATION

If a number is too large or too small to be displayed neatly on the screen, it will be expressed in scientific notation, which is the form $a \times 10^k$ where $1 \leqslant a < 10$ and $k$ is an integer.

To evaluate $2300^3$, press 2300 $\boxed{\wedge}$ 3 $\boxed{\text{ENTER}}$ . The answer displayed is 1.2167E10, which means $1.2167 \times 10^{10}$.

To evaluate $\frac{3}{20\,000}$, press 3 $\boxed{\div}$ 20 000 $\boxed{\text{ENTER}}$ . The answer displayed is 1.5E−4, which means $1.5 \times 10^{-4}$.

You can enter values in scientific notation using the EE function, which is accessed by pressing $\boxed{\text{2nd}}$ $\boxed{,}$ .

For example, to evaluate $\frac{2.6 \times 10^{14}}{13}$, press 2.6 $\boxed{\text{2nd}}$ $\boxed{,}$ 14 $\boxed{\div}$ 13 $\boxed{\text{ENTER}}$ . The answer is $2 \times 10^{13}$.

```
2300^3
              1.2167E10
3/20000
               1.5E-4
```

```
2.6E14/13
                  2E13
```

## SECONDARY FUNCTION AND ALPHA KEYS

The **secondary function** of each key is displayed in blue above the key. It is accessed by pressing the $\boxed{\text{2nd}}$ key, followed by the key corresponding to the desired secondary function.

For example, to calculate $\sqrt{36}$, press $\boxed{\text{2nd}}$ $\boxed{x^2}$ ($\sqrt{\phantom{x}}$) 36 $\boxed{)}$ $\boxed{\text{ENTER}}$ .

The **alpha function** of each key is displayed in green above the key. It is accessed by pressing the $\boxed{\text{ALPHA}}$ key followed by the key corresponding to the desired letter. The main purpose of the alpha keys is to store values into memory which can be recalled later.

## MEMORY

Utilising the memory features of your calculator allows you to recall calculations you have performed previously. This not only saves time, but also enables you to maintain accuracy in your calculations.

## SPECIFIC STORAGE TO MEMORY

Values can be stored into the variable letters A, B, ...., Z. Storing a value in memory is useful if you need that value multiple times.

Suppose we wish to store the number 15.4829 for use in a number of calculations. To store this number in variable A, type in the number, then press  STO▶  ALPHA  MATH  (A)  ENTER .

We can now add 10 to this value by pressing  ALPHA  MATH   +  10  ENTER , or cube this value by pressing  ALPHA  MATH   ^  3  ENTER .

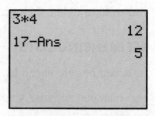

## ANS VARIABLE

The variable **Ans** holds the most recent evaluated expression, and can be used in calculations by pressing  2nd  (−) .

For example, suppose you evaluate $3 \times 4$, and then wish to subtract this from 17. This can be done by pressing 17  −   2nd  (−)  ENTER .

If you start an expression with an operator such as  +  ,  −  , etc, the previous answer **Ans** is automatically inserted ahead of the operator. For example, the previous answer can be halved simply by pressing  ÷  2  ENTER .

If you wish to view the answer in fractional form, press  MATH  1  ENTER .

## RECALLING PREVIOUS EXPRESSIONS

The **ENTRY** function recalls previously evaluated expressions, and is used by pressing  2nd   ENTER .

This function is useful if you wish to repeat a calculation with a minor change, or if you have made an error in typing.

Suppose you have evaluated $100 + \sqrt{132}$. If you now want to evaluate $100 + \sqrt{142}$, instead of retyping the command, it can be recalled by pressing  2nd   ENTER .

The change can then be made by moving the cursor over the 3 and changing it to a 4, then pressing  ENTER .

If you have made an error in your original calculation, and intended to calculate $1500 + \sqrt{132}$, again you can recall the previous command by pressing  2nd   ENTER .

Move the cursor to the first 0.

You can insert the 5, rather than overwriting the 0, by pressing  2nd  DEL  (INS) 5  ENTER .

# LISTS

Lists are used for a number of purposes on the calculator. They enable us to store sets of data, which we can then analyse and compare.

## CREATING A LIST

Press [STAT] 1 to access the **list editor** screen.

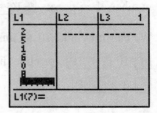

To enter the data {2, 5, 1, 6, 0, 8} into **List 1**, start by moving the cursor to the first entry of **L₁**. Press 2 [ENTER] 5 [ENTER] .... and so on until all the data is entered.

## DELETING LIST DATA

To delete a list of data from the list editor screen, move the cursor to the heading of the list you want to delete then press [CLEAR] [ENTER] .

## REFERENCING LISTS

Lists can be referenced by using the secondary functions of the keypad numbers 1-6.

For example, suppose you want to add 2 to each element of **List1** and display the results in **List2**. To do this, move the cursor to the heading of **L₂** and press [2nd] 1 [+] 2 [ENTER] .

# STATISTICS

Your graphics calculator is a useful tool for analysing data and creating statistical graphs. We will first produce descriptive statistics and graphs for the data set:

$$5\ 2\ 3\ 3\ 6\ \ 4\ 5\ 3\ 7\ 5\ \ 7\ 1\ 8\ 9\ 5.$$

Enter the data set into **List 1**. To obtain descriptive statistics of the data set, press [STAT] [▶] **1:1-Var Stats** [2nd] 1 (**L₁**) [ENTER] .

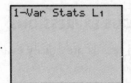
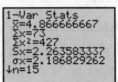

To obtain a boxplot of the data, press [2nd] [Y=] (**STAT PLOT**) 1 and set up **Statplot1** as shown. Press [ZOOM] **9:ZoomStat** to graph the boxplot with an appropriate window.

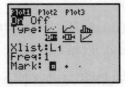
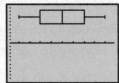

To obtain a vertical bar chart of the data, press [2nd] [Y=] 1, and change the type of graph to a vertical bar chart as shown. Press [ZOOM] **9:ZoomStat** to draw the bar chart. Press [WINDOW] and set the **Xscl** to 1, then [GRAPH] to redraw the bar chart.

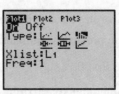
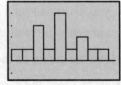

We will now enter a second set of data, and compare it to the first.

Enter the data set   9 6 2 3 5 5 7 5 6 7 6 3 4 4 5 8 4   into **List 2**, press 2nd Y= 1, and change the type of graph back to a boxplot as shown. Move the cursor to the top of the screen and select **Plot2**. Set up **Statplot2** in the same manner, except set the **XList** to **L2**. Press ZOOM 9:ZoomStat to draw the side-by-side boxplots.

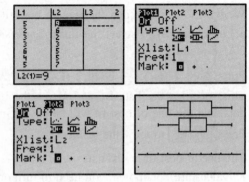

## STATISTICS FROM GROUPED DATA

To obtain descriptive statistics for the data in the table alongside, enter the data values into **List 1**, and the frequency values into **List 2**.

Press STAT ▶ 1 : 1-Var Stats 2nd 1 (L₁) , 2nd 2 (L₂) ENTER .

| Data | Frequency |
|------|-----------|
| 2 | 3 |
| 3 | 4 |
| 4 | 8 |
| 5 | 5 |

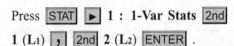

# TWO VARIABLE STATISTICS

Consider the data

| $x$ | 1 | 2 | 3 | 4 | 5 | 6 | 7 |
|-----|---|---|----|----|----|----|----|
| $y$ | 5 | 8 | 10 | 13 | 16 | 18 | 20 |

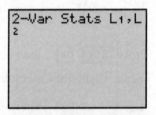

To find $s_x$ and $s_y$, the standard deviations of $x$ and $y$, enter the $x$ values into **List 1** and the $y$ values into **List 2** using the instructions on page **30**.

Press STAT ▶ 2:2-Var Stats, then 2nd 1 (L₁) , 2nd 2 (L₂) ENTER to obtain the two variable statistics.

$s_x$ is given by $\sigma_X = 2$. Use the ▼ key to scroll down to find $s_y$, which is given by $\sigma_y \approx 5.08$.

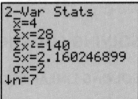

### FINDING $r$ AND THE LINE OF BEST FIT

We can use our graphics calculator to find the line of best fit connecting two variables. We can also find the values of Pearson's correlation coefficient $r$ and the coefficient of determination $r^2$, which measure the strength of the linear correlation between the two variables.

We will examine the relationship between the variables $x$ and $y$ for the data above.

Enter the $x$ values into **List 1** and the $y$ values into **List 2**.

To produce a scatter diagram, press 2nd Y= (STAT PLOT) 1, and set up **Statplot 1** as shown. Press ZOOM 9 : **ZoomStat** to draw the scatter diagram.

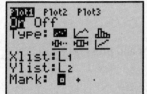

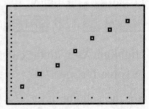

We will now find $r$ and the line of best fit. Press STAT →
4:LinReg(ax+b) to select the linear regression option from the
CALC menu.

```
LinReg(ax+b) L₁,
L₂,Y₁
```

Press 2nd 1 ($L_1$) , 2nd 2 ($L_2$) , VARS → 1 1 ($Y_1$).
This specifies the lists $L_1$ and $L_2$ as the lists which hold the
data, and the line of best fit will be pasted into the function $Y_1$.
Press ENTER to view the results.

The line of best fit is given as $y \approx 2.54x + 2.71$. If the $r$ and
$r^2$ values are not shown, you need to turn on the Diagnostic by
pressing 2nd 0 (CATALOG) and selecting DiagnosticOn.

```
LinReg
 y=ax+b
 a=2.535714286
 b=2.714285714
 r²=.9954581359
 r=.9977264835
```

The $r$ value of $\approx 0.998$ indicates a very strong positive
correlation between $x$ and $y$.

You can view the line of best fit by pressing GRAPH .

## CALCULATING $\chi^2$

To calculate $\chi^2$ for the data alongside,
enter the values of the table into matrix
A, using the instructions given on page
36.

|        | $A_1$ | $A_2$ |
|--------|-------|-------|
| $B_1$  | 21    | 28    |
| $B_2$  | 13    | 24    |

```
MATRIX[A] 2 ×2
[ 21    28    ]
[ 13    24    ]
```

Press STAT ◄ , then select C:$\chi^2$-Test... from the TESTS
menu. Highlight Calculate, then press ENTER .

So, $\chi^2 \approx 0.526$. The $p$-value and the degrees of freedom are
also given. The expected values are stored in matrix B.

```
χ²-Test
 χ²=.5258652317
 P=.4683504083
 df=1
```

# SOLVING EQUATIONS

## SOLVING LINEAR EQUATIONS

To solve the linear equation $3.2x - 4.2 = 7.4$, we rearrange
the equation to $3.2x - 11.6 = 0$, so that one side is equal to
zero.

```
EQUATION SOLVER
eqn:0=3.2X-11.6
```

Press MATH then 0 to select 0:Solver...

Press ▲ , then enter the equation into eqn:0= by pressing 3.2
X,T,θ,n − 11.6 ENTER .

```
3.2X-11.6=0
•X=3.625
  bound={-1ᴇ99,1...
•left-rt=0
```

Highlight X= with the cursor and press ALPHA ENTER (SOLVE)
to solve for $x$.

So, the solution is $x = 3.625$.

## SOLVING QUADRATIC EQUATIONS

The TI-84 Plus does not have a built-in method to solve quadratic equations. We must write our own program. Note that this program can not be taken into examinations.

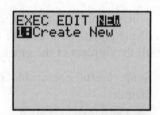

To solve the quadratic equation $3x^2 + 2x - 11 = 0$,

press $\boxed{\text{PRGM}}$ $\boxed{\blacktriangleleft}$ **1** to create a new program, label the program QUADRAT, then press $\boxed{\text{ENTER}}$ .

Enter the code for the program as shown alongside.

The *Disp* and *Prompt* commands are accessed from the **I/O** menu of the **PRGM** screen. You can enter $=$ by pressing $\boxed{\text{2nd}}$ $\boxed{\text{MATH}}$ **1**.

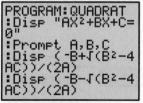

Press $\boxed{\text{2nd}}$ $\boxed{\text{MODE}}$ (**QUIT**) when you are done.

To use the program, press $\boxed{\text{PRGM}}$ , then **1:QUADRAT**. Press $\boxed{\text{ENTER}}$ to start the program.

As prompted, enter the coefficients A, B and C, pressing $\boxed{\text{ENTER}}$ after each one.

So the solutions are $x \approx -2.28$ and $1.61$.

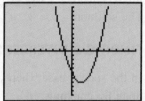

# WORKING WITH FUNCTIONS

### GRAPHING FUNCTIONS

Pressing $\boxed{\text{Y=}}$ selects the **Y=** editor, where you can store functions to graph. Delete any unwanted functions by scrolling down to the function and pressing $\boxed{\text{CLEAR}}$ .

To graph the function $y = x^2 - 3x - 5$, move the cursor to **Y**$_1$, and press $\boxed{\text{X,T,}\theta,n}$ $\boxed{x^2}$ $\boxed{-}$ 3 $\boxed{\text{X,T,}\theta,n}$ $\boxed{-}$ 5 $\boxed{\text{ENTER}}$ . This stores the function into **Y**$_1$. Press $\boxed{\text{GRAPH}}$ to draw a graph of the function.

To view a table of values for the function, press $\boxed{\text{2nd}}$ $\boxed{\text{GRAPH}}$ (**TABLE**). The starting point and interval of the table values can be adjusted by pressing $\boxed{\text{2nd}}$ $\boxed{\text{WINDOW}}$ (**TBLSET**).

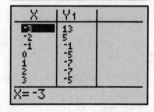

## ADJUSTING THE VIEWING WINDOW

When graphing functions it is important that you are able to view all the important features of the graph. As a general rule it is best to start with a large viewing window to make sure all the features of the graph are visible. You can then make the window smaller if necessary.

Some useful commands for adjusting the viewing window include:

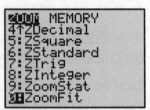

ZOOM 0:ZoomFit :    This command scales the $y$-axis to fit the minimum and maximum values of the displayed graph within the current $x$-axis range.

ZOOM 6:ZStandard : This command returns the viewing window to the default setting of $-10 \leqslant x \leqslant 10$, $-10 \leqslant y \leqslant 10$.

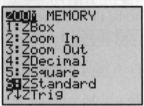

If neither of these commands are helpful, the viewing window can be adjusted manually by pressing WINDOW and setting the minimum and maximum values for the $x$ and $y$ axes.

## FINDING POINTS OF INTERSECTION

It is often useful to find the points of intersection of two graphs, for instance, when you are trying to solve simultaneous equations.

We can solve $y = 11 - 3x$ and $y = \dfrac{12 - x}{2}$ simultaneously by finding the point of intersection of these two lines.

Press Y= , then store $11 - 3x$ into Y₁ and $\dfrac{12 - x}{2}$ into Y₂. Press GRAPH to draw a graph of the functions.

To find their point of intersection, press 2nd TRACE (CALC) 5:intersect. Press ENTER twice to specify the functions Y₁ and Y₂ as the functions you want to find the intersection of, then use the arrow keys to move the cursor close to the point of intersection and press ENTER once more.
The solution $x = 2$, $y = 5$ is given.

## FINDING $x$-INTERCEPTS

In the special case when you wish to solve an equation of the form $f(x) = 0$, this can be done by graphing $y = f(x)$ and then finding when this graph cuts the $x$-axis.

For example, to solve $x^3 - 3x^2 + x + 1 = 0$, press Y= and store $x^3 - 3x^2 + x + 1$ into Y₁. Then press GRAPH .

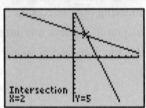

To find where this function first cuts the $x$-axis, press 2nd TRACE (CALC) 2:zero.

Move the cursor to the left of the first zero and press $\boxed{\text{ENTER}}$ , then move the cursor to the right of the first zero and press $\boxed{\text{ENTER}}$ . Finally, move the cursor close to the first zero and press $\boxed{\text{ENTER}}$ once more. The solution $x \approx -0.414$ is given.

Repeat this process to find the remaining solutions $x = 1$ and $x \approx 2.414$.

## TURNING POINTS

To find the turning point or vertex of $y = -x^2 + 2x + 3$, press $\boxed{\text{Y=}}$ and store $-x^2 + 2x + 3$ into **Y**₁. Press $\boxed{\text{GRAPH}}$ to draw the graph.

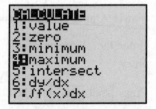

From the graph, it is clear that the vertex is a maximum, so press $\boxed{\text{2nd}}$ $\boxed{\text{TRACE}}$ (**CALC**) **4:maximum**.

Move the cursor to the left of the vertex and press $\boxed{\text{ENTER}}$ , then move the cursor to the right of the vertex and press $\boxed{\text{ENTER}}$. Finally, move the cursor close to the vertex and press $\boxed{\text{ENTER}}$ once more. The vertex is $(1, 4)$.

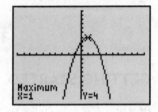

## FINDING THE TANGENT TO A FUNCTION

To find the equation of the tangent to $y = x^2$ when $x = 2$, we first draw the graph of $y = x^2$. Press $\boxed{\text{2nd}}$ $\boxed{\text{PRGM}}$ (**DRAW**) **5:Tangent**, then press **2** $\boxed{\text{ENTER}}$ to draw the tangent at $x = 2$.

The tangent has gradient 4, and equation $y = 4x - 4$.

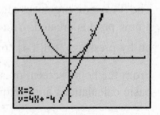

## FINANCIAL MATHEMATICS

Suppose we invest $5000 at 7.2% p.a. compounded annually. To find the value of the investment after 10 years, press (**APPS**) **1:Finance...** to display the finance menu, then **1** to select **1:TVM Solver...**

Set up the TVM screen as shown:

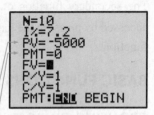

**Note:** All money being invested is considered as outgoings and is entered as a negative value.

There are no payments into the account during the term of the investment, so **PMT** is set to 0.

Highlight **FV** and press $\boxed{\text{ALPHA}}$ $\boxed{\text{ENTER}}$ (**SOLVE**) to find the future value. The investment amounts to $10 021.16.

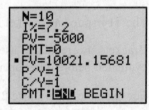

# MATRICES

## STORING MATRICES

To store the matrix $\begin{pmatrix} 2 & 3 \\ 1 & 4 \\ 5 & 0 \end{pmatrix}$, press 2nd $x^{-1}$ (**MATRIX**) to

display the matrices screen, and use ▶ to select the **EDIT** menu. This is where you define matrices and enter the elements.

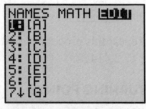

Press **1** to select **1:[A]**. Press 3 ENTER 2 ENTER to define matrix **A** as a $3 \times 2$ matrix.

Enter the elements of the matrix, pressing ENTER after each entry.

Press 2nd MODE (**QUIT**) when you are done.

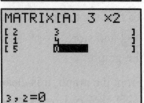

---

## C | TEXAS INSTRUMENTS TI-$n$SPIRE

## GETTING STARTED

Pressing 🏠 takes you to the **home screen**, where you can choose which application you wish to use.

The TI-$n$spire organises any work done into **pages**. Every time you start a new application, a new page is created. You can navigate back and forth between the pages you have worked on by pressing ctrl ◀ or ctrl ▶

From the home screen, press **1** to open the Calculator application. This is where most of the basic calculations are performed.

## SECONDARY FUNCTION KEY

The secondary function of each key is displayed in grey above the primary function. It is accessed by pressing the ctrl key followed by the key corresponding to the desired secondary function.

## BASIC FUNCTIONS

### GROUPING SYMBOLS (BRACKETS)

The TI-$n$spire has bracket keys that look like (( and )) .

Brackets are regularly used in mathematics to indicate an expression which needs to be evaluated before other operations are carried out.

For example, to evaluate $2 \times (4 + 1)$ we type   2 × (( 4 + 1 )) enter .

We also use brackets to make sure the calculator understands the expression we are typing in.

For example, to evaluate $\frac{2}{4+1}$ we type   2 ÷ ( 4 + 1 ) enter .

If we typed   2 ÷ 4 + 1 enter   the calculator would think we meant $\frac{2}{4} + 1$.

In general, it is a good idea to place brackets around any complicated expressions which need to be evaluated separately.

## POWER KEYS

The TI-$n$spire has a power key that looks like ∧ . We type the base first, press the power key, then enter the index or exponent.

For example, to evaluate $25^3$ we type   25 ∧ 3 enter .

Numbers can be squared on the TI-$n$spire using the special key $x^2$ .

For example, to evaluate $25^2$ we type   25 $x^2$ enter .

## ROOTS

To enter roots on the TI-$n$spire we need to use the secondary function ctrl .

We enter square roots by pressing   ctrl $x^2$ .

For example, to evaluate $\sqrt{36}$ we press   ctrl $x^2$ 36 enter .

Higher roots are entered by pressing   ctrl ∧ , which creates the $\sqrt[\Box]{\Box}$ template.

Enter the root number in the first entry, and the number you wish to find the root of in the second entry. Use the arrow keys to navigate around the template.

## ROUNDING OFF

You can instruct the TI-$n$spire to round off values to a fixed number of decimal places.

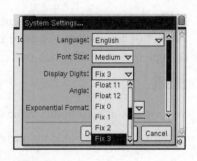

For example, to round to 3 decimal places, from the home screen select **8 : System Info > 2 : System Settings...** Press the tab button until the **Display Digits** drop-box is highlighted. Use the ▼ key to select *Fix 3*, then press enter three times to return to the page you were working on.

To unfix the number of decimal places, select *Float* from the **Display Digits** drop-box.

## DECIMAL EXPANSION OF FRACTIONS

If you press   5 ÷ 8 enter , the calculator will simply return the fraction $\frac{5}{8}$. To find the decimal expansion of $\frac{5}{8}$, press   5 ÷ 8 ctrl enter .

## INVERSE TRIGONOMETRIC FUNCTIONS

The inverse trigonometric functions $\sin^{-1}$, $\cos^{-1}$ and $\tan^{-1}$ are the secondary functions of [sin] , [cos] and [tan] respectively. They are accessed by using the secondary function key [ctrl] .

For example, if $\cos x = \frac{3}{5}$, then $x = \cos^{-1}\left(\frac{3}{5}\right)$.

To calculate this, press [ctrl] [cos] 3 [÷] 5 [)] [enter] .

## SCIENTIFIC NOTATION

You can enter very large or very small values by expressing them in scientific notation, which is in the form $a \times 10^k$ where $1 \leqslant a < 10$ and $k$ is an integer. You can do this using the [EE] button.

For example, to evaluate $\dfrac{2.6 \times 10^{14}}{13}$, press 2.6 [EE] 14 [÷] 13 [enter] . The answer is $2 \times 10^{13}$.

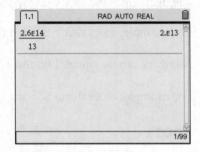

# MEMORY

Utilising the memory features of your calculator allows you to recall calculations you have performed previously. This not only saves time, but also enables you to maintain accuracy in your calculations.

### SPECIFIC STORAGE TO MEMORY

Values can be stored into the variable letters A, B, ...., Z. Storing a value in memory is useful if you need that value multiple times.

Suppose we wish to store the number 15.4829 for use in a number of calculations. To store this number in variable A, type in the number then press [ctrl] [var] (**sto▶**) (A) [enter] .

We can now add 10 to this value by pressing (A) [+] 10 [enter] or cube this value by pressing (A) [∧] 3 [enter] .

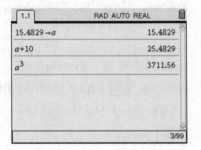

### ANS VARIABLE

The variable **Ans** holds the most recent evaluated expression, and can be used in calculations by pressing [ctrl] [(−)] .

For example, suppose you evaluate $3 \times 4$, and then wish to subtract this from 17. This can be done by pressing 17 [−] [ctrl] [(−)] [enter] .

If you start an expression with an operator such as $\boxed{+}$ , $\boxed{-}$ , etc, the previous answer **Ans** is automatically inserted ahead of the operator. For example, the previous answer can be doubled simply by pressing $\boxed{\times}$ 2 $\boxed{\text{enter}}$ .

### RECALLING PREVIOUS EXPRESSIONS

Pressing the $\boxed{\blacktriangle}$ key allows you to recall and edit previously evaluated expressions.

To recall a previous expression, press the $\boxed{\blacktriangle}$ key until the desired expression is highlighted, and press $\boxed{\text{enter}}$ . The expression then appears in the current entry line, where it can be edited.

## LISTS

Lists are used for a number of purposes on the calculator. They enable us to store sets of data, which we can then analyse and compare.

In order to perform many of the operations involving data lists on the TI-*n*spire, you need to **name** your lists as you define them.

### CREATING A LIST

Selecting **3 : Lists & Spreadsheet** from the home screen takes you to the **list editor** screen.

To enter the data $\{2,\ 5,\ 1,\ 6,\ 0,\ 8\}$ into **List A**, start by moving the cursor to the first entry of **List A**. Press 2 $\boxed{\text{enter}}$ 5 $\boxed{\text{enter}}$ .... and so on until all the data is entered.

Move the cursor to the heading of **List A** and use the green alphabet keys to enter a name for the list, for example *data*.

### DELETING LIST DATA

To delete a list of data from the list editor screen, move the cursor to the heading of that list, and press $\boxed{\blacktriangle}$ to highlight the whole column. Press $\boxed{\leftarrow}$ to delete the list.

### REFERENCING LISTS

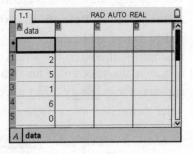

Once you have named a list, you can use that name to reference the list in other operations.

Suppose you want to add 2 to each element of the *data* list we created in the above example, and display the results in **List B**. Move the cursor to the shaded row of **List B**, and press $\boxed{=}$ *data* $\boxed{+}$ 2 $\boxed{\text{enter}}$ .

## STATISTICS

Your graphics calculator is a useful tool for analysing data and creating statistical graphs.

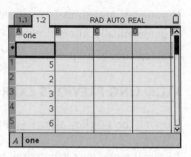

We will first produce descriptive statistics and graphs for the data set:

$$5\ 2\ 3\ 3\ 6\quad 4\ 5\ 3\ 7\ 5\quad 7\ 1\ 8\ 9\ 5.$$

Enter the data into **List A** and name this list *one*.

To obtain the descriptive statistics, press 🏠 **1 : Calculator** to open the Calculator application, press menu , then select **5 : Statistics** > **1 : Statistical Calculations** > **1 : One-Variable Statistics**.

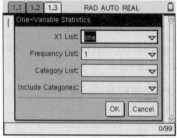

Press enter to choose 1 list. Select *one* from the **X1 List** drop-box, and press enter .

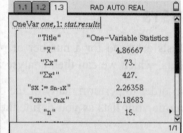

We will now draw some statistical graphs for the data. Press 🏠 **5 : Data & Statistics** to open the Data and Statistics application. You will see the data points randomly scattered on the screen. Move the cursor to the bottom of the screen until the "Click to add variable" box appears. Press enter , then select *one*. The points will order themselves into a dotplot along the horizontal axis.

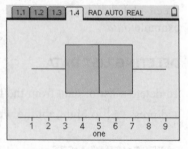

To obtain a vertical bar chart of the data, press menu , then select
**1 : Plot Type** > ...
**3 : Histogram**.

To obtain a boxplot of the data, press menu ,
then select **1 : Plot Type** > **2 : Box Plot**.

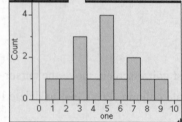

We will now add a second set of data, and compare it to the first.
Use the ctrl ◄ command to return to the page containing the list of data.
Enter the set $9\ 6\ 2\ 3\ 5\ 5\ 7\ 5\ 6\ 7\ 6\ 3\ 4\ 4\ 5\ 8\ 4$ into **List B**, and name the list *two*.
Use the ctrl ► command to navigate back to the page containing the boxplot of *one*.

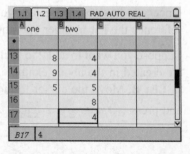

To view boxplots of both data sets, we need to split the page into two sections. Press [ctrl] [⌂] , then select **5 : Page Layout** > **2 : Select Layout** > **3 : Layout 3**. Press [ctrl] [tab] to navigate between the sections, then press [menu] **5** to open a new Data and Statistics application. Draw another boxplot in this section, this time using the data in *two*.

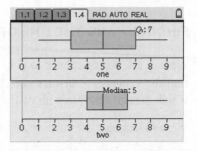

In order to compare the boxplots, the horizontal scales should be the same. Press [menu] , then select **5 : Window/Zoom** > **1 : Window Settings**.

Set the X range from 0 to 10. Press [ctrl] [tab] , and do the same with the other boxplot.

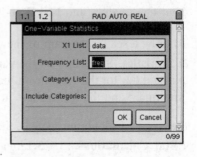

## STATISTICS FROM GROUPED DATA

To obtain descriptive statistics for the data in the table alongside, enter the data values into **List A**, and label the list *data*. Enter the frequency values into **List B**, and label the list *freq*.

| Data | Frequency |
|------|-----------|
| 2 | 3 |
| 3 | 4 |
| 4 | 8 |
| 5 | 5 |

Press [⌂] **1 : Calculator** to open the Calculator application. Press [menu] , then select **5 : Statistics** > **1 : Stat Calculations ...** > **1 : One-Variable Statistics**. Press [enter] to choose 1 list. Select *data* from the **X1 List** drop-box and *freq* from the **Frequency List** drop-box, then press [enter] .

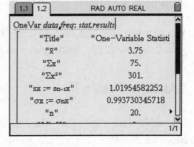

## TWO VARIABLE STATISTICS

Consider the data

| $x$ | 1 | 2 | 3 | 4 | 5 | 6 | 7 |
|-----|---|---|---|----|----|----|----|
| $y$ | 5 | 8 | 10 | 13 | 16 | 18 | 20 |

To find $s_x$ and $s_y$, the standard deviations of $x$ and $y$, enter the $x$ values into **List A** and label the list *one*, then enter the $y$ values into **List B** and label the list *two*.

Press **1:Calculator** to open the Calculator application, press menu , select **5:Statistics > 1:Stat Calculations... > 2:Two-Variable Statistics**. Select *one* from the **X List** drop-box, *two* from the **Y List** drop-box, then press enter to display the two variable statistics.

Scroll up through the results to find $s_x$, which is given by $\sigma_x = 2$, and $s_y$, which is given by $\sigma_y \approx 5.08$.

| 1.1 | 1.2 | DEG AUTO REAL | |
| --- | --- | --- | --- |
| "$\sigma x := \sigma_n x$" | | 2. | |
| "n" | | 7. | |
| "$\bar{y}$" | | 12.8571 | |
| "$\Sigma y$" | | 90. | |
| "$\Sigma y^2$" | | 1338. | |
| "sy := s$_{n-1}$y" | | 5.49025 | |
| "$\sigma y := \sigma_n y$" | | 5.08298 | |
| "$\Sigma xy$" | | 431. | |

## FINDING $r$ AND THE LINE OF BEST FIT

We can use our calculator to find the line of best fit connecting two variables. We can also find the values of Pearson's correlation coefficient $r$ and the coefficient of determination $r^2$, which measure the strength of the linear correlation between the two variables.

We will examine the relationship between the variables $x$ and $y$ for the data above.

Enter the $x$ values into **List A** and label the list *one*, then enter the $y$ values into **List B** and label the list *two*.

To draw a scatter diagram of the data, press **5:Data & Statistics**. Select *one* for the variable on the horizontal axis and *two* for the variable on the vertical axis. We will now find $r$ and the line of best fit.

Press **1:Calculator** menu , then select **5:Statistics > 1:Stat Calculations... > 3:Linear Regression (mx+b)**. Select *one* from the **X List** drop-box, *two* from the **Y List** drop-box, then press enter .

We can see that the line of best fit is $y \approx 2.54x + 2.71$, and that $r \approx 0.998$.

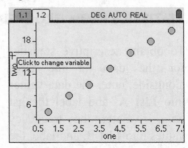

| 1.1 | 1.2 | DEG AUTO REAL | |
| --- | --- | --- | --- |
| "Title" | "Linear Regression (mx+b)" | | |
| "RegEqn" | "m*x+b" | | |
| "m" | 2.53571 | | |
| "b" | 2.71429 | | |
| "r²" | 0.995458 | | |
| "r" | 0.997726 | | |
| "Resid" | "{...}" | | |

## CALCULATING $\chi^2$

To calculate $\chi^2$ for the data alongside, enter the values of the table into matrix **A**, using the instructions given on page **44**.

|  | $A_1$ | $A_2$ |
| --- | --- | --- |
| $B_1$ | 21 | 28 |
| $B_2$ | 13 | 24 |

Press menu , then select **5:Statistics > 7:Stat Tests... > 8:$\chi^2$2-way Test**. Select $a$ from the drop-box, then select **OK**.

So, $\chi^2 \approx 0.526$. The $p$-value and the degrees of freedom are also given.

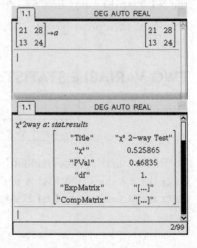

| 1.1 | DEG AUTO REAL | |
| --- | --- | --- |
| $\chi^2$2way $a$: stat.results | | |
| "Title" | "$\chi^2$ 2-way Test" | |
| "$\chi^2$" | 0.525865 | |
| "PVal" | 0.46835 | |
| "df" | 1. | |
| "ExpMatrix" | "[...]" | |
| "CompMatrix" | "[...]" | |

# SOLVING EQUATIONS

## SOLVING LINEAR EQUATIONS

To solve the linear equation $3.2x - 4.2 = 7.4$,
press menu from the Calculator application and select
**3:Calculations > 1:Numerical Solve**.

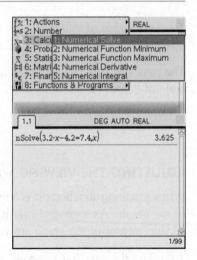

Enter the equation by pressing $3.2$ ⊗ − $4.2$ = $7.4$,
then press , ⊗ enter .

The solution is $x = 3.625$.

## SOLVING QUADRATIC EQUATIONS

We will write our own program to solve quadratic
equations. Note that this program can not be taken into
examinations.

To solve the quadratic equation $3x^2 + 2x - 11 = 0$,
press menu from the Calculator application, then select
**8:Functions and Programs > 1:Program Editor >
1:New...** . Label the program *quadrat*, and select **OK**.

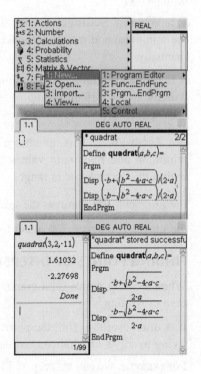

Enter the code for *quadrat* $(a, b, c)$ as shown alongside.
You can enter *Disp* by pressing menu **6:I/O > 1:Disp**.

When you are done, press menu , then select **2:Check
Syntax & Store > 1:Check Syntax & Store** to store the
program.

Press ctrl tab to move the cursor to the other side of
the screen, and enter *quadrat* $(3, 2, -11)$ enter .

So, the solutions are $x \approx -2.28$ or $1.61$.

# WORKING WITH FUNCTIONS

## GRAPHING FUNCTIONS

Selecting **2 : Graphs & Geometry** from the home screen
opens the graphing application, where you can graph
functions.

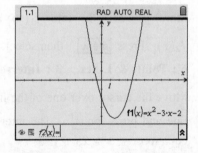

To graph the function $y = x^2 - 3x - 2$, press ⊗ $x^2$
− $3$ ⊗ − $2$ enter .

To view a table of values for the function, press menu ,
then select **2 : View > 9 : Add Function Table**.

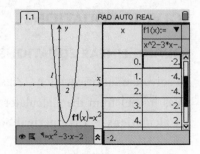

The page splits into 2, with the graph on one side and the
table of values on the other side.

## ADJUSTING THE VIEWING WINDOW

When graphing functions it is important that you are able to view all the important features
of the graph. As a general rule it is best to start with a large viewing window to make sure
all the features of the graph are visible. You can then make the window smaller if necessary.

To adjust the viewing window, press menu then select **4 : Window** . The most useful
options are:

**1 : Window Settings** :   With this option you can set
the minimum and maximum values for the $x$ and $y$ axes
manually.

**5 : Zoom-Standard** :   This option returns the viewing
window to the default setting of $-10 \leqslant x \leqslant 10$,
$-\frac{20}{3} \leqslant y \leqslant \frac{20}{3}$.

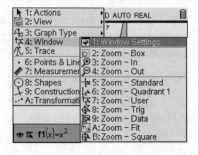

**A : Zoom-Fit** :   This option scales the $y$-axis to fit the
minimum and maximum values of the displayed graph
within the current $x$-axis range.

Pressing ctrl G removes the function entry line, allowing you to use the full screen to view
the graph. Press ctrl G again to bring the function entry line back.

## FINDING POINTS OF INTERSECTION

When locating points on a graph, it is advised that you set the accuracy level to *Float 4* for
ease of reading.

It is often useful to find the points of intersection of two graphs, for instance, when you are
trying to solve simultaneous equations.

For example, we can solve $y = 11 - 3x$ and $y = \dfrac{12 - x}{2}$
simultaneously by finding the point of intersection of
these two lines.

Store $y = 11 - 3x$ into $f_1(x)$ and $y = \dfrac{12 - x}{2}$ into
$f_2(x)$. Press menu , then select

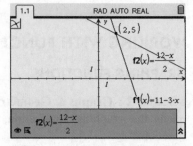

**6 : Points & Lines > 3 : Intersection Point(s)**.

Move the cursor over one of the lines and press enter , then move the cursor over the other
line and press enter . The intersection point $(2, 5)$ is displayed. So, the solution to the
equations is $x = 2$, $y = 5$.

## FINDING $x$-INTERCEPTS

In the special case when you wish to solve an equation of the form $f(x) = 0$, this can be done by graphing $y = f(x)$ and then finding when the graph cuts the $x$-axis.

For example, to solve $x^3 - 3x^2 + x + 1 = 0$, store $x^3 - 3x^2 + x + 1$ into $f_1(x)$.

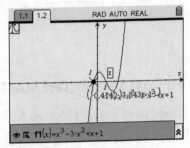

To find where this graph cuts the $x$-axis, press menu , then select **5 : Trace > 1 : Graph Trace**. Use the ◄ key to move the cursor along the curve until you reach the zero. A $z$ will appear on the screen.

If you need to move the coordinates to make them easier to read, press enter to paste the coordinates to the screen, then esc to exit the trace command. Move the cursor over the coordinates, and hold the ⊕ key until the hand closes. Use the cursor keys to drag the coordinates, then press esc .

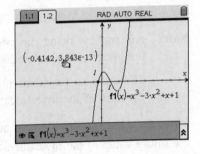

The solution $x \approx -0.414$ is given. Repeat this process to find the remaining solutions $x = 1$ and $x \approx 2.414$.

## TURNING POINTS

To find the turning point or vertex of $y = -x^2 + 2x + 3$, store $-x^2 + 2x + 3$ into $f_1(x)$.

Press menu , then select **5 : Trace > 1 : Graph Trace**.

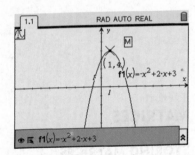

Use the ► key to move the cursor along the curve until the vertex is reached. An $M$ will appear on the screen to indicate a local maximum. The vertex is at $(1, 4)$.

## FINDING THE TANGENT TO A FUNCTION

To find the equation of the tangent to $y = x^2$ when $x = 1$, we first draw the graph of $y = x^2$. Press menu then select **5 : Trace > 1 : Graph Trace**. Press 1 enter , and the point $(1, 1)$ is located. Press enter esc to store the point.

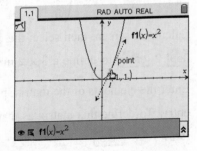

Press menu , then select
**6 : Points & Lines > 7 : Tangent**.

Move the cursor towards the point $(1, 1)$ until the word *point* appears, then press enter to draw the tangent.

To find the equation of the tangent, press esc to exit the tangent command, and move the cursor over the tangent until the word *line* appears. Press ctrl menu and select **6 : Coordinates and Equations**. The tangent has gradient 2, and equation $y = 2x - 1$.

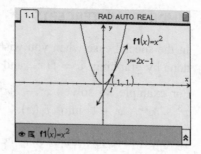

# FINANCIAL MATHEMATICS

Suppose we invest $5000 at 7.2% compounded annually. To find the value of the investment after 10 years, press menu from the Calculator application and select **7:Finance > 1:Finance Solver**. Set up the screen as shown.

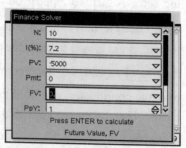

**Note:** All money being invested is considered as outgoings and is entered as a negative value.

There are no payments into the account during the term of the investment, so **Pmt** is set to 0.

Move the cursor to the **FV** field and press enter to find the future value of the investment.

The investment amounts to $10 021.16.

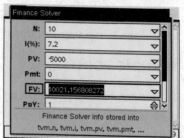

# MATRICES

## STORING MATRICES

To store the matrix $\begin{pmatrix} 2 & 3 \\ 1 & 4 \\ 5 & 0 \end{pmatrix}$, press ctrl × from the

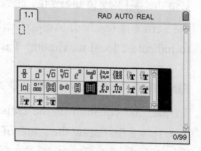

Calculator screen, then select the [⊞] template. Press 3 tab 2 enter to define a $3 \times 2$ matrix.

Enter the elements of the matrix, pressing tab after each entry. To define this matrix as matrix **A**, press ctrl var (sto►) Ⓐ enter .

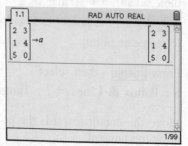

# Chapter 1

# Number properties

**Contents:**

## OPENING PROBLEM

## LEGEND OF THE AMBALAPPUZHA PAAL PAYASAM

According to Hindu legend, Lord Krishna once appeared as a sage before the king who ruled a region of India, and challenged him to a game of chess. The prize if Lord Krishna won was based on the chessboard: that the king would provide him with a single grain of rice for the first square, two grains of rice for the second square, four grains of rice for the third square, and so on doubling the rice on each successive square on the board. Lord Krishna of course did win, and the king was most unhappy when he realised he owed more rice than there was in the world.

**Things to think about:**

a How can we describe the number of grains of rice on each square?

b How many grains of rice would there be on the 40th square?

c Find the total number of grains of rice that the king owed.

In this chapter we revise some of the properties of numbers. We consider operations with numbers and the order in which operations should be performed.

# A        WORDS USED IN MATHEMATICS

Many words used in mathematics have special meanings. It is important to learn what each word means so we can use it correctly.

For example, when we write any number, we write some combination of the ten symbols: 1, 2, 3, 4, 5, 6, 7, 8, 9 and 0. These symbols are called **digits**.

There are four **basic operations** that are carried out with numbers:

> **Addition** $+$ to find the **sum**
>
> **Subtraction** $-$ to find the **difference**
>
> **Multiplication** $\times$ to find the **product**
>
> **Division** $\div$ to find the **quotient**

## SUMS AND DIFFERENCES

- To find the **sum** of two or more numbers, we *add* them.
  The sum of 3 and 16 is $3 + 16 = 19$.
- To find the **difference** between two numbers, we *subtract* the smaller from the larger.
  The difference between 3 and 16 is $16 - 3 = 13$.
- When adding or subtracting **zero (0)**, the number remains unchanged.
  So, $23 + 0 = 23$, $23 - 0 = 23$.
- When **adding** several numbers, we do not have to carry out the addition in the given order. Sometimes it is easier to change the order.

**Example 1**                                                    🔊 **Self Tutor**

Find:   a   the sum of 187, 369 and 13      b   the difference between 37 and 82.

a      $187 + 369 + 13$                    b      The difference between 37 and 82
  $= 187 + 13 + 369$                           $= 82 - 37$
  $= 200 + 369$                                $= 45$
  $= 569$

## PRODUCTS AND QUOTIENTS

- The word **product** is used to describe the result of a multiplication.
  The product of 3 and 5 is  $3 \times 5 = 15$.
  We say that 3 and 5 are **factors** of 15.

- The word **quotient** is used to describe the result of a division.
  The quotient of 15 and 3 is  $15 \div 3 = 5$.
  We say that 15 is the **dividend** and that 3 is the **divisor**.

- Multiplying by **one (1)** does not change the value of a number.
  So,  $17 \times 1 = 17$,  $1 \times 17 = 17$.

- Multiplying by **zero (0)** produces zero.
  So,  $17 \times 0 = 0$,  $0 \times 17 = 0$.

- Division by zero **(0)** is meaningless. We say the result is **undefined**.
  So,  $0 \div 4 = 0$  but  $4 \div 0$  is undefined.

- The order in which numbers are multiplied does **not** change the resultant number.
  So,  $3 \times 7 \times 2 = 2 \times 3 \times 7 = 42$.

## EXERCISE 1A

1 Find:

   a  the sum of 4, 8 and 11                    b  the difference between 23 and 41

   c  the sum of the first 12 positive whole numbers

   d  by how much 407 exceeds 239.

2 Solve the following problems:

   a  What number must be increased by 249 to get 752?

   b  What number must be decreased by 385 to get 2691?

3 Jose received €285 in wages whereas Juan received
  €312. How much more did Juan receive than Jose?

4 Emma's horse float has mass 406 kg. Her two horses
  weigh 517 kg and 561 kg. If Emma's car is allowed to
  tow 1500 kg, is she allowed to transport both horses at
  the same time?

5 To help buy an apartment, Agneta borrowed $26 200
  from her parents.  She has already paid them back
  amounts of $515, $872 and $664.  How much does
  Agneta still owe her parents?

6   Find:

   a   the product of 19 and 23                    b   the quotient of 1008 and 36
   c   the product of the first 6 positive whole numbers.

7   How many £3 buckets of chips must I sell to earn £246?

8   My orchard contains 8 rows of 12 apple trees. If each tree produces 400 fruit, how many apples can I harvest?

9   How many laps of a 400 m track does an athlete need to complete to run 10 000 m?

10   An apartment complex has 6 buildings, each 28 storeys high, and on each storey there are 5 apartments.

   a   How many apartments are there in total?
   b   If each apartment owner has to pay $3400 per year to maintain the buildings, what is the total annual budget for maintenance?

11   A cargo plane can carry 115 tonnes. How many plane loads are needed to transport 7245 tonnes of supplies?

# B    INDEX NOTATION

A convenient way to write a product of *identical factors* is to use **index** or **exponential notation**.

For example,  32 can be written as  $2 \times 2 \times 2 \times 2 \times 2$.

> There are five identical factors, each a 2.
>
> We can write  $2 \times 2 \times 2 \times 2 \times 2$  as  $2^5$.
>
> The small 5 is called the **index** or **exponent**, and the 2 is called the **base**.

Another example is:      $7^4$  ⟵  index or exponent
                                ⟵  base number

which tells us there are 4 factors of 7 multiplied together, or  $7 \times 7 \times 7 \times 7$.

The following table shows how the index form relates to the factorised numbers.

| Natural number | Factorised form | Index form | Spoken form |
|:---:|:---:|:---:|:---:|
| 2 | 2 | $2^1$ | two |
| 4 | $2 \times 2$ | $2^2$ | two squared |
| 8 | $2 \times 2 \times 2$ | $2^3$ | two cubed |
| 16 | $2 \times 2 \times 2 \times 2$ | $2^4$ | two to the fourth |
| 32 | $2 \times 2 \times 2 \times 2 \times 2$ | $2^5$ | two to the fifth |

Any non-zero number raised to the power zero is equal to 1.

$$a^0 = 1, \quad a \neq 0$$

$0^0$ is undefined.

---

**Example 2**   ◀)) **Self Tutor**

Write in index form:     $2 \times 2 \times 2 \times 2 \times 3 \times 3 \times 3$

$2 \times 2 \times 2 \times 2 \times 3 \times 3 \times 3 = 2^4 \times 3^3$     {4 factors of 2, and 3 factors of 3}

---

**Example 3**   ◀)) **Self Tutor**

Write as a natural number:
$2^3 \times 3^2 \times 5$

$2^3 \times 3^2 \times 5$
$= 2 \times 2 \times 2 \times 3 \times 3 \times 5$
$= 8 \times 9 \times 5$
$= 40 \times 9$
$= 360$

---

## CALCULATOR USE

The **power key** of your calculator may look like $\boxed{\wedge}$ , $\boxed{x^y}$  or $\boxed{y^x}$ . It can be used to enter numbers in index form into the calculator.

---

**Example 4**   ◀)) **Self Tutor**

Use your calculator to convert   $2^3 \times 3^4 \times 11^2$   into natural number form.

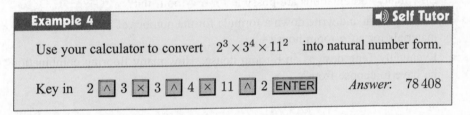

Key in   2 $\boxed{\wedge}$ 3 $\boxed{\times}$ 3 $\boxed{\wedge}$ 4 $\boxed{\times}$ 11 $\boxed{\wedge}$ 2 $\boxed{\text{ENTER}}$     *Answer*:   78 408

---

You will need to check if your calculator uses the same key sequence as in the example. If not, work out the sequence which gives you the correct answers.

## EXERCISE 1B.1

**1**  Copy and complete the values of these common powers:

    **a**  $5^1 = ....,\ 5^2 = ....,\ 5^3 = ....,\ 5^4 = ....$

    **b**  $6^1 = ....,\ 6^2 = ....,\ 6^3 = ....,\ 6^4 = ....$

    **c**  $7^1 = ....,\ 7^2 = ....,\ 7^3 = ....,\ 7^4 = ....$

**2**  Write each number in index form:

    **a**  $2 \times 3 \times 3$
    **b**  $3 \times 3 \times 7 \times 7$
    **c**  $2 \times 2 \times 5 \times 5 \times 7$

    **d**  $3 \times 5 \times 5 \times 5 \times 11$
    **e**  $2 \times 2 \times 3 \times 3 \times 3$
    **f**  $3 \times 3 \times 5 \times 7 \times 7 \times 7$

**3** Convert each product into natural number form:

    **a** $2 \times 5 \times 7$             **b** $2 \times 3^2$             **c** $3^3 \times 5$

    **d** $2^2 \times 3^3$            **e** $2^3 \times 3 \times 5^2$       **f** $2^4 \times 5^2 \times 11^2$

**4** Use your calculator to convert each product into natural number form:

    **a** $2^4 \times 3^5$            **b** $3^3 \times 5^5 \times 7$       **c** $2^5 \times 3^3 \times 11^2$

    **d** $7^4 \times 11^3 \times 13$      **e** $2 \times 3^6 \times 5^2$      **f** $2^2 \times 5^4 \times 7^3$

**5** Consider $2^1, 2^2, 2^3, 2^4, 2^5, \dots$. Look for a pattern and hence find the last digit of $2^{111}$.

**6**   **a** Copy and complete:

$$2^1 = \dots$$
$$2^1 + 2^2 = \dots$$
$$2^1 + 2^2 + 2^3 = \dots$$
$$2^1 + 2^2 + 2^3 + 2^4 = \dots$$

$$2^2 - 2 =$$
$$2^3 - 2 =$$
$$2^4 - 2 =$$
$$2^5 - 2 =$$

    **b** Use the results of **a** to predict an expression for $2^1 + 2^2 + 2^3 + \dots + 2^7$. Check your prediction using your calculator.

**7** Answer the **Opening Problem** on page **46**. Use question **6** to help you with part **c**.

**8** Teng is designing a house, and in each room he can choose from tiles, floorboards or carpet for the floor.

    **a** How many combinations of flooring materials are possible if he designs a 2-room "studio"?

    **b** How many flooring combinations are possible for a 3-room apartment?

    **c** How many combinations are possible for a 4-room flat?

    **d** Find a pattern and write down a formula for the number of combinations of flooring materials for an $n$-room house.

    **e** Eventually Teng designs an 8-room house. How many flooring combinations does he have to choose from?

## NEGATIVE BASES

Consider the statements below:

$$(-1)^1 = -1$$
$$(-1)^2 = -1 \times -1 = 1$$
$$(-1)^3 = -1 \times -1 \times -1 = -1$$
$$(-1)^4 = -1 \times -1 \times -1 \times -1 = 1$$

$$(-2)^1 = -2$$
$$(-2)^2 = -2 \times -2 = 4$$
$$(-2)^3 = -2 \times -2 \times -2 = -8$$
$$(-2)^4 = -2 \times -2 \times -2 \times -2 = 16$$

From these patterns we can see that:

> A **negative** base raised to an **odd** power is **negative**.
> A **negative** base raised to an **even** power is **positive**.

### Example 5

🔊 **Self Tutor**

Evaluate:   **a** $(-5)^2$   **b** $-5^2$   **c** $(-5)^3$   **d** $-(-5)^3$

| **a** $(-5)^2$ | **b** $-5^2$ | **c** $(-5)^3$ | **d** $-(-5)^3$ |
|---|---|---|---|
| $= 25$ | $= -1 \times 5^2$ | $= -125$ | $= -1 \times (-5)^3$ |
| | $= -25$ | | $= -1 \times -125$ |
| | | | $= 125$ |

Notice the effect of the brackets.

### Example 6

🔊 **Self Tutor**

Find, using your calculator:   **a** $(-5)^4$   **b** $-7^4$

|   |   |   | *Answer* |
|---|---|---|---|
| **a** | Press: | $($ $(-)$ 5 $)$ $\wedge$ 4 ENTER | 625 |
| **b** | Press: | $(-)$ 7 $\wedge$ 4 ENTER | $-2401$ |

## EXERCISE 1B.2

**1** Simplify:

   **a** $(-1)^2$       **b** $(-1)^5$       **c** $(-1)^8$       **d** $(-1)^{23}$

   **e** $(-1)^{10}$      **f** $-1^{10}$       **g** $-(-1)^{10}$     **h** $(-3)^2$

   **i** $(-4)^3$       **j** $-4^3$        **k** $-(-7)^2$      **l** $-(-3)^3$

**2** Use your calculator to find the following, recording the entire display:

   **a** $2^9$        **b** $(-3)^5$      **c** $-5^5$       **d** $9^3$       **e** $6^4$

   **f** $(-9)^4$      **g** $-9^4$      **h** $1.16^{11}$     **i** $-0.981^{14}$    **j** $(-1.14)^{23}$

## C     FACTORS OF POSITIVE INTEGERS

The **factors** of a positive integer are the positive integers which divide exactly into it.

For example, the factors of 8 are   1, 2, 4 and 8   since

$$8 \div 1 = 8$$
$$8 \div 2 = 4$$
$$8 \div 4 = 2$$
$$\text{and } 8 \div 8 = 1.$$

3 is not a factor of 8 since $8 \div 3 = 2$ with remainder 2. We say that 8 is not *divisible* by 3.

All positive integers can be split into **factor pairs**.

For example,     $8 = 1 \times 8$  or  $2 \times 4$

$132 = 11 \times 12$

> When we write a number as a product of factors, we say it is **factorised**.

10 may be factorised as a product of two factors in two ways:  $1 \times 10$  or  $2 \times 5$.

12 has factors  1, 2, 3, 4, 6, and 12,  and can be factorised as a product of two factors in three ways:  $1 \times 12$,  $2 \times 6$,  and  $3 \times 4$.

## EVEN AND ODD NUMBERS

> A whole number is **even** if it has 2 as a factor and thus is divisible by 2.
>
> A whole number is **odd** if it is not divisible by 2.

## EXERCISE 1C.1

1    a  List all the factors of 15.          b  List all the factors of 16.
    c  Copy and complete this equation:  $21 = 3 \times ....$
    d  Write another pair of factors which multiply to give 21.

2  List *all* the factors of each of the following numbers:
    a  9               b  17              c  22              d  24
    e  28              f  42              g  60              h  108

3  Complete the factorisations below:
    a  $36 = 6 \times ....$          b  $38 = 2 \times ....$          c  $48 = 12 \times ....$
    d  $90 = 5 \times ....$          e  $88 = 8 \times ....$          f  $54 = 3 \times ....$
    g  $72 = 12 \times ....$         h  $46 = 2 \times ....$          i  $60 = 12 \times ....$

4  Write the largest factor other than itself, for each of the following numbers:
    a  18              b  30              c  35              d  49
    e  88              f  143             g  126             h  219

5    a  Beginning with 6, write three consecutive even numbers.
    b  Beginning with 11, write five consecutive odd numbers.

6    a  Write two consecutive even numbers which add to 34.
    b  Write two non-consecutive odd numbers which add to 8.
    c  Write all the pairs of two non-consecutive odd numbers which add to 16.

7  Use the words "even" and "odd" to complete these sentences correctly:
    a  The sum of two even numbers is always ......
    b  The sum of two odd numbers is always ......

   **c** The sum of three even numbers is always ......

   **d** The sum of three odd numbers is always ......

   **e** The sum of an odd number and an even number is always ......

   **f** When an even number is subtracted from an odd number the result is ......

   **g** When an odd number is subtracted from an odd number the result is ......

   **h** The product of two odd numbers is always ......

   **i** The product of an even and an odd number is always ......

## PRIMES AND COMPOSITES

Some numbers can be written as the product of only one pair of factors, one and the number itself.

For example, the only two factors of 3 are 3 and 1, and of 11 are 11 and 1.

Numbers of this type are called **prime numbers**. They have important uses in coding and cryptography.

> A **prime** number is a natural number which has exactly two different factors.
>
> A **composite** number is a natural number which has more than two factors.

From the definition of prime and composite numbers we can see that

> the number 1 is neither prime nor composite.

## PRIME FACTORS

8 is a **composite number** since it has 4 factors: 1, 8, 2, 4.

We can write 8 as the product $2 \times 4$, or as the product of prime factors $2 \times 2 \times 2$.

The **fundamental theorem of arithmetic** is:

> Every composite number can be written as the product of prime factors in exactly one way (ignoring order).

So, although $252 = 2^2 \times 3^2 \times 7$ or $3^2 \times 7 \times 2^2$, the factors of 252 cannot involve different prime base numbers.

If 1 was a prime number then there would not be only one factorisation for each composite number. For example, $252 = 1^3 \times 2^2 \times 3^2 \times 7$ or $1^7 \times 2^2 \times 3^2 \times 7$. For this reason 1 is neither prime nor composite.

To express a composite number as the **product of prime numbers**, we systematically divide the number by the prime numbers which are its factors, starting with the smallest.

When we write a number as the product of prime factors, it is usual to express it in index form.

### Example 7

Express 252 as the product of prime factors.

| 2 | 252 |
|---|-----|
| 2 | 126 |
| 3 | 63 |
| 3 | 21 |
| 7 | 7 |
|   | 1 |

$$\therefore \quad 252 = 2 \times 2 \times 3 \times 3 \times 7$$
$$= 2^2 \times 3^2 \times 7$$

## EXERCISE 1C.2

1  a  List all the prime numbers less than 60.

   b  How many prime numbers are even? List them.

2  Show that the following are composites by finding a factor other than 1 or itself:

   a  985          b  7263          c  5840          d  1001

3  Express each of the following numbers as a product of prime factors:

   a  14          b  20          c  28          d  32          e  40

4  Use your list of prime numbers to help you find:

   a  the smallest one-digit odd prime

   b  all odd two-digit composite numbers less than 30

   c  a prime number whose two digits differ by 7.

## HIGHEST COMMON FACTOR

A number which is a factor of two or more other numbers is called a **common factor** of these numbers.

For example, 5 is a common factor of 25 and 35.

We can use the method of expressing a number as the product of its prime factors to find the **highest common factor (HCF)** of two or more natural numbers.

### Example 8

Find the highest common factor (HCF) of 18 and 24.

| 2 | 18 |
|---|-----|
| 3 | 9 |
| 3 | 3 |
|   | 1 |

| 2 | 24 |
|---|-----|
| 2 | 12 |
| 2 | 6 |
| 3 | 3 |
|   | 1 |

$18 = 2 \times 3 \times 3$

$24 = 2 \times 2 \times 2 \times 3$

$2 \times 3$ is common to the factorisations of both 18 and 24.

So, the highest common factor of 18 and 24 is $2 \times 3 = 6$.

## EXERCISE 1C.3

**1** Find the highest common factor of:

a 8, 12     b 9, 15     c 14, 21     d 27, 36

e 26, 39     f 18, 30     g 18, 24, 45     h 32, 60, 108

**2** Alice has a packet containing 48 green lollies. Bob has a packet containing 56 red lollies. What is the highest number of friends, including Alice and Bob, that the lollies can be shared amongst so that each person receives the same number of green lollies and each person receives the same number of red lollies?

---

### INVESTIGATION        WHEEL FACTORISATION

There are several different methods for finding prime numbers. For small prime numbers, a common way to search is to start with all numbers up to a particular limit and then remove the composite numbers and one. This is called a **sieve** method.

In this investigation we use a sieve method called **wheel factorisation** to remove *most* of the composite numbers up to 100.

**What to do:**

**1** The smallest prime numbers are 2 and 3.
$2 \times 3 = 6$, so we write the numbers from 1 to 6 in a circle.

**2** We continue to write the numbers all the way to 100 by adding more circles as shown. Notice how the lines of numbers extend out like the spokes of a wheel.
Click on the icon to load a completed printable wheel.

DEMO

**3** Cross out the number 1, since this is not prime.

**4** For spokes 2 and 3, which were the prime numbers used in step **1**, cross out all numbers except these primes.

**5** For spokes 4 and 6, which are composite numbers, cross out all numbers.

**6** The remaining numbers in the wheel are *mostly* primes. Sort through them and identify those which are not. What do you notice about the prime factors of these numbers?

**MULTIPLES OF POSITIVE INTEGERS**

The **multiples** of any whole number have that number as a factor. They are obtained by multiplying the number by 1, then 2, then 3, then 4, and so on.

The multiples of 10 are  $1 \times 10$,  $2 \times 10$,  $3 \times 10$,  $4 \times 10$,  $5 \times 10$, ....

or  10, 20, 30, 40, 50, ....

Likewise, the multiples of 15 are  15, 30, 45, 60, 75, ....

The number 30 is a multiple of both 10 and 15, so we say 30 is a **common multiple** of 10 and 15. Notice that 10 and 15 are both factors of 30.

In fact, 30 has the factors  1, 2, 3, 5, 6, 10, 15, and 30,  and 30 is a *common multiple* of each of these factors.

---

**Example 9**    ◀) **Self Tutor**

Find common multiples of 4 and 6 between 20 and 40.

The multiples of 4 are  4, 8, 12, 16, 20, 24, 28, 32, 36, 40, ....

The multiples of 6 are  6, 12, 18, 24, 30, 36, 42, ....

∴  the common multiples between 20 and 40 are  24 and 36.

---

## LOWEST COMMON MULTIPLE

The **lowest common multiple (LCM)** of two or more numbers is the smallest number which is a multiple of *each* of these numbers.

---

**Example 10**    ◀) **Self Tutor**

Find the lowest common multiple of 9 and 12.

The multiples of 9 are:   9, 18, 27, 36, 45, 54, 63, 72, 81, ....

The multiples of 12 are:   12, 24, 36, 48, 60, 72, 84, ....

∴  the common multiples are 36, 72, .... and 36 is the smallest of these

∴  the LCM is 36.

---

## EXERCISE 1D

1  List the first six multiples of:

   a  4          b  5          c  7          d  11

2  Find the:

   a  fourth multiple of 6          b  sixth multiple of 9.

**3** List the numbers from 1 to 40.

   **a** Put a circle around each multiple of 3.

   **b** Put a square around each multiple of 5.

   **c** List the common multiples of 3 and 5 which are less than 40.

**4** Consider the following list of multiples of 12:   12  24  36  48  60  72  84  96  108  120
State the numbers from the list which are common multiples of:

   **a** 9 and 12        **b** 12 and 15        **c** 9, 12 and 15

**5** Find the lowest common multiple of the following sets:

   **a** 2, 5        **b** 3, 7        **c** 4, 5        **d** 6, 8

   **e** 6, 9        **f** 10, 12        **g** 4, 5 and 7        **h** 6, 9 and 12

**6** Find:    **a** the smallest multiple of 7 that is greater than 100

            **b** the greatest multiple of 9 that is less than 200.

**7** Three clocks start chiming at exactly the same instant. One chimes every 3 hours, one every 4 hours, and the other every six hours. When will they next chime together?

**8** The football fields at three different schools were measured, and it was found that their perimeters were 320 m, 360 m, and 400 m. If the students at each school are to run the same distance, and this must be a whole number of laps, what is the shortest distance they need to run?

## E     ORDER OF OPERATIONS

When two or more operations are carried out, different answers can result depending on the **order** in which the operations are performed.

For example, consider the expression $11 - 4 \times 2$.

Bruce decided to subtract first, then multiply:

$$11 - 4 \times 2$$
$$= 7 \times 2$$
$$= 14$$

Poj decided to multiply first, then subtract:

$$11 - 4 \times 2$$
$$= 11 - 8$$
$$= 3$$

Which answer is correct, 14 or 3?

To avoid this problem, a set of rules for the **order of performing operations** has been agreed upon by all mathematicians.

### RULES FOR ORDER OF OPERATIONS

- Perform operations within **Brackets** first.
- Calculate any part involving **Exponents**.
- Starting from the left, perform all **Divisions** and **Multiplications** as you come to them.
- Finally, working from the left, perform all **Additions** and **Subtractions**.

The word **BEDMAS** may help you remember this order.

**Note:**
- If an expression contains more than one set of brackets, evaluate the innermost brackets first.
- The division line of fractions behaves like a set of brackets. This means that the numerator and denominator must each be found before doing the division.

Using these rules, Poj's method is correct in the above example, and $11 - 4 \times 2 = 3$.

---

**Example 11**  ◀) **Self Tutor**

Evaluate:   $35 - 10 \div 2 \times 5 + 3$

$\phantom{=}35 - 10 \div 2 \times 5 + 3$
$= 35 - 5 \times 5 + 3$   {division and multiplication working from left}
$= 35 - 25 + 3$
$= 10 + 3$   {subtraction and addition working from left}
$= 13$

---

## EXERCISE 1E.1

**1** Evaluate the following:

| | | |
|---|---|---|
| **a** $6 - 3 + 4$ | **b** $7 \times 4 \div 2$ | **c** $3 + 2 \times 5$ |
| **d** $3 \times 2 - 1$ | **e** $16 \div 4 \times 2$ | **f** $15 \div 5 + 2$ |
| **g** $9 - 6 \div 3$ | **h** $4 + 7 - 3 \times 2$ | **i** $3 \times 4 - 2 \times 5$ |
| **j** $3 + 9 \div 3 - 2$ | **k** $7 - 9 \div 3 \times 2$ | **l** $13 - 2 \times 6 + 7$ |

---

**Example 12**  ◀) **Self Tutor**

Evaluate:   $2 \times (3 \times 6 - 4) + 7$

$\phantom{=}2 \times (3 \times 6 - 4) + 7$
$= 2 \times (18 - 4) + 7$   {inside brackets, multiply}
$= 2 \times 14 + 7$   {complete brackets}
$= 28 + 7$   {multiplication next}
$= 35$   {addition last}

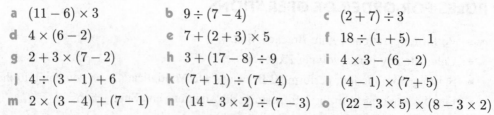

If you do not follow the order rules, you are likely to get the wrong answer.

---

**2** Evaluate the following:

| | | |
|---|---|---|
| **a** $(11 - 6) \times 3$ | **b** $9 \div (7 - 4)$ | **c** $(2 + 7) \div 3$ |
| **d** $4 \times (6 - 2)$ | **e** $7 + (2 + 3) \times 5$ | **f** $18 \div (1 + 5) - 1$ |
| **g** $2 + 3 \times (7 - 2)$ | **h** $3 + (17 - 8) \div 9$ | **i** $4 \times 3 - (6 - 2)$ |
| **j** $4 \div (3 - 1) + 6$ | **k** $(7 + 11) \div (7 - 4)$ | **l** $(4 - 1) \times (7 + 5)$ |
| **m** $2 \times (3 - 4) + (7 - 1)$ | **n** $(14 - 3 \times 2) \div (7 - 3)$ | **o** $(22 - 3 \times 5) \times (8 - 3 \times 2)$ |

**Example 13** ◀)) **Self Tutor**

Evaluate the innermost brackets first.

Evaluate:   $5 + [13 - (8 \div 4)]$

$5 + [13 - (8 \div 4)]$
$= 5 + [13 - 2]$     {innermost brackets first}
$= 5 + 11$     {remaining brackets next}
$= 16$     {addition last}

**3**  Simplify:

  **a**  $3 \times [2 + (7 - 5)]$      **b**  $3 + [2 \times (7 - 5)]$      **c**  $[(13 - 7) \div 2] + 11$

  **d**  $[14 \div (2 + 5)] \times 3$      **e**  $3 + [32 \div (2 + 6)] \div 2$      **f**  $3 \times [(32 \div 2) + 6] - 2$

**Example 14** ◀)) **Self Tutor**

Evaluate:   $\dfrac{16 - (4 - 2)}{14 \div (3 + 4)}$

$\dfrac{16 - (4 - 2)}{14 \div (3 + 4)}$

$= \dfrac{16 - 2}{14 \div 7}$     {brackets first}

$= \dfrac{14}{2}$     {evaluate numerator, denominator}

$= 7$     {do the division}

In a fraction we need to evaluate the numerator and denominator separately and then perform the division.

**4**  Simplify:

  **a**  $\dfrac{19 - 3}{2}$      **b**  $\dfrac{11 - 6}{4 \times 5}$      **c**  $\dfrac{6 \times (7 - 2)}{10}$      **d**  $\dfrac{18 - 2 \times 7}{6 \div 3}$

**5**  Simplify:

  **a**  $3 + 5^2$      **b**  $7^2 - 18$      **c**  $5^2 - 6 \times 2$

  **d**  $(13 - 4) \div 3^2$      **e**  $48 \div (5 - 3)^2$      **f**  $2 \times 3^3 - (11 - 7)^2$

**6**  Simplify:

  **a**  $3 \times -2 + 18$      **b**  $-3 \times -2 - 18$      **c**  $23 - 5 \times -3$

  **d**  $[3 - (-2 + 7)] + 4$      **e**  $(18 \div 3) \times -2$      **f**  $2(7 - 13) - (6 - 12)$

  **g**  $-6 \times (2 - 7)$      **h**  $-(14 - 8) \div -2$      **i**  $-18 - (8 - 15)$

  **j**  $-52 \div (6 - 19)$      **k**  $\dfrac{38 - -4}{6 \times -7}$      **l**  $\dfrac{28 - (-3 \times 4)}{10 \times -2}$

## USING A CALCULATOR

Modern calculators are designed to use BEDMAS automatically. However, unless your calculator has a *natural mathematics* mode, you need to be careful with fractions that you place the numerator in brackets and also the denominator in brackets.

For example:

Instructions for using your calculator can be found at the start of the book.

- to calculate   $15 \times 60 \div (8 + 7)$

  press  15 ☒ 60 ☒ ☒ 8 ☒ 7 ☒ ENTER    *Answer:* 60

- to calculate  $\dfrac{27 + 13}{5 \times 4}$  we first write the fraction as  $\dfrac{(27 + 13)}{(5 \times 4)}$

  then press  ☒ 27 ☒ 13 ☒ ☒ ☒ 5 ☒ 4 ☒ ENTER

  *Answer:* 2

Notice that by pressing  27 ☒ 13 ☒ 5 ☒ 4 ENTER  we would

be finding the value of a very different expression:  $27 + \dfrac{13}{5} \times 4$

which has result $37.4$.

## EXERCISE 1E.2

1 Use your calculator to simplify:

   **a** $6 \times 8 - 18 \div (2 + 4)$       **b** $10 \div 5 + 20 \div (4 + 1)$

   **c** $5 + (2 \times 10 - 5) - 6$       **d** $18 - (15 \div 3 + 4) + 1$

   **e** $(2 \times 3 - 4) + (33 \div 11 + 5)$       **f** $(18 \div 3 + 3) \div (4 \times 4 - 7)$

   **g** $(50 \div 5 + 6) - (8 \times 2 - 4)$       **h** $(10 \times 3 - 20) + 3 \times (9 \div 3 + 2)$

   **i** $(7 - 3 \times 2) \div (8 \div 4 - 1)$       **j** $(5 + 3) \times 2 + 10 \div (8 - 3)$

   **k** $\dfrac{27 - (18 \div 3) + 3}{3 \times 4}$       **l** $\dfrac{620 - 224}{9 \times 4 \times 11}$

---

## REVIEW SET 1A

**1** Find:

   **a** the sum of 28 and 18       **b** the quotient of 425 and 17

   **c** the difference between 246 and 81       **d** the product of 29 and 12.

**2** If Arnold does 37 situps on Wednesday, 45 on Thursday and 29 on Friday, how many has he done over the three day period?

**3** Write  $2 \times 2 \times 5 \times 5 \times 5 \times 7$:

   **a** in index form       **b** as a natural number.

**4** Evaluate:

   **a** $3^2$      **b** $(-5)^2$      **c** $-7^2$      **d** $-2^3$

**5** The ancient Greeks compared the brightness of stars by giving them a "magnitude number". They said a magnitude 1 star (the brightest) was twice as bright as a magnitude 2 star, which was twice as bright as a magnitude 3 star, and so on.

  **a** How many times brighter was a magnitude 1 star than a magnitude 3 star?

  **b** The lowest magnitude was 6. How many times brighter was the brightest star than the faintest star?

**6** List all the:

  **a** multiples of 7 between 80 and 100

  **b** prime numbers between 30 and 40

  **c** pairs of even numbers that add to 22.

**7** List all the factors of:

  **a** 28 **b** 31 **c** 36 **d** 16

**8** Find the highest common factor of:

  **a** 16, 20 **b** 54, 72 **c** 56, 70

**9** Find the lowest common multiple of:

  **a** 6, 10 **b** 7, 8 **c** 3, 4 and 5

**10** Evaluate:

  **a** $12 + 27 \div 3$ **b** $3 \times (5 - 2)$ **c** $(11 - 5) \times (3 + 4)$

**11** Simplify:

  **a** $\dfrac{7 + 17}{3 - 1}$ **b** $7^2 - 4 \times 5$ **c** $-6 - 5 - 4$

## REVIEW SET 1B

**1** Zhang starts the day with \$487 in his wallet. During the day he buys lunch for \$12, pays \$175 in rent and buys \$29 worth of phone credit. How much money is left in Zhang's wallet?

**2** Every hour, a factory produces 23 boxes of soap. Each box contains 25 bars of soap. How many bars of soap are produced in an 8 hour working day?

**3** Simplify:

  **a** $(-1)^4$ **b** $(-1)^{13}$ **c** $-(-2)^5$ **d** $-7.1^2$

**4** Find the sum of all the odd numbers between 70 and 80.

**5** Show that 2241 is a composite number.

**6** Express the following numbers as the products of prime factors in index form:

  **a** 33 **b** 60 **c** 56

**7** **a** List all the pairs of factors of 42.

  **b** Write down all the factors of 18.

**8** Find the:

    **a** HCF of 48 and 45                       **b** LCM of 12 and 20.

**9** A shop runs a promotion in which every 500th customer receives a free gift, every 800th customer receives a voucher and every 1200th customer gets a discount on their purchases. Which customer is the first to receive a free gift, a voucher *and* a discount?

**10** Evaluate:

    **a** $[8 - (1 + 2)] \times 3$       **b** $15 \div (2 + 3)$       **c** $6^2 \div 2 + 4$

**11** Simplify:

    **a** $-3 \times (5 + 7)$       **b** $\dfrac{-4 \times 8}{24 \div 3}$       **c** $6 - (2 - 8)$

# Chapter 2

# Measurement

**Syllabus reference: 2.2, 2.3, 2.4**

**Contents:**

## DISCUSSION

Write down five quantities which we commonly *measure*.

What devices do we use to measure these quantities?

What units are these quantities measured in?

What errors are associated with our measurements?

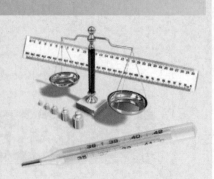

## OPENING PROBLEM

On September 28, 2008, Ethiopian runner Haile Gebrselassie won the 42.195 km Berlin Marathon in the world record time of 2 hours 3 minutes and 59 seconds.

**Things to think about:**

**a** What is the length of the marathon in metres?

**b** Can you write the time taken by Haile in:

    **i** seconds                 **ii** hours?

**c** What was Haile's average speed for the marathon?

# A                              TIME

For thousands of years people measured time by observing the passage of day and night, the stars, and the changes of season. This was necessary to help them with farming and other aspects of daily life.

© iStockphoto

The earliest inventions for measuring time included the sundial, the hourglass, and the waterclock or *clepsydra*.

Over the centuries many different devices were made to measure time more accurately, eventually leading to the watches and clocks we use today. The most accurate clock in the world, the cesium fountain atomic clock, is inaccurate by only one second every 20 million years.

© iStockphoto

Musée de l'Agora antique d'Athènes, photo from Wikimedia Commons

## UNITS OF TIME

The units of time we use are based on the sun, the moon, and the Earth's rotation.

The most common units are related as follows:

> 1 minute = 60 seconds
> 1 hour = 60 minutes = 3600 seconds
> 1 day = 24 hours
> 1 week = 7 days
> 1 year = 12 months = $365\frac{1}{4}$ days

For times which are longer or shorter we either multiply or divide by powers of 10:

$$1 \text{ millisecond} = \frac{1}{1000} \text{ second}$$

$$1 \text{ microsecond} = \frac{1}{1\,000\,000} \text{ second}$$

> 1 decade = 10 years
> 1 century = 100 years
> 1 millennium = 1000 years

### Example 1 — ◀⦁ Self Tutor

Convert   3 hours 26 minutes 18 seconds  into seconds.

> 3 h 26 min 18 s
> $= (3 \times 3600) \text{ s} + (26 \times 60) \text{ s} + 18 \text{ s}$
> $= 12\,378 \text{ s}$

We use h for hours, min for minutes, s for seconds.

### Example 2 — ◀⦁ Self Tutor

What is the time difference between 11.43 am and 3.18 pm?

> 11.43 am to 12 noon = 17 min
> 12 noon to 3 pm = 3 h
> 3 pm to 3.18 pm = 18 min
> $\therefore$   the total is   3 h 35 min

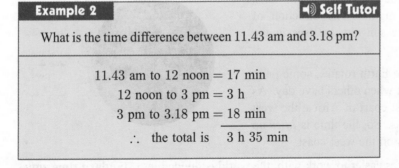

### Example 3 — ◀⦁ Self Tutor

What is the time  $3\frac{1}{2}$ hours before 1.15 pm?

> 1.15 pm $- 3\frac{1}{2}$ hours
> $= 1.15 \text{ pm} - 3 \text{ h} - 30 \text{ min}$
> $= 10.15 \text{ am} - 30 \text{ min}$
> $= 9.45 \text{ am}$

# EXERCISE 2A.1

1 Convert into seconds:

  a  45 minutes        b  1 hour 10 minutes      c  2 hours 5 minutes 28 seconds

2 Convert into minutes:

  a  $3\frac{1}{2}$ hours                        b  1440 seconds

  c  5 hours 13 minutes                          d  3 days 1 hour 48 minutes

3 Find the time difference between:

  a  2.30 am  and  7.20 am                       b  10.14 am  and  1.51 pm

  c  5.18 pm  and  11.32 pm                      d  3.42 pm  and  6.08 am  the next day.

4 Joseph caught the 7.54 am train into town, arriving in the main station at 8.47 am.  It took him 16 minutes to walk from the station to work.

  a  How long was Joseph's train journey?    b  At what time did Joseph arrive at work?

5 Find the time that is:

  a  3 hours after 7.15 am                       b  $5\frac{1}{2}$ hours before 10.26 am

  c  $4\frac{1}{2}$ hours after 11.50 am         d  $6\frac{1}{2}$ hours before 2.35 am.

6 I left for work $1\frac{1}{4}$ hours after I woke up.  If I left at 8.05 am, at what time did I wake up?

7 My brother overseas telephoned me at 3.47 am.  I was very angry and told him I would ring him back when I woke up in the morning.  If I woke up at 7.04 am, how long did my brother have to wait for the return call?

# TIME ZONES (EXTENSION)

The Earth rotates about its north-south axis, resulting in day and night.  The direction of rotation means that the sun always rises in the east and sets in the west.

Because of the way the Earth rotates, some parts of the world have night when others have day.  As the sun rises on the east coast of Africa, the west coast is still in darkness.  So, the time is *later* on the east coast than it is on the west coast.

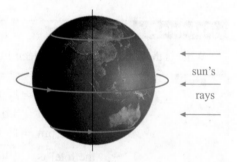

sun's

rays

To make time differences easier to work with, the world is divided into **standard time zones** which are measured in 1 hour units.

The **prime meridian** is the line of longitude which passes through Greenwich, near London.  Times along this prime meridian have **Greenwich Mean Time (GMT)**.

There are 12 time zones to the east of the prime meridian which are **ahead** of GMT.

There are 12 time zones to the west of the prime meridian which are **behind** GMT.

The $+12$ and $-12$ time zones meet at the **international date line**, at which point we take off 24 hours when stepping from west to east.

A Standard Time Zone map is shown on page **67**.

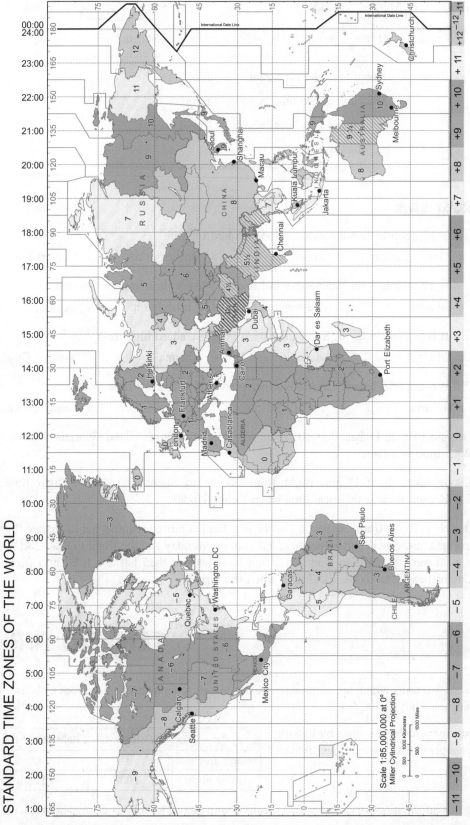

STANDARD TIME ZONES OF THE WORLD

Scale 1:85,000,000 at 0°
Miller Cylindrical Projection

https://www.cia.gov/library/publications/the-world-factbook/reference_maps/pdf/time_zones.pdf

### Example 4    ◄》 Self Tutor

If it is 3 pm in Dubai, what time is it in Macau?

Dubai is in the time zone +4 hours.

Macau is in the time zone +8 hours.

∴    Macau is 4 hours ahead of Dubai.

∴    the time is 7 pm.

## EXERCISE 2A.2

**1**  If it is 12 noon in London, what is the standard time in:

   **a** Dar es Salaam    **b** Seoul    **c** Buenos Aires    **d** Calgary?

**2**  If it is 12 midnight on Wednesday in London, what is the standard time in:

   **a** Macau    **b** Washington DC    **c** Christchurch    **d** Seattle?

**3**  If it is 6 pm on Friday in Sao Paulo, what is the standard time in:

   **a** Madrid    **b** Helsinki    **c** Chennai    **d** Mexico City?

**4**  If it is 8 am on Thursday in Melbourne, what is the standard time in:

   **a** Jakarta    **b** Port Elizabeth    **c** Caracas    **d** Casablanca?

**5**  Georgio lives in Dubai. It is 10.30 am when he phones his friend Gabriela in Amman. What time is it there?

**6**  Keong takes the 8.15 pm flight from Jakarta to Shanghai.  If the flight time is 6 h 15 min, what is the local time when Keong lands?

**7**  Beatrix is flying from Quebec to Casablanca, but her airline requires her to change flights in Frankfurt. She departs Quebec at 9.35 pm on Monday and the flight to Frankfurt takes 8 h 25 min. She has to wait 3 h 5 min in Frankfurt, then has a 3 h 20 min flight to Casablanca. What is the local time when she arrives?

## B    TEMPERATURE

There are two units which are commonly used to measure temperature:  degrees Celsius (°C) and  degrees Fahrenheit (°F).

We can compare the two units by looking at the temperatures at which water freezes and boils.

|  | Celsius (°C) | Fahrenheit (°F) |
|---|---|---|
| water freezes | 0 | 32 |
| water boils | 100 | 212 |

Using this information we can construct a **conversion graph** to help us change between units.

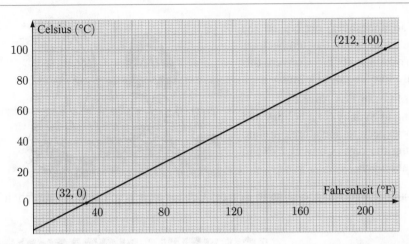

## CONVERSION FORMULAE

To convert between the temperature units more exactly we can use the following conversion formulae:

> If $C$ is in degrees Celsius and $F$ is in degrees Fahrenheit then:
>
> - to convert °C to °F, use $F = \frac{9}{5}C + 32$
> - to convert °F to °C, use $C = \frac{5}{9}(F - 32)$

---

**Example 5** ◀) **Self Tutor**

Convert:  a  392°F to °C          b  30°C to °F

a
$$C = \tfrac{5}{9}(F - 32)$$
$$\therefore \ C = \tfrac{5}{9}(392 - 32)$$
$$\therefore \ C = 200$$
So, $392°F = 200°C$

b
$$F = \tfrac{9}{5}C + 32$$
$$\therefore \ F = \tfrac{9}{5} \times 30 + 32$$
$$\therefore \ F = 86$$
So, $30°C = 86°F$

---

## EXERCISE 2B

1  Estimate the temperature in degrees Celsius for:
   a  60°F          b  180°F          c  10°F

2  Estimate the temperature in degrees Fahrenheit for:
   a  60°C          b  30°C          c  15°C

3  Convert the following into °C:
   a  0°F          b  100°F          c  20°F

4  Convert the following into °F:
   a  70°C          b  −10°C          c  400°C

5  Rearrange $F = \frac{9}{5}C + 32$ to show $C = \frac{5}{9}(F - 32)$.

DEMO

**6**  **a**  Jonte, in Johannesburg, notices on the Weather Channel that the temperature in New York is $-16^o$F.  Convert this temperature into degrees Celsius.

    **b**  Mary-Lou lives in Los Angeles. She is going to Sydney for a holiday and is told to expect temperatures around $25^o$C during the day.  Convert $25^o$C to degrees Fahrenheit.

**7**  Find the temperature which is the same in degrees Celsius as it is in degrees Fahrenheit.

# C | SCIENTIFIC NOTATION (STANDARD FORM)

Many people doing scientific work deal with very large or very small numbers.  To avoid having to write and count lots of zeros, they use **scientific notation** to write numbers.

Observe the pattern:

$$10\,000 = 10^4$$
$$1000 = 10^3$$
$$100 = 10^2$$
$$10 = 10^1$$
$$1 = 10^0$$
$$\tfrac{1}{10} = 10^{-1}$$
$$\tfrac{1}{100} = 10^{-2}$$
$$\tfrac{1}{1000} = 10^{-3}$$

(with $\div 10$ and $-1$ shown at each step)

As we divide by 10, the **index** or **exponent** of 10 decreases by one.

We can use this pattern to simplify the writing of very large and very small numbers.

For example,    $5\,000\,000$          and          $0.000\,003$

$$= 5 \times 1\,000\,000 \qquad\qquad = \tfrac{3}{1\,000\,000}$$
$$= 5 \times 10^6 \qquad\qquad\qquad = 3 \times \tfrac{1}{1\,000\,000}$$
$$= 3 \times 10^{-6}$$

> **Scientific notation** or **standard form** involves writing any given number as a *number between* 1 *and* 10, multiplied by a *power of* 10.
>
> i.e.,  $a \times 10^k$  where  $1 \leqslant a < 10$  and $k$ is an integer.

| **Example 6** | ◆) **Self Tutor** |
|---|---|

Write in scientific notation:

   **a**  9 448 800 000             **b**  0.000 000 053 04

| | |
|---|---|
| **a**   9 448 800 000 | **b**   0.000 000 053 04 |
| $= 9.4488 \times 1\,000\,000\,000$ | $= 5.304 \div 100\,000\,000$ |
| So, $a = 9.4488$ and $k = 9$ | So, $a = 5.304$ and $k = -8$ |
| The number is $9.4488 \times 10^9$. | The number is $5.304 \times 10^{-8}$. |

A number such as 4.62 is already between 1 and 10. We write it in scientific notation as $4.62 \times 10^0$ since $10^0 = 1$.

Your calculator is able to display numbers using scientific notation. For help with this, consult the **graphics calculator instructions** at the start of this book.

## EXERCISE 2C

**1**  Which of the following numbers are *not* written in scientific notation?

    **a**  $3.7 \times 10^4$     **b**  $4.2 \times 10^{-7}$     **c**  $0.3 \times 10^5$     **d**  $21 \times 10^{11}$

**2**  Copy and complete:

$$1000 = 10^3$$
$$100 = 10^2$$
$$10 =$$
$$1 =$$
$$0.1 =$$
$$0.01 = 10^{-2}$$
$$0.001 =$$
$$0.0001 =$$

**3**  Write as decimal numbers:

    **a**  $8.2 \times 10^4$     **b**  $3.6 \times 10^1$     **c**  $8.7 \times 10^0$     **d**  $4.9 \times 10^2$

    **e**  $7.8 \times 10^{-3}$     **f**  $5.5 \times 10^{-2}$     **g**  $3.76 \times 10^{-1}$     **h**  $2.02 \times 10^{-3}$

**4**  Write in scientific notation:

    **a**  3900     **b**  17 000     **c**  0.04     **d**  0.000 071

    **e**  85     **f**  6.3     **g**  2 480 000     **h**  0.000 000 108

**5**  Write these calculator display numbers in scientific notation:

    **a**  $\boxed{4.5E07}$     **b**  $\boxed{3.8E\text{-}04}$     **c**  $\boxed{2.1E05}$     **d**  $\boxed{4.0E\text{-}03}$

    **e**  $\boxed{6.1E03}$     **f**  $\boxed{1.6E\text{-}06}$     **g**  $\boxed{3.9E04}$     **h**  $\boxed{6.7E\text{-}02}$

**6**  Write the numbers displayed in question **5** as decimal numbers.

    For example,  $\boxed{3.9E06}$  is    $3.9 \times 10^6$

$$= 3.900\,000 \times 1\,000\,000$$
$$= 3\,900\,000$$

> In an exam it is **not** acceptable to write your answer as a calculator display.

**7** Write as a decimal number:

   **a** The estimated population of the world in the year 2010 is $6.8 \times 10^9$ people.

   **b** The pressure at the edge of the Earth's thermosphere is about $1.0 \times 10^{-7}$ Pa.

   **c** The diameter of the Milky Way is $1.4 \times 10^5$ light years.

   **d** The mass of a proton is about $1.67 \times 10^{-27}$ kg.

**8** Express the following in scientific notation:

   **a** The Jurassic period lasted about 54 400 000 years.

   **b** The ball bearing in a pen nib has diameter 0.003 m.

   **c** There are about 311 900 000 different 5-card poker hands which can be dealt.

   **d** The wavelength of blue light is about 0.000 000 47 m.

## D    INTERNATIONAL SYSTEM (SI) UNITS

The **International system of Units**, abbreviated SI from the French *le Système international d'unités*, is the world's most widely used system of measurement.

It is founded on seven base units:

| Quantity | Name | Symbol |
|---|---|---|
| Distance | metre | m |
| Mass | kilogram | kg |
| Time | second | s |
| Electric current | ampere | A |
| Temperature | kelvin | K |
| Intensity of light | candela | cd |
| Amount of substance | mole | mol |

Other SI units, called **derived units**, are defined algebraically in terms of the base units.

Some of the common SI derived units are:

| Quantity | Name | Symbol |
|---|---|---|
| Area | square metre | $m^2$ |
| Volume | cubic metre | $m^3$ |
| Mass | gram | g |
| Velocity | metres per second | $m\,s^{-1}$ |
| Angle | radian | rad |

| Quantity | Name | Symbol |
|---|---|---|
| Force | newton | N |
| Pressure | pascal | Pa |
| Energy | joule | J |
| Power | watt | W |
| Frequency | hertz | Hz |

When we multiply one unit by another, we leave a short space between the unit symbols.

When we divide one unit by another, we use an oblique line between the unit symbols, or a negative index. For example, we write metres per second as m/s or $m\,s^{-1}$.

### Example 7

**a** Density is defined as mass per unit volume. Write the SI unit for density.

**b** A newton is defined as the force which accelerates a mass of 1 kilogram at the rate of 1 metre per second per second. Write down the combination of SI units which defines a newton.

**a** The unit for mass is kg, and the unit for volume is $m^3$.

∴ the unit for density is $kg/m^3$ or $kg\,m^{-3}$.

**b** 1 newton = 1 kilogram × 1 metre per second per second = $1\ kg\,m\,s^{-2}$

In addition to the base and derived units, the SI allows the use of other units, such as:

| Quantity | Name | Symbol | SI equivalent |
|---|---|---|---|
| Time | minute | min | 60 s |
| | hour | h | 3600 s |
| Mass | tonne | t | 1000 kg |
| Capacity | litre | L | 0.001 $m^3$ |
| Area | hectare | ha | 10 000 $m^2$ |
| Angle | degree | o | $\frac{\pi}{180}$ rad |
| Temperature | degree Celsius | °C | $K - 273.15$ |
| Pressure | millibar | mb | 100 Pa |
| Distance at sea | Nautical mile | Nm | 1.852 km |
| Speed at sea | Knot | kn | 1.852 $km\,h^{-1}$ |
| Energy | Kilowatt hour | kWh | 3.6 MJ |

The symbol for litre can be l or L depending on the country. We use L here to avoid confusion with the number 1.

Smaller or larger multiples of these units are obtained by combining the base unit with a prefix chosen from a progression of powers of 10. The most commonly used are:

| | | |
|---|---|---|
| nano | n | $10^{-9} = \frac{1}{1\,000\,000\,000}$ |
| micro | $\mu$ | $10^{-6} = \frac{1}{1\,000\,000}$ |
| milli | m | $10^{-3} = \frac{1}{1000}$ |

| | | |
|---|---|---|
| kilo | k | $10^3 = 1000$ |
| mega | M | $10^6 = 1\,000\,000$ |
| giga | G | $10^9 = 1\,000\,000\,000$ |

The SI also accepts the prefix "centi" ($10^{-2}$) which is not strictly a SI unit but can be used in conjunction with metre, litre, or gram.

When stating the value of a measurement, the prefix chosen should give the value as a number between 0.1 and 1000. Thus, one nautical mile is written as 1.852 km, not 1852 m.

The SI does not allow the use of other units. Imperial units of measurement, as used in the United States for example, are not acceptable in the international system.

For more information on SI units, visit: http//www.bipm.org/en/si/si_brochure/

---

**Example 8**                                                    ◀) **Self Tutor**

Convert:

a   3540 millimetres into metres          b   7.14 kilograms into grams

c   4 hours and 12 minutes into seconds   d   15 knots into kilometres per hour

---

a            $1 \text{ mm} = 10^{-3} \text{ m}$                  b            $1 \text{ kg} = 1000 \text{ g}$

∴  $3540 \text{ mm} = 3540 \times 10^{-3}$              ∴  $7.14 \text{ kg} = 7.14 \times 1000$

$= 3.54 \text{ m}$                                  $= 7140 \text{ g}$

c            $1 \text{ h} = 3600 \text{ s}$                      d            $1 \text{ kn} = 1.852 \text{ km h}^{-1}$

$1 \text{ min} = 60 \text{ s}$                          ∴  $15 \text{ kn} = 15 \times 1.852$

∴  $4 \text{ h } 12 \text{ min} = (4 \times 3600) + (12 \times 60)$          $= 27.78 \text{ km h}^{-1}$

$= 15\,120 \text{ s}$

---

## EXERCISE 2D

1   How many millilitres are there in 1 kilolitre?

2   How many micrometres are there in a:

   a   millimetre               b   kilometre?

3   How many $\mu$Pa are there in 1 MPa?

4   Convert the following:

   a   0.025 L into mL          b   26 580 ns into $\mu$s          c   45 km into mm

   d   5840 kg into t           e   54 kWh into MJ            f   60 km h$^{-1}$ into m s$^{-1}$

   g   0.14 m$^2$ into mm$^2$       h   16 m s$^{-1}$ into km h$^{-1}$    i   36 kn into km h$^{-1}$

5   Calculate the area of a rectangle with side lengths of 440 m and 75 m. Give your answer in hectares.

6   A kilowatt hour is the accepted commercial unit for selling energy.  If 60 kWh are purchased, how many joules of energy have been bought?

7   A joule is defined as the energy required to exert a force of 1 newton for a distance of 1 metre. Write down the combination of SI units which describe a joule.

8   A ship has travelled 48 km in the past 3 hours. Calculate the average speed of the ship in knots.

---

**E**                               # ROUNDING NUMBERS

There are many occasions when it is sensible to give an **approximate** answer.

For example, it is unreasonable to give the exact population of a country since the number is continually changing. We would not say that the population of Turkey is  71 158 647 people. It is more sensible to say that the population of Turkey is about 71 million people.

We use the symbol $\approx$ or sometimes $\doteqdot$ to show that an answer has been approximated.

**Rules for rounding off** are:

- If the digit after the one being rounded off is **less than 5**  (0, 1, 2, 3 or 4)  we round **down**.

- If the digit after the one being rounded off is **5 or more**  (5, 6, 7, 8, 9)  we round **up**.

| Example 9 | ◀) **Self Tutor** |
|---|---|

Round off to the nearest 10:

    **a**  48          **b**  583          **c**  5705

    **a**  $48 \approx 50$     {Round up, as 8 is greater than 5}

    **b**  $583 \approx 580$     {Round down, as 3 is less than 5}

    **c**  $5705 \approx 5710$     {Round up, halfway is always rounded up}

## EXERCISE 2E.1

**1** Round off to the nearest 10:

| | | | |
|---|---|---|---|
| **a**  75 | **b**  78 | **c**  298 | **d**  637 |
| **e**  3994 | **f**  1651 | **g**  9797 | **h**  1015 |
| **i**  783 | **j**  835 | **k**  2119 | **l**  1995 |

| Example 10 | ◀) **Self Tutor** |
|---|---|

Round off to the nearest 100:      **a**  452      **b**  37 239

    **a**  $452 \approx 500$     {Round up for 5 or more}

    **b**  $37\,239 \approx 37\,200$     {Round down, as 3 is less than 5}

**2** Round off to the nearest 100:

| | | | |
|---|---|---|---|
| **a**  78 | **b**  468 | **c**  923 | **d**  954 |
| **e**  5449 | **f**  4765 | **g**  13 066 | **h**  43 951 |

**3** Round off to the nearest 1000:

| | | | |
|---|---|---|---|
| **a**  748 | **b**  5500 | **c**  9990 | **d**  3743 |
| **e**  65 438 | **f**  123 456 | **g**  434 576 | **h**  570 846 |

**4** Round off to the accuracy given:

    **a**  the cost of an overseas holiday is $15 387 (to the nearest $1000)

    **b**  the mass of a horse is 468 kg (to the nearest ten kg)

    **c**  a weekly wage of €610 (to the nearest €100)

    **d**  a distance of 5735 km (to the nearest 100 km)

    **e**  the annual amount of water used in a household was 117 489 litres (to the nearest kilolitre)

    **f**  the monthly income for a business was £28 817 (to the nearest £1000)

**g** the box-office takings for a new movie were $6 543 722 (to the nearest hundred thousand dollars)

**h** the area of a country is 32 457 hectares (to the nearest thousand hectares)

**i** the number of times the average heart will beat in one year is 35 765 280 times (to the nearest million)

**j** a year's loss by a large mining company was $1 322 469 175 (to the nearest billion dollars).

## ROUNDING DECIMAL NUMBERS

If a traffic survey showed that 1852 cars carried 4376 people, it would not be sensible to give the average number of people per car as 2.362 850 972. An approximate answer of 2.4 is more appropriate.

There is clearly a need to **round off** decimal numbers which have more figures in them than are required.

We can round off to the certain number of **decimal places** or **significant figures**.

---

**Example 11**                                                    ◀) **Self Tutor**

Round:    **a** 3.27 to one decimal place        **b** 6.3829 to two decimal places.

**a** 3.27   has 2 in the *first* decimal place
        and 7 in the *second* decimal place.
   Since 7 is in the second decimal place and is greater than 5, we increase the digit in the first decimal place by 1 and delete what follows. So, $3.27 \approx 3.3$

**b** 6.3829   has 8 in the *second* decimal place
        and 2 in the *third* decimal place.
   Since 2 is less than 5, we retain the 8 and delete all digits after it.
   So, $6.3829 \approx 6.38$

---

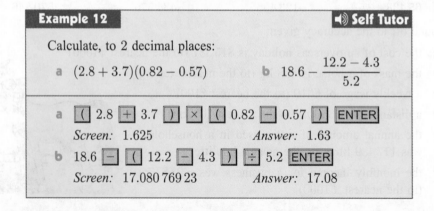

**Example 12**                                                    ◀) **Self Tutor**

Calculate, to 2 decimal places:

**a** $(2.8 + 3.7)(0.82 - 0.57)$        **b** $18.6 - \dfrac{12.2 - 4.3}{5.2}$

**a** [(] 2.8 [+] 3.7 [)] [×] [(] 0.82 [−] 0.57 [)] [ENTER]
   *Screen:* 1.625             *Answer:* 1.63

**b** 18.6 [−] [(] 12.2 [−] 4.3 [)] [÷] 5.2 [ENTER]
   *Screen:* 17.080 769 23        *Answer:* 17.08

## EXERCISE 2E.2

1 Round the following to the number of decimal places stated in brackets.

  a  3.47        [1]        b  5.362       [2]        c  7.164        [1]

  d  15.234      [2]        e  9.0246      [3]        f  12.6234       [1]

  g  0.4372      [2]        h  9.276 43    [2]        i  0.0099        [2]

2 Find, giving your answers correct to 2 decimal places where necessary:

  a  $(16.8 + 12.4) \times 17.1$        b  $16.8 + 12.4 \times 17.1$        c  $127 \div 9 - 5$

  d  $127 \div (9 - 5)$        e  $37.4 - 16.1 \div (4.2 - 2.7)$        f  $\dfrac{16.84}{7.9 + 11.2}$

  g  $\dfrac{27.4}{3.2} - \dfrac{18.6}{16.1}$        h  $\dfrac{27.9 - 17.3}{8.6} + 4.7$        i  $\dfrac{0.0768 + 7.1}{18.69 - 3.824}$

## ROUNDING OFF TO SIGNIFICANT FIGURES

> To round off to $n$ significant figures, we look at the $(n + 1)$th digit.
> - If it is 0, 1, 2, 3 or 4 we do not change the $n$th digit.
> - If it is 5, 6, 7, 8 or 9 we increase the $n$th digit by 1.
>
> Delete all digits after the $n$th digit, replacing by 0s if necessary.

DEMO

| Example 13 | ◀》 Self Tutor |
|---|---|

Round:  a  7.182 to 2 significant figures       b  0.001 32 to 2 significant figures
        c  423 to 1 significant figure       d  4.057 to 3 significant figures.

a  $7.182 \approx 7.2$  (2 s.f.)

 This is the 2nd significant figure, so we look at the next digit which is 8.
 The 8 tells us to round the 1 up to a 2 and leave off the remaining digits.

b  $0.001 32 \approx 0.0013$  (2 s.f.)

 These zeros at the front are place holders and so must stay. The first significant
 figure is the 1. The third significant figure, 2, tells us to leave the 3 as it is and
 leave off the remaining digits.

c  $423 \approx 400$  (1 s.f.)

 4 is the first significant figure so it has to be rounded. The second figure, 2, tells
 us to keep the original 4 in the hundreds place. We convert the 23 into 00. These
 two zeros are place holders. They are not 'significant figures' but they need to be
 there to make sure the 4 has value 400.

d  $4.057 \approx 4.06$  (3 s.f.)

 This 0 is significant as it lies between two non-zero digits. The fourth significant
 figure, 7, tell us to round the 5 up to a 6 and leave off remaining digits.

In IB examinations you are expected to give answers to 3 significant figures unless otherwise specified in the question.

## EXERCISE 2E.3

1  Write correct to 2 significant figures:

    **a**  567      **b**  16 342      **c**  70.7      **d**  3.001      **e**  0.716

    **f**  49.6      **g**  3.046      **h**  1760      **i**  0.0409      **j**  45 600

2  Write correct to 3 significant figures:

    **a**  43 620      **b**  10 076      **c**  $0.\overline{6}$      **d**  0.036 821      **e**  0.318 6

    **f**  0.719 6      **g**  $0.6\overline{3}$      **h**  0.063 71      **i**  18.997      **j**  256 800

3  Write correct to 4 significant figures:

    **a**  28.039 2      **b**  0.005 362      **c**  23 683.9      **d**  42 366 709

    **e**  0.038 792      **f**  0.006 377 9      **g**  0.000 899 9      **h**  43.076 321

4  The crowd at an ice hockey match was officially 5838 people.

    **a**  Round the crowd size to:

        **i**  1 significant figure

        **ii**  2 significant figures.

    **b**  Which of these figures would be used by the media to indicate crowd size?

5  Calculate the following, giving answers in scientific notation correct to three significant figures where necessary:

    **a**  $0.002 \times 0.003 \div 15\,000$      **b**  $70\,000 \times 500^3$      **c**  $\sqrt{0.000\,078\,2}$

    **d**  $1250^2 \times 650^3$      **e**  $(0.000\,172)^4$      **f**  $\dfrac{385 \times 1250}{0.000\,006\,7}$

6  A rocket travels at $2.8 \times 10^4$ km h$^{-1}$ in space. Find how far it would travel in:

    **a**  5 hours      **b**  a day      **c**  a year.

    Give your answers in scientific notation correct to 2 significant figures.

    Assume that 1 year $\approx 365.25$ days.

7  Evaluate, giving your answers in standard form correct to 3 significant figures:

    **a**  $234\,000\,000 \times 289\,800\,000$      **b**  $998\,600\,000\,000 \times 122\,000\,000$

    **c**  $0.4569 \times 0.000\,000\,399\,3$      **d**  $0.000\,000\,988 \times 0.000\,000\,768$

    **e**  $(394\,550\,000)^2$      **f**  $(0.000\,000\,120\,34)^2$

8  **a**  If there are 365 days in a year, show that there are 31 536 000 seconds in a year. Express this value in scientific notation, correct to 4 significant figures.

    **b**  Light travels approximately $9.4488 \times 10^{15}$ m in a year.

    How far does light travel in one second?

    Give your answer in scientific notation, correct to 4 significant figures.

**Example 14**                                                         ◄)) **Self Tutor**

Use your calculator to simplify, correct to 3 significant figures:

a $(3.2 \times 10^4) \times (8.6 \times 10^{-16})$          b $\dfrac{2.8 \times 10^5}{6.4 \times 10^{-8}}$

a Press:  3.2 [2nd] [EE] 4 [×] 8.6 [2nd] [EE]

[(–)] 16 [ENTER]

*Answer:* $2.75 \times 10^{-11}$

```
3.2E4*8.6E-16
          2.75E-11
■
```

b Press:  2.8 [EXP] 5 [÷] 6.4 [EXP] [(–)] 8 [EXE]

*Answer:* $4.38 \times 10^{12}$

```
2.8E5÷6.4E-8
         4.38E+12
```

**9** Use your calculator to answer the following, correct to 3 significant figures:

a $(4.7 \times 10^5) \times (8.5 \times 10^7)$          b $(2.7 \times 10^{-3}) \times (9.6 \times 10^9)$

c $(3.4 \times 10^7) \div (4.8 \times 10^{15})$          d $(7.3 \times 10^{-7}) \div (1.5 \times 10^4)$

e $(2.83 \times 10^3)^2$                                f $(5.96 \times 10^{-5})^2$

**10** Use your calculator to answer the following, correct to 3 significant figures where necessary.

a A rocket travels in space at $4 \times 10^5$ km h$^{-1}$. How far does it travel in:   i 30 days   ii 20 years?

b An electron travels $5 \times 10^3$ km in $2 \times 10^{-5}$ hours. Find its average speed in kilometres per hour.

c A bullet travelling at an average speed of $2 \times 10^3$ km h$^{-1}$ hits a target 500 m away. Find the time of flight of the bullet in seconds.

d The planet Mars is $2.28 \times 10^8$ km from the sun whilst Mercury is $5.79 \times 10^7$ km from the sun. How many times further from the sun is Mars than Mercury?

e Microbe C has mass $2.63 \times 10^{-5}$ g, whereas microbe D has mass $8 \times 10^{-7}$ g. Which microbe is heavier? How many times heavier is it than the other one?

There are 365.25 days in a year.

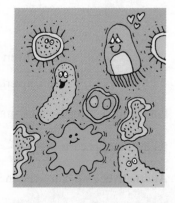

# F RATES

A **rate** is an ordered comparison of quantities of **different** kinds.

Some examples of rates are shown in the following table:

| Rate | Example of units |
|------|------------------|
| rates of pay | dollars per hour, euros per hour |
| petrol consumption | litres per 100 km |
| annual rainfall | mm per year |
| unit cost | dollars per kilogram, pounds per kilogram |
| population density | people per square km |

## RESEARCH RATE DATA

1   Obtain data from the internet for the average rainfall of your city, and the breakdown into average monthly rates. Compare these with rates for other cities.

2   Compare the rates of petrol consumption for different cars. Also compare the rates for 4 cylinder and 6 cylinder cars.

## SPEED

One of the most common rates we use is **speed**, which is a comparison between the *distance travelled* and the *time taken*.

$$\text{Average speed} = \frac{\text{distance travelled}}{\text{time taken}} \qquad \text{Time taken} = \frac{\text{distance travelled}}{\text{average speed}}$$

$$\text{Distance travelled} = \text{average speed} \times \text{time taken}$$

Because we are comparing quantities of different kinds, the units cannot be omitted as they are with ratios. In most cases we express speed in either kilometres per hour ($km\,h^{-1}$) or in metres per second ($m\,s^{-1}$).

$$1 \text{ km}\,h^{-1} = \frac{1000 \text{ m}}{3600 \text{ s}} = \tfrac{1}{3.6} \text{ m}\,s^{-1}$$

To convert $km\,h^{-1}$ into $m\,s^{-1}$, we divide by 3.6.

To convert $m\,s^{-1}$ into $km\,h^{-1}$, we multiply by 3.6.

For example, suppose a car travels 144 km in 2 hours.

Its average speed is $\dfrac{144 \text{ km}}{2 \text{ h}} = 72 \text{ km}\,h^{-1}$.

Alternatively, we can write the speed as $\dfrac{72}{3.6} = 20 \text{ m}\,s^{-1}$.

**Example 15**                                                                          ◄᎒ **Self Tutor**

A car is travelling a distance of 325 km.

**a**  What is its average speed if the trip takes 4 h 17 min?

**b**  What is the time taken if the average speed is 93 $km\,h^{-1}$?

**a**    average speed

$= \dfrac{\text{distance travelled}}{\text{time taken}}$

$= \dfrac{325 \text{ km}}{4 \text{ h } 17 \text{ min}}$

$\approx 75.9 \text{ km} \, h^{-1}$

Using a **Texas Instruments TI-84 Plus**

325 ÷ 4 [2nd] [APPS] (ANGLE) 1 (1:°) 17 [2nd] [APPS] (ANGLE) 2 (2:') [ENTER]

Using a **Casio fx-9860G**

325 ÷ 4 [OPTN] [F6] (▷) [F5] (ANGL) [F4] (o, ") 17 [F4] (o' ") [EXE]

**b**    time taken

$= \dfrac{\text{distance travelled}}{\text{average speed}}$

$= \dfrac{325 \text{ km}}{93 \text{ km} \, h^{-1}}$

$\approx 3 \text{ h } 29 \text{ min } 41 \text{ s}$

Using a **Texas Instruments TI-84 Plus**

325 ÷ 93 [ENTER] [2nd] [MATRX] (ANGLE) 4 (4:▶DMS) [ENTER]

Using a **Casio fx-9860G**

325 ÷ 93 [EXE] [OPTN] [F6] (▷) [F5] (ANGL) [F5] (o, ")

## EXERCISE 2F.1

**1**  Find the average speed of a car travelling:

    **a**  71.2 km in 51 minutes         **b**  468 km in 5 hours 37 minutes.

**2**  The flight from London to Frankfurt is 634 km and takes 86 minutes. What is the average speed of the plane in $km\,h^{-1}$?

**3**  What is faster, 100 $km\,h^{-1}$ or 30 $m\,s^{-1}$?

**4**  Find the distance you would travel if you:

    **a**  drove at an average speed of 95 $km\,h^{-1}$ for 3 h 23 min

    **b**  rode at an average speed of 25.3 km $h^{-1}$ for 1 h 17.5 min.

**5**  How long would it take to travel 42.3 km at an average walking speed of 5.7 $km\,h^{-1}$?

**INVESTIGATION 1**                                                    **STOPPING DISTANCES**

A car does *not* stop the instant you want it to. It travels on for quite some distance before coming to rest. Two factors control how far a car travels between you seeing a problem and the car coming to a halt.

The first is called the **reaction time**, the time for the driver to react and hit the brake pedal. The distance travelled during this time is called the **reaction distance**. The second is the **braking distance**, the distance the car travels after the brakes are applied.

$$\text{Stopping distance} \quad = \quad \frac{\text{distance travelled}}{\text{whilst reacting}} \quad + \quad \frac{\text{distance travelled}}{\text{whilst braking}}$$

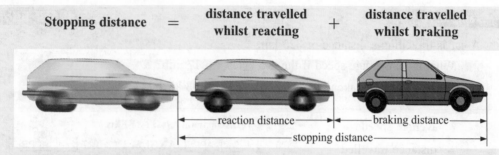

reaction distance ——— braking distance

stopping distance

## MEASURING REACTION TIME

*Materials:*
- Electronic timer (measuring to hundredths of a second) with remote switching capability
- Pedal simulator
- Light for timer mechanism

The driver is to have his or her foot resting on the accelerator pedal. When the light flashes, the foot is moved rapidly to the brake pedal to press it.

Do this test five times, and average the reaction times obtained.

## CALCULATING REACTION DISTANCE

Now that you have a good estimate of your personal reaction time, you can calculate your reaction distance for any given vehicle speed. To do this, multiply your reaction time by the vehicle speed in metres per second.

For example, if you are travelling at $30 \text{ km h}^{-1}$ and your reaction time is 0.5 s, then

*Step 1:* $30 \text{ km h}^{-1} = (30 \div 3.6) \text{ m s}^{-1} = 8.333 \text{ m s}^{-1}$

*Step 2:* Distance travelled $= 0.5 \times 8.333 = 4.166$ m *before* you hit the brake pedal.

**What to do:**

1 Convert $60 \text{ km h}^{-1}$ to $\text{m s}^{-1}$.

2 Calculate the reaction distance for a reaction time of 0.5 s and a vehicle speed of $60 \text{ km h}^{-1}$.

3 Using your own reaction time, repeat the calculations above to find your reaction distance for a vehicle speed of $60 \text{ km h}^{-1}$.

4 Having calculated your reaction distance for $60 \text{ km h}^{-1}$ in part **3**, now use your personal reaction time to calculate reaction distances for each of the following speeds. Remember, this is the distance covered *before the car even begins to slow down!*

| *Speed in $km\,h^{-1}$* | 30 | 40 | 50 | 60 | 70 | 80 | 90 | 100 | 110 | 120 |
|---|---|---|---|---|---|---|---|---|---|---|
| *Speed in $m\,s^{-1}$* | 8.33 | | | | | | | | | |
| *Reaction distance* | | | | | | | | | | |

**Simple reaction time** is the measure of a fully prepared person waiting for a signal and then reacting to that signal. This is what you measured in the above exercises. In the real world of driving, many things can distract or impair a driver, resulting in much longer reaction times.

**5** As a class, discuss factors that could increase your reaction time. List these on the board.

## CALCULATING BRAKING DISTANCES

The **braking distance** is the distance you travel *after* you have applied the brakes as the car slows to a stop.

On a good bitumen surface, with a car in perfect condition, it takes about 28 m to stop while travelling at $60 \text{ km h}^{-1}$. The distance is longer on wet roads or gravel surfaces.

We can calculate the effects of different road surfaces on braking distances using the following formula:

**distance travelled (in m) = speed (in $\text{m s}^{-1}$) $\times$ (2.08 + 0.96 $\times$ surface factor)**

**What to do:**

Calculate the braking distances for each of the speeds and surface conditions listed in the table alongside.

Copy and complete the table which follows:

You may like to set up a **spreadsheet** to do this.

| Surface factor | |
|---|---|
| dry asphalt | 1.4 |
| wet asphalt | 1.7 |
| gravel | 2.1 |
| hard snow | 6.7 |
| ice | 14.4 |

| Speed ($\text{km h}^{-1}$) | Speed ($\text{m s}^{-1}$) | Dry asphalt | Wet asphalt | Gravel | Snow | Ice |
|---|---|---|---|---|---|---|
| 50 | | | | | | |
| 60 | | | | | | |
| 70 | | | | | | |
| 80 | | | | | | |
| ⋮ | | | | | | |
| 120 | | | | | | |

## CALCULATING STOPPING DISTANCE

Remember: **Stopping distance = Reaction distance + Braking distance**

**What to do:**

Using your personal reaction distances, find your total stopping distances for the conditions listed previously. Copy and complete a table like the one following or set up a **spreadsheet**:

| Condition | Personal reaction distance | Braking distance | Stopping distance |
|---|---|---|---|
| 30 km h$^{-1}$, dry bitumen | | | |
| 50 km h$^{-1}$, dry bitumen | | | |
| 60 km h$^{-1}$, dry bitumen | | | |
| 80 km h$^{-1}$, dry bitumen | | | |
| ⋮ | | | |

## OTHER RATES PROBLEMS

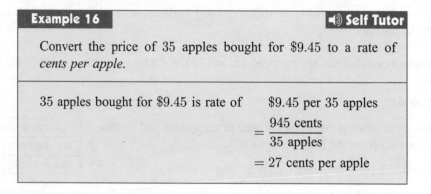

**Example 16**    ◀)) **Self Tutor**

Convert the price of 35 apples bought for $9.45 to a rate of *cents per apple*.

35 apples bought for $9.45 is rate of     $9.45 per 35 apples

$$= \frac{945 \text{ cents}}{35 \text{ apples}}$$

$$= 27 \text{ cents per apple}$$

## EXERCISE 2F.2

1 Copy and complete:

   a If 24 kg of peas are sold for $66.24, they earn me $...... per kg.

   b My car uses 18 L of petrol every 261 km. The rate of petrol consumption is ...... km per litre.

   c 675 litres of water are pumped into a tank in 25 minutes. This is a rate of ...... L min$^{-1}$.

   d Jasmin is paid $87 for 6 hours work. This is a rate of $...... per hour.

   e A temperature rise of 14 degrees in $3\frac{1}{2}$ hours is a rate of ...... degrees per hour.

   f 38.5 kg of seed spread over 7 m$^2$ is a rate of ...... kg m$^{-2}$.

   g $173.47 for 1660 kWh of power is a rate of ...... cents per kWh.

   h Dominic types 220 words in 4 minutes. This rate is ..... words per minute.

2 A worker in a local factory earns €14.67 per hour.

   a How much does he earn in a 40 hour week?

   b If he receives the same weekly wage but only works a 35 hour week, what is his hourly rate for that week?

---

**Example 17**    🔊 **Self Tutor**

Suburb A covers 6.3 km² and has a population of 28 700 people.
Suburb B covers 3.9 km² and has a population of 16 100 people.
Which suburb is more heavily populated?

Suburb A has $\dfrac{28\,700 \text{ people}}{6.3 \text{ km}^2} \approx 4556$  people per km².

Suburb B has $\dfrac{16\,100 \text{ people}}{3.9 \text{ km}^2} \approx 4128$  people per km².

∴  suburb A is more heavily populated.

---

**3**  A farmer harvested 866 bags of wheat from an 83 hectare paddock (A) and 792 bags from a 68 hectare paddock (B). Which paddock yielded the better crop?

**4**  When the local netball club decided the winner of the trophy for the highest number of goals thrown per match, there were two contenders:  Pat, who threw 446 goals in 18 matches, and Jo, who threw 394 goals in 15 matches.  Who won the trophy?

**5**  A family uses 46 kilolitres of water in 90 days.
  **a**  Find the rate in litres per day.
  **b**  If the water board charges 65 cents per kilolitre, how much do they need to pay for the water used:
    **i**  over the 90 day period          **ii**  per day?

**6**  Phillipa types at a rate of 50 words per minute.
  **a**  How long would it take her to type a 500 word essay at this rate?
  **b**  How much longer would it take Kurt to type this essay if he types at 35 words per minute?

**7**  The cost of electricity is 13.49 cents/kWh for the first 300 kWh, then 10.25 cents/kWh for the remainder.
  **a**  How much does 2050 kWh of power cost?
  **b**  What is the overall rate in cents/kWh?

**8**  The temperature at 2.30 pm was 11°C and fell steadily until it reached −2°C at 1.45 am.
  **a**  Find the decrease in temperature.
  **b**  Find the average rate of decrease per hour correct to 2 decimal places.

**9**  Convert:
  **a**  $12 per hour into cents per minute
  **b**  240 000 litres per minute into kilolitres per second
  **c**  30 mL per second into litres per hour
  **d**  $2.73 per gram into dollars per kilogram
  **e**  1 death every 10 minutes into deaths per year.

# G    ACCURACY OF MEASUREMENTS

Examine a variety of measuring instruments at school and at home. Make a list of the names of these instruments, what they measure, what their units are, and the degree of accuracy to which they can measure.

For example:

A ruler measures length. In the Metric System it measures in centimetres and millimetres and can measure to the nearest millimetre.

Record your findings in a table.

When we take measurements, we are usually reading some sort of scale.

The scale of a ruler may have millimetres marked on it, but when we measure the length of an object, it is likely to fall between two divisions. So, when we **estimate** to the nearest millimetre, our answer may be inaccurate by up to a half a millimetre.

A measurement is accurate to $\pm\frac{1}{2}$ of the smallest division on the scale.

### Example 18                                         ◀) Self Tutor

Ling uses a ruler to measure the length of her pencil case. She writes down the result 18.7 cm.

Find the range of values in which the length may lie.

18.7 cm is 187 mm, so the measuring device must be accurate to the nearest half mm.

∴ the range of values is $187 \pm \frac{1}{2}$ mm

The actual length is in the range $186\frac{1}{2}$ mm to $187\frac{1}{2}$ mm, which is 18.65 cm to 18.75 cm.

## EXERCISE 2G

1   State the accuracy of the following measuring devices:

   a   a tape measure marked in cm

   b   a measuring cylinder with 1 mL graduations

   c   a beaker with 100 mL graduations

   d   a set of scales with marks every 500 g.

2   Roni checks his weight every week using scales with 1 kg graduations. This morning he recorded a weight of 68 kg. In what range of values does Roni's actual weight lie?

**3** Find the range of values for the following measurements:

   **a** 27 mm            **b** 38.3 cm           **c** 4.8 m

   **d** 1.5 kg           **e** 25 g              **f** 3.75 kg

**4** Tom's digital thermometer said his temperature was 36.4°C. In what range of values did Tom's actual temperature lie?

**5** Four students measured the width of their classroom using the same tape measure. The measurements were 6.1 m, 6.4 m, 6.0 m, 6.1 m.

   **a** Which measurement is likely to be incorrect?

   **b** What answer would you give for the width of the classroom?

   **c** What graduations do you think were on the tape measure?

---

**Example 19**

A rectangular block of wood was measured as 78 cm by 24 cm. What are the boundary limits of its perimeter?

The length of 78 cm could be from $77\frac{1}{2}$ cm to $78\frac{1}{2}$ cm.

The width of 24 cm could be from $23\frac{1}{2}$ cm to $24\frac{1}{2}$ cm.

$\therefore$ the perimeter's lower boundary is $2 \times 77\frac{1}{2} + 2 \times 23\frac{1}{2} = 202$ cm

and the perimeter's upper boundary is $2 \times 78\frac{1}{2} + 2 \times 24\frac{1}{2} = 206$ cm

So, the perimeter is between 202 cm and 206 cm, which is $204 \pm 2$ cm.

---

**6** A rectangular bath mat was measured as 86 cm by 38 cm.
What are the boundary limits of its perimeter?

**7** A rectangular garden bed is measured to have dimensions 252 cm by 143 cm. Between what two values could the total length of edging required to border the garden bed be?

---

**Example 20** 🔊 Self Tutor

A paver is measured as 18 cm × 10 cm. What are the boundary values of its actual area?

The length of the paver could be from $17\frac{1}{2}$ cm to $18\frac{1}{2}$ cm.

The width of the paver could be from $9\frac{1}{2}$ cm to $10\frac{1}{2}$ cm.

$\therefore$ the lower boundary of the area is $17\frac{1}{2} \times 9\frac{1}{2} = 166.25$ cm$^2$

and the upper boundary of the area is $18\frac{1}{2} \times 10\frac{1}{2} = 194.25$ cm$^2$.

So, the area is between 166.25 cm$^2$ and 194.25 cm$^2$

This could also be represented as $\dfrac{166.25 + 194.25}{2} \pm 14$ cm$^2$

which is $180.25 \pm 14$ cm$^2$.

**8** A rectangle is measured to be 6 cm by 8 cm. What is:

    **a** the largest area it could have          **b** the smallest area it could have?

**9** Find the boundary values for the actual area of a glass window measured as 42 cm by 26 cm.

**10** The base of a triangle is measured as 9 cm and its height is measured as 8 cm. What are the boundary values for its actual area?

**11** Find boundary values for the actual volume of a box measuring 4 cm by 8 cm by 6 cm.

**12** Find the boundary values for the actual volume of a house brick measuring 21.3 cm by 9.8 cm by 7.3 cm.

**13** A cylinder is measured to have radius 5 cm and height 15 cm. Use the formula $V = \pi r^2 h$ to find the boundary values for the cylinder's volume.

**14** A cone is measured to have radius 8.4 cm and height 4.6 cm. Use the formula $V = \frac{1}{3}\pi r^2 h$ to find the boundary values for the cone's volume.

# H ERROR AND PERCENTAGE ERROR

An **approximation** is a value given to a number which is close to, but not equal to, its true value.

Approximations often occur when we round off results obtained by measurement.
For example, 36.428 97 is approximately 36.4.

An **estimation** is a value which has been found by judgement or prediction instead of carrying out a more accurate measurement.

For example, we can estimate $38.7 \times 5.1$ to be $40 \times 5 = 200$ whereas its true value is 197.37. A good approximation of this true value would be 197.

In order to make reasonable estimations we often appeal to our previous experience.

## INVESTIGATION 3      A GRAM IN THE HAND IS WORTH ....

**What to do:**

**1** Measure in mm the length and width of a sheet of 80 gsm A4 photocopying paper.

**2** What is its area in $m^2$ and how many sheets make up $1\ m^2$?

**3** 80 gsm means 80 grams per square metre. What is the mass of one sheet of A4 paper?

**4** What is the approximate mass of this part of the sheet?

6 cm

**5** Crumple the 6 cm strip into your hand and feel how heavy it is.

# ERROR

Whenever we measure a quantity there is almost always a difference between our measurement and the actual value. We call this difference the **error**.

If the actual or exact value is $V_E$ and the approximate value is $V_A$ then the

$$\text{error} = V_A - V_E$$

Error is often expressed as a percentage of the exact value, and in this case we call it **percentage error**.

$$\text{Percentage error} \quad E = \frac{V_A - V_E}{V_E} \times 100\%$$

The **absolute percentage error** is the *size* of the percentage error, ignoring its sign. To indicate this we use a **modulus** sign.

$$\text{Absolute percentage error} = |E| = \frac{|V_A - V_E|}{V_E} \times 100\%$$

---

**Example 21**                                                   ◀)) **Self Tutor**

You estimate a fence's length to be 70 m but when you measure it, you find its true length is 78.3 m. Find, correct to one decimal place:

  **a** the error     **b** the percentage error   **c** the absolute percentage error.

---

**a** error $= V_A - V_E$   **b** percentage error   **c** absolute percentage error

$\phantom{a}\quad = 70 - 78.3$     $= \dfrac{V_A - V_E}{V_E} \times 100\%$    $\approx |-10.6\%|$

$\phantom{a}\quad = -8.3 \text{ m}$     $\phantom{a}\approx 10.6\%$

$\phantom{aaaaaaaa}= \dfrac{-8.3}{78.3} \times 100\%$

$\phantom{aaaaaaaa}\approx -10.6\%$

---

## EXERCISE 2H

**1** Find **i** the error  **ii** the percentage error  in rounding:

  **a** the yearly profit of €1 367 540 made by a company to €1.37 million.

  **b** a population of 31 467 people to 31 000 people

  **c** a retail sales figure of $458 110 to $460 000

  **d** the number of new cars sold by a company in a year from 2811 to 3000.

**2** Find **i** the error  **ii** the absolute percentage error  if you estimate:

  **a** the mass of a brick to be 5 kg when its measured mass is 6.238 kg

  **b** the perimeter of a property to be 100 m when its measured length is 97.6 m

  **c** the capacity of a container to be 20 L when its measured capacity is 23.8 L

  **d** the time to solve a problem to be 50 hours when it actually took 72 hours.

**3** Jon's lounge room is a 10.3 m by 9.7 m rectangle.

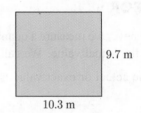

**a** Estimate the floor area by rounding each length to the nearest metre.

**b** What is the actual area of the floor?

**c** What is the error in your calculation in **a**?

**d** What percentage error was made?

9.7 m

10.3 m

**4** The cost of freight on a parcel is dependent on its volume. Justine lists the dimensions of a parcel as 24 cm by 15 cm by 9 cm on the consignment note. The actual dimensions are 23.9 cm × 14.8 cm × 9.2 cm.

**a** Calculate the actual volume of the parcel.

**b** Calculate the volume given on the consignment note.

**c** Find the rounding error in the calculation.

**d** What percentage error was made?

**5** Luigi estimates that he can travel at an average of 70 km h$^{-1}$ between his house and the nearest town, 87 km away. On one particular journey it took him 1 hour and 20 minutes.

**a** Calculate his average speed for this journey.

**b** Find the error in his estimate.

**c** Find the absolute percentage error in his estimate.

## ESTIMATION OR MEASUREMENT?

Sometimes it is better to estimate rather than take measurements. However, it will only make sense if our estimation is reasonably accurate.

Factors which influence our decision to estimate or measure include:

- the time required to measure and calculate
- the difficulty of measuring
- the accuracy needed.

### INVESTIGATION 4    ESTIMATING AND ACCURACY

In this investigation you will make estimates of angle size, length, mass, temperature, and time. You can then check your estimates by taking actual measurements.

**What to do:**

**1  Angle size**    *Equipment needed:*  Protractor

**a** Draw three angles: one acute, one reflex and one obtuse.

**b** Estimate the size of each angle in degrees.

**c** Cut out an angle of exactly 30$^o$ using a protractor. Use this angle to help you re-estimate the three angle sizes.

**d** Measure each angle with a protractor, and hence complete the table alongside:

| angle | estimate 1 | estimate 2 | measured size |
|-------|-----------|-----------|---------------|
| **i** | | | |
| **ii** | | | |
| **iii** | | | |

**e** For each angle, find the errors in each estimate and determine the percentage errors.

**f** Did the 30° angle help to improve your estimates?

**2 Length**   *Equipment needed:*  Large tape measure or trundle wheel

   **a** Estimate the length and width of *one* of the following:

- your school tennis courts  (backstop to backstop)
- your school gym  (wall to wall)
- a rectangular school building  (wall to wall)

   **b** Use paces to estimate the lengths more accurately.

   **c** Check your estimates using a tape measure or trundle wheel.

   **d** Find the percentage error in each of your estimates.

**3 Thickness**   *Equipment needed:*  Vernier callipers

   **a** Ask your teacher to demonstrate the correct use of the vernier callipers.

   **b** Estimate the thickness of:

      **i**  your pen or pencil   **ii**  your textbook   **iii**  one page of your textbook.

   **c** Use the vernier callipers to find the thickness of the items in **b**.
**Hint:** In **iii** find the thickness of 100 pages.

   **d** Determine the percentage errors of your estimates in **b**.

**4 Mass**   *Equipment needed:*  Kitchen scales, digital bathroom scales

   **a** Examine a set of kitchen scales and a set of digital bathroom scales. Comment on the degree of accuracy of each measuring device.

   **b** Estimate the mass of a textbook, a pencil, a shoe, a student desk, and someone in the room who does not mind being weighed.

   **c** Which, if either, of the measuring devices is suitable for measuring the masses of these objects?

   **d** Weigh each object as accurately as you can. Record the results in a table such as the one alongside:

| Object | Estimate | Measured | Error | % Error |
|--------|----------|----------|-------|---------|
| | | | | |
| ⋮ | | | | |

   **e** Try again with another set of objects to see if you can improve your estimates.

**5 Temperature**   *Equipment needed:*  Thermometer in °C

   **a** Make an estimate of the temperature of:

      **i**  air in the classroom                  **ii**  air outside the classroom
      **iii**  water from the cold tap            **iv**  water from the hot tap (careful!)

   **b**  Use a thermometer to measure the temperature of the air and water in **a**.

   **c**  Comment on the accuracy of your estimates.

**6**  **Time**   *Equipment needed:*  Stopwatch or watch with seconds

   **a**  In pairs test each other at estimating a time interval of one minute.

   **b**  Can you find a way to improve your method of estimating?

## REVIEW SET 2A

**1**  Find the time difference between 10.35 am and 4.52 pm.

**2**  What is the time:

   **a**  $4\frac{1}{4}$ hours after 11.20 pm        **b**  $3\frac{1}{2}$ hours before 1.20 pm?

**3**  A racehorse weighs 440 kg. Calculate its mass in grams.

**4**  It is $35°C$ in a town in Mexico. Use the formula  $F = \frac{9}{5}C + 32$  to calculate this temperature in degrees Fahrenheit.

**5**  Express the following quantities as ordinary decimal numbers:

   **a**  Jupiter has a radius of  $1.43 \times 10^5$ km

   **b**  a baker's yeast cell is approximately  $4.5 \times 10^{-6}$ m  in diameter.

**6**  Sound travels along a telephone cable at  $1.91 \times 10^8$ m s$^{-1}$. Use your calculator to find how long it takes Tetsuo's voice to travel from his office phone in Tokyo to his:

   **a**  wife's phone, 3740 m away   **b**  brother in Beijing, $2.1 \times 10^6$ m away.

**7**  **a**  Round 6.376 to:   **i**  1 decimal place   **ii**  3 significant figures.

   **b**  Round 0.0473 to:   **i**  2 decimal places   **ii**  2 significant figures.

**8**  **a**  How accurate is a tape measure marked in cm?

   **b**  Find the range of possible values for a measurement of 36 cm.

   **c**  A square has sides measured to be 36 cm. What are the boundary values for its actual area?

**9**  A cyclist is travelling a distance of 134 km.

   **a**  What is her average speed, if the trip takes 5 hours and 18 minutes?

   **b**  If her average speed is 24 km h$^{-1}$, how long does the trip take?

**10**  Find the  **i**  error  **ii**  percentage error  if you:

   **a**  estimate your credit card balance to be $2000 when it is $2590

   **b**  round 26.109 cm to 26 cm.

**11**  A photograph was measured as 15 cm by 10 cm. What are the boundary values for its perimeter?

**12**  If it is 12 noon in Greenwich, what is the standard time in Islamabad if Islamabad is 5 hours ahead of GMT?

## REVIEW SET 2B

**1**  Convert $2\frac{3}{4}$ hours to minutes.

**2**  Aniko left for work at 7.39 am and returned home at 6.43 pm. How long was she away from home?

**3**  Use the formula   $C = \frac{5}{9}(F - 32)$   to convert 84°F to degrees Celsius.

**4**  Bianca is 1.68 m tall. Calculate her height in cm.

**5**  Write as decimal numbers:

    **a**  $4.6 \times 10^{11}$         **b**  $1.9 \times 10^{0}$         **c**  $3.2 \times 10^{-3}$

**6**  Write in scientific notation:

    **a**  The diameter of the earth is approximately 12.76 million metres.

    **b**  A bacterium has a diameter of 0.000 000 42 cm.

**7**  Sheets of paper are  $3.2 \times 10^{-4}$ m  in thickness. Use your calculator to find how many sheets are required to make a pile of paper 10 cm high.

**8**  **a**  Round 59.397 to:     **i**  1 decimal place     **ii**  4 significant figures.
    **b**  Round 0.008 35 to:     **i**  2 decimal places     **ii**  2 significant figures.

**9**  The cost of water is \$0.97 per kL for the first 120 kL, then \$1.88 per kL for the remainder. How much does 361 kL of water cost?

**10**  Jenny estimated the length of her front fence to be 32 m. When she measured it, its exact length was 34.3 m. Find, correct to one decimal place:

    **a**  the error         **b**  the absolute percentage error.

**11**  **a**  Jorg works at a supermarket for 38 hours each week. He earns £332.50 per week. What is his hourly rate?

    **b**  After a promotion, he earns £10.25 per hour, and only works 35 hours each week. What is this change in weekly income?

**12**  Nairobi is 2 hours ahead of GMT and Honolulu is 10 hours behind GMT. Calculate the standard time in Nairobi when it is 2 pm in Honolulu.

## REVIEW SET 2C

**1** Find the time difference between 11.17 am and 5.09 pm.

**2** Calculate the time:

 **a** $5\frac{1}{2}$ hours after 9.17 am   **b** $4\frac{1}{4}$ hours before 1.48 pm.

**3** Use $C = \frac{5}{9}(F - 32)$ to convert $50°F$ to degrees Celsius.

**4** A yacht travels 26 nautical miles in 2 hours. Find the average speed of the yacht in kilometres per hour.

**5** Write the following as decimal numbers:

 **a** $5.73 \times 10^{-3}$   **b** $3.02 \times 10^{3}$   **c** $9.875 \times 10^{2}$

**6** Find, giving your answers correct to 3 significant figures:

 **a** $(17.5 - 4.3) \div 3.2$   **b** $\dfrac{16.52 - 0.041}{4.2 + 1.35}$

**7**  **a** How long would it take to travel 45.8 km at an average speed of $21.3 \ km\,h^{-1}$?

 **b** A car travels 20 km in 24 minutes. Find the average speed of the car in kilometres per hour.

**8** Store A sells 200 g packets of sugar for \$1.79, while store B sells 500 g packets of sugar for \$4.40. Which store offers better value for money?

**9** The two shorter sides of a right angled triangle are measured as 6 cm and 8 cm. What are the boundary limits for the area of the triangle?

**10** A circular gazebo has a diameter of 2.8 m. In calculating the area of the gazebo, the diameter is rounded to the nearest metre.

 **a** Find the actual area and the calculated area of the gazebo.

 **b** Find the error in the calculation.

 **c** What is the percentage error in the calculation?

**11** An architect designs a support beam to be $\sqrt{5}$ metres long. The builder working from the architect's plans converts this length to a decimal number.

 **a** Write down the length of the support beam correct to the nearest:

  **i** metre   **ii** centimetre   **iii** millimetre.

 **b** For each answer in **a**, write down how many significant figures were specified.

 **c** The architect insists that there be no more than 1% error. Which lengths from **a**, if any, will satisfy this?

**12** Brisbane is 10 hours ahead of GMT and Santiago is 5 hours behind GMT. Calculate the standard time in Santiago if it is 7 pm in Brisbane.

# Chapter 3

# Sets and Venn diagrams

## OPENING PROBLEM

A city has three football teams $A$, $B$ and $C$, in the national league. In the last season, 20% of the city's population went to see team $A$ play, 24% saw team $B$, and 28% saw team $C$. Of these, 4% saw both $A$ and $B$, 5% saw both $A$ and $C$, and 6% saw both $B$ and $C$. 1% saw all three teams play.

**Things to think about:**

**a**  How can we represent this information on a diagram?

**b**  What percentage of the population:

  **i**   saw only team $A$ play

  **ii**  saw team $A$ *or* team $B$ play but not team $C$

  **iii** did not see any of the teams play?

# A          SET NOTATION

A **set** is a collection of numbers or objects.

For example, the set of all digits we use to write numbers is $\{0, 1, 2, 3, 4, 5, 6, 7, 8, 9\}$.

Notice how the ten digits have been written within the brackets "{" and "}", and how they are separated by commas.

We usually use capital letters to represent sets, so we can refer to the set easily.

For example, if $V$ is the set of all vowels, then $V = \{a, e, i, o, u\}$.

Every number or object in a set is called an **element** or **member** of the set.

We use the symbol $\in$ to mean *is an element of* and $\notin$ to mean *is not an element of*.

So, for the set $A = \{1, 2, 3, 4, 5, 6, 7\}$ we can say $4 \in A$ but $9 \notin A$.

The set $\{\,\}$ or $\varnothing$ is called the **empty set** and contains no elements.

## COUNTING ELEMENTS OF SETS

The number of elements in set $A$ is written $n(A)$.

For example, the set $A = \{2, \;\; 3, \;\; 5, \;\; 8, 13, 21\}$ has 6 elements, so we write $n(A) = 6$.

  1st 2nd 3rd

A set which has a finite number of elements is said to be a **finite set**.

For example:  $A = \{2, 3, 5, 8, 13, 21\}$ is a finite set.

  $\varnothing$ is also a finite set, since $n(\varnothing) = 0$.

**Infinite sets** are sets which have infinitely many elements.

For example, the set of counting numbers 1, 2, 3, 4, .... does not have a largest element, but rather keeps on going forever. It is therefore an infinite set.

## SUBSETS

Suppose $P$ and $Q$ are two sets. $P$ is a **subset** of $Q$ if every element of $P$ is also an element of $Q$. We write $P \subseteq Q$.

For example, $\{2, 3, 5\} \subseteq \{1, 2, 3, 4, 5, 6\}$ as every element in the first set is also in the second set.

We say $P$ is a **proper subset** of $Q$ if $P$ is a subset of $Q$ but is *not equal to Q*. We write $P \subset Q$.

## UNION AND INTERSECTION

If $P$ and $Q$ are two sets then:

Every element in $P$ and every element in $Q$ is found in $P \cup Q$.

- $P \cap Q$ is the **intersection** of $P$ and $Q$ and consists of all elements which are in **both $P$ and $Q$**.
- $P \cup Q$ is the **union** of $P$ and $Q$ and consists of all elements which are in $P$ **or** $Q$.

For example, if $P = \{1, 3, 4\}$ and $Q = \{2, 3, 5\}$ then

DEMO

$$P \cap Q = \{3\} \quad \text{and} \quad P \cup Q = \{1, 2, 3, 4, 5\}.$$

## DISJOINT SETS

Two sets are **disjoint** or **mutually exclusive** if they have no elements in common.

| Example 1 | ◄) Self Tutor |
|---|---|

$M = \{2, 3, 5, 7, 8, 9\}$ and $N = \{3, 4, 6, 9, 10\}$

a True or false?   i $4 \in M$   ii $6 \notin M$

b List the sets:   i $M \cap N$   ii $M \cup N$

c Is   i $M \subseteq N$   ii $\{9, 6, 3\} \subseteq N$?

To write down $M \cup N$, start with $M$ and add to it the elements of $N$ which are not in $M$.

a  i 4 is not an element of $M$, so $4 \in M$ is false.
   ii 6 is not an element of $M$, so $6 \notin M$ is true.

b  i $M \cap N = \{3, 9\}$ since 3 and 9 are elements of both sets.
   ii Every element which is in either $M$ or $N$ is in the union of $M$ and $N$.
   $\therefore M \cup N = \{2, 3, 4, 5, 6, 7, 8, 9, 10\}$

c  i No. Not every element of $M$ is an element of $N$.
   ii Yes, as 9, 6 and 3 are also in $N$.

## EXERCISE 3A

**1** Write using set notation:

    **a** 5 is an element of set $D$        **b** 6 is not an element of set $G$

    **c** $d$ is not an element of the set of all English vowels

    **d** $\{2, 5\}$ is a subset of $\{1, 2, 3, 4, 5, 6\}$

    **e** $\{3, 8, 6\}$ is not a subset of $\{1, 2, 3, 4, 5, 6\}$.

**2** Find **i** $A \cap B$ **ii** $A \cup B$ for:

    **a** $A = \{6, 7, 9, 11, 12\}$ and $B = \{5, 8, 10, 13, 9\}$

    **b** $A = \{1, 2, 3, 4\}$ and $B = \{5, 6, 7, 8\}$

    **c** $A = \{1, 3, 5, 7\}$ and $B = \{1, 2, 3, 4, 5, 6, 7, 8, 9\}$

**3** Write down the number of elements in the following sets:

    **a** $A = \{0, 3, 5, 8, 14\}$        **b** $B = \{1, 4, 5, 8, 11, 13\}$

    **c** $A \cap B$        **d** $A \cup B$

**4** Describe the following sets as either finite or infinite:

    **a** the set of counting numbers between 10 and 20

    **b** the set of counting numbers greater than 5.

**5** Which of these pairs of sets are disjoint?

    **a** $A = \{3, 5, 7, 9\}$ and $B = \{2, 4, 6, 8\}$

    **b** $P = \{3, 5, 6, 7, 8, 10\}$ and $Q = \{4, 9, 10\}$

**6** True or false? If $R$ and $S$ are two non-empty sets and $R \cap S = \varnothing$ then $R$ and $S$ are disjoint.

## B    SPECIAL NUMBER SETS

The following is a list of some special number sets you should be familiar with:

$\mathbb{N} = \{0, 1, 2, 3, 4, 5, 6, 7, ....\}$ is the set of all **natural** or **counting numbers**.

$\mathbb{Z} = \{0, \pm1, \pm2, \pm3, \pm4, ....\}$ is the set of all **integers**.

$\mathbb{Z}^+ = \{1, 2, 3, 4, 5, 6, 7, ....\}$ is the set of all **positive integers**.

$\mathbb{Z}^- = \{-1, -2, -3, -4, -5, ....\}$ is the set of all **negative integers**.

$\mathbb{Q}$ is the set of all **rational numbers**, or numbers which can be written in the form $\dfrac{p}{q}$ where $p$ and $q$ are integers and $q \neq 0$.

$\mathbb{R}$ is the set of all **real numbers**, which are all numbers which can be placed on the number line.

Notice that the set of integers is made up of the set of negative integers, zero, and the set of positive integers.

$$\mathbb{Z} = (\mathbb{Z}^- \cup \{0\} \cup \mathbb{Z}^+)$$

The sets $\mathbb{N}$, $\mathbb{Z}$, $\mathbb{Z}^+$, $\mathbb{Z}^-$, $\mathbb{Q}$ and $\mathbb{R}$ are all infinite sets.

### Example 2 ◀》 Self Tutor

Explain why:   a   any positive integer is also a rational number

   b   $-7$ is a rational number

   a   We can write any positive integer as a fraction where the number itself is the numerator, and the denominator is 1.

   For example, $5 = \frac{5}{1}$.

   So, all positive integers are rational numbers.

   b   $-7 = \frac{-7}{1}$,   so $-7$ is rational.

### Example 3 ◀》 Self Tutor

Show that the following are rational numbers:

   a   0.47          b   0.135

   a   $0.47 = \frac{47}{100}$,   so 0.47 is rational.

   b   $0.135 = \frac{135}{1000} = \frac{27}{200}$,   so 0.135 is rational.

> All terminating decimal numbers are rational numbers.

## EXERCISE 3B.1

1   Show that 8 and $-11$ are rational numbers.

2   Why is $\frac{4}{0}$ not a rational number?

3   True or false?

   a   $\mathbb{Z}^+ \subseteq \mathbb{N}$          b   $\mathbb{N} \subset \mathbb{Z}$          c   $\mathbb{N} = \mathbb{Z}^+$          d   $\mathbb{Z}^- \subseteq \mathbb{Z}$

   e   $\mathbb{Q} \subset \mathbb{Z}$          f   $\{0\} \subseteq \mathbb{Z}$          g   $\mathbb{Z} \subseteq \mathbb{Q}$          h   $\mathbb{Z}^+ \cup \mathbb{Z}^- = \mathbb{Z}$

4   Show that the following are rational numbers:

   a   0.8          b   0.71          c   0.45          d   0.219          e   0.864

5   True or false?

   a   $127 \in \mathbb{N}$          b   $\frac{138}{279} \in \mathbb{Q}$          c   $3\frac{1}{7} \notin \mathbb{Q}$          d   $-\frac{4}{11} \in \mathbb{Q}$

6   Describing the following sets as either finite or infinite:

   a   the set of all rational numbers $\mathbb{Q}$

   b   the set of all rational numbers between 0 and 1.

## RECURRING DECIMALS (EXTENSION)

All **recurring decimal numbers** can be shown to be rational.

| Example 4 | ◀)) Self Tutor |
|---|---|

Show that:    a   $0.777\,777\,7....$      b   $0.363\,636....$      are rational.

a   Let  $x = 0.777\,777\,7....$

$\therefore \;\; 10x = 7.777\,777\,7....$

$\therefore \;\; 10x = 7 + 0.777\,777....$

$\therefore \;\; 10x = 7 + x$

$\therefore \;\; 9x = 7$

$\therefore \;\; x = \frac{7}{9}$

So,  $0.777\,777.... = \frac{7}{9}$,

which is rational.

b   Let  $x = 0.363\,636....$

$\therefore \;\; 100x = 36.363\,636....$

$\therefore \;\; 100x = 36 + 0.363\,636....$

$\therefore \;\; 100x = 36 + x$

$\therefore \;\; 99x = 36$

$\therefore \;\; x = \frac{36}{99}$

$\therefore \;\; x = \frac{4}{11}$

So,  $0.363\,636.... = \frac{4}{11}$,

which is rational.

**7**   Show that these are rational:

a   $0.444\,444....$      b   $0.212\,121....$      c   $0.325\,325\,325....$

## IRRATIONAL NUMBERS

All real numbers are either rational or irrational.

> **Irrational numbers** cannot be written in the form $\dfrac{p}{q}$
>
> where $p$ and $q$ are integers, $q \neq 0$.
>
> The set of irrational numbers is denoted by $\mathbb{Q}'$.

Numbers such as  $\sqrt{2}$, $\sqrt{3}$, $\sqrt{5}$, and $\sqrt{7}$  are all irrational.

This means that their decimal expansions neither terminate nor recur.

Other irrationals include  $\pi \approx 3.141\,593....$  which is the ratio of a circle's circumference to its diameter, and exponential  $e \approx 2.718\,281\,828\,235....$  which has applications in finance and modelling.

The following shows the relationship between various number sets:

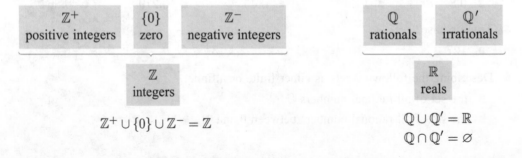

| $\mathbb{Z}^+$ positive integers | $\{0\}$ zero | $\mathbb{Z}^-$ negative integers | | $\mathbb{Q}$ rationals | $\mathbb{Q}'$ irrationals |

| $\mathbb{Z}$ integers | | $\mathbb{R}$ reals |

$$\mathbb{Z}^+ \cup \{0\} \cup \mathbb{Z}^- = \mathbb{Z}$$

$$\mathbb{Q} \cup \mathbb{Q}' = \mathbb{R}$$
$$\mathbb{Q} \cap \mathbb{Q}' = \varnothing$$

## EXERCISE 3B.2

**1** Which of the following are irrational numbers?

    **a** 3.127　　　　　**b** $\sqrt{8}$　　　　　**c** $\sqrt{4}$　　　　　**d** $\sqrt{1}$

**2** Show that $\sqrt{\frac{9}{25}}$ is a rational number.

**3** On the table, indicate with a tick or cross whether the numbers in the left hand column belong to $\mathbb{Q}$, $\mathbb{R}$, $\mathbb{Z}$, $\mathbb{Q}'$ or $\mathbb{N}$.

| | $\mathbb{Q}$ | $\mathbb{R}$ | $\mathbb{Z}$ | $\mathbb{Q}'$ | $\mathbb{N}$ |
|---|---|---|---|---|---|
| $\sqrt{2}$ | | | | | |
| $5$ | | | | | |
| $-\frac{1}{3}$ | | | | | |
| $2.17$ | | | | | |
| $-9$ | | | | | |

## C     SET BUILDER NOTATION

$A = \{x \mid -2 \leqslant x \leqslant 4, \ x \in \mathbb{Z}\}$ reads "the set of all $x$ such that $x$ is an integer between $-2$ and $4$, including $-2$ and $4$."

       └─ such that
       └─ the set of all

We can represent $A$ on a number line as:

We see that $A$ is a finite set, and that $n(A) = 7$.

$B = \{x \mid -2 \leqslant x < 4, \ x \in \mathbb{R}\}$ reads "the set of all real $x$ such that $x$ is greater than or equal to $-2$ and less than $4$."

We represent $B$ on a number line as:

filled in circle indicates $-2$ is included　　　　open circle indicates $4$ is not included

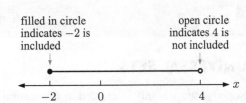

$B$ is an infinite set, and $n(B) = \infty$.

---

| **Example 5** | ◆) **Self Tutor** |
|---|---|

Suppose $A = \{x \mid 3 < x \leqslant 10, \ x \in \mathbb{Z}\}$.

  **a** Write down the meaning of the set builder notation.

  **b** List the elements of set $A$.     **c** Find $n(A)$.

  **a** The set of all $x$ such that $x$ is an integer between $3$ and $10$, including $10$.

  **b** $A = \{4, 5, 6, 7, 8, 9, 10\}$     **c** There are 7 elements, so $n(A) = 7$.

## EXERCISE 3C

1 Explain whether the following sets are finite or infinite:

    **a** $\{x \mid -2 \leqslant x \leqslant 1, \ x \in \mathbb{Z}\}$          **b** $\{x \mid -2 \leqslant x \leqslant 1, \ x \in \mathbb{R}\}$

    **c** $\{x \mid x \geqslant 5, \ x \in \mathbb{Z}\}$              **d** $\{x \mid 0 \leqslant x \leqslant 1, \ x \in \mathbb{Q}\}$

2 For the following sets:

    **i** Write down the meaning of the set builder notation.

    **ii** If possible, list the elements of $A$.          **iii** Find $n(A)$.

    **a** $A = \{x \mid -1 \leqslant x \leqslant 7, \ x \in \mathbb{Z}\}$      **b** $A = \{x \mid -2 < x < 8, \ x \in \mathbb{N}\}$

    **c** $A = \{x \mid 0 \leqslant x \leqslant 1, \ x \in \mathbb{R}\}$       **d** $A = \{x \mid 5 \leqslant x \leqslant 6, \ x \in \mathbb{Q}\}$

3 Write in set builder notation:

    **a** the set of all integers between $-100$ and $100$

    **b** the set of all real numbers greater than $1000$

    **c** the set of all rational numbers between 2 and 3, including 2 and 3.

4 $\{a\}$ has two subsets, $\varnothing$ and $\{a\}$. $\{a, b\}$ has four subsets: $\varnothing$, $\{a\}$, $\{b\}$, and $\{a, b\}$.

    **a** List the subsets of   **i** $\{a, b, c\}$   **ii** $\{a, b, c, d\}$   and state the number of subsets in each case.

    **b** Copy and complete: "If a set has $n$ elements then it has ...... subsets."

5 Is $A \subseteq B$ in these cases?

    **a** $A = \varnothing$ and $B = \{2, 5, 7, 9\}$         **b** $A = \{2, 5, 8, 9\}$ and $B = \{8, 9\}$

    **c** $A = \{x \mid 2 \leqslant x \leqslant 3, \ x \in \mathbb{R}\}$ and $B = \{x \mid x \in \mathbb{R}\}$

    **d** $A = \{x \mid 3 \leqslant x \leqslant 9, \ x \in \mathbb{Q}\}$ and $B = \{x \mid 0 \leqslant x \leqslant 10, \ x \in \mathbb{R}\}$

    **e** $A = \{x \mid -10 \leqslant x \leqslant 10, \ x \in \mathbb{Z}\}$ and $B = \{z \mid 0 \leqslant z \leqslant 5, \ z \in \mathbb{Z}\}$

    **f** $A = \{x \mid 0 \leqslant x \leqslant 1, \ x \in \mathbb{Q}\}$ and $B = \{y \mid 0 < y \leqslant 2, \ y \in \mathbb{Q}\}$

# D             COMPLEMENTS OF SETS

## UNIVERSAL SETS

Suppose we are only interested in the natural numbers from 1 to 20, and we want to consider subsets of this set. We say the set $U = \{x \mid 1 \leqslant x \leqslant 20, \ x \in \mathbb{N}\}$ is the *universal set* in this situation.

> The symbol $U$ is used to represent the **universal set** under consideration.

## COMPLEMENTARY SETS

If the universal set $U = \{1, 2, 3, 4, 5, 6, 7, 8\}$, and the set $A = \{1, 3, 5, 7, 8\}$, then the complement of $A$ is $A' = \{2, 4, 6\}$.

> The **complement** of $A$, denoted $A'$, is the set of all elements of $U$ which are **not** in $A$.

Three obvious relationships are observed connecting $A$ and $A'$. These are:

- $A \cap A' = \varnothing$        as $A'$ and $A$ have no common members.
- $A \cup A' = U$        as all elements of $A$ and $A'$ combined make up $U$.
- $n(A) + n(A') = n(U)$

### Example 6        ◄◈ Self Tutor

Find $C'$ given that:

**a** $U = \{$all positive integers$\}$ and $C = \{$all even integers$\}$

**b** $C = \{x \mid x \geqslant 2, \ x \in \mathbb{Z}\}$ and $U = \mathbb{Z}$

---

**a** $C' = \{$all odd integers$\}$        **b** $C' = \{x \mid x \leqslant 1, \ x \in \mathbb{Z}\}$

### Example 7        ◄◈ Self Tutor

If $U = \{x \mid -5 \leqslant x \leqslant 5, \ x \in \mathbb{Z}\}$, $A = \{x \mid 1 \leqslant x \leqslant 4, \ x \in \mathbb{Z}\}$ and
$B = \{x \mid -3 \leqslant x < 2, \ x \in \mathbb{Z}\}$, list the elements of these sets:

| | | | |
|---|---|---|---|
| **a** $A$ | **b** $B$ | **c** $A'$ | **d** $B'$ |
| **e** $A \cap B$ | **f** $A \cup B$ | **g** $A' \cap B$ | **h** $A' \cup B'$ |

---

**a** $A = \{1, 2, 3, 4\}$        **b** $B = \{-3, -2, -1, 0, 1\}$

**c** $A' = \{-5, -4, -3, -2, -1, 0, 5\}$        **d** $B' = \{-5, -4, 2, 3, 4, 5\}$

**e** $A \cap B = \{1\}$        **f** $A \cup B = \{-3, -2, -1, 0, 1, 2, 3, 4\}$

**g** $A' \cap B = \{-3, -2, -1, 0\}$

**h** $A' \cup B' = \{-5, -4, -3, -2, -1, 0, 2, 3, 4, 5\}$

## EXERCISE 3D

**1** Find the complement of $C$ given that:

**a** $U = \{$letters of the English alphabet$\}$ and $C = \{$vowels$\}$

**b** $U = \{$integers$\}$ and $C = \{$negative integers$\}$

**c** $U = \mathbb{Z}$ and $C = \{x \mid x \leqslant -5, \ x \in \mathbb{Z}\}$

**d** $U = \mathbb{Q}$ and $C = \{x \mid x \leqslant 2 \ \text{ or } \ x \geqslant 8, \ x \in \mathbb{Q}\}$

**2** If $U = \{x \mid 0 \leqslant x \leqslant 8, \ x \in \mathbb{Z}\}$, $A = \{x \mid 2 \leqslant x \leqslant 7, \ x \in \mathbb{Z}\}$ and
$B = \{x \mid 5 \leqslant x \leqslant 8, \ x \in \mathbb{Z}\}$ list the elements of:

| | | | |
|---|---|---|---|
| **a** $A$ | **b** $A'$ | **c** $B$ | **d** $B'$ |
| **e** $A \cap B$ | **f** $A \cup B$ | **g** $A \cap B'$ | |

**3** If $n(U) = 15$, $n(P) = 6$ and $n(Q') = 4$ where $P$ and $Q'$ are subsets of $U$, find:

**a** $n(P')$        **b** $n(Q)$

**4** True or false?

    **a** If $n(U) = a$ and $n(A) = b$ then $n(A') = b - a$.

    **b** If $Q$ is a subset of $U$ then $Q' = \{x \mid x \notin Q,\ x \in U\}$.

**5** If $U = \{x \mid 0 < x \leqslant 12,\ x \in \mathbb{Z}\}$, $A = \{x \mid 2 \leqslant x \leqslant 7,\ x \in \mathbb{Z}\}$,
    $B = \{x \mid 3 \leqslant x \leqslant 9,\ x \in \mathbb{Z}\}$, and $C = \{x \mid 5 \leqslant x \leqslant 11,\ x \in \mathbb{Z}\}$,
    list the elements of:

| | | | |
|---|---|---|---|
| **a** $B'$ | **b** $C'$ | **c** $A'$ | **d** $A \cap B$ |
| **e** $(A \cap B)'$ | **f** $A' \cap C$ | **g** $B' \cup C$ | **h** $(A \cup C) \cap B'$ |

---

**Example 8**  ◀)) **Self Tutor**

Suppose $U = \{\text{positive integers}\}$, $P = \{\text{multiples of 4 less than 50}\}$ and $Q = \{\text{multiples of 6 less than 50}\}$.

    **a** List $P$ and $Q$.     **b** Find $P \cap Q$.     **c** Find $P \cup Q$.

    **d** Verify that $n(P \cup Q) = n(P) + n(Q) - n(P \cap Q)$.

---

    **a** $P = \{4, 8, 12, 16, 20, 24, 28, 32, 36, 40, 44, 48\}$
       $Q = \{6, 12, 18, 24, 30, 36, 42, 48\}$

    **b** $P \cap Q = \{12, 24, 36, 48\}$

    **c** $P \cup Q = \{4, 6, 8, 12, 16, 18, 20, 24, 28, 30, 32, 36, 40, 42, 44, 48\}$

    **d** $n(P \cup Q) = 16$ and $n(P) + n(Q) - n(P \cap Q) = 12 + 8 - 4 = 16$
       So, $n(P \cup Q) = n(P) + n(Q) - n(P \cap Q)$ is verified.

---

**6** Suppose $U = \mathbb{Z}^+$, $P = \{\text{prime numbers} < 25\}$, and $Q = \{2, 4, 5, 11, 12, 15\}$.

    **a** List $P$.     **b** Find $P \cap Q$.     **c** Find $P \cup Q$.

    **d** Verify that $n(P \cup Q) = n(P) + n(Q) - n(P \cap Q)$.

**7** Suppose $U = \mathbb{Z}^+$, $P = \{\text{factors of 30}\}$, and $Q = \{\text{factors of 40}\}$.

    **a** List $P$ and $Q$.     **b** Find $P \cap Q$.     **c** Find $P \cup Q$.

    **d** Verify that $n(P \cup Q) = n(P) + n(Q) - n(P \cap Q)$.

**8** Suppose $U = \mathbb{Z}^+$, $M = \{\text{multiples of 4 between 30 and 60}\}$, and $N = \{\text{multiples of 6 between 30 and 60}\}$.

    **a** List $M$ and $N$.     **b** Find $M \cap N$.     **c** Find $M \cup N$.

    **d** Verify that $n(M \cup N) = n(M) + n(N) - n(M \cap N)$.

**9** Suppose $U = \mathbb{Z}$, $R = \{x \mid -2 \leqslant x \leqslant 4,\ x \in \mathbb{Z}\}$, and $S = \{x \mid 0 \leqslant x < 7,\ x \in \mathbb{Z}\}$.

    **a** List $R$ and $S$.     **b** Find $R \cap S$.     **c** Find $R \cup S$.

    **d** Verify that $n(R \cup S) = n(R) + n(S) - n(R \cap S)$.

**10** Suppose $U = \mathbb{Z}$, $C = \{y \mid -4 \leqslant y \leqslant -1, y \in \mathbb{Z}\}$, and $D = \{y \mid -7 \leqslant y < 0, y \in \mathbb{Z}\}$.

    **a** List $C$ and $D$.     **b** Find $C \cap D$.     **c** Find $C \cup D$.

    **d** Verify that $n(C \cup D) = n(C) + n(D) - n(C \cap D)$.

**11** Suppose $U = \mathbb{Z}^+$, $P = \{$factors of 12$\}$, $Q = \{$factors of 18$\}$, and $R = \{$factors of 27$\}$.

   **a** List the sets $P$, $Q$, and $R$.

   **b** Find:    **i** $P \cap Q$        **ii** $P \cap R$        **iii** $Q \cap R$

              **iv** $P \cup Q$        **v** $P \cup R$        **vi** $Q \cup R$

   **c** Find:    **i** $P \cap Q \cap R$        **ii** $P \cup Q \cup R$

**12** Suppose $U = \mathbb{Z}^+$, $A = \{$multiples of 4 less than 40$\}$,
   $B = \{$multiples of 6 less than 40$\}$, and $C = \{$multiples of 12 less than 40$\}$.

   **a** List the sets $A$, $B$ and $C$.

   **b** Find:    **i** $A \cap B$    **ii** $B \cap C$    **iii** $A \cap C$    **iv** $A \cap B \cap C$

   **c** Find $A \cup B \cup C$.

   **d** Verify that $n(A \cup B \cup C) = n(A) + n(B) + n(C) - n(A \cap B) - n(B \cap C)$
                                  $- n(A \cap C) + n(A \cap B \cap C)$.

**13** Suppose $U = \mathbb{Z}^+$, $A = \{$multiples of 6 less than 31$\}$,
               $B = \{$factors of 30$\}$, and $C = \{$primes $< 30\}$.

   **a** List the sets $A$, $B$ and $C$.

   **b** Find:    **i** $A \cap B$    **ii** $B \cap C$    **iii** $A \cap C$    **iv** $A \cap B \cap C$

   **c** Find $A \cup B \cup C$.

   **d** Verify that $n(A \cup B \cup C) = n(A) + n(B) + n(C) - n(A \cap B) - n(B \cap C)$
                                    $- n(A \cap C) + n(A \cap B \cap C)$.

# E       VENN DIAGRAMS

Venn diagrams are often used to represent sets of objects, numbers, or things.

> A **Venn diagram** consists of a universal set $U$ represented by a rectangle.
>
> Sets within the universal set are usually represented by circles.

For example: 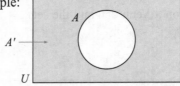   is a Venn diagram which shows set $A$ within the universal set $U$.

$A'$, the complement of $A$, is the shaded region outside the circle.

Suppose $U = \{2, 3, 5, 7, 8\}$, $A = \{2, 7, 8\}$ and $A' = \{3, 5\}$.

We can represent these sets by:

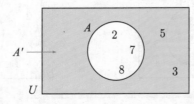

## SUBSETS

If $B \subseteq A$ then every element of $B$ is also in $A$.

The circle representing $B$ is placed within the circle representing $A$.

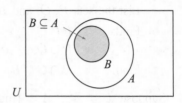

## INTERSECTION

$A \cap B$ consists of all elements common to both $A$ and $B$.

It is the shaded region where the circles representing $A$ and $B$ overlap.

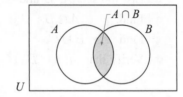

## UNION

$A \cup B$ consists of all elements in $A$ or $B$ or both.

It is the shaded region which includes everywhere in either circle.

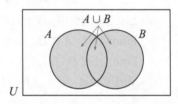

## DISJOINT OR MUTUALLY EXCLUSIVE SETS

Disjoint sets do not have common elements.

They are represented by non-overlapping circles.

For example, if $A = \{2, 3, 8\}$ and $B = \{4, 5, 9\}$
then $A \cap B = \varnothing$.

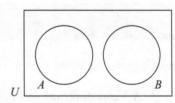

| Example 9 | ◀️ Self Tutor |
|---|---|

Given $U = \{1, 2, 3, 4, 5, 6, 7, 8\}$, illustrate on a Venn diagram the sets:

**a** $A = \{1, 3, 6, 8\}$ and $B = \{2, 3, 4, 5, 8\}$

**b** $A = \{1, 3, 6, 7, 8\}$ and $B = \{3, 6, 8\}$.

**a** $A \cap B = \{3, 8\}$

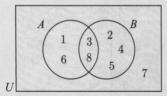

**b** $A \cap B = \{3, 6, 8\}$, $B \subseteq A$

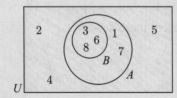

**Example 10**    ◀ŵ **Self Tutor**

Given $U = \{1, 2, 3, 4, 5, 6, 7, 8, 9\}$, illustrate on a Venn diagram the sets $A = \{2, 4, 8\}$ and $B = \{1, 3, 5, 9\}$.

Since $A$ and $B$ are disjoint, their circles are separated.

$A \cap B = \varnothing$

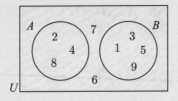

## EXERCISE 3E

1 Represent sets $A$ and $B$ on a Venn diagram, given:

a $U = \{2, 3, 4, 5, 6, 7\}$, $A = \{2, 4, 6\}$, and $B = \{5, 7\}$

b $U = \{2, 3, 4, 5, 6, 7\}$, $A = \{2, 4, 6\}$, and $B = \{3, 5, 7\}$

c $U = \{1, 2, 3, 4, 5, 6, 7\}$, $A = \{2, 4, 5, 6\}$, and $B = \{1, 4, 6, 7\}$

d $U = \{3, 4, 5, 7\}$, $A = \{3, 4, 5, 7\}$, and $B = \{3, 5\}$

2 Suppose $U = \{x \mid 1 \leqslant x \leqslant 10, \ x \in \mathbb{Z}\}$, $A = \{\text{odd numbers} < 10\}$, and $B = \{\text{primes} < 10\}$.

a List sets $A$ and $B$.

b Find $A \cap B$ and $A \cup B$.

c Represent the sets $A$ and $B$ on a Venn diagram.

3 Suppose $U = \{x \mid 1 \leqslant x \leqslant 9, \ x \in \mathbb{Z}\}$, $A = \{\text{factors of } 6\}$, and $B = \{\text{factors of } 9\}$.

a List sets $A$ and $B$.

b Find $A \cap B$ and $A \cup B$.

c Represent the sets $A$ and $B$ on a Venn diagram.

4 Suppose $U = \{\text{even numbers between 0 and 30}\}$,
  $P = \{\text{multiples of 4 less than 30}\}$, and
  $Q = \{\text{multiples of 6 less than 30}\}$.

a List sets $P$ and $Q$.

b Find $P \cap Q$ and $P \cup Q$.

c Represent the sets $P$ and $Q$ on a Venn diagram.

5 Suppose $U = \{x \mid x \leqslant 30, \ x \in \mathbb{Z}^+\}$, $R = \{\text{primes less than 30}\}$, and $S = \{\text{composites less than 30}\}$.

a List sets $R$ and $S$.

b Find $R \cap S$ and $R \cup S$.

c Represent the sets $R$ and $S$ on a Venn diagram.

6   List the elements of set:

a $A$

b $B$

c $A'$

d $B'$

e $A \cap B$

f $A \cup B$

g $(A \cup B)'$

h $A' \cup B'$

**7**

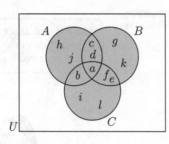

This Venn diagram consists of three overlapping circles $A$, $B$ and $C$.

**a**  List the letters in set:

|  |  |  |
|---|---|---|
| **i**   $A$ | **ii**   $B$ | **iii**   $C$ |
| **iv**   $A \cap B$ | **v**   $A \cup B$ | **vi**   $B \cap C$ |
| **vii**   $A \cap B \cap C$ | **viii**   $A \cup B \cup C$ | |

**b**  Find:

   **i**  $n(A \cup B \cup C)$

   **ii**  $n(A) + n(B) + n(C) - n(A \cap B) - n(A \cap C) - n(B \cap C) + n(A \cap B \cap C)$

## F       VENN DIAGRAM REGIONS

We use shading to show various sets being considered.

For example, for two intersecting sets $A$ and $B$:

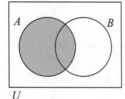  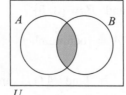  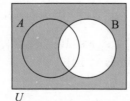  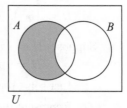

    $A$ is shaded         $A \cap B$ is shaded         $B'$ is shaded         $A \cap B'$ is shaded

| **Example 11** | ◄)) **Self Tutor** |
|---|---|

On separate Venn diagrams, shade these regions for two intersecting sets $A$ and $B$:

  **a**  $A \cup B$         **b**  $A' \cap B$         **c**  $(A \cap B)'$

**a**         **b**         **c**

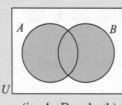  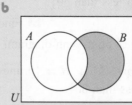  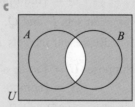

   (in $A$, $B$ or both)     (outside $A$, intersected     (outside $A \cap B$)

                    with $B$)

Click on the icon to **practise shading regions** representing various subsets. You can practise with both two and three intersecting sets.

**DEMO**

## EXERCISE 3F

**1**

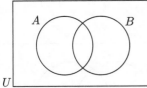

Draw separate Venn diagrams showing shading regions for:

  **a** $A \cap B$          **b** $A \cap B'$

  **c** $A' \cup B$          **d** $A \cup B'$

  **e** $(A \cap B)'$        **f** $(A \cup B)'$

PRINTABLE
VENN DIAGRAMS
(OVERLAPPING)

**2**

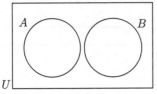

Suppose $A$ and $B$ are two disjoint sets. Shade on separate Venn diagrams:

  **a** $A$            **b** $B$

  **c** $A'$          **d** $B'$

  **e** $A \cap B$      **f** $A \cup B$

  **g** $A' \cap B$      **h** $A \cup B'$

  **i** $(A \cap B)'$

PRINTABLE VENN
DIAGRAMS (DISJOINT)

**3**

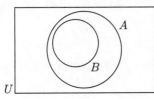

Suppose $B \subseteq A$, as shown in the given Venn diagram. Shade on separate Venn diagrams:

  **a** $A$            **b** $B$

  **c** $A'$          **d** $B'$

  **e** $A \cap B$      **f** $A \cup B$

  **g** $A' \cap B$      **h** $A \cup B'$

  **i** $(A \cap B)'$

PRINTABLE VENN
DIAGRAMS (SUBSET)

**4**

This Venn diagram consists of three intersecting sets. On separate Venn diagrams shade:

  **a** $A$             **b** $B'$

  **c** $B \cap C$        **d** $A \cup B$

  **e** $A \cap B \cap C$    **f** $A \cup B \cup C$

  **g** $(A \cap B \cap C)'$   **h** $(A \cup B) \cap C$

  **i** $(B \cap C) \cup A$

PRINTABLE VENN
DIAGRAMS (3 SETS)

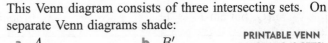

# **G**    NUMBERS IN REGIONS

We have seen that there are four regions on a Venn diagram which contains two overlapping sets $A$ and $B$.

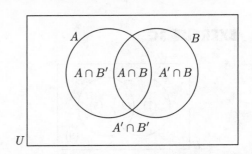

There are many situations where we are only interested in the *number of elements* of $U$ that are in each region.

We do not need to show all the elements on the diagram, so instead we simply write the number of elements in each region in brackets.

For example, the Venn diagram opposite shows there are 4 elements in both sets $A$ and $B$, and 3 elements in neither set $A$ nor $B$.

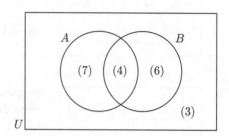

Every element in $U$ belongs in only one region of the Venn diagram. So, in total there are $7 + 4 + 6 + 3 = 20$ elements in the universal set $U$.

---

**Example 12**                                                      ◀) **Self Tutor**

If (3) means that there are 3 elements in the set $P \cap Q$, how many elements are there in:

| | |
|---|---|
| **a** $P$ | **b** $Q'$ |
| **c** $P \cup Q$ | **d** $P$, but not $Q$ |
| **e** $Q$, but not $P$ | **f** neither $P$ nor $Q$? |

| | |
|---|---|
| **a** $n(P) = 7 + 3 = 10$ | **b** $n(Q') = 7 + 4 = 11$ |
| **c** $n(P \cup Q) = 7 + 3 + 11$ $= 21$ | **d** $n(P, \text{ but not } Q) = 7$ |
| **e** $n(Q, \text{ but not } P) = 11$ | **f** $n(\text{neither } P \text{ nor } Q) = 4$ |

---

Venn diagrams allow us to easily visualise identities such as

$$n(A \cap B') = n(A) - n(A \cap B)$$
$$n(A' \cap B) = n(B) - n(A \cap B)$$

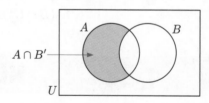

## EXERCISE 3G

**1**

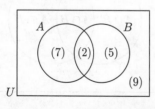

If (2) means that there are 2 elements in the set $A \cap B$, give the number of elements in:

| | |
|---|---|
| **a** $B$ | **b** $A'$ |
| **c** $A \cup B$ | **d** $A$, but not $B$ |
| **e** $B$, but not $A$ | **f** neither $A$ nor $B$ |

**2**

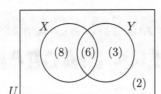

Give the number of elements in:

a  $X'$                          b  $X \cap Y$
c  $X \cup Y$                    d  $X$, but not $Y$
e  $Y$, but not $X$             f  neither $X$ nor $Y$

**3**

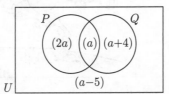

In the Venn diagram given, $(a)$ means that there are $a$ elements in the shaded region.

Notice that $n(A) = a + b$.

Find:

a  $n(B)$          b  $n(A')$          c  $n(A \cap B)$
d  $n(A \cup B)$   e  $n((A \cap B)')$  f  $n((A \cup B)')$

**4**

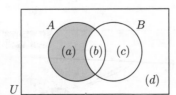

The Venn diagram shows that $n(P \cap Q) = a$ and $n(P) = 3a$.

a  Find:

  i  $n(Q)$                    ii  $n(P \cup Q)$
  iii  $n(Q')$                 iv  $n(U)$

b  Find $a$ if:

  i  $n(U) = 29$              ii  $n(U) = 31$

Comment on your results.

---

**Example 13**    ◄)) **Self Tutor**

Given  $n(U) = 30$,  $n(A) = 14$,  $n(B) = 17$  and  $n(A \cap B) = 6$,  find:

a  $n(A \cup B)$                b  $n(A$, but not $B)$

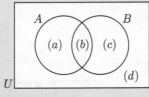

We see that   $b = 6$        {as $n(A \cap B) = 6$}
              $a + b = 14$    {as $n(A) = 14$}
              $b + c = 17$    {as $n(B) = 17$}
              $a + b + c + d = 30$   {as $n(U) = 30$}

Since  $b = 6$,  $a = 8$  and  $c = 11$.

So,  $8 + 6 + 11 + d = 30$  and hence  $d = 5$.

a  $n(A \cup B) = a + b + c = 25$          b  $n(A$, but not $B) = a = 8$

---

**5**  Given  $n(U) = 26$,  $n(A) = 11$,  $n(B) = 12$  and  $n(A \cap B) = 8$,  find:

a  $n(A \cup B)$                b  $n(B$, but not $A)$

**6**  Given  $n(U) = 32$,  $n(M) = 13$,  $n(M \cap N) = 5$  and  $n(M \cup N) = 26$,  find:

a  $n(N)$                      b  $n((M \cup N)')$

**7**  Given  $n(U) = 50$,  $n(S) = 30$,  $n(R) = 25$  and  $n(R \cup S) = 48$,  find:

a  $n(R \cap S)$               b  $n(S$, but not $R)$

# H    PROBLEM SOLVING WITH VENN DIAGRAMS

In this section we use Venn diagrams to illustrate real world situations. We can solve problems by considering the number of elements in each region.

## Example 14    ◀)) Self Tutor

A squash club has 27 members. 19 have black hair, 14 have brown eyes, and 11 have both black hair and brown eyes.

  **a**  Place this information on a Venn diagram.

  **b**  Hence find the number of members with:

    **i**  black hair or brown eyes

    **ii**  black hair, but not brown eyes.

**a**  Let $Bl$ represent the black hair set and $Br$ represent the brown eyes set.

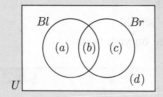

$$a + b + c + d = 27$$
$$a + b = 19$$
$$b + c = 14$$
$$b = 11$$
$$\therefore \ a = 8, \ c = 3, \ d = 5$$

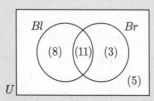

**b**  **i**  $n(Bl \cup Br) = 8 + 11 + 3$
$$= 22$$

    **ii**  $n(Bl \cap Br') = 8$

## Example 15    ◀)) Self Tutor

A platform diving squad of 25 has 18 members who dive from 10 m and 17 who dive from 5 m. How many dive from both platforms?

Let $T$ represent those who dive from 10 m and $F$ represent those who dive from 5 m.

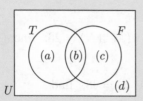

$d = 0$  {as all divers in the squad must dive from at least one of the platforms}

$$a + b = 18$$
$$b + c = 17$$
$$a + b + c = 25$$

$\therefore \ a = 8, \ b = 10, \ c = 7.$

$$n(\text{both } T \text{ and } F) = n(T \cap F)$$
$$= 10$$

So, 10 members dive from both platforms.

## EXERCISE 3H

**1** Pelé has 14 cavies as pets. Five have long hair and 8 are brown. Two are both brown and have long hair.

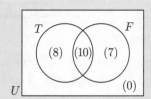

**a** Place this information on a Venn diagram.

**b** Hence find the number of cavies that:

   **i** do not have long hair

   **ii** have long hair and are not brown

   **iii** are neither long-haired nor brown.

**2**

During a 2 week period, Murielle took her umbrella with her on 8 days. It rained on 9 days, and Murielle took her umbrella on five of the days when it rained.

**a** Display this information on a Venn diagram.

**b** Hence find the number of days that:

   **i** Murielle did not take her umbrella and it rained

   **ii** Murielle did not take her umbrella and it did not rain.

**3** A badminton club has 31 playing members. 28 play singles and 16 play doubles. How many play both singles and doubles?

**4** In a factory, 56 people work on the assembly line. 47 work day shifts and 29 work night shifts. How many work both day shifts and night shifts?

**5**

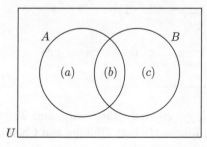

Use the figure given to show that:
$$n(A \cup B) = n(A) + n(B) - n(A \cap B)$$

**Example 16**    ◀) **Self Tutor**

A city has three football teams $A$, $B$ and $C$, in the national league.

In the last season, 20% of the city's population went to see team $A$ play, 24% saw team $B$, and 28% saw team $C$. Of these, 4% saw both $A$ and $B$, 5% saw both $A$ and $C$, and 6% saw both $B$ and $C$. 1% saw all three teams play.

Using a Venn diagram, find the percentage of the city's population which:

  **a**  saw only team $A$ play

  **b**  saw team $A$ or team $B$ play but not team $C$

  **c**  did not see any of the teams play.

We construct the Venn diagram in terms of percentages.

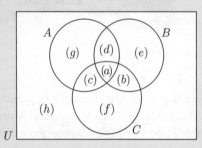

Using the given information,

$$a = 1 \quad \{1\% \text{ saw all three teams play}\}$$
$$a + d = 4 \quad \{4\% \text{ saw } A \text{ and } B\}$$
$$a + b = 6 \quad \{6\% \text{ saw } B \text{ and } C\}$$
$$a + c = 5 \quad \{5\% \text{ saw } A \text{ and } C\}$$

$$\therefore \ d = 3, \ b = 5 \ \text{and} \ c = 4$$

Also, 20% saw team $A$ play,
so $g + 1 + 4 + 3 = 20 \quad \therefore \ g = 12$

24% saw team $B$ play,
so $e + 1 + 5 + 3 = 24 \quad \therefore \ e = 15$

28% saw team $C$ play,
so $f + 1 + 5 + 4 = 28 \quad \therefore \ f = 18$

In total we cover 100% of the population,
so $h = 42$.

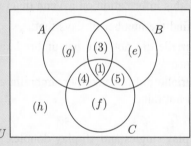

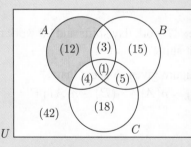

  **a**  $n(\text{saw } A \text{ only}) = 12\%$  {shaded}

  **b**  $n(A \text{ or } B, \text{ but not } C)$
    $= 12\% + 3\% + 15\%$
    $= 30\%$

  **c**  $n(\text{saw none of the teams}) = 42\%$

**6**  In a year group of 63 students 22 study Biology, 26 study Chemistry, and 25 study Physics. 18 study both Physics and Chemistry, four study both Biology and Chemistry, and three study both Physics and Biology. One studies all three subjects. How many students study:

  **a**  Biology only                **b**  Physics or Chemistry

  **c**  none of Biology, Physics or Chemistry    **d**  Physics but not Chemistry?

**7**  36 students participated in the mid-year adventure trip. 19 students went paragliding, 21 went abseiling, and 16 went white water rafting. 7 did abseiling and rafting, 8 did paragliding and rafting, and 11 did paragliding and abseiling. 5 students did all three activities. Find the number of students who:

    **a**  went paragliding or abseiling     **b**  only went white water rafting

    **c**  did not participate in any of the activities mentioned

    **d**  did exactly two of the activities mentioned.

**8**  There are 32 students in the woodwind section of the school orchestra. 11 students can play the flute, 15 can play the clarinet, and 12 can play the saxophone. Two can play the flute and the saxophone, two can play the flute and the clarinet, and 6 can play the clarinet and the saxophone. One student can play all three instruments. Find the number of students who can play:

    **a**  none of the instruments mentioned

    **b**  only the saxophone

    **c**  the saxophone and the clarinet but not the flute

    **d**  only one of the clarinet, saxophone, or flute.

**9**  In a particular region, most farms have livestock and crops. A survey of 21 farms showed that 15 grow crops, 9 have cattle, and 11 have sheep. Four have sheep and cattle, 7 have cattle and crops, and 8 have sheep and crops. Three have cattle, sheep, and crops. Find the number of farms with:

    **a**  only crops     **b**  only animals     **c**  exactly one type of animal, and crops.

## REVIEW SET 3A

**1**  If  $S = \{x \mid 2 < x \leqslant 7, \ x \in \mathbb{Z}\}$:

    **a**  list the elements of $S$     **b**  find  $n(S)$.

**2**  For each of the following numbers, state if they are rational or irrational. If the number is rational, prove your claim.

    **a**  $\frac{4}{7}$     **b**  $0.165$     **c**  $\frac{8}{0}$

    **d**  $56$     **e**  $\sqrt{5}$     **f**  $0.181\,818\ldots$

**3**  Determine whether  $A \subseteq B$  for the following sets:

    **a**  $A = \{2, 4, 6, 8\}$  and  $B = \{x \mid 0 < x < 10, \ x \in \mathbb{Z}\}$

    **b**  $A = \varnothing$  and  $B = \{x \mid 2 < x < 3, \ x \in \mathbb{R}\}$

    **c**  $A = \{x \mid 2 < x \leqslant 4, \ x \in \mathbb{Q}\}$  and  $B = \{x \mid 0 \leqslant x < 4, \ x \in \mathbb{R}\}$

    **d**  $A = \{x \mid x < 3, \ x \in \mathbb{R}\}$  and  $B = \{y \mid y \leqslant 4, \ y \in \mathbb{R}\}$

**4**  Find the complement of $X$ given that:

    **a**  $U = \{\text{the 7 colours of the rainbow}\}$  and  $X = \{\text{red, indigo, violet}\}$

    **b**  $U = \{x \mid -5 \leqslant x \leqslant 5, \ x \in \mathbb{Z}\}$  and  $X = \{-4, -1, 3, 4\}$

    **c**  $U = \{x \mid x \in \mathbb{Q}\}$  and  $X = \{y \mid y < -8, \ y \in \mathbb{Q}\}$

**5** On separate Venn diagrams like the one alongside, shade:

    **a** $N'$        **b** $M \cap N$      **c** $M \cap N'$

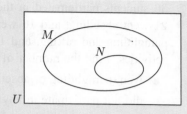

**6** Let $U = \{$the letters in the English alphabet$\}$, $A = \{$the letters in "springbok"$\}$, and $B = \{$the letters in "waterbuck"$\}$.

    **a** Find:    **i** $A \cup B$    **ii** $A \cap B$    **iii** $A \cap B'$

    **b** Write a description for each of the sets in **a**.

    **c** Show $U$, $A$ and $B$ on a Venn diagram.

**7** Let $U = \{x \mid x \leqslant 30,\ x \in \mathbb{Z}^+\}$, $P = \{$factors of 24$\}$, and $Q = \{$factors of 30$\}$.

    **a** List the elements of:

        **i** $P$        **ii** $Q$        **iii** $P \cap Q$        **iv** $P \cup Q$

    **b** Illustrate the sets $P$ and $Q$ on a Venn diagram.

**8** A school has 564 students. 229 of them were absent for at least one day during Term 1 due to sickness, and 111 students missed some school because of family holidays. 296 students attended every day of Term 1.

    **a** Display this information on a Venn diagram.

    **b** Find how many students:

        **i** missed school for both illness and holidays

        **ii** were away for holidays but not sickness

        **iii** were absent during Term 1 for any reason.

**9** The main courses at a restaurant all contain rice or onion. Of the 23 choices, 17 contain onion and 14 have rice. If Elke dislikes onion, how many choices does she have?

**10** 38 students were asked what life skills they had. 15 could swim, 12 could drive and 23 could cook. 9 could cook and swim, 5 knew how to swim and drive, and 6 could drive and cook. There was a student who could do all three. Find the number of students who:

    **a** could cook only

    **b** could not do any of these things

    **c** had exactly two life skills.

**11** Consider the sets $U = \{x \mid x \leqslant 10,\ x \in \mathbb{Z}^+\}$, $P = \{$odd numbers less than 10$\}$, and $Q = \{$even numbers less than 11$\}$.

    **a** List the sets $P$ and $Q$.    **b** What can be said about sets $P$ and $Q$?

    **c** Illustrate sets $P$ and $Q$ on a Venn diagram.

## REVIEW SET 3B

**1** True or false:

    **a** $\mathbb{N} \subset \mathbb{Q}$                 **b** $0 \in \mathbb{Z}^+$               **c** $0 \in \mathbb{Q}$

    **d** $\mathbb{R} \subseteq \mathbb{Q}$             **e** $\mathbb{Z}^+ \cap \mathbb{Z}^- = \{0\}$

**2**  **a** Write in set builder notation:

      **i** the real numbers between 5 and 12

      **ii** the integers between $-4$ and 7, including $-4$

      **iii** the natural numbers greater than 45.

    **b** Which sets in **a** are finite and which are infinite?

**3** List the subsets of $\{1, 3, 5\}$.

**4** Let  $U = \{x \mid 0 < x < 10, \ x \in \mathbb{Z}\}$,  $A = \{$the even integers between 0 and 9$\}$, and  $B = \{$the factors of 8$\}$.

    **a** List the elements of:      **i** $A$      **ii** $A \cap B$      **iii** $(A \cup B)'$

    **b** Represent this information on a Venn diagram.

**5** If $S$ and $T$ are disjoint sets, $n(S) = s$ and $n(T) = t$, find:

    **a** $S \cap T$               **b** $n(S \cup T)$

**6**

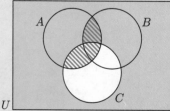

Give an expression for the region shaded in:

    **a** blue          **b** red.

**7** In a car club, 13 members drive a manual and 15 members have a sunroof on their car. 5 have manual cars with a sunroof, and 4 have neither.

    **a** Display this information on a Venn diagram.

    **b** How many members:

      **i** are in the club

      **ii** drive a manual car without a sunroof

      **iii** do not drive a manual?

**8** All attendees of a camp left something at home. 11 forgot to bring their towel, and 23 forgot their hat. Of the 30 campers, how many had neither a hat nor a towel?

**9** Consider the sets  $U = \{x \mid x \leqslant 60, \ x \in \mathbb{Z}^+\}$,  $A = \{$factors of 60$\}$, and  $B = \{$factors of 30$\}$.

    **a** List the sets $A$ and $B$.          **b** What can be said about sets $A$ and $B$?

    **c** Illustrate sets $A$ and $B$ on a Venn diagram.

**10** At a conference, the 58 delegates speak many different languages.    28 speak Arabic, 27 speak Chinese, and 39 speak English.  12 speak Arabic and Chinese, 16 speak both Chinese and English, and 17 speak Arabic and English.  2 speak all three languages. How many delegates speak:

  **a**  Chinese only

  **b**  none of these languages

  **c**  neither Arabic nor Chinese?

# Chapter 4

# Laws of algebra

**Contents:**

In this chapter we review some important laws that deal with algebraic expressions. These include the **index laws** which describe what happens when different operations are performed on expressions containing indices, and the **expansion laws** which describe how brackets can be removed from expressions.

## OPENING PROBLEM

Fill out the table below:

| $b$ | $(5+b)^2$ | $(5-b)^2$ | $(5+b)^2 - (5-b)^2$ |
|-----|-----------|-----------|---------------------|
| 0   |           |           |                     |
| 1   |           |           |                     |
| 2   |           |           |                     |
| 3   |           |           |                     |
| 4   |           |           |                     |
| 5   |           |           |                     |

Can you explain why $(5+b)^2 - (5-b)^2$ is always equal to $20b$?

# A     INDEX LAWS

## INVESTIGATION 1

In this investigation we discover the index laws by observing patterns involving indices.

**What to do:**

**1** Write out the first 10 powers of:   **a** 2   **b** 3   **c** 5

**2** **a** Use your calculator to fill in the first column of numbers. Then use your answers to **1** to complete the second column.

$$2^3 \times 2^2 = \quad 32 \quad = \quad 2^5$$
$$2^2 \times 2^7 = \qquad =$$
$$2^5 \times 2^3 = \qquad =$$
$$3^4 \times 3^1 = \qquad =$$
$$3^3 \times 3^5 = \qquad =$$
$$3^2 \times 3^2 = \qquad =$$
$$5^3 \times 5^4 = \qquad =$$

**b** Use your observations from **a** to fill in these statements:

**i** $2^m \times 2^n = \ldots$   **ii** $3^m \times 3^n = \ldots$   **iii** $a^m \times a^n = \ldots$

**3**   **a**   As in **2**, fill in the following using your calculator and your answers to **1**.

$$\frac{2^5}{2^2} = \quad = \qquad \frac{3^8}{3^3} = \quad = \qquad \frac{5^6}{5^5} = \quad =$$

$$\frac{2^6}{2^3} = \quad = \qquad \frac{3^4}{3^3} = \quad = \qquad \frac{5^9}{5^2} = \quad =$$

**b**   Fill in these statements:

**i**  $\dfrac{2^m}{2^n} = ....$       **ii**  $\dfrac{5^m}{5^n} = ....$       **iii**  $\dfrac{a^m}{a^n} = ....$

**4**   **a**   Use your calculator and earlier answers to complete this table:

$$(2^3)^2 = \quad 64 \quad = \quad 2^6$$
$$(2^4)^2 = \qquad =$$
$$(3^1)^3 = \qquad =$$
$$(3^2)^5 = \qquad =$$
$$(5^3)^3 = \qquad =$$
$$(5^2)^4 = \qquad =$$

**b**   Complete:

**i**  $(3^m)^n = ....$       **ii**  $(5^m)^n = ....$       **iii**  $(a^m)^n = ....$

**5**   **a**   Use your calculator to find:

**i**  $2^0$       **ii**  $5^0$       **iii**  $79^0$       **iv**  $148^0$

**b**   Write a rule showing what you have found.

**6**   **a**   Evaluate using a calculator:

**i**  $\dfrac{1}{5^3}$       **ii**  $\dfrac{1}{3^1}$       **iii**  $\dfrac{1}{3^4}$       **iv**  $\dfrac{1}{5^2}$       **v**  $\dfrac{1}{2^1}$

**vi**  $5^{-3}$       **vii**  $3^{-1}$       **viii**  $3^{-4}$       **ix**  $5^{-2}$       **x**  $2^{-1}$

**b**   Complete:

**i**  $\dfrac{1}{3^n} = ....$       **ii**  $\dfrac{1}{5^n} = ....$       **iii**  $\dfrac{1}{a^n} = ....$

The following are **laws of indices** for $m$, $n \in \mathbb{Z}$:

| | |
|---|---|
| $a^m \times a^n = a^{m+n}$ | To **multiply** numbers with the **same base**, keep the base and **add** the indices. |
| $\dfrac{a^m}{a^n} = a^{m-n}, \ a \neq 0$ | To **divide** numbers with the **same base**, keep the base and **subtract** the indices. |
| $(a^m)^n = a^{m \times n}$ | When **raising** a **power** to a **power**, keep the base and **multiply** the indices. |
| $(ab)^n = a^n b^n$ | The power of a product is the product of the powers. |
| $\left(\dfrac{a}{b}\right)^n = \dfrac{a^n}{b^n}, \ b \neq 0$ | The power of a quotient is the quotient of the powers. |

$a^0 = 1, \ a \neq 0$      Any non-zero number raised to the power of zero is 1.

$a^{-n} = \dfrac{1}{a^n}$ and $\dfrac{1}{a^{-n}} = a^n$ and in particular $a^{-1} = \dfrac{1}{a}, \ a \neq 0.$

---

**Example 1**    ◀) **Self Tutor**

Simplify:    **a** $\ 7^4 \times 7^5$      **b** $\ p^6 \times p^2$

     **a**   $7^4 \times 7^5$     **b**   $p^6 \times p^2$
        $= 7^{4+5}$          $= p^{6+2}$
        $= 7^9$            $= p^8$

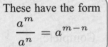

These have the form
$a^m \times a^n = a^{m+n}$

---

**Example 2**    ◀) **Self Tutor**

Simplify:    **a** $\ \dfrac{5^6}{5^3}$      **b** $\ \dfrac{x^{11}}{x^6}$

     **a**   $\dfrac{5^6}{5^3}$     **b**   $\dfrac{x^{11}}{x^6}$
        $= 5^{6-3}$        $= x^{11-6}$
        $= 5^3$          $= x^5$

These have the form
$\dfrac{a^m}{a^n} = a^{m-n}$

---

**Example 3**    ◀) **Self Tutor**

Simplify:    **a** $\ (3^5)^2$      **b** $\ (x^3)^k$

     **a**   $(3^5)^2$     **b**   $(x^3)^k$
        $= 3^{5 \times 2}$       $= x^{3 \times k}$
        $= 3^{10}$         $= x^{3k}$

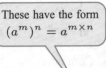

These have the form
$(a^m)^n = a^{m \times n}$

---

## EXERCISE 4A.1

**1** Simplify using $a^m \times a^n = a^{m+n}$:

   **a** $\ k^4 \times k^2$      **b** $\ 5^2 \times 5^6$      **c** $\ d^3 \times d^7$      **d** $\ 11^4 \times 11^a$

   **e** $\ p^6 \times p$      **f** $\ c^8 \times c^m$      **g** $\ x^k \times x^2$      **h** $\ r^2 \times r^5 \times r^4$

**2** Simplify using $\dfrac{a^m}{a^n} = a^{m-n}$:

   **a** $\ \dfrac{7^8}{7^3}$      **b** $\ \dfrac{b^7}{b^5}$      **c** $\ 5^9 \div 5^6$      **d** $\ \dfrac{m^{10}}{m^4}$

   **e** $\ \dfrac{k^{12}}{k^a}$      **f** $\ \dfrac{y^6}{y}$      **g** $\ \dfrac{t^m}{t^4}$      **h** $\ \dfrac{x^{3a}}{x^2}$

**3** Simplify using $(a^m)^n = a^{m \times n}$:

   **a** $(5^3)^2$          **b** $(c^4)^3$          **c** $(3^8)^4$          **d** $(v^5)^5$

   **e** $(7^6)^d$          **f** $(g^k)^8$          **g** $(m^3)^t$          **h** $(11^x)^{2y}$

**4** Simplify:

   **a** $b^5 \times b^7$        **b** $\dfrac{t^9}{t^2}$        **c** $(p^6)^3$        **d** $\dfrac{7^6}{7^n}$

   **e** $(x^{2s})^3$        **f** $d^k \div d^3$        **g** $3^2 \times 3^7 \times 3^4$        **h** $(j^4)^{3x}$

   **i** $11^6 \times 11$        **j** $\dfrac{z^7}{z^{4t}}$        **k** $(13^c)^{5d}$        **l** $w^{7p} \div w$

---

### Example 4     ◀) Self Tutor

Write as powers of 2:

   **a** 16        **b** $\frac{1}{16}$        **c** 1        **d** $4 \times 2^n$        **e** $\dfrac{2^m}{8}$

| **a** $16$ | **b** $\dfrac{1}{16}$ | **c** $1$ | **d** $4 \times 2^n$ | **e** $\dfrac{2^m}{8}$ |
|---|---|---|---|---|
| $= 2 \times 2 \times 2 \times 2$ | $= \dfrac{1}{2^4}$ | $= 2^0$ | $= 2^2 \times 2^n$ | $= \dfrac{2^m}{2^3}$ |
| $= 2^4$ | $= 2^{-4}$ | | $= 2^{2+n}$ | $= 2^{m-3}$ |

---

### Example 5     ◀) Self Tutor

Express in simplest form with a prime number base:

   **a** $9^4$        **b** $\dfrac{3^x}{9^y}$        **c** $25^x$

Decide first what the prime number base should be.

| **a** $9^4$ | **b** $\dfrac{3^x}{9^y}$ | **c** $25^x$ |
|---|---|---|
| $= (3^2)^4$ | $= \dfrac{3^x}{(3^2)^y}$ | $= (5^2)^x$ |
| $= 3^{2 \times 4}$ | $= \dfrac{3^x}{3^{2y}}$ | $= 5^{2x}$ |
| $= 3^8$ | $= 3^{x-2y}$ | |

---

**5** Write as a power of 2:

   **a** 4      **b** $\frac{1}{4}$      **c** 8      **d** $\frac{1}{8}$      **e** 32      **f** $\frac{1}{32}$

   **g** 2      **h** $\frac{1}{2}$      **i** 64      **j** $\frac{1}{64}$      **k** 128      **l** $\frac{1}{128}$

**6** Write as powers of 3:

   **a** 9      **b** $\frac{1}{9}$      **c** 27      **d** $\frac{1}{27}$      **e** 3      **f** $\frac{1}{3}$

   **g** 81      **h** $\frac{1}{81}$      **i** 1      **j** 243      **k** $\frac{1}{243}$

**7** Write as a single power of 2:

   **a** $2 \times 2^a$     **b** $4 \times 2^b$     **c** $8 \times 2^t$     **d** $(2^x)^2$     **e** $(2^{-n})^{-1}$

   **f** $\dfrac{2^c}{4}$     **g** $\dfrac{2^m}{2^{-m}}$     **h** $\dfrac{4}{2^{1-n}}$     **i** $\dfrac{2^{x+1}}{2^x}$     **j** $\dfrac{4^x}{2^{1-x}}$

**8** Write as a single power of 3:

   **a** $9 \times 3^p$     **b** $27^a$     **c** $3 \times 9^n$     **d** $27 \times 3^d$     **e** $9 \times 27^t$

   **f** $\dfrac{3^y}{3}$     **g** $\dfrac{3}{3^y}$     **h** $\dfrac{9}{27^t}$     **i** $\dfrac{9^a}{3^{1-a}}$     **j** $\dfrac{9^{n+1}}{3^{2n-1}}$

**9** Express in simplest form with a prime number base:

   **a** $32$     **b** $49$     **c** $25^3$     **d** $4^5$

   **e** $16^p$     **f** $27^t$     **g** $5^a \times 25$     **h** $4^n \times 8^n$

   **i** $\dfrac{8^m}{16^n}$     **j** $\dfrac{25^p}{5^4}$     **k** $\dfrac{2^{x+2}}{2^{x-1}}$     **l** $9^{t+2}$

   **m** $32^{2-r}$     **n** $\dfrac{81}{3^{y+1}}$     **o** $\dfrac{16^k}{4^k}$     **p** $\dfrac{5^{a+1} \times 125}{25^{2a}}$

---

**Example 6**      🔊 **Self Tutor**

Write without brackets:

   **a** $(3x)^3$         **b** $\left(\dfrac{x}{y}\right)^4$

   **a**   $(3x)^3$      **b**   $\left(\dfrac{x}{y}\right)^4$

      $= 3^3 \times x^3$

      $= 27x^3$             $= \dfrac{x^4}{y^4}$

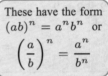

These have the form $(ab)^n = a^n b^n$ or $\left(\dfrac{a}{b}\right)^n = \dfrac{a^n}{b^n}$

**10** Write without brackets:

   **a** $(2a)^2$     **b** $(3n)^2$     **c** $(5m)^3$     **d** $(mn)^3$

   **e** $\left(\dfrac{a}{2}\right)^3$     **f** $\left(\dfrac{3}{m}\right)^2$     **g** $\left(\dfrac{p}{q}\right)^4$     **h** $\left(\dfrac{t}{5}\right)^2$

---

**Example 7**      🔊 **Self Tutor**

Simplify, giving answers in simplest rational form:

   **a** $7^0$     **b** $3^{-2}$     **c** $3^0 - 3^{-1}$     **d** $\left(\dfrac{5}{3}\right)^{-2}$

   **a**  $7^0$    **b**  $3^{-2}$    **c**  $3^0 - 3^{-1}$   **d**  $\left(\dfrac{5}{3}\right)^{-2}$

     $= 1$        $= \dfrac{1}{3^2}$      $= 1 - \frac{1}{3}$      $= \left(\dfrac{3}{5}\right)^2$

              $= \dfrac{1}{9}$          $= \frac{2}{3}$        $= \dfrac{9}{25}$

Notice that $\left(\dfrac{a}{b}\right)^{-2} = \left(\dfrac{b}{a}\right)^2$

**Example 8** ◄) **Self Tutor**

Write without negative indices:

a  $3x^{-1}$    b  $(3x)^{-1}$    c  $\left(\dfrac{3}{x}\right)^{-2}$

$a^{-n} = \dfrac{1}{a^n}$

a  $3x^{-1}$

$= \dfrac{3}{x}$

b  $(3x)^{-1}$

$= \dfrac{1}{3x}$

c  $\left(\dfrac{3}{x}\right)^{-2}$

$= \left(\dfrac{x}{3}\right)^2$

$= \dfrac{x^2}{3^2}$

$= \dfrac{x^2}{9}$

**11** Simplify, giving answers in simplest rational form:

a  $4^0$         b  $3^{-1}$         c  $7^{-2}$         d  $x^{-3}$

e  $5^0 + 5^{-1}$     f  $\left(\frac{5}{3}\right)^0$     g  $\left(\frac{7}{4}\right)^{-1}$     h  $\left(\frac{1}{6}\right)^{-1}$

i  $\left(\frac{4}{3}\right)^{-2}$     j  $2^1 + 2^{-1}$     k  $\left(1\frac{2}{3}\right)^{-3}$     l  $5^2 + 5^1 + 5^{-1}$

**12** Write without negative indices:

a  $5n^{-1}$     b  $(5n)^{-1}$     c  $\left(\dfrac{5}{n}\right)^{-1}$     d  $\left(\dfrac{n}{5}\right)^{-2}$

e  $(mn)^{-1}$     f  $m^{-1}n$     g  $mn^{-1}$     h  $\left(\dfrac{m}{n}\right)^{-1}$

## SIMPLIFYING ALGEBRAIC EXPRESSIONS

When given an algebraic expression we can use the index laws to write it in **simplest form**. The resulting expression should not contain brackets or negative indices.

**Example 9** ◄) **Self Tutor**

Express the following in simplest form, without brackets:

a  $(2c^3d)^4$         b  $\left(\dfrac{3f}{g^4}\right)^2$

a  $(2c^3d)^4$
$= 2^4 \times (c^3)^4 \times d^4$
$= 16 \times c^{12} \times d^4$
$= 16c^{12}d^4$

b  $\left(\dfrac{3f}{g^4}\right)^2$
$= \dfrac{3^2 \times f^2}{(g^4)^2}$
$= \dfrac{9f^2}{g^8}$

**Example 10**                                                    ◀ᴺ **Self Tutor**

Simplify using the index laws:

  a   $4x^3 \times 2x^6$        b   $\dfrac{15t^7}{3t^5}$        c   $\dfrac{k^2 \times k^6}{(k^3)^2}$

a     $4x^3 \times 2x^6$

    $= 4 \times 2 \times x^3 \times x^6$

    $= 8 \times x^{3+6}$

    $= 8x^9$

b     $\dfrac{15t^7}{3t^5}$

    $= \frac{15}{3} \times t^{7-5}$

    $= 5t^2$

c     $\dfrac{k^2 \times k^6}{(k^3)^2}$

    $= \dfrac{k^{2+6}}{k^{3\times 2}}$

    $= \dfrac{k^8}{k^6}$

    $= k^2$

## EXERCISE 4A.2

**1** Express the following in simplest form, without brackets:

  a   $(2a)^2$        b   $(6b^2)^2$        c   $\left(\dfrac{5k}{m}\right)^2$        d   $\left(\dfrac{t}{2s}\right)^3$

  e   $(2a)^3$        f   $(3m^2n^2)^3$        g   $\left(\dfrac{y^2}{3z}\right)^3$        h   $\left(\dfrac{c}{3d^2}\right)^0$

  i   $(2ab^4)^4$        j   $\left(\dfrac{2a^2}{b^2}\right)^3$        k   $\left(\dfrac{4a^3}{b}\right)^2$        l   $\left(\dfrac{3p^2}{q^3}\right)^2$

**2** Simplify the following using one or more of the index laws:

  a   $\dfrac{4b^5}{b^2}$        b   $2w^4 \times 3w$        c   $\dfrac{12p^4}{3p^2}$        d   $5c^7 \times 6c^4$

  e   $\dfrac{d^2 \times d^7}{d^5}$        f   $\dfrac{18a^2b^3}{6ab}$        g   $\dfrac{24m^2n^4}{6m^2n}$        h   $\dfrac{t^5 \times t^8}{(t^2)^3}$

  i   $5s^2t \times 4t^3$        j   $\dfrac{(k^4)^5}{k^3 \times k^6}$        k   $\dfrac{12x^2y^5}{8xy^2}$        l   $\dfrac{(b^3)^4 \times b^5}{b^2 \times b^6}$

**Example 11**                                                    ◀ᴺ **Self Tutor**

Write without negative indices:

  a   $(2c^3)^{-4}$        b   $\dfrac{a^{-3}b^2}{c^{-1}}$

a   $(2c^3)^{-4} = \dfrac{1}{(2c^3)^4}$

             $= \dfrac{1}{2^4 c^{3\times 4}}$

             $= \dfrac{1}{16c^{12}}$

b     $a^{-3} = \dfrac{1}{a^3}$   and   $\dfrac{1}{c^{-1}} = c^1$

   $\therefore \;\; \dfrac{a^{-3}b^2}{c^{-1}} = \dfrac{b^2c}{a^3}$

3   Write without negative indices:

a   $ab^{-2}$

b   $(ab)^{-2}$

c   $(2ab^{-1})^2$

d   $(5m^2)^{-2}$

e   $(3a^{-2}b)^2$

f   $(3xy^4)^{-3}$

g   $\dfrac{a^2b^{-1}}{c^2}$

h   $\dfrac{a^2b^{-1}}{c^{-2}}$

i   $\dfrac{1}{a^{-3}}$

j   $\dfrac{a^{-2}}{b^{-3}}$

k   $\dfrac{2a^{-1}}{d^2}$

l   $\dfrac{12a}{m^{-3}}$

# WORKING WITH FRACTIONS

| Example 12 | ◀)) Self Tutor |
|---|---|
| Write $\dfrac{1}{2^{1-n}}$ in non-fractional form. | $\begin{aligned}\dfrac{1}{2^{1-n}} &= 2^{-(1-n)} \\ &= 2^{-1+n} \\ &= 2^{n-1}\end{aligned}$ |

| Example 13 | ◀)) Self Tutor |
|---|---|

Write in non-fractional form:

a   $\dfrac{x^2 + 3x + 2}{x}$

b   $\dfrac{x^3 + 5x - 3}{x^2}$

c   $\dfrac{2x^5 + x^2 + 3x}{x^{-2}}$

a   $\dfrac{x^2 + 3x + 2}{x}$

$= \dfrac{x^2}{x} + \dfrac{3x}{x} + \dfrac{2}{x}$

$= x + 3 + 2x^{-1}$

b   $\dfrac{x^3 + 5x - 3}{x^2}$

$= \dfrac{x^3}{x^2} + \dfrac{5x}{x^2} - \dfrac{3}{x^2}$

$= x + 5x^{-1} - 3x^{-2}$

c   $\dfrac{2x^5 + x^2 + 3x}{x^{-2}}$

$= \dfrac{2x^5}{x^{-2}} + \dfrac{x^2}{x^{-2}} + \dfrac{3x}{x^{-2}}$

$= 2x^{5-(-2)} + x^{2-(-2)}$

$\qquad\qquad + 3x^{1-(-2)}$

$= 2x^7 + x^4 + 3x^3$

## EXERCISE 4A.3

1   Write in non-fractional form:

a   $\dfrac{1}{a^n}$

b   $\dfrac{1}{b^{-n}}$

c   $\dfrac{1}{3^{2-n}}$

d   $\dfrac{a^n}{b^{-m}}$

e   $\dfrac{a^{-n}}{a^{2+n}}$

2   Write in non-fractional form:

a   $\dfrac{x+3}{x}$

b   $\dfrac{3-2x}{x}$

c   $\dfrac{5-x}{x^2}$

d   $\dfrac{x+2}{x^3}$

e   $\dfrac{x^2+5}{x}$

f   $\dfrac{x^2+x-2}{x}$

g   $\dfrac{2x^2-3x+4}{x}$

h   $\dfrac{x^3-3x+5}{x^2}$

i   $\dfrac{5-x-x^2}{x}$

j   $\dfrac{8+5x-2x^3}{x}$

k   $\dfrac{16-3x+x^3}{x^2}$

l   $\dfrac{5x^4-3x^2+x+6}{x^2}$

**3** Write in non-fractional form:

a $\dfrac{4 + 2x}{x^{-1}}$

b $\dfrac{5 - 4x}{x^{-2}}$

c $\dfrac{6 + 3x}{x^{-3}}$

d $\dfrac{x^2 + 3}{x^{-1}}$

e $\dfrac{x^2 + x - 4}{x^{-2}}$

f $\dfrac{x^3 - 3x + 6}{x^{-3}}$

g $\dfrac{x^3 - 6x + 10}{x^{-2}}$

# B   THE DISTRIBUTIVE LAW

To find the product of 4 and 103, it is helpful to write 103 as $100 + 3$. We can then split the product into two simpler products, and add the results:

$$4 \times 103 = 4(100 + 3)$$
$$= 4 \times 100 + 4 \times 3 \qquad \{4 \text{ lots of } 103 = 4 \text{ lots of } 100 + 4 \text{ lots of } 3\}$$
$$= 400 + 12$$
$$= 412$$

This method uses the fact that $4(100 + 3) = 4 \times 100 + 4 \times 3$, which is an example of the **distributive law**:

$$a(b + c) = ab + ac$$

Each term inside the brackets is multiplied by the value outside the brackets.

---

**Example 14**                                        ◀) **Self Tutor**

Expand the following:

a $3(x + 5)$         b $4x(x - 2)$         c $-2x(x - 5)$

a $\quad 3(x + 5)$
$\quad = 3 \times x + 3 \times 5$
$\quad = 3x + 15$

b $\quad 4x(x - 2)$
$\quad = 4x \times x + 4x \times -2$
$\quad = 4x^2 - 8x$

c $\quad -2x(x - 5)$
$\quad = -2x \times x + -2x \times -5$
$\quad = -2x^2 + 10x$

---

## EXERCISE 4B

**1** A collection of balls has been arranged into a rectangle with $a$ rows, as illustrated alongside. The rectangle consists of $b$ columns of green balls and $c$ columns of red balls.

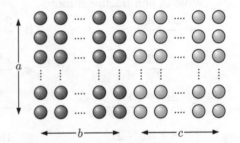

a Explain why there are $a(b + c)$ balls in total.

b Find an expression for the number of:

    i green balls         ii red balls.

c Hence, show that $a(b + c) = ab + ac$.

**2** Expand and simplify:

  **a** $4(x+3)$        **b** $5(x-2)$        **c** $8(3-x)$

  **d** $-(2x+5)$      **e** $-3(x-7)$      **f** $2x(x+6)$

  **g** $-6x(x+5)$     **h** $4x(3x-5)$     **i** $-5x(x-2)$

  **j** $-3x(6-5x)$     **k** $7x^2(x-4)$     **l** $-9x(4x^2-9)$

---

### Example 15      ◀) Self Tutor

Expand and simplify:

  **a** $3(4x+1)+2(3x-4)$      **b** $x(3x+2)-4x(1-x)$

  **a**    $3(4x+1)+2(3x-4)$     **b**    $x(3x+2)-4x(1-x)$

      $=12x+3+6x-8$           $=3x^2+2x-4x+4x^2$

      $=18x-5$                 $=7x^2-2x$

We simplify by **collecting like terms**.

---

**3** Expand and simplify:

  **a** $2(2x+3)+5(3x+1)$        **b** $4x+3(6x-5)$

  **c** $3(3x-4)-2(x-7)$        **d** $-2(4x+3)-3(8-5x)$

  **e** $x(2x-1)+3x(x+4)$       **f** $3x(x-9)+5(5x+2)$

  **g** $4x(2x-5)-(3x+7)$       **h** $3x(7x-2)-x(6-x)$

  **i** $-8x(4-3x)-5x(3x-2)$     **j** $-6x(2x-3)-4(5-3x)$

---

## C    THE PRODUCT $(a+b)(c+d)$

We can find the product $(a+b)(c+d)$ by using the distributive law several times.

$$(a+b)(c+d) = a(c+d)+b(c+d) \qquad \{(a+b)X = aX+bX\}$$
$$= ac+ad+bc+bd$$

$$(a+b)(c+d) = ac+ad+bc+bd$$

This expansion is sometimes called the **FOIL** rule.

Notice that this final result contains four terms.

  $ac$ is the product of the **F**irst terms of each bracket.

  $ad$ is the product of the **O**uter terms of each bracket.

  $bc$ is the product of the **I**nner terms of each bracket.

  $bd$ is the product of the **L**ast terms of each bracket.

We can also demonstrate this rule using areas.

We can find an expression for the shaded area in two ways:

- Shaded area $= (a+b)(c+d)$
  {area of large rectangle}

- Shaded area $= ac + ad + bc + bd$
  {sum of areas of the 4 smaller rectangles}

So, $(a+b)(c+d) = ac + ad + bc + bd.$

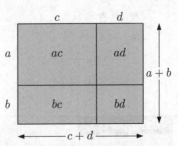

---

**Example 16**    ◀)) **Self Tutor**

Expand and simplify:    a  $(x+4)(x+5)$    b  $(3x+1)(4x-3)$

a    $(x+4)(x+5)$

$= x \times x + x \times 5 + 4 \times x + 4 \times 5$

$= x^2 + 5x + 4x + 20$

$= x^2 + 9x + 20$

b    $(3x+1)(4x-3)$

$= 3x \times 4x + 3x \times -3 + 1 \times 4x + 1 \times -3$

$= 12x^2 - 9x + 4x - 3$

$= 12x^2 - 5x - 3$

---

## EXERCISE 4C

1  Expand and simplify:

  a  $(x+2)(x+7)$
  b  $(x+8)(x-3)$
  c  $(x-5)(x+4)$
  d  $(x-3)(x-6)$
  e  $(2x+3)(x-4)$
  f  $(3x-5)(2x+7)$
  g  $(5x-2)(4x-5)$
  h  $(3+x)(4x-1)$
  i  $(5-3x)(x+4)$
  j  $(6x-1)(8-3x)$
  k  $(9-x)(3x+4)$
  l  $(7x-3)(4-5x)$

---

**Example 17**    ◀)) **Self Tutor**

Expand and simplify:    a  $(2x+5)(2x-5)$    b  $(3x+4)^2$

a    $(2x+5)(2x-5)$
$= 4x^2 - 10x + 10x - 25$
$= 4x^2 - 25$

b    $(3x+4)^2$
$= (3x+4)(3x+4)$
$= 9x^2 + 12x + 12x + 16$
$= 9x^2 + 24x + 16$

What do you notice about the middle two terms in **a**?

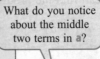

---

2  Expand and simplify:

  a  $(x+4)(x-4)$
  b  $(a+6)(a-6)$
  c  $(7+x)(7-x)$
  d  $(3x+1)(3x-1)$
  e  $(4k+3)(4k-3)$
  f  $(5+6a)(5-6a)$

3  Expand and simplify:

  a  $(x+7)^2$
  b  $(x-5)^2$
  c  $(2x-3)^2$
  d  $(5+3x)^2$
  e  $(7-2x)^2$
  f  $(4x+y)^2$

# D  DIFFERENCE OF TWO SQUARES

Consider the product $(a+b)(a-b)$.

Using the FOIL rule to expand this product, $(a+b)(a-b) = a^2 - ab + ab - b^2$
$$= a^2 - b^2$$

$$\boxed{(a+b)(a-b) = a^2 - b^2}$$

This expansion rule is called the **difference of two squares** since the expression on the right hand side is the difference between the two perfect squares $a^2$ and $b^2$.

This result can be demonstrated geometrically.

In the figure alongside,
the shaded area = area of large square
$\qquad$ − area of small square
$$= a^2 - b^2$$

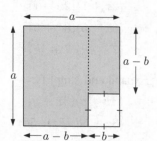

If the rectangle on the right hand side is rotated and placed on top of the remaining shaded area, we form a new rectangle.

Now, the shaded area $= (a+b)(a-b)$

So, $(a+b)(a-b) = a^2 - b^2$.

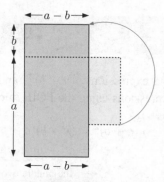

DEMO

| Example 18 | ◀ Self Tutor |
|---|---|

Expand and simplify:
**a** $(x+8)(x-8)$  $\qquad$ **b** $(4-y)(4+y)$

**a** $\quad (x+8)(x-8)$  $\qquad$ **b** $\quad (4-y)(4+y)$
$\quad = x^2 - 8^2$  $\qquad\qquad = 4^2 - y^2$
$\quad = x^2 - 64$  $\qquad\qquad\; = 16 - y^2$

## EXERCISE 4D

**1** Expand and simplify:

**a** $(x+3)(x-3)$  $\qquad$ **b** $(x-1)(x+1)$  $\qquad$ **c** $(6+x)(6-x)$

**d** $(10-x)(10+x)$  $\qquad$ **e** $(x-10)(x+10)$  $\qquad$ **f** $(a-7)(a+7)$

**g** $(9+y)(9-y)$  $\qquad$ **h** $(k+5)(k-5)$  $\qquad$ **i** $(x+y)(x-y)$

**Example 19**    ◄ᴗ **Self Tutor**

Expand and simplify:

    **a**  $(3x + 2)(3x - 2)$         **b**  $(4x - 3y)(4x + 3y)$

| | |
|---|---|
| **a**     $(3x + 2)(3x - 2)$ | **b**     $(4x - 3y)(4x + 3y)$ |
| $= (3x)^2 - 2^2$ | $= (4x)^2 - (3y)^2$ |
| $= 9x^2 - 4$ | $= 16x^2 - 9y^2$ |

**2** Expand and simplify:

    **a**  $(2x + 1)(2x - 1)$       **b**  $(5x - 3)(5x + 3)$       **c**  $(4x + 7)(4x - 7)$

    **d**  $(6x - 5)(6x + 5)$       **e**  $(8t + 1)(8t - 1)$       **f**  $(5 - 9x)(5 + 9x)$

    **g**  $(7 - 4k)(7 + 4k)$       **h**  $(10 + 3m)(10 - 3m)$     **i**  $(1 - 12z)(1 + 12z)$

**3** Expand and simplify:

    **a**  $(3x + y)(3x - y)$       **b**  $(m - 4n)(m + 4n)$       **c**  $(3p + 7q)(3p - 7q)$

    **d**  $(8c - 5d)(8c + 5d)$       **e**  $(9x - 2y)(9x + 2y)$      **f**  $(5x + 6y)(6y - 5x)$

## E    PERFECT SQUARES EXPANSIONS

The expressions $(a + b)^2$ and $(a - b)^2$ are known as **perfect squares**. Expanding the expressions using the FOIL rule, we get:

$$(a + b)^2 = (a + b)(a + b)$$
$$= a^2 + \underbrace{ab + ab} + b^2$$
the middle two terms
are identical
$$= a^2 + 2ab + b^2$$

and

$$(a - b)^2 = (a - b)(a - b)$$
$$= a^2 \underbrace{- ab - ab} + b^2$$
the middle two terms
are identical
$$= a^2 - 2ab + b^2$$

So, the perfect square expansion rules are:

$$(a + b)^2 = a^2 + 2ab + b^2$$
$$(a - b)^2 = a^2 - 2ab + b^2$$

A useful way to remember the perfect square expansion rules is:

*Step 1:*    Square the *first term*.

*Step 2:*    Double the product of the *first* and *last terms*, adding or subtracting according to the sign between the terms.

*Step 3:*    Add on the square of the *last term*.

**Example 20**                                         ◀)) **Self Tutor**

Expand and simplify:

    **a**  $(x+5)^2$         **b**  $(x-4)^2$

**a**    $(x+5)^2$       **b**    $(x-4)^2$

$= x^2 + 2 \times x \times 5 + 5^2$     $= x^2 - 2 \times x \times 4 + 4^2$

$= x^2 + 10x + 25$         $= x^2 - 8x + 16$

## EXERCISE 4E

**1** Use the rule $(a+b)^2 = a^2 + 2ab + b^2$ to expand and simplify:

    **a** $(x+3)^2$       **b** $(x+6)^2$       **c** $(x+2)^2$

    **d** $(a+9)^2$       **e** $(5+k)^2$       **f** $(7+t)^2$

**2** Use the rule $(a-b)^2 = a^2 - 2ab + b^2$ to expand and simplify:

    **a** $(x-3)^2$       **b** $(x-1)^2$       **c** $(x-8)^2$

    **d** $(b-2)^2$       **e** $(4-x)^2$       **f** $(7-y)^2$

**Example 21**                                         ◀)) **Self Tutor**

Expand and simplify using the perfect square expansion rules:

    **a**  $(3x+2)^2$           **b**  $(1-5x)^2$

**a**    $(3x+2)^2$       **b**    $(1-5x)^2$

$= (3x)^2 + 2 \times 3x \times 2 + 2^2$     $= 1^2 - 2 \times 1 \times 5x + (5x)^2$

$= 9x^2 + 12x + 4$         $= 1 - 10x + 25x^2$

**3** Expand and simplify using the perfect square expansion rules:

    **a** $(3x+5)^2$       **b** $(4a-2)^2$       **c** $(2b+7)^2$

    **d** $(3k+1)^2$       **e** $(5y-4)^2$       **f** $(3-2x)^2$

    **g** $(4+3y)^2$       **h** $(1+5z)^2$       **i** $(2-3n)^2$

**Example 22**                                         ◀)) **Self Tutor**

Expand and simplify:     **a**  $(3x^2-1)^2$   **b**  $4 - (x+3)^2$

**a**    $(3x^2-1)^2$       **b**    $4 - (x+3)^2$

$= (3x^2)^2 - 2 \times 3x^2 \times 1 + 1^2$     $= 4 - (x^2 + 6x + 9)$

$= 9x^4 - 6x^2 + 1$         $= 4 - x^2 - 6x - 9$

                             $= -x^2 - 6x - 5$

**4** Expand and simplify:

  **a** $(x^2 + 3)^2$        **b** $(y^2 - 7)^2$        **c** $(5z^2 + 1)^2$

  **d** $(3 - 2a^2)^2$        **e** $(m^2 + n^2)^2$        **f** $(x^2 - y^2)^2$

**5** Expand and simplify:

  **a** $2x + 5 - (x + 2)^2$            **b** $4 - 3x + (x - 1)^2$

  **c** $(x + 3)(x - 3) + (x + 2)^2$      **d** $(x + 7)(x - 7) - (x + 4)^2$

  **e** $(5 - x)^2 - (x + 3)(x - 2)$     **f** $(2 - 3x)^2 + (x - 4)(x + 1)$

  **g** $(3x + 1)(3x - 1) + (x - 7)^2$    **h** $(2x - 5)(x + 3) - (1 - x)^2$

  **i** $(x - 2)^2 + (3x - 4)^2$        **j** $(4 - x)^2 - (x - 3)^2$

**6** Revisit the **Opening Problem** and answer the questions.

## F    FURTHER EXPANSION

When expressions containing more than two terms are multiplied together, we can still use the distributive law to expand the brackets. Each term in the first set of brackets is multiplied by each term in the second set of brackets.

If there are 2 terms in the first brackets and 3 terms in the second brackets, there will be $2 \times 3 = 6$ terms in the expansion. However, when we simplify by collecting like terms, the final answer may contain fewer terms.

**Example 23**        ◀◎ **Self Tutor**

Expand and simplify:    $(3x + 2)(x^2 - 4x + 1)$

$(3x + 2)(x^2 - 4x + 1)$

$= 3x^3 - 12x^2 + 3x$     {$3x$ multiplied by each term in the 2nd brackets}

$\phantom{=}\; + 2x^2 - 8x + 2$    {2 multiplied by each term in the 2nd brackets}

$= 3x^3 - 10x^2 - 5x + 2$   {collecting like terms}

> When expanding, each term in the first brackets is multiplied by each term in the second brackets.

## EXERCISE 4F

**1** Expand and simplify:

  **a** $(x + 2)(x^2 + 3x + 5)$      **b** $(x + 3)(x^2 - 4x + 2)$

  **c** $(x + 5)(x^2 + x + 2)$        **d** $(x - 2)(x^2 + 3x - 4)$

  **e** $(2x + 3)(x^2 - 2x + 1)$     **f** $(4x - 1)(x^2 - x - 1)$

  **g** $(2 - x)(x^2 + 7x - 3)$      **h** $(3x + 2)(2x^2 - 5x + 3)$

**Example 24**                                    ◀) **Self Tutor**

Expand and simplify:  $(x+3)^3$

$(x+3)^3$
$= (x+3) \times (x+3)^2$
$= (x+3)(x^2 + 6x + 9)$
$= x^3 + 6x^2 + 9x$        {$x \times$ each term in the 2nd brackets}
$\quad + 3x^2 + 18x + 27$  {$3 \times$ each term in the 2nd brackets}
$= x^3 + 9x^2 + 27x + 27$  {collecting like terms}

**2** Expand and simplify:

   **a**  $(x+2)^3$             **b**  $(x+1)^3$             **c**  $(x-1)^3$

   **d**  $(x-2)^3$             **e**  $(3x+1)^3$          **f**  $(2x-3)^3$

**Example 25**                                    ◀) **Self Tutor**

Expand and simplify:    **a**  $x(x+3)(x+2)$   **b**  $(x+2)(x-3)(x+1)$

   **a**    $x(x+3)(x+2)$
      $= (x^2 + 3x)(x+2)$        {$x \times$ each term in the first brackets}
      $= x^3 + 2x^2 + 3x^2 + 6x$  {expanding remaining factors}
      $= x^3 + 5x^2 + 6x$        {collecting like terms}

   **b**    $(x+2)(x-3)(x+1)$
      $= (x^2 - 3x + 2x - 6)(x+1)$  {expanding first two factors}
      $= (x^2 - x - 6)(x+1)$       {collecting like terms}
      $= x^3 + x^2 - x^2 - x - 6x - 6$  {expanding remaining factors}
      $= x^3 - 7x - 6$             {collecting like terms}

**3** Expand and simplify:

   **a**  $x(x+1)(x+2)$        **b**  $x(x-2)(x+3)$        **c**  $x(x-4)(x-1)$

   **d**  $2x(x+2)(x+1)$       **e**  $2x(x-3)(x-4)$       **f**  $-x(2+x)(x-3)$

   **g**  $-3x(x+4)(x-5)$      **h**  $3x(2-x)(x-1)$       **i**  $-x(x+6)(1-x)$

**4** Expand and simplify:

   **a**  $(x+1)(x+3)(x+2)$            **b**  $(x-3)(x+2)(x-1)$

   **c**  $(x-2)(x-4)(x-6)$            **d**  $(x+1)(x-2)(x-1)$

   **e**  $(2x-3)(x+2)(x-1)$          **f**  $(2x+3)(2x-3)(x-2)$

   **g**  $(2-x)(4x-1)(x+5)$          **h**  $(2+x)(5-x)(3x+1)$

**5** State how many terms would be in the expansion of the following:

   **a** $(a+b)(c+d)$

   **b** $(a+b+c)(d+e)$

   **c** $(a+b)(c+d+e)$

   **d** $(a+b+c)(d+e+f)$

   **e** $(a+b+c+d)(e+f)$

   **f** $(a+b+c+d)(e+f+g)$

   **g** $(a+b)(c+d)(e+f)$

   **h** $(a+b+c)(d+e)(f+g)$

---

## INVESTIGATION 2        THE EXPANSION OF $(a+b)^3$

The purpose of this investigation is to discover the expansion for $(a+b)^3$.

### What to do:

**1** Find a large potato and cut it to obtain a 4 cm by 4 cm by 4 cm cube.

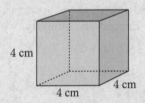

**2** By making 3 cuts parallel to the cube's surfaces, divide the cube into 8 rectangular prisms as shown.

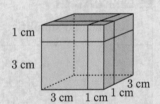

**3** Find how many prisms are:

   **a** 3 by 3 by 3

   **b** 3 by 3 by 1

   **c** 3 by 1 by 1

   **d** 1 by 1 by 1

**4** Now instead of 3 cm and 1 cm dimensions, suppose the potato was cut to give dimensions $a$ cm and $b$ cm.

How many prisms are:

   **a** $a$ by $a$ by $a$

   **b** $a$ by $a$ by $b$

   **c** $a$ by $b$ by $b$

   **d** $b$ by $b$ by $b$?

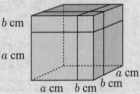

**5** Explain why the volume of the cube in **4** is given by $(a+b)^3$.

**6** By adding the volumes of the 8 rectangular prisms, find an expression for the total volume. Hence write down the expansion formula for $(a+b)^3$.

## REVIEW SET 4A

**1** Simplify:  **a** $x^4 \times x^2$  **b** $\left(2^{-1}\right)^7$  **c** $\left(ab^3\right)^6$

**2** Write without negative indices:

**a** $3^{-3}$  **b** $x^{-1}y$  **c** $\left(\dfrac{a}{b}\right)^{-1}$

**3** Express in simplest form with a prime number base:

**a** $27$  **b** $9^t$  **c** $\dfrac{4}{2^{m-1}}$

**4** Simplify using one or more of the index laws:

**a** $\dfrac{15xy^2}{3y^4}$  **b** $\dfrac{j^6}{j^5 \times j^8}$  **c** $\dfrac{36g^3h^5}{12h^2}$

**5** Express the following in simplest form, without brackets:

**a** $\left(\dfrac{t}{4s}\right)^3$  **b** $\left(\dfrac{m^2}{5n}\right)^0$  **c** $\left(5p^3q\right)^2$

**6** Write in non-fractional form:

**a** $\dfrac{x^2+8}{x}$  **b** $\dfrac{4+x+x^3}{x^{-2}}$  **c** $\dfrac{k^{-x}}{k^{x+6}}$

**7** Expand and simplify:

**a** $7x(x-7)$  **b** $x(3-x) - 7x(x+5)$

**8** Expand and simplify:

**a** $(x-3)(x+3)$  **b** $(2x-5)(x+6)$  **c** $(7x-y)^2$

**9** Expand and simplify:

**a** $(x+4)(x+9) + (x+6)(x-6)$  **b** $(x-5)(x^2+7x-2)$

**10** How many terms are in the expansion of:

**a** $(a+b+c)(d+e)$  **b** $(a+b)(c+d+e+f)$?

## REVIEW SET 4B

**1** Simplify:  **a** $\dfrac{m^9}{m^5}$  **b** $y^0$  **c** $\left(\dfrac{7z}{w}\right)^{-2}$

**2** Simplify:  **a** $\dfrac{k^x}{k^2}$  **b** $11^r \times 11^{-4}$  **c** $9 \times 3^b$

**3** Write in non-fractional form:

**a** $\dfrac{1}{11}$  **b** $\dfrac{a}{b^2}$  **c** $\dfrac{jk^4}{l^a}$

**4** Express in simplest form with a prime number base:

   **a** $\frac{1}{16}$        **b** $3^k \times 81$        **c** $\frac{125^a}{5^b}$

**5** Write in simplest rational form:

   **a** $2^{-3}$        **b** $7^0$        **c** $3^{-1} + 3^1$

**6** Simplify, writing your answer without brackets:

   **a** $\left(\frac{2a^6}{8b^2}\right)^3$        **b** $\left(5d \times d^{-5}\right)^2$        **c** $\frac{16z^2 \times z^5}{(2z)^3}$

**7** Expand and simplify:

   **a** $4x(5 - x)$        **b** $(3x + 2)(2x + 3)$

**8** Expand and simplify:

   **a** $(x - 9)(x + 4)$        **b** $(x + 7)^2$        **c** $(2 - x)(x + 3)$

**9** Expand and simplify:

   **a** $7 - (x + 4)^2$        **b** $(6x + 1)(x + 5) + (x - 2)^2$

**10** Expand and simplify:

   **a** $(x + 7)(x - 2)(2x + 3)$        **b** $(x - 1)^3$

# Chapter 5

# Equations and formulae

**Syllabus reference: 2.7, 4.8**

Algebra is a tool which we use to write mathematical ideas in a convenient way. In algebra we use letters or symbols to represent unknown quantities, or values which can vary depending on the situation.

There are several important words associated with algebra that you should be familiar with:

- $2x + 3$ is an **expression** for the quantity which is three more than twice $x$.
- $2x + 3 = 5$ is an **equation** which says that the quantity $2x + 3$ has the value 5. We can **solve** the equation to find the value of $x$.
- $2x + 3 > 5$ is an **inequality** or **inequation** which says that the value of $2x + 3$ is more than 5.
- $y = 2x + 3$ is a **formula** which connects the two **variables** $x$ and $y$. If we know the value of one of the variables then we can **substitute** this value to determine the other variable. We can also **rearrange** formulae to write them in other more convenient forms.

## OPENING PROBLEM

Holly is offered two different mobile phone plans. Plan A costs €25 for the monthly access fee and calls are billed at 17 cents per minute. Plan B costs only €10 for the monthly access fee but calls are billed at 23 cents per minute.

**Things to think about:**

**a** Can you write a *formula* that connects the total cost €$C$ with the number of minutes $m$ used per month for *each* plan?

**b** Use the formula to find the total *cost* for each plan if Holly uses her phone for:
  **i** 150 minutes per month
  **ii** 300 minutes per month.

**c** Find the monthly usage such that the cost of each plan is the same.

**d** What advice would you give to Holly regarding her choice of plans?

## A    ALGEBRAIC SUBSTITUTION

We can think of an expression as a number crunching machine. We feed an input number into the machine and the machine produces a related output number.

For example, the machine for the expression $4x - 1$ starts with the input number $x$, multiplies it by 4, and then subtracts 1.

If we feed the number 3 into the machine, the machine **substitutes** the number 3 in place of $x$, then **evaluates** the result.

$$4x - 1 = 4 \times 3 - 1$$
$$= 12 - 1$$
$$= 11$$

So, the machine produces the output number 11.

When we substitute a negative value, we place it in brackets to make sure the negative sign does not become confusing.

For example, if we feed the number $-5$ into the machine, the machine calculates

$$4x - 1 = 4 \times (-5) - 1$$
$$= -20 - 1$$
$$= -21$$

---

### Example 1 ◀)) Self Tutor

If $p = -2$, $q = 3$ and $r = 4$, find the value of:

**a** $p + 5q$      **b** $pr - 7q$      **c** $\dfrac{2r - 4q}{qr + p - 1}$

| | | |
|---|---|---|
| **a** $\quad p + 5q$ | **b** $\quad pr - 7q$ | **c** $\quad \dfrac{2r - 4q}{qr + p - 1}$ |
| $= (-2) + 5 \times 3$ | $= (-2) \times 4 - 7 \times 3$ | $= \dfrac{2 \times 4 - 4 \times 3}{3 \times 4 + (-2) - 1}$ |
| $= -2 + 15$ | $= -8 - 21$ | $= \dfrac{8 - 12}{12 - 2 - 1}$ |
| $= 13$ | $= -29$ | $= \dfrac{-4}{9}$ |

---

## EXERCISE 5A

**1** If $l = 2$, $m = -3$ and $n = -1$, find the value of:

  **a** $4l$      **b** $-n$      **c** $2mn$      **d** $lmn$

  **e** $2l + m$      **f** $4m - 3l$      **g** $ml - 2n$      **h** $nl - 2mn$

**2** If $e = 4$, $f = 2$ and $g = -3$, evaluate:

  **a** $\dfrac{g}{e}$      **b** $\dfrac{e + f}{g}$      **c** $\dfrac{2g + e}{f}$      **d** $\dfrac{3f - e}{2f - g}$

  **e** $g - \dfrac{e}{f}$      **f** $\dfrac{fg}{e}$      **g** $\dfrac{2g + f}{e}$      **h** $\dfrac{g - f}{e + g}$

### Example 2    ◀) Self Tutor

If $x = 2$, $y = -4$ and $z = -5$, evaluate:

a $y^2$          b $yz^3 - 3x$

Notice the use of brackets.

| a | $y^2$ | b | $yz^3 - 3x$ |
|---|---|---|---|
| | $= (-4)^2$ | | $= (-4) \times (-5)^3 - 3 \times 2$ |
| | $= 16$ | | $= 494$ |

**3** If $a = 4$, $b = -1$ and $c = -3$, evaluate:

a $b^2$          b $c^3$          c $a^2 + c^2$          d $(a + c)^2$

e $a^3 + b^3$          f $(a + b)^3$          g $(2c)^2$          h $2c^2$

### Example 3    ◀) Self Tutor

If $k = 5$, $l = -1$, and $m = 2$, evaluate:

a $\sqrt{k + l}$          b $\sqrt{m^2 + 3k}$

| a | $\sqrt{k + l}$ | b | $\sqrt{m^2 + 3k}$ |
|---|---|---|---|
| | $= \sqrt{5 + (-1)}$ | | $= \sqrt{2^2 + 3(5)}$ |
| | $= \sqrt{4}$ | | $= \sqrt{19}$ |
| | $= 2$ | | $\approx 4.36$ {3 significant figures} |

**4** If $k = -2$, $l = 3$, and $m = 7$, evaluate:

a $\sqrt{l + k}$          b $\sqrt{m + 3l}$          c $\sqrt{m - k}$          d $\sqrt{lm - 2k}$

e $\sqrt{k^2 + m^2}$          f $\sqrt{l^2 - m}$          g $\sqrt{2m + 6l - 5k}$          h $\sqrt{m^2 - l^2 + 2k}$

## B          LINEAR EQUATIONS

Many problems can be written as **equations** using algebraic notation. So, it is essential we are able to **solve** equations.

**Linear equations** are equations which can be written in the form $ax + b = 0$ where $x$ is the **variable** or **unknown** and $a$, $b$ are constants.

To solve linear equations we need to rearrange the equation to **isolate** the unknown. We first look at how the equation is constructed, then perform **inverse operations** to undo how the expression involving the unknown was built up. The inverse operations are performed on both sides of the equation in order to **maintain the balance**.

Once you have found a solution, you should check it is correct by **substitution** back into the original equation.

### Example 4

◄ᴼ **Self Tutor**

Solve for $x$:    **a** $2x - 3 = 5$    **b** $8 - 4x = -2$

> The inverse of $-3$ is $+3$.
> The inverse of $\times 2$ is $\div 2$.

**a**    $2x - 3 = 5$

$2x - 3 + 3 = 5 + 3$    {adding 3 to both sides}

$\therefore \ 2x = 8$

$\therefore \ \dfrac{2x}{2} = \dfrac{8}{2}$    {dividing both sides by 2}

$\therefore \ x = 4$    *Check:* $2 \times 4 - 3 = 8 - 3 = 5$ ✓

**b**    $8 - 4x = -2$

$\therefore \ 8 - 4x - 8 = -2 - 8$    {subtracting 8 from both sides}

$\therefore \ -4x = -10$

$\therefore \ \dfrac{-4x}{-4} = \dfrac{-10}{-4}$    {dividing both sides by $-4$}

$\therefore \ x = \dfrac{5}{2}$    *Check:* $8 - 4 \times \left(\dfrac{5}{2}\right) = 8 - 10 = -2$ ✓

### Example 5

◄ᴼ **Self Tutor**

Solve for $x$:    **a** $\dfrac{x}{4} + 7 = 5$    **b** $\dfrac{1}{3}(x + 2) = 6$

**a**    $\dfrac{x}{4} + 7 = 5$

$\therefore \ \dfrac{x}{4} + 7 - 7 = 5 - 7$    {subtracting 7 from both sides}

$\therefore \ \dfrac{x}{4} = -2$

$\therefore \ \dfrac{x}{4} \times 4 = -2 \times 4$    {multiplying both sides by 4}

$\therefore \ x = -8$    *Check:* $\dfrac{-8}{4} + 7 = -2 + 7 = 5$ ✓

**b**    $\dfrac{1}{3}(x + 2) = 6$

$\therefore \ \dfrac{1}{3}(x + 2) \times 3 = 6 \times 3$    {multiplying both sides by 3}

$\therefore \ x + 2 = 18$

$\therefore \ x + 2 - 2 = 18 - 2$    {subtracting 2 from both sides}

$\therefore \ x = 16$    *Check:* $\dfrac{1}{3}(16 + 2) = \dfrac{1}{3} \times 18 = 6$ ✓

## EXERCISE 5B.1

**1** Solve for $x$:

**a** $x + 5 = 3$    **b** $4x = 28$    **c** $-18 = -3x$    **d** $7 - x = 11$

**e** $2x + 3 = 14$    **f** $3x - 4 = -13$    **g** $5 - 2x = -9$    **h** $7 = 11 - 3x$

**2** Solve for $x$:

**a** $\dfrac{x}{3} = 15$    **b** $\dfrac{1}{4}x = 16$    **c** $1 = \dfrac{x}{-3}$    **d** $\dfrac{x}{2} - 4 = 7$

e  $\dfrac{x-4}{3} = -1$    f  $\frac{1}{2}(x+5) = 6$    g  $\dfrac{2x-3}{5} = 4$    h  $\frac{1}{3}(2-x) = -5$

## EQUATIONS WITH A REPEATED UNKNOWN

Sometimes the unknown will appear more than once. In these situations we **expand** any brackets then **collect like terms**. We perform inverse operations so the terms involving the unknown are on one side of the equation and the remaining terms are on the other side. We can then simplify the equation and solve for the unknown.

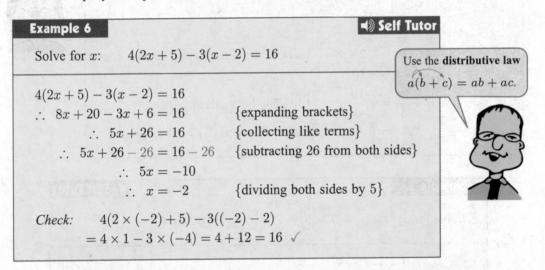

**Example 6**    ◀)) **Self Tutor**

Solve for $x$:    $4(2x+5) - 3(x-2) = 16$

Use the **distributive law**
$a(b+c) = ab + ac$.

$4(2x+5) - 3(x-2) = 16$
$\therefore \ 8x + 20 - 3x + 6 = 16$    {expanding brackets}
$\therefore \ 5x + 26 = 16$    {collecting like terms}
$\therefore \ 5x + 26 - 26 = 16 - 26$    {subtracting 26 from both sides}
$\therefore \ 5x = -10$
$\therefore \ x = -2$    {dividing both sides by 5}

*Check:*  $4(2 \times (-2) + 5) - 3((-2) - 2)$
$= 4 \times 1 - 3 \times (-4) = 4 + 12 = 16$ ✓

**Example 7**    ◀)) **Self Tutor**

Solve for $x$:    a  $4x - 3 = 3x + 7$    b  $5 - 3(-1 + x) = x$

a        $4x - 3 = 3x + 7$
$\therefore \ 4x - 3 - 3x = 3x + 7 - 3x$    {subtracting $3x$ from both sides}
$\therefore \ x - 3 = 7$
$\therefore \ x - 3 + 3 = 7 + 3$    {adding 3 to both sides}
$\therefore \ x = 10$
*Check:*  LHS $= 4 \times 10 - 3 = 37$,    RHS $= 3 \times 10 + 7 = 37$. ✓

b    $5 - 3(-1 + x) = x$
$\therefore \ 5 + 3 - 3x = x$    {expanding the brackets}
$\therefore \ 8 - 3x = x$
$\therefore \ 8 - 3x + 3x = x + 3x$    {adding $3x$ to both sides}
$\therefore \ 8 = 4x$
$\therefore \ \dfrac{8}{4} = \dfrac{4x}{4}$    {dividing both sides by 4}
$\therefore \ 2 = x \ \text{or} \ x = 2$
*Check:*  LHS $= 5 - 3(-1 + 2) = 5 - 3 \times 1 = 2 =$ RHS ✓

## EXERCISE 5B.2

1 Solve for $x$:

a $3(x+2) + 2(x+4) = 19$

b $2(x-7) - 5(x+1) = -7$

c $3(x-3) - 4(x-5) = 2$

d $5(2x+1) - 3(x-1) = -6$

e $2(3x-2) + 7(2x+1) = 13$

f $4(x+4) + 3(5-2x) = 19$

2 Solve for $x$:

a $5x - 5 = 4x + 1$

b $2x - 3 = 6 - x$

c $1 - 3x = 2x - 9$

d $-4x = 8 - 2x$

e $9 - 5x = x + 6$

f $4x - 7 = x + 3$

g $6 - x + 3(1-x) = 7 - 2x$

h $8 - 5(3-x) = 9 + x$

i $6 + 7x - 2(3-x) = 5x - 8$

j $5(3x+1) - 4x = x - 2$

3 Solve for $x$:

a $5(2x-1) + 2 = 10x - 3$

b $2(9x-1) = 6(3x+1)$

c Comment on your solutions to a and b.

## OTHER EXPANSIONS

Sometimes when more complicated equations are expanded and simplified, a linear equation results.

You will need to remember the expansion laws:

$$a(b+c) = ab + ac$$
$$(a+b)(c+d) = ac + ad + bc + bd$$
$$(a+b)^2 = a^2 + 2ab + b^2$$
$$(a-b)^2 = a^2 - 2ab + b^2$$
$$(a+b)(a-b) = a^2 - b^2$$

### Example 8

◄)) **Self Tutor**

Solve for $x$:  $(x-3)^2 = (4+x)(2+x)$

$(x-3)^2 = (4+x)(2+x)$

$\therefore \quad x^2 - 6x + 9 = 8 + 4x + 2x + x^2$  {expanding each side}

$\therefore \quad x^2 - 6x + 9 - x^2 = 8 + 4x + 2x + x^2 - x^2$  {subtracting $x^2$ from both sides}

$\therefore \quad -6x + 9 = 8 + 6x$

$\therefore \quad -6x + 9 + 6x = 8 + 6x + 6x$  {adding $6x$ to both sides}

$\therefore \quad 9 = 12x + 8$

$\therefore \quad 9 - 8 = 12x + 8 - 8$  {subtracting 8 from both sides}

$\therefore \quad 1 = 12x$

$\therefore \quad \dfrac{1}{12} = \dfrac{12x}{12}$  {dividing both sides by 12}

$\therefore \quad x = \frac{1}{12}$

## EXERCISE 5B.3

1 Solve for $x$:

a $x(x+5) = (x-4)(x-3)$

b $x(2x+1) - 2(x+1) = 2x(x-1)$

c $(x+3)(x-2) = (4-x)^2$

d $x^2 - 3 = (2+x)(3+x)$

e $(x+2)(2x-1) = 2x(x+3)$

f $(x+4)^2 = (x-1)(x+3)$

g $(x+3)(x-3) = x(1+x)$

h $(x-2)^2 = (x-1)(x+1)$

# C  FRACTIONAL EQUATIONS

When equations involve fractions, we start by writing all fractions with their **lowest common denominator** (LCD).

For example:    In    $\dfrac{2x}{3} = \dfrac{x}{4}$  the LCD is 12.

In    $\dfrac{3}{2x} = \dfrac{x}{4}$  the LCD is $4x$.

In    $\dfrac{x-7}{3} = \dfrac{x}{2x-1}$  the LCD is  $3(2x-1)$.

Once the fractions are all written with their lowest common denominator, we can **equate the numerators**.

---

**Example 9**    ◄) **Self Tutor**

Solve for $x$:    $\dfrac{2-x}{3} = \dfrac{x}{5}$

Notice how we insert the brackets.

$\dfrac{2-x}{3} = \dfrac{x}{5}$    {LCD of fractions = 15}

$\therefore \left(\dfrac{2-x}{3}\right) \times \dfrac{5}{5} = \dfrac{x}{5} \times \dfrac{3}{3}$    {to create the common denominator}

$\therefore \dfrac{5(2-x)}{15} = \dfrac{3x}{15}$

$\therefore 5(2-x) = 3x$    {equating numerators}

$\therefore 10 - 5x = 3x$    {expanding the brackets}

$\therefore 10 - 5x + 5x = 3x + 5x$    {adding $5x$ to both sides}

$\therefore 10 = 8x$

$\therefore \dfrac{10}{8} = \dfrac{8x}{8}$    {dividing both sides by 8}

$\therefore \dfrac{5}{4} = x$

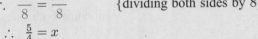

**Example 10**                                                      ◄) **Self Tutor**

Solve for $x$:   $\dfrac{3x+2}{1-2x}=\dfrac{1}{6}$

$$\dfrac{3x+2}{1-2x}=\dfrac{1}{6} \qquad \{\text{LCD of fractions}=6(1-2x)\}$$

$$\therefore \left(\dfrac{3x+2}{1-2x}\right)\times\dfrac{6}{6}=\dfrac{1}{6}\times\left(\dfrac{1-2x}{1-2x}\right) \quad \{\text{to create the common denominator}\}$$

$$\therefore \dfrac{6(3x+2)}{6(1-2x)}=\dfrac{(1-2x)}{6(1-2x)}$$

$$\therefore\ 6(3x+2)=1-2x \qquad \{\text{equating numerators}\}$$

$$\therefore\ 18x+12=1-2x \qquad \{\text{expanding the brackets}\}$$

$$\therefore\ 18x+12+2x=1-2x+2x \qquad \{\text{adding } 2x \text{ to both sides}\}$$

$$\therefore\ 20x+12=1$$

$$\therefore\ 20x+12-12=1-12 \qquad \{\text{subtracting 12 from both sides}\}$$

$$\therefore\ 20x=-11$$

$$\therefore\ \dfrac{20x}{20}=\dfrac{-11}{20} \qquad \{\text{dividing both sides by 20}\}$$

$$\therefore\ x=-\tfrac{11}{20}$$

## EXERCISE 5C

**1** Solve for $x$:

**a** $\dfrac{x}{5}=\dfrac{2}{3}$  **b** $\dfrac{5}{6}=\dfrac{x}{5}$  **c** $\dfrac{x-3}{2}=\dfrac{1}{5}$

**d** $\dfrac{x}{4}=\dfrac{1+x}{3}$  **e** $\dfrac{2-x}{3}=\dfrac{8x}{5}$  **f** $\dfrac{2x-1}{5}=-\dfrac{3x}{7}$

**g** $\dfrac{1-3x}{4}=\dfrac{2+x}{3}$  **h** $\dfrac{7-x}{5}=\dfrac{3x+1}{8}$  **i** $\dfrac{3-2x}{5}=\dfrac{2+5x}{-3}$

**2** Solve for $x$:

**a** $\dfrac{3}{x}=\dfrac{2}{5}$  **b** $\dfrac{2}{x}=\dfrac{1}{3}$  **c** $\dfrac{7}{x}=\dfrac{3}{4}$

**d** $\dfrac{3}{4x}=\dfrac{5}{3}$  **e** $\dfrac{5}{4x}=\dfrac{3}{2}$  **f** $\dfrac{2}{3x}=-\dfrac{4}{9}$

**g** $\dfrac{4}{x+1}=\dfrac{5}{3}$  **h** $\dfrac{3}{1-x}=\dfrac{2}{5}$  **i** $\dfrac{1}{5}=\dfrac{4}{3x+2}$

**3** Solve for $x$:   $\dfrac{4}{3x}=\dfrac{5}{4x}$   Comment on your answer.

4   Solve for $x$:

   **a**  $\dfrac{1}{x} = \dfrac{2}{x+1}$

   **b**  $\dfrac{2x-1}{1-x} = \dfrac{1}{2}$

   **c**  $\dfrac{3x+1}{x+2} = 4$

   **d**  $\dfrac{3x-2}{1-2x} = -\dfrac{1}{3}$

   **e**  $\dfrac{3}{2x-1} = \dfrac{5}{3x}$

   **f**  $\dfrac{1-5x}{4+x} = -\dfrac{3}{4}$

   **g**  $\dfrac{3-2x}{x+1} = -7$

   **h**  $\dfrac{4x+3}{1-2x} = \dfrac{3}{8}$

   **i**  $\dfrac{4}{3x+2} = \dfrac{7}{2-5x}$

## D │ SOLVING LINEAR EQUATIONS USING TECHNOLOGY

You can use a graphics calculator to solve linear equations. For assistance you should refer to the **graphics calculator instructions** at the start of the book.

---

**Example 11**    ◀ঠ) **Self Tutor**

Solve this equation using technology:   $4.6x - 8.9 = 7.2$

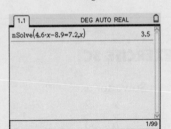

| **Casio fx-9860G** | **TI-84 Plus** | **TI-$n$Spire** |

Using technology, $x = 3.5$

---

## EXERCISE 5D

1   Use technology to solve the following:

   **a**  $5.4x + 7.2 = 15.6$

   **b**  $0.05x - 9.6 = 3.5$

   **c**  $23.24 - 13.08x = 8.94$

   **d**  $1234.32 + 37.56x = 259.04$

2   Use technology to solve the following, giving your answers as fractions:

   **a**  $\dfrac{3x+2}{5} = -1$

   **b**  $5x + 3 = 2 - 8x$

   **c**  $\dfrac{2x+3}{x-4} = -5$

3   When $w$ grams of weight are placed on a spring balance, the scale reads $R$ mm. The reading is given by the formula  $R = 0.4w + 5$.
   Find $w$ when:

   **a**  $R = 27$

   **b**  $R = 42$

**4** In the United States of America, temperature is measured in degrees Fahrenheit ($^o$F) rather than in degrees Celsius ($^o$C). The rule showing the relationship between these two temperature scales is  $F = 1.8C + 32$.  What temperature in $^o$C corresponds to a temperature of:    **a**   40$^o$F    **b**   0$^o$F    **c**   200$^o$F?

**5** The total cost of sinking a bore is given by the rule  $C = 15d + 350$ dollars  where $d$ is the depth in metres. How deep a bore can a farmer obtain for a cost of:

   **a**   $2000    **b**   $3200?

**6** Use technology to solve:

    **a**   $3x + 2 = 5x - 17$                      **b**   $3.6x - 1.8 = 2.7x + 4.1$

    **c**   $3.56x + 13.67 = 1.05x + 39.97$      **d**   $21.67 + 3.67x = 5.83x - 58.88$

## E    PROBLEM SOLVING WITH LINEAR EQUATIONS

Many problems can be translated into **algebraic equations**. When problems are solved using algebra, we follow these steps:

> *Step 1:*   Determine what the unknown quantity is and use a letter or symbol to represent it.
>
> *Step 2:*   Decide which operations are involved.
>
> *Step 3:*   Translate the problem into an equation.
>
> *Step 4:*   Solve the equation by isolating the unknown.
>
> *Step 5:*   Check that your solution does satisfy the original problem.
>
> *Step 6:*   Write your answer in sentence form.

### Example 12      ◀⁾ Self Tutor

When a number is doubled and subtracted from 3, the result is $-17$. Find the number.

Let $x$ be the number.

∴ $2x$ is the number doubled.

∴ $3 - 2x$ is this number subtracted from 3.

$$So, \quad 3 - 2x = -17$$
$$∴ \quad 3 - 2x - 3 = -17 - 3 \quad \text{\{subtracting 3 from both sides\}}$$
$$∴ \quad -2x = -20$$
$$∴ \quad x = 10 \qquad \text{\{dividing both sides by } -2\text{\}}$$

So, the number is 10.        *Check:* $3 - 2 \times 10 = 3 - 20 = -17$ ✓

**Example 13**    ◀)) **Self Tutor**

Malikah's mum is presently four times as old as Malikah. In 6 years' time her mum will only be three times as old as she is then. How old is Malikah now?

Let Malikah's present age be $x$ years.

$\therefore$ her mother's present age is $4x$ years.

|         | Now | 6 years' time |
|---------|-----|---------------|
| Malikah | $x$ | $x + 6$       |
| Mother  | $4x$| $4x + 6$      |

So,   $4x + 6 = 3(x + 6)$    {her mum is three times as old}

$\therefore \ 4x + 6 = 3x + 18$

$\therefore \ 4x + 6 - 3x = 3x + 18 - 3x$

$\therefore \quad x + 6 = 18$

$\therefore \quad x = 12$    $\therefore$  Malikah's present age is 12 years.

## EXERCISE 5E

1  I take a certain number and multiply it by 5. I subtract the resulting product from 24 to get $-11$. What was my original number?

2  Doubling a certain number and subtracting 5 gives the same result as subtracting 10 from the number then multiplying by 7. Find the number.

3  Fayyad and Malik start with the same number. Fayyad divides the number by 3 then adds 3, while Malik subtracts 7 from the number and then multiplies the result by 3. They now both have the same number. What number did they start with?

4  Jordana visits a furniture shop and sees a table she likes. She measures it to be 9 handspans and 4 cm long, but then she sees a label that says the table is 166 cm long. How wide is Jordana's handspan?

5  Farmer Giles walks down one side of his chicken coop and sees it is just 30 cm less than 8 paces. He walks along the next side, taking 15 paces to arrive 25 cm short of the end. He knows that the second side is twice as long as the first.

   a  How long is Farmer Giles' pace?

   b  What are the dimensions of the chicken coop?

6  Mira's mother is presently three times as old as Mira. In 11 years' time her mother will be twice as old as her. How old is Mira now?

7  At Ferenc's birth, his mother was 27 years old. At what age will Ferenc be 40% of his mother's age?

**Example 14**    ◀)) **Self Tutor**

Carl has only 20 cent coins and 50 cent coins in his wallet. He has three more 50 cent coins than 20 cent coins, and their total value is $2.90. How many 20 cent coins does Carl have?

If Carl has $x$ 20 cent coins then he has $(x+3)$ 50 cent coins.

| Coin | Number | Value |
|---|---|---|
| 20 cent | $x$ | $20x$ cents |
| 50 cent | $x+3$ | $50(x+3)$ cents |

$\therefore\ 20x + 50(x+3) = 290$    {equating values in cents}

$\therefore\ 20x + 50x + 150 = 290$

$\therefore\ \ \ 70x + 150 = 290$

$\therefore\ \ \ \ \ \ \ \ \ 70x = 140$

$\therefore\ \ \ \ \ \ \ \ x = 2$    So, Carl has two 20 cent coins.

**8** Wayne has a collection of 2 cent and 5 cent stemps. He has three times as many 2 cent stamps as 5 cent stamps, and the total value of the stamps is 66 cents. How many 5 cent stamps does Wayne have?

**9** Louise has only 5 cent, 10 cent and 20 cent coins in her purse. She has 30 coins in total, and she has two more 10 cent coins than 5 cent coins. If the total value of her coins is $3.80, how many 10 cent coins does she have?

**10** Theresa sells lemonade for £1, juice for £1.50, and coffee for £2. On one day, the number of coffees she sells is twice the number of lemonades she sells, and 4 more than the number of juices she sells. If she earns a total of £74, how many lemonades did she sell?

# F    FORMULA SUBSTITUTION

A **formula** is an equation which connects two or more variables.

The plural of formula is **formulae** or **formulas**.

In a formula it is common for one of the variables to be on one side of the equation and the other variable(s) and constants to be on the other side.

The variable on its own is called the **subject** of the formula.

If the formula contains two or more variables and we know the value of all but one of them, we can use the formula to find the value of the unknown variable.

*Step 1:*    Write down the formula and state the values of the known variables.

*Step 2:*    Substitute the known values into the formula to form a one variable equation.

*Step 3:*    Solve the equation for the unknown variable.

### Example 15    ◀) Self Tutor

The acceleration of a falling raindrop is given by $a = g - 1.96v$ m s$^{-2}$ where $g = 9.8$ m s$^{-2}$ is the gravitational constant and $v$ is the speed of the raindrop.

Find:

  **a**  the acceleration of the raindrop before it starts falling

  **b**  the acceleration of the raindrop when its speed reaches 3 m s$^{-1}$

  **c**  the speed of the raindrop for which it does not accelerate.

**a**    $a = g - 1.96v$ where $g = 9.8$ and $v = 0$

    $\therefore \; a = 9.8 - 1.96 \times 0$

    $\therefore \; a = 9.8$ m s$^{-2}$

**b**    $a = g - 1.96v$ where $g = 9.8$ and $v = 3$

    $\therefore \; a = 9.8 - 1.96 \times 3$

    $\therefore \; a = 3.92$ m s$^{-2}$

**c**    $a = g - 1.96v$ where $a = 0$ and $g = 9.8$

    $\therefore \; 0 = 9.8 - 1.96v$

    $\therefore \; 1.96v = 9.8$

    $\therefore \; v = \dfrac{9.8}{1.96}$

    $\therefore \; v = 5$ m s$^{-1}$

We use more than 3 significant figures in our working to ensure the answer is correct to at least this accuracy.

## EXERCISE 5F

**1**  The formula for the circumference $C$ of a circle of diameter $d$, is $C = \pi d$ where $\pi \approx 3.14159$ is a constant. Find:

  **a**  the circumference of a circle of diameter 11.4 cm

  **b**  the diameter of a circle with circumference 250 cm

  **c**  the radius of a circle of circumference 100 metres.

**2**  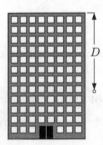

A tennis ball is dropped from the top of a tall building. The total distance it has fallen is given by the formula $D = \frac{1}{2}gt^2$ where $D$ is the distance in metres and $t$ is the time taken in seconds. Given that $g = 9.8$ m s$^{-2}$, find:

  **a**  the total distance fallen in the first 3 seconds of fall

  **b**  the height of the building, to the nearest metre, if the ball takes 5.13 seconds to reach the ground.

**3**  When a car travels a distance $d$ kilometres in time $t$ hours, the average speed for the journey is given by  $s = \dfrac{d}{t}$  km h$^{-1}$.  Find:

   **a**  the average speed of a car which travels 200 km in $2\frac{1}{2}$ hours

   **b**  the distance travelled by a car in $3\frac{1}{4}$ hours if its average speed is 80 km h$^{-1}$

   **c**  the time taken, to the nearest minute, for a car to travel 865 km at an average speed of 110 km h$^{-1}$.

**4**  The area of a circle of radius $r$ is given by  $A = \pi r^2$.  Find:

   **a**  the area of a circle of radius 5.6 cm

   **b**  the radius of a circular pond which has an area of 200 m$^2$.

**5**  The potential difference $V$ across an $R$ ohm resistor is given by  $V = IR$ volts,  where $I$ is the current in amps flowing through the circuit.  Find:

   **a**  the potential difference across a 6 ohm resistor if the current in the circuit is 0.08 amps

   **b**  the resistance in a circuit with current 0.2 amps if the potential difference is 12 volts.

**6**  The volume of a cylinder of radius $r$ and height $h$ is given by  $V = \pi r^2 h$.  Find:

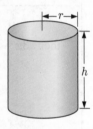

   **a**  the volume of a cylindrical tin can of radius 12 cm and height 17.5 cm

   **b**  the height of a cylinder of radius 4 cm if its volume is 80 cm$^3$

   **c**  the radius, in mm, of copper wire with volume 100 cm$^3$ and length 0.2 km.

**7**

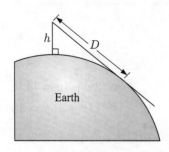

Earth

The formula  $D = 3.56\sqrt{h}$  estimates the distance in kilometres to the horizon which can be seen by a person with eye level $h$ metres above the level of the sea.

Find:

   **a**  the distance to the horizon when a person's eye level is 10 m above sea level

   **b**  how far above sea level a person's eye must be for the horizon to be 30 km away.

**8**  The total surface area of a sphere of radius $r$ is given by  $A = 4\pi r^2$.  Find:

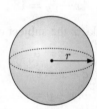

   **a**  the total surface area of a sphere of radius 6.9 cm

   **b**  the radius (in cm) of a spherical balloon which has a surface area of 1 m$^2$.

## G          FORMULA REARRANGEMENT

Consider the formula $V = \frac{1}{3}\pi r^2 h$, which gives the volume of a cone with radius $r$ and height $h$.

We say that $V$ is the **subject** of the formula because $V$ is expressed in terms of the other variables $r$ and $h$.

The formula can be **rearranged** to make **equivalent** formulae where the other variables are the subjects:

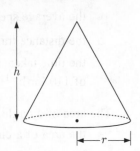

$$h = \frac{3V}{\pi r^2} \qquad r = \sqrt{\frac{3V}{\pi h}}$$

We rearrange formulae using the same methods which we used to solve equations. We perform **inverse operations** to isolate the variable we wish to make the subject.

---

**Example 16**                                              ◀)) **Self Tutor**

Make $y$ the subject of $3x - 7y = 22$.

$$\begin{aligned} \text{If } \quad 3x - 7y &= 22 \\ \text{then } \quad 3x - 7y - 3x &= 22 - 3x && \{\text{subtracting } 3x \text{ from both sides}\} \\ \therefore \quad -7y &= 22 - 3x \\ \therefore \quad 7y &= 3x - 22 && \{\text{multiplying both sides by } -1\} \\ \therefore \quad \frac{7y}{7} &= \frac{3x - 22}{7} && \{\text{dividing both sides by } 7\} \\ \therefore \quad y &= \frac{3x - 22}{7} \end{aligned}$$

---

## EXERCISE 5G.1

**1** Make $y$ the subject of:

    **a** $x + 2y = 4$          **b** $2x + 6y = 7$          **c** $3x + 4y = 11$

    **d** $5x + 4y = 8$          **e** $7x + 2y = 20$        **f** $11x + 15y = 38$

**2** Make $y$ the subject of:

    **a** $x - 2y = 4$          **b** $2x - 6y = 7$          **c** $3x - 4y = -12$

    **d** $4x - 5y = 18$         **e** $7x - 6y = 42$        **f** $12x - 13y = -44$

**3** Make $x$ the subject of:

    **a** $a + x = b$           **b** $ax = b$             **c** $2x + a = d$

    **d** $c + x = t$           **e** $7x + 3y = d$         **f** $ax + by = c$

    **g** $mx - y = c$         **h** $c - 2x = p$         **i** $a - 3x = t$

    **j** $n - kx = 5$          **k** $a - bx = n$         **l** $p = a - nx$

**Example 17**    ◀⑴ **Self Tutor**

Make $z$ the subject

of $y = \dfrac{x}{z}$.

$$y = \frac{x}{z}$$

$$\therefore \quad y \times z = \frac{x}{z} \times z \qquad \text{\{multiplying both sides by } z\text{\}}$$

$$\therefore \quad yz = x$$

$$\therefore \quad \frac{yz}{y} = \frac{x}{y} \qquad \text{\{dividing both sides by } y\text{\}}$$

$$\therefore \quad z = \frac{x}{y}$$

**4**  Make $x$ the subject of:

**a**  $a = \dfrac{x}{b}$      **b**  $\dfrac{a}{x} = d$      **c**  $p = \dfrac{2}{x}$      **d**  $\dfrac{x}{2} = n$      **e**  $\dfrac{m}{x} = \dfrac{x}{n}$

## REARRANGEMENT AND SUBSTITUTION

In the previous section on formula substitution, the variables were replaced by numbers and then the equation was solved. However, often we need to substitute several values for the unknowns and solve the equation for each case. In this situation it is quicker to **rearrange** the formula **before substituting**.

**Example 18**    ◀⑴ **Self Tutor**

The circumference of a circle is given by $C = 2\pi r$, where $r$ is the circle's radius. Rearrange this formula to make $r$ the subject, and hence find the radius when the circumference is:

     **a**  10 cm          **b**  20 cm          **c**  50 cm.

$2\pi r = C,$   so   $r = \dfrac{C}{2\pi}.$

   **a**  When $C = 10,$   $r = \dfrac{10}{2\pi} \approx 1.59$     $\therefore$   the radius is about 1.59 cm.

   **b**  When $C = 20,$   $r = \dfrac{20}{2\pi} \approx 3.18$     $\therefore$   the radius is about 3.18 cm.

   **c**  When $C = 50,$   $r = \dfrac{50}{2\pi} \approx 7.96$     $\therefore$   the radius is about 7.96 cm.

## EXERCISE 5G.2

**1**  The equation of a straight line is $5x + 3y = 18$. Rearrange this formula into the form $y = mx + c$, and hence state the gradient $m$ and the $y$-intercept $c$.

**2**  **a**  Make $a$ the subject of the formula $K = \dfrac{d}{2ab}$.

     **b**  Find the value of $a$ when:

         **i**  $K = 112,$   $d = 24,$   $b = 2$          **ii**  $K = 400,$   $d = 72,$   $b = 0.4.$

**3** When a car travels a distance $d$ kilometres in time $t$ hours, the average speed $s$ for the journey is given by the formula   $s = \dfrac{d}{t}$ $\text{km h}^{-1}$.

  **a** Make $d$ the subject of the formula. Hence find the distance travelled by a car if:
   **i** the average speed is $60$ $\text{km h}^{-1}$ and the time travelled is $3$ hours
   **ii** the average speed is $80$ $\text{km h}^{-1}$ and the time travelled is $1\frac{1}{2}$ hours
   **iii** the average speed is $95$ $\text{km h}^{-1}$ and the time travelled is $1$ h $20$ min.

  **b** Make $t$ the subject of the formula. Hence find the time required for a car to travel:
   **i** $180$ km at an average speed of $60$ $\text{km h}^{-1}$
   **ii** $140$ km at an average speed of $35$ $\text{km h}^{-1}$
   **iii** $220$ km at an average speed of $100$ $\text{km h}^{-1}$.

**4** The simple interest $\$I$ paid on an investment of $\$C$ is determined by the annual rate of interest $r$ (as a percentage) and the duration of the investment, $n$ years. The interest is given by the formula   $I = \dfrac{Crn}{100}$.

  **a** Make $n$ the subject of the formula.

  **b**  **i** Find the time required to generate $\$1050$ interest on an investment of $\$6400$ at an interest rate of $8\%$ per annum.

   **ii** Find the time required for an investment of $\$1000$ to double at an interest rate of $10\%$ per annum.

# H   LINEAR SIMULTANEOUS EQUATIONS

In some situations we may have several equations that must be true at the same time. We call these **simultaneous equations**.

To solve simultaneous equations we require values for the variables which satisfy each equation. These values are the **simultaneous solution** of the equations.

In this chapter we will consider systems of two linear simultaneous equations containing two unknowns. In these systems there will be infinitely many solutions which satisfy the first equation, and infinitely many solutions which satisfy the second equation. However, in general there will only be one solution which satisfies both equations at the same time.

## INVESTIGATION                         IMPORTING RACKETS

Kobeng imports two brands of racket for his store.
In one shipment he buys $x$ Asway rackets at $\$40$ each, and $y$ Onex rackets at $\$60$ each.

In total Kobeng buys $50$ rackets, so   $x + y = 50$.

The total price is $\$2640$, so   $40x + 60y = 2640$.

To find out how many of each brand Kobeng buys, we need to solve simultaneously the

equations $\begin{cases} x + y = 50 \\ 40x + 60y = 2640. \end{cases}$

**What to do:**

SPREADSHEET

**1** Click on the icon to open a spreadsheet. The first row displays all the possible values for $x$, from 0 to 50.

| | A | B | C | D | E | F | G | H |
|---|---|---|---|---|---|---|---|---|
| 1 | Number of Asway rackets, x | 0 | 1 | 2 | 3 | 4 | 5 | .... |
| 2 | Number of Onex rackets, y | | | | | | | |
| 3 | Total cost | | | | | | | |

**2** Kobeng buys 50 rackets in total, so $x + y = 50$, which means that $y = 50 - x$. Enter the formula = 50-B1 into cell **B2**, and fill the formula across.

**3** The total cost of $x$ Asway rackets and $y$ Onex rackets is $40x + 60y$ dollars. Enter the formula = 40*B1 + 60*B2 into cell **B3**, and fill the formula across.

**4** Find the combination of rackets which results in a total cost of $2640.

**5** Verify that the values for $x$ and $y$ found in **4** satisfy both $x + y = 50$ and $40x + 60y = 2640$.

In the investigation we used trial and error to find a simultaneous solution to the system of equations. This method can be very tedious, however, so instead we need some alternative methods.

# SOLUTION BY SUBSTITUTION

The method of **solution by substitution** is used when at least one equation is given with either $x$ or $y$ as the **subject** of the formula, or if it is easy to make $x$ or $y$ the subject.

| **Example 19** | ◀)) **Self Tutor** |
|---|---|

Solve by substitution: $\begin{cases} y = 3 + x \\ 2x - 4y = -16 \end{cases}$

$y$ is the subject of (1) so we substitute $3 + x$ for $y$ in (2).

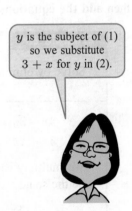

$\begin{aligned} y = 3 + x \quad &\dots (1) \\ 2x - 4y = -16 \quad &\dots (2) \end{aligned}$

Substituting (1) into (2) gives $2x - 4(3 + x) = -16$

$\therefore \ 2x - 12 - 4x = -16$

$\therefore \ -2x = -4$

$\therefore \ x = 2$

Substituting $x = 2$ into (1) gives $y = 3 + 2 = 5$

So, $x = 2$ and $y = 5$.

*Check:* In (2), $2 \times 2 - 4 \times 5 = 4 - 20 = -16 \ \checkmark$

## EXERCISE 5H.1

**1**  Solve simultaneously by substitution:

**a** $\begin{cases} y = x - 3 \\ 2x + y = 12 \end{cases}$

**b** $\begin{cases} x = y - 1 \\ 4x - 3y = 0 \end{cases}$

**c** $\begin{cases} y = x + 6 \\ 3y + 2x = 13 \end{cases}$

**d** $\begin{cases} y = -2x \\ 3x - y = 10 \end{cases}$

**e** $\begin{cases} 3x - 5y = -9 \\ y = x + 3 \end{cases}$

**f** $\begin{cases} 2x = y \\ 2y - x = 1 \end{cases}$

**2**  Use substitution to solve simultaneously:

**a** $\begin{cases} x = -2 - 3y \\ 2x + 5y = -5 \end{cases}$

**b** $\begin{cases} y = 4 - x \\ y = 3x + 3 \end{cases}$

**c** $\begin{cases} x = 2y - 5 \\ 4x + 3y = 13 \end{cases}$

**d** $\begin{cases} y = 4x \\ 3x - 2y = 10 \end{cases}$

**e** $\begin{cases} x = -6 - 5y \\ 5x + 3y = 14 \end{cases}$

**f** $\begin{cases} 4x - 2y = -3 \\ y = 3x + 1 \end{cases}$

**3**  **a**  Try to solve using the method of substitution: $\begin{cases} y = 2x + 5 \\ y = 2x + 1 \end{cases}$

   **b**  What is the simultaneous solution for the equations in **a**?

**4**  **a**  Try to solve using the method of substitution: $\begin{cases} y = 2x + 5 \\ 2y = 4x + 10 \end{cases}$

   **b**  How many simultaneous solutions do the equations in **a** have?

## SOLUTION BY ELIMINATION

In many problems which require the simultaneous solution of linear equations, each equation will be of the form $ax + by = c$. Solution by substitution is often tedious in such situations and the method of **elimination** of one of the variables is preferred.

In this method we multiply each equation by a constant so that the coefficients of either $x$ or $y$ are the **same size** but **opposite in sign**.

We then **add the equations** to eliminate one variable.

| Example 20 | ◀)) Self Tutor |
|---|---|

Solve by elimination:    $\begin{cases} 2x - 3y = 4 \\ 3x + 2y = 19 \end{cases}$

$2x - 3y = 4$    .... (1)

$3x + 2y = 19$    .... (2)

We multiply each equation by a constant so the coefficients of $y$ will be the same size but opposite in sign.

$\qquad 4x - 6y = 8 \qquad \{2 \times (1)\}$

$\qquad \underline{9x + 6y = 57} \qquad \{3 \times (2)\}$

Adding,  $13x \qquad = 65$

$\qquad \therefore \ x = 5$

Substituting $x = 5$ into (1), $2 \times 5 - 3y = 4$

$$\therefore \ 10 - 3y = 4$$
$$\therefore \ 6 = 3y$$
$$\therefore \ 2 = y$$

So, $x = 5$ and $y = 2$

*Check:* In (2), $3x + 2y = 3 \times 5 + 2 \times 2 = 15 + 4 = 19$ ✓

## EXERCISE 5H.2

**1** What equation results when the following are added vertically?

**a** $3x + 2y = 7$
$x - 2y = 8$

**b** $2x - y = 8$
$-2x + 3y = 4$

**c** $x - 5y = -3$
$4x + 5y = 13$

**d** $5x + 3y = 15$
$3x - 3y = 1$

**e** $-2x + 3y = 5$
$2x - 5y = -3$

**f** $-x + 5y = 3$
$x - 2y = -6$

**2** Solve using the method of elimination:

**a** $\begin{cases} 2x + y = 5 \\ x - y = 1 \end{cases}$

**b** $\begin{cases} 3x - 2y = 5 \\ -x + 2y = 1 \end{cases}$

**c** $\begin{cases} 2x + y = 8 \\ -2x + 3y = 0 \end{cases}$

**d** $\begin{cases} 2x + 5y = -1 \\ 3x - 5y = 11 \end{cases}$

**e** $\begin{cases} -2x - 2y = -5 \\ -8x + 2y = 0 \end{cases}$

**f** $\begin{cases} 2x - y = 3 \\ -2x - 5y = -1 \end{cases}$

**3** Give the equation which results when both sides of:

**a** $x - y = 2$ are multiplied by 3

**b** $2x + y = -1$ are multiplied by $-1$

**c** $-x + 3y = 2$ are multiplied by 2

**d** $3x - 2y = 4$ are multiplied by 3.

**4** Solve using the method of elimination:

**a** $\begin{cases} x + 2y = 4 \\ 3x + y = 7 \end{cases}$

**b** $\begin{cases} 3x + 2y = 3 \\ 5x - y = -8 \end{cases}$

**c** $\begin{cases} -x + 2y = 6 \\ 3x - 5y = -14 \end{cases}$

**d** $\begin{cases} 2x - 3y = 12 \\ 5x + 2y = 11 \end{cases}$

**e** $\begin{cases} x + 6y = 1 \\ -3x + 2y = 7 \end{cases}$

**f** $\begin{cases} 2x + 3y = 5 \\ 3x - 2y = 27 \end{cases}$

**g** $\begin{cases} 6x - 5y = 4 \\ -3x + 2y = -2 \end{cases}$

**h** $\begin{cases} 3x - y = 8 \\ 4x + 2y = -1 \end{cases}$

**i** $\begin{cases} -x - 2y = 9 \\ 2x + y = 3 \end{cases}$

**5** Try to solve the following by elimination. Comment on your results.

**a** $\begin{cases} 5x + 2y = 6 \\ 15x + 6y = 18 \end{cases}$

**b** $\begin{cases} 3x - y = 2 \\ -6x + 2y = -3 \end{cases}$

## USING TECHNOLOGY

You can solve linear simultaneous equations using your graphics calculator. For instructions on how to do this, click on the icon alongside corresponding to your calculator model.

For the **TI-84 Plus**, you will need to download the application **Polysmlt 2** from
http://education.ti.com/educationportal/sites/US/productDetail/us_poly_83_84.html

---

**Example 21**                                                    ◆)) **Self Tutor**

Use technology to solve: $\begin{cases} 2x - 3y = 4 \\ 3x + 2y = 19 \end{cases}$

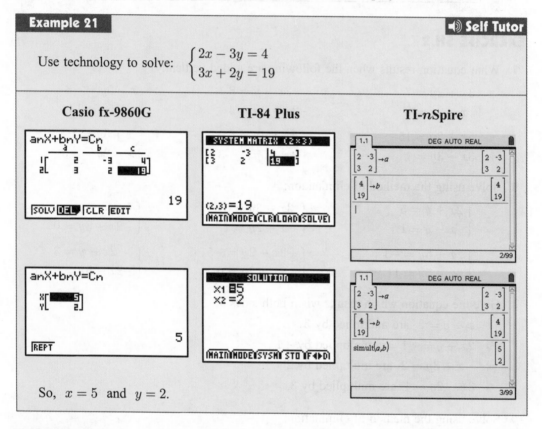

So, $x = 5$ and $y = 2$.

---

## EXERCISE 5H.3

**1** Use technology to solve these simultaneous equations:

a $\begin{cases} 3x + 4y = 1 \\ x - 2y = 7 \end{cases}$

b $\begin{cases} x + 4y = -2 \\ -3x + 2y = 13 \end{cases}$

c $\begin{cases} 6x + y = 13 \\ 2x - 3y = 16 \end{cases}$

d $\begin{cases} x + 3y = 1 \\ -3x + 7y = 21 \end{cases}$

e $\begin{cases} 1.4x - 2.3y = -1.3 \\ 5.7x - 3.4y = 12.6 \end{cases}$

f $\begin{cases} 3.6x - 0.7y = -11.37 \\ 4.9x + 2.7y = -1.23 \end{cases}$

**2** Try to solve $\begin{cases} 0.2x + 0.9y = 5 \\ 0.6x + 2.7y = -3 \end{cases}$ using technology. Comment on your result.

# PROBLEM SOLVING WITH SIMULTANEOUS EQUATIONS

Many problems can be described using a pair of linear equations. We saw an example of this in the investigation on page **156** in which Kobeng was importing rackets.

You should follow these steps to solve problems involving simultaneous equations:

> *Step 1:* Decide on the two unknowns; call them $x$ and $y$, say. Do not forget the units.
>
> *Step 2:* Write down **two** equations connecting $x$ and $y$.
>
> *Step 3:* Solve the equations simultaneously.
>
> *Step 4:* Check your solutions with the original data given.
>
> *Step 5:* Give your answer in sentence form.

The form of the original equations will help you decide whether to use the substitution method or the elimination method.

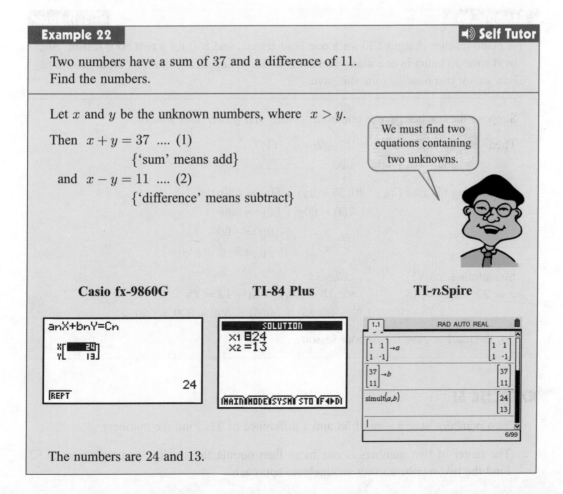

### Example 22   ◀) Self Tutor

Two numbers have a sum of 37 and a difference of 11.
Find the numbers.

Let $x$ and $y$ be the unknown numbers, where $x > y$.

Then $x + y = 37$ .... (1)
　　　 {'sum' means add}

and $x - y = 11$ .... (2)
　　　 {'difference' means subtract}

> We must find two equations containing two unknowns.

**Casio fx-9860G**　　**TI-84 Plus**　　**TI-nSpire**

The numbers are 24 and 13.

**Example 23**    ◀)) **Self Tutor**

Two adults' tickets and three children's tickets to a baseball match cost $45, while three adults' and four children's tickets cost $64. Find the cost of an adult's ticket using an algebraic method.

Let $x be the cost of an adult's ticket and $y be the cost of a child's ticket.

So,   $2x + 3y = 45$  .... (1)   and   $3x + 4y = 64$  .... (2)

$\therefore \quad 6x + 9y = 135 \qquad \{(1) \times 3\}$
$\underline{-6x - 8y = -128} \qquad \{(2) \times -2\}$

Adding,       $y = 7$

Substituting into (1),   $2x + 3(7) = 45$       *Check:*
$\qquad\qquad\qquad \therefore \quad 2x = 24$       (1)  $2(12) + 3(7) = 24 + 21 = 45 \ \checkmark$
$\qquad\qquad\qquad \therefore \quad x = 12$       (2)  $3(12) + 4(7) = 36 + 28 = 64 \ \checkmark$

So, an adult's ticket costs $12.

---

**Example 24**    ◀)) **Self Tutor**

A piano teacher charges $30 for a one hour lesson, and $50 for a two hour lesson. She works for 25 hours in one week, and earns $690. Using an algebraic method, determine how many two hour lessons she gave.

Suppose the teacher gave $x$ one hour lessons and $y$ two hour lessons.

Then   $x + 2y = 25$,  so  $x = 25 - 2y$   .... (1)
and   $30x + 50y = 690$        .... (2)

Substituting (1) into (2),   $30(25 - 2y) + 50y = 690$
$\qquad\qquad\qquad \therefore \quad 750 - 60y + 50y = 690$
$\qquad\qquad\qquad\qquad \therefore \quad -10y = -60$
$\qquad\qquad\qquad\qquad\qquad \therefore \quad y = 6$

Substituting into (1),       *Check:*
$x = 25 - 2(6) = 13$         $13 + 2(6) = 13 + 12 = 25 \ \checkmark$
$\qquad\qquad\qquad\qquad\qquad 30(13) + 50(6) = 390 + 300 = 690 \ \checkmark$

So, the teacher gave 6 two hour lessons.

---

# EXERCISE 51

1  Two numbers have a sum of 58 and a difference of 22. Find the numbers.

2  The larger of two numbers is one more than double the smaller, and their sum is 82. Find the two numbers using an algebraic approach.

**3** A hairdresser has 13 small and 14 large cans of hair spray, giving a total of 9 L of hairspray. At this time last year she had 4 small and 12 large cans, totalling 6 L of hairspray. How much spray is in each size can?

**4** A violinist is learning a waltz and a sonatina. One day she practices for 33 minutes by playing the waltz 4 times and the sonatina 3 times. The next day she plays the waltz 6 times and the sonatina only once, for a total of 25 minutes. Using an algebraic method, determine the length of each piece.

**5** A shop sells two lengths of extension cable. Tomasz buys 2 short cables and 5 long cables for a total length of 26 m. Alicja buys 24.3 m of cabling by getting 3 short and 4 long cables. Find the two different lengths of the extension cables.

**6** In an archery competition, competitors fire 8 arrows at a target. They are awarded points based on which region of the target is hit. The results for two of the competitors are shown opposite.

How many points are awarded for hitting the:
  **a** red     **b** blue region?

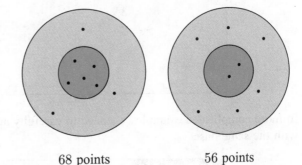

68 points                    56 points

**7** Find the length of the longest side of this rectangle:

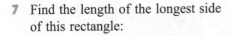

$(2a+5)$ m

$(3a-1)$ m          $(b+2)$ m

$3b$ m

**8** Find the length of wire required to construct this pentagon:

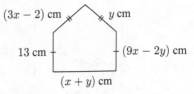

$(3x-2)$ cm     $y$ cm

13 cm          $(9x-2y)$ cm

$(x+y)$ cm

**9** A hardware store sells 3 litre paint cans for £15 and 5 litre paint cans for £20. In one day the store sells 71 litres of paint, worth a total of £320. How many paint cans did the store sell?

**10** Kristen can run at 15 km h$^{-1}$, and walk at 5 km h$^{-1}$. She completed a 42 km marathon in 4 hours. What distance did Kristen run during the marathon?

# J          EXPONENTIAL EQUATIONS

An **exponential equation** is an equation in which the unknown occurs as part of the index or exponent.

For example, $3^x = 27$ and $2^{1-x} = \frac{1}{4}$ are both exponential equations.

To solve exponential equations we first look to see if both sides can be written as powers with the **same base**. If the base numbers are the same then we can **equate indices**.

$$\text{If } a^x = a^k \text{ then } x = k.$$

---

**Example 25**    ◀)) **Self Tutor**

Solve for $x$:    **a** $3^x = 27$    **b** $2^{1-x} = \frac{1}{4}$

**a**    $3^x = 27$
$\therefore 3^x = 3^3$
$\therefore x = 3$

**b**    $2^{1-x} = \frac{1}{4}$
$\therefore 2^{1-x} = 2^{-2}$
$\therefore 1 - x = -2$
$\therefore -x = -3$
$\therefore x = 3$

---

In more complicated examples we need to carefully apply the index laws to write both sides with the same base.

---

**Example 26**    ◀)) **Self Tutor**

Solve for $x$:

**a** $8^x = \frac{1}{16}$    **b** $25^{x+1} = \left(\frac{1}{5}\right)^x$

**a**    $8^x = \frac{1}{16}$
$\therefore (2^3)^x = 2^{-4}$
$\therefore 2^{3x} = 2^{-4}$
$\therefore 3x = -4$
$\therefore x = -\frac{4}{3}$

**b**    $25^{x+1} = \left(\frac{1}{5}\right)^x$
$\therefore (5^2)^{x+1} = (5^{-1})^x$
$\therefore 5^{2(x+1)} = 5^{-x}$
$\therefore 2(x + 1) = -x$
$\therefore 2x + 2 = -x$
$\therefore 3x = -2$
$\therefore x = -\frac{2}{3}$

---

## EXERCISE 5J.1

**1** Solve for $x$:

**a** $2^x = 8$    **b** $5^x = 25$    **c** $3^x = 81$    **d** $7^x = 1$

**e** $3^x = \frac{1}{3}$    **f** $4^x = \frac{1}{16}$    **g** $5^x = \frac{1}{125}$    **h** $4^{x+1} = 64$

2   Solve for $x$:

  a   $2^{x-2} = \frac{1}{32}$

  b   $3^{1-x} = \frac{1}{27}$

  c   $7^{x+1} = 343$

  d   $5^{1-2x} = \frac{1}{5}$

  e   $8^x = 16$

  f   $4^x = \frac{1}{8}$

  g   $25^x = \frac{1}{5}$

  h   $9^x = \frac{1}{27}$

  i   $27^x = \frac{1}{9}$

  j   $16^x = \frac{1}{32}$

  k   $4^{x+2} = 128$

  l   $25^{1-x} = \frac{1}{125}$

  m   $9^{x-3} = 27$

  n   $4^{4x-1} = \frac{1}{2}$

  o   $\left(\frac{1}{2}\right)^x = 8$

  p   $\left(\frac{1}{3}\right)^{2x} = 9$

  q   $81^x = 27^{-x}$

  r   $\left(\frac{1}{8}\right)^{1-x} = 32$

  s   $\left(\frac{1}{3}\right)^{-x} = 243$

  t   $\left(\frac{1}{7}\right)^x = 49$

3   Solve for $x$:

  a   $4^{2x+1} = 8^{1-x}$

  b   $9^{2-x} = \left(\frac{1}{3}\right)^{2x+1}$

  c   $2^x \times 8^{1-x} = \frac{1}{4}$

4   Solve for $x$:

  a   $3 \times 2^x = 12$

  b   $7 \times 2^x = 56$

  c   $3 \times 2^{x+2} = 24$

  d   $12 \times 3^{-x} = \frac{4}{3}$

  e   $4 \times \left(\frac{1}{3}\right)^x = 36$

  f   $5 \times \left(\frac{1}{2}\right)^x = 20$

## SOLVING EXPONENTIAL EQUATIONS WITH TECHNOLOGY

Often we cannot write both sides of an exponential equation with the same base. In these cases a **graphics calculator** can be used to solve the equation. Refer to the **graphics calculator instructions** at the start of the book if you require assistance.

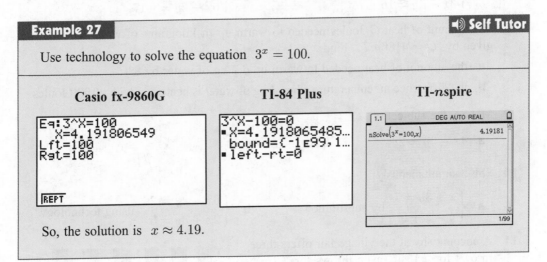

**Example 27**                                                                ◀》 **Self Tutor**

Use technology to solve the equation  $3^x = 100$.

So, the solution is  $x \approx 4.19$.

## EXERCISE 5J.2

1   Solve the following exponential equations using technology:

  a   $2^x = 20$

  b   $2^x = 100$

  c   $2^x = 5000$

  d   $2^x = 80\,000$

  e   $3^x = 30$

  f   $5^x = 0.567$

  g   $12^x = 23\,000$

  h   $(1.04)^x = 4.238$

  i   $3 \times 2^x = 93$

  j   $5 \times 2^x = 420$

  k   $8 \times 3^x = 120$

  l   $21 \times (1.05)^x = 34$

## REVIEW SET 5A

**1** If $r = 2$, $s = -5$ and $t = -1$, find the value of:

    **a** $(rs)^2$
    **b** $\dfrac{t - 2r}{3s}$
    **c** $\sqrt{t + 5r}$

**2** Solve for $x$:

    **a** $2(x - 3) + 5(1 - x) = 2$
    **b** $(x - 5)(x + 4) = (x - 2)^2$

**3** Solve for $x$:

    **a** $\dfrac{6 - 5x}{4x + 3} = -2$
    **b** $\dfrac{1}{x} = \dfrac{3}{x + 8}$

**4** Use technology to solve the following:

    **a** $3.75x + 2.663 = 1.7255$
    **b** $\dfrac{3 - 2x}{x + 5} = -1$

**5** When a certain number is trebled then decreased by 1, the result is twice as much as 5 more than the number. What is the number?

**6** A post office has two lengths of mailing tube, 45 cm and 75 cm. They have 15 more short tubes than long tubes, and if the tubes were laid end to end they would cover 1995 cm. How many 75 cm tubes does the post office have?

**7** Solve using the method of elimination:

    **a** $\begin{cases} -2x + 5y = -3 \\ 3x + 4y = 16 \end{cases}$
    **b** $\begin{cases} x - 8y = 1 \\ 6x - 2y = -17 \end{cases}$

**8** The amount of heat $Q$ Joules needed to warm up $m$ kilograms of water by $T°C$ is given by $Q = 4186mT$. Find:

    **a** the amount of heat needed to warm up 6.7 kg of water by $8°C$

    **b** the difference in temperature when 4 kg of water is heated up with 20 000 Joules.

**9** Make $y$ the subject of:

    **a** $4x - 3y = 28$
    **b** $cy + d = k$
    **c** $\dfrac{p}{y} = q$

**10** Solve simultaneously:

    **a** $\begin{cases} x + 3y = 7 \\ y = x + 5 \end{cases}$ by substitution
    **b** $\begin{cases} 6x - 2y = 26 \\ 2x + 3y = 5 \end{cases}$ using technology.

**11** A coconut shy at the village fair offers three throws for £1, or seven throws for £2. In one hour, 187 throws are made, and the attendant takes £57. How many people bought three throws?

**12** Use technology to solve for $x$:

    **a** $2^x = 7$         **b** $(1.08)^x = 8.501$         **c** $4 \times 5^x = 109$

**13** Seven adults' tickets and eight children's tickets to an exhibition cost £255, while three adults' tickets and twenty three children's tickets cost £305. Find the cost of a child's ticket.

## REVIEW SET 5B

**1** If $a = 3$, $b = -4$, and $c = 7$, find the value of:

    **a** $b^2 - c^2$         **b** $\dfrac{3a + 4b}{c(b - 1)}$         **c** $\sqrt{b(a - c)}$

**2** Solve for $x$:

    **a** $x - 14 = 6$         **b** $\dfrac{4x - 9}{2} = 8$         **c** $2x - 9 = 5(x + 1)$

**3** Solve for $x$:

    **a** $\dfrac{2}{x} = \dfrac{8}{7}$         **b** $\dfrac{x + 6}{-4} = \dfrac{x - 1}{3}$

**4** Use technology to solve the following:

    **a** $3.98k - 5.89 = 12.816$         **b** $\dfrac{12a - 5}{a + 5} = 1$

**5** If the current price of bread dropped by 44 cents, 9 loaves of bread would cost as much as 7 do now. What is the current price of bread?

**6** The population density of a region with population $N$ and area $A$ km$^2$ is given by $D = \dfrac{N}{A}$ people per square kilometre.

    **a** Find the population density of Liechtenstein, which has around 35 500 people living in 160 km$^2$.

    **b** India has a population density of approximately 357 people per square kilometre. If 1 170 000 000 people live there, how big is India?

**7** The profit $P$ of a business that sells all $n$ items it produces is given by $P = Sn - Cn$, where $S$ is the selling price and $C$ is the cost price of each item.

    **a** Make $n$ the subject of the formula.

    **b** Veronika is a jeweller. She imports watches for €205 and sells them for €215. How many must she sell to make €970 profit?

    **c** Now rearrange the formula to make $S$ the subject.

    **d** Veronika also aims to make €360 from selling earrings. She estimates that she can sell 75 pairs of earrings, with production costs of €24.50 per pair. At what price should she sell the earrings?

**8** Solve simultaneously:

    **a** $\begin{cases} x = 2y - 4 \\ -3x + 2y = -1 \end{cases}$ by substitution     **b** $\begin{cases} 6x + y = 22 \\ 4x + 3y = -4 \end{cases}$ using technology.

**9**  A machine tests car batteries for faults. A functional battery takes 2 minutes to test, but a faulty battery requires 5 minutes to detect and repair. In an 83 minute session, 37 batteries were tested. How many were faulty?

**10**  Find the lengths of the sides of the rectangle:

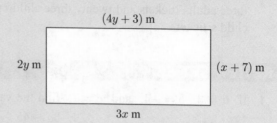

**11**  Solve for $x$:

**a**  $2^x = \frac{1}{16}$

**b**  $5^{-4x+1} = \left(\frac{1}{25}\right)^{x+1}$

**c**  $8 \times 3^{x-4} = 72$

**12**  A football club was counting gate receipts for their last home game. They know that there were 250 more adults than children at the game, and the total value of tickets sold was €29 030. If a child's ticket cost €7, and an adult's ticket cost €12, how many adults and how many children attended?

# Chapter **6**

# Pythagoras' theorem

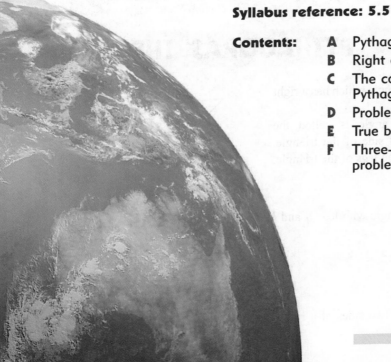

**Syllabus reference: 5.5**

## OPENING PROBLEM

Joy has a hiking stick which collapses down to 55 cm in length. She wants to pack it in a small suitcase which is $45 \text{ cm} \times 30 \text{ cm} \times 30 \text{ cm}$.

**a** Will the hiking stick fit flat in the bottom of the case?

**b** Can Joy fit the hiking stick in the case?

We see $90°$ angles or **right angles** every day in buildings, boxes, books, and many other places. For thousands of years the construction of right angles has been an important skill, for example, in the great pyramids of Egypt.

In this chapter we look at **Pythagoras' theorem** which relates to right angles in triangles. We can use this rule to find unknown side lengths in figures known to have right angles, and also to test for right angles.

## HISTORICAL NOTE

**Pythagoras of Samos** was a Greek philosopher in the late 6th century BC. He was an influential teacher and leader of the group called the **Pythagoreans**, a secretive sect who believed that everything was related to mathematics and numbers.

Pythagoras did not discover the theorem that bears his name. We know this because it was used previously by the Babylonians and Indians. Some claim that Pythagoras constructed the first proof of the theorem, but no writings of Pythagoras survive to give evidence supporting this claim.

## A    PYTHAGORAS' THEOREM

A **right angled triangle** is a triangle which has a right angle as one of its angles.

The side opposite the right angle is called the **hypotenuse**, and is the longest side of the triangle. The other two sides are called the **legs** of the triangle.

**Pythagoras' theorem** states:

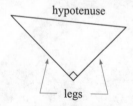

In a right angled triangle with legs $a$ and $b$, and hypotenuse $c$,

$$a^2 + b^2 = c^2$$

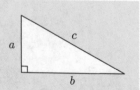

If we know the lengths of any two sides of a right angled triangle, we can use Pythagoras' theorem to find the third side.

**Example 1**   ◀)) **Self Tutor**

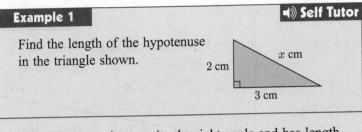

Find the length of the hypotenuse
in the triangle shown.

If $x^2 = k$, then
$x = \pm\sqrt{k}$. We reject
$-\sqrt{k}$ as lengths must
be positive!

The hypotenuse is opposite the right angle and has length
$x$ cm.

$$\therefore \quad x^2 = 3^2 + 2^2 \quad \{\text{Pythagoras}\}$$
$$\therefore \quad x^2 = 9 + 4$$
$$\therefore \quad x^2 = 13$$
$$\therefore \quad x = \sqrt{13} \qquad \{\text{as } x > 0\}$$

So, the hypotenuse is $\sqrt{13}$ cm long.

## ACCURACY OF ANSWERS

In the example above, the solution $\sqrt{13}$ in surd form is exact, and is acceptable since it is
irrational. If the answer was $\sqrt{16}$, you would be expected to simplify it to 4.

Answers given in surd form may not always be practical in real contexts. For example, if we
needed to draw a line $\sqrt{13}$ centimetres long using a ruler, we would approximate the value
to 3.6 cm using a calculator.

Within all IB Mathematics courses, final answers should be given either exactly or correct
to 3 significant figures. Rounding to 3 significant figures should only occur at the end of a
calculation and not at intermediate steps.

## EXERCISE 6A

1   Find the length of the hypotenuse in the following triangles, leaving your answer in surd
(square root) form if appropriate:

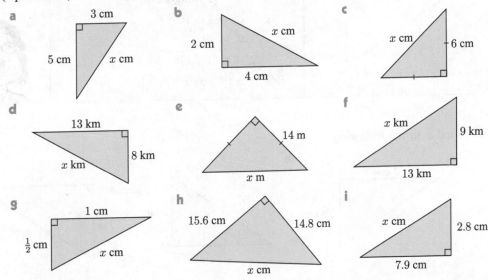

### Example 2

🔊 Self Tutor

Find the length of the third side of the given triangle.

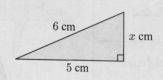

The hypotenuse has length 6 cm.

$$\therefore \quad x^2 + 5^2 = 6^2 \qquad \{\text{Pythagoras}\}$$
$$\therefore \quad x^2 + 25 = 36$$
$$\therefore \quad x^2 = 11$$
$$\therefore \quad x = \sqrt{11} \qquad \{\text{as } x > 0\}$$

So, the third side is $\sqrt{11}$ cm long.

**2**  Find the length of the third side of the following right angled triangles.
Where appropriate leave your answer in surd (square root) form.

**a**
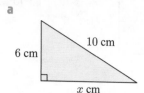

**b**
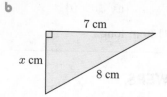

**c**
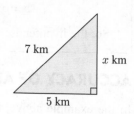

**d**
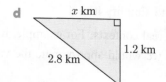

**e**
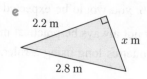

**f**
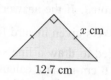

### Example 3

🔊 Self Tutor

Find $x$ in the following:

The hypotenuse has length $x$ cm.

$$\therefore \quad x^2 = 2^2 + (\sqrt{10})^2$$
$$\qquad \{\text{Pythagoras}\}$$
$$\therefore \quad x^2 = 4 + 10$$
$$\therefore \quad x^2 = 14$$
$$\therefore \quad x = \pm\sqrt{14}$$

But $x > 0$, so $x = \sqrt{14}$.

Remember that $(\sqrt{a})^2 = a$.

**3**  Find $x$ in the following:

**a**
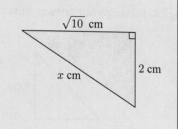

**b**
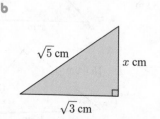

**c**
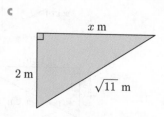

**d**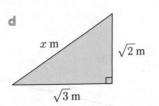

**e**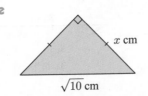

**f**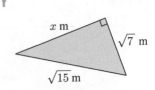

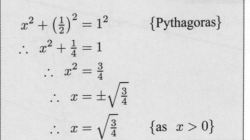

**Example 4** ◀) **Self Tutor**

Solve for $x$:

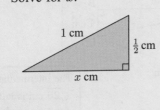

1 cm, $\frac{1}{2}$ cm, $x$ cm

$x^2 + \left(\frac{1}{2}\right)^2 = 1^2 \qquad$ {Pythagoras}

$\therefore \ x^2 + \frac{1}{4} = 1$

$\therefore \ x^2 = \frac{3}{4}$

$\therefore \ x = \pm\sqrt{\frac{3}{4}}$

$\therefore \ x = \sqrt{\frac{3}{4}} \qquad$ {as $\ x > 0$}

**4** Solve for $x$:

**a**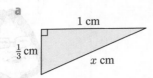

**b**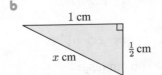

**c**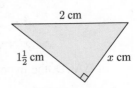

**d**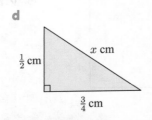

**e**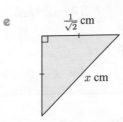

**f**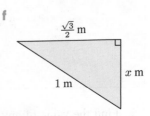

**Example 5** ◀) **Self Tutor**

Find the value of $x$:

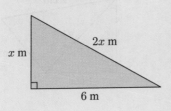

$x$ m, $2x$ m, 6 m

$(2x)^2 = x^2 + 6^2 \quad$ {Pythagoras}

$\therefore \ 4x^2 = x^2 + 36$

$\therefore \ 3x^2 = 36$

$\therefore \ x^2 = 12$

$\therefore \ x = \pm\sqrt{12}$

$\therefore \ x = \sqrt{12} \qquad$ {as $\ x > 0$}

The use of brackets here is essential.

**5** Find the value of $x$:

**a**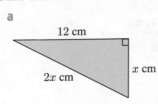

**b**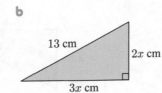

**c**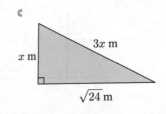

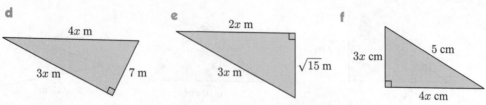

**d** $4x$ m, $3x$ m, $7$ m

**e** $2x$ m, $3x$ m, $\sqrt{15}$ m

**f** $3x$ cm, $5$ cm, $4x$ cm

---

**Example 6**    🔊 **Self Tutor**

Find the value of any unknowns:

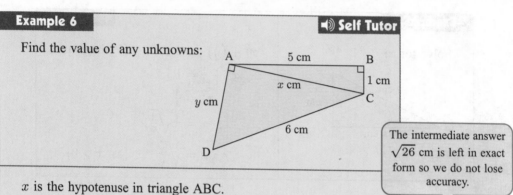

A — 5 cm — B
$x$ cm, 1 cm
$y$ cm, C
6 cm
D

The intermediate answer $\sqrt{26}$ cm is left in exact form so we do not lose accuracy.

$x$ is the hypotenuse in triangle ABC.

$$\therefore \quad x^2 = 5^2 + 1^2 \quad \{\text{Pythagoras}\}$$
$$\therefore \quad x^2 = 26$$
$$\therefore \quad x = \sqrt{26} \qquad \{\text{as } x > 0\}$$

In $\triangle ACD$, the hypotenuse is 6 cm long.

$$\therefore \quad y^2 + (\sqrt{26})^2 = 6^2 \qquad \{\text{Pythagoras}\}$$
$$\therefore \quad y^2 + 26 = 36$$
$$\therefore \quad y^2 = 10$$
$$\therefore \quad y = \sqrt{10} \quad \{\text{as } y > 0\}$$

**6** Find the value of any unknowns:

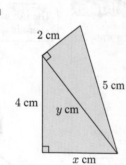

**a** 2 cm, 5 cm, 4 cm, $y$ cm, $x$ cm

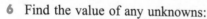

**b** 1 cm, 5 cm, $x$ cm, $y$ cm, 2 cm

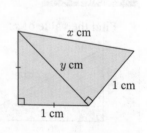

**c** $x$ cm, $y$ cm, 1 cm, 1 cm

**7** Find $x$:

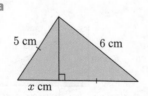

**a** 5 cm, 6 cm, $x$ cm

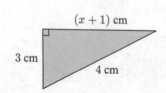

**b** $(x+1)$ cm, 3 cm, 4 cm

**8**  Find the length of AC in:

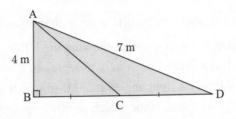

**9**  In the following figures, draw additional lines to complete right angled triangles. Apply Pythagoras' theorem to find the unknown distance AB.

**a**

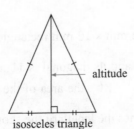

**b**

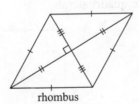

**c**

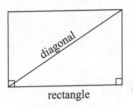

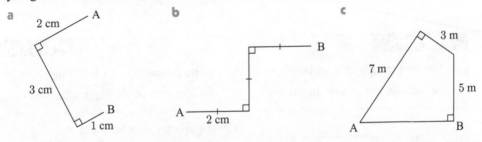

# RIGHT ANGLES IN GEOMETRY

There are many geometric figures which involve right angles.  It is important to recognise these because it tells us when we can apply Pythagoras' theorem.

## POLYGONS

A **rectangle** is a quadrilateral in which all four angles are right angles.

We can form right angled triangles by drawing in a **diagonal** of the rectangle.

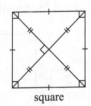

rectangle

A **rhombus** is a quadrilateral which has sides equal in length. Its diagonals bisect each other at right angles.

rhombus

A **square** is both a rectangle *and* a rhombus, so contains many right angles.

square

An **isosceles triangle** has two sides which are equal in length.

isosceles triangle

An **equilateral triangle** has all three sides equal in length.

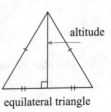

equilateral triangle

For both isosceles and equilateral triangles, the altitude bisects the base at right angles.

To solve problems involving geometric figures:

- Draw a neat diagram showing the information given.
- Use a symbol such as $x$ to represent the unknown length.
- Identify a right angled triangle to which you can apply Pythagoras' theorem.
- Solve the equation which results from Pythagoras' theorem.
- Specify an exact answer or round to 3 significant figures.
- If appropriate, write the answer in sentence form.

### Example 7 | ◀ Self Tutor

The longer side of a rectangle is 12 cm and its diagonal is 13 cm. Find:

**a** the length of the shorter side     **b** the area of the rectangle.

**a**
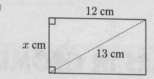

Let the shorter side be $x$ cm.

$$\therefore \quad x^2 + 12^2 = 13^2$$
$$\therefore \quad x^2 + 144 = 169$$
$$\therefore \quad x^2 = 25$$
$$\therefore \quad x = \pm 5$$

But $x > 0$, so $x = 5$

So, the shorter side is 5 cm long.

**b**  Area = length × width
$$= 12 \times 5$$
$$= 60 \text{ cm}^2$$

## EXERCISE 6B.1

**1** Find the lengths of the diagonals of these quadrilaterals:

**a**
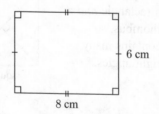

6 cm

8 cm

**b**
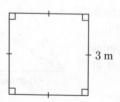

3 m

**2** Find the lengths of the diagonals of a 12 mm × 16 mm rectangle.

**3** The shorter side of a rectangle is 5 mm, and its diagonal is 11 mm. Find:

**a** the length of the longer side     **b** the area of the rectangle.

**4** The longer side of a rectangle is three times the length of the shorter side. Find the exact dimensions of the rectangle if the diagonal has length $\sqrt{1000}$ m.

**Example 8**    🔊 **Self Tutor**

A rhombus has diagonals of length 6 cm and 8 cm.
Find the length of its sides.

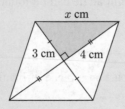

The diagonals of a rhombus *bisect at right angles.*

Let each side be $x$ cm long.

$\therefore \; x^2 = 3^2 + 4^2$    {Pythagoras}

$\therefore \; x^2 = 9 + 16$

$\therefore \; x^2 = 25$

$\therefore \; x = 5$    {as  $x > 0$}

So, the sides are 5 cm in length.

**5**   A rhombus has diagonals of length 2 cm and 4 cm. Find the length of its sides in surd form.

**6**   Find the side length of a square with diagonals 18 cm long.

**7**   A rhombus has sides of length 8 m. Its shorter diagonal is 10 m long. Find:

   **a**   the length of the longer diagonal      **b**   the area of the rhombus.

**Example 9**    🔊 **Self Tutor**

  **a**   Find the altitude of an equilateral triangle with sides 6 m long.

  **b**   Hence find the area of the triangle.

**a**

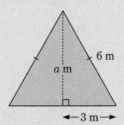

Let the altitude be $a$ m.
The altitude bisects the base at right angles.

$\therefore \; a^2 + 3^2 = 6^2$    {Pythagoras}

$\therefore \; a^2 + 9 = 36$

$\therefore \; a^2 = 27$

$\therefore \; a = \sqrt{27}$  {as  $a > 0$}

So, the altitude of the triangle is
about 5.20 m.

**b**   Area $= \frac{1}{2} \times$ base $\times$ height

       $= \frac{1}{2} \times 6 \times \sqrt{27}$

       $\approx 15.6$ m$^2$

**8**   An isosceles triangle has equal sides of length 6 cm. Its third side is 8 cm long. Find:

   **a**   the altitude of the triangle      **b**   the area of the triangle.

**9**   The base of an isosceles triangle is 6 cm long, and its area is 12 cm$^2$. Find the length of the two equal sides.

**10**   The altitude of an equilateral triangle is $2\sqrt{3}$ mm in length. Find the perimeter of the triangle.

---

## INVESTIGATION 1          RIGHT ANGLES IN GEOMETRIC FIGURES

In this investigation we will discover how a right angle can be found within a common geometric figure.

**What to do:**

**1**   Mark two points A and B about 10 cm apart on a piece of blank paper.

**2**   Join A and B with a straight line.

**3**   Place a set square on the paper so that A and B lie along the set square edges that are at right angles to each other. Mark the point where the right angle lies.

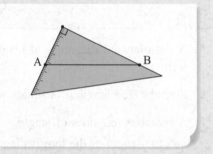

**4**   Repeat step **3** 15 times, with the right angled corner at a different position each time. Make sure the hypotenuse of the set square is always on the same side of AB.

**5**   If we continued this process, the **locus** of points would form a familiar shape. What is it?

**6**   Let C be any point on the locus. Copy and complete: *"The angle ACB on a ..... is always a ....."*

---

## CIRCLES

There are several situations where right angles are involved with circles.
The circle theorems which follow are not part of this course, but provide useful applications of Pythagoras' theorem.

### ANGLE IN A SEMI-CIRCLE

In the previous investigation you should have found that:

The angle in a semi-circle is
always a right angle.

## THE CHORD OF A CIRCLE

Consider the chord AB of a circle.

Since the radius of the circle is AO = BO, triangle ABO is isosceles.

Using the isosceles triangle theorem:

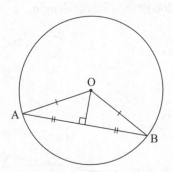

> The line drawn from the centre of a circle, at right angles to a chord, bisects the chord.

---

**Example 10**                                   ◀)) **Self Tutor**

A circle has a chord of length 10 cm, and the radius of the circle is 8 cm.
Find the shortest distance from the centre of the circle to the chord.

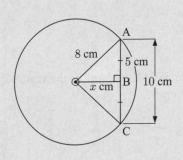

The shortest distance is the 'perpendicular distance'.
The line drawn from the centre of a circle, at right angles to a chord, bisects the chord, so

$$AB = BC = 5 \text{ cm}.$$

In $\triangle AOB$, $5^2 + x^2 = 8^2$ {Pythagoras}

$$\therefore \ x^2 = 64 - 25 = 39$$
$$\therefore \ x = \sqrt{39} \ \{\text{as } x > 0\}$$
$$\therefore \ x \approx 6.24$$

Thus the shortest distance is 6.24 cm.

---

## THE TANGENT TO A CIRCLE

A **tangent** to a circle touches the circle but does not cut it. The radius from the centre to the point of contact is at right angles to the tangent.

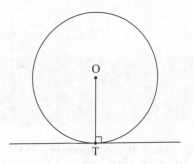

## EXERCISE 6B.2

1  Consider the circle with diameter PQ alongside.

   **a**  What is the measure of $\widehat{PRQ}$?

   **b**  Write down an equation relating $a$, $b$ and $c$.

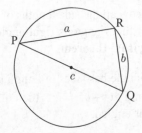

**2** Find the unknown length:

**a**

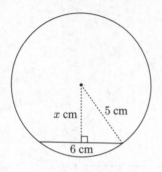

**b**

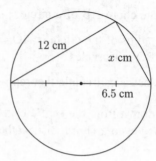

**c**

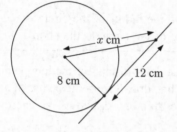

**3** The chord of a circle is 8 cm long. The closest point of the chord to the centre of the circle is 3 cm away from it. Find the radius of the circle.

**4** Find the radius of this semi-circle.

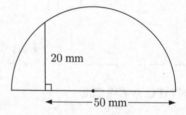

# C    THE CONVERSE OF PYTHAGORAS' THEOREM

There are many situations in real life where we need to know whether an angle is a right angle. For example, to make sure that this flag pole is not leaning to one side, we need to determine whether triangle ABC is right angled at B.

If we know all the side lengths of a triangle, we can determine whether the triangle is right angled by using the **converse of Pythagoras' theorem**.

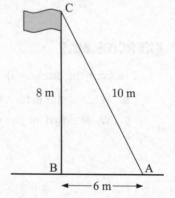

If a triangle has sides of length $a$, $b$ and $c$ units and $a^2 + b^2 = c^2$, then the triangle is right angled.

**GEOMETRY PACKAGE**

**Example 11**

◀») **Self Tutor**

The dimensions marked on this triangle are correct, but the triangle is not drawn to scale. Is it a right angled triangle?

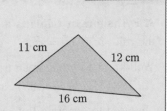

The two shorter sides have lengths 11 cm and 12 cm.

Now $11^2 + 12^2 = 121 + 144 = 265$

whereas $16^2 = 256$

Since $11^2 + 12^2 \neq 16^2$, the triangle is not right angled.

## EXERCISE 6C

1 The following figures are not drawn accurately. Which of the triangles are right angled?

a

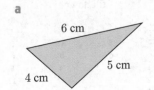

b

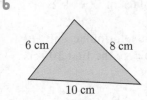

c

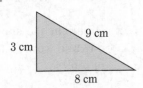

d

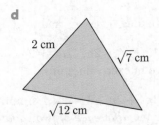

e

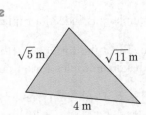

f

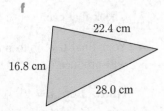

2 If any of the following triangles (not drawn accurately) is right angled, find the right angle:

a

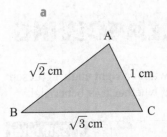

b

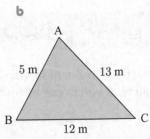

c

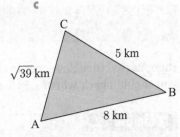

3 Explain how the converse of Pythagoras' theorem can be used to test for right angled corners in a building frame.

## INVESTIGATION 2                    PYTHAGOREAN TRIPLES SPREADSHEET

A **Pythagorean triple** is a set of three integers which obeys the rule $a^2 + b^2 = c^2$.

SPREADSHEET

Well known Pythagorean triples include $\{3, 4, 5\}$, $\{5, 12, 13\}$, $\{7, 24, 25\}$ and $\{8, 15, 17\}$.

Formulae can be used to generate Pythagorean triples.

An example is $2n + 1$, $2n^2 + 2n$, $2n^2 + 2n + 1$ where $n$ is a positive integer.

A spreadsheet can quickly generate sets of Pythagorean triples using such formulae.

**What to do:**

1  Open a new spreadsheet and enter the following:

   **a**  in column A, the values of $n$ for $n = 1, 2, 3, 4, 5, \dots$

   **b**  in column B, the values of $2n + 1$

   **c**  in column C, the values of $2n^2 + 2n$

   **d**  in column D, the values of $2n^2 + 2n + 1$.

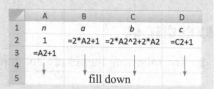

|   | A | B | C | D |
|---|---|---|---|---|
| 1 | n | a | b | c |
| 2 | 1 | =2*A2+1 | =2*A2^2+2*A2 | =C2+1 |
| 3 | =A2+1 | | | |
| 4 | ↓ | ↓ | ↓ | ↓ |
| 5 | | | fill down | |

2  Highlight the appropriate formulae and **fill down** to Row 11 to generate the first 10 sets of triples.

|   | A | B | C | D |
|---|---|---|---|---|
| 1 | n | a | b | c |
| 2 | 1 | 3 | 4 | 5 |
| 3 | 2 | 5 | 12 | 13 |
| 4 | 3 | 7 | 24 | 25 |
| 5 | 4 | 9 | 40 | 41 |

3  Check that each set of numbers is indeed a triple by finding $a^2 + b^2$ and $c^2$.

4  Your final task is to prove that the formulae $\{2n + 1, \ 2n^2 + 2n, \ 2n^2 + 2n + 1\}$ will produce sets of Pythagorean triples for all positive integer values of $n$.

**Hint:**  Let $a = 2n + 1$, $b = 2n^2 + 2n$ and $c = 2n^2 + 2n + 1$, then simplify $c^2 - b^2 = (2n^2 + 2n + 1)^2 - (2n^2 + 2n)^2$ using the *difference of two squares* factorisation.

## D          PROBLEM SOLVING

Right angled triangles occur frequently in **problem solving**. Any time a right angle is present you should check whether Pythagoras' theorem can be used and whether it is beneficial.

### Example 12                                        ◄)) Self Tutor

A rectangular gate is 3 m wide and has a 3.5 m diagonal. How high is the gate?

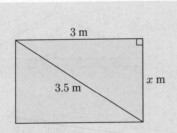

Let $x$ m be the height of the gate.

Now $(3.5)^2 = x^2 + 3^2$    {Pythagoras}

$\therefore\ 12.25 = x^2 + 9$

$\therefore\ \ 3.25 = x^2$

$\therefore\ \ x = \sqrt{3.25}$    {as $x > 0$}

$\therefore\ \ x \approx 1.803$

The gate is about 1.80 m high.

---

**Example 13**    ◄)) **Self Tutor**

Bjorn suspects that the corner A of a tennis court is not a right angle.
With a measuring tape he finds that AB = 3.72 m,  BC = 4.56 m,  and AC = 2.64 m.
Is Bjorn's suspicion correct?

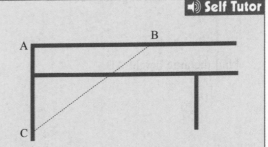

$$BC^2 = 4.56^2 \approx 20.8$$
$$\text{and}\ \ AB^2 + AC^2 = 3.72^2 + 2.64^2 \approx 20.8\ \ (3\ \text{s.f.})$$

Within the limitations of accuracy of the measurements, the angle at A is a right angle.

## EXERCISE 6D

1   Find, correct to 3 significant figures, the value of $x$ in:

**a**

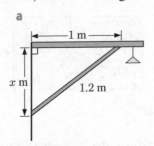

**b**

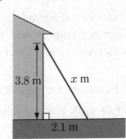

**c**

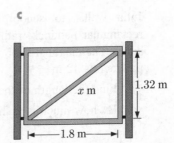

2   The size of a movie screen is the length across its diagonal. The largest screen in the world is at LG IMAX, Sydney, measuring 35.73 m across and 29.42 m high. What is its size?

3   A surveyor is trying to mark out a rectangle. She measures the sides to be 13.3 m and 17.9 m, and a diagonal to be 22.3 m. Is the angle between the sides a right angle?

4   After takeoff, an aeroplane climbs at a constant angle until it reaches an elevation of 12 000 m. If the flight distance reads 39 km, how much ground has the plane covered?

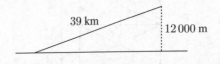

**5**  Find the length of roof truss AB.

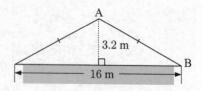

**6**  Rohan is building a rabbit hutch in the shape of an equilateral triangular prism.

  **a**  If the height is 80 cm, how long are the sides of the triangle?

  **b**  Find the area of ground covered by the rabbit hutch.

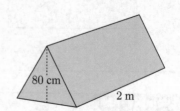

**7**  Find the attic height AB.

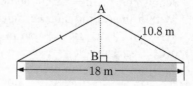

**8**  A projector is 40 m from the middle of a screen which is 15 m high. How much further away from the projector is the top edge than the centre of the screen?

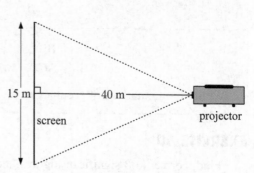

**9**  Julia walks to school across the diagonal of a rectangular paddock, rather than walking around two sides. The diagonal is 85 metres long. One side of the paddock is 42 m.

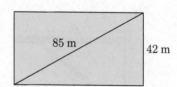

  **a**  Find the length of the other side of the paddock.

  **b**  By how much is it shorter to walk across the diagonal?

**10**

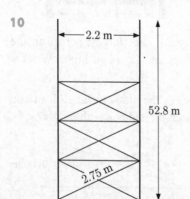

A steel frame office building has the framework section shown in the diagram. The vertical supports are 2.2 m apart and 52.8 m high. If the diagonal braces have length 2.75 m, how many are needed for this section?

**11** A power station P supplies two towns A and B with power. New underground power lines to each town are required. The towns are connected by a straight highway through A and B and the power station is 42 km from this highway.

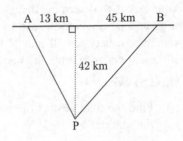

  **a** Find the length of power line required from P to each town.

  **b** Find the total cost of the new power line given that each kilometre will cost $2350.

**12** The diagram shows various measurements of a field. Calculate the perimeter of the field to the nearest metre.

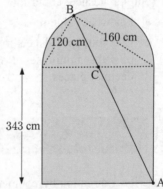

**13**

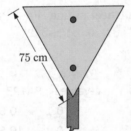

A traffic sign is an equilateral triangle with edges 75 cm long. It will be fixed to its post with bolts 5 cm in from the top and bottom of the sign. How far apart will the bolts be?

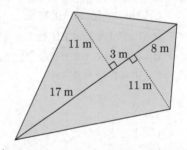

**14** The doorway alongside is rectangular at the bottom with a semi-circular arch at the top.

  **a** Find the radius of the semi-circle.

  **b** Find the length of line segment AC.

  **c** Hence find the length of the line segment AB which passes through the circle's centre C.

A and B are two homesteads which are 4 km and 3 km away from a water pipeline. M and N are the nearest points (on the pipeline) to A and B respectively, and MN = 6 km. The cost of running a spur pipeline across country from the pipeline is $3000 per km and the cost of a pump is $8000.

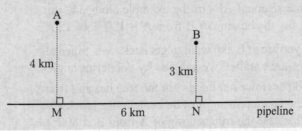

Your task is to determine the most economic way of pumping the water from the pipeline to A and B. Should you use two pumps located at M and N, or use one pump located somewhere between M and N knowing that one pump would be satisfactory to pump sufficient water to meet the needs of both homesteads?

**What to do:**

1   Find the total cost of the pumps and pipelines if two pumps are used, one at M and the other at N.

2   Suppose one pump is used and it is located at P, the midpoint of MN.

   **a**  Find PA and PB to the nearest metre.

   **b**  Find the total cost of the pipeline and pump in this case.

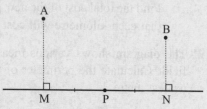

3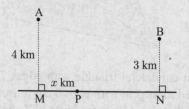

Suppose P is $x$ km from M.

   **a**  Show that  PA + PB  is given by $\sqrt{x^2 + 16} + \sqrt{x^2 - 12x + 45}$ km.

   **b**  Use a **spreadsheet** to find  PA + PB  for  $x = 0.1, 0.2, 0.3, ...., 5.9$.

4   Your spreadsheet could look like:

   **a**  For what value of $x$ is  PA + PB  least?

   **b**  Use your spreadsheet to calculate the value of $x$ that minimises  PA + PB, correct to 3 decimal places.

|   | A | B | C |
|---|---|---|---|
| 1 | $x$ -values | PA+PB | |
| 2 | | 0.1 | 10.620 |
| 3 | | 0.2 | 10.535 |
| 4 | | 0.3 | 10.453 |

# E    TRUE BEARINGS

We describe a direction by comparing it with the **true north direction**. This measurement is called a **true bearing**. It is taken in the **clockwise** direction from true north.

Imagine you are standing at point A, and want to describe the direction to point B. Start by facing north, and measure how far you have to turn clockwise to face B. This angle is the **bearing of B from A**.

On a diagram, this is the clockwise angle from a line pointing north to the line segment AB. In the example alongside this angle is $120°$. So, the bearing of B from A is $120°$T or $120°$.

Now suppose you are at B and want to get back to A. Since all true north lines are parallel, we can see by cointerior angles that  $A\hat{B}C = 60°$. However, this is not the true bearing from B to A since the measurement must be made in the clockwise direction. In this case the true bearing of A from B is $300°$T.

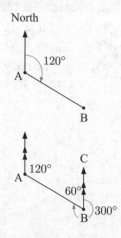

**Note:**
- A true bearing is always written using three digits. For example, we write $070^o$ rather than $70^o$.
- The bearings of A from B and B from A always differ by $180^o$. You should be able to explain this using angle pair properties for parallel lines.

---

**Example 14**    ◀️) **Self Tutor**

Kimi leaves point A and heads east for 5 km. He then heads south for 6 km. How far is he now from point A?

By Pythagoras,
$$x^2 = 5^2 + 6^2$$
$$\therefore \ x^2 = 61$$
$$\therefore \ \ x = \sqrt{61} \quad \{\text{as} \ \ x > 0\}$$
$$\therefore \ \ x \approx 7.81$$

So, Kimi is 7.81 km from A.

---

## EXERCISE 6E

**1** A schooner sails 46 km north then 74 km east.

  **a** Draw a fully labelled diagram of the ship's course.

  **b** How far is the ship from its starting point?

**2** A runner is 22 km east and 15 km south of her starting point.

  **a** How far is she from her starting point?

  **b** How long would it take her to return to her starting point in a direct line if she can run at $10 \ \text{km} \, \text{h}^{-1}$?

---

**Example 15**    ◀️) **Self Tutor**

A man cycles due east at $16 \ \text{km} \, \text{h}^{-1}$. His son cycles due south at $20 \ \text{km} \, \text{h}^{-1}$.
How far apart are they after 4 hours, if they both leave point A at the same time?

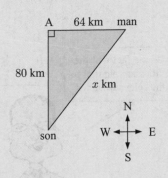

After 4 hours the man has travelled $4 \times 16 = 64$ km and his son has travelled $4 \times 20 = 80$ km.

Thus $x^2 = 64^2 + 80^2 \quad \{\text{Pythagoras}\}$
$$\therefore \ \ x^2 = 4096 + 6400$$
$$\therefore \ \ x^2 = 10\,496$$
$$\therefore \ \ x = \sqrt{10\,496} \quad \{\text{as} \ x > 0\}$$
$$\therefore \ \ x \approx 102.4$$

So, they are about 102 km apart after 4 hours.

**3** Captain Jack and Captain Will leave Bridgetown at the same time. Jack sails due east at a constant speed of $15$ km h$^{-1}$, and Will sails due south at a constant speed of $19$ km h$^{-1}$.

   **a** How far has each captain travelled after two hours?

   **b** Find the distance between them after 2 hours.

**4** Queensville is 210 km north of Rosebank and 130 km west of Springfield. There is a highway direct from Rosebank to Springfield with speed limit $90$ km h$^{-1}$, and a train line from Rosebank through Queensville to Springfield.

   **a** How long does it take to drive from Rosebank to Springfield?

   **b** If the train goes at an average of $135$ km h$^{-1}$, how long does the Rosebank - Queensville - Springfield journey take?

   **c** Which option is quicker?

**5**

Police Officer Francisca has had her bicycle stolen. She walks north from the police station trying to find it. Officer Gisela also searches by travelling west of the station, and she goes at twice the speed because her bike wasn't stolen. After 2 hours, their walkie-talkies are just out of their 12 km range. How fast did each officer travel?

---

**Example 16**    ◄⏺ **Self Tutor**

A helicopter starts at base station S. It flies on a true bearing of $074°$ for 112 km to outpost A, then travels 134 km on a true bearing of $164°$ to outpost B.
How far is outpost B from base station S?

Let  SB $= x$ km.

From the diagram we see that  $\widehat{SAB} = 90°$.

$\Delta SAB$ is therefore a right angled triangle.

By Pythagoras,  $x^2 = 112^2 + 134^2$

$\therefore\ x = \sqrt{(112^2 + 134^2)}$

$\therefore\ x \approx 174.6$

Outpost B is about 175 km from base station S.

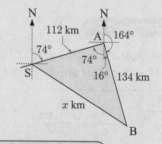

> We use the fact that the north lines are parallel to find the relevant angles.

**6** Jan walks 450 m from home on a true bearing of $127^o$. She then walks 710 m on a true bearing of $217^o$.

   **a** Draw a fully labelled sketch of Jan's path as in **Example 16**.

   **b** Find how far Jan is from her starting point.

**7**

Two rally car drivers set off from town C at the same time. A travels in the direction $063^o$ at 120 $km\,h^{-1}$ and B travels in the direction $333^o$ at 135 $km\,h^{-1}$. How far apart are they after one hour?

**8** Two ships B and C leave port A at the same time. B travels in the direction $067^oT$ at a constant speed of 36 $km\,h^{-1}$. C travels in the direction $157^o$ at a constant speed of 28 $km\,h^{-1}$. Two hours go by.

   **a** How far does B travel in the two hours?

   **b** How far does C travel in the two hours?

   **c** Draw a fully labelled sketch of the situation.

   **d** Find the distance between the ships after two hours.

# F    THREE-DIMENSIONAL PROBLEMS

When we deal with three-dimensional objects, it is common to find right angled triangles. We can use Pythagoras' theorem in the normal way by looking for right angled triangles with two known lengths.

In many three-dimensional problems we need to use Pythagoras' theorem *twice*.

---

**Example 17**                                                   ◀ŷ) **Self Tutor**

Michael's coffee mug is 90 mm high and 73 mm in diameter. It is filled to the brim with steaming hot coffee. Michael does not like sugar, but he always stirs in his milk. What is the minimum length stirrer Michael needs so that if he drops it in, it will not disappear in the coffee?

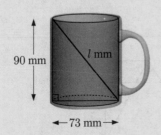

Let the stirrer have length $l$ mm.

If the stirrer fits exactly in the mug, we have a right angled triangle.

By Pythagoras,   $l^2 = 73^2 + 90^2$

$$\therefore \ l = \sqrt{(73^2 + 90^2)} \quad \{\text{as } l > 0\}$$

$$\therefore \ l \approx 115.9 \text{ mm}$$

So, the stirrer must be at least 116 mm long.

## EXERCISE 6F

**1**  An ice cream cone is 8 cm tall and its slant height
is 10 cm. Find the radius of the circle at the top
of the cone.

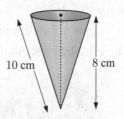

**2**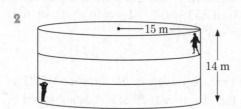

An actor stands at the back of the stage
of Shakespeare's Globe theatre, which is
cylindrical. How far must his voice reach so that
he can be heard by the audience member furthest
away from him?

**3**  A cylindrical soft drink can is 8 cm wide and
12 cm high, with a hole in the middle of the top
for the straw. How long must the straw be so that
all of the soft drink can be reached, and there is
2 cm of straw sticking out at the top?

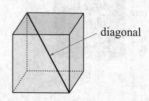

---

**Example 18**                                        ◆) **Self Tutor**

Skyways Airlines has the policy that passengers cannot carry on luggage with diagonal
measurement of more than 56 cm. Katie's bag is 40 cm × 30 cm × 25 cm. Is she
allowed to carry it on board the plane?

We first consider the distance BC across the
base.

By Pythagoras,  $BC^2 = 40^2 + 30^2$

Now triangle ABC is right angled at B.

So, by Pythagoras,    $AC^2 = AB^2 + BC^2$

$\therefore\ AC^2 = 25^2 + 40^2 + 30^2$

$\therefore\ AC = \sqrt{(25^2 + 40^2 + 30^2)}$    {as  $AC > 0$}

$\therefore\ AC \approx 55.9$ cm

So, Katie is just allowed to carry her bag on the plane.

---

**4**  A cube has sides of length 2 cm. Find
the length of a diagonal of the cube.

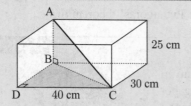

diagonal

**5**  A room is 6 m by 5 m and has a height of 3 m. Find the distance from a corner point on the floor to the opposite corner of the ceiling.

**6**  A room is 7 m long, 4.5 m wide and 2.4 m high. A motion sensor is attached to an upper corner of the room. What range must it have to 'see' the opposite corner?

**7**  A cube has sides of length 2 m. B is at the centre of one face, and A is an opposite vertex. Find the direct distance from A to B.

**8**  Answer the **Opening Problem** on page **170**.

---

### Example 19
🔊 **Self Tutor**

A pyramid of height 40 m has a square base with edges 50 m. Determine the length of the slant edges.

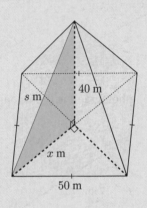

Let a slant edge have length $s$ m.

Let half a diagonal have length $x$ m.

Using

$$x^2 + x^2 = 50^2 \qquad \text{\{Pythagoras\}}$$
$$\therefore \ 2x^2 = 2500$$
$$\therefore \ x^2 = 1250$$

Using

$$s^2 = x^2 + 40^2 \qquad \text{\{Pythagoras\}}$$
$$\therefore \ s^2 = 1250 + 1600$$
$$\therefore \ s^2 = 2850$$
$$\therefore \ s = \sqrt{2850} \qquad \text{\{as } s > 0\text{\}}$$
$$\therefore \ s \approx 53.4$$

So, each slant edge is about 53.4 m long.

---

**9**  A camping tent is 2 metres wide, 3 metres long, and 1.5 metres high. It has been decorated with diagonal stripes as illustrated. Find the length of each stripe.

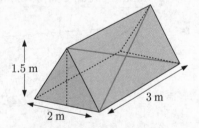

**10**

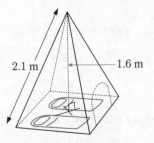

A square-based pyramid tent has a centre pole 1.6 m high and edge poles 2.1 m long. What is the maximum possible height of a camper who sleeps along the edge of the tent?

## REVIEW SET 6A

**1**  The shadecloth outside a workplace is 3 m long. The building is 2.4 m high. How far are the pegs from the base of the building?

**2**  A city park is a square with sides 320 metres long. The council decides to build a new walkway from one corner to the opposite corner. How long will the walkway be?

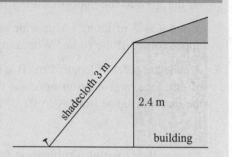

**3**  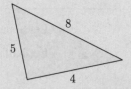  Find the length of the truss AB for the roof structure shown.

**4**  Is this triangle right angled? Give evidence for your answer.

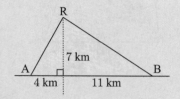

**5**  A photograph has a diagonal 15 cm long. One side of the photograph is 9 cm long. Find the perimeter of the photograph.

**6**  A reservoir R supplies two towns Alton and Barnsville with water. The pipelines from R to each town are being replaced to cope with increased demand. The towns are connected by a straight road through them and the reservoir is 7 km from this road.

**a**  Find the distances AR and BR to the nearest metre.

**b**  Find the total cost of the new pipelines given that each 100 m will cost €2550.

**7**  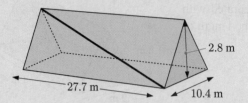  A pipe runs diagonally across a roof 2.8 m high, 27.7 m long and 10.4 m wide. How long is the pipe?

**8**  Kate and Ric leave home at the same time. Kate walks north at 5 km h$^{-1}$ and Ric walks west at 6.5 km h$^{-1}$.

**a**  How far do they each walk in 30 minutes?

**b**  How far apart are they at that time?

**9**  Will a 10 m long piece of timber fit in a rectangular shed of dimensions 8 m by 5 m by 3 m? Give evidence for your answer.

**10**  A fishing boat leaves port and sails 12 km east then 5 km south. How far must it sail to return to port by the shortest route?

**11**  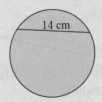 A 14 cm long cut is made across a circular pizza. The shortest distance from the cut to the centre of the pizza is 9 cm. Find the radius of the pizza.

## REVIEW SET 6B

**1**   How high is the roof above the walls in the roof structure shown?

**2**  A ladder is 2 m long. It leans against a wall so that it is 90 cm from the base of the wall. How far up the wall does the ladder reach?

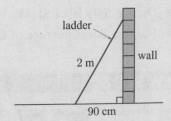

**3**  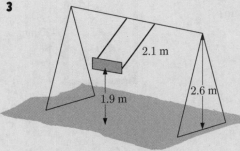 Erik is pushing his son on a swing. He can reach 1.9 m into the air. The swing stand is 2.6 m high and the swing is 2.1 m long. How far back should Erik stand?

**4**  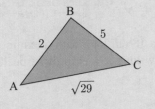 Show that this triangle is right angled and state which vertex is the right angle.

**5**  A softball diamond has sides of length 30 m. Determine the distance the catcher must throw the ball from the home base to reach second base.

**6**  A pyramid of height 30 m has a square base with edges 40 m. Determine the length of the slant edges.

**7**

53 km

Teslatown

48 km

Franklinville

A powerline must go from Franklinville to Teslatown.  Roads go through both towns, meeting at right angles as shown.

**a** The line could follow the roads, costing $375 000 per km.  How much would this cost?

**b** The line could go cross country from Teslatown to Franklinville, at a cost of $475 000 per km.  How much would this cost?

**c** Which option is cheaper?

**8** If the diameter of a circle is 24 cm, find the shortest distance from a chord of length 18 cm to the centre of the circle.

**9** An aeroplane departs A and flies in the direction 143°T for 368 km. It then changes direction to 233°T and flies a further 472 km to town C.

**a** Draw a fully labelled sketch of the flight.

**b** Find the direct distance of C from A.

## REVIEW SET 6C

**1** A graduation certificate has a validation thread across one diagonal and around the edges. How much thread is required for each certificate?

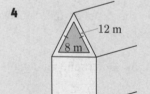

420 mm

←297 mm→

**2** For the roof structure given:

**a** Find the height QS of the roof above the walls.

**b** Find the length of the roof truss PQ.

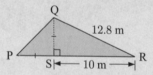

**3**

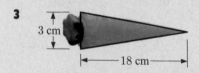

3 cm

|←——18 cm——→|

A carrot is 18 cm long with maximum diameter 3 cm. How long is a strip of its peel?

**4**

12 m

8 m

A chalet roof is shaped as shown.  There is a triangular window at the front.

**a** Find the height of the window.

**b** Find the area of glass for the window.

**5** In the local park there is a 50 m long slide running down the hill. From an overhead map, Nancy knows the slide covers a horizontal distance of 34 m. The platform of the slide is 1.5 m above the top of the hill. How high is the hill?

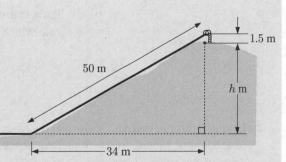

**6** Eli thinks he has laid a rectangular slab of concrete for the floor of his toolshed. It measures 3.2 m long and 2.1 m wide. The diagonal measures 3.83 m. Check that Eli's concrete is rectangular.

**7** A cubic iron grid has sides of length 10 m. Find the length of a diagonal brace of the cube.

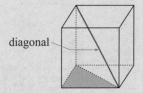

**8** A room is 7 m by 4 m and has a height of 3 m. Find the distance from a corner point on the floor to the opposite corner of the ceiling.

**9** Find the length AC.

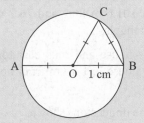

**10** A boat leaves port and sails 14.8 km in the direction 125°T. It turns and sails 5.3 km in the direction 215°T, then returns directly to port.

   **a** Draw a fully labelled sketch of the boat trip.

   **b** How far did the boat sail on this trip?

## REVIEW SET 6D

**1** As Margorita sits on the park bench, her eyes are 1 metre above the ground, 5 metres from the base of the lamp-post, and 7 metres from its top. Find the height of the lamp-post.

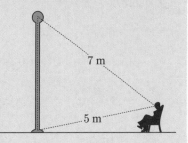

**2**

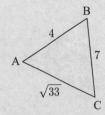

Show that the triangle alongside is right angled and state which vertex is the right angle.

**3** Examine this tile pattern. Show that the sides of the largest square are twice as long as the sides of the smallest square.

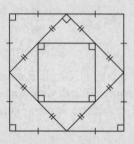

**4**

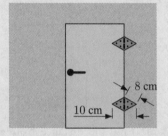

When a door is closed, its hinge is in the shape of a rhombus. The edges of the hinge are 8 cm, and one of its diagonals is 10 cm long. Find the length of the other diagonal.

**5** A soccer pitch is marked out on a field. To ensure it is rectangular, the size of the pitch is measured. It is 101.6 m long and 76.2 m wide, and the diagonal measures 127 m. Is the pitch rectangular?

**6** Lisa leaves her friend's house and runs east for 900 m, and then south until she arrives home. If Lisa's house is 1.5 km from her friend's house, how far south did she run?

**7** A rectangular box has the dimensions shown. B is an LED at the centre of the top face. Find the direct distance from A to B.

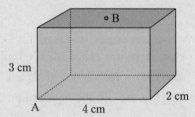

**8** A symmetrical square-based pyramid has base edges 20 m and slant edges 25 m. Find the height of the pyramid.

**9** A chord is 8 cm from the centre of a circle of radius 11 cm. Find the length of the chord.

# Chapter 7

# Descriptive statistics

## OPENING PROBLEM

A farmer is investigating the effect of a new organic fertiliser on his crops of peas. He has divided a small garden into two equal plots and planted many peas in each. Both plots have been treated the same except that fertiliser has been used on one but not the other.

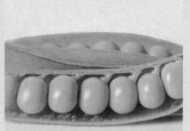

© iStockphoto

A random sample of 150 pods is harvested from each plot at the same time, and the number of peas in each pod is counted. The results are:

**Without fertiliser**

```
4 6 5 6 5 6 4 6 4 9 5 3 6 8 5 4 6 8 6 5 6 7 4 6 5 2 8 6 5 6 5 5 5 4 4 4 6 7 5 6
7 5 5 6 4 8 5 3 7 5 3 6 4 7 5 6 5 7 5 7 6 7 5 4 7 5 5 5 6 6 5 6 7 5 8 6 8 6 7 6
6 3 7 6 8 3 3 4 4 7 6 5 6 4 5 7 3 7 7 6 7 7 4 6 6 5 6 7 6 3 4 6 6 3 7 6 7 6 8 6
6 6 6 4 7 6 6 5 3 8 6 7 6 8 6 7 6 6 6 8 4 4 8 6 6 2 6 5 7 3
```

**With fertiliser**

```
6 7 7 4 9 5 5 5 8 9 8 9 7 7 5 8 7 6 6 7 9 7 7 7 8 9 3 7 4 8 5 10 8 6 7 6 7 5 6 8
7 9 4 4 9 6 8 5 8 7 7 4 7 8 10 6 10 7 7 7 9 7 7 8 6 8 6 8 7 4 8 6 8 7 3 8 7 6 9 7
6 9 7 6 8 3 9 5 7 6 8 7 9 7 8 4 8 7 7 6 6 8 6 3 8 5 8 7 6 7 4 9 6 6 6 8 4 7 8
9 7 7 4 7 5 7 4 7 6 4 6 7 7 6 7 8 7 6 6 7 8 6 7 10 5 13 4 7 11
```

### Things to think about:

- Can you state clearly the problem that the farmer wants to solve?
- How has the farmer tried to make a fair comparison?
- How could the farmer make sure that his selection was at random?
- What is the best way of organising this data?
- What are suitable methods of displaying the data?
- Are there any abnormally high or low results and how should they be treated?
- How can we best describe the most typical pod size?
- How can we best describe the spread of possible pod sizes?
- Can the farmer make a reasonable conclusion from his investigation?

In statistics we collect information about a group of individuals, then analyse this information to draw conclusions about those individuals.

You should already be familiar with these words which are commonly used in statistics:

- **Population**    A defined collection of individuals or objects about which we want to draw conclusions.
- **Census**    The collection of information from the **whole population**.
- **Sample**    A subset of the population. It is important to choose a sample at **random** to avoid **bias** in the results.
- **Survey**    The collection of information from a **sample**.

- **Data** (singular **datum**)    Information about individuals in a population.
- **Parameter**    A numerical quantity measuring some aspect of a population.
- **Statistic**    A quantity calculated from data gathered from a sample. It is usually used to estimate a population parameter.

# A    TYPES OF DATA

When we collect data, we measure or observe a particular feature or **variable** associated with the population. The variables we observe are described as either categorical or numerical.

## CATEGORICAL VARIABLES

A **categorical variable** describes a particular quality or characteristic.

The data is divided into **categories**, and the information collected is called **categorical data**.

Some examples of categorical data are:

- *computer operating system:*    the categories could be Windows, Macintosh or Linux.
- *gender:*    the categories are male and female.

## QUANTITATIVE OR NUMERICAL VARIABLES

A **quantitative variable** has a numerical value. The information collected is called **numerical data**.

Quantitative variables can either be discrete or continuous.

A **quantitative discrete variable** takes exact number values and is often a result of **counting**.

Some examples of quantitative discrete variables are:

- *the number of apricots on a tree:*    the variable could take the values 0, 1, 2, 3, .... up to 1000 or more.
- *the number of players in a game of tennis:*    the variable could take the values 2 or 4.

A **quantitative continuous variable** can take any numerical value within a certain range. It is usually a result of **measuring**.

Some examples of quantitative continuous variables are:

- *the times taken to run a 100 m race:*    the variable would likely be between 9.8 and 25 seconds.
- *the distance of each hit in baseball:*    the variable could take values from 0 m to 100 m.

---

**Example 1**                                               🔊 **Self Tutor**

Classify these variables as categorical, quantitative discrete or quantitative continuous:
  a  the number of heads when 3 coins are tossed
  b  the brand of toothpaste used by the students in a class
  c  the heights of a group of 15 year old children.

---

a  The values of the variables are obtained by counting the number of heads. The result can only be one of the values 0, 1, 2 or 3. It is a quantitative discrete variable.

b  The variable describes the brands of toothpaste. It is a categorical variable.

c  This is a numerical variable which can be measured. The data can take any value between certain limits, though when measured we round off the data to an accuracy determined by the measuring device. It is a quantitative continuous variable.

## EXERCISE 7A

1  Classify the following variables as categorical, quantitative discrete or quantitative continuous:
  a  the number of brothers a person has
  b  the colours of lollies in a packet
  c  the time children spend brushing their teeth each day
  d  the height of trees in a garden
  e  the brand of car a person drives
  f  the number of petrol pumps at service stations
  g  the most popular holiday destinations
  h  the scores out of 10 in a diving competition
  i  the amount of water a person drinks each day
  j  the number of hours spent per week at work
  k  the average temperatures of various cities
  l  the items students ate for breakfast before coming to school
  m  the number of televisions in each house.

2  For each of the variables in 1:
  •  if the variable is categorical, list some possible categories for the variable
  •  if the variable is quantitative, give the possible values or range of values the variable may take.

---

# B    SIMPLE QUANTITATIVE DISCRETE DATA

## ORGANISATION AND DISPLAY

There are several different ways we can organise and display quantitative discrete data. One of the simplest ways to organise the data is using a **frequency table**.

For example, consider the **Opening Problem** in which the quantitative discrete variable is *the number of peas in a pod*. For the data without fertiliser we count the data systematically using a **tally**.

The **frequency** of a data value is the number of times that value occurs in the data set.

We can also add a column for **relative frequency**, which is the frequency divided by the total number of recorded values. The relative frequency gives the proportion of results which take that value.

| Number of peas in pod | Tally | Frequency | Relative frequency |
|---|---|---|---|
| 1 | | 0 | 0 |
| 2 | \|\| | 2 | 0.013 |
| 3 | ⊬⊬ ⊬⊬ \| | 11 | 0.073 |
| 4 | ⊬⊬ ⊬⊬ ⊬⊬ \|\|\|\| | 19 | 0.127 |
| 5 | ⊬⊬ ⊬⊬ ⊬⊬ ⊬⊬ ⊬⊬ \|\|\|\| | 29 | 0.193 |
| 6 | ⊬⊬ ⊬⊬ ⊬⊬ ⊬⊬ ⊬⊬ ⊬⊬ ⊬⊬ ⊬⊬ ⊬⊬ ⊬⊬ \| | 51 | 0.34 |
| 7 | ⊬⊬ ⊬⊬ ⊬⊬ ⊬⊬ ⊬⊬ | 25 | 0.167 |
| 8 | ⊬⊬ ⊬⊬ \|\| | 12 | 0.08 |
| 9 | \| | 1 | 0.007 |
| | Total | 150 | |

We can then display the data using a **column graph**. For this graph:

- the range of scores is on the horizontal axis
- the frequency of scores is on the vertical axis
- the column widths are equal and the column height represents frequency
- there are gaps between columns to indicate the data is discrete.

We can also turn the column graph into a **frequency polygon** by connecting the midpoints of the tops of the columns with straight line segments.

A column graph and frequency polygon for *the number of peas in a pod without fertiliser* is shown alongside.

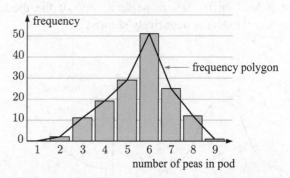

**Number of peas in a pod without fertiliser**

Another way to organise and display the data is to use a **dot plot**. In this case the range of values is again on the horizontal axis, and we place one dot for each recorded value. The height of the resulting column indicates the frequency for that data value.

The dot plot for *the number of peas in a pod without fertiliser* is shown alongside.

**Number of peas in a pod without fertiliser**

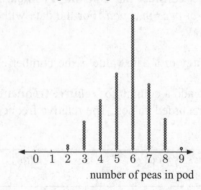

number of peas in pod

In both a column graph and a dot plot, the **mode** of the data has the highest column. In this case the mode is 6 peas in a pod.

**DISCUSSION**

Are there any advantages or disadvantages in using a dot plot rather than a column graph?

## DESCRIBING THE DISTRIBUTION OF THE DATA SET

Many data sets show **symmetry** or **partial symmetry** about the mode.

If we place a curve over the column graph we see that this curve shows symmetry. We have a **symmetrical distribution** of the data.

Comparing the peas in a pod without fertiliser data with the symmetrical distribution, we can see it has been 'stretched' on the left or negative side of the mode. We say the data is **negatively skewed**.

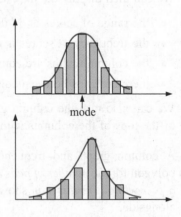

mode

So, we have:

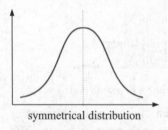

symmetrical distribution

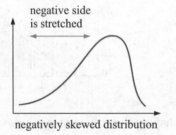

negative side is stretched

negatively skewed distribution

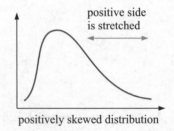

positive side is stretched

positively skewed distribution

## OUTLIERS

**Outliers** are data values that are either much larger or much smaller than the general body of data. Outliers appear separated from the body of data on a column graph.

For example, if the farmer in the **Opening Problem** found one pod without fertiliser that contained 13 peas, then the data value 13 would be considered an outlier. It is much larger than the other data in the sample. On the column graph it appears separated.

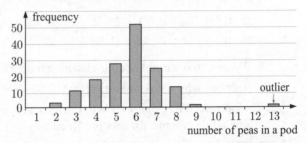

---

**Example 2**    ◀)) **Self Tutor**

30 children attended a library holiday programme. Their year levels at school were:

| | | | | | | | | | | | | | | |
|---|---|---|---|---|---|---|---|---|---|---|---|---|---|---|
| 8 | 7 | 6 | 7 | 7 | 7 | 9 | 7 | 7 | 11 | 8 | 10 | 8 | 8 | 9 |
| 10 | 7 | 7 | 8 | 8 | 8 | 8 | 7 | 6 | 6 | 6 | 6 | 9 | 6 | 9 |

**a** Record this information in a frequency table. Include a column for relative frequency.

**b** Construct a column graph and frequency polygon to display the data.

**c** What is the modal year level of the children?

**d** Describe the shape of the distribution. Are there any outliers?

**e** What percentage of the children were in year 8 or below?

**f** What percentage of the children were above year 9?

**a**

| Year level | Tally | Frequency | Relative frequency |
|---|---|---|---|
| 6 | ⊞ | 6 | 0.2 |
| 7 | ⊞ IIII | 9 | 0.3 |
| 8 | ⊞ III | 8 | 0.267 |
| 9 | IIII | 4 | 0.133 |
| 10 | II | 2 | 0.067 |
| 11 | I | 1 | 0.033 |
| | Total | 30 | |

**b**

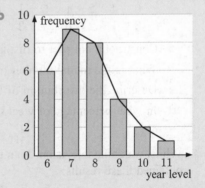

**c** The modal year level is year 7.

**d** The distribution of children's year levels is positively skewed. There are no outliers.

**e** $\dfrac{6+9+8}{30} \times 100\% \approx 76.7\%$ were in year 8 or below.

*or* the sum of the relative frequencies is $0.2 + 0.3 + 0.267 = 0.767$

∴ 76.7% were in year 8 or below.

**f** $\dfrac{2+1}{30} \times 100\% = 10\%$ were above year 9.

*or* $0.067 + 0.033 = 0.1$     ∴ 10% were above year 9.

## EXERCISE 7B

1   In the last football season, the Flames scored the
    following numbers of goals in each game:

    2  0  1  4  0  1  2  1  1  0  3  1
    3  0  1  1  6  2  1  3  1  2  0  2

    a   What is the variable being considered here?
    b   Explain why the data is discrete.
    c   Construct a frequency table to organise the data.
        Include a column for relative frequency.
    d   Draw a column graph and frequency polygon to display the data.
    e   What is the modal score for the team?
    f   Describe the distribution of the data. Are there any outliers?
    g   In what percentage of games did the Flames fail to score?

2   Prince Edward High School prides itself on the
    behaviour of its students. However, from time to time
    they do things they should not, and as a result are placed
    on detention. The studious school master records the
    number of students on detention each week throughout
    the year:

    0  2  1  5  0  1  4  2  3  1
    4  3  0  2  9  2  1  5  0  3
    6  4  2  1  5  1  0  2  1  4
    3  1  2  0  4  3  2  1  2  3

    a   Construct a dot plot to display the data.
    b   What is the modal number of students on detention in a week?
    c   Describe the distribution of the data, including the presence of outliers.
    d   In what percentage of weeks were more than 4 students on detention?

3   Whilst watching television, Joan recorded the number of commercials in each break. She
    obtained these results:

    5  7  6  4  6  5  6  7  5  8
    7  6  9  8  7  6  6  9  6  7
    6  4  7  5  8  7  6  8  7  8
    5  6  9  7

    a   Construct a frequency table to organise the data. Include a column for relative
        frequency.
    b   Draw a column graph and frequency polygon to display the data.
    c   Find the mode of the data.
    d   Describe the distribution of the data. Are there any outliers?
    e   What percentage of breaks contained at least 6 commercials?

4   A random sample of people were asked "How many times did you eat at a restaurant last week?" A column graph was used to display the results.

a   How many people were surveyed?

b   Find the mode of the data.

c   How many people surveyed did not eat at a restaurant at all last week?

d   What percentage of people surveyed ate at a restaurant more than three times last week?

e   Describe the distribution of the data.

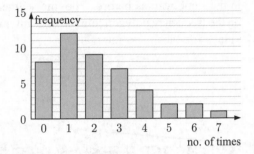

5   Consider *the number of peas in a pod with fertiliser* in the **Opening Problem**.

a   Construct a frequency table to organise the data. Include a column for relative frequency.

b   Draw a column graph and frequency polygon to display the data.

c   Describe fully the distribution of the data.

d   Is there evidence to suggest that the fertiliser increases the number of peas in each pod?

e   Is it reasonable to say that using the fertiliser will increase the farmer's profits?

## C   GROUPED QUANTITATIVE DISCRETE DATA

A local kindergarten is concerned about the number of vehicles passing by between 8.45 am and 9.00 am. Over 30 consecutive week days they recorded data:

27, 30, 17, 13, 46, 23, 40, 28, 38, 24, 23, 22, 18, 29, 16,
35, 24, 18, 24, 44, 32, 52, 31, 39, 32,  9, 41, 38, 24, 32

In situations like this there are many different data values with very low frequencies. This makes it difficult to study the data distribution. It is more statistically meaningful to group the data into **class intervals** and then compare the frequency for each class.

For the data given we use class intervals of length 10. The frequency table is shown opposite.

We see the **modal class**, or class with the highest frequency, is from 20 to 29 cars.

| Number of cars | Tally | Frequency | Relative Frequency |
|---|---|---|---|
| 0 to 9 | \| | 1 | 0.033 |
| 10 to 19 | ⦀⦀ | 5 | 0.167 |
| 20 to 29 | ⦀⦀ ⦀⦀ | 10 | 0.333 |
| 30 to 39 | ⦀⦀ \|\|\|\| | 9 | 0.3 |
| 40 to 49 | \|\|\|\| | 4 | 0.133 |
| 50 to 59 | \| | 1 | 0.033 |
| | Total | 30 | |

Due to rounding, the relative frequencies will not always add to *exactly* 1.

We can construct a **column graph** and **frequency polygon** for grouped discrete data in the same way as before. The line segments on the frequency polygon join the **mid-interval values** for each class interval.

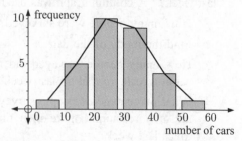

Vehicles passing kindergarten between 8.45 am and 9.00 am

## DISCUSSION

- If we are given a set of raw data, how can we efficiently find the lowest and highest data values?
- If the data values are grouped in classes on a frequency table or column graph, do we still know what the highest and lowest values are?
- Is there another way to display data in groups without 'losing' information about the highest and lowest values?

## STEM AND LEAF PLOTS

A **stem and leaf plot** or **stem plot** is a method of writing data in groups without losing information about the actual data values. At the same time it allows us to compare the frequencies of each group.

For numbers with two digits, the first digit forms part of the **stem** and the second digit forms a **leaf**.

For example, for the first vehicle data value, 27, the stem is 2 and the leaf is 7.

Once a stem and leaf plot has been constructed, we can write the leaves in order to form an **ordered stem and leaf plot**.

For the data on vehicles passing the kindergarten, we have:

| **Stem and leaf plot** | | **Ordered stem and leaf plot** | |
|---|---|---|---|
| Stem | Leaf | Stem | Leaf |
| 0 | 9 | 0 | 9 |
| 1 | 7 3 8 6 8 | 1 | 3 6 7 8 8 |
| 2 | 7 3 8 4 3 2 9 4 4 4 | 2 | 2 3 3 4 4 4 4 7 8 9 |
| 3 | 0 8 5 2 1 9 2 8 2 | 3 | 0 1 2 2 2 5 8 8 9 |
| 4 | 6 0 4 1 | 4 | 0 1 4 6 |
| 5 | 2 | 5 | 2 |

Scale:  $1 \mid 7 = 17$    Scale:  $1 \mid 7 = 17$

Notice that:

- we write a **scale** to show the place value of each leaf
- the lowest data value is 9 and the highest data value is 52
- the modal class is 20 to 29 cars.

## BACK TO BACK STEM AND LEAF PLOTS

A **back to back stem and leaf plot** allows us to compare data sets which are related.

For example, this back to back stem plot represents the times for the 100 metre freestyle recorded by members of a swimming squad.

We can see that the fastest time for a girl is 33.4 seconds and the slowest time for a girl is 41.1 seconds.

We see that the times for the boys are generally a little faster and less widely spread than the times for the girls. However, the modal class for the two data sets is the same.

| Girls | | Boys |
|---:|:---:|:---|
| | 32 | 1 |
| 4 | 33 | 0 2 2 7 |
| 7 6 3 | 34 | 1 3 4 4 8 |
| 8 7 4 3 0 | 35 | 0 2 4 7 9 9 |
| 8 8 3 3 | 36 | 7 8 8 |
| 7 6 6 6 | 37 | 0 |
| 6 | 38 | |
| 0 | 39 | |
| | 40 | |
| 1 | 41 | |

*Scale:*   $32 \mid 1 = 32.1$ seconds

---

**Example 3**    ◀) Self Tutor

A company recorded the number of truck loads of ore mined each day in a lead-zinc mine over a 21 day period.

| *Zinc ore:* | 33 | 40 | 28 | 26 | 55 | 32 | 48 | 37 | 39 | 38 | 51 |
|---|---|---|---|---|---|---|---|---|---|---|---|
| | 22 | 65 | 43 | 32 | 43 | 36 | 25 | 29 | 24 | 34 | |
| *Lead ore:* | 15 | 10 | 13 | 30 | 25 | 20 | 14 | 8 | 11 | 28 | 22 |
| | 17 | 23 | 14 | 9 | 18 | 22 | 27 | 10 | 24 | 11 | |

**a**  Draw an ordered back to back stem and leaf plot of the data.

**b**  What are the modal classes of the two distributions?

**c**  Describe the distributions, comparing zinc ore production to lead ore production.

---

**a**            **Truck loads of ore**

| Lead | | Zinc |
|---:|:---:|:---|
| 9 8 | 0 | |
| 8 7 5 4 4 3 1 1 0 0 | 1 | |
| 8 7 5 4 3 2 2 0 | 2 | 2 4 5 6 8 9 |
| 0 | 3 | 2 2 3 4 6 7 8 9 |
| | 4 | 0 3 3 8 |
| | 5 | 1 5 |
| | 6 | 5 |

*Scale:*  $2 \mid 2$ means 22 truck loads

**b**  The zinc ore has modal class 30 to 39 truck loads, and the lead ore has modal class 10 to 19 truck loads.

**c**  The zinc ore distribution is positively skewed, whereas the lead ore distribution is approximately symmetric. From the stem and leaf plot it is clear that, on average, more zinc ore than lead ore is produced by the mine.

## EXERCISE 7C

**1**  Arthur catches the train to school from a busy train station. Over the course of 30 days he counts the number of people waiting at the station when the train arrives.

$$
\begin{array}{cccccccccc}
17 & 25 & 32 & 19 & 45 & 30 & 22 & 15 & 38 & 8 \\
21 & 29 & 37 & 25 & 42 & 35 & 19 & 31 & 26 & 7 \\
22 & 11 & 27 & 44 & 24 & 22 & 32 & 18 & 40 & 29
\end{array}
$$

   **a**  Construct a tally and frequency table for this data using class intervals  0 - 9, 10 - 19, ...., 40 - 49.

   **b**  On how many days were there less than 10 people at the station?

   **c**  On what percentage of days were there at least 30 people at the station?

   **d**  Draw a column graph and frequency polygon for the data.

   **e**  Find the modal class of the data.

**2**  A selection of businesses were asked how many employees they had.  A column graph was constructed to display the results.

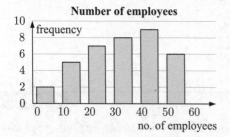

**Number of employees**

   **a**  How many businesses were surveyed?

   **b**  Find the modal class.

   **c**  Describe the distribution of the data.

   **d**  What percentage of businesses surveyed had less than 30 employees?

   **e**  Can you determine the highest number of employees a business had?

**3**  **a**  For the ordered stem and leaf plot given, find:

    **i**  the minimum value

    **ii**  the maximum value

    **iii**  the number of data with a value of at least 60

    **iv**  the number of data with a value less than 45

    **v**  the percentage of the data with a value greater than 53.

| Stem | Leaf |
|---|---|
| 3 | 8 9 |
| 4 | 0 3 6 7 7 8 |
| 5 | 1 3 4 5 5 6 7 9 9 |
| 6 | 2 2 5 6 7 7 8 8 9 |
| 7 | 0 0 1 2 4 5 6 8 |
| 8 | |
| 9 | 1 |

*Scale:*  7 | 0 means 70

   **b**  How would you describe the distribution of the data?
   **Hint:** Turn the stem plot on its side.

**4**  A city council does a survey of the number of houses per street in some of its suburbs.

$$
\begin{array}{cccccccccccccc}
42 & 15 & 20 & 6 & 34 & 19 & 8 & 5 & 11 & 38 & 56 & 23 & 24 & 24 \\
35 & 47 & 22 & 36 & 39 & 18 & 14 & 44 & 25 & 6 & 34 & 35 & 28 & 12 \\
27 & 32 & 36 & 34 & 30 & 40 & 32 & 12 & 17 & 6 & 37 & 32
\end{array}
$$

   **a**  Construct a stem and leaf plot for this data using  0, 1, 2, 3, 4 and 5 as the stems.

   **b**  Redraw the stem and leaf plot so that it is ordered.

   **c**  What advantage does a stem and leaf plot have over a frequency table?

   **d**  What is the  **i** least  **ii** most  number of houses on a street?

   **e**  If the council decides to construct a footpath down all streets with more than 25 houses, what percentage of the streets will have a footpath?

   **f**  What percentage of streets have less than 30 houses on them?

**5** A bakery keeps a record of how many pies and pasties they sell each day for a month.

| Pies | | | | | | | |
|---|---|---|---|---|---|---|---|
| 62 | 76 | 55 | 65 | 49 | 78 | 71 | 82 |
| 79 | 47 | 60 | 72 | 58 | 82 | 76 | 67 |
| 50 | 61 | 70 | 85 | 77 | 69 | 48 | 74 |
| 63 | 56 | 81 | 75 | 63 | 74 | 54 | |

| Pasties | | | | | | | |
|---|---|---|---|---|---|---|---|
| 37 | 52 | 71 | 59 | 63 | 47 | 56 | 68 |
| 43 | 67 | 38 | 73 | 54 | 55 | 61 | 49 |
| 50 | 48 | 53 | 39 | 45 | 60 | 46 | 51 |
| 38 | 57 | 41 | 72 | 50 | 44 | 76 | |

   **a** Draw a back to back stem plot to display this data.

   **b** Find the modal class for each data set.

   **c** Does the bakery generally sell more pies or pasties?

**6** A bus and tram travel the same route many times during the day. The drivers counted the number of passengers on each trip one day, as listed below.

| Bus | | | | | | |
|---|---|---|---|---|---|---|
| 30 | 43 | 40 | 53 | 70 | 50 | 63 |
| 41 | 38 | 21 | 28 | 23 | 43 | 48 |
| 20 | 26 | 35 | 48 | 41 | 33 | |

| Tram | | | | | |
|---|---|---|---|---|---|
| 58 | 68 | 43 | 45 | 70 | 79 |
| 38 | 23 | 30 | 22 | 63 | 73 |
| 25 | 35 | 60 | 53 | | |

   **a** Construct a back to back stem and leaf plot for this information.

   **b** Compare the numbers of passengers who travelled on the bus and tram.

---

## INVESTIGATION 1                               TAXI SIR?

Taxi drivers Peter and Ivan are friendly rivals. Each claims that he is the more successful driver. They agree to randomly select 25 days on which they work, and record the daily fare totals. The data collected to the nearest dollar was:

| Peter | 194 | 99 | 188 | 208 | 95 | 168 | 205 | 196 | 233 |
|---|---|---|---|---|---|---|---|---|---|
| | 116 | 132 | 153 | 205 | 191 | 182 | 118 | 140 | 270 |
| | 183 | 155 | 93 | 154 | 190 | 223 | 147 | | |
| Ivan | 260 | 152 | 127 | 163 | 180 | 161 | 110 | 153 | 139 |
| | 139 | 142 | 161 | 97 | 116 | 129 | 215 | 241 | 160 |
| | 110 | 159 | 147 | 174 | 162 | 158 | 223 | | |

**What to do:**

**1** Produce a back to back stem and leaf plot to display this data.

**2** Explain why "the amount of money collected per hour" would have been a better variable to use than "the daily fare totals".

**3** The amount of money collected per hour on each of these days is given below:

| Peter | 17.3 | 11.3 | 15.7 | 18.9 | 9.6 | 13.0 | 19.1 | 16.7 | 11.7 |
|---|---|---|---|---|---|---|---|---|---|
| | 15.8 | 12.8 | 24.0 | 15.0 | 12.9 | 20.1 | 18.6 | 18.9 | 13.9 |
| | 11.7 | 15.5 | 15.2 | 18.3 | 12.3 | 18.6 | 22.8 | | |
| Ivan | 23.7 | 13.3 | 12.2 | 14.2 | 15.7 | 14.0 | 10.0 | 10.0 | 12.2 |
| | 13.5 | 18.6 | 13.3 | 12.7 | 13.5 | 8.8 | 11.1 | 12.3 | 18.9 |
| | 20.1 | 13.8 | 14.6 | 13.3 | 13.4 | 13.6 | 14.2 | | |

Produce a back to back stem and leaf plot to display this data. Use the stems 8, 9, 10, ...., 23 and the leaves should represent tenths of a dollar.

**4** Present a brief written report of about 250 words to summarise your findings and draw a conclusion.

# D │ QUANTITATIVE CONTINUOUS DATA

When we measure data that is **continuous**, we cannot write down an exact value. Instead we write down an approximation which is only as accurate as the measuring device.

Since no two data values will be *exactly* the same, it does not make sense to talk about the frequency of particular values. Instead we group the data into **class intervals** of **equal width**. We can then talk about the frequency of each class interval.

A special type of graph called a **frequency histogram** or just **histogram** is used to display the data. This is similar to a column graph but, to account for the continuous nature of the variable, a number line is used for the horizontal axis and the 'columns' are joined together.

The **modal class**, or class of values that appears most often, is easy to identify from a frequency histogram.

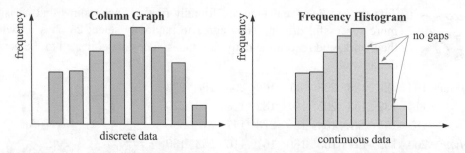

## INVESTIGATION 2                    CHOOSING CLASS INTERVALS

 When dividing data values into intervals, the choice of how many intervals to use, and hence the width of each class, is important.

**What to do:**

**1** Click on the icon to experiment with various data sets and the number of classes. How does the number of classes alter the way we can interpret the data?

**2** Write a brief account of your findings.

As a rule of thumb we use approximately $\sqrt{n}$ classes for a data set of $n$ individuals. For very large sets of data we use more classes rather than less.

**Example 4**                                                    ◀ Self Tutor

A sample of 20 juvenile lobsters was randomly selected from a tank containing several hundred. Each lobster was measured for length (in cm) and the results were:

| 4.9 | 5.6 | 7.2 | 6.7 | 3.1 | 4.6 | 6.0 | 5.0 | 3.7 | 7.3 |
| 6.0 | 5.4 | 4.2 | 6.6 | 4.7 | 5.8 | 4.4 | 3.6 | 4.2 | 5.4 |

Organise the data using a frequency table, and hence graph the data.

The variable 'the length of a lobster' is *continuous* even though lengths have been rounded to the nearest mm.

The shortest length is 3.1 cm and the longest is 7.3 cm, so we will use class intervals of length 1 cm.

| Length (cm) | Frequency |
|-------------|-----------|
| $3 \leqslant l < 4$ | 3 |
| $4 \leqslant l < 5$ | 6 |
| $5 \leqslant l < 6$ | 5 |
| $6 \leqslant l < 7$ | 4 |
| $7 \leqslant l < 8$ | 2 |

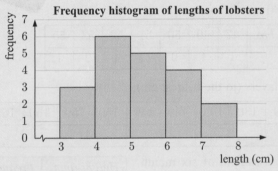

Frequency histogram of lengths of lobsters

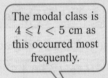

The modal class is $4 \leqslant l < 5$ cm as this occurred most frequently.

## EXERCISE 7D

1   A frequency table for the heights of a volleyball squad is given alongside.

| Height (cm) | Frequency |
|-------------|-----------|
| $170 \leqslant H < 175$ | 1 |
| $175 \leqslant H < 180$ | 8 |
| $180 \leqslant H < 185$ | 9 |
| $185 \leqslant H < 190$ | 11 |
| $190 \leqslant H < 195$ | 9 |
| $195 \leqslant H < 200$ | 3 |
| $200 \leqslant H < 205$ | 3 |

   a   Explain why 'height' is a continuous variable.

   b   Construct a frequency histogram for the data. The axes should be carefully marked and labelled, and you should include a heading for the graph.

   c   What is the modal class? Explain what this means.

   d   Describe the distribution of the data.

2   A school has conducted a survey of 60 students to investigate the time it takes for them to travel to school. The following data gives the travel times to the nearest minute.

| 12 | 15 | 16 | 8  | 10 | 17 | 25 | 34 | 42 | 18 | 24 | 18 | 45 | 33 | 38 |
| 45 | 40 | 3  | 20 | 12 | 10 | 10 | 27 | 16 | 37 | 45 | 15 | 16 | 26 | 32 |
| 35 | 8  | 14 | 18 | 15 | 27 | 19 | 32 | 6  | 12 | 14 | 20 | 10 | 16 | 14 |
| 28 | 31 | 21 | 25 | 8  | 32 | 46 | 14 | 15 | 20 | 18 | 8  | 10 | 25 | 22 |

   a   Is travel time a discrete or continuous variable?

   b   Construct an ordered stem plot for the data using stems 0, 1, 2, ....

   c   Describe the distribution of the data.

   d   What is the modal travelling time?

**3** A group of 25 young athletes participated in a javelin throwing competition. They achieved the following distances in metres:

| | | | | | | | | |
|---|---|---|---|---|---|---|---|---|
| 17.6 | 25.7 | 21.3 | 30.9 | 13.0 | 31.6 | 22.3 | 28.3 | 7.4 |
| 38.4 | 19.1 | 24.0 | 40.0 | 16.2 | 42.9 | 31.9 | 28.1 | 41.8 |
| 13.6 | 27.4 | 33.7 | 9.2 | 23.3 | 39.8 | 25.1 | | |

**a** Choose suitable class intervals to group the data.

**b** Organise the data in a frequency table.

**c** Draw a frequency histogram to display the data.

**d** Find the modal class.

**e** What percentage of athletes threw the javelin 30 metres or further?

**4** For the following data, state whether a frequency histogram or a column graph should be used and draw the appropriate graph.

**a** The number of matches in 30 match boxes:

| Number of matches per box | 47 | 49 | 50 | 51 | 52 | 53 | 55 |
|---|---|---|---|---|---|---|---|
| Frequency | 1 | 1 | 9 | 12 | 4 | 2 | 1 |

**b** The heights of 25 hockey players (to the nearest cm):

| Height (cm) | 120 - 129 | 130 - 139 | 140 - 149 | 150 - 159 | 160 - 169 |
|---|---|---|---|---|---|
| Frequency | 1 | 2 | 7 | 14 | 1 |

**5** A plant inspector takes a random sample of six month old seedlings from a nursery and measures their heights to the nearest mm.

The results are shown in the table alongside.

| Height (mm) | Frequency |
|---|---|
| 300 - 324 | 12 |
| 325 - 349 | 18 |
| 350 - 374 | 42 |
| 375 - 399 | 28 |
| 400 - 424 | 14 |
| 425 - 449 | 6 |

**a** Represent the data on a frequency histogram.

**b** How many of the seedlings are 400 mm or more?

**c** What percentage of the seedlings are between 349 and 400 mm?

**d** The total number of seedlings in the nursery is 1462. Estimate the number of seedlings which measure: **i** less than 400 mm   **ii** between 374 and 425 mm.

**6** The weights, in grams, of 50 laboratory rats are given below.

| | | | | | | | | |
|---|---|---|---|---|---|---|---|---|
| 261 | 133 | 173 | 295 | 265 | 142 | 140 | 271 | 185 |
| 251 | 166 | 100 | 292 | 107 | 201 | 234 | 239 | 159 |
| 153 | 263 | 195 | 151 | 156 | 117 | 144 | 189 | 234 |
| 171 | 233 | 182 | 165 | 122 | 281 | 149 | 152 | 289 |
| 168 | 260 | 256 | 156 | 239 | 203 | 101 | 268 | 241 |
| 217 | 254 | 240 | 214 | 221 | | | | |

**a** Choose suitable class intervals to group the data.

**b** Organise the data in a frequency table.

**c** Draw a frequency histogram to display the data.

**d** What percentage of the rats weigh less than 200 grams?

# MEASURING THE CENTRE OF DATA

We can get a better understanding of a data set if we can locate its **middle** or **centre**, and also get an indication of its **spread** or **dispersion**. Knowing one of these without the other is often of little use.

There are *three statistics* that are used to measure the **centre** of a data set. These are the **mode**, the **mean**, and the **median**.

## THE MODE

For discrete numerical data, the **mode** is the most frequently occuring value in the data set.

For continuous numerical data, we cannot talk about a mode in this way because no two data values will be *exactly* equal. Instead we talk about a **modal class**, which is the class that occurs most frequently.

If a set of scores has two modes we say it is **bimodal**. If there are more than two modes then we do not use them as a measure of the centre.

## THE MEAN

The **mean** of a data set is the statistical name for its arithmetic average.

$$\text{mean} = \frac{\textbf{sum of all data values}}{\textbf{the number of data values}}$$

The mean gives us a single number which indicates a centre of the data set. It is usually not a member of the data set.

For example, a mean test mark of 73% tells us that there are several marks below 73% and several above it. 73% is at the centre, but it does not necessarily mean that one of the students scored 73%.

We denote the **mean** for an entire population by $\mu$, which we read as "mu".

However, in many cases we do not have data for all of the population, and so the exact value of $\mu$ is unknown. Instead we obtain data from a **sample** of the population and use the mean of the sample, $\overline{x}$, as an *approximation* for $\mu$.

Suppose $x$ is a numerical variable. We let:

$x_i$ be the $i$th data value

$n$ be the number of data values in the sample

$\overline{x}$ represent the mean of the sample, so $\overline{x} = \dfrac{\sum\limits_{i=1}^{n} x_i}{n}$

where $\sum\limits_{i=1}^{n} x_i$ means the **sum** of all $n$ data values, $x_1 + x_2 + .... + x_n$.

## THE MEDIAN

The **median** is the *middle value* of an ordered data set.

An ordered data set is obtained by listing the data, usually from smallest to largest.

The median splits the data in halves. Half of the data are less than or equal to the median and half are greater than or equal to it.

For example, if the median mark for a test is 73% then you know that half the class scored less than or equal to 73% and half scored greater than or equal to 73%.

For an **odd number** of data, the median is one of the original data values.

For an **even number** of data, the median is the average of the two middle values, and may not be in the original data set.

If there are $n$ data values, find $\dfrac{n+1}{2}$. The median is the $\left(\dfrac{n+1}{2}\right)$th data value.

For example:

If $n = 13$, $\dfrac{n+1}{2} = \dfrac{13+1}{2} = 7$, so the median = 7th ordered data value.

**DEMO**

If $n = 14$, $\dfrac{n+1}{2} = \dfrac{14+1}{2} = 7.5$, so the median = average of the 7th and 8th ordered data values.

---

**Example 5**                                          ◀) **Self Tutor**

Find the mean, mode and median of the following data sets:

  **a**   3, 6, 5, 6, 4, 5, 5, 6, 7       **b**   13, 12, 15, 13, 18, 14, 16, 15, 15, 17

**a**   mean $= \dfrac{3+6+5+6+4+5+5+6+7}{9} = \dfrac{47}{9} \approx 5.2$

The scores 5 and 6 occur with highest frequency.
∴ the data set is bimodal with modes 5 and 6.
Listing the set in order of size: 3, 4, 5, 5, 5, 6, 6, 6, 7    {as $n = 9$, $\frac{n+1}{2} = 5$}

                           ↑
                    middle score

∴ the median is 5.

**b**   mean $= \dfrac{13+12+15+13+18+14+16+15+15+17}{10} = \dfrac{148}{10} = 14.8$

The score 15 occurs most frequently, so the mode is 15.
Listing the set in order of size:

       12, 13, 13, 14, 15, 15, 15, 16, 17, 18      {as $n = 10$, $\frac{n+1}{2} = 5.5$}

                  ↑
             middle scores

The median is the average of the two middle scores, which is 15.

**Example 6**                                                    ◀)) **Self Tutor**

If 6 people have a mean mass of 53.7 kg, find their total mass.

$$\frac{\text{sum of masses}}{6} = 53.7 \text{ kg}$$

∴   the total mass $= 53.7 \times 6 = 322.2$ kg.

## EXERCISE 7E.1

1  Find the  **i** mean  **ii** median  **iii** mode   for each of the following data sets:

   **a**  2, 3, 3, 3, 4, 4, 4, 5, 5, 5, 5, 6, 6, 6, 6, 6, 7, 7, 8, 8, 8, 9, 9

   **b**  10, 12, 12, 15, 15, 16, 16, 17, 18, 18, 18, 18, 19, 20, 21

   **c**  22.4, 24.6, 21.8, 26.4, 24.9, 25.0, 23.5, 26.1, 25.3, 29.5, 23.5

2  Consider the following    *Data set A:*  3, 4, 4, 5, 6, 6, 7, 7, 7, 8, 8, 9, 10
   two data sets:        *Data set B:*  3, 4, 4, 5, 6, 6, 7, 7, 7, 8, 8, 9, 15

   **a**  Find the mean for both data set A and data set B.

   **b**  Find the median of both data set A and data set B.

   **c**  Explain why the mean of data set A is less than the mean of data set B.

   **d**  Explain why the median of data set A is the same as the median of data set B.

3  The scores obtained by two ten-pin bowlers over a 10 game series are:

   Gordon:   160,   175,   142,   137,   151,   144,   169,   182,   175,   155
   Ruth:      157,   181,   164,   142,   195,   188,   150,   147,   168,   148

   Who has the higher mean score?

4  Phil kept a record of the number of cups of coffee he drank each day for 15 days:
                     2, 3, 1, 1, 0, 0, 4, 3, 0, 1, 2, 3, 2, 1, 4

   Find the   **a** mode   **b** mean   **c** median of the data.

5  A basketball team scored 43, 55, 41 and 37 points in their first four matches.

   **a**  What is the mean number of points scored for the first four matches?

   **b**  What score will the team need to shoot in
      their next match so that they maintain the
      same mean score?

   **c**  The team scores only 25 points in the fifth
      match. What is the mean number of points
      scored for the five matches?

   **d**  The team scores 41 points in their sixth and
      final match. Will this increase or decrease
      their previous mean score? What is the mean
      score for all six matches?

6  The mean monthly sales for a clothing store total $15 467. Calculate the total sales for
the store for the year.

**7**  While on an outback safari, Bill drove an average of 262 km per day for a period of 12 days. How far did Bill drive in total while on safari?

**8**  Towards the end of the season, a netballer had played 14 matches and had scored an average of 16.5 goals per game. In the final two matches of the season she threw 21 goals and 24 goals. Find the netballer's new average.

**9**  Find $x$ if  5, 9, 11, 12, 13, 14, 17 and $x$  have a mean of 12.

**10**  Find $a$ given that  3, 0, $a$, $a$, 4, $a$, 6, $a$ and 3  have a mean of 4.

**11**  Over the complete assessment period, Aruna averaged 35 out of 40 marks for her maths tests. However, when checking her files, she could only find 7 of the 8 tests. For these she scored 29, 36, 32, 38, 35, 34 and 39.  Determine how many marks out of 40 she scored for the eighth test.

**12**  A sample of 10 measurements has a mean of 15.7 and a sample of 20 measurements has a mean of 14.3. Find the mean of all 30 measurements.

**13**  The mean and median of a set of 9 measurements are both 12. If 7 of the measurements are  7, 9, 11, 13, 14, 17 and 19,  find the other two measurements.

**14**  Jana took seven spelling tests, each with twelve words, but she could only find the results of five of them. These were: 9, 5, 7, 9 and 10.  She asked her teacher for the other two results and the teacher said that the mode of her scores was 9 and the mean was 8. Given that Jana knows her worst result was a 5, find the two missing results.

## INVESTIGATION 3                            EFFECTS OF OUTLIERS

We have seen that an **outlier** or **extreme value** is a value which is much greater than, or much less than, the other values.

Your task is to examine the effect of an outlier on the three measures of central tendency.

**What to do:**

**1**  Consider the set of data:  4, 5, 6, 6, 6, 7, 7, 8, 9, 10.  Calculate:

   **a**  the mean          **b**  the mode          **c**  the median.

**2**  We now introduce the extreme value 100 to the data, so the data set is now: 4, 5, 6, 6, 6, 7, 7, 8, 9, 10, 100.   Calculate:

   **a**  the mean          **b**  the mode          **c**  the median.

**3**  Comment on the effect that the extreme value has on:

   **a**  the mean          **b**  the mode          **c**  the median.

**4**  Which of the three measures of central tendency is most affected by the inclusion of an outlier? Discuss your findings with your class.

## CHOOSING THE APPROPRIATE MEASURE

The mean, mode and median can all be used to indicate the centre of a set of numbers. The most appropriate measure will depend upon the type of data under consideration. When selecting which one to use for a given set of data, you should keep the following properties in mind.

| | |
|---|---|
| **Mode:** | • gives the most usual value<br>• only takes common values into account<br>• not affected by extreme values |
| **Mean:** | • commonly used and easy to understand<br>• takes all values into account<br>• affected by extreme values |
| **Median:** | • gives the halfway point of the data<br>• only takes middle values into account<br>• not affected by extreme values |

For example:

- A shoe store is investigating the sizes of shoes sold over one month. The mean shoe size is not very useful to know, but the mode shows at a glance which size the store most commonly has to restock.

- On a particular day a computer sales department sells computers for $900, $1250, $1000, $1700, $1140, $1100, $1495, $1250, $1090 and $1075. Here the mode is meaningless, the median is $1120, and the mean is $1200. The mean is the best measure of centre as the salesman can use it to predict average profit.

- When looking at real estate prices, the mean is distorted by the few sales of very expensive houses. For a typical house buyer, the median will best indicate the price they should expect to pay in a particular area.

## EXERCISE 7E.2

1 The selling prices of the last 10 houses sold in a certain district were as follows:

$146 400,   $127 600,   $211 000,   $192 500,
$256 400,   $132 400,   $148 000,   $129 500,
$131 400,   $162 500

  a Calculate the mean and median selling prices and comment on the results.

  b Which measure would you use if you were:

    i a vendor wanting to sell your house

    ii looking to buy a house in the district?

2 The annual salaries of ten office workers are:
$23 000,   $46 000,   $23 000,   $38 000,   $24 000
$23 000,   $23 000,   $38 000,   $23 000,   $32 000

  a Find the mean, median and modal salaries of this group.

**b** Explain why the mode is an unsatisfactory measure of the middle in this case.

**c** Is the median a satisfactory measure of the middle of this data set?

**3** The following raw data is the daily rainfall, to the nearest millimetre, for the month of July 2007 in the desert:

3, 1, 0, 0, 0, 0, 0, 2, 0, 0, 3, 0, 0, 0, 7, 1, 1, 0, 3, 8, 0, 0, 0, 42, 21, 3, 0, 3, 1, 0, 0

**a** Find the mean, median and mode for the data.

**b** Give a reason why the median is not the most suitable measure of centre for this set of data.

**c** Give a reason why the mode is not the most suitable measure of centre for this set of data.

**d** Are there any outliers in this data set?

**e** On some occasions outliers are removed because they must be due to errors in observation or calculation. If the outliers in the data set were accurately found, should they be removed before finding the measures of the middle?

## MEASURES OF THE CENTRE FROM OTHER SOURCES

When the same data appears several times we often summarise the data in table form.

Consider the data in the given table:

We can find the measures of the centre directly from the table.

**The mode**

There are 15 of data value 7, which is more than for any other data value.

The mode is therefore 7.

**The mean**

| Data value $(x)$ | Frequency $(f)$ | Product $(fx)$ |
|---|---|---|
| 3 | 1 | $1 \times 3 = 3$ |
| 4 | 1 | $1 \times 4 = 4$ |
| 5 | 3 | $3 \times 5 = 15$ |
| 6 | 7 | $7 \times 6 = 42$ |
| 7 | 15 | $15 \times 7 = 105$ |
| 8 | 8 | $8 \times 8 = 64$ |
| 9 | 5 | $5 \times 9 = 45$ |
| Total | $\sum f = 40$ | $\sum fx = 278$ |

Adding a 'Product' column to the table helps to add all scores.

For example, there are 15 data of value 7 and these add to $15 \times 7 = 105$.

Remembering that the mean $= \dfrac{\text{sum of all data values}}{\text{the number of data values}}$, we find

$$\overline{x} = \frac{\sum_{i=1}^{k} f_i x_i}{n} \quad \text{where} \quad n = \sum_{i=1}^{k} f_i \text{ is the total number of data, and}$$

$$k \text{ is the number of } \textit{different} \text{ data values.}$$

This formula is often abbreviated as $\overline{x} = \dfrac{\sum fx}{\sum f}$.

In this case the mean $= \dfrac{278}{40} = 6.95$.

## The median

There are 40 data values, an even number, so there are *two middle* data values.

As the sample size $n = 40$,

$$\frac{n+1}{2} = \frac{41}{2} = 20.5 .$$

So, the median is the average of the 20th and 21st data values.

In the table, the blue numbers show us accumulated values, or the **cumulative frequency**.

| Data Value | Frequency | Cumulative Frequency | |
|---|---|---|---|
| 3 | 1 | 1 | ← 1 number is 3 |
| 4 | 1 | 2 | ← 2 numbers are 4 or less |
| 5 | 3 | 5 | ← 5 numbers are 5 or less |
| 6 | 7 | 12 | ← 12 numbers are 6 or less |
| 7 | 15 | 27 | ← 27 numbers are 7 or less |
| 8 | 8 | 35 | ← 35 numbers are 8 or less |
| 9 | 5 | 40 | ← all numbers are 9 or less |
| Total | 40 | | |

We can see that the 20th and 21st data values (in order) are both 7s.

So, the median $= \dfrac{7 + 7}{2} = 7$.

---

**Example 7**    ◀) **Self Tutor**

The table shows the number of aces served by tennis players in their first sets of a tournament.

| Number of aces | 1 | 2 | 3 | 4 | 5 | 6 |
|---|---|---|---|---|---|---|
| Frequency | 4 | 11 | 18 | 13 | 7 | 2 |

Determine the:  **a**  mean number of aces for these sets
**b**  median number of aces for these sets    **c**  mode.

| No. of aces (x) | Freq. (f) | Product (fx) | Cumul. freq. |
|---|---|---|---|
| 1 | 4 | 4 | 4 |
| 2 | 11 | 22 | 15 |
| 3 | 18 | 54 | 33 |
| 4 | 13 | 52 | 46 |
| 5 | 7 | 35 | 53 |
| 6 | 2 | 12 | 55 |
| Total | $\sum f = 55$ | $\sum fx = 179$ | |

In this case $\dfrac{\sum fx}{\sum f}$ is

short for $\dfrac{\sum\limits_{i=1}^{6} f_i x_i}{\sum\limits_{i=1}^{6} f_i}$ .

**a**  $\overline{x} = \dfrac{\sum fx}{\sum f} = \dfrac{179}{55} \approx 3.25$ aces

**b**  There are 55 data values, so  $n = 55$.  $\dfrac{n+1}{2} = 28$,  so the median is the 28th data value. We use the cumulative frequency column to help us find this data value.
Data values 16 to 33 are 3 aces, so the 28th data value is 3 aces.
∴  the median is 3 aces.

**c**  Looking down the frequency column, the highest frequency is 18. This corresponds to 3 aces, so the mode is 3 aces.

The publishers acknowledge the late Mr Jim Russell, General Features for the reproduction of this cartoon.

© Jim Russell, General Features Pty Ltd.

## EXERCISE 7E.3

1   The table alongside shows the results when 3 coins were tossed simultaneously 30 times. Calculate the:

   a   mode      b   median

   c   mean.

| Number of heads | Number of times occurred |
|---|---|
| 0 | 4 |
| 1 | 12 |
| 2 | 11 |
| 3 | 3 |
| Total | 30 |

2   The following frequency table records the number of phone calls made in a day by 50 fifteen year olds.

   a   For this data, find the:

      i   mean     ii   median     iii   mode.

   b   Construct a column graph for the data and show the position of the mean, median, and mode on the horizontal axis.

   c   Describe the distribution of the data.

   d   Why is the mean larger than the median for this data?

   e   Which measure of centre would be the most suitable for this data set?

| No. of phone calls | Frequency |
|---|---|
| 0 | 5 |
| 1 | 8 |
| 2 | 13 |
| 3 | 8 |
| 4 | 6 |
| 5 | 3 |
| 6 | 3 |
| 7 | 2 |
| 8 | 1 |
| 11 | 1 |

3   A company claims that their match boxes contain, on average, 50 matches per box. On doing a survey, the Consumer Protection Society recorded the following results:

   a   For the CPS data, calculate the:

      i   mode     ii   median     iii   mean.

   b   Do the results of this survey support the company's claim?

   c   In a court for 'false advertising', the company won their case against the Consumer Protection Society. Suggest how they did this.

| Number in a box | Frequency |
|---|---|
| 47 | 5 |
| 48 | 4 |
| 49 | 11 |
| 50 | 6 |
| 51 | 3 |
| 52 | 1 |
| Total | 30 |

4  Families at a school in Australia were surveyed, and the number of children in each family recorded. The results of the survey are shown alongside.

| Number of children | Frequency |
|---|---|
| 1 | 5 |
| 2 | 28 |
| 3 | 15 |
| 4 | 8 |
| 5 | 2 |
| 6 | 1 |
| Total | 59 |

    a  Calculate the:

       i  mean      ii  mode      iii  median.

    b  The average Australian family has 2.2 children. How does this school compare to the national average?

    c  The data set is skewed.   Is the skewness positive or negative?

    d  How has the skewness of the data affected the measures of its centre?

5  Consider again the **Opening Problem** on page **198**.

    a  Use a frequency table for the *Without fertiliser* data to find the:

       i  mean        ii  mode        iii  median  number of peas per pod.

    b  Use a frequency table for the *With fertiliser* data to find the:

       i  mean        ii  mode        iii  median  number of peas per pod.

    c  Which of the measures of centre is appropriate to use in a report on this data?

    d  Has the application of fertiliser significantly improved the number of peas per pod?

## DATA IN CLASSES

When information has been gathered in classes we use the **midpoint** or **mid-interval value** of the class to represent all scores within that interval.

We are assuming that the scores within each class are evenly distributed throughout that interval. The mean calculated is an **approximation** of the true value, and we cannot do better than this without knowing each individual data value.

### Example 8        ◀ᴺ Self Tutor

Estimate the mean of the following *ages of bus drivers* data, to the nearest year:

| Age (yrs) | 21 - 25 | 26 - 30 | 31 - 35 | 36 - 40 | 41 - 45 | 46 - 50 | 51 - 55 |
|---|---|---|---|---|---|---|---|
| Frequency | 11 | 14 | 32 | 27 | 29 | 17 | 7 |

| Age (yrs) | Frequency ($f$) | Midpoint ($x$) | $f x$ |
|---|---|---|---|
| 21 - 25 | 11 | 23 | 253 |
| 26 - 30 | 14 | 28 | 392 |
| 31 - 35 | 32 | 33 | 1056 |
| 36 - 40 | 27 | 38 | 1026 |
| 41 - 45 | 29 | 43 | 1247 |
| 46 - 50 | 17 | 48 | 816 |
| 51 - 55 | 7 | 53 | 371 |
| Total | $\sum f = 137$ | | $\sum f x = 5161$ |

$$\bar{x} = \frac{\sum f x}{\sum f}$$

$$= \frac{5161}{137}$$

$$\approx 37.7$$

∴  the mean age of the drivers is about 38 years.

## EXERCISE 7E.4

**1** 50 students sit for a mathematics test. Given the results in the table, estimate the mean score.

| Score | 0-9 | 10-19 | 20-29 | 30-39 | 40-49 |
|---|---|---|---|---|---|
| Frequency | 2 | 5 | 7 | 27 | 9 |

**2** The table shows the petrol sales in one day by a number of city service stations.

| Litres (L) | Frequency |
|---|---|
| 2000 to 2999 | 4 |
| 3000 to 3999 | 4 |
| 4000 to 4999 | 9 |
| 5000 to 5999 | 14 |
| 6000 to 6999 | 23 |
| 7000 to 7999 | 16 |

a How many service stations were involved in the survey?

b Estimate the total amount of petrol sold for the day by the service stations.

c Find the approximate mean sales of petrol for the day.

**3** Following is a record of the number of points Chloe has scored in her basketball matches.

$$15 \quad 8 \quad 6 \quad 10 \quad 0 \quad 9 \quad 2 \quad 16 \quad 11 \quad 14 \quad 13 \quad 17 \quad 16 \quad 12 \quad 13 \quad 12 \quad 10$$
$$3 \quad 13 \quad 5 \quad 18 \quad 14 \quad 19 \quad 4 \quad 15 \quad 15 \quad 19 \quad 19 \quad 14 \quad 6 \quad 11 \quad 8 \quad 9 \quad 3$$
$$9 \quad 7 \quad 15 \quad 19 \quad 12 \quad 17 \quad 14$$

a Find the mean number of points per match.

b Estimate the mean by grouping the data into the intervals:

  i  0 - 4, 5 - 9, 10 - 14, 15 - 19    ii  0 - 3, 4 - 7, 8 - 11, 12 - 15, 16 - 19

c Comment on the accuracy of your answers from a and b.

**4** Kylie pitched a softball 50 times. The speeds of her pitches are shown in the table.
Estimate the mean speed of her pitches.

| Speed (km $h^{-1}$) | Frequency |
|---|---|
| 80 - < 85 | 8 |
| 85 - < 90 | 14 |
| 90 - < 95 | 22 |
| 95 - < 100 | 6 |

**5** The table shows the sizes of land blocks on a suburban street.
Estimate the mean land block size.

| Size ($m^2$) | Frequency |
|---|---|
| 500 - < 600 | 5 |
| 600 - < 700 | 11 |
| 700 - < 800 | 23 |
| 800 - < 900 | 14 |
| 900 - < 1000 | 9 |

**6** This frequency histogram illustrates the results of an aptitude test given to a group of people seeking positions in a company.

a How many people sat for the test?

b Estimate the mean score for the test.

c What fraction of the people scored less than 100 for the test?

d If the top 20% of the people are offered positions in the company, estimate the minimum mark required.

# F   MEASURING THE SPREAD OF DATA

To accurately describe a distribution we need to measure both its **centre** and its **spread** or **dispersion**.

The given distributions have the same mean, but clearly they have different spreads. The A distribution has most scores close to the mean whereas the C distribution has the greatest spread.

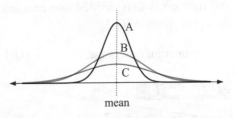

Three common measures of spread are **range**, **interquartile range (IQR)**, and **standard deviation**. We consider the first two of these measures here, and standard deviation later in the chapter.

## THE RANGE

The **range** is the difference between the maximum (largest) and the minimum (smallest) data value.

---

**Example 9**   ◀)) Self Tutor

A library surveys 20 borrowers each day from Monday to Friday, and records the number who are not satisfied with the range of reading material. The results are: 3  7  6  8  11.

The following year the library receives a grant that enables the purchase of a large number of books. The survey was then repeated, with results: 2  3  5  4  6.

Find the range of data in each survey.

The range is the maximum minus the minimum data value.

So, for the first survey, the range is $11 - 3 = 8$.

For the second survey, the range is $6 - 2 = 4$.

---

The **range** is not considered to be a particularly reliable measure of spread as it uses only two data values. It may be influenced by extreme values or outliers.

## THE QUARTILES AND THE INTERQUARTILE RANGE

The median divides an ordered data set into two halves, and these halves are divided in half again by the **quartiles**.

The middle value of the lower half is called the **lower quartile** or **25th percentile**. One quarter or 25% of the data have values less than or equal to the lower quartile. 75% of the data have values greater than or equal to the lower quartile.

The middle value of the upper half is called the **upper quartile** or **75th percentile**. One quarter or 25% of the data have values greater than or equal to the upper quartile. 75% of the data have values less than or equal to the upper quartile.

The **interquartile range** is the range of the middle half or 50% of the data.

> **interquartile range = upper quartile − lower quartile**

The data set is thus divided into quarters by the lower quartile ($Q_1$), the median ($Q_2$), and the upper quartile ($Q_3$).

So, the interquartile range,    $$IQR = Q_3 - Q_1.$$

---

**Example 10**    ◀ Self Tutor

For the data set    7, 3, 1, 7, 6, 9, 3, 8, 5, 8, 6, 3, 7, 1, 9,    find the:

**a** median    **b** lower quartile    **c** upper quartile    **d** interquartile range.

The ordered data set is:

~~1, 1, 3, 3, 3, 5, 6,~~ 6, ~~7, 7, 7, 8, 8, 9, 9~~    (15 of them)

**a** As $n = 15$, $\dfrac{n+1}{2} = 8$    $\therefore$ the median = 8th data value = 6

**b/c** As the median is a data value we now ignore it and split the remaining data into two:

         lower        upper

    $\overbrace{1\ 1\ 3\ 3\ 3\ 5\ 6}$   $\overbrace{7\ 7\ 7\ 8\ 8\ 9\ 9}$    $Q_1$ = median of lower half = 3

                                            $Q_3$ = median of upper half = 8

**d** $IQR = Q_3 - Q_1 = 8 - 3 = 5$

---

**Example 11**    ◀ Self Tutor

For the data set  6, 4, 9, 15, 5, 13, 7, 12, 8, 10, 4, 1, 13, 1, 6, 4, 5, 2, 8, 2,  find:

**a** the median    **b** $Q_1$    **c** $Q_3$    **d** the interquartile range.

The ordered data set is:

~~1 1 2 2 4 4 4 5 5~~ 6 6 ~~7 8 8 9 10 12 13 13 15~~    (20 of them)

**a** As $n = 20$, $\dfrac{n+1}{2} = 10.5$

    $\therefore$ the median = $\dfrac{\text{10th value} + \text{11th value}}{2} = \dfrac{6+6}{2} = 6$

**b/c** As we have an even number of data values, we split the data into two:

       lower            upper

  $\overbrace{1\ 1\ 2\ 2\ 4\ 4\ 4\ 5\ 5\ 6}$   $\overbrace{6\ 7\ 8\ 8\ 9\ 10\ 12\ 13\ 13\ 15}$

    $\therefore\ Q_1 = \dfrac{4+4}{2} = 4, \quad Q_3 = \dfrac{9+10}{2} = 9.5$

**d** $IQR = Q_3 - Q_1$
        $= 9.5 - 4$
        $= 5.5$

Some computer packages calculate quartiles differently.

## EXERCISE 7F

1 For each of the following data sets, make sure the data is ordered and then find:

    **i** the median     **ii** the upper and lower quartiles

    **iii** the range     **iv** the interquartile range.

  **a** 2, 3, 3, 3, 4, 4, 4, 5, 5, 5, 5, 6, 6, 6, 6, 6, 7, 7, 8, 8, 8, 9, 9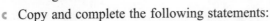

  **b** 10, 12, 15, 12, 24, 18, 19, 18, 18, 15, 16, 20, 21, 17, 18, 16, 22, 14

  **c** 21.8, 22.4, 23.5, 23.5, 24.6, 24.9, 25, 25.3, 26.1, 26.4, 29.5

2 The times spent (in minutes) by 20 people waiting in a queue at a bank for a teller were:

  3.4   2.1   3.8   2.2   4.5   1.4   0    0   1.6   4.8

  1.5   1.9   0    3.6   5.2   2.7   3.0   0.8   3.8   5.2

  **a** Find the median waiting time and the upper and lower quartiles.

  **b** Find the range and interquartile range of the waiting times.

  **c** Copy and complete the following statements:

    **i** "50% of the waiting times were greater than ...... minutes."

    **ii** "75% of the waiting times were less than ...... minutes."

    **iii** "The minimum waiting time was ...... minutes and the maximum waiting time was ...... minutes. The waiting times were spread over ...... minutes."

3 For the data set given, find:

  **a** the minimum value     **b** the maximum value

  **c** the median     **d** the lower quartile

  **e** the upper quartile     **f** the range

  **g** the interquartile range.

| Stem | Leaf |
|------|------|
| 0 | 3 4 7 9 |
| 1 | 0 3 4 6 7 8 |
| 2 | 0 0 3 5 6 9 9 9 |
| 3 | 1 3 7 8 |
| 4 | 2      3 \| 7 means 37 |

4 The heights of 20 ten year olds are recorded in the following stem and leaf plot:

  **a** Find the:   **i** median height

               **ii** upper and lower quartiles of the data.

  **b** Copy and complete the following statements:

    **i** "Half of the children are no more than ...... cm tall."

    **ii** "75% of the children are no more than ...... cm tall."

  **c** Find the:   **i** range      **ii** interquartile range for the height of the ten year olds.

  **d** Copy and complete:

  "The middle 50% of the children have heights spread over ...... cm."

| Stem | Leaf |
|------|------|
| 10 | 9 |
| 11 | 1 3 4 4 8 9 |
| 12 | 2 2 4 4 6 8 9 9 |
| 13 | 1 2 5 8 8 |

10 \| 9 means 109 cm

5 Revisit the **Opening Problem** on page **198**.

  **a** For the *Without fertiliser* data, find:

    **i** the range     **ii** the median     **iii** the lower quartile

    **iv** the upper quartile     **v** the interquartile range.

**b** Repeat **a** for the *With fertiliser* data.

**c** Consider again the questions posed in the **Opening Problem**. Amend your solutions where appropriate.

# G    BOX AND WHISKER PLOTS

A **box and whisker plot** (or simply a **box plot**) is a visual display of some of the descriptive statistics of a data set. It shows:

- the minimum value
- the lower quartile ($Q_1$)
- the median ($Q_2$)
- the upper quartile ($Q_3$)
- the maximum value

These five numbers form the **five-number summary** of the data set.

For the data set in **Example 11** on page **224**, the five-number summary and box plot are:

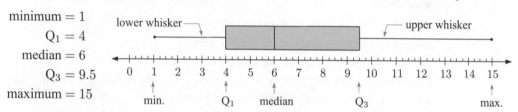

minimum $= 1$
$Q_1 = 4$
median $= 6$
$Q_3 = 9.5$
maximum $= 15$

The rectangular box represents the 'middle' half of the data set.

The lower whisker represents the 25% of the data with smallest values.

The upper whisker represents the 25% of the data with greatest values.

## Example 12    ◀) Self Tutor

Consider the data set:    8 2 3 9 6 5 3 2 2 6 2 5 4 5 5 6

**a** Construct a five-number summary for this data.    **b** Draw a box plot.

**c** Find the:    **i** range    **ii** interquartile range of the data.

**d** Find the percentage of data values less than 3.

**a** The ordered data set is:

2  2  2  2  3  3  4  5  5  5  5  6  6  6  8  9    (16 of them)

$Q_1 = 2.5$    median $= 5$    $Q_3 = 6$

So, the 5-number summary is:    $\begin{cases} \text{minimum} = 2 & Q_1 = 2.5 \\ \text{median} = 5 & Q_3 = 6 \\ \text{maximum} = 9 \end{cases}$

**b**

> **c   i**   range = maximum − minimum
> $$= 9 - 2$$
> $$= 7$$
>
> **ii**   IQR = $Q_3 - Q_1$
> $$= 6 - 2.5$$
> $$= 3.5$$
>
> **d**   25% of the data values are less than 3.

## EXERCISE 7G.1

**1**

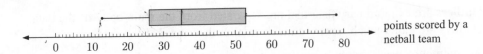

points scored by a netball team

**a**   The box plot given summarises the points scored by a netball team. Locate:

   **i**   the median      **ii**   the maximum value      **iii**   the minimum value

   **iv**   the upper quartile      **v**   the lower quartile

**b**   Calculate:   **i**   the range      **ii**   the interquartile range.

**2**

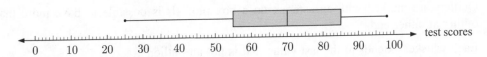

test scores

The box plot above summarises the class results for a test out of 100 marks.

  **a**   Copy and complete the following statements about the test results:

    **i**   The highest mark scored for the test was ......, and the lowest mark was ......

    **ii**   Half of the class scored a mark greater than or equal to ......

    **iii**   The top 25% of the class scored at least ...... marks for the test.

    **iv**   The middle half of the class had scores between ...... and ...... for this test.

  **b**   Find the range of the data set.

  **c**   Find the interquartile range of the data set.

  **d**   Estimate the mean mark for these test scores.

**3**   For the following data sets:

    **i**   construct a 5-number summary      **ii**   draw a box plot

    **iii**   find the range      **iv**   find the interquartile range.

  **a**   3, 5, 5, 7, 10, 9, 4, 7, 8, 6, 6, 5, 8, 6

  **b**   3, 7, 0, 1, 4, 6, 8, 8, 8, 9, 7, 5, 6, 8, 7, 8, 8, 2, 9

  **c**

| Stem | Leaf |
|------|------|
| 11 | 7 |
| 12 | 0 3 6 6 8 |
| 13 | 0 1 1 1 3 5 5 7 |
| 14 | 4 7 7 9 9 |
| 15 | 1 |

    11 | 7 represents 117

**4**  Ranji counts the number of bolts in several boxes and tabulates the data as follows:

| Number of bolts | 33 | 34 | 35 | 36 | 37 | 38 | 39 | 40 |
|---|---|---|---|---|---|---|---|---|
| Frequency | 1 | 5 | 7 | 13 | 12 | 8 | 0 | 1 |

    **a**  Find the five-number summary for this data set.

    **b**  Find the:    **i**  range    **ii**  IQR  for this data set.

    **c**  Construct a box plot for the data set.

## BOX PLOTS AND OUTLIERS

**Outliers** are extraordinary data that are separated from the main body of the data. Outliers are either much larger or much smaller than most of the data.

A commonly used test to identify outliers involves the calculation of upper and lower boundaries:

- **The upper boundary = upper quartile + 1.5 × IQR.**
  Any data larger than the upper boundary is an outlier.
- **The lower boundary = lower quartile − 1.5 × IQR.**
  Any data smaller than the lower boundary is an outlier.

Outliers are marked with an asterisk on a box plot. It is possible to have more than one outlier at either end.

Each whisker extends to the last value that is not an outlier.

---

**Example 13**                                               ◀)) **Self Tutor**

Test the following data for outliers and hence construct a box plot for the data:

$$3, \ 7, \ 8, \ 8, \ 5, \ 9, \ 10, \ 12, \ 14, \ 7, \ 1, \ 3, \ 8, \ 16, \ 8, \ 6, \ 9, \ 10, \ 13, \ 7$$

The ordered data set is:

$$1 \ \ 3 \ \ 3 \ \ 5 \ \ 6 \ \ 7 \ \ 7 \ \ 7 \ \ 8 \ \ 8 \ \ 8 \ \ 8 \ \ 9 \ \ 9 \ \ 10 \ \ 10 \ \ 12 \ \ 13 \ \ 14 \ \ 16 \quad \{n = 20\}$$

$\text{Min}_x = 1 \qquad Q_1 = 6.5 \qquad \text{median} = 8 \qquad Q_3 = 10 \qquad \text{Max}_x = 16$

$\text{IQR} = Q_3 - Q_1 = 3.5$

*Test for outliers:*  

| upper boundary | and | lower boundary |
|---|---|---|
| = upper quartile + 1.5 × IQR | | = lower quartile − 1.5 × IQR |
| = 10 + 1.5 × 3.5 | | = 6.5 − 1.5 × 3.5 |
| = 15.25 | | = 1.25 |

16 is above the upper boundary, so it is an outlier.
1 is below the lower boundary, so it is an outlier.

So, the box plot is:

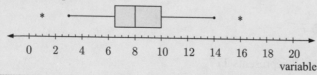

Each whisker is drawn to the last value that is not an outlier.

## EXERCISE 7G.2

1   A set of data has a lower quartile of 31.5, a median of 37, and an upper quartile of 43.5.

   a   Calculate the interquartile range for this data set.

   b   Calculate the boundaries that identify outliers.

   c   Which of the data 22, 13.2, 60, 65 would be outliers?

2   Julie examines a new variety of bean and does a count on the number of beans in 33 pods. Her results were:

   5, 8, 10, 4, 2, 12, 6, 5, 7, 7, 5, 5, 5, 5, 13, 9, 3, 4, 4, 7, 8, 9, 5, 5, 4, 3, 6, 6, 6, 6, 9, 8, 7, 6

   a   Find the median, lower quartile, and upper quartile of the data set.

   b   Find the interquartile range of the data set.

   c   What are the lower and upper boundaries for outliers?

   d   Are there any outliers according to c?     e   Draw a box plot of the data set.

## PARALLEL BOX PLOTS

A parallel box plot enables us to make a *visual comparison* of the distributions of two data sets. We can easily compare descriptive statistics such as their median, range, and interquartile range.

| Example 14 | ◄») Self Tutor |
|---|---|

A hospital is trialling a new anaesthetic drug and has collected data on how long the new and old drugs take before the patient becomes unconscious. They wish to know which drug acts faster and which is more reliable.

   *Old drug times (s):*   8, 12, 9, 8, 16, 10, 14, 7, 5, 21,
                           13, 10, 8, 10, 11, 8, 11, 9, 11, 14

   *New drug times (s):*   8, 12, 7, 8, 12, 11, 9, 8, 10, 8,
                           10, 9, 12, 8, 8, 7, 10, 7, 9, 9

Prepare a parallel box plot for the data sets and use it to compare the two drugs for speed and reliability.

---

The 5-number summaries are:

For the old drug:   $\min_x = 5$          For the new drug:   $\min_x = 7$
                    $Q_1 = 8$                                  $Q_1 = 8$
                    median $= 10$                              median $= 9$
                    $Q_3 = 12.5$                               $Q_3 = 10$
                    $\max_x = 21$                              $\max_x = 12$

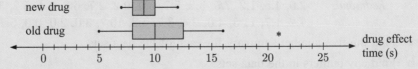

Using the median, 50% of the time the new drug takes 9 seconds or less, compared with 10 seconds for the old drug. So, the new drug is generally a little quicker.

Comparing the spread:

range for old drug $= 21 - 5$          range for new drug $= 12 - 7$
$= 16$                                                $= 5$
$IQR = Q_3 - Q_1$                         $IQR = Q_3 - Q_1$
$= 12.5 - 8$                               $= 10 - 8$
$= 4.5$                                     $= 2$

These measures indicate that the new drug times are less 'spread out' than the old drug times. They are more predictable or reliable.

## EXERCISE 7G.3

1 The amounts of money withdrawn from an ATM were recorded on a Friday and a Saturday. The results are displayed on the parallel box plot alongside.

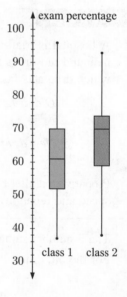

a Find the five-number summary for each set of data.

b Determine the   i range   ii interquartile range   for each set of data.

2 After the final examination, two classes studying the same subject compiled this parallel box plot to show their results.

a In which class was:
   i the highest mark        ii the lowest mark
   iii there a larger spread of marks?

b Find:   i the interquartile range of class 1
           ii the range of class 2.

c If students who scored at least 70% received an achievement award, what percentage of students received an award in:   i class 1   ii class 2?

d Describe the distribution of marks in:
   i class 1        ii class 2.

e Copy and complete:
   The students in class ...... generally scored higher marks.
   The marks in class ...... were more varied.

3 Below are the durations, in minutes, of Paul and Redmond's last 25 mobile phone calls.

Paul:        1.7, 2.0, 3.9, 3.4, 0.9, 1.4, 2.5, 1.1, 5.1, 4.2, 1.5, 2.6, 0.8,
             4.0, 1.5, 1.0, 2.9, 3.2, 2.5, 0.8, 1.8, 3.1, 6.9, 2.3, 1.2

Redmond:     2.0, 4.8, 1.2, 7.5, 3.2, 5.7, 3.9, 0.2, 2.7, 6.8, 3.4, 5.2, 3.2,
             7.2, 1.7, 11.5, 4.0, 2.4, 3.7, 4.2, 10.7, 3.0, 2.0, 0.9, 5.7

a Find the five-number summary for each of the data sets.

b Find any outliers in the data sets.

c Display the data in a parallel box plot.

d Compare and comment on the distributions of the data.

# CUMULATIVE FREQUENCY GRAPHS

In addition to the median, it is often useful to know the number or proportion of scores that lie above or below a particular value. To study this we calculate the **cumulative frequency** for each data value, which is the sum of the frequencies of the data values up to the one in question.

We construct a **cumulative frequency distribution table** to show this information.

We then construct a **cumulative frequency graph** by plotting the cumulative frequencies against the upper end points of each class interval, and then joining the points with a smooth curve.

The cumulative frequency curve should always be **increasing** as we look from left to right. The cumulative frequency value we read from the graph indicates the number of data that are less than the corresponding data value.

## PERCENTILES

A **percentile** is the score below which a certain percentage of the data lies.

For example:
- the 85th percentile is the score below which 85% of the data lies.
- If your score in a test is the 95th percentile, then 95% of the class have scored less than you.

Notice that:
- the **lower quartile** ($Q_1$) is the 25th percentile
- the **median** ($Q_2$) is the 50th percentile
- the **upper quartile** ($Q_3$) is the 75th percentile.

A cumulative frequency graph provides a convenient way to find percentiles.

---

**Example 15**    ◄) **Self Tutor**

The data shows the results of the women's marathon at the 2008 Olympics, for all competitors who finished the race.

a Construct a cumulative frequency distribution table.

b Represent the data on a cumulative frequency graph.

c Use your graph to estimate the:

  i median finishing time

  ii number of competitors who finished in a time less than 2 hours 35 minutes

  iii percentage of competitors who took more than 2 hours 39 minutes to finish

  iv time taken by a competitor who finished in the top 20% of those who completed the marathon.

| Finishing time (t hours & mins) | Frequency |
|---|---|
| $2\text{ h }26 \leqslant t < 2\text{ h }28$ | 8 |
| $2\text{ h }28 \leqslant t < 2\text{ h }30$ | 3 |
| $2\text{ h }30 \leqslant t < 2\text{ h }32$ | 9 |
| $2\text{ h }32 \leqslant t < 2\text{ h }34$ | 11 |
| $2\text{ h }34 \leqslant t < 2\text{ h }36$ | 12 |
| $2\text{ h }36 \leqslant t < 2\text{ h }38$ | 7 |
| $2\text{ h }38 \leqslant t < 2\text{ h }40$ | 5 |
| $2\text{ h }40 \leqslant t < 2\text{ h }48$ | 8 |
| $2\text{ h }48 \leqslant t < 2\text{ h }56$ | 6 |

**a**

| Finishing time (t hours & mins) | Frequency | Cumulative Frequency | |
|---|---|---|---|
| 2 h 26 $\leqslant t <$ 2 h 28 | 8 | 8 | |
| 2 h 28 $\leqslant t <$ 2 h 30 | 3 | 11 | ← This is $8 + 3$. |
| 2 h 30 $\leqslant t <$ 2 h 32 | 9 | 20 | ← This is $8 + 3 + 9$. |
| 2 h 32 $\leqslant t <$ 2 h 34 | 11 | 31 | |
| 2 h 34 $\leqslant t <$ 2 h 36 | 12 | 43 | |
| 2 h 36 $\leqslant t <$ 2 h 38 | 7 | 50 | ← This 50 means that 50 |
| 2 h 38 $\leqslant t <$ 2 h 40 | 5 | 55 | competitors completed the |
| 2 h 40 $\leqslant t <$ 2 h 48 | 8 | 63 | marathon in less than |
| 2 h 48 $\leqslant t <$ 2 h 56 | 6 | 69 | 2 hours 38 minutes. |

**b**

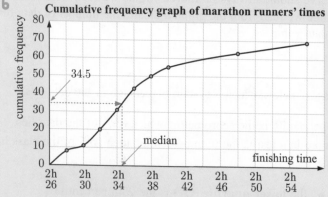

Cumulative frequency graph of marathon runners' times

The cumulative frequency gives a *running total* of the number of runners finishing by a given time.

**c**

**i** The median is estimated using the 50th percentile. As 50% of 69 is 34.5, we start with the cumulative frequency of 34.5 and find the corresponding time. So, the median is approximately 2 hours 34.5 minutes.

**ii** There are approximately 37 competitors who took less than 2 h 35 min to complete the race.

**iii** There are $69 - 52 = 17$ competitors who took more than 2 hours 39 min. So, $\frac{17}{69} \approx 26.4\%$ took more than 2 hours 39 minutes.

**iv** The time taken is estimated using the 20th percentile. As 20% of 69 is 13.8, we find the time corresponding to a cumulative frequency of approximately 14. About 20% of the competitors took less than 2 hours 30 minutes and 40 seconds.

Another way to calculate percentiles is to add a separate scale to a cumulative frequency graph. On the graph alongside, the cumulative frequency is read from the axis on the left side, and each value corresponds to a percentage on the right side.

We can use the percentage scale to help find the quartiles and other percentiles.

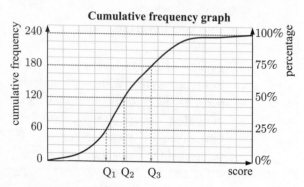

Cumulative frequency graph

## EXERCISE 7H

1   The following frequency distribution was obtained by asking 50 randomly selected people the lengths of their feet. Their answers were given to the nearest centimetre.

| Foot length (cm) | 20 | 21 | 22 | 23 | 24 | 25 | 26 | 27 | 28 | 29 | 30 |
|---|---|---|---|---|---|---|---|---|---|---|---|
| Frequency | 1 | 1 | 0 | 3 | 5 | 13 | 17 | 7 | 2 | 0 | 1 |

Draw a cumulative frequency graph for the data and use it to find:

  a   the median foot length

  b   how many people had a foot length of:      i   25 cm or more      ii   26 cm or less.

2   The following data shows the lengths of 30 trout caught in a lake during a fishing competition. The measurements were rounded down to the next centimetre.

31   38   34   40   24   33   30   36   38   32   35   32   36   27   35
40   34   37   44   38   36   34   33   31   38   35   36   33   33   28

  a   Construct a cumulative frequency table for trout lengths, $x$ cm, using the intervals $24 \leqslant x < 27$, $27 \leqslant x < 30$, and so on.

  b   Draw a cumulative frequency graph for the data.

  c   Use b to find the median length.

  d   Use the original data to find its median and compare your answer with c. Comment on your results.

3   A botanist has measured the heights of 60 seedlings and has presented her findings on the cumulative frequency graph below.

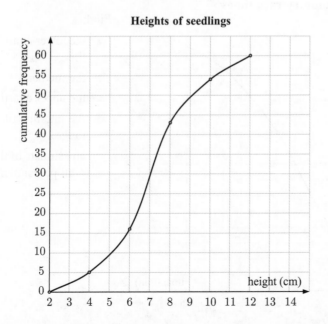

Heights of seedlings

  a   How many seedlings have heights of 5 cm or less?

  b   What percentage of seedlings are taller than 8 cm?

  c   What is the median height?

  d   What is the interquartile range for the heights?

  e   Find the 90th percentile for the data and explain what your answer means.

**4** In an examination the following scores were achieved by a group of students:

Draw a cumulative frequency graph for the data and use it to find:

  **a** the median examination mark

  **b** how many students scored less than 65 marks

  **c** how many students scored between 55 and 70 marks

  **d** how many students failed, given that the pass mark was 45

  **e** the credit mark, given that the top 16% of students were awarded credits.

| Score | Frequency |
|-------|-----------|
| $10 \leqslant x < 20$ | 2 |
| $20 \leqslant x < 30$ | 5 |
| $30 \leqslant x < 40$ | 7 |
| $40 \leqslant x < 50$ | 21 |
| $50 \leqslant x < 60$ | 36 |
| $60 \leqslant x < 70$ | 40 |
| $70 \leqslant x < 80$ | 27 |
| $80 \leqslant x < 90$ | 9 |
| $90 \leqslant x < 100$ | 3 |

**5** The following table gives the age groups of car drivers involved in accidents in a city for a given year. Draw a cumulative frequency graph for the data and use it to find:

  **a** the median age of the drivers involved in the accidents

  **b** the percentage of drivers involved in accidents who had an age of 23 or less.

  **c** Estimate the probability that a driver involved in an accident is:

   **i** aged less than or equal to 27 years

   **ii** aged 27 years.

| Age (in years) | No. of accidents |
|----------------|------------------|
| $16 \leqslant x < 20$ | 59 |
| $20 \leqslant x < 25$ | 82 |
| $25 \leqslant x < 30$ | 43 |
| $30 \leqslant x < 35$ | 21 |
| $35 \leqslant x < 40$ | 19 |
| $40 \leqslant x < 50$ | 11 |
| $50 \leqslant x < 60$ | 24 |
| $60 \leqslant x < 80$ | 41 |

**6** The following cumulative frequency graph displays the performance of 80 competitors in a cross-country race.

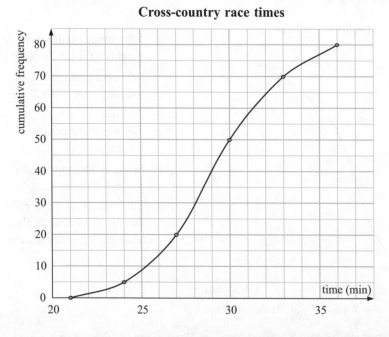

**Cross-country race times**

Find:

  **a** the lower quartile time

  **b** the median

  **c** the upper quartile

  **d** the interquartile range

  **e** an estimate of the 40th percentile.

**7**  The table below gives the distribution of the life of electric light globes.

Draw a cumulative frequency graph for the data and use it to estimate:

  **a**  the median life of a globe

  **b**  the percentage of globes which had a life of 2700 hours or less

  **c**  the number of globes which had a life between 1500 and 2500 hours.

| Life (hours) | Number of globes |
|---|---|
| $0 \leqslant l < 500$ | 5 |
| $500 \leqslant l < 1000$ | 17 |
| $1000 \leqslant l < 2000$ | 46 |
| $2000 \leqslant l < 3000$ | 79 |
| $3000 \leqslant l < 4000$ | 27 |
| $4000 \leqslant l < 5000$ | 4 |

 # STATISTICS USING TECHNOLOGY

## GRAPHICS CALCULATOR

A **graphics calculator** can be used to find descriptive statistics and to draw some types of graphs. For instructions on how to do this, consult the graphics calculator instructions at the start of the book.

Consider the data set:  5 2 3 3 6 4 5 3 7 5 7 1 8 9 5

You should be able to:

- Enter the data as a **list**.
- Enter the **statistics calculation** part of the menu and obtain the descriptive statistics like these shown.

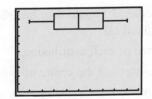

$\overline{x}$ is the mean

five number summary

- Obtain a box and whisker plot, column graph, or histogram.

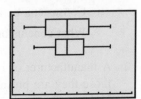

- Enter a second data set into another list and obtain a parallel box plot for comparison with the first one.

  Use the data:   9 6 2 3 5 5 7 5 6 7 6 3 4 4 5 8 4

You will need to change the **viewing window** as appropriate.

## STATISTICS FROM A COMPUTER PACKAGE

Click on the icon to load our **statistics package**.

    Enter data set 1:  5 2 3 3 6 4 5 3 7 5 7 1 8 9 5
    Enter data set 2:  9 6 2 3 5 5 7 5 6 7 6 3 4 4 5 8 4

STATISTICS PACKAGE

Examine the side by side column graphs.

Click on the Box and Whisker tab to view the parallel box plot.

Click on the Statistics tab to obtain the descriptive statistics.

## EXERCISE 7I

Use technology to answer the following questions:

**1** **a** Enter the data set:   5 2 3 3 6 4 5 3 7 5 7 1 8 9 5   and obtain the mean and the 5-number summary. This is the data used in the screendumps on page **235**, so you can use them to check your results.

   **b** Construct the box plot for the data in **a**.

   **c** Construct the column graph for the data in **a**.

   **d** Enter the data set:   9 6 2 3 5 5 7 5 6 7 6 3 4 4 5 8 4   into a second list. Find the mean and 5-number summary. Create a parallel box plot comparing the data sets.

**2** Shane and Brett play in the same cricket team and are fierce but friendly rivals when it comes to bowling. During a season the number of wickets taken in each innings by the bowlers were:

| *Shane:* | 1 | 6 | 2 | 0 | 3 | 4 | 1 | 4 | 2 | 3 | 0 | 3 | 2 | 4 | 3 | 4 | 3 | 3 |
|---|---|---|---|---|---|---|---|---|---|---|---|---|---|---|---|---|---|---|
|  | 3 | 4 | 2 | 4 | 3 | 2 | 3 | 3 | 0 | 5 | 3 | 5 | 3 | 2 | 4 | 3 | 4 | 3 |

| *Brett:* | 7 | 2 | 4 | 8 | 1 | 3 | 4 | 2 | 3 | 0 | 5 | 3 | 5 | 2 | 3 | 1 | 2 | 0 |
|---|---|---|---|---|---|---|---|---|---|---|---|---|---|---|---|---|---|---|
|  | 4 | 3 | 4 | 0 | 3 | 3 | 0 | 2 | 5 | 1 | 1 | 2 | 2 | 5 | 1 | 4 | 0 | 1 |

   **a** Is the variable discrete or continuous?

   **b** Enter the data into a graphics calculator or statistics package.

   **c** Produce a vertical column graph for each data set.

   **d** Are there any outliers? Should they be deleted before we start to analyse the data?

   **e** Describe the shape of each distribution.

   **f** Compare the measures of the centre of each distribution.

   **g** Compare the spreads of each distribution.

   **h** Construct a parallel box plot.

   **i** What conclusions, if any, can be drawn from the data?

**3** A manufacturer of light globes claims that their new design has a 20% longer life than those they are presently selling. Forty of each globe are randomly selected and tested. Here are the results to the nearest hour:

| | | | | | | | | | | | | | | |
|---|---|---|---|---|---|---|---|---|---|---|---|---|---|---|
| | 103 | 96 | 113 | 111 | 126 | 100 | 122 | 110 | 84 | 117 | 103 | 113 | 104 | 104 |
| *Old type:* | 111 | 87 | 90 | 121 | 99 | 114 | 105 | 121 | 93 | 109 | 87 | 118 | 75 | 111 |
| | 87 | 127 | 117 | 131 | 115 | 116 | 82 | 130 | 113 | 95 | 108 | 112 | | |

| | | | | | | | | | | | | | | |
|---|---|---|---|---|---|---|---|---|---|---|---|---|---|---|
| | 146 | 131 | 132 | 160 | 128 | 119 | 133 | 117 | 139 | 123 | 109 | 129 | 109 | 131 |
| *New type:* | 191 | 117 | 132 | 107 | 141 | 136 | 146 | 142 | 123 | 144 | 145 | 125 | 164 | 125 |
| | 133 | 124 | 153 | 129 | 118 | 130 | 134 | 151 | 145 | 131 | 133 | 135 | | |

**a** Is the variable discrete or continuous?

**b** Enter the data into a graphics calculator or statistics package.

**c** Are there any outliers? Should they be deleted before we start to analyse the data?

**d** Compare the measures of centre and spread.

**e** Construct a parallel box plot.

**f** Describe the shape of each distribution.

**g** What conclusions, if any, can be drawn from the data?

# J | STANDARD DEVIATION

The problem with using the range and the IQR as measures of spread or dispersion of scores is that both of them only use two values in their calculation. Some data sets have their spread characteristics hidden when the range or IQR are quoted, and so we need a better way of describing spread.

The **standard deviation** of a distribution takes into account the **deviation** of **each score** from the mean. It is therefore a good measure of the **dispersion** of the data.

Consider a data set of $n$ values: $x_1$, $x_2$, $x_3$, $x_4$, ...., $x_n$, with mean $\overline{x}$.

For a data set of $n$ values, $s_n = \sqrt{\dfrac{\sum\limits_{i=1}^{n} (x_i - \overline{x})^2}{n}}$ is called the **standard deviation**.

Notice in this formula that:

- $(x_i - \overline{x})^2$ is a measure of how far $x_i$ deviates from $\overline{x}$.

- If $\sum\limits_{i=1}^{n} (x_i - \overline{x})^2$ is small, it will indicate that most of the data values are close to $\overline{x}$.

- Dividing by $n$ gives an indication of how far, on average, the data is from the mean.

- The square root is used to correct the units.

The standard deviation is a **non-resistant** measure of spread. This is due to its dependence on the mean of the sample and because extreme data values will give large values for $(x_i - \overline{x})^2$.

It is only a useful measure if the distribution is close to symmetrical. The IQR and percentiles are more appropriate tools for measuring spread if the distribution is considerably skewed.

In this course you will only be required to calculate standard deviation using a calculator. You can learn how to do this in the **graphics calculator instructions** chapter.

However, in the following example we demonstrate how to calculate the standard deviation from first principles, giving you an understanding of how it works.

**Example 16**    ◀)) **Self Tutor**

Calculate the standard deviation of the data set:   2, 5, 4, 6, 7, 5, 6.

$$\overline{x} = \frac{2+5+4+6+7+5+6}{7} = 5$$

$$s = \sqrt{\frac{\sum(x - \overline{x})^2}{n}}$$

$$= \sqrt{\frac{16}{7}} \approx 1.51$$

| Score $(x)$ | $x - \overline{x}$ | $(x - \overline{x})^2$ |
|---|---|---|
| 2 | $-3$ | 9 |
| 4 | $-1$ | 1 |
| 5 | 0 | 0 |
| 5 | 0 | 0 |
| 6 | 1 | 1 |
| 6 | 1 | 1 |
| 7 | 2 | 4 |
| 35 | | 16 |

The following screendumps indicate the result when we calculate the standard deviation for this data set:

| Casio fx-9860G | TI-84 Plus | TI-$n$spire |
|---|---|---|

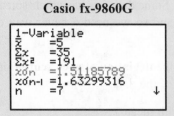
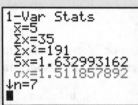
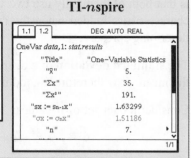

## SAMPLING FROM A POPULATION

Populations are often huge, and gathering data from every individual is impossible due to time constraints and cost.

Consequently, a **random sample** is taken from the population with the hope that it will truly reflect the characteristics of the population. To ensure this, the sample must be sufficiently large, and be taken in such a way that the results are unbiased.

To help distinguish between a sample and the whole population, we use different notation for both the mean and standard deviation. This is shown in the table opposite.

| | sample | population |
|---|---|---|
| mean | $\overline{x}$ | $\mu$ |
| standard deviation | $s_n$ | $\sigma$ |

In general, the population mean $\mu$ and standard deviation $\sigma$ will be unknown.

However, given statistics from a sample, we can make **inferences** about the population using the following results which are assumed without proof:

When a sample of size $n$ is used to draw inference about a population:
- the mean of the sample $\overline{x}$ is an unbiased estimate of $\mu$
- $s_n$ is an estimate of the standard deviation $\sigma$.

## EXERCISE 7J.1

1   A company recorded the following weekly petrol usage (in litres) by its salespersons:

62, 40, 52, 48, 64, 55, 44, 75, 40, 68, 60, 42, 70, 49, 56

   a   Use the formula method to find the mean and standard deviation of the petrol used.

   b   Use your graphics calculator to find the mean and standard deviation.

2   The weights of a group of cooking chickens in kilograms are:

1.5, 1.8, 1.7, 1.4, 1.7, 1.8, 2.0, 1.5, 1.6, 1.6, 1.9, 1.7, 1.4, 1.7, 1.8, 2.0

Use your graphics calculator to find the mean and standard deviation of weights.

3   A random sample of 87 deer from a huge herd had a mean weight of 93.8 kg with standard deviation 6.77 kg. Estimate the mean and standard deviation of the whole herd.

4   The weights (in grams) of a random sample of sparrows are as follows:

87  75  68  69  81  89  73  66  91  77  84  83  77  84  80  76  67

   a   Find the mean and standard deviation of the sample.

   b   Estimate the mean and standard deviation of the population from which the sample was taken.

## STANDARD DEVIATION FOR GROUPED DATA

For grouped data, the standard deviation is   $s_n = \sqrt{\dfrac{\sum f_i (x_i - \overline{x})^2}{\sum f_i}}$

where   $x_i$ is the $i$th score,

       $\overline{x}$ is the **mean**,

and   $f_i$ is the **frequency** of the $i$th score.

For **continuous** data, or data that has been grouped in **classes**, we use the **mid-interval values** to represent all data in that interval.

| Example 17 | | | | ◆) Self Tutor |
|---|---|---|---|---|

Use technology to find the standard deviation for this distribution of examination scores:

| Mark | Frequency | Mark | Frequency |
|---|---|---|---|
| 0 - 9 | 1 | 50 - 59 | 16 |
| 10 - 19 | 1 | 60 - 69 | 24 |
| 20 - 29 | 2 | 70 - 79 | 13 |
| 30 - 39 | 4 | 80 - 89 | 6 |
| 40 - 49 | 11 | 90 - 99 | 2 |

In order to find the standard deviation of already grouped data, the mid-interval values are used to represent all data in that interval.

We then use technology to find the standard deviation.

| Class interval | Mid-interval value | Frequency | Class interval | Mid-interval value | Frequency |
|---|---|---|---|---|---|
| 0 - 9 | 4.5 | 1 | 50 - 59 | 54.5 | 16 |
| 10 - 19 | 14.5 | 1 | 60 - 69 | 64.5 | 24 |
| 20 - 29 | 24.5 | 2 | 70 - 79 | 74.5 | 13 |
| 30 - 39 | 34.5 | 4 | 80 - 89 | 84.5 | 6 |
| 40 - 49 | 44.5 | 11 | 90 - 99 | 94.5 | 2 |

**Casio fx-9860G**

```
1-Variable
x̄    =59.75
Σx   =4780
Σx²  =308200
xσn  =16.8058769
xσn-1 =16.9119087
n    =80          ↓
```

**TI-84 Plus**

```
1-Var Stats
x̄=59.75
Σx=4780
Σx²=308200
Sx=16.91190877
σx=16.80587695
↓n=80
```

**TI-nspire**

```
1.1  1.2        DEG AUTO REAL

OneVar one,two: stat.results

   "Title"      "One-Variable Statistics
   "x̄"                   59.75
   "Σx"                  4780.
   "Σx²"                308200.
   "sx := sn-1x"         16.9119
   "σx := σnx"           16.8059
   "n"                   80.
                                      1/1
```

So, the standard deviation $s \approx 16.8$.

## EXERCISE 7J.2

**1** Below is a sample of family sizes taken at random from people in a city.

| Number of children, $x$ | 0 | 1 | 2 | 3 | 4 | 5 | 6 | 7 |
|---|---|---|---|---|---|---|---|---|
| Frequency, $f$ | 14 | 18 | 13 | 5 | 3 | 2 | 2 | 1 |

   **a** Find the sample mean and standard deviation.

   **b** Estimate the mean and standard deviation of the population from which the sample was taken.

**2** Below is a random sample of the ages of squash players at the Junior National Squash Championship.

| Age | 11 | 12 | 13 | 14 | 15 | 16 | 17 | 18 |
|---|---|---|---|---|---|---|---|---|
| Frequency | 2 | 1 | 4 | 5 | 6 | 4 | 2 | 1 |

Find the mean and standard deviation of the ages.

**3** The local Health and Fitness Centre recorded the following number of clients per week during the last year:

Calculate the average number of clients per week and the standard deviation from this number.

| Number of clients | Frequency |
|---|---|
| 36 | 2 |
| 39 | 5 |
| 44 | 9 |
| 45 | 11 |
| 46 | 15 |
| 48 | 5 |
| 50 | 4 |
| 52 | 1 |
| Total | 52 |

4   The lengths of 30 randomly selected 12-day old babies were measured and the following data obtained:

a   Estimate the mean length and the standard deviation of the lengths.

b   Estimate the mean and standard deviation of the population from which the sample was taken.

| Length (cm) | Frequency |
|---|---|
| $40 \leqslant l < 42$ | 1 |
| $42 \leqslant l < 44$ | 1 |
| $44 \leqslant l < 46$ | 3 |
| $46 \leqslant l < 48$ | 7 |
| $48 \leqslant l < 50$ | 11 |
| $50 \leqslant l < 52$ | 5 |
| $52 \leqslant l < 54$ | 2 |

5   The weekly wages (in dollars) of 200 randomly selected steel workers are given alongside:
Estimate the mean and the standard deviation of the wages.

| Wage ($) | Number of workers |
|---|---|
| 360 - 369.99 | 17 |
| 370 - 379.99 | 38 |
| 380 - 389.99 | 47 |
| 390 - 399.99 | 57 |
| 400 - 409.99 | 18 |
| 410 - 419.99 | 10 |
| 420 - 429.99 | 10 |
| 430 - 439.99 | 3 |

6   The hours worked last week by 40 employees of a local clothing factory were as follows:

38   40   46   32   41   39   44   38   40   42   38   40   43   41   47   36   38   39   34   40
48   30   49   40   40   43   45   36   35   39   42   44   48   36   38   42   46   38   39   40

a   Calculate the mean and standard deviation for this data.

b   Now group the data into classes 30 - 33, 34 - 37, and so on. Calculate the mean and standard deviation using these groups. Examine any differences in the two sets of answers.

c   Draw a cumulative frequency graph for the data and determine its interquartile range.

d   Represent this data on a box plot.

7   A traffic survey by the highways department revealed that the following number of vehicles passed through a suburban intersection in 15 minute intervals during the day.

a   Calculate the mean and the standard deviation for the data.

b   Draw a cumulative frequency graph of the data and determine its interquartile range.

| Number of vehicles | Frequency |
|---|---|
| 1 - 5 | 4 |
| 6 - 10 | 16 |
| 11 - 15 | 22 |
| 16 - 20 | 28 |
| 21 - 25 | 14 |
| 26 - 30 | 9 |
| 31 - 35 | 5 |
| 36 - 40 | 2 |

## COMPARING THE SPREAD OF TWO DATA SETS

We have seen how the **mean** of two data sets is a useful comparison of their centres. To compare the spread or dispersion of two data sets we can use their **standard deviations**.

---

**Example 18**    ◀)) **Self Tutor**

The following exam results were recorded by two classes of students studying Spanish:

*Class A:*    64  69  74  67  78  88  76  90  89  84  83  87  78  80  95  75  55  78  81
*Class B:*    94  90  88  81  86  96  92  93  88  72  94  61  87  90  97  95  77  77  82  90

Compare the results of the two classes including their spread.

Using technology we obtain the mean and standard deviation for each class:

|         | Mean | Standard deviation |
|---------|------|--------------------|
| Class A | 78.5 | 9.63               |
| Class B | 86.5 | 8.92               |

Class B has a higher mean than class A, indicating that the students in class B generally performed better in the exam.
Class A has a higher standard deviation than class B, indicating that the results in class A were more dispersed.

---

## EXERCISE 7J.3

1   The column graphs show two distributions:

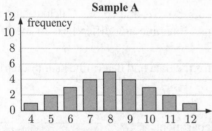  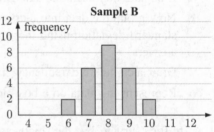

a   By looking at the graphs, which distribution appears to have wider spread?

b   Find the mean of each sample.

c   Find the standard deviation of each sample. Comment on your answers.

2   The number of points scored by Andrew and Brad in the last 8 basketball matches are tabulated below.

| Points by Andrew | 23 | 17 | 31 | 25 | 25 | 19 | 28 | 32 |
|------------------|----|----|----|----|----|----|----|----|
| Points by Brad   |  9 | 29 | 41 | 26 | 14 | 44 | 38 | 43 |

a   Find the mean and standard deviation of the number of points scored by each player.

b   Which of the two players is more consistent?

**3** A manufacturer of soft drinks employs a statistican for quality control. He needs to check that 375 mL of drink goes into each can, but realises the machine which fills the cans will slightly vary each delivery.

    **a** Would you expect the standard deviation for the whole production run to be the same for one day as it is for one week? Explain your answer.

    **b** If samples of 125 cans are taken each day, what measure would be used to:

       **i** check that an average of 375 mL of drink goes into each can

      **ii** check the variability of the volume of drink going into each can?

    **c** What is the significance of a low standard deviation in this case?

---

## INVESTIGATION 4                    HEART STOPPERS

A new drug is claimed to lower the cholesterol level in humans. To test this claim, a heart specialist enlisted the help of 50 of his patients.

The patients agreed to take part in an experiment in which 25 of them would be randomly allocated to take the new drug and the other 25 would take an identical looking pill that was actually a *placebo*, or sugar pill that would have no effect.

All participants had their cholesterol level measured before starting the course of pills, and then again after they had taken the pills for two months.

The data collected by the doctor is given below:

| | |
|---|---|
| cholesterol levels of **all** participants **before** the experiment | 7.1 8.2 8.4 6.5 6.5 7.1 7.2 7.1 6.1 6.0 8.5 5.0 6.3<br>6.7 7.3 8.9 6.2 6.3 7.1 8.4 7.4 7.6 7.5 6.6 8.1 6.2<br>6.2 7.0 8.1 8.4 6.4 7.6 8.6 7.5 7.9 6.2 6.8 7.5<br>6.0 5.0 8.3 7.9 6.7 7.3 6.0 7.4 7.4 8.6 6.5 7.6 |
| cholesterol levels of the 25 participants who took the drug | 4.8 5.6 4.7 4.2 4.8 4.6 4.8 5.2 4.8 5.0 4.7 5.1 4.7<br>4.4 4.7 4.9 6.2 4.7 4.7 4.4 5.6 3.2 4.4 4.6 5.2 |
| cholesterol levels of the 25 participants who took the placebo | 7.0 8.4 8.8 6.1 6.6 7.6 6.5 7.9 6.2 6.8 7.5 6.0 8.2<br>5.7 8.3 7.9 6.7 7.3 6.1 7.4 8.4 6.6 6.5 7.6 6.1 |

### What to do:

**1** Produce stem plots showing the cholesterol levels of the three groups in the table.

                                                                  STATISTICS<br>                                                                    PACKAGE

**2** Use technology to calculate the relevant statistical data for each group.

**3**   Use the data to complete the table:

| Cholesterol Level | Before the Experiment | 25 participants taking the drug | 25 participants taking the placebo |
|---|---|---|---|
| $4.0 \leqslant l < 4.5$ | | | |
| $4.5 \leqslant l < 5.0$ | | | |
| $5.0 \leqslant l < 5.5$ | | | |
| $5.5 \leqslant l < 6.0$ | | | |
| ⋮ | | | |
| $8.5 \leqslant l < 9.0$ | | | |

**4**   Calculate the mean and standard deviation for each group in the table.

**5**   Write a report presenting your findings.

---

## RESEARCH PROJECT

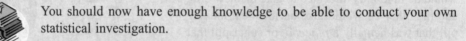

You should now have enough knowledge to be able to conduct your own statistical investigation.

First, choose a problem or issue that you find interesting. Find a question that you can investigate, making sure that you can find useful data for it. Some ideas to get you started are listed at the end of these instructions. Think about how you will organise and display your data when you have collected it. Then talk about your question and plans for analysis with your teacher, and make changes to the problem or your research plan if necessary.

Collect your data, making sure that it is randomly selected, and that you have enough to make a fair conclusion. Use technology to produce appropriate graphs or statistical calculations. In your analysis, you may need to consider:

- Is the data categorical, quantitative discrete, or quantitative continuous?
- Do you need to group any of the data?
- Are there any outliers?
- Should you find measures for the centre or spread? If so, which ones should you use?

Write a report of your investigation as a newspaper article, a slideshow presentation, or a word processed document. Your report should include:

- an explanation of the overall problem you researched
- a simple description of your method of investigation
- the analysis you carried out including raw data and any summary statistics, graphs, or tables that you produced
- your conclusion, with the reasons you came to that decision
- a discussion of any flaws in your method that might weaken your conclusion.

**Project ideas:**

United Nations demographics page (international population, trade, housing, wealth):
*http://unstats.un.org/unsd/demographic/default.htm*

Food and Agriculture Organisation of the United Nations (food trade and consumption)
*http://faostat.fao.org/site/342/default.aspx*

World Health Organisation (disease and health care):
*http://www.who.int/research/en/*

International Baccalaureate (IB education):  *http://www.ibo.org/facts/*

**MORE PROJECTS**

Alternatively, you could research your favourite sport, a large business, climate, or a community issue. Some further ideas are included in the link.

## REVIEW SET 7A

**1** Classify the following data as categorical, quantitative discrete, or quantitative continuous:

   **a** the number of pages in a daily newspaper

   **b** the maximum daily temperature in the city

   **c** the manufacturer of a television

   **d** the preferred football code

   **e** the position taken by a player on a lacrosse field

   **f** the time it takes 15 year olds to run one kilometre

   **g** the length of people's feet

   **h** the number of goals shot by a soccer player

   **i** the cost of a bicycle.

**2** The data given below are the lengths, in metres, of yachts competing in a sailing race.

| | | | | | | | | | |
|---|---|---|---|---|---|---|---|---|---|
| 14.7 | 14.1 | 21.6 | 16.2 | 15.7 | 12.8 | 10.1 | 13.9 | 14.4 | 13.0 |
| 11.7 | 14.6 | 17.2 | 13.4 | 12.1 | 11.3 | 13.1 | 21.6 | 23.5 | 16.4 |
| 14.4 | 15.8 | 12.6 | 19.7 | 18.0 | 16.2 | 27.4 | 21.9 | 14.4 | 12.4 |

   **a** Produce a frequency histogram of the data.

   **b** Find the    **i** median      **ii** range   of the yacht lengths.

   **c** Comment on the skewness of the data.

**3** Find $a$ given that the data set   2, $a$, 5, 4, 1, 2, 3, 5   has a mean of 3.

**4** The following marks were scored for a test where the maximum score was 50:

    47   32   32   29   36   39   40   46   43   39   44   18   38   45   35   46   7   44   27   48

   **a** Construct an ordered stem plot for the data.

   **b** What percentage of the students scored 40 or more marks?

   **c** What percentage of the students scored less than 30 marks?

   **d** If a score of 25 or more is a pass, what percentage of the students passed?

   **e** Describe the distribution of the data.

**5** The back to back stem plot alongside represents the age at first marriage for a collection of males and females.

**a** Copy and complete the following table:

| Distribution | Females | Males |
|---|---|---|
| shape | | |
| median | | |
| range | | |

**b** Compare the distributions of age at first marriage for males and females. What conclusion can you make?

**Age at first marriage**

| Females | | Males |
|---:|:---:|:---|
| 8 | 19 | |
| | 20 | |
| 9 | 21 | |
| 9 4 0 | 22 | |
| 6 4 4 4 1 | 23 | 2 4 |
| 8 5 3 | 24 | 1 |
| 3 2 | 25 | 2 2 4 6 |
| 9 2 | 26 | 5 5 6 7 8 |
| 0 | 27 | 3 7 8 |
| 4 | 28 | 5 7 8 |
| 8 | 29 | 2 6 |

*Scale:* 23 | 2 means 23.2 years

**6** Draw a box and whisker plot for the following data:

11, 12, 12, 13, 14, 14, 15, 15, 15, 16, 17, 17, 18.

**7** 120 people caught whooping cough in an outbreak. The times for them to recover were recorded and the results were used to produce the cumulative frequency graph shown.

Estimate:

**a** the median

**b** the interquartile range.

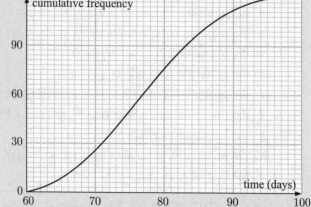

**8** Find, using your calculator, the mean and standard deviation of these sets of data:

**a** 117, 129, 105, 124, 123, 128, 131, 124, 123, 125, 108

**b** 6.1, 5.6, 7.2, 8.3, 6.6, 8.4, 7.7, 6.2

## REVIEW SET 7B

**1** A sample of lamp-posts were surveyed for the following data. Classify the data as categorical, quantitative discrete or quantitative continuous:

**a** the diameter of the lamp-post measured 1 metre from its base

**b** the material from which the lamp-post is made

**c** the location of the lamp-post (inner, outer, North, South, East or West)

**d** the height of the lamp-post

**e** the time since the last inspection

**f** the number of inspections since installation

**g** the condition of the lamp-post (very good, good, fair, unsatisfactory).

**2**  The data below shows the distance in metres that Thabiso threw a baseball:

| 71.2 | 65.1 | 68.0 | 71.1 | 74.6 | 68.8 | 83.2 | 85.0 | 74.5 | 87.4 |
| 84.3 | 77.0 | 82.8 | 84.4 | 80.6 | 75.9 | 89.7 | 83.2 | 97.5 | 82.9 |
| 90.5 | 85.5 | 90.7 | 92.9 | 95.6 | 85.5 | 64.6 | 73.9 | 80.0 | 86.5 |

  **a**  Determine the highest and lowest value for the data set.

  **b**  Choose between 6 and 12 groups into which all the data values can be placed.

  **c**  Prepare a frequency distribution table.

  **d**  Draw a frequency histogram for the data.

  **e**  Determine:    **i**  the mean    **ii**  the median.

**3**  Consider the following distribution of continuous grouped data:

| Scores | 0 to 9.9 | 10 to 19.9 | 20 to 29.9 | 30 to 39.9 | 40 to 49.9 |
|---|---|---|---|---|---|
| Frequency | 1 | 13 | 27 | 17 | 2 |

  **a**  Construct a cumulative frequency graph for the data.

  **b**  Find the median of the data.        **c**  Find the interquartile range.

  **d**  Find the mean and standard deviation.

**4**  The daily profits of a shop over the last 20 days, in pounds, are:

| 324 | 348 | 352 | 366 | 346 | 329 | 375 | 353 | 336 | 368 |
| 336 | 375 | 356 | 358 | 353 | 311 | 365 | 376 | 343 | 331 |

  **a**  Find the:    **i**  median    **ii**  lower quartile    **iii**  upper quartile.

  **b**  Find the interquartile range of the data set.

  **c**  Find the mean and standard deviation of the daily profits.

**5**  This cumulative frequency curve shows the times taken for 200 students to travel to school by bus.

  **a**  Estimate how many of the students spent between 10 and 20 minutes travelling to school.

  **b**  If 30% of the students spent more than $m$ minutes travelling to school, estimate the value of $m$.

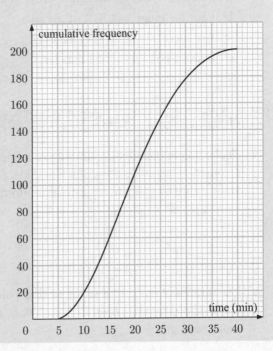

**6** The playing time, in minutes, of CDs purchased by a random sample of shoppers is shown alongside.

| Playing time (minutes) | Number of CDs |
|---|---|
| $30 \leqslant t < 35$ | 5 |
| $35 \leqslant t < 40$ | 13 |
| $40 \leqslant t < 45$ | 17 |
| $45 \leqslant t < 50$ | 29 |
| $50 \leqslant t < 55$ | 27 |
| $55 \leqslant t < 60$ | 18 |
| $60 \leqslant t < 65$ | 7 |

 **a** Find the mean and standard deviation of the playing time of CDs purchased.

 **b** Estimate the mean and standard deviation for the population this sample comes from.

**7** Find the range, lower quartile, upper quartile and standard deviation for the following data:    120, 118, 132, 127, 135, 116, 122, 128.

**8** A confectioner claims to sell an average of 30 liquorice allsorts per bag. The results from a survey of bags are shown in the table below.

| Number of allsorts | 27 | 28 | 29 | 30 | 31 | 32 |
|---|---|---|---|---|---|---|
| Frequency | 23 | 29 | 41 | 37 | 22 | 32 |

 **a** Find the mean and standard deviation for this data.

 **b** Is the confectioner's claim justified?

**9** Consider this set of data:

   19, 7, 22, 15, 14, 10, 8, 28, 14, 18, 31, 13, 18, 19, 11, 3, 15, 16, 19, 14

 **a** Find the 5-number summary for the data.

 **b** Find the range and IQR of the data.

 **c** Are there any outliers in the data?

 **d** Draw a box plot of the data set.

## REVIEW SET 7C

**1** The winning margin in 100 rugby games was recorded. The results are given alongside.

Draw a column graph to represent this information.

| Margin (points) | Frequency |
|---|---|
| 1 - 10 | 13 |
| 11 - 20 | 35 |
| 21 - 30 | 27 |
| 31 - 40 | 18 |
| 41 - 50 | 7 |

**2** The mean and mode of a set of 14 data points are both 7.
The data points are:   6, 8, 7, 7, 5, 7, 6, 8, 6, 9, 6, 7, $p$, $q$.
Find $p$ and $q$.

**3** The table alongside shows the number of patrons visiting an art gallery on various days.
Find the mean number of patrons per day.

| No. of patrons | Frequency |
|---|---|
| 250 - 299 | 14 |
| 300 - 349 | 34 |
| 350 - 399 | 68 |
| 400 - 449 | 72 |
| 450 - 499 | 54 |
| 500 - 549 | 23 |
| 550 - 599 | 7 |

**4** The given parallel box plots represent the 100 metre sprint times for the members of two athletics squads.

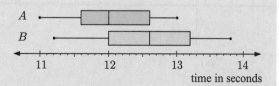

**a** Determine the 5-number summaries for both $A$ and $B$.

**b** Determine:   **i** the range   **ii** the interquartile range   for each group.

**c** Copy and complete:

   **i** We know the members of squad ...... generally ran faster because ......

   **ii** We know the times in squad ...... are more varied because ......

**5** A random sample of the weekly supermarket bills for a number of families was observed and recorded in the table given.

**a** Find the mean bill and the standard deviation of the bills.

**b** Estimate the mean and standard deviation of the population that the data was taken from.

| Bill (€) | No. of families |
|---|---|
| 70 - 79.99 | 27 |
| 80 - 89.99 | 32 |
| 90 - 99.99 | 48 |
| 100 - 109.99 | 25 |
| 110 - 119.99 | 37 |
| 120 - 129.99 | 21 |
| 130 - 139.99 | 18 |
| 140 - 149.99 | 7 |

**6** An examination worth 100 marks was given to 800 biology students. The cumulative frequency graph for the students' results is shown on the following page.

**a** Find the number of students who scored 45 marks or less for the test.

**b** Find the median score.

**c** Between what values do the middle 50% of test results lie?

**d** Find the interquartile range of the data.

**e** What percentage of students obtained a mark of 55 or more?

**f** If a 'distinction' is awarded to the top 10% of students, what score is required to receive this honour?

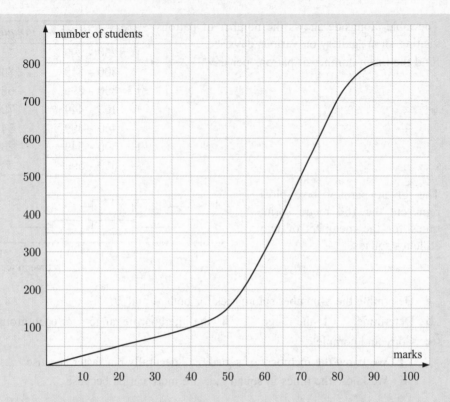

**7** The number of peanuts in a jar varies slightly from jar to jar. A sample of 30 jars for two brands X and Y was taken and the number of peanuts in each jar was recorded.

| | | *Brand X* | | | | | | *Brand Y* | | | |
|---|---|---|---|---|---|---|---|---|---|---|---|
| 871 | 885 | 878 | 882 | 889 | 885 | 909 | 906 | 913 | 891 | 898 | 901 |
| 916 | 913 | 886 | 905 | 907 | 898 | 894 | 894 | 928 | 893 | 924 | 892 |
| 874 | 904 | 901 | 894 | 897 | 899 | 927 | 907 | 901 | 900 | 907 | 913 |
| 908 | 901 | 898 | 894 | 895 | 895 | 921 | 904 | 903 | 896 | 901 | 895 |
| 910 | 904 | 896 | 893 | 903 | 888 | 917 | 903 | 910 | 903 | 909 | 904 |

**a** Produce a back to back stem plot for the data for each brand.

**b** Copy and complete this table:

| | Brand X | Brand Y |
|---|---|---|
| outliers | | |
| shape | | |
| centre (median) | | |
| spread (range) | | |

**c** Use the above information to compare Brand X and Brand Y.

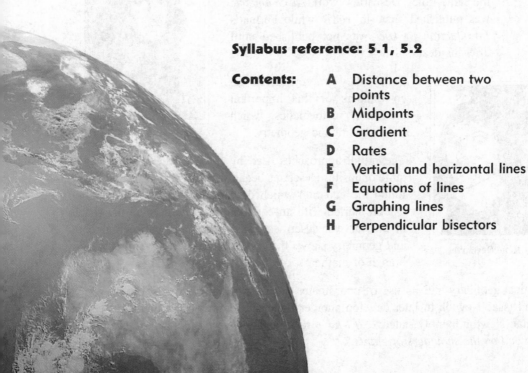

# Chapter **8**

# Coordinate geometry

**Syllabus reference: 5.1, 5.2**

## OPENING PROBLEM

A city has two hospitals:
Ridgehaven located at R(6, −9),
and Sunport located at S(−8, 5).

**Things to think about:**

a  Trish lives at T(4, 4). Which hospital is Trish closest to?

b  Can you find the point midway between the hospitals?

c  The city's planning council wants to define a 'boundary line' so that people will go to the hospital closest to them. Can you find the equation of this boundary line?

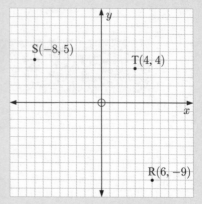

## HISTORICAL NOTE

History now shows that the two Frenchmen René Descartes and Pierre de Fermat arrived at the idea of **analytical geometry** at about the same time. Descartes' work *La Geometrie* was published first, in 1637, while Fermat's *Introduction to Loci* was not published until after his death.

**Pierre de Fermat**

Today, they are considered the co-founders of this important branch of mathematics, which links algebra and geometry.

**Réne Descartes**

The initial approaches used by these mathematicians were quite opposite. Descartes began with a line or curve and then found the equation which described it. Fermat, to a large extent, started with an equation and investigated the shape of the curve it described. This interaction between algebra and geometry shows the power of **analytical geometry** as a branch of mathematics.

Analytical geometry and its use of coordinates provided the mathematical tools which enabled Isaac Newton to later develop another important branch of mathematics called **calculus**. Newton humbly stated: *"If I have seen further than Descartes, it is because I have stood on the shoulders of giants."*

# THE NUMBER PLANE

The position of any point in the **number plane** can be specified in terms of an **ordered pair** of numbers $(x, y)$, where:

DEMO

$x$ is the **horizontal step** from a fixed point or **origin** O, and
$y$ is the **vertical step** from O.

Once the origin O has been given, two perpendicular axes are drawn. The **x-axis** is horizontal and the **y-axis** is vertical. The axes divide the number plane into four **quadrants**.

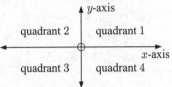

The number plane is also known as either:

- the **2-dimensional plane**, or
- the **Cartesian plane**, named after **René Descartes**.

In the diagram, the point P is at $(a, b)$.
  $a$ and $b$ are referred to as the **coordinates** of P.
  $a$ is called the **x-coordinate**.
  $b$ is called the **y-coordinate**.

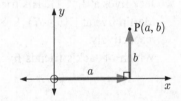

**Examples:**  The coordinates of the given points are

$$A(4, 2)$$
$$B(0, 2)$$
$$C(-3, 1)$$
$$D(-1, 0)$$
$$E(1, -2).$$

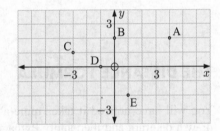

# A  DISTANCE BETWEEN TWO POINTS

Suppose we have the points A$(1, 2)$ and B$(5, 4)$, and we want to find the distance $d$ between A and B.

By drawing line segments AC and BC along the grid lines, we form a right angled triangle with hypotenuse AB.

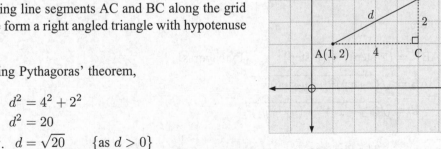

Now, using Pythagoras' theorem,

$$d^2 = 4^2 + 2^2$$
$$\therefore \quad d^2 = 20$$
$$\therefore \quad d = \sqrt{20} \quad \{\text{as } d > 0\}$$

So, the distance between A and B is $\sqrt{20}$ units.

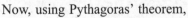

## EXERCISE 8A.1

**1** Use Pythagoras' theorem where appropriate to find the distance between:

    **a** A and B         **b** D and E

    **c** A and E         **d** F and H

    **e** D and F         **f** B and F

    **g** C and D        **h** H and B.

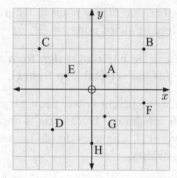

**2** Jack lives at J(2, 1). His friends Kevin, Ling, and Martin live at K(5, −7), L(8, 7), and M(−5, −4) respectively.

Which of Jack's friends lives closest to him?

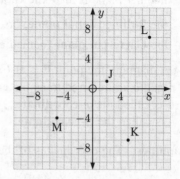

## THE DISTANCE FORMULA

You will have noticed it takes quite a lot of time to draw a diagram and then apply Pythagoras' theorem.

To make the process quicker, we can develop a formula.

To go from $A(x_1, y_1)$ to $B(x_2, y_2)$, we find the

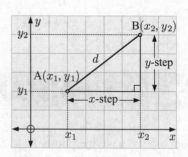

$$x\text{-step} = x_2 - x_1$$
and $y\text{-step} = y_2 - y_1.$

As before,

$$(AB)^2 = (x\text{-step})^2 + (y\text{-step})^2 \qquad \{\text{Pythagoras}\}$$

$$\therefore \ AB = \sqrt{(x\text{-step})^2 + (y\text{-step})^2}$$

$$\therefore \ d = \sqrt{(x_2 - x_1)^2 + (y_2 - y_1)^2}.$$

> The distance between two points $A(x_1, y_1)$ and $B(x_2, y_2)$
> is given by $\mathbf{AB} = \sqrt{(x_2 - x_1)^2 + (y_2 - y_1)^2}.$

### Example 1

**Self Tutor**

Find the distance between $A(6, 3)$ and $B(8, -2)$.

$\underset{\underset{x_1 \ y_1}{\uparrow \ \uparrow}}{A(6, 3)} \qquad \underset{\underset{x_2 \ y_2}{\uparrow \ \uparrow}}{B(8, -2)}$

$$\begin{aligned} AB &= \sqrt{(8-6)^2 + (-2-3)^2} \\ &= \sqrt{2^2 + (-5)^2} \\ &= \sqrt{4 + 25} \\ &= \sqrt{29} \text{ units} \end{aligned}$$

> The distance formula saves us having to graph the points each time we want to find a distance.

## EXERCISE 8A.2

1 Find the distance from:

  **a** $A(2, 6)$ to $B(3, 3)$       **b** $C(-2, 3)$ to $D(1, 5)$

  **c** $M(2, 4)$ to $N(-1, -3)$    **d** $O(0, 0)$ to $P(-2, 4)$

  **e** $R(3, -2)$ to $S(5, -2)$    **f** $T(0, 3)$ to $U(2, -1)$

  **g** $W(-4, 0)$ to $X(0, 3)$    **h** $Y(-1, -4)$ to $Z(-3, 3)$.

2 In the map alongside, each grid unit represents 1 km.

Find the distance between:

  **a** the lighthouse and the tree

  **b** the jetty and the lighthouse

  **c** the well and the tree

  **d** the lighthouse and the well.

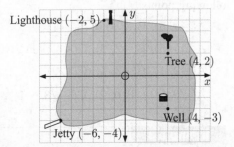

### Example 2

**Self Tutor**

The points $A(2, -1)$, $B(5, 1)$ and $C(0, 2)$ form a triangle ABC.

  **a** Use the distance formula to classify the triangle as equilateral, isosceles, or scalene.

  **b** Does the triangle have a right angle?

**a**

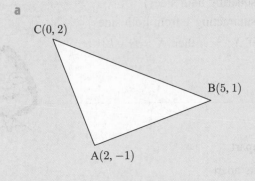

$$\begin{aligned} AB &= \sqrt{(5-2)^2 + (1--1)^2} \\ &= \sqrt{3^2 + 2^2} \\ &= \sqrt{13} \text{ units} \end{aligned}$$

$$\begin{aligned} AC &= \sqrt{(0-2)^2 + (2--1)^2} \\ &= \sqrt{(-2)^2 + 3^2} \\ &= \sqrt{13} \text{ units} \end{aligned}$$

$$\begin{aligned} BC &= \sqrt{(0-5)^2 + (2-1)^2} \\ &= \sqrt{(-5)^2 + 1^2} \\ &= \sqrt{26} \text{ units} \end{aligned}$$

Since $AB = AC$ but not $BC$, triangle ABC is isosceles.

**b**    $AB^2 + AC^2 = 13 + 13$
$$= 26$$
$$= BC^2$$

So, using the converse of Pythagoras' theorem, triangle ABC is right angled.
The right angle is opposite the longest side, so the right angle is at A.

**3** Use the distance formula to classify triangle ABC as either equilateral, isosceles or scalene.

  **a** A(−1, 0), B(−2, 3), C(−5, 4)     **b** A(−2, −4), B(1, 4), C(2, −3)

  **c** A(0, 1), B(0, −1), C(−$\sqrt{3}$, 0)     **d** A(0, −4), B($\sqrt{3}$, 1), C(3$\sqrt{3}$, −5)

**4** Use the distance formula to see if the following triangles are right angled. If they are, state the vertex where the right angle is.

  **a** A(1, −1), B(−1, 2), C(7, 3)     **b** A(−1, 2), B(3, 4), C(5, 0)

  **c** A(−2, 3), B(−5, 4), C(1, 2)     **d** A(5, 4), B(−4, 6), C(−3, 2)

**5** Fully classify the triangles formed by the following points:

  **a** A(−4, 5), B(3, 4), C(8, −1)

  **b** A(2, −5), B(−2, 2), C(−4, −1)

  **c** A(−2, 1), B(−3, 4), C(1, 2)

  **d** A($\sqrt{3}$, −1), B(0, 2), C(−$\sqrt{3}$, −1)

> Classify the triangles according to side length *and* the presence of a right angle.

---

**Example 3**　　　　　　　　　　　　　　　　　**◄)) Self Tutor**

Find $q$ given that P(−2, 4) and Q(−1, $q$) are $\sqrt{10}$ units apart.

From P to Q, the $x$-step $= -1 - -2 = 1$
   and the $y$-step $= q - 4$

$\therefore \sqrt{1^2 + (q-4)^2} = \sqrt{10}$
$\therefore 1 + (q-4)^2 = 10$    {squaring both sides}
$\therefore (q-4)^2 = 9$    {subtracting 1 from both sides}
$\therefore q - 4 = \pm 3$    {if $X^2 = k$ then $X = \pm\sqrt{k}$}
$\therefore q = 4 \pm 3$
So, $q = 1$ or 7.

> This example has two possible solutions. Draw a diagram to see why this is so.

**6** Find $q$ given that:

  **a** P(2, 1) and Q($q$, −3) are 5 units apart

  **b** P($q$, 6) and Q(−2, 1) are $\sqrt{29}$ units apart

  **c** P($q$, $q$) is $\sqrt{8}$ units from the origin

  **d** Q(3, $q$) is equidistant from A(−1, 5) and B(6, 4)

**7** Classify the triangle formed by the points A($a$, $b$), B($a$, $-b$), and C(1, 0) as scalene, isosceles, or equilateral.

# B                                                                      MIDPOINTS

The point M halfway between points A and B is called the **midpoint** of AB.

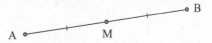

Consider the points A(3, 1) and B(5, 5). M is at (4, 3) on the line segment connecting A and B.

Using the distance formula, we can see that
AM = $\sqrt{(4-3)^2 + (3-1)^2} = \sqrt{5}$ units,  and
MB = $\sqrt{(5-4)^2 + (5-3)^2} = \sqrt{5}$ units.

So, M is the midpoint of AB.

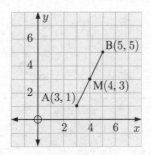

The $x$-coordinate of M is the *average* of the $x$-coordinates of A and B.

The $y$-coordinate of M is the *average* of the $y$-coordinates of A and B.

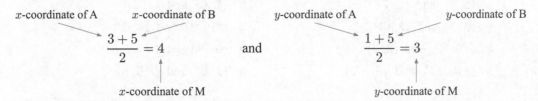

$x$-coordinate of A        $x$-coordinate of B        $y$-coordinate of A        $y$-coordinate of B

$$\frac{3+5}{2} = 4 \qquad \text{and} \qquad \frac{1+5}{2} = 3$$

$x$-coordinate of M        $y$-coordinate of M

## THE MIDPOINT FORMULA

If A is the point ($x_1$, $y_1$) and B is ($x_2$, $y_2$), then the **midpoint** M of AB has coordinates

$$\left( \frac{x_1 + x_2}{2}, \frac{y_1 + y_2}{2} \right).$$

### Example 4                                                            ◀ Self Tutor

Find the coordinates of M, the midpoint of AB, given A($-1$, 3) and B(5, $-2$).

The $x$-coordinate of M          The $y$-coordinate of M

$= \dfrac{-1+5}{2}$                  $= \dfrac{3+-2}{2}$

$= \dfrac{4}{2}$                     $= \dfrac{1}{2}$

$= 2$

∴ the midpoint of AB is M(2, $\frac{1}{2}$).

## EXERCISE 8B

**1  a** Use the distance formula to check that:

    **i** M is the midpoint of AB

    **ii** N is the midpoint of CD.

  **b** Use the midpoint formula to check your answers to part **a**.

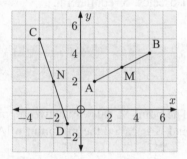

**2**

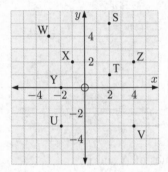

Using the diagram only, find the coordinates of the midpoint of the line segment:

**a** ST            **b** UV

**c** WX          **d** YZ

**e** SV            **f** UT

**g** YT           **h** TV

**3** Find the coordinates of the midpoint of the line segment that joins:

**a** $(2, 5)$ and $(4, 7)$              **b** $(1, 6)$ and $(4, 2)$

**c** $(0, 3)$ and $(2, 0)$              **d** $(3, -2)$ and $(3, 2)$

**e** $(-1, 4)$ and $(2, 2)$           **f** $(0, -3)$ and $(-2, 5)$

**g** $(-4, -1)$ and $(3, -2)$        **h** $(1, 0)$ and $(-6, 8)$.

---

| Example 5 | ◀) Self Tutor |
|---|---|

M is the midpoint of AB. If A is $(-1, 4)$ and M is $(2, 3)$, find the coordinates of B.

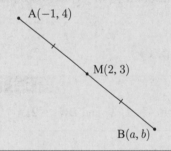

Let B have coordinates $(a, b)$.

$$\therefore \quad \frac{a + (-1)}{2} = 2 \quad \text{and} \quad \frac{b + 4}{2} = 3$$

$$\therefore \quad a - 1 = 4 \quad \text{and} \quad b + 4 = 6$$

$$\therefore \quad a = 5 \quad \text{and} \quad b = 2$$

So, B is the point $(5, 2)$.

---

**4** M is the midpoint of AB. Find the coordinates of B if:

**a** A is $(1, 3)$ and M is $(2, -1)$       **b** A is $(2, 1)$ and M is $(0, 2)$

**c** A is $(-2, 1)$ and M is $(-1\frac{1}{2}, 3)$     **d** A is $(3, -2)$ and M is $(3\frac{1}{2}, -2)$

**e** A is $(0, 0)$ and M is $(2, -\frac{1}{2})$       **f** A is $(-3, \frac{1}{2})$ and M is $(0, 0)$.

**Example 6**    ◄ᴺ) **Self Tutor**

M is the midpoint of AB. Use *equal steps* to find the coordinates of B, given A is $(-4, 3)$ and M is $(-1, 2)$.

A$(-4, 3)$    $+3$

$-1$    $+3$

M$(-1, 2)$

$-1$

B$(a, b)$

$x$-step:    $-4 \xrightarrow{+3} -1 \xrightarrow{+3} 2$

$y$-step:    $3 \xrightarrow{-1} 2 \xrightarrow{-1} 1$

$\therefore$  B is $(2, 1)$

**5**  Check your answers to questions **4a** and **4b** using equal steps.

**6**  If P is the midpoint of IJ, find the coordinates of I for:

  **a**  P$(2, -6)$  and  J$(4, -3)$          **b**  P$(0, -2)$  and  J$(-5, 1)$.

**7**  PQ is the diameter of a circle, centre C. If P is $(4, -7)$ and Q is $(-2, -3)$, find the coordinates of C.

**8**  AB is a diameter of a circle, centre $(3\frac{1}{2}, -1)$. Find the coordinates of A given that B is $(2, 0)$.

**9**  Torvald gets into a rowboat at A$(1, 2)$ on one side of a circular lake. He rows in a straight line towards the other side. He stops in the middle of the lake for a rest, at M$(-2, 3)$.

  **a**  What are the coordinates of the point Torvald is aiming for?

  **b**  If distances are in km, how much further does he have to row?

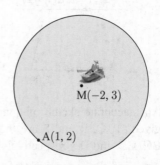

**10**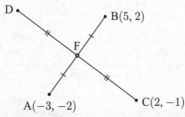

A flagpole at F is held by four wires pegged into the ground at A, B, C and D. Opposite pegs are the same distance away from the pole. What are the coordinates of D?

**11**  Molly the cat stands at A$(-1, -2)$, watching in fear as Susan and Sandra throw water balloons at each other. Susan is at B$(2, 3)$, and Sandra is at C$(0, 4)$. The two girls throw at the same time, and their balloons collide and explode midway between them. Units are given in metres.

  **a**  Find the coordinates of the explosion point.

  **b**  How far is Molly from the explosion?

### Example 7

🔊 **Self Tutor**

Use midpoints to find the fourth vertex of the given parallelogram:

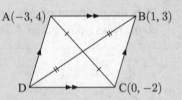

Since ABCD is a parallelogram, the diagonals bisect each other.

∴ the midpoint of DB is the same as the midpoint of AC.

If D is $(a, b)$, then
$$\frac{a+1}{2} = \frac{-3+0}{2} \quad \text{and} \quad \frac{b+3}{2} = \frac{4+-2}{2}$$
$$\therefore \quad a+1 = -3 \quad \text{and} \quad b+3 = 2$$
$$\therefore \quad a = -4 \quad \text{and} \quad b = -1$$

So, D is $(-4, -1)$.

**12** Use midpoints to find the fourth vertex of the given parallelograms:

a
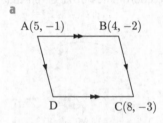

b
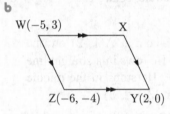

c
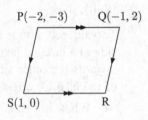

**13** An inaccurate sketch of quadrilateral ABCD is given. P, Q, R and S are the midpoints of AB, BC, CD and DA respectively.

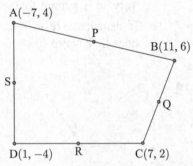

a Find the coordinates of:
   i P    ii Q    iii R    iv S

b Find the length of:
   i PQ    ii QR    iii RS    iv SP

c What can be deduced about quadrilateral PQRS from **b**?

## C                                                    GRADIENT

Consider the following lines. Which do you think is the steepest?

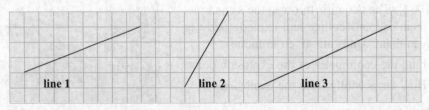

line 1          line 2          line 3

We can see that line 2 rises much faster than the other two lines, so line 2 is the steepest. However, most people would find it hard to tell which of lines 1 and 3 is steeper just by looking at them. We therefore need a more precise way to measure the steepness of a line.

> The **gradient** of a line is a measure of its steepness.

To calculate the gradient of a line, we first choose any two distinct points on the line. We can move from one point to the other by making a positive **horizontal step** followed by a **vertical step**.

If the line is sloping upwards, the vertical step will be positive.

If the line is sloping downwards, the vertical step will be negative.

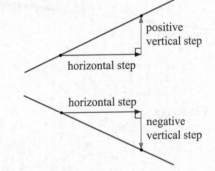

The gradient is calculated by dividing the vertical step by the horizontal step.

$$\text{The } \textbf{gradient} \text{ of a line} = \frac{\text{vertical step}}{\text{horizontal step}} \quad \text{or} \quad \frac{\textit{y}\textbf{-step}}{\textit{x}\textbf{-step}}.$$

For lines with the same horizontal step, as the lines get steeper the vertical step increases. This results in a higher gradient.

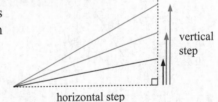

---

**Example 8**    ◀️ **Self Tutor**

Find the gradient of each line segment:

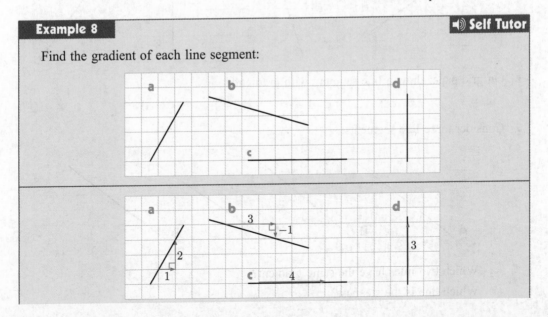

| a | gradient $= \frac{2}{1}$ $= 2$ | b | gradient $= \frac{-1}{3}$ $= -\frac{1}{3}$ | c | gradient $= \frac{0}{4}$ $= 0$ | d | gradient $= \frac{3}{0}$ which is undefined |

From the previous example, you should have found that:

> • the gradient of **horizontal** lines is **0**
> • the gradient of **vertical** lines is **undefined**.

Lines like  are upwards sloping and have **positive gradients**.

Lines like  are downwards sloping and have **negative gradients**.

## EXERCISE 8C.1

1 Find the gradient of each line segment:

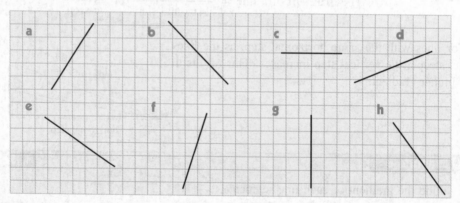

2 On grid paper draw a line segment with gradient:

a $\frac{3}{4}$    b $-2$    c $4$    d $-\frac{1}{4}$    e $0$    f $\frac{4}{7}$

3 Consider these line segments:

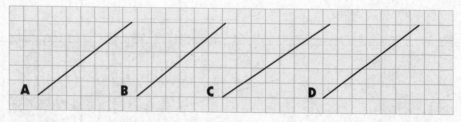

a Which two lines have the same gradient?

b Which line is the steepest?

**Example 9**                                              ◄ঠ) **Self Tutor**

Draw a line through $(1, 3)$ with gradient $-\frac{1}{2}$.

Plot the point $(1, 3)$.

The gradient $= \dfrac{y\text{-step}}{x\text{-step}} = \dfrac{-1}{2}$

$\therefore$ let $y\text{-step} = -1, \; x\text{-step} = 2$.

We use these steps to find another point and draw the line through these points.

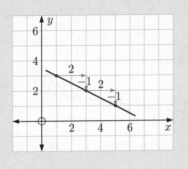

**4** On the same set of axes, draw lines through $(2, 3)$ with gradients $\frac{1}{3}, \frac{3}{4}, 2$ and $4$.

**5** On the same set of axes, draw lines through $(-1, 2)$ with gradients $0, -\frac{2}{5}, -2$ and $-5$.

## THE GRADIENT FORMULA

If a line passes through $A(x_1, y_1)$ and $B(x_2, y_2)$, then the horizontal or $x$-step is $x_2 - x_1$, and the vertical or $y$-step is $y_2 - y_1$.

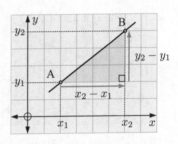

The **gradient** of the line passing through $A(x_1, y_1)$ and $B(x_2, y_2)$ is $\dfrac{y_2 - y_1}{x_2 - x_1}$.

**Example 10**                                             ◄ঠ) **Self Tutor**

Find the gradient of the line through $(-2, 1)$ and $(2, 9)$.

$$\underset{x_1 \; y_1}{(-2, 1)} \quad \underset{x_2 \; y_2}{(2, 9)}$$

$$\begin{aligned} \text{gradient} &= \frac{y_2 - y_1}{x_2 - x_1} \\ &= \frac{9 - 1}{2 - (-2)} \\ &= \frac{8}{4} \\ &= 2 \end{aligned}$$

## EXERCISE 8C.2

1   Find the gradients of the line segments joining the following pairs of points:

   a   $(1, 3)$  and  $(6, 8)$       b   $(-4, 5)$  and  $(4, 3)$       c   $(0, 0)$  and  $(3, 5)$

   d   $(5, 2)$  and  $(2, 9)$       e   $(1, -4)$  and  $(-5, -2)$     f   $(-3, 4)$  and  $(2, 4)$

   g   $(-6, 0)$  and  $(0, -4)$     h   $(-3, 5)$  and  $(-3, 1)$      i   $(-5, -8)$  and  $(3, 4)$.

2   Find the gradient of line:

   a   1                b   2

   c   3                d   4

   e   5                f   6

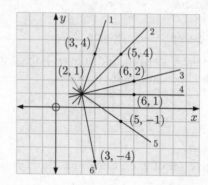

---

### Example 11                                                    ◀)) Self Tutor

Find $a$ given that the line joining P$(a, -4)$ to Q$(1, 8)$ has gradient 3.

The gradient of PQ $= 3$,   so   $\dfrac{8 - (-4)}{1 - a} = 3$        {gradient formula}

$$\therefore \ 12 = 3(1 - a)$$
$$\therefore \ 12 = 3 - 3a$$
$$\therefore \ 3a = -9$$
$$\therefore \ a = -3$$

---

3   Find $a$ given that the line joining:

   a   P$(1, 5)$  to  Q$(4, a)$  has gradient 2

   b   M$(-2, a)$  to  N$(0, -2)$  has gradient $-4$

   c   A$(a, 8)$  to  B$(-3, -4)$  has gradient $\frac{2}{3}$.

4   A line with gradient $-2$ passes through the point $(-1, 10)$. Determine where this line cuts the $x$-axis.

   **Hint:** A point on the $x$-axis has coordinates $(a, 0)$.

## PARALLEL LINES

The figure ABCD alongside is a trapezium, with AB parallel to DC.

DC has a gradient of $\frac{1}{3}$, and AB has a gradient of $\frac{3}{9} = \frac{1}{3}$.

Thus, AB and DC have the same gradient.

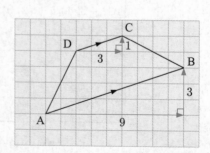

- If two lines are **parallel**, they have **equal gradient**.
- If two lines have **equal gradient**, they are **parallel**.

# PERPENDICULAR LINES

The figure alongside is a square, so AB
is perpendicular to BC.

AB has a gradient of $\frac{3}{2}$, and BC has a gradient
of $\frac{-2}{3} = -\frac{2}{3}$.

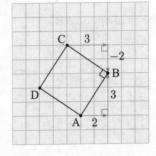

The gradients are *negative reciprocals* of each
other and their product is $\frac{3}{2} \times -\frac{2}{3} = -1$.

For lines which are not horizontal or vertical:

- if the lines are **perpendicular**, their gradients are **negative reciprocals**.
- if the gradients are **negative reciprocals**, the lines are **perpendicular**.

---

**Example 12**                                                    ◀) **Self Tutor**

If a line has gradient $\frac{2}{5}$, find the gradient of all lines:

a   parallel to the given line                    b   perpendicular to the given line.

a   The original line has gradient $\frac{2}{5}$, so the gradient of all parallel lines is also $\frac{2}{5}$.

b   The gradient of all perpendicular lines is $-\frac{5}{2}$.    {the negative reciprocal}

---

# EXERCISE 8C.3

1   Find the gradient of all lines   i   parallel   ii   perpendicular  to a line with gradient:

   a   $\frac{3}{4}$   b   $\frac{1}{5}$   c   4   d   $-3$   e   $-\frac{3}{7}$   f   $-4\frac{1}{2}$   g   0   h   $-1$

2   The gradients of several pairs of lines are listed below.
    Which of the line pairs are perpendicular?

   a   $2, \frac{1}{2}$   b   $\frac{3}{5}, -\frac{3}{5}$   c   $4, -\frac{1}{4}$   d   $\frac{3}{4}, 1\frac{1}{3}$   e   $-\frac{2}{5}, 2\frac{1}{2}$   f   $-\frac{3}{8}, 2\frac{1}{3}$

3   Consider the line segments below.

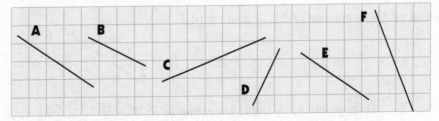

Identify any pairs of lines which are:

   a   parallel                          b   perpendicular.

**Example 13**                                      ◀) **Self Tutor**

Find $t$ given that the line joining A$(1, 4)$ to B$(5, t)$ is perpendicular to a line with gradient $\frac{2}{3}$.

The gradient of AB $= -\dfrac{3}{2}$    {perpendicular to line with gradient $\frac{2}{3}$}

$\therefore \dfrac{t - 4}{5 - 1} = -\dfrac{3}{2}$    {gradient formula}

$\therefore \dfrac{t - 4}{4} = \dfrac{-6}{4}$    {writing fractions with equal denominators}

$\therefore t - 4 = -6$    {equating numerators}

$\therefore t = -2$

**4**  Find $t$ given that the line joining:

**a**  C$(2, 5)$ and D$(4, t)$ is perpendicular to a line with gradient $\frac{1}{4}$.

**b**  X$(-3, -1)$ and Y$(t, 1)$ is perpendicular to a line with gradient $3\frac{1}{2}$.

**5**  Given the points A$(1, 2)$, B$(-3, 0)$, C$(5, 3)$, and D$(3, k)$, find $k$ if:

**a**  AB is parallel to CD          **b**  AC is parallel to DB

**c**  AB is perpendicular to CD     **d**  AD is perpendicular to BC.

**6**  Consider the triangle ABC alongside.

**a**  Find the length of each side. Hence, show that the triangle is right angled at B.

**b**  Find the gradients of AB and BC. Hence verify that AB is perpendicular to BC.

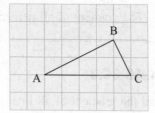

## COLLINEAR POINTS

> Three or more points are **collinear** if they lie on the same straight line.

Consider the three collinear points A, B, and C, which all lie on the line $L$.

gradient of AB = gradient of BC = gradient of $L$.

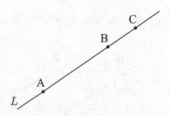

> Three points A, B, and C are **collinear** if:
>
> gradient of AB = gradient of BC (= gradient of AC)

**Example 14**    ◀)) **Self Tutor**

Show that the points  A($-5$, $-3$), B($-1$, $-1$), and C($7$, $3$) are collinear.

The gradient of  $AB = \dfrac{-1 - (-3)}{-1 - (-5)}$    The gradient of  $BC = \dfrac{3 - (-1)}{7 - (-1)}$

$\qquad\qquad\qquad = \frac{2}{4} = \frac{1}{2}$    $\qquad\qquad\qquad = \frac{4}{8} = \frac{1}{2}$

AB and BC have equal gradients, and so A, B, and C are collinear.

## EXERCISE 8C.4

1  Determine whether the following sets of three points are collinear:

   **a**  A($-1$, $7$), B($1$, $1$), C($4$, $-8$)    **b**  P($-4$, $2$), Q($-1$, $3$), R($5$, $6$)

   **c**  R($-2$, $1$), S($4$, $11$), T($-5$, $-4$)    **d**  X($7$, $-5$), Y($2$, $-1$), Z($-6$, $5$)

2  Find $n$ given that:

   **a**  A($-7$, $-8$), B($-1$, $1$),  and  C($3$, $n$) are collinear.

   **b**  P($3$, $-11$), Q($n$, $-2$), and R($-5$, $13$) are collinear.

# D  RATES

In the previous section we considered the gradients of straight lines and the gradient between points.

We see gradients every day in the real world when we consider the slope of a hill or ramp. The sign alongside indicates to drivers that the road ahead is steeply downhill.

Gradients are also important when we consider how quantities are related. If we draw the graph relating two quantities, the gradient of the line describes the **rate** at which one quantity changes relative to the other.

One of the most common examples of a rate is **speed**, which is the rate at which something is travelling.

For example, a cheetah sprinting after its prey can travel 20 m every second.

If we plot the distance the cheetah travels against the time taken, the gradient of the graph

$$= \frac{y\text{-step}}{x\text{-step}} = \frac{80}{4} = 20.$$

In comparison, the speed of the cheetah

$$= \frac{\text{distance travelled}}{\text{time taken}} = \frac{80 \text{ m}}{4 \text{ s}} = 20 \text{ m s}^{-1}.$$

So, the gradient of the graph gives the speed at which the cheetah is running.

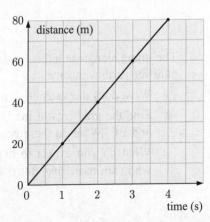

## EXERCISE 8D

**1**

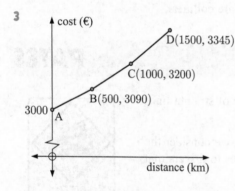

The graph alongside displays the mass of various volumes of silver.

   **a** Find the gradient of the line.

   **b** Interpret the gradient found in **a**.

   **c**   **i** What is the mass of 3 cm³ of silver?

   **ii** What is the volume of 100 g of silver?

**2** A motorcyclist makes a day's journey and plots her progress on the graph alongside. Find:

   **a** the average speed for the whole trip

   **b** the average speed from

   **i** O to A       **ii** B to C

   **c** the time interval over which her average speed was greatest.

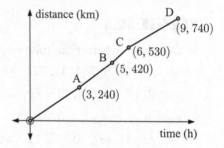

**3**

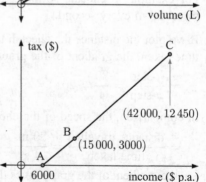

Harriet buys a car. Every 500 km she records how much she has spent on petrol and upkeep costs. She then plots the results on the graph shown.

   **a** How much did the car cost?

   **b** What is the gradient of AB? What does this represent?

   **c** Find the gradient of the straight line segment from A to D. What does this gradient mean?

**4** The graphs alongside show the energy per litre of biodiesel and ethanol.

   **a** Find the gradient of each line.

   **b** Which type of fuel gives more energy per litre?

**5** The graph alongside indicates the amount of tax paid for various incomes.

   **a** What does the value at A mean?

   **b** Find the gradients of the line segments AB and BC. What do these gradients indicate?

   **c** What do you expect to happen for people who earn more than $42 000 p.a.?

## E | VERTICAL AND HORIZONTAL LINES

### VERTICAL LINES

The graph opposite shows a vertical line passing through $(2, -1)$ and $(2, 3)$.

The gradient of the line is $\dfrac{3 - -1}{2 - 2} = \dfrac{4}{0}$ which is undefined.

All points on the line have $x$-coordinate 2, so the **equation** of the line is $x = 2$.

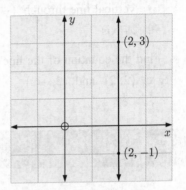

> All **vertical** lines have equations of the form $x = a$ where $a$ is a constant.
>
> The gradient of a vertical line is **undefined**.

### HORIZONTAL LINES

This graph shows a horizontal line passing through $(-3, 1)$ and $(2, 1)$.

The gradient of the line is $\dfrac{1 - 1}{2 - -3} = \dfrac{0}{5} = 0$.

All points on the line have $y$-coordinate 1, so the **equation** of the line is $y = 1$.

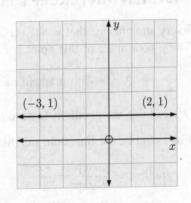

> All **horizontal** lines have equations of the form $y = b$ where $b$ is a constant.
>
> The gradient of a horizontal line is **zero**.

### EXERCISE 8E

1   Find the equations of the lines labelled **A** to **D**:

a

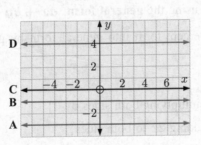

b

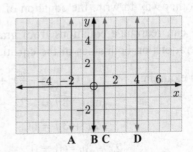

2   Identify as either a vertical or horizontal line and hence plot the graph of:

   **a** $x = 1$        **b** $y = 2$        **c** $x = -4$        **d** $y = -2$

**3** Find the equation of the:

**a** horizontal line through $(3, -4)$    **b** vertical line which cuts the $x$-axis at 5

**c** vertical line through $(-1, -3)$    **d** horizontal line which cuts the $y$-axis at 2

**e** $x$-axis    **f** $y$-axis

**4** Find the equation of the line passing through:

**a** $(2, 2)$ and $(2, -2)$    **b** $(2, -2)$ and $(-2, -2)$.

## F    EQUATIONS OF LINES

The **equation of a line** is an equation which connects the $x$ and $y$ values for every point on the line.

## GRADIENT-INTERCEPT FORM

Every straight line that is not vertical will cut the $y$-axis at a single point. The $y$-coordinate of this point is called the **$y$-intercept** of the line.

A line with gradient $m$ and $y$-intercept $c$ has equation $y = mx + c$.

We call this the **gradient-intercept form** of the equation of a line.

For example, the line alongside has

$$\text{gradient} = \frac{y\text{-step}}{x\text{-step}} = \frac{-2}{3}$$

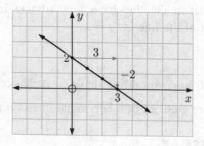

and its $y$-intercept is 2.

So, its equation is $y = -\frac{2}{3}x + 2$.

## GENERAL FORM

Another way to write the equation of a line is using the **general form** $ax + by + d = 0$.

We can rearrange equations from gradient-intercept form into general form by performing operations on both sides of the equation.

For example,    if $y = -\frac{2}{3}x + 2$

then  $3y = -2x + 6$    {multiplying both sides by 3}

$\therefore \quad 2x + 3y = 6$    {adding $2x$ to both sides}

$\therefore \quad 2x + 3y - 6 = 0$    {subtracting 6 from both sides}

So, the line with gradient-intercept form $y = -\frac{2}{3}x + 2$ has general form $2x + 3y - 6 = 0$.

# FINDING THE EQUATION OF A LINE

In order to find the equation, we need to know some information about the line.

Suppose we know the gradient of the line is 2 and that the line passes through $(4, 1)$.

We suppose $(x, y)$ is any point on the line.

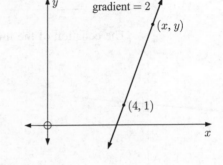

The gradient between $(4, 1)$ and $(x, y)$ is $\dfrac{y - 1}{x - 4}$, and this gradient must equal 2.

So, $\dfrac{y - 1}{x - 4} = 2$

$\therefore \; y - 1 = 2(x - 4)$   {multiplying both sides by $(x - 4)$}

$\therefore \; y - 1 = 2x - 8$   {expanding the brackets}

$\qquad \therefore \; y = 2x - 7$   {adding 1 to both sides}

This is the equation of the line in gradient-intercept form.

We can find the equation of a line if we know:

- its **gradient** and the **coordinates of any point** on the line, or
- the **coordinates of two distinct points** on the line.

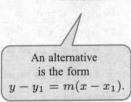

If a straight line has gradient $m$ and passes through the point $(x_1, y_1)$ then its equation is $\dfrac{y - y_1}{x - x_1} = m$.

We can rearrange this equation into either gradient-intercept or general form.

> An alternative is the form $y - y_1 = m(x - x_1)$.

---

**Example 15**   ◄ᴺ **Self Tutor**

Find, in *gradient-intercept form*, the equation of the line through $(-1, 3)$ with a gradient of 5.

The equation of the line is

$\qquad y = mx + c$ where $m = 5$.

When $x = -1$, $y = 3$

$\qquad 3 = 5(-1) + c$

$\therefore \; 3 = c - 5$

$\therefore \; c = 8$

Thus, $y = 5x + 8$ is the equation.

*or*   The equation of the line is

$\qquad \dfrac{y - 3}{x - -1} = 5$

$\therefore \; \dfrac{y - 3}{x + 1} = 5$

$\therefore \; y - 3 = 5(x + 1)$

$\therefore \; y - 3 = 5x + 5$

$\therefore \; y = 5x + 8$

### Example 16                                         ◀) Self Tutor

Find, in *general form*, the equation of the line with gradient $\frac{3}{4}$
which passes through $(5, -2)$.

The equation of the line is         $\dfrac{y - -2}{x - 5} = \dfrac{3}{4}$

$\therefore \ \dfrac{y + 2}{x - 5} = \dfrac{3}{4}$

$\therefore \ 4(y + 2) = 3(x - 5)$

$\therefore \ 4y + 8 = 3x - 15$

$\therefore \ 3x - 4y - 23 = 0$

### Example 17                                         ◀) Self Tutor

Find the equation of the line which passes through the points $A(-1, 5)$ and $B(2, 3)$.

The gradient of the line is   $\dfrac{3 - 5}{2 - -1} = \dfrac{-2}{3}$.

Using A, the equation is            *or*     Since $m = -\frac{2}{3}$, we have $y = -\frac{2}{3}x + c$.

$\dfrac{y - 5}{x - -1} = \dfrac{-2}{3}$                    Using A, we substitute $x = -1$, $y = 5$

$\therefore \ \dfrac{y - 5}{x + 1} = \dfrac{-2}{3}$                   $\therefore \ 5 = \left(-\frac{2}{3}\right)(-1) + c$

$\therefore \ 3(y - 5) = -2(x + 1)$             $\therefore \ 5 = \frac{2}{3} + c$

$\therefore \ 3y - 15 = -2x - 2$               $\therefore \ c = 5 - \frac{2}{3} = \frac{13}{3}$

$\therefore \ 2x + 3y - 13 = 0$                $\therefore \ y = -\frac{2}{3}x + \frac{13}{3}$

We would get the same
equations using point B.
Try it yourself.

## EXERCISE 8F.1

1  Find the equation of the line with:

    **a**  gradient 1 and $y$-intercept $-2$          **b**  gradient $-1$ and $y$-intercept 4

    **c**  gradient 2 and $y$-intercept 0           **d**  gradient $-\frac{1}{2}$ and $y$-intercept 3.

2  Find, in *gradient-intercept form*, the equation of the line through:

    **a**  $(2, -5)$ with gradient 4               **b**  $(-1, -2)$ with gradient $-3$

    **c**  $(7, -3)$ with gradient $-5$             **d**  $(1, 4)$ with gradient $\frac{1}{2}$

    **e**  $(-1, 3)$ with gradient $-\frac{1}{3}$           **f**  $(2, 6)$ with gradient 0.

**3** Find, in *general form*, the equation of the line through:

    **a** $(2, 5)$ having gradient $\frac{2}{3}$         **b** $(-1, 4)$ having gradient $\frac{3}{5}$

    **c** $(5, 0)$ having gradient $-\frac{1}{3}$       **d** $(6, -2)$ having gradient $-\frac{2}{7}$

    **e** $(-3, -1)$ having gradient $4$         **f** $(5, -3)$ having gradient $-2$

    **g** $(4, -5)$ having gradient $-3\frac{1}{2}$       **h** $(-7, -2)$ having gradient $6$.

**4** Find, in *gradient-intercept form*, the equation of the line which passes through the points:

    **a** A$(2, 3)$ and B$(4, 8)$         **b** A$(0, 3)$ and B$(-1, 5)$

    **c** A$(-1, -2)$ and B$(4, -2)$       **d** C$(-3, 1)$ and D$(2, 0)$

    **e** P$(5, -1)$ and Q$(-1, -2)$       **f** R$(-1, -3)$ and S$(-4, -1)$.

**5** Find, in *general form*, the equation of the line which passes through:

    **a** $(0, 1)$ and $(3, 2)$     **b** $(1, 4)$ and $(0, -1)$     **c** $(2, -1)$ and $(-1, -4)$

    **d** $(0, -2)$ and $(5, 2)$     **e** $(3, 2)$ and $(-1, 0)$     **f** $(-1, -1)$ and $(2, -3)$.

---

**Example 18**     🔊 **Self Tutor**

Find the equation of the line with graph:

**a** 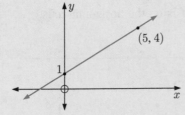      **b**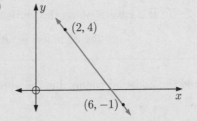

**a** Two points on the line are $(0, 1)$ and $(5, 4)$

    $\therefore$ gradient $m = \dfrac{4-1}{5-0} = \frac{3}{5}$

    and the $y$-intercept $c = 1$

    $\therefore$ the equation is $y = \frac{3}{5}x + 1$

    {gradient-intercept form}

**b** Two points on the line are $(2, 4)$ and $(6, -1)$

    $\therefore$ gradient $m = \dfrac{-1-4}{6-2} = -\frac{5}{4}$

    As we do not know the $y$-intercept we use the general form.

    The equation is $\dfrac{y-4}{x-2} = -\dfrac{5}{4}$

    $\therefore \ 4(y-4) = -5(x-2)$

    $\therefore \ 4y - 16 = -5x + 10$

    $\therefore \ 5x + 4y - 26 = 0$

---

**6** Find the equations of the illustrated lines:

    **a** 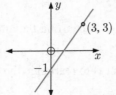     **b** 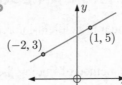     **c**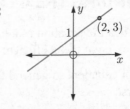

**d**

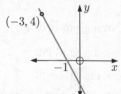

**e**

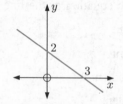

**f**

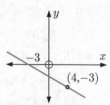

---

### Example 19    ◄⟩ Self Tutor

Find the equation connecting
the variables in:

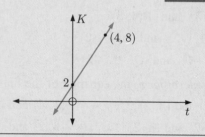

$(0, 2)$ and $(4, 8)$ lie on the straight line

$\therefore$ the gradient $m = \dfrac{8 - 2}{4 - 0} = \dfrac{6}{4} = \dfrac{3}{2}$, and the $y$-intercept $c = 2$.

In this case $K$ is on the vertical axis and $t$ is on the horizontal axis.

$\therefore$ the equation is $K = \frac{3}{2}t + 2$.

---

**7** Find the equation connecting the variables given:

**a**

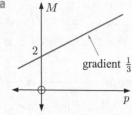

**b**

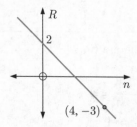

**c**

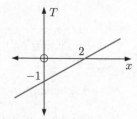

**d**

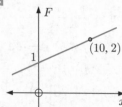

**e**

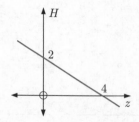

**f**

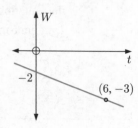

## FINDING THE GRADIENT FROM AN EQUATION

When the equation of a line is written in gradient-intercept form, we can find the gradient by looking at the coefficient of $x$.

For equations in general form, one method of finding the gradient is to rearrange the equation first.

### Example 20
◀)) **Self Tutor**

Find the gradient of the line $2x + 5y - 17 = 0$.

$$2x + 5y - 17 = 0$$
$$\therefore \ 5y = -2x + 17$$
$$\therefore \ y = -\tfrac{2}{5}x + \tfrac{17}{5}$$

So, the gradient is $-\tfrac{2}{5}$.

You will learn in the exercise a faster way of finding the gradient of a line with equation written in general form.

## EXERCISE 8F.2

1   Find the gradient of the line with equation:

a  $y = 3x + 2$          b  $y = 3 - 2x$          c  $y = 0$

d  $x = 5$          e  $y = \dfrac{2x + 1}{3}$          f  $y = \dfrac{3 - 4x}{5}$

2   Find the gradient of the line with equation:

a  $3x + y - 7 = 0$          b  $2x - 7y = 8$          c  $2x + 7y - 8 = 0$

d  $3x - 4y = 11$          e  $4x + 11y - 9 = 0$          f  $7x - 9y = 63$

3   a   Find the gradient of the line with equation $ax + by + d = 0$.

b   *Hence* find the gradient of the line with equation:

i   $2x + 5y + 1 = 0$          ii   $3x - 2y = 0$          iii   $5x + 4y - 10 = 0$

iv   $-x + 3y - 2 = 0$          v   $-2x + y = -3$          vi   $x - 4y = 6$

## DOES A POINT LIE ON A LINE?

A point lies on a line if its coordinates satisfy the equation of the line.

### Example 21
◀)) **Self Tutor**

Does $(3, -2)$ lie on the line with equation $5x - 2y = 20$?

Substituting $(3, -2)$ into $5x - 2y = 20$
$$\text{gives} \ 5(3) - 2(-2) = 20$$
$$\text{or} \ 19 = 20 \ \text{which is false.}$$

$\therefore \ (3, -2)$ does not lie on the line.

## EXERCISE 8F.3

1   **a**   Does $(3, 4)$ lie on the line with equation $3x - 2y - 1 = 0$?

    **b**   Does $(-2, 5)$ lie on the line with equation $5x + 3y = -5$?

    **c**   Does $(6, -\frac{1}{2})$ lie on the line with equation $3x - 8y - 22 = 0$?

    **d**   Does $(8, -\frac{2}{3})$ lie on the line with equation $x - 9y = 14$?

2   Find $k$ if:

    **a**   $(3, 4)$ lies on the line with equation $x - 2y - k = 0$

    **b**   $(1, 5)$ lies on the line with equation $4x - 2y = k$

    **c**   $(1, 5)$ lies on the line with equation $6x + 7y = k$

    **d**   $(-2, -3)$ lies on the line with equation $4x - 3y - k = 0$

3   Find $a$ given that:

    **a**   $(a, 3)$ lies on the line with equation $y = 2x - 1$

    **b**   $(-2, a)$ lies on the line with equation $y = 1 - 3x$

    **c**   $(a, 5)$ lies on the line with equation $y = 3x + 4$

4   A straight road is to pass through points A$(5, 3)$ and B$(1, 8)$.

    **a**   Find where this road meets the road given by:

        **i**   $x = 3$       **ii**   $y = 4$

    **b**   If we wish to refer to the points on road AB that are *between* A and B, how can we indicate this?

    **c**   Does C$(23, -20)$ lie on the road?

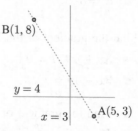

---

# G        GRAPHING LINES

**DISCUSSION**                                    **GRAPHING LINES**

Discuss the easiest way to graph a line when its equation is given in the form:

- $y = mx + c$         such as   $y = 2x + 3$
- $ax + by + d = 0$    such as   $2x + 3y - 12 = 0$.

## GRAPHING FROM THE GRADIENT-INTERCEPT FORM

The easiest way to graph lines with equations given in gradient-intercept form is to use the $y$-intercept and one other point on the graph. The other point can be found by substitution or by using the gradient.

**Example 22**                                                                    ◀) **Self Tutor**

Graph the line with equation   $y = \frac{5}{2}x - 2$.

*Method 1:*

The $y$-intercept is $-2$.

When $x = 2$, $y = 5 - 2 = 3$

$\therefore$ $(0, -2)$ and $(2, 3)$ lie on the line.

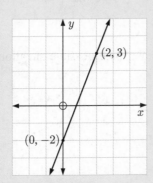

*Method 2:*

The $y$-intercept is $-2$

and the gradient $= \frac{5}{2}$ ◀—— $\dfrac{y\text{-step}}{x\text{-step}}$

So, we start at $(0, -2)$ and move to another point by moving across 2, then up 5.

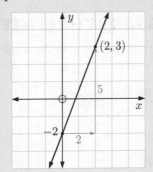

## GRAPHING FROM THE GENERAL FORM

The easiest way to graph lines given in general form is to use the axes intercepts.

> The $x$-intercept is found by letting $y = 0$.
> The $y$-intercept is found by letting $x = 0$.

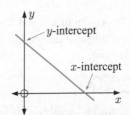

**Example 23**                                                                    ◀) **Self Tutor**

Graph the line with equation  $3x + 5y + 30 = 0$.

When $x = 0$, $5y + 30 = 0$

$\qquad\qquad \therefore\ y = -6$

So, the $y$-intercept is $-6$.

When $y = 0$, $3x + 30 = 0$

$\qquad\qquad \therefore\ x = -10$

So, the $x$-intercept is $-10$.

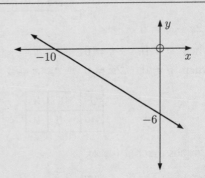

## EXERCISE 8G.1

**1** Draw the graph of the line with equation:

   **a**   $y = \frac{1}{2}x + 2$        **b**   $y = 2x + 1$        **c**   $y = -x + 3$

   **d**   $y = -3x + 2$       **e**   $y = -\frac{1}{2}x$         **f**   $y = -2x - 2$

   **g**   $y = \frac{3}{2}x$          **h**   $y = \frac{2}{3}x + 2$      **i**   $y = -\frac{3}{4}x - 1$

**2** Use axes intercepts to sketch the graphs of:

   **a**   $x + 2y = 8$        **b**   $4x + 3y - 12 = 0$     **c**   $2x - 3y = 6$

   **d**   $3x - y - 6 = 0$     **e**   $x + y = 5$          **f**   $x - y = -5$

   **g**   $2x - y + 4 = 0$     **h**   $9x - 2y = 9$        **i**   $3x + 4y = -15$

## FINDING WHERE LINES MEET

When we graph two lines on the same set of axes, there are three possible situations which may occur:

    *Case 1:*                          *Case 2:*                       *Case 3:*

| The lines meet in a single **point of intersection**. | The lines are **parallel** and **never meet**. There is no point of intersection. | The lines are **coincident**. There are infinitely many points of intersection. |

We saw these situations in **Chapter 5** when we solved simultaneous equations. In general there was a single solution, but in some special cases there was either no solution or infinitely many solutions.

---

### Example 24          ◀》 Self Tutor

Use graphical methods to find where the lines $x + y = 6$ and $2x - y = 6$ meet.

For $x + y = 6$

   when $x = 0$,   $y = 6$

   when $y = 0$,   $x = 6$

| $x$ | 0 | 6 |
|-----|---|---|
| $y$ | 6 | 0 |

For $2x - y = 6$

   when $x = 0$,   $-y = 6$    $\therefore$   $y = -6$

   when $y = 0$,   $2x = 6$    $\therefore$   $x = 3$

| $x$ | 0 | 3 |
|-----|----|---|
| $y$ | -6 | 0 |

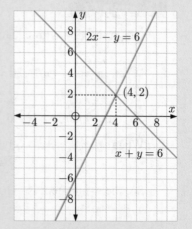

The graphs meet at $(4, 2)$.

*Check:* $4 + 2 = 6$ ✓ and $2 \times 4 - 2 = 6$ ✓

## EXERCISE 8G.2

**1** Use graphical methods to find the point of intersection of:

**a** $y = x - 3$
$y = 1 - x$

**b** $x - y - 1 = 0$
$y = 2x$

**c** $4x + 3y + 12 = 0$
$x - 2y + 3 = 0$

**d** $3x + y + 3 = 0$
$2x - 3y + 24 = 0$

**e** $3x + y = 9$
$3x - 2y = -12$

**f** $x - 3y = -9$
$2x - 3y = -12$

**g** $2x - y = 6$
$x + 2y = 8$

**h** $y = 2x - 4$
$2x - y - 2 = 0$

**i** $y = -x - 5$
$2x + 2y = -10$

**2** How many points of intersection do the following pairs of lines have?
Explain, but **do not** graph them.

**a** $3x + y - 5 = 0$
$3x + y - 8 = 0$

**b** $3x + y + 5 = 0$
$6x + 2y + 10 = 0$

**c** $3x - y + 5 = 0$
$3x - y + k = 0$  where $k$ is a constant.

**ACTIVITY**

Two candles are lit at the same time. The first candle is 20 cm long and burns at a rate of 2.5 mm per hour. The second candle is 24.5 cm long and burns at a rate of 3.5 mm per hour.

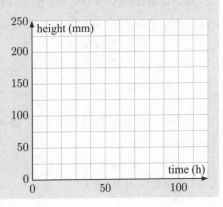

**What to do:**

**1** Explain why the heights of the candles after $t$ hours are given by $h_1 = 200 - 2.5t$ mm for the first candle and $h_2 = 245 - 3.5t$ mm for the second candle.

**2** Use the equations in **1** to determine how long each candle will last.

**3** Graph each equation on the same set of axes.

**4** At what time will the candles have the same height?

**5** If you want the candles to 'go out' together, which candle would you light first? How long after this would you light the other one?

## USING TECHNOLOGY TO FIND WHERE LINES MEET

We can plot straight lines using a **graphing package** or a **graphics calculator**. We can also use technology to find the point of intersection of a pair of lines. This is often much easier than doing the algebra by hand, particularly when the answers are not integers.

However, most graphing packages and graphics calculators need to have the equations of the lines in the form $y = mx + c$. This means that if the equation of a line is given in **general form** we will have to rearrange it into **gradient-intercept form**.

Suppose we wish to find the point of intersection of $2x - 3y - 5 = 0$ and $x - 4y + 1 = 0$.

*Step 1:*  Rearrange each equation into the form $y = mx + c$.

$$2x - 3y - 5 = 0 \qquad \text{and} \qquad x - 4y + 1 = 0$$
$$\therefore \ 3y = 2x - 5 \qquad\qquad \therefore \ 4y = x + 1$$
$$\therefore \ y = \tfrac{2}{3}x - \tfrac{5}{3} \qquad\qquad \therefore \ y = \tfrac{1}{4}x + \tfrac{1}{4}$$

*Step 2:*  If you are using the **graphing package**, click on the icon and enter the two equations.

If you are using a **graphics calculator**, enter the two equations in the appropriate window. See the instructions at the start of the book for further help.

GRAPHING PACKAGE

*Step 3:*  Solve the equations using technology.

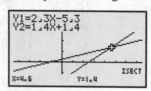

For this example, the point of intersection is (4.6, 1.4).

## EXERCISE 8G.3

**1**  Use technology to find the point of intersection of:

  **a**  $y = x + 5$
  $x + 2y - 1 = 0$

  **b**  $5x + 2y - 13 = 0$
  $y = 3x + 1$

  **c**  $2x + y - 6 = 0$
  $4x - 3y - 5 = 0$

  **d**  $7x + 3y + 3 = 0$
  $x - y - 4 = 0$

**2**  If you can, find the point(s) of intersection of the following using technology:

  **a**  $y = 2x + 5$
  $2x - y - 2 = 0$

  **b**  $4x - 3y + 6 = 0$
  $y = \tfrac{4}{3}x + 2$

Explain your results.

**3**  A potter knows that if he makes $x$ pots per day, his costs are $y = 200 + 4x$ pounds. His income from selling the pots is $y = 17x + 5$ pounds. He always sells all the pots he makes.

  **a**  Graph these two equations using technology, and find their point of intersection.

  **b**  What does this point represent?

# H PERPENDICULAR BISECTORS

We have already seen that the **midpoint** M of the line segment AB is the point on the line segment that is halfway between A and B.

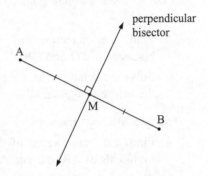

perpendicular bisector

> The **perpendicular bisector** of AB is the set of *all* points which are the same distance from A and B.

The perpendicular bisector is a line which passes through M and which is perpendicular to AB. It divides the Cartesian plane into two regions: the set of points closer to A than to B, and the set of points closer to B than to A.

---

**Example 25** ◀)) Self Tutor

Find the equation of the perpendicular bisector of AB given A(−1, 2) and B(3, 4).

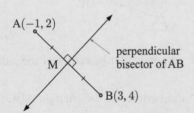

A(−1, 2)

M

perpendicular bisector of AB

B(3, 4)

The midpoint M of AB is $\left(\dfrac{-1+3}{2},\ \dfrac{2+4}{2}\right)$

or M(1, 3).

The gradient of AB is $\dfrac{4-2}{3--1} = \dfrac{2}{4} = \dfrac{1}{2}$

∴ the gradient of the perpendicular bisector is $-\dfrac{2}{1}$

The equation of the perpendicular bisector is $\dfrac{y-3}{x-1} = -2$

$$\therefore\ y - 3 = -2(x - 1)$$
$$\therefore\ y - 3 = -2x + 2$$
$$\therefore\ y = -2x + 5$$

---

## EXERCISE 8H

1 Find the equation of the perpendicular bisector of AB given:

    **a** A(3, −3) and B(1, −1)
    **b** A(1, 3) and B(−3, 5)

    **c** A(3, 1) and B(−3, 6)
    **d** A(4, −2) and B(4, 4).

2 Two post offices are located at P(3, 8) and Q(7, 2) on a Council map. Each post office services those houses which are closer to them than the other post office. Find the equation of the boundary between the regions.

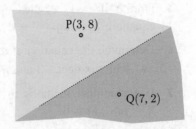

P(3, 8)

Q(7, 2)

**3** Answer the **Opening Problem** on page **252**.

**4** The perpendicular bisector of a chord of a circle passes through the centre of the circle.

A circle passes through points P(5, 7), Q(7, 1) and R(−1, 5).

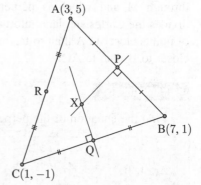

    **a** Find the equations of the perpendicular bisectors of PQ and QR.

    **b** Solve the equations in **a** simultaneously to find the centre of the circle.

**5** Triangle ABC has the vertices shown.

    **a** Find the coordinates of P, Q and R, the midpoints of AB, BC and AC respectively.

    **b** Find the equation of the perpendicular bisector of:

        **i** AB    **ii** BC    **iii** AC

    **c** Find the coordinates of X, the point of intersection of the perpendicular bisector of AB and the perpendicular bisector of BC.

    **d** Does the point X lie on the perpendicular bisector of AC?

    **e** What does your result from **d** suggest about the perpendicular bisectors of the sides of a triangle?

    **f** What is special about the point X in relation to the vertices of the triangle ABC?

## REVIEW SET 8A

**1**   **a** Find the distance between the points A(−3, 2) and B(1, 5).

    **b** Find the gradient of the line perpendicular to a line with gradient $\frac{3}{4}$.

    **c** Find the midpoint of the line segment joining C(−3, 1) to D(5, 7).

**2** Find the axes intercepts and gradient of the line with equation $5x - 2y + 10 = 0$.

**3** Determine the equation of the illustrated line:

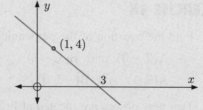

**4** Find $a$ given that P(−3, 4), Q(2, 6) and R(5, $a$) are collinear.

**5** Find $c$ if (−1, $c$) lies on the line with equation $3x - 2y + 7 = 0$.

**6** Determine the equation of the line:

    **a** with gradient −3 and $y$-intercept 4    **b** through the points (−3, 4) and (3, 1).

**7** Use graphical methods to find the point of intersection of $y = 2x - 9$ and $x + 4y - 36 = 0$.

**8**  Find the distance between  P$(-4, 7)$  and  Q$(-1, 3)$.

**9**  **a**  Find the gradient of the line  $y = -4x + 7$.

   **b**  Line $L$ is perpendicular to  $y = -4x + 7$.   What is its gradient?

   **c**  $L$ passes through the point $(-2, 1)$.  Find the equation of $L$.

**10**  Use midpoints to find the fourth vertex of the given parallelogram:

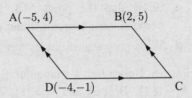

**11**  Find $k$ given that  $(-3, k)$  is 7 units away from  $(2, 4)$.

## REVIEW SET 8B

**1**  Determine the midpoint of the line segment joining  K$(3, 5)$  to  L$(7, -2)$.

**2**  Find the gradient of the following lines:

   **a**    **b**    **c**    **d**

**3**  Find, in gradient-intercept form, the equation of the line through:

   **a**  $(2, -1)$ with gradient $-3$      **b**  $(3, -2)$ and $(-1, 4)$.

**4**  Find where the following lines cut the axes:

   **a**  $y = -\frac{3}{2}x + 7$      **b**  $5x - 3y - 12 = 0$

**5**  Does $(2, -5)$ lie on the line with equation  $3x + 4y + 14 = 0$?

**6**  If  $3x + ky = 7$  and  $y = 3 - 4x$  are the equations of two lines, find $k$ if:

   **a**  the lines are parallel      **b**  the lines are perpendicular.

**7**  Use graphical methods to find where the line through  A$(-5, 0)$  and  B$(3, 10)$  meets the line with equation  $3x + 2y - 7 = 0$.

**8**  Find the equation of the:

   **a**  horizontal line through $(-4, 3)$      **b**  vertical line through $(-6, 1)$.

**9**  Find the equation of the perpendicular bisector of the line segment joining  P$(7, -1)$  to  Q$(-3, 5)$.

**10** The illustrated circle has centre $(3, 2)$ and radius 5. The points $A(8, 2)$, $B(6, -2)$ lie on the circle.

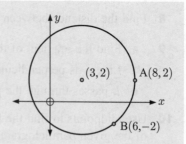

**a** Find the midpoint of chord AB.

**b** Hence, find the equation of the perpendicular bisector of the chord.

**c** Show that the point $(3, 2)$ lies on the perpendicular bisector found in **b**.

**d** What property of circles has been checked in **c**?

**11** Farmer Huber has a triangular field with corners $A(-1, 1)$, $B(1, 5)$ and $C(5, 1)$. There are gates at M and N, the midpoints of AB and BC respectively. A straight path goes from M to N.

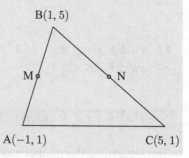

**a** Use gradients to show that the path is parallel to AC.

**b** Show that the path is half as long as the fenceline AC.

## REVIEW SET 8C

**1** Find, in general form, the equation of the line through:

**a** $(1, -5)$ with gradient $\frac{2}{3}$

**b** $(2, -3)$ and $(-4, -5)$.

**2** If $5x - 7y - 8 = 0$ and $3x + ky + 11 = 0$ are the equations of two lines, find the value of $k$ for which:

**a** the lines are parallel

**b** the lines are perpendicular.

**3** A point T on the $y$-axis is 3 units from the point $A(-1, 2)$. Find:

**a** the possible coordinates of T

**b** the equation of the line AT, given that T has a positive $y$-coordinate.

**4** A truck driver plots his day's travel on the graph alongside.

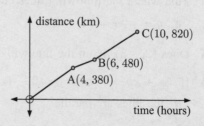

**a** Find the gradient of AB.

**b** Find the gradient of OC.

**c** Interpret your answers to **a** and **b**.

**5** Fully classify triangle KLM for $K(-5, -2)$, $L(0, 1)$ and $M(3, -4)$.

**6**

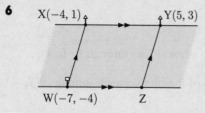

Navigation signs are posted on the bank of a river at W, X and Y as shown alongside. The local council plans to place another sign at Z such that WXYZ is a parallelogram. Use midpoints to find the coordinates of Z.

**7** Draw the graph of the line with equation:

    **a** $y = -\frac{1}{3}x + 4$         **b** $5x - 2y + 1 = 0$

**8** Two primary schools are located at P(5, 12) and Q(9, 4) on a council map. If the Local Education Authority wishes to zone the region so that children must attend the closest school to their place of residence, what is the equation of the line that forms this boundary?

**9** Given A(6, 8), B(14, 6), C(−1, −3) and D(−9, −1):

    **a** Use the gradient to show that:

        **i** AB is parallel to DC     **ii** BC is parallel to AD.

    **b** What kind of figure is ABCD?

    **c** Check that AB = DC and BC = AD using the distance formula.

    **d** Find the midpoints of diagonals:   **i** AC   **ii** BD.

    **e** What property of parallelograms has been checked in **d**?

> For figures named ABCD, the labelling is in cyclic order.

**10** Copy and complete:

| | Equation of line | Gradient | x-intercept | y-intercept |
|---|---|---|---|---|
| **a** | $5x - 2y - 10 = 0$ | | | |
| **b** | $4x + 5y = 20$ | | | |
| **c** | $y = -2x + 5$ | | | |
| **d** | $x = 8$ | | | |
| **e** | $y = 5$ | | | |
| **f** | $x + y = 11$ | | | |

**11** Consider the points A(1, 3), B(6, 3), C(3, −1) and D(−2, −1).

    **a** Use the distance formula to show that ABCD is a rhombus.

    **b** Find the midpoints of AC and BD.

    **c** Use gradients to show that AC and BD are perpendicular.

## REVIEW SET 8D

**1** For the points P(1, −3) and Q(−4, 0), find:

    **a** the distance between P and Q

    **b** the gradient of PQ

    **c** the equation of the line passing through P and Q.

**2** Fully classify triangle ABC for A(5, −1), B(−2, 3) and C(0, 8).

**3** Find $k$ given that the line joining A(5, $k$) and B(2, 4) is perpendicular to the line with equation $x - 3y - 7 = 0$.

**4** Use midpoints to find the fourth vertex K of parallelogram HIJK for H(3, 4), I(−3, −1), and J(4, 10).

**5**

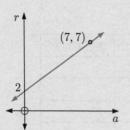

volume of water (L)

D(120, 2795)

C(80, 2075)

B(45, 1095)

330 A

time (minutes)

Jalen monitors the amount of water in his rainwater tank during a storm.

**a** How much water was in the tank before the storm?

**b** When was it raining the hardest?

**c** At what rate is the tank filling between C and D?

**d** What is the average water collection rate during the whole storm?

**6** Find $c$ given that P(5, 9), Q(−2, $c$) and R(−5, 4) are collinear.

**7** Find the gradient of the line with equation:

**a** $y = \dfrac{4 - 3x}{2}$ **b** $5x + 3y + 6 = 0$

**8** Find the equation linking the variables in these graphs:

**a**

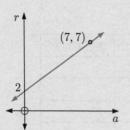

$r$

(7, 7)

2

$a$

**b**

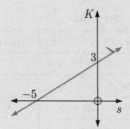

$K$

3

−5

$s$

**9** Find $t$ if:

**a** (−2, 4) lies on the line with equation $2x - 7y = t$

**b** (3, $t$) lies on the line with equation $4x + 5y = -1$.

**10** Consider P(1, 5), Q(5, 7), and R(3, 1).

**a** Show that triangle PQR is isosceles.

**b** Find the midpoint M of QR.

**c** Use the gradient to verify that PM is perpendicular to QR.

**d** Draw a sketch to illustrate what you have found in **a**, **b** and **c**.

**11** The Circular Gardens are bounded by East Avenue and Diagonal Road. Diagonal Road intersects North Street at C and East Avenue at D. Diagonal Rd is tangential to the Circular Gardens at B.

**a** Find the equation of:

**i** East Avenue     **ii** North Street

**iii** Diagonal Road.

**b** Where does Diagonal Road intersect:

**i** East Avenue     **ii** North Street?

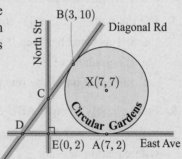

B(3, 10)

North Str

Diagonal Rd

X(7, 7)

C

Circular Gardens

D

E(0, 2)   A(7, 2)   East Ave

# Chapter 9

# Quadratic algebra

## OPENING PROBLEM

A small aeroplane flies 1000 km at speed $v$ km h$^{-1}$.

If the aeroplane's speed was 120 km h$^{-1}$ less, the flight would have taken a half an hour longer.

**Things to think about:**

**a** Can you explain why the flight took $\dfrac{1000}{v}$ hours?

**b** Can you explain why $\dfrac{1000}{v} = \dfrac{1000}{v - 120} - \frac{1}{2}$?

**c** Can you rearrange the equation in **b** to show that $v^2 - 120v - 240\,000 = 0$?

**d** Can you solve the equation in **c** to find the speed of the aeroplane?

We have seen previously that a **linear expression** is an expression of the form $ax + b$ where $a$ and $b$ are constants and $a \neq 0$.

A **quadratic expression** in $x$ is an expression of the form $ax^2 + bx + c$ where $x$ is the variable and $a$, $b$ and $c$ represent constants, $a \neq 0$.

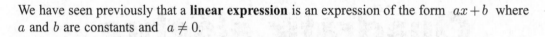

$$ax^2 \qquad + \qquad bx \qquad + \qquad c$$

the $x^2$ term        the $x$ term        the constant term

For example: $x^2 - 3x + 2$, $2x^2 + x$ and $-x^2 + 3x - 1$ are all quadratic expressions.

In $ax^2 + bx + c$, we say that $a$ is the **coefficient** of $x^2$, $b$ is the **coefficient** of $x$, and $c$ is the **constant term**.

You will have seen many quadratic expressions in this course already. They result whenever we expand the product of two linear expressions.

expansion

$$(x + 3)(x - 1) = x^2 + 2x - 3$$

The reverse process of expansion is called **factorisation**. It is the process of writing an expression as a product of factors.

$(x + 3)$ and $(x - 1)$ are *factors* of $x^2 + 2x - 3$.

factorisation

$$x^2 + 2x - 3 = (x + 3)(x - 1)$$

# A     FACTORISATION WITH COMMON FACTORS

Whenever we are asked to factorise an expression, the first thing we look for is a **common factor** in the terms of the expression. We write the highest common factor of the terms in front of a set of brackets and apply the reverse of the **distributive law**.

$$ab + ac = a(b + c)$$

$ab$ and $ac$ have the common factor $a$.

---

### Example 1    ◀ Self Tutor

Factorise by removing a common factor:

a   $3x^2 - 2x$       b   $-2x^2 + 8x$

a    $3x^2 - 2x$
$= 3 \times x \times x - 2 \times x$
$= x(3x - 2)$   {HCF is $x$}

b    $-2x^2 + 8x$
$= -2 \times x \times x + 2 \times x \times 4$
$= 2x(-x + 4)$   {HCF is $2x$}
$= 2x(4 - x)$

---

### Example 2    ◀ Self Tutor

Factorise by removing a common factor:

a   $(x + 2)(x - 1) - 3(x + 2)$      b   $x(x + 3) - (x + 3)^2$

a    $(x + 2)(x - 1) - 3(x + 2)$
$= (x + 2)(x - 1 - 3)$
         {HCF is $(x + 2)$}
$= (x + 2)(x - 4)$

b    $x(x + 3) - (x + 3)^2$
$= x(x + 3) - (x + 3)(x + 3)$
$= (x + 3)[x - (x + 3)]$
         {HCF is $(x + 3)$}
$= (x + 3)[\cancel{x} - \cancel{x} - 3]$
$= -3(x + 3)$

---

## EXERCISE 9A

**1** Find the highest common factor of:

a   $x^2$ and $3x$              b   $2x^2$ and $6x$

c   $x + 1$ and $(x + 1)^2$      d   $(x - 1)(x - 2)$ and $2(x - 1)$

e   $-3x(1 - x)$ and $9x^2$     f   $(x + 3)(1 - x)$ and $4(x - 1)$

**2** Fully factorise:

a  $2x^2 + 3x$      b  $4x^2 - 7x$      c  $-3x^2 + 15x$

d  $5x^2 + 25x$     e  $-8x^2 + 2x$     f  $2x^2 - 12$

g  $3x - 6x^2$      h  $4x^2 + 10x$     i  $12x - 21x^2$

Check your factorisations by expansion.

**3** Fully factorise:

a  $(x + 3)(x - 2) + 4(x + 3)$      b  $(x + 4)(x - 1) - 5(x - 1)$

c  $(x + 1)(x + 2) - (x + 2)^2$      d  $(x + 4)(x - 3) - 2(x + 4)^2$

e  $5(x - 2) - (x - 2)(x - 6)$

f  $x^2 - x(x - 5)$

g  $4(x - 1)^2 - 2(x + 3)(x - 1)$

h  $8x^2 - 6x(3 - x)$

i  $(x + 7)(2 - x) + 5(x - 2)$

# B   THE DIFFERENCE OF TWO SQUARES FACTORISATION

We have seen previously that the expansion of $(a + b)(a - b)$ is the **difference of two squares** $a^2 - b^2$.

We can factorise the difference of two squares by reversing this process:

$$a^2 - b^2 = (a + b)(a - b)$$

Note that in contrast, we cannot factorise the sum of two squares $a^2 + b^2$ into two real linear factors.

---

**Example 3**                          ◀ Self Tutor

Fully factorise:   a  $16 - x^2$          b  $9x^2 - 4$

a    $16 - x^2$            b    $9x^2 - 4$
   $= 4^2 - x^2$              $= (3x)^2 - 2^2$
   $= (4 + x)(4 - x)$         $= (3x + 2)(3x - 2)$

---

**Example 4**                    ◀ Self Tutor

Fully factorise:   $12x^2 - 27$

$12x^2 - 27$
$= 3(4x^2 - 9)$          {HCF is 3}
$= 3((2x)^2 - 3^2)$      {difference of two squares}
$= 3(2x + 3)(2x - 3)$

Always look first for a common factor.

At this stage we can see that
$$x^2 - 1 = (x+1)(x-1)$$
$$x^2 - 4 = (x+2)(x-2)$$
$$x^2 - 9 = (x+3)(x-3) \text{ and so on.}$$

But what do we do with $x^2 - 2$, where 2 is not a perfect square?

We can still use the difference of two squares factorisation by noting that $2 = (\sqrt{2})^2$.

So, $x^2 - 2 = x^2 - (\sqrt{2})^2$
$$= (x + \sqrt{2})(x - \sqrt{2})$$

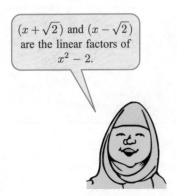

$(x + \sqrt{2})$ and $(x - \sqrt{2})$ are the linear factors of $x^2 - 2$.

---

**Example 5**    ◀) **Self Tutor**

Factorise into linear factors:

  **a**   $7 - x^2$            **b**   $(x+1)^2 - 11$

  **a**    $7 - x^2$
       $= (\sqrt{7})^2 - x^2$
       $= (\sqrt{7} + x)(\sqrt{7} - x)$

  **b**    $(x+1)^2 - 11$
       $= (x+1)^2 - (\sqrt{11})^2$
       $= [(x+1) + \sqrt{11}][(x+1) - \sqrt{11}]$
       $= (x + 1 + \sqrt{11})(x + 1 - \sqrt{11})$

---

## EXERCISE 9B

**1** Fully factorise:

  **a**   $x^2 - 25$      **b**   $9 - x^2$      **c**   $a^2 - 64$      **d**   $100 - x^2$

  **e**   $4x^2 - 49$      **f**   $1 - 16x^2$      **g**   $25t^2 - 81$      **h**   $49 - 36x^2$

**2** Fully factorise:

  **a**   $5x^2 - 20$      **b**   $2 - 98x^2$      **c**   $-7x^2 + 63$      **d**   $100 - 4a^2$

  **e**   $27x^2 - 48$      **f**   $50 - 8k^2$      **g**   $36x^2 - 4$      **h**   $-2x^2 + 72$

**3** If possible, factorise into linear factors:

  **a**   $x^2 - 5$            **b**   $14 - x^2$            **c**   $x^2 + 8$

  **d**   $(x+2)^2 - 6$      **e**   $(x-3)^2 + 7$      **f**   $(x+4)^2 - 10$

**4** Fully factorise:

  **a**   $2x^2 - 50$        **b**   $81 - x^2$        **c**   $x^2 - 3$

  **d**   $64 - 16t^2$      **e**   $(x+5)^2 - 7$      **f**   $49x^2 - 9$

  **g**   $21 - x^2$        **h**   $(x-1)^2 - 5$      **i**   $100 - 36a^2$

**Example 6**    ◀)) Self Tutor

Fully factorise:

a $(2x - 1)^2 - 16$

b $(x + 1)^2 - (x - 2)^2$

a $\quad (2x - 1)^2 - 16$
$\quad = (2x - 1)^2 - 4^2$
$\quad = [(2x - 1) + 4][(2x - 1) - 4]$
$\quad = [2x + 3][2x - 5]$

b $\quad (x + 1)^2 - (x - 2)^2$
$\quad = [(x + 1) + (x - 2)][(x + 1) - (x - 2)]$
$\quad = [x + 1 + x - 2][x + 1 - x + 2]$
$\quad = [2x - 1][3]$
$\quad = 3(2x - 1)$

5 Fully factorise:

a $(2x + 3)^2 - 16$

b $(5 - x)^2 - 36$

c $25 - (3x + 4)^2$

d $(x + 6)^2 - 4x^2$

e $(3x + 5)^2 - (x + 2)^2$

f $(4x - 3)^2 - (x - 5)^2$

## C | PERFECT SQUARE FACTORISATION

The perfect squares $(x + a)^2$ and $(x - a)^2$ have expansions in which the middle term involves $2ax$.

$$(x + a)^2 = x^2 + 2ax + a^2$$
$$(x - a)^2 = x^2 - 2ax + a^2$$

So, if we are given a quadratic expression of the form $x^2 + 2ax + a^2$ or $x^2 - 2ax + a^2$, we can use a perfect square factorisation:

$$x^2 + 2ax + a^2 = (x + a)^2$$
$$x^2 - 2ax + a^2 = (x - a)^2$$

**Example 7**    ◀)) Self Tutor

Fully factorise:

a $x^2 + 6x + 9$

b $x^2 - 12x + 36$

a $\quad x^2 + 6x + 9$
$\quad = x^2 + 2 \times 3 \times x + 3^2$
$\quad = (x + 3)^2$

b $\quad x^2 - 12x + 36$
$\quad = x^2 - 2 \times 6 \times x + 6^2$
$\quad = (x - 6)^2$

**Example 8**    ◀)) Self Tutor

Fully factorise:

a $4x^2 + 12x + 9$

b $-18x^2 + 12x - 2$

**a**  $4x^2 + 12x + 9$
$= (2x)^2 + 2 \times 3 \times (2x) + 3^2$
$= (2x + 3)^2$

**b**  $-18x^2 + 12x - 2$
$= -2(9x^2 - 6x + 1)$    {HCF $= -2$}
$= -2((3x)^2 - 2 \times 1 \times (3x) + 1^2)$
$= -2(3x - 1)^2$

## EXERCISE 9C

**1** Fully factorise:

  **a**  $x^2 + 10x + 25$        **b**  $x^2 - 14x + 49$        **c**  $t^2 - 20t + 100$
  **d**  $x^2 + 4x + 4$          **e**  $b^2 - 2b + 1$          **f**  $x^2 + 16x + 64$
  **g**  $k^2 - 6k + 9$          **h**  $x^2 - 8x + 16$         **i**  $z^2 + 18z + 81$

**2** Fully factorise:

  **a**  $4x^2 - 20x + 25$       **b**  $9x^2 + 12x + 4$        **c**  $16x^2 - 8x + 1$
  **d**  $9n^2 - 30n + 25$       **e**  $36x^2 - 12x + 1$       **f**  $2x^2 + 24x + 72$
  **g**  $-3x^2 - 6x - 3$        **h**  $32x^2 - 48x + 18$      **i**  $-100x^2 + 40x - 4$

# D | SUM AND PRODUCT FACTORISATION

The quadratic expression $x^2 + bx + c$ is a **quadratic trinomial** because it has three terms.

We have already seen how the special quadratic trinomials $x^2 + 2ax + a^2$ and $x^2 - 2ax + a^2$ can be factorised as perfect squares. However, most quadratic trinomials cannot be factorised in this way.

Consider the expansion  $(x + p)(x + q) = x^2 + qx + px + pq$
$$= x^2 + \underbrace{(p + q)}_{\text{sum of } p \text{ and } q} x + \underbrace{pq}_{\text{product of } p \text{ and } q}$$

So, the expression  $x^2 + (p + q)x + pq$  can be factorised using the **sum and product factorisation**

$$x^2 + \underbrace{(p + q)}_{\text{sum of } p \text{ and } q} x + \underbrace{pq}_{\text{product of } p \text{ and } q} = (x + p)(x + q)$$

| **Example 9** | ◀) **Self Tutor** |
|---|---|

Fully factorise:

  **a**  $x^2 + 2x - 8$          **b**  $x^2 + 8x + 15$

**a**  $x^2 + 2x - 8$  has  $p + q = 2$  and
$pq = -8$
$\therefore$  $p$ and $q$ are $-2$ and $4$
So,  $x^2 + 2x - 8 = (x - 2)(x + 4)$

**b**  $x^2 + 8x + 15$  has  $p + q = 8$  and
$pq = 15$
$\therefore$  $p$ and $q$ are $3$ and $5$
So,  $x^2 + 8x + 15 = (x + 3)(x + 5)$

**Example 10**    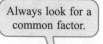 Self Tutor

Fully factorise:

  a   $2x^2 - 10x + 12$          b   $-3x^2 + 12x + 15$

> Always look for a common factor.

  a     $2x^2 - 10x + 12$

      $= 2(x^2 - 5x + 6)$      {HCF is 2}

      $= 2(x - 2)(x - 3)$     { $p + q = -5$ and $pq = 6$

                              so $p$ and $q$ are $-2$ and $-3$}

  b     $-3x^2 + 12x + 15$

      $= -3(x^2 - 4x - 5)$     {HCF is $-3$}

      $= -3(x - 5)(x + 1)$   { $p + q = -4$ and $pq = -5$

                              so $p$ and $q$ are $-5$ and $1$}

## EXERCISE 9D

**1** Fully factorise:

  a   $x^2 + 5x + 4$          b   $x^2 + 2x - 15$          c   $x^2 - x - 12$

  d   $x^2 - 10x + 21$        e   $x^2 + 3x - 18$          f   $a^2 + 11a + 18$

  g   $x^2 + 2x - 63$         h   $x^2 + 14x + 33$        i   $x^2 - 19x - 20$

  j   $x^2 - 16x + 64$        k   $x^2 - 49$               l   $x^2 + 8x - 48$

**2** Fully factorise:

  a   $2x^2 - 6x - 20$        b   $3x^2 + 24x + 36$        c   $5x^2 - 5x - 100$

  d   $-x^2 + 9x - 14$       e   $4x^2 - 16x - 48$        f   $-2x^2 + 4x + 48$

  g   $7x^2 - 7x - 42$       h   $-3x^2 - 30x - 27$     i   $-5x^2 + 40x - 80$

# E | FACTORISATION OF $ax^2 + bx + c$

We now have several techniques for factorising the quadratic trinomial $ax^2 + bx + c$. These techniques can be used when $a = 1$, or when $a$ is a common factor of $b$ and $c$ which can be taken out.

Use the following steps to factorise quadratic expressions:

  *Step 1:*   If the expression has a **common factor,** take it out.

  *Step 2:*   Look for the **difference of two squares:**     $x^2 - a^2 = (x + a)(x - a)$

  *Step 3:*   Look for a **perfect square** factorisation:     $x^2 + 2ax + a^2 = (x + a)^2$

                             or   $x^2 - 2ax + a^2 = (x - a)^2$

  *Step 4:*   Look for the **sum and product** type: $x^2 + (p + q)x + pq = (x + p)(x + q)$

## EXERCISE 9E.1

**1** Fully factorise:

    **a** $4x^2 + 8x$              **b** $5x - x^2$              **c** $6x^2 - 4x$

    **d** $3x^2 + 15$            **e** $-2x^2 + 10x$        **f** $18x - 12x^2$

**2** Fully factorise:

    **a** $x^2 - 81$             **b** $x^2 + 2x + 1$       **c** $x^2 + 12x + 27$

    **d** $x^2 - 20x + 36$     **e** $x^2 - 22$           **f** $t^2 - 10t + 25$

    **g** $x^2 + 7x - 60$      **h** $x^2 + 24x + 144$    **i** $k^2 - 2k - 48$

**3** Fully factorise:

    **a** $5x^2 + 30x + 40$    **b** $3x^2 - 12$         **c** $6x^2 - 36x + 54$

    **d** $-2x^2 + 20x - 32$   **e** $49x^2 - 28x + 4$    **f** $-3x^2 + 30x - 72$

    **g** $80 - 5x^2$         **h** $4x^2 - 44x - 48$    **i** $-32x^2 + 16x - 2$

## 'SPLITTING' THE $x$-TERM

For other quadratic expressions of the form $ax^2 + bx + c$ we can try 'splitting' the $x$-term. This is the direct reverse of the expansion process.

For example, consider the expansion     $(3x + 1)(2x - 3)$
$$= 6x^2 - 9x + 2x - 3$$
$$= 6x^2 - 7x - 3$$

Reversing this process,     $6x^2 - 7x - 3$

$$= 6x^2 - 9x + 2x - 3 \quad \text{\{'splitting' the } x\text{-term\}}$$
$$= (6x^2 - 9x) + (2x - 3) \quad \text{\{grouping the terms in pairs\}}$$
$$= 3x(2x - 3) + (2x - 3) \quad \text{\{factorising each pair separately\}}$$
$$= (3x + 1)(2x - 3) \quad \text{\{completing the factorisation\}}$$

But how do we know to 'split' $-7x$ into $-9x + 2x$? We could have written $-7x$ as $-4x - 3x$ instead, or many other possibilities.

The clue is that in $6x^2 - 9x + 2x - 3$, we see that    $-9 \times 2 = -18$
                          and that   $6 \times -3 = -18$.

So, when 'splitting' the $x$-term we look for two numbers whose sum is $-7$ and whose product is $-18$. These numbers are $-9$ and $2$.

> To factorise $ax^2 + bx + c$ by 'splitting' the $x$-term:
>
> *Step 1:*   Find $ac$. Look for two factors of $ac$ which add to $b$.
>
> *Step 2:*   If the factors are $p$ and $q$, then replace $bx$ by $px + qx$.
>
> *Step 3:*   Complete the factorisation.

**Example 11**                                                    ◀) **Self Tutor**

Show how to split the $x$-term of the following so that factorisation can occur:

  a  $4x^2 + 9x + 2$                          b  $8x^2 - 2x - 3$

  a  In $4x^2 + 9x + 2$, $ac = 4 \times 2 = 8$ and $b = 9$.
     We need two numbers with a product of 8 and a sum of 9.
     These are 8 and 1.
     So, the split is  $9x = 8x + x$.

  b  In $8x^2 - 2x - 3$, $ac = 8 \times -3 = -24$ and $b = -2$.
     We need two numbers with a product of $-24$ and a sum of $-2$.
     These are $-6$ and 4.
     So, the split is  $-2x = -6x + 4x$.

**Example 12**                                                    ◀) **Self Tutor**

Factorise by 'splitting' the $x$-term:

  a  $3x^2 + 14x + 8$                          b  $4x^2 - 8x - 5$

It does not matter
what order you write
the 'split' terms in.

  a  $3x^2 + 14x + 8$ has $ac = 24$ and $b = 14$.
     We need two numbers with a product of 24 and a sum of 14.
     Searching amongst the factors of 24, only 2 and 12 have a sum of 14.

   $\therefore \quad 3x^2 + 14x + 8$
   $= 3x^2 + 2x + 12x + 8$        {splitting the $x$-term}
   $= x(3x + 2) + 4(3x + 2)$      {factorising in pairs}
   $= (3x + 2)(x + 4)$            {taking out the common factor}

  b  $4x^2 - 8x - 5$ has $ac = -20$ and $b = -8$.
     We need two numbers with a product of $-20$ and a sum of $-8$.
     Searching amongst the factors of $-20$, only $-10$ and 2 have a sum of $-8$.

   $\therefore \quad 4x^2 - 8x - 5$
   $= 4x^2 - 10x + 2x - 5$        {splitting the $x$-term}
   $= 2x(2x - 5) + 1(2x - 5)$     {factorising in pairs}
   $= (2x - 5)(2x + 1)$           {taking out the common factor}

## EXERCISE 9E.2

1  Show how to split the $x$-term so that factorisation can occur:

   a  $2x^2 + 7x + 3$          b  $3x^2 + 5x - 2$          c  $4x^2 + 11x + 6$
   d  $4x^2 - 6x - 4$          e  $8x^2 + 14x - 4$          f  $10x^2 - 19x - 15$

2  Fully factorise:

   a  $2x^2 + 5x + 3$          b  $3x^2 + 11x + 6$          c  $3x^2 + 7x + 2$
   d  $6x^2 + 7x + 2$          e  $5x^2 + 13x + 6$          f  $6x^2 + 11x + 3$
   g  $4x^2 + 12x + 9$         h  $9x^2 + 9x + 2$           i  $10x^2 + 29x + 10$

3 Fully factorise:

a $2x^2 - x - 6$      b $3x^2 - 10x - 8$      c $4x^2 - 8x + 3$

d $5x^2 - 17x + 6$      e $4x^2 + 4x - 15$      f $6x^2 - 7x - 5$

g $10x^2 + 3x - 4$      h $9x^2 - 6x - 8$      i $8x^2 - 14x + 3$

j $15x^2 - x - 6$      k $12x^2 - 17x + 6$      l $7x^2 - 9x - 10$

4 Fully factorise by first removing $-1$ as a common factor:

a $-3x^2 - 5x - 2$      b $-4x^2 - 16x - 15$      c $-5x^2 + 7x + 6$

d $-6x^2 - 11x + 7$      e $-9x^2 + 9x + 10$      f $-10x^2 + 27x - 18$

# F     QUADRATIC EQUATIONS

A **quadratic equation** in $x$ is an equation which can be written in the form $ax^2 + bx + c = 0$ where $a$, $b$ and $c$ are constants and $a \neq 0$.

The solutions of the equation are the values of $x$ which make the equation true. We call these the **roots** of the equation, and they are also the **zeros** of the quadratic expression $ax^2 + bx + c$.

## SOLUTION OF $x^2 = k$

Just as for linear equations, we can perform operations on both sides of a quadratic equation so as to maintain the balance.

Many quadratic equations can thus be rearranged into the form $x^2 = k$.

If $k$ is positive then $\sqrt{k}$ exists such that $(\sqrt{k})^2 = k$ and $(-\sqrt{k})^2 = k$.

Thus the solutions are $x = \pm\sqrt{k}$.

If $x^2 = k$ then $\begin{cases} x = \pm\sqrt{k} & \text{if } k > 0 \\ x = 0 & \text{if } k = 0 \\ \text{there are no real solutions if } k < 0. \end{cases}$

$\pm\sqrt{k}$ is read as 'plus or minus the square root of $k$'

**Example 13**      ◀ᴐ **Self Tutor**

Solve for $x$:    a $3x^2 - 1 = 8$    b $5 - 2x^2 = 11$

a $3x^2 - 1 = 8$

$\therefore \; 3x^2 = 9$      {adding 1 to both sides}

$\therefore \; x^2 = 3$      {dividing both sides by 3}

$\therefore \; x = \pm\sqrt{3}$

b $5 - 2x^2 = 11$

$\therefore \; -2x^2 = 6$      {subtracting 5 from both sides}

$\therefore \; x^2 = -3$      {dividing both sides by $-2$}

which has no solutions as $x^2$ cannot be negative.

We can apply this same method of solution whenever there is a perfect square on the left hand side.

**Example 14**                                    ◀⑴ **Self Tutor**

Solve for $x$:

a  $(x+3)^2 = 36$            b  $(x-4)^2 = 7$

| | |
|---|---|
| a  $(x+3)^2 = 36$ | b  $(x-4)^2 = 7$ |
| $\therefore\ x+3 = \pm\sqrt{36}$ | $\therefore\ x-4 = \pm\sqrt{7}$ |
| $\therefore\ x+3 = \pm 6$ | $\therefore\ x = 4 \pm \sqrt{7}$ |
| $\therefore\ x = -3 \pm 6$ | |
| $\therefore\ x = 3$ or $-9$ | |

For equations of the form $(x \pm a)^2 = k$ we do not need to expand the brackets.

## EXERCISE 9F

1  Solve for $x$:

a  $x^2 = 4$            b  $3x^2 = 48$            c  $4x^2 = 4$

d  $5x^2 = 35$            e  $2x^2 = -10$            f  $6x^2 = 0$

g  $2x^2 + 9 = 27$            h  $4x^2 - 5 = 15$            i  $7 - 3x^2 = 19$

2  Solve for $x$:

a  $(x-3)^2 = 16$            b  $(x+1)^2 = 9$            c  $(x+4)^2 = -25$

d  $(x-2)^2 = 10$            e  $(x+4)^2 = 13$            f  $(x-3)^2 = -9$

g  $(x-7)^2 = 0$            h  $(2x-3)^2 = 25$            i  $\frac{1}{2}(3x+1)^2 = 7$

# G    THE NULL FACTOR LAW

We have seen that a linear equation such as  $2x + 3 = 11$  will usually have *one* solution. In contrast, a quadratic equation may have *two*, *one*, or *zero* solutions.

Here are some simple quadratic equations which clearly show the truth of this statement:

| Equation | $ax^2 + bx + c = 0$ form | $a$ | $b$ | $c$ | Solutions | No. of solutions |
|---|---|---|---|---|---|---|
| $x^2 - 4 = 0$ | $x^2 + 0x - 4 = 0$ | 1 | 0 | $-4$ | $x = 2$  or  $x = -2$ | **two** |
| $(x-2)^2 = 0$ | $x^2 - 4x + 4 = 0$ | 1 | $-4$ | 4 | $x = 2$ | **one** |
| $x^2 + 4 = 0$ | $x^2 + 0x + 4 = 0$ | 1 | 0 | 4 | none as $x^2$ is always $\geqslant 0$ | **zero** |

For quadratic equations which are not of the form  $x^2 = k$,  we can try to **factorise** the quadratic and then apply the **Null Factor law**.

The Null Factor law states:

When the product of two (or more) numbers is zero then at least one of them must be zero.

So, if  $ab = 0$  then  $a = 0$  or  $b = 0$.

**Example 15**    ◄)) **Self Tutor**

Solve for $x$ using the Null Factor law:

**a** $3x(x - 5) = 0$          **b** $(x - 4)(3x + 7) = 0$

**a**              $3x(x - 5) = 0$
∴  $3x = 0$  or  $x - 5 = 0$
∴       $x = 0$ or $5$

**b**              $(x - 4)(3x + 7) = 0$
∴  $x - 4 = 0$  or  $3x + 7 = 0$
∴      $x = 4$  or  $3x = -7$
∴      $x = 4$ or $-\frac{7}{3}$

## EXERCISE 9G.1

**1** Solve for the unknown using the Null Factor law:

**a** $3x = 0$          **b** $a \times 8 = 0$          **c** $-7y = 0$

**d** $ab = 0$          **e** $2xy = 0$          **f** $abc = 0$

**g** $a^2 = 0$          **h** $pqrs = 0$          **i** $a^2 b = 0$

**2** Solve for $x$ using the Null Factor law:

**a** $x(x - 5) = 0$          **b** $2x(x + 3) = 0$          **c** $(x + 1)(x - 3) = 0$

**d** $3x(7 - x) = 0$          **e** $-2x(x + 1) = 0$          **f** $4(x + 6)(2x - 3) = 0$

**g** $(2x + 1)(2x - 1) = 0$          **h** $11(x + 2)(x - 7) = 0$          **i** $-6(x - 5)(3x + 2) = 0$

**j** $x^2 = 0$          **k** $4(5 - x)^2 = 0$          **l** $-3(3x - 1)^2 = 0$

## STEPS FOR SOLVING QUADRATIC EQUATIONS

To use the **Null Factor law** when solving equations, we must have one side of the equation *equal to zero*.

> *Step 1:*    If necessary, rearrange the equation so one side is **zero**.
> *Step 2:*    **Fully factorise** the other side (usually the LHS).
> *Step 3:*    Use the **Null Factor law**.
> *Step 4:*    **Solve** the resulting linear equations.
> *Step 5:*    **Check** at least one of your solutions.

**Caution:**    Do not be tempted to divide both sides by an expression involving $x$.
If you do this then you may lose one of the solutions.

For example,  consider  $x^2 = 5x$.

*Incorrect solution*

$$x^2 = 5x$$

$$\therefore \quad \frac{x^2}{x} = \frac{5x}{x}$$

$$\therefore \quad x = 5$$

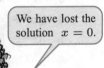

We have lost the solution $x = 0$.

*Correct solution*

$$x^2 = 5x$$

$$\therefore \quad x^2 - 5x = 0$$

$$\therefore \quad x(x - 5) = 0$$

$$\therefore \quad x = 0 \text{ or } 5$$

**Example 16**   ◀) Self Tutor

Solve for $x$:   **a** $3x^2 + 5x = 0$   **b** $x^2 = 5x + 6$

| | |
|---|---|
| **a** $\quad 3x^2 + 5x = 0$ | **b** $\qquad\qquad x^2 = 5x + 6$ |
| $\therefore \ x(3x + 5) = 0$ | $\therefore \ x^2 - 5x - 6 = 0$ |
| $\therefore \quad x = 0$ or $3x + 5 = 0$ | $\therefore \ (x - 6)(x + 1) = 0$ |
| $\therefore \quad x = 0$ or $\qquad x = -\frac{5}{3}$ | $\therefore \quad x = 6$ or $-1$ |

## EXERCISE 9G.2

**1** Factorise and hence solve for $x$:

**a** $3x^2 + 6x = 0$      **b** $2x^2 + 5x = 0$      **c** $4x^2 - 3x = 0$

**d** $4x^2 = 5x$      **e** $3x^2 = 9x$      **f** $4x = 8x^2$

**2** Solve for $x$:

**a** $x^2 + 9x + 14 = 0$      **b** $x^2 + 11x + 30 = 0$      **c** $x^2 + 2x = 15$

**d** $x^2 + x = 12$      **e** $x^2 + 6 = 5x$      **f** $x^2 + 4 = 4x$

**g** $x^2 = x + 6$      **h** $x^2 = 7x + 60$      **i** $x^2 = 3x + 70$

**j** $10 - 3x = x^2$      **k** $x^2 + 12 = 7x$      **l** $9x + 36 = x^2$

**Example 17**   ◀) Self Tutor

Solve for $x$:   $5x^2 = 3x + 2$

| | |
|---|---|
| $5x^2 = 3x + 2$ | |
| $\therefore \ 5x^2 - 3x - 2 = 0$ | {making the RHS $= 0$} |
| $\therefore \ 5x^2 - 5x + 2x - 2 = 0$ | {$ac = -10$, $b = -3$ |
| $\therefore \ 5x(x - 1) + 2(x - 1) = 0$ | $\therefore$ numbers are $-5$ and $+2$} |
| $\therefore \ (x - 1)(5x + 2) = 0$ | {factorising} |
| $\therefore \ x - 1 = 0$ or $5x + 2 = 0$ | {Null Factor law} |
| $\therefore \ x = 1$ or $-\frac{2}{5}$ | {solving the linear equations} |

**3** Solve for $x$:

**a** $2x^2 + 2 = 5x$      **b** $3x^2 + 8x = 3$      **c** $3x^2 + 17x + 20 = 0$

**d** $2x^2 + 5x = 3$      **e** $2x^2 + 5 = 11x$      **f** $2x^2 + 7x + 5 = 0$

**g** $3x^2 + 13x + 4 = 0$      **h** $5x^2 = 13x + 6$      **i** $2x^2 + 17x = 9$

**j** $2x^2 + 3x = 5$      **k** $3x^2 + 2x = 8$      **l** $2x^2 + 9x = 18$

**4** Solve for $x$:

**a** $6x^2 + 13x = 5$      **b** $6x^2 = x + 2$      **c** $6x^2 + 5x + 1 = 0$

**d** $21x^2 = 62x + 3$      **e** $10x^2 + x = 2$      **f** $10x^2 = 7x + 3$

**5**  Solve for $x$:

    **a**  $x(x+5)+2(x+6)=0$          **b**  $x(1+x)+x=3$

    **c**  $(x-1)(x+9)=8x$             **d**  $3x(x+2)-5(x-3)=17$

    **e**  $4x(x+1)=-1$                **f**  $2x(x-6)=x-20$

---

### Example 18         ◀) Self Tutor

Solve for $x$:    $3x+\dfrac{2}{x}=-7$

$$3x+\frac{2}{x}=-7$$

$$\therefore\ x\left(3x+\frac{2}{x}\right)=-7x \qquad \{\text{multiplying both sides by } x\}$$

$$\therefore\ 3x^2+2=-7x \qquad \{\text{expanding the brackets}\}$$

$$\therefore\ 3x^2+7x+2=0 \qquad \{\text{making the RHS}=0\}$$

$$\therefore\ (x+2)(3x+1)=0 \qquad \{\text{factorising}\}$$

$$\therefore\ x=-2 \text{ or } -\tfrac{1}{3}$$

---

**6**  Solve for $x$ by first eliminating the algebraic fractions:

    **a**  $\dfrac{x}{3}=\dfrac{2}{x}$            **b**  $\dfrac{4}{x}=\dfrac{x}{2}$            **c**  $\dfrac{x}{5}=\dfrac{2}{x}$

    **d**  $\dfrac{x-1}{4}=\dfrac{3}{x}$        **e**  $\dfrac{x-1}{x}=\dfrac{x+11}{5}$      **f**  $\dfrac{x}{x+2}=\dfrac{1}{x}$

    **g**  $\dfrac{2x}{3x+1}=\dfrac{1}{x+2}$     **h**  $\dfrac{2x+1}{x}=3x$       **i**  $\dfrac{x+2}{x-1}=\dfrac{x}{2}$

---

## H ┃ THE QUADRATIC FORMULA (EXTENSION)

Acme Leather Jacket Co. makes and sells $x$ leather jackets each week and their profit function is given by  $P=-12.5x^2+550x-2125$ dollars.

How many jackets must be made and sold each week in order to obtain a weekly profit of $3000?

Clearly we need to solve the equation:

$$-12.5x^2+550x-2125=3000$$

We can rearrange the equation to give

$$12.5x^2-550x+5125=0,$$

which is of the form  $ax^2+bx+c=0$  and is thus a quadratic equation.

Quadratic equations like this are too difficult to solve by factorising. Instead we use the **quadratic formula:**

$$\text{If } ax^2 + bx + c = 0, \quad \text{then} \quad x = \frac{-b \pm \sqrt{b^2 - 4ac}}{2a}.$$

In the Acme Leather Jacket Co. equation $12.5x^2 - 550x + 5125 = 0$ we have
$a = 12.5, \quad b = -550, \quad c = 5125$

$$\therefore \quad x = \frac{550 \pm \sqrt{(-550)^2 - 4 \times 12.5 \times 5125}}{2(12.5)}$$

$$= \frac{550 \pm \sqrt{46\,250}}{25}$$

$$\approx 30.60 \quad \text{or} \quad 13.40$$

However, $x$ needs to be a whole number, so $x = 13$ or 31 would produce a profit of around \$3000 each week.

---

**Example 19**    ◀)) **Self Tutor**

Solve for $x$:    **a** $x^2 - 2x - 6 = 0$    **b** $2x^2 + 3x - 6 = 0$

**a** $x^2 - 2x - 6 = 0$ has
$a = 1, \quad b = -2, \quad c = -6$

$$\therefore \quad x = \frac{-(-2) \pm \sqrt{(-2)^2 - 4(1)(-6)}}{2(1)}$$

$$\therefore \quad x = \frac{2 \pm \sqrt{4 + 24}}{2}$$

$$\therefore \quad x = \frac{2 \pm \sqrt{28}}{2}$$

$$\therefore \quad x = \frac{2 \pm 2\sqrt{7}}{2}$$

$$\therefore \quad x = 1 \pm \sqrt{7}$$

**b** $2x^2 + 3x - 6 = 0$ has
$a = 2, \quad b = 3, \quad c = -6$

$$\therefore \quad x = \frac{-3 \pm \sqrt{3^2 - 4(2)(-6)}}{2(2)}$$

$$\therefore \quad x = \frac{-3 \pm \sqrt{9 + 48}}{4}$$

$$\therefore \quad x = \frac{-3 \pm \sqrt{57}}{4}$$

---

## EXERCISE 9H

**1** Use the quadratic formula to solve exactly for $x$:

**a** $x^2 - 4x - 3 = 0$    **b** $x^2 + 6x + 7 = 0$    **c** $x^2 + 1 = 4x$

**d** $x^2 + 4x = 1$    **e** $x^2 - 4x + 2 = 0$    **f** $2x^2 - 2x - 3 = 0$

**g** $(3x + 1)^2 = -2x$    **h** $(x + 3)(2x + 1) = 9$

**2** Use the quadratic formula to solve exactly for $x$:

**a** $(x + 2)(x - 1) = 2 - 3x$    **b** $(2x + 1)^2 = 3 - x$    **c** $(x - 2)^2 = 1 + x$

**d** $\dfrac{x - 1}{2 - x} = 2x + 1$    **e** $x - \dfrac{1}{x} = 1$    **f** $2x - \dfrac{1}{x} = 3$

# SOLVING QUADRATIC EQUATIONS USING TECHNOLOGY

You can use your graphics calculator to solve quadratic equations.

The method for doing this is more complicated than for solving linear equations because there may be more than one solution. Instructions can be found in the **graphics calculator instructions** at the front of the book.

### Example 20
🔊 **Self Tutor**

Use technology to solve $2x^2 + 4x = 7$.

$$2x^2 + 4x = 7$$
$$\therefore \quad 2x^2 + 4x - 7 = 0$$

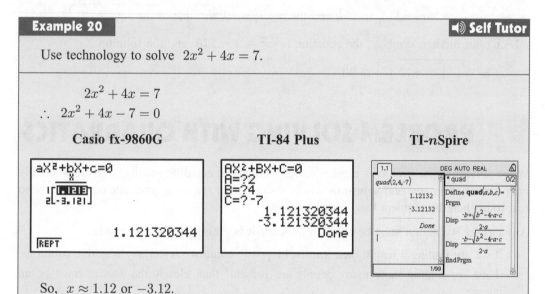

**Casio fx-9860G**　　　　**TI-84 Plus**　　　　**TI-$n$Spire**

So, $x \approx 1.12$ or $-3.12$.

## EXERCISE 9I

**1** Use technology to solve these equations:

a $x^2 + 5x + 3 = 0$

b $3x^2 - 2x - 4 = 0$

c $-2x^2 + x + 9 = 0$

d $4x^2 - 5 = 2x$

e $5x^2 + 3x = 6$

f $\dfrac{5}{x} - 4x = 2$

### HISTORICAL NOTE
### BABYLONIAN ALGEBRA

The mathematics used by the **Babylonians** was recorded on clay tablets in cuneiform. One such tablet which has been preserved is called *Plimpton 322*, written around 1600 BC.

The Ancient Babylonians were able to solve difficult equations using the rules we use today, such as transposing terms, multiplying both sides by like quantities to remove fractions, and factorisation.

They could, for example, add $4xy$ to $(x - y)^2$ to obtain $(x + y)^2$.

This was all achieved without the use of letters for unknown quantities. However, they often used words for the unknown.

Consider the following example from about 4000 years ago:

**Problem:**    *"I have subtracted the side of my square from the area and the result is 870. What is the side of the square?"*

**Solution:**    Take half of 1, which is $\frac{1}{2}$, and multiply $\frac{1}{2}$ by $\frac{1}{2}$ which is $\frac{1}{4}$;

add this to 870 to get $870\frac{1}{4}$. This is the square of $29\frac{1}{2}$.

Now add $\frac{1}{2}$ to $29\frac{1}{2}$ and the result is 30, the side of the square.

Using our modern symbols, the equation is $x^2 - x = 870$ and the solution is

$$x = \sqrt{\left(\tfrac{1}{2}\right)^2 + 870} + \tfrac{1}{2} = 30.$$

# J    PROBLEM SOLVING WITH QUADRATICS

When solving some problems algebraically, a quadratic equation results. We are generally only interested in any **real solutions** which result. If the resulting quadratic equation has no real roots then the problem has no real solution.

Any answer we obtain must be checked to see if it is reasonable. For example:

- if we are finding a length then it must be positive and we reject any negative solutions
- if we are finding 'how many people are present' then clearly the answer must be an integer.

We employ the following general problem solving method:

*Step 1:*    If the information is given in words, translate it into algebra using a pronumeral such as $x$ for the unknown. Write down the resulting equation.

*Step 2:*    Solve the equation by a suitable method.

*Step 3:*    Examine the solutions carefully to see if they are acceptable.

*Step 4:*    Give your answer in a sentence.

---

**Example 21**                                                              ◀)) **Self Tutor**

A rectangle has length 3 cm longer than its width. Its area is 42 cm². Find its width.

If the width is $x$ cm then the length is $(x + 3)$ cm.

$$\therefore \ x(x + 3) = 42 \quad \{\text{equating areas}\}$$
$$\therefore \ x^2 + 3x - 42 = 0$$
$$\therefore \ x \approx -8.15 \text{ or } 5.15 \quad \{\text{using technology}\}$$

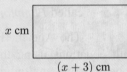

$x$ cm

$(x + 3)$ cm

We reject the negative solution as lengths are positive.

So, the width $\approx 5.15$ cm.

**Example 22**    ◀) **Self Tutor**

Is it possible to bend a 12 cm length of wire to form the shorter sides of a right angled triangle with area 20 cm$^2$?

Suppose the wire is bent $x$ cm from one end.

The area  $A = \frac{1}{2}x(12 - x)$

$\therefore \quad \frac{1}{2}x(12 - x) = 20$

$\therefore \quad x(12 - x) = 40$

$\therefore \quad 12x - x^2 - 40 = 0$

$\therefore \quad x^2 - 12x + 40 = 0$

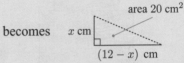 becomes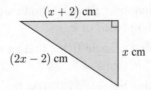

Using technology, there are no real solutions, indicating this situation is impossible.

## EXERCISE 9J

1   Two integers differ by 12 and the sum of their squares is 74. Find the integers.

2   The sum of a number and its reciprocal is $5\frac{1}{5}$. Find the number.

3   The sum of a natural number and its square is 210. Find the number.

4   The product of two consecutive even numbers is 360. Find the numbers.

5   The product of two consecutive odd numbers is 255. Find the numbers.

6   The number of diagonals of an $n$-sided polygon is given by the formula  $D = \dfrac{n}{2}(n - 3)$.

A polygon has 90 diagonals. How many sides does it have?

7   The length of a rectangle is 4 cm longer than its width. Find its width given that its area is 26 cm$^2$.

8   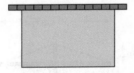   A rectangular pig pen is built against an existing brick fence. 24 m of fencing was used to enclose 70 m$^2$. Find the dimensions of the pen.

9   Use the theorem of Pythagoras to find $x$ given:

a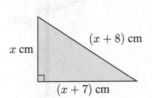

b

10   Is it possible to bend a 20 cm length of wire into the shape of a rectangle which has an area of 30 cm$^2$?

**11** A rectangular box has a square base, and its height is 1 cm longer than the length of each side of its base.

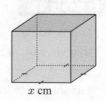

    **a** If each side of its base has length $x$ cm, show that its total surface area is given by $A = 6x^2 + 4x$ cm$^2$.

    **b** If the total surface area is 240 cm$^2$, find the dimensions of the box.

**12**

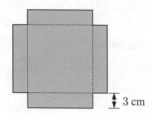

3 cm

An open box can hold 80 cm$^3$. It is made from a square piece of tinplate with 3 cm squares cut from each of its 4 corners. Find the dimensions of the original piece of tinplate.

**DEMO**

**13** A triangular paddock has a road AB forming its longest side. AB is 3 km long. The fences AC and CB are at right angles. If BC is 400 m longer than AC, find the area of the paddock in hectares.

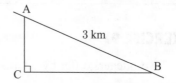

**14** A uniform concrete path is paved around a 30 m by 40 m rectangular lawn. The concrete has area one quarter of the area of the lawn. Find the width of the path.

**15** Answer the **Opening Problem** on page **288**.

**16** Two trains travel a 160 km track each day. The express travels 10 km h$^{-1}$ faster and takes 30 minutes less time than the normal train. Find the speed of the express.

**17** A rectangular swimming pool is 12 m long by 6 m wide. It is surrounded by a pavement of uniform width, the area of the pavement being $\frac{7}{8}$ of the area of the pool.

    **a** If the pavement is $x$ m wide, show that the area of the pavement is $4x^2 + 36x$ m$^2$.

    **b** Hence, show that $4x^2 + 36x - 63 = 0$.

    **c** How wide is the pavement?

**18** Chermaine is making a kite by lashing together two pieces of bamboo, one 80 cm long and the other 50 cm long. The pieces are tied so that the material for the kite has right angles on the sides as shown. Let the distance AO from the tip of the kite to the lashing be $x$ cm.

    **a** Using triangle AOB, find an expression for AB in terms of $x$.

    **b** Using triangle BOC, find an expression for BC in terms of $x$.

    **c** Using triangle ABC, find the value of $x$.

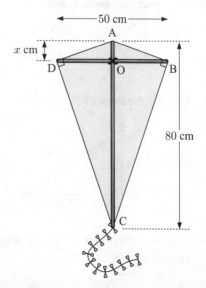

## REVIEW SET 9A

**1** Fully factorise:

   **a** $x^2 - 4x - 21$   **b** $4t^2 - 25$     **c** $3x^2 - 6x - 72$   **d** $6x^2 + x - 2$

**2** Solve for $x$:

   **a** $x^2 + 24 = 11x$               **b** $10x^2 - 11x - 6 = 0$

**3** Solve for $x$:

   **a** $(x - 2)^2 = 25$             **b** $x(x - 4) - (x - 6) = 0$

**4** Solve for $x$ by first eliminating the algebraic fractions:

   **a** $\dfrac{4}{x} = \dfrac{x}{7}$             **b** $\dfrac{x + 1}{x + 3} = \dfrac{x}{2}$

**5** The width of a rectangle is 7 cm less than its length and its area is 260 cm². Find its dimensions.

**6** A sailboat has two triangular sails with dimensions shown alongside. The hypotenuses of the two sails are equal. Find $x$.

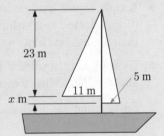

**7** Solve using the quadratic formula:

   $x^2 + 6x - 11 = 0$

## REVIEW SET 9B

**1** Fully factorise:

   **a** $x^2 - 8x - 33$     **b** $y^2 + 4y - 32$     **c** $x^2 - 10x + 25$

**2** Solve for $x$:

   **a** $x^2 + 5x = 24$     **b** $2x^2 - 18 = 0$     **c** $8x^2 + 2x - 3 = 0$

**3** Solve for $x$:

   **a** $(x + 3)^2 = 5x + 29$         **b** $2x^2 - 108 = 6x$

**4** Solve for $x$ using technology:

   **a** $x^2 + 6x - 2 = 0$         **b** $-3x^2 + 5x + 14 = 0$

**5**

ABCD is a rectangle in which AB = 21 cm. The square AXYD is removed and the remaining rectangle has area 80 cm². Find the length of BC.

**6** When the square of a number is increased by 10, the result is seven times the original number. Find the number.

**7** Solve using the quadratic formula:  $x^2 - 2x = 100$

## REVIEW SET 9C

**1** Factorise into linear factors:

   **a** $13 - x^2$       **b** $(x-1)(2x+5) - 3(x-1)^2$

**2** Factorise:

   **a** $x^2 - 7x - 18$   **b** $4x^2 - 49$     **c** $2k^2 - 14k - 60$  **d** $5x^2 + 12x + 4$

**3** Solve for $x$:

   **a** $x^2 + 6 = 5x$       **b** $x^2 + 16 = 8x$       **c** $3x^2 = 2x + 21$

**4** Using technology, solve for $x$:

   **a** $7.4x^2 - 153x + 289.6 = 0$        **b** $\dfrac{x-4}{2x+1} = \dfrac{5x}{x-9}$

**5** A right angled triangle has its hypotenuse one centimetre more than twice the length of the shortest side, while the other side is 7 cm longer than the shortest side. Find the length of each of the sides of the triangle.

**6** Over 65 km, I cycled 7 km per hour faster than my sister and finished 45 minutes ahead of her. What was my speed?

**7** Solve using the quadratic formula: $\;x^2 - 14x + 7 = 0$

## REVIEW SET 9D

**1** Fully factorise:

   **a** $4x^2 - 36$      **b** $a^2 - 7a - 30$       **c** $6x^2 - x - 12$

**2** Solve for $x$:

   **a** $2x^2 - 5x = 0$   **b** $x^2 - 12 = 4x$       **c** $4x^2 - 5x = 6$

**3** Solve for $x$:

   **a** $(x+3)^2 = 36$   **b** $x(x+4) + 2(x+5) = 5$   **c** $3x(x-2) = 2 - 11x$

**4** Richard has an elder sister who is twice his age, and a younger sister who is two years younger than him. If the product of his sisters' ages is 70, how old is Richard?

**5** Iain throws a ball into the air. Its height above the ground after $x$ seconds is $2 + 4x - 4.9x^2$ metres. How long does it take for the ball to hit the ground?

**6** I have a square block of land. My neighbour has a rectangular block, which is the same width as my block, but is 1 km longer. The combined area of our land is 6 km$^2$. What are the dimensions of my block of land?

**7** Solve using the quadratic formula: $\;2x^2 - 5x + 1 = 0$

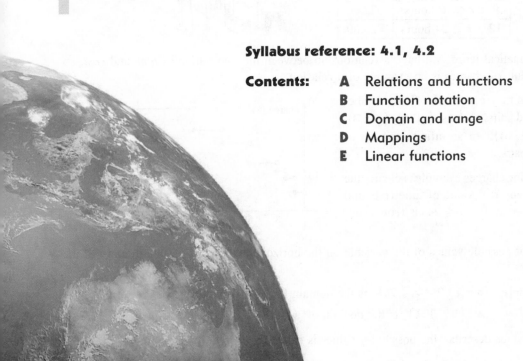

# Chapter **10**

# Functions

**Syllabus reference: 4.1, 4.2**

**Contents:**  **A**  Relations and functions
**B**  Function notation
**C**  Domain and range
**D**  Mappings
**E**  Linear functions

## A    RELATIONS AND FUNCTIONS

The charges for parking a car in a short-term car park at an airport are given in the table alongside.

There is an obvious relationship between the time spent in the car park and the cost. The cost is *dependent* on the length of time the car is parked.

Looking at this table we might ask: How much would be charged for *exactly* one hour? Would it be $5 or $9?

To make the situation clear, and to avoid confusion, we could adjust the table and draw a graph. We need to indicate that 2-3 hours really means a time over 2 hours up to and including 3 hours. So, $2 < t \leqslant 3$.

| Car park charges | |
|---|---|
| *Period (t)* | *Charge* |
| 0 - 1 hours | $5.00 |
| 1 - 2 hours | $9.00 |
| 2 - 3 hours | $11.00 |
| 3 - 6 hours | $13.00 |
| 6 - 9 hours | $18.00 |
| 9 - 12 hours | $22.00 |
| 12 - 24 hours | $28.00 |

We now have:

| Car park charges | |
|---|---|
| *Period* | *Charge* |
| $0 < t \leqslant 1$ hours | $5.00 |
| $1 < t \leqslant 2$ hours | $9.00 |
| $2 < t \leqslant 3$ hours | $11.00 |
| $3 < t \leqslant 6$ hours | $13.00 |
| $6 < t \leqslant 9$ hours | $18.00 |
| $9 < t \leqslant 12$ hours | $22.00 |
| $12 < t \leqslant 24$ hours | $28.00 |

In mathematical terms, we have a relationship between the two variables *time* and *cost*, so the schedule of charges is an example of a **relation**.

A relation may consist of a finite number of ordered pairs, such as $\{(1, 5), (-2, 3), (4, 3), (1, 6)\}$, or an infinite number of ordered pairs.

The parking charges example is clearly the latter as any real value of time ($t$ hours) in the interval $0 < t \leqslant 24$ is represented.

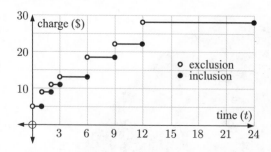

The set of possible values of the variable on the horizontal axis is called the **domain** of the relation.

For example:  • $\{t \mid 0 < t \leqslant 24\}$ is the domain for the car park relation
  • $\{-2, 1, 4\}$ is the domain of $\{(1, 5), (-2, 3), (4, 3), (1, 6)\}$.

The set which describes the possible $y$-values is called the **range** of the relation.

For example:  • the range of the car park relation is $\{5, 9, 11, 13, 18, 22, 28\}$
  • the range of $\{(1, 5), (-2, 3), (4, 3), (1, 6)\}$ is $\{3, 5, 6\}$.

We will now look at relations and functions more formally.

# RELATIONS

> A **relation** is any set of points on the Cartesian plane.

A relation is often expressed in the form of an **equation** connecting the **variables** $x$ and $y$.

For example, $y = x + 3$ and $x = y^2$ are the equations of two relations.

These equations generate sets of ordered pairs.

Their graphs are:

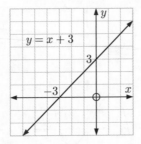 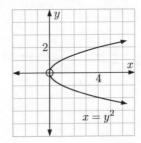

However, a relation may not be able to be defined by an equation. Below are two examples which show this:

**(1)** 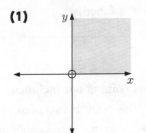  All points in the first quadrant are a relation.

$x > 0, \ y > 0$

**(2)** 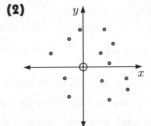  These 13 points form a relation.

# FUNCTIONS

> A **function**, sometimes called a **mapping**, is a relation in which no two different ordered pairs have the same $x$-coordinate or first member.

We can see from this definition that a function is a special type of relation.

## TESTING FOR FUNCTIONS

**Algebraic Tests:**

> If a relation is given as an equation, and the substitution of any value for $x$ results in one and only one value of $y$, we have a function.

For example:

- $y = 3x - 1$ is a function, as for any value of $x$ there is only one value of $y$.
- $x = y^2$ is not a function since if $x = 4$ then $y = \pm 2$.

**Geometric Test** or **Vertical Line Test**:

> If we draw all possible vertical lines on the graph of a relation, the relation:
> - is a function if each line cuts the graph no more than once
> - is not a function if at least one line cuts the graph more than once.

## Example 1

◀)) **Self Tutor**

Which of the following relations are functions?

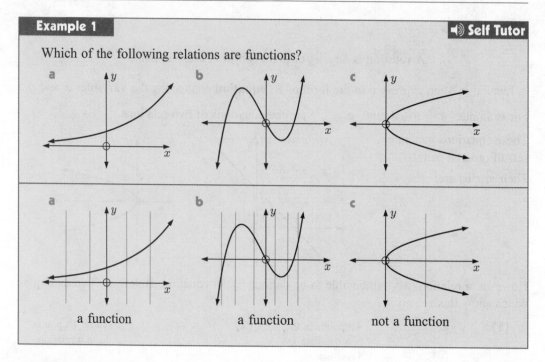

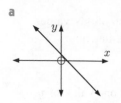

a function

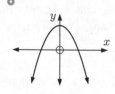

a function

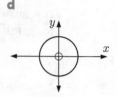

not a function

## GRAPHICAL NOTE

- If a graph contains a small **open circle** such as ——○—— , this point is **not included**.
- If a graph contains a small **filled-in circle** such as ——● , this point **is included**.
- If a graph contains an **arrow head** at an end such as ——▶ , then the graph continues indefinitely in that general direction, or the shape may repeat as it has done previously.

## EXERCISE 10A

1 Which of the following sets of ordered pairs are functions? Give reasons.

  a  $\{(1, 3), (2, 4), (3, 5), (4, 6)\}$

  b  $\{(1, 3), (3, 2), (1, 7), (-1, 4)\}$

  c  $\{(2, -1), (2, 0), (2, 3), (2, 11)\}$

  d  $\{(7, 6), (5, 6), (3, 6), (-4, 6)\}$

  e  $\{(0, 0), (1, 0), (3, 0), (5, 0)\}$

  f  $\{(0, 0), (0, -2), (0, 2), (0, 4)\}$

2 Use the vertical line test to determine which of the following relations are functions:

  a        b        c        d

  e        f        g        h

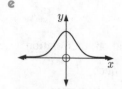
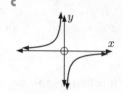
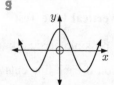
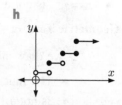
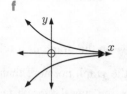

**3**  Will the graph of a straight line always be a function?  Give evidence to support your answer.

**4**  Give algebraic evidence to show that the relation  $x^2 + y^2 = 9$  is not a function.

## B          FUNCTION NOTATION

**Function machines** are sometimes used to illustrate how functions behave.

For example:

If 4 is fed into the machine, $2(4) + 3 = 11$  comes out.

The above 'machine' has been programmed to perform a particular function.

If  $f$  is used to represent that particular function we can write:

$f$  is the function that will convert $x$ into  $2x + 3$.

So,  $f$  would convert    2  into    $2(2) + 3 = 7$    and

$-4$  into   $2(-4) + 3 = -5$.

This function can be written as:

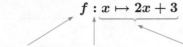

$$f : x \mapsto 2x + 3$$

function $f$     such that     $x$ is converted into  $2x + 3$

Two other equivalent forms we use are:  $f(x) = 2x + 3$  or  $y = 2x + 3$

$f(x)$  is the value of $y$ for a given value of $x$,  so  $y = f(x)$.

Notice that for  $f(x) = 2x + 3$,  $f(2) = 2(2) + 3 = 7$  and  $f(-4) = 2(-4) + 3 = -5$.

Consequently,   $f(2) = 7$  indicates that the point $(2, 7)$ lies on the graph of the function.

Likewise,        $f(-4) = -5$  indicates that the point $(-4, -5)$ also lies on the graph.

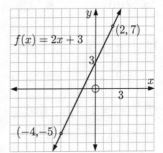

**Note:**

- $f(x)$  is read as  "$f$ of $x$".
- $f$  is the function which converts $x$ into  $f(x)$, so we write  $f : x \mapsto f(x)$.
- $y = f(x)$  is sometimes called the **image** of $x$.

> **Example 2**                                          ◄)) **Self Tutor**
>
> If $f : x \mapsto 2x^2 - 3x$,  find the value of:     a  $f(5)$     b  $f(-4)$
>
> ---
>
> $f(x) = 2x^2 - 3x$
>
> a  $f(5) = 2(5)^2 - 3(5)$           {replacing $x$ with $(5)$}
> $\qquad = 2 \times 25 - 15$
> $\qquad = 35$
>
> b  $f(-4) = 2(-4)^2 - 3(-4)$        {replacing $x$ with $(-4)$}
> $\qquad\ = 2(16) + 12$
> $\qquad\ = 44$

> **Example 3**                                          ◄)) **Self Tutor**
>
> If $f(x) = 5 - x - x^2$,  find in simplest form:     a  $f(-x)$     b  $f(x+2)$
>
> ---
>
> a  $f(-x) = 5 - (-x) - (-x)^2$          {replacing $x$ with $(-x)$}
> $\qquad\ = 5 + x - x^2$
>
> b  $f(x+2) = 5 - (x+2) - (x+2)^2$        {replacing $x$ with $(x+2)$}
> $\qquad\quad = 5 - x - 2 - [x^2 + 4x + 4]$
> $\qquad\quad = 3 - x - x^2 - 4x - 4$
> $\qquad\quad = -x^2 - 5x - 1$

## EXERCISE 10B

**1**  If $f : x \mapsto 3x + 2$,  find the value of:

    a  $f(0)$      b  $f(2)$      c  $f(-1)$      d  $f(-5)$      e  $f(-\tfrac{1}{3})$

**2**  If $f : x \mapsto 3x - x^2 + 2$,  find the value of:

    a  $f(0)$      b  $f(3)$      c  $f(-3)$      d  $f(-7)$      e  $f(\tfrac{3}{2})$

**3**  If $g : x \mapsto x - \dfrac{4}{x}$,  find the value of:

    a  $g(1)$      b  $g(4)$      c  $g(-1)$      d  $g(-4)$      e  $g\left(-\tfrac{1}{2}\right)$

**4**  If $f(x) = 7 - 3x$,  find in simplest form:

    a  $f(a)$    b  $f(-a)$    c  $f(a+3)$   d  $f(b-1)$   e  $f(x+2)$   f  $f(x+h)$

**5**  If $F(x) = 2x^2 + 3x - 1$,  find in simplest form:

    a  $F(x+4)$   b  $F(2-x)$   c  $F(-x)$    d  $F(x^2)$     e  $F(x^2-1)$   f  $F(x+h)$

**6** Suppose $G(x) = \dfrac{2x + 3}{x - 4}$.

   **a** Evaluate:   **i** $G(2)$   **ii** $G(0)$   **iii** $G\left(-\frac{1}{2}\right)$

   **b** Find a value of $x$ such that $G(x)$ does not exist.

   **c** Find $G(x + 2)$ in simplest form.

   **d** Find $x$ if $G(x) = -3$.

**7** $f$ represents a function. What is the difference in meaning between $f$ and $f(x)$?

**8** The value of a photocopier $t$ years after purchase is given by $V(t) = 9650 - 860t$ euros.

   **a** Find $V(4)$ and state what $V(4)$ means.

   **b** Find $t$ when $V(t) = 5780$ and explain what this represents.

   **c** Find the original purchase price of the photocopier.

**9** On the same set of axes draw the graphs of three different functions $f(x)$ such that $f(2) = 1$ and $f(5) = 3$.

**10** Find a linear function $f(x) = ax + b$ for which $f(2) = 1$ and $f(-3) = 11$.

**11** Find constants $a$ and $b$ if $f(x) = ax + \dfrac{b}{x}$, $f(1) = 1$, and $f(2) = 5$.

**12** Given $T(x) = ax^2 + bx + c$, find $a$, $b$ and $c$ if $T(0) = -4$, $T(1) = -2$ and $T(2) = 6$.

**13** If $f(x) = 2^x$, show that $f(a)f(b) = f(a + b)$.

## C    DOMAIN AND RANGE

> The **domain** of a relation is the set of permissible values that $x$ may have.
>
> The **range** of a relation is the set of permissible values that $y$ may have.

The domain and range of a relation are often described using **interval notation**.

For example:

**(1)**

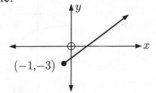

All values of $x \geqslant -1$ are permissible.
So, the domain is $\{x \mid x \geqslant -1\}$.
All values of $y \geqslant -3$ are permissible.
So, the range is $\{y \mid y \geqslant -3\}$.

**(2)**

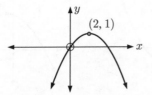

$x$ can take any value.
So, the domain is $\{x \mid x \in \mathbb{R}\}$.
$y$ cannot be $> 1$.
So, the range is $\{y \mid y \leqslant 1\}$.

**(3)**

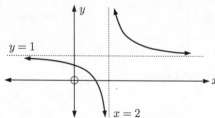

$x$ can take all values except $x = 2$.
So, the domain is $\{x \mid x \neq 2\}$.
Likewise, the range is $\{y \mid y \neq 1\}$.

**(4)**  For the profit function alongside:

- the domain is $\{x \mid x \geqslant 0\}$
- the range is $\{y \mid y \leqslant 100\}$.

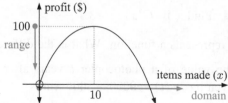

Click on the icon to obtain software for finding the domain and range of different functions.

**DOMAIN AND RANGE**

---

**Example 4**  ◀) **Self Tutor**

For each of the following graphs, state the domain and range:

a

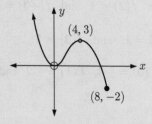

b

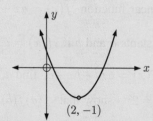

a   Domain is   $\{x \mid x \leqslant 8\}$
    Range is    $\{y \mid y \geqslant -2\}$

b   Domain is   $\{x \mid x \in \mathbb{R}\}$
    Range is    $\{y \mid y \geqslant -1\}$

---

## EXERCISE 10C

**1**  For each of the following graphs, find the domain and range:

a

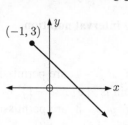

b

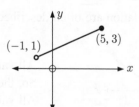

c

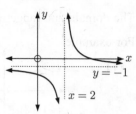

d

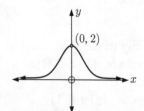

e

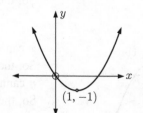

f

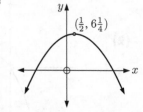

**g**
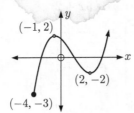

**h**
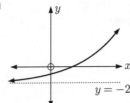

**i**
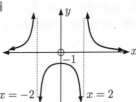

**2** For each of the following functions, state the values of $x$ for which $f(x)$ is undefined:

    **a** $f(x) = \sqrt{x + 6}$      **b** $f : x \mapsto \dfrac{1}{x^2}$      **c** $f(x) = \dfrac{-7}{\sqrt{3 - 2x}}$

**3** Use technology to help sketch graphs of the following functions. Find the domain and range of each.     **DOMAIN AND RANGE**

    **a** $f(x) = \sqrt{x}$                        **b** $f : x \mapsto \dfrac{1}{x^2}$

    **c** $f : x \mapsto \sqrt{4 - x}$            **d** $y = x^2 - 7x + 10$

    **e** $f : x \mapsto 5x - 3x^2$         **f** $f : x \mapsto x + \dfrac{1}{x}$

    **g** $y = \dfrac{x + 4}{x - 2}$                **h** $y = x^3 - 3x^2 - 9x + 10$

    **i** $f : x \mapsto \dfrac{3x - 9}{x^2 - x - 2}$       **j** $y = x^2 + x^{-2}$

    **k** $y = x^3 + \dfrac{1}{x^3}$               **l** $f : x \mapsto x^4 + 4x^3 - 16x + 3$

# D                                      **MAPPINGS**

In the previous section, we introduced functions as 'machines' which convert $x$ into $f(x)$.

The function $f : x \mapsto f(x)$ **maps** elements from the **domain** of the function onto elements in the **range** of the function.

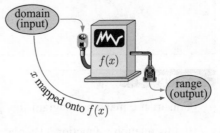

For example, the function $f : x \mapsto 5x + 2$ maps $x$ onto 'two more than five lots of $x$'.

We can specify a domain to limit the input possibilities.

For the domain $\{x \mid 1 \leqslant x \leqslant 4, \ x \in \mathbb{Z}\}$, the permissible values of $f(x)$ are restricted to:

    $f(1) = 5(1) + 2 = 7$
    $f(2) = 5(2) + 2 = 12$
    $f(3) = 5(3) + 2 = 17$
    $f(4) = 5(4) + 2 = 22$

We can represent $f : x \mapsto 5x + 2$ for this domain using a **mapping diagram**:

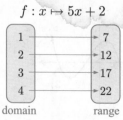

$f : x \mapsto 5x + 2$

domain          range

In this case each element in the domain $\{1, 2, 3, 4\}$ corresponds to a single element in the range $\{7, 12, 17, 22\}$.

For a **relation**:

- multiple elements in the domain may correspond to the **same** element in the range.
- an element in the domain may have more than one corresponding element in the range.

For a **function**, however, each element in the domain corresponds to exactly one element in the range.

---

**Example 5**    ◀)) **Self Tutor**

Construct a mapping diagram for $f : x \mapsto x^2$ on the domain $\{-2, -1, 0, 1, 2\}$.

Is this relation a function? Display the results on a set of axes.

| $x$ | $-2$ | $-1$ | $0$ | $1$ | $2$ |
|-----|------|------|-----|-----|-----|
| $f(x)$ | $4$ | $1$ | $0$ | $1$ | $4$ |

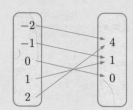

This relation is a function since each element in the domain corresponds to exactly one element in the range.

---

**Example 6**    ◀)) **Self Tutor**

Construct a mapping diagram for $p : x \mapsto \pm\sqrt{x}$ on the domain $\{0, 1, 4, 9\}$.

Is this relation a function? Display the results on a set of axes.

| $x$ | $0$ | $1$ | $4$ | $9$ |
|-----|-----|-----|-----|-----|
| $p(x)$ | $0$ | $\pm 1$ | $\pm 2$ | $\pm 3$ |

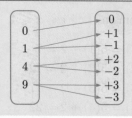

The mapping diagram shows single elements of the domain mapping to *multiple* elements within the range. This relation is not a function.

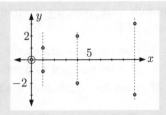

## EXERCISE 10D

1 For the following relations on $-2 \leqslant x \leqslant 2$, $x \in \mathbb{Z}$:

    **i** draw a mapping diagram to represent the relation

    **ii** list the elements of the range using set notation

    **iii** determine if the relation is a function

    **iv** illustrate the relation on a set of axes.

**a** $f(x) = 3x - 1$      **b** $f(x) = x^2 + 1$      **c** $f(x) = 3 - 4x$

**d** $f : x \mapsto 3 \pm x$      **e** $f(x) = 2x^2 - x + 1$      **f** $f(x) = x^3$

**g** $f(x) = 3^x$      **h** $f : x \mapsto \dfrac{1}{x+3}$      **i** $f(x) = \dfrac{x+3}{x}$, $x \neq 0$

---

### Example 7      ◀） Self Tutor

The diagram shows a function $f$ mapping members of set $X$ to members of set $Y$.

**a** Using set notation, write down the members of the domain and range.

**b** Find the equation of the function $f$.

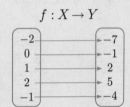

$f : X \to Y$

**a** Domain $= \{-2, -1, 0, 1, 2\}$, Range $= \{-7, -4, -1, 2, 5\}$

**b** We use the mapping diagram to construct a table of values:

| $x$ | $-2$ | $-1$ | $0$ | $1$ | $2$ |
|-----|------|------|-----|-----|-----|
| $f(x)$ | $-7$ | $-4$ | $-1$ | $2$ | $5$ |

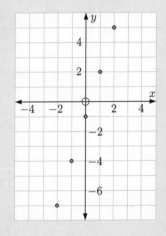

Plotting the points on a set of axes, we see that the points form a straight line.

So, $f(x) = mx + c$ where

$$m = \frac{5 - 2}{2 - 1} \quad \{\text{using } (2, 5) \text{ and } (1, 2)\}$$

$$\therefore \quad m = 3$$

The $y$-intercept $c = -1$.

$$\therefore \quad f(x) = 3x - 1 \quad \text{or} \quad f : x \mapsto 3x - 1$$

on the domain $\{x \mid -2 \leqslant x \leqslant 2, \ x \in \mathbb{Z}\}$.

**2** In the following mapping diagrams, the function $f$ maps the elements of $X$ onto the elements of $Y$.

    **i** Use set notation to write down the domain of $f$.

    **ii** Use set notation to write down the range of $f$.

    **iii** Find the equation of the function $f$.

**a**
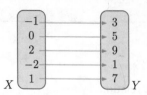

**b**
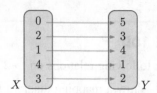

**c**
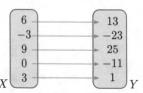

**d**
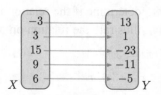

**3** In the following mapping diagrams, the function $f$ maps $X$ onto $Y$.

    **i** Sketch the function $f$ on a set of axes.

    **ii** Find the equation of the function $f$.

**a**
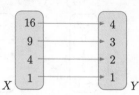

**b**
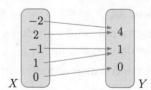

**c**
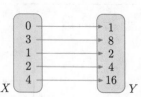

**d**
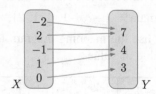

To find the equations of the functions, it may help to compare the graphs with those in question **1**.

# E | LINEAR FUNCTIONS

A **linear function** is a function of the form $f(x) = ax + b$ or $f : x \mapsto ax + b$ where $a$ and $b$ are constants, $a \neq 0$.

## GRAPHS OF LINEAR FUNCTIONS

Consider the function $f(x) = ax + b$.

The graph of $y = f(x)$ is a **straight line** with gradient $a$ and $y$-intercept $b$.

The $x$-intercept is where the graph cuts the $x$-axis. It is found by solving the equation $f(x) = 0$.

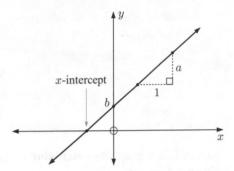

## INVESTIGATION                                    BAMBOO

Bamboo is the fastest growing plant in the world, with some species growing up to 1 metre per day.

Xuanyu planted a 30 cm high bamboo plant in her garden bed. She found that with consistent weather it grew 10 cm each day.

**What to do:**

**1** Copy and complete this table of values which gives the height $H$ of the bamboo after $t$ days.

| $t$ (days) | 0 | 1 | 2 | 3 | 4 | 5 | 6 |
|---|---|---|---|---|---|---|---|
| $H$ (cm) | 30 | 40 | | | | | |

**2** Plot the points on a set of axes and connect them with straight line segments.

**3** Explain why it is reasonable to connect the points with straight line segments.

**4** Discuss whether it is reasonable to continue the line for $t < 0$ and for $t > 6$ days. Hence state the domain of the function $H(t)$.

**5** Find the '$H$-intercept' and gradient of the line.

**6** Find an equation for the function $H(t)$.

**7** Use your equation to find the value of $H(10)$. Explain what this value represents.

**8** How long will it take for the bamboo to be 1 m high?

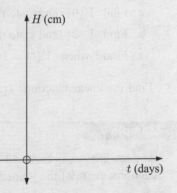

| Example 8 | ◆)) Self Tutor |
|---|---|

The cost of hiring a tennis court is given by the formula $C(h) = 5h + 8$ dollars where $h$ is the number of hours the court is hired for. Find the cost of hiring the tennis court for:    **a**    4 hours    **b**    10 hours.

The formula is $C(h) = 5h + 8$.

**a**  Substituting $h = 4$ we get
$$C(4) = 5(4) + 8$$
$$= 20 + 8$$
$$= 28$$
It costs $28 to hire the court for 4 hours.

**b**  Substituting $h = 10$ we get
$$C(10) = 5(10) + 8$$
$$= 50 + 8$$
$$= 58$$
It costs $58 to hire the court for 10 hours.

You can use a **graphics calculator** or **graphing package** to help you in the following exercise.

GRAPHING PACKAGE

## EXERCISE 10E

1  The cost of staying at a hotel is given by the formula $C(d) = 50d + 20$ euros where $d$ is the number of days a person stays. Find the cost of staying for:

    **a**  3 days        **b**  6 days        **c**  2 weeks

2  The thermometer on Charlotte's kitchen oven uses the Celsius scale, but her recipe book gives the required temperature on the Fahrenheit scale. The formula which links the two temperature scales is $T_C(F) = \frac{5}{9}(F - 32)$ where $T_C$ is the temperature in degrees Celsius and $F$ is the temperature in degrees Fahrenheit.
Convert the following Fahrenheit temperatures into Celsius:

    **a**  212°F        **b**  32°F        **c**  104°F        **d**  374°F

3  The value of a car $t$ years after its purchase is given by $V(t) = 25\,000 - 3000t$ pounds.

    **a**  Find $V(0)$ and state the meaning of $V(0)$.

    **b**  Find $V(3)$ and state the meaning of $V(3)$.

    **c**  Find $t$ when $V(t) = 10\,000$ and explain what this represents.

4  Find the linear function $f(x) = ax + b$ such that $f(2) = 7$ and $f(-1) = -5$.

| Example 9 | ◆)) Self Tutor |
|---|---|

Ace taxi services charge $3.30 for stopping to pick up a passenger and then $1.75 for each kilometre of the journey.

    **a**  Copy and complete:

| Distance ($d$ km) | 0 | 2 | 4 | 6 | 8 | 10 |
|---|---|---|---|---|---|---|
| Cost ($C) | | | | | | |

**b** Graph $C$ against $d$.

**c** Find the function $C(d)$ which connects the variables.

**d** Find the cost of a 9.4 km journey.

**a**

| Distance ($d$ km) | 0 | 2 | 4 | 6 | 8 | 10 |
|---|---|---|---|---|---|---|
| Cost ($\$C$) | 3.30 | 6.80 | 10.30 | 13.80 | 17.30 | 20.80 |

adding $2 \times \$1.75 = \$3.50$ each time.

**b**

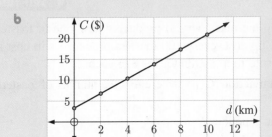

**c** The 'y-intercept' is 3.30 and

the gradient $= \dfrac{20.80 - 17.30}{10 - 8}$

$= 1.75$

$\therefore\ C(d) = 1.75d + 3.3$

**d** $C(9.4) = 1.75 \times 9.4 + 3.3$

$= 19.75$

$\therefore$ the cost is $\$19.75$

**5** An electrician charges \$60 for calling and \$45 per hour he spends on the job.

  **a** From a table of values, plot the amount $\$C$ the electrician charges against the hours $t$ he works for $t = 0,\ 1,\ 2,\ 3,\ 4$ and 5.

  **b** Use your graph to determine the cost function $C$ in terms of $t$.

  **c** Use the cost function to determine the electrician's total cost for a job lasting $6\frac{1}{2}$ hours. Use your graph to check your answer.

**6** A rainwater tank contains 265 litres. The tap is left on and 11 litres escape per minute.

  **a** Construct a table of values for the volume $V$ litres left in the tank after $t$ minutes for $t = 0,\ 1,\ 2,\ 3,\ 4$ and 5.

  **b** Use your table to graph $V$ against $t$.

  **c** Use your graph to determine the function $V(t)$.

  **d** Use your function to determine:

   **i** how much water is left in the tank after 15 minutes

   **ii** the time taken for the tank to empty.

  **e** Use your graph to check your answers to **d i** and **d ii**.

**7** The cost of running a truck is €158 plus €365 for every one thousand kilometres driven.

  **a** Without graphing, determine the cost €$C$ in terms of the number of thousands of kilometres $n$.

  **b** Find the cost of running the truck a distance of 3750 km.

  **c** How far could the truck travel if €5000 was available?

**8** A salesperson's wage is determined from the graph alongside.

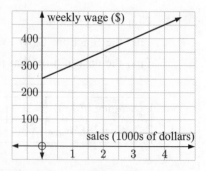

a Determine the weekly wage $W in terms of the sales $s thousand dollars.

b Find the weekly wage if the salesperson made $33 500 worth of sales.

c Determine the sales necessary for a weekly wage of $830.

---

**Example 10**    ◀ﺔ Self Tutor

An appliance manufacturer can set up the machinery to produce a new line of toaster for $12 000. Following this initial setup cost, every 100 toasters produced will cost a further $1000. The toasters are then sold to a distributor for $25 each.

a Determine the cost of production function $C(n)$ where $n$ is the number of toasters manufactured.

b Determine the income or revenue function $R(n)$.

c Graph $C(n)$ and $R(n)$ on the same set of axes for $0 \leqslant n \leqslant 1500$.

d How many toasters need to be produced and sold in order to 'break even'?

e Calculate the profit or loss made when

   i 400 toasters       ii 1500 toasters    are produced and sold.

---

a After the fixed cost of $12 000, each toaster costs $10 to produce.

  ∴ $C(n) = 10n + 12\,000$ dollars     {gradient = cost/item = $10}

b Each toaster is sold for $25, so $R(n) = 25n$ dollars.

c

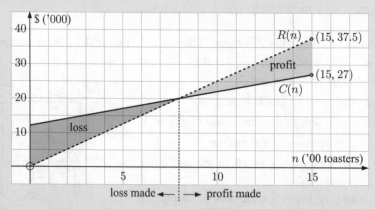

d To the left of the point of intersection, $C(n) > R(n)$, so a loss is made.

The manufacturer 'breaks even' where $C(n) = R(n)$

$$\therefore \quad 10n + 12\,000 = 25n$$

$$\therefore \quad 12\,000 = 15n$$

$$\therefore \quad n = 800$$

800 toasters must be produced and sold in order to 'break even'.

e    Profit $= R(n) - C(n)$          i   $P(400) = 15 \times 400 - 12\,000$
   $\therefore\ P(n) = 25n - (10n + 12\,000)$                     $= -\$6000$
          $= 15n - 12\,000$              This is a loss of $6000.

                                    ii  $P(1500) = 15 \times 1500 - 12\,000$
                                              $= \$10\,500$
                                        This is a profit of $10\,500.

**9**   Self adhesive label packs are produced with cost function $C(n) = 3n + 20$ dollars and revenue function $R(n) = 5n + 10$ dollars where $n$ is the number of packs produced.

   **a**   Graph each function on the same set of axes, clearly labelling each graph.

   **b**   Determine the number of packs which must be produced and sold to 'break even'. Check your answer algebraically.

   **c**   For what values of $n$ is a profit made?

   **d**   How many self adhesive label packs need to be produced and sold to make a profit of $100?

**10**   Two way adaptors sell for £7 each. The adaptors cost £2.50 each to make with fixed costs of £300 per day regardless of the number made.

   **a**   Find revenue and cost functions in terms of the number $n$ of adaptors manufactured per day.

   **b**   Graph the revenue and cost functions on the same set of axes.

   **c**   Determine the 'break even' level of production and check your answer algebraically.

   **d**   How many adaptors must be made and sold every day to make a profit of £1000?

**11**   A new novel is being printed. The plates required for the printing process cost €6000, after which the printing costs €3250 per thousand books. The books are to sell at €9.50 each with an unlimited market.

   **a**   Determine cost and revenue functions for the production of the novel.

   **b**   Graph the cost and revenue functions on the same set of axes.

   **c**   How many books must be sold in order to 'break even'? Check your answer algebraically.

   **d**   What level of production and sale will produce a €10 000 profit?

**12**   Waverley Manufacturing produces carburettors for motor vehicles. Each week there is a fixed cost of $2100 to keep the factory running. Each carburettor costs $13.20 in materials and $14.80 in labour to produce. Waverley is able to sell the carburettors to the motor vehicle manufacturers at $70 each.

   **a**   Determine Waverley's cost and revenue functions in terms of the number $n$ manufactured per week.

   **b**   Draw graphs of the cost and revenue functions on the same set of axes. Use your graph to find the 'break even' point.

c Find the expression for the profit function and check your answer for the 'break even' value of $n$.

d Use your profit function to find:

   i the weekly profit for producing and selling 125 carburettors

   ii the number of carburettors required to make a profit of at least $1300.

## REVIEW SET 10A

**1** If $f(x) = 2x - x^2$ find:   **a** $f(2)$   **b** $f(-3)$   **c** $f(-\frac{1}{2})$

**2** If $f(x) = ax + b$ where $a$ and $b$ are constants, find $a$ and $b$ for $f(1) = 7$ and $f(3) = -5$.

**3** If $g(x) = x^2 - 3x$, find in simplest form:   **a** $g(x+1)$   **b** $g(x^2 - 2)$

**4** For each of the following graphs determine:

   **i** the range and domain       **ii** whether it is a function.

**a**

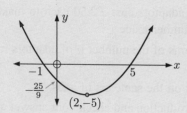

**b**

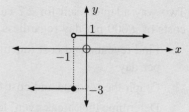

**5** Consider $f(x) = \dfrac{2}{x^2}$.

   **a** For what value of $x$ is $f(x)$ meaningless?

   **b** Sketch the graph of this function using technology.

   **c** State the domain and range of the function.

**6**   **a** Construct a mapping diagram for $f : x \mapsto x^2 - 4$ on the domain $\{-2, -1, 0, 1, 2\}$.

   **b** List the elements of the range of $f$ using set notation.

   **c** Determine whether $f$ is a function.

   **d** Draw the graph of $f$.

**7** A marquee hire company charges £130 for setting up and packing down, and £80 per day of use.

   **a** Construct a table of values showing the cost £$C$ of hiring a marquee for $d$ days, where $d = 0, 1, 2, 3, 4$.

   **b** Use your table to graph $C$ against $d$.

   **c** Use your graph to find the function linking $C$ and $d$.

   **d** The company offers a special deal in which the total cost of a week's hire is £650. How much money does this save?

## REVIEW SET 10B

**1** Use the vertical line test to determine which of the following relations are functions:

   **a**                **b**                         **c**

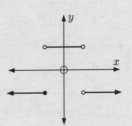
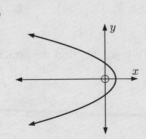

**2** If $f : x \mapsto 3x - 5$, find:

   **a** $f(2)$         **b** $f(0)$         **c** $f(x + 1)$         **d** $f(x^2 - x)$

**3** Find constants $a$ and $b$ if $f(x) = \dfrac{a}{x - 2} + b$, $f(1) = -4$ and $f(5) = 0$.

**4** For each of the following graphs, find the domain and range:

   **a**                         **b**

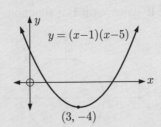
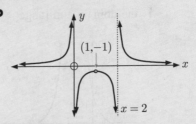

**5** For each of the following functions, state the values of $x$ for which $f(x)$ is undefined:

   **a** $f(x) = \dfrac{1}{x^3}$         **b** $f : x \mapsto \sqrt{x - 2}$         **c** $f(x) = 3x + 7$

**6** For the following functions on $-2 \leqslant x \leqslant 2$ where $x \in \mathbb{Z}$:

   **i** draw a mapping diagram to represent $f(x)$

   **ii** list the elements of the domain of $f(x)$ using set notation

   **iii** list the elements of the range of $f(x)$ using set notation.

   **a** $f : x \mapsto 2x + 5$             **b** $f(x) = x^2 - x + 2$

**7** The amount of oil $O$ left in a leaky barrel after $t$ minutes is shown on the graph alongside.

   **a** Express the amount of oil left after $t$ minutes as a formula.

   **b** How much oil is left after 15 minutes?

   **c** How long will it take before:

      **i** there are only 50 litres of oil left

      **ii** the barrel is empty?

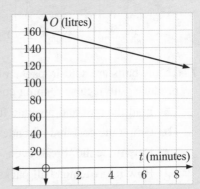

## REVIEW SET 10C

**1** Which of these sets of ordered pairs are functions? Give reasons for your answers.

  **a** $\{(1, 2), (-1, 2), (0, 5), (2, -7)\}$      **b** $\{(0, 1), (1, 3), (2, 5), (0, 7)\}$

  **c** $\{(6, 1), (6, 2), (6, 3), (6, 4)\}$

**2** For each of the following graphs, find the domain and range:

  **a**

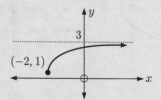

  **b**

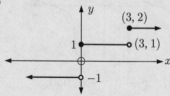

**3** Draw a possible graph of a function $g(x)$ where $g(2) = 5$, $g(4) = 7$ and $g(6) = -1$.

**4** Find $a$, $b$ and $c$ if $f(0) = 5$, $f(-2) = 21$, $f(3) = -4$ and $f(x) = ax^2 + bx + c$.

**5** For each of the following graphs determine:

  **i** the domain and range      **ii** whether it is a function.

  **a**

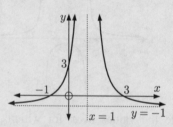

  **b**

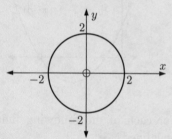

**6** In the following mapping diagrams, the function $f$ maps $X$ onto $Y$.

  **i** Use set notation to write down the domain and range of $f$.

  **ii** Sketch the function $f$ on a set of axes.

  **iii** Find the equation of the function $f$.

  **a**

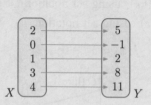

  **b**

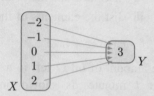

**7** Tennis balls are sold in packs of 3 for $11 per pack. The balls cost $2.40 each to produce with factory running costs of $1750 per day.

  **a** Find the cost and revenue functions for making $n$ tennis balls in a day.

  **b** Graph the cost and revenue functions on the same set of axes.

  **c** Determine the 'break even' production level. Check your answer algebraically.

  **d** How many tennis ball packs must be sold to make $400 profit per day?

# Chapter

# 11

# Perimeter, area and volume

**Syllabus reference: 2.4, 5.5**

**Contents:**

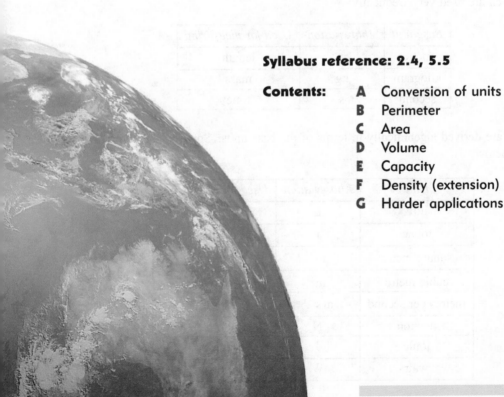

## OPENING PROBLEM                                BRICK EDGING

You are asked to quote on the supply and installation of bricks around a lawn. The bricks are expensive and are not returnable. Consequently, you need to accurately calculate how many are needed and what they will cost. You draw a rough sketch of what the house owner wants. You take it back to your office to do the calculations.

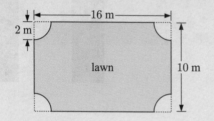

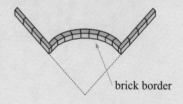

brick border

**Things to think about:**

- How far is it around the lawn?
- How many bricks will you need?
- What will be the cost of the bricks needed to do the job?
- Set up a spreadsheet to handle the calculations. This is particularly useful for a company expecting dozens of similar jobs in the future.

- What is the length of one brick?
- What is the cost of one brick?

In **Chapter 2** we saw that the **International System of Units** or **SI** has seven base units, three of which are used very frequently:

| Base unit | Abbreviation | Used for measuring |
|-----------|--------------|---------------------|
| metre | m | length |
| kilogram | kg | mass |
| second | s | time |

Other units are derived algebraically in terms of the base units. Some of the common ones are shown below:

| Unit | Abbreviation | Used for measuring |
|------|--------------|---------------------|
| litre | L | capacity |
| tonne | t | heavy masses |
| square metre | $m^2$ | area |
| cubic metre | $m^3$ | volume |
| metres per second | $m\,s^{-1}$ | speed |
| newton | N | force |
| joule | J | energy |
| watt | W | power |

# A    CONVERSION OF UNITS

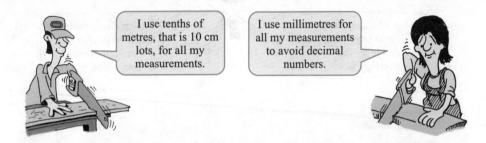

I use tenths of metres, that is 10 cm lots, for all my measurements.

I use millimetres for all my measurements to avoid decimal numbers.

## DISCUSSION

Discuss why we need to convert from one set of units to another.

When we work in the SI system, we often use units that are related to the base units by powers of ten. We use prefixes such as kilo, centi, and milli to indicate these units.

## CONVERSION DIAGRAM

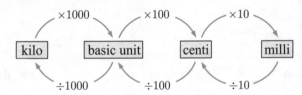

For example, to convert **milli**metres into **centi**metres we divide by 10.

## LENGTH CONVERSIONS

The following table shows the relationship between various **length units**:

| 1 m = 100 cm | 1 km = 1000 m | 1 cm = 10 mm | 1 mm = $\frac{1}{10}$ cm |
|---|---|---|---|
| = 1000 mm | = 100 000 cm | = $\frac{1}{100}$ m | = $\frac{1}{1000}$ m |
| = $\frac{1}{1000}$ km | = 1 000 000 mm | | |

However, you may find it easier to use the following **conversion diagram**:

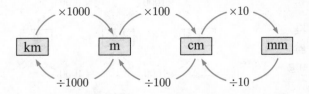

When changing from smaller to larger units, divide by the conversion factor.

When changing from larger to smaller units, multiply by the conversion factor.

### Example 1
🔊 Self Tutor

Convert:    **a**  16.73 m to cm    **b**  48 380 cm to km

**a**  We convert from larger to smaller units, so we need to multiply.
$$16.73 \text{ m} = (16.73 \times 100) \text{ cm}$$
$$= 1673 \text{ cm}$$

**b**  We convert from smaller to larger units, so we need to divide.
$$48\,380 \text{ cm} = (48\,380 \div 100 \div 1000) \text{ km}$$
$$= 0.4838 \text{ km}$$

## EXERCISE 11A.1

**1**  Convert:

|   |   |   |
|---|---|---|
| **a**  8250 cm to m | **b**  295 mm to cm | **c**  6250 m to km |
| **d**  73.8 m to cm | **e**  24.63 cm to m | **f**  9.761 m to km |

**2**  Convert:

|   |   |   |
|---|---|---|
| **a**  413 cm to mm | **b**  3754 km to m | **c**  4.829 km to cm |
| **d**  26.9 m to mm | **e**  0.47 km to cm | **f**  3.88 km to mm |

**3**  I have 55 reels of garden hose, each with 132 m of hose.  How many kilometres of garden hose do I have?

**4**  Phyllis is a candlemaker.  The wick of each of her candles is 27.5 cm.  If Phyllis has 4.95 km of wick, how many candles can she make?

## MASS CONVERSIONS

| **Mass** |
|---|
| 1 t = 1000 kg |
| 1 kg = 1000 g |
| 1 g = 1000 mg |

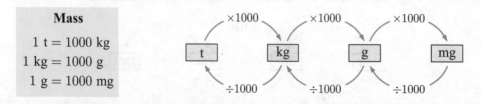

| **Example 2** | ◆) **Self Tutor** |
|---|---|

Convert:    a   2.3 kg to grams       b   8 470 000 g to tonnes

| | |
|---|---|
| a    2.3 kg<br>= (2.3 × 1000) g<br>= 2300 g | b    8 470 000 g<br>= (8 470 000 ÷ 1000 ÷ 1000) tonnes<br>= 8.47 tonnes |

## EXERCISE 11A.2

1  Convert:

a  5.9 kg to g        b  2600 g to kg        c  3750 g to t

d  15 kg to mg        e  4.8 t to g          f  1600 mg to kg

g  1.7385 g to mg     h  46 218 g to t       i  0.0361 kg to mg

2  How many 6 gram nails can be made from 0.12 t of iron?

3  Dominic found that the average banana weight on his plantation was 138 grams. That year he exported 45 000 bananas.

a  How many tonnes of bananas did he export?

b  If each truck carried 700 kg of bananas to the port, how many truck loads were required that year?

---

| **B** | **PERIMETER** |
|---|---|

## PERIMETER

> The **perimeter** of a figure is the measurement of the distance around its boundary.
>
> For a **polygon**, the perimeter is obtained by adding the lengths of all of its sides.
>
> For a **circle**, the perimeter has a special name, the **circumference**.

**DEMO**

Following is a summary of some **perimeter formulae**:

| *Shape* | *Formula* | *Shape* | *Formula* |
|---|---|---|---|
| square  $l$ | $P = 4l$ | rectangle $w$ $l$ | $P = 2l + 2w$<br>*or*  $P = 2(l + w)$ |
|  polygon  $a$ $e$ $b$ $d$ $c$ | $P = a + b + c + d + e$ | $d$ $r$ | $C = \pi d$<br>*or*  $C = 2\pi r$ |

**Example 3**  ◀) **Self Tutor**

Find the perimeter of:

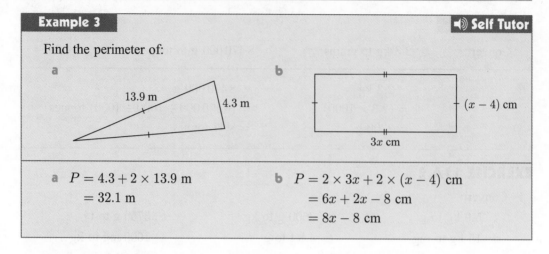

**a** $P = 4.3 + 2 \times 13.9$ m
 $= 32.1$ m

**b** $P = 2 \times 3x + 2 \times (x - 4)$ cm
 $= 6x + 2x - 8$ cm
 $= 8x - 8$ cm

## EXERCISE 11B

**1** Find the perimeter of the following figures:

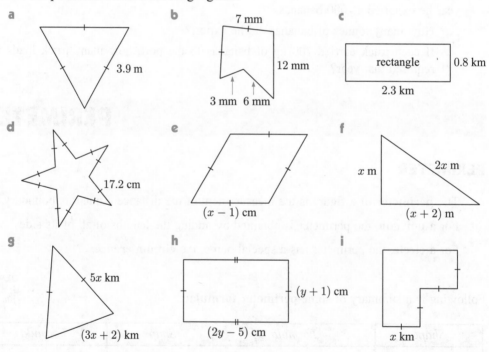

**2** A rectangular field 220 metres long and 300 metres wide is to be fenced.
 **a** Draw and label a diagram of the field.
 **b** Find the total length of fencing required.

**3** A sailing crew races around the course shown on the diagram. The race is 4 laps long. What distance do they travel?

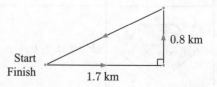

**4** A farmer wants to fence his private garden to keep out his sheep. The garden measures 26 m × 40 m. The fence has 5 strands of wire, and posts are placed every 2 metres.

    **a** Calculate the perimeter of the garden.

    **b** What length of wire is needed?

    **c** How many posts are needed?

    **d** Find the total cost of the fence if wire costs $0.28 per metre and each post costs $3.95.

**5** A room has the shape and dimensions shown. Skirting board was laid around the edge of the room.

    **a** How much skirting board was needed?

    **b** Skirting comes in 2.4 metre lengths which can be cut. If each length costs $2.48, what was the cost of the skirting board?

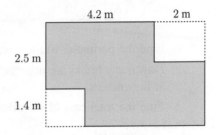

---

**Example 4**     🔊 **Self Tutor**

Find, to 3 significant figures, the perimeter of:

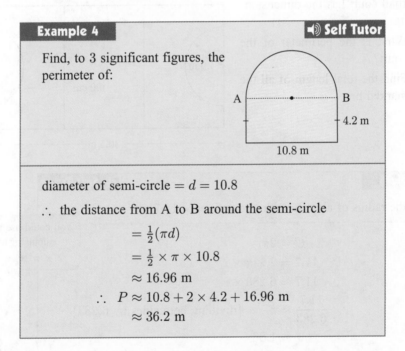

diameter of semi-circle $= d = 10.8$

$\therefore$ the distance from A to B around the semi-circle

$$= \tfrac{1}{2}(\pi d)$$
$$= \tfrac{1}{2} \times \pi \times 10.8$$
$$\approx 16.96 \text{ m}$$
$$\therefore \quad P \approx 10.8 + 2 \times 4.2 + 16.96 \text{ m}$$
$$\approx 36.2 \text{ m}$$

---

**6** Find, to 3 significant figures, the perimeter of:

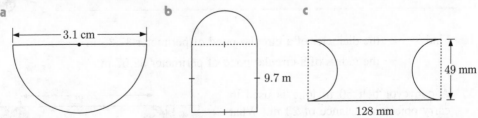

**7** My bike wheels have a diameter of 32 centimetres. When I ride to school the wheels complete 239 revolutions. How far do I live from my school?

**8** Consider the lawn in the **Opening Problem** on page **330**. Bricks of length 220 mm, each costing $4.70, are used to form its border.

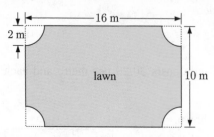

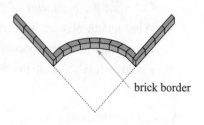

brick border

**a** Find the perimeter of the lawn.

**b** How many bricks are necessary to border the lawn? Allow 2% extra for their overlap at the corners.

**c** Find the total cost of the bricks.

**9** A netball court has the dimensions shown.

**a** What is the perimeter of the court?

**b** Find the total length of all the marked lines.

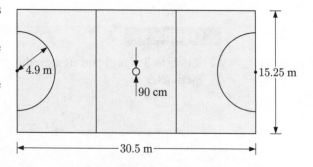

---

Find the radius of a circle with circumference 11.7 m.

> You could use a graphics calculator to solve
> $2 \times \pi \times r = 11.7$

$$C = 2\pi r$$
$$\therefore \quad 11.7 = 2 \times \pi \times r$$
$$\therefore \quad 11.7 \approx 6.283 \times r$$
$$\therefore \quad \frac{11.7}{6.283} \approx r \qquad \{\text{dividing both sides by } 6.283\}$$
$$\therefore \quad r \approx 1.86$$

$\therefore$   the radius is approximately 1.86 m.

**10** Find:   **a** the diameter of a circular pond of perimeter 37.38 m

**b** the radius of a circular pond of perimeter 32.67 m.

**11** A conveyor belt 50 m long is used to carry objects a distance of 23 m. What depth is the recess needed to exactly contain the belt rollers?

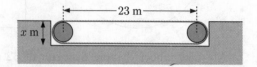

**AREA**

The **area** of a closed figure is the number of square units it contains.

The relationships between the various units of area can be obtained using the conversions for length.

For example,  since  $1 \text{ cm} = 10 \text{ mm}$,
$$1 \text{ cm} \times 1 \text{ cm} = 10 \text{ mm} \times 10 \text{ mm}$$
$$\therefore \ 1 \text{ cm}^2 = 100 \text{ mm}^2$$

## AREA UNITS

Area conversions are shown in the following table and conversion diagram:

| | | | |
|---|---|---|---|
| $1 \text{ cm}^2 = 10 \text{ mm} \times 10 \text{ mm}$ | $= 100 \text{ mm}^2$ | $\{1 \text{ cm}^2 \text{ is 1 square centimetre}\}$ |
| $1 \text{ m}^2 = 100 \text{ cm} \times 100 \text{ cm}$ | $= 10\,000 \text{ cm}^2$ | $\{1 \text{ m}^2 \text{ is 1 square metre}\}$ |
| $1 \text{ ha} = 100 \text{ m} \times 100 \text{ m}$ | $= 10\,000 \text{ m}^2$ | $\{1 \text{ ha is 1 hectare}\}$ |
| $1 \text{ km}^2 = 1000 \text{ m} \times 1000 \text{ m}$ | $= 1\,000\,000 \text{ m}^2$ | or 100 ha |

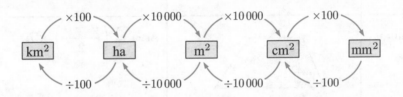

---

**Example 6**                                         ◀) **Self Tutor**

Convert:    a  $650\,000 \text{ m}^2$ into ha        b  $2.5 \text{ m}^2$ into $\text{mm}^2$

a  We convert from smaller to larger units, so we need to divide.
$$650\,000 \text{ m}^2$$
$$= (650\,000 \div 10\,000) \text{ ha}$$
$$= 65 \text{ ha}$$

b  We convert from larger to smaller units, so we need to multiply.
$$2.5 \text{ m}^2$$
$$= (2.5 \times 10\,000 \times 100) \text{ mm}^2$$
$$= 2\,500\,000 \text{ mm}^2$$

## EXERCISE 11C.1

1  Convert:

  a  $560 \text{ cm}^2$ to $\text{m}^2$      b  $4.8 \text{ km}^2$ to ha      c  $55 \text{ mm}^2$ to $\text{cm}^2$

  d  $0.13 \text{ km}^2$ to $\text{m}^2$      e  $46\,170 \text{ mm}^2$ to $\text{m}^2$      f  $7.21$ ha to $\text{km}^2$

  g  $8.43 \text{ m}^2$ to $\text{km}^2$      h  $0.0059$ ha to $\text{m}^2$      i  $9\,890\,000 \text{ cm}^2$ to $\text{km}^2$

2  a  There are around $56\,800$ houses built on 4800 hectares of land in my city. Find, in square metres, the average lot size for a house.

  b  A glazing company manufactures glass in $9.9 \text{ m}^2$ sheets which it then cuts exactly into $550 \text{ cm}^2$ panels. How many panels can it cut from each sheet?

## AREA FORMULAE

The formulae for calculating the area of the most commonly occurring shapes are given below:

| Shape | Figure | Formula |
|---|---|---|
| **Rectangle** | width, length | **Area = length × width** |
| **Triangle** | height, base, base | **Area = $\frac{1}{2}$ × base × height**    DEMO |
| **Parallelogram** | height, base | **Area = base × height**    DEMO |
| **Trapezium** | $a$, $h$, $b$ | **Area = $\left(\dfrac{a+b}{2}\right) \times h$**    DEMO |
| **Circle** | $r$ | **Area = $\pi r^2$**    DEMO |

---

**Example 7**    ◀) **Self Tutor**

Find, to 3 significant figures, the areas of the following figures:

**a**

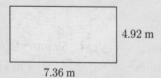

4.92 m

7.36 m

**b**

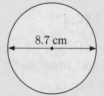

8.7 cm

**a**   $A = lw$
  $= 7.36 \times 4.92$
  $\approx 36.2 \text{ m}^2$

**b**   $A = \pi r^2$   where   $r = \dfrac{8.7}{2} = 4.35$
  $\therefore \ A = \pi \times (4.35)^2$
  $\therefore \ A \approx 59.4 \text{ cm}^2$

## EXERCISE 11C.2

**1** Find the area of:

   **a** a square cattle ranch with sides of length 16.72 km

   **b** a rectangular housing block which is 42.7 m by 21.3 m

   **c** a triangular garden patch with base 12.7 m and altitude 10.5 m

   **d** a circular pond of radius 23.8 m.

**2** Write down and then simplify expressions for the areas of the following:

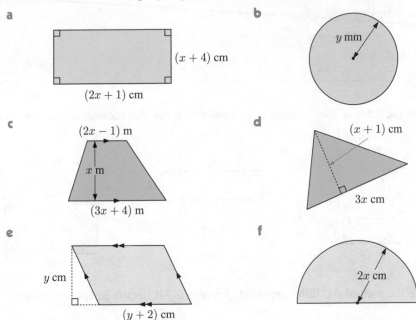

**3** Write down and simplify expressions for the areas of the following figures. Note that some of the information given is unnecessary!

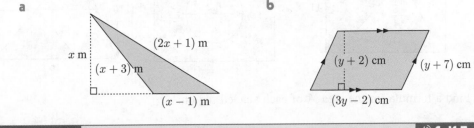

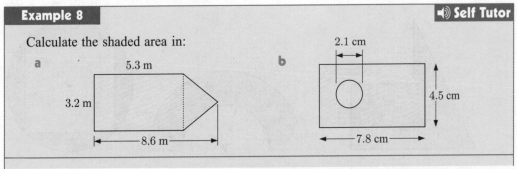

**a** The required area is the sum of 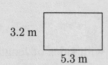 and

$\therefore$  area = area of rectangle + area of triangle
$$= 5.3 \times 3.2 + \tfrac{1}{2} \times 3.2 \times 3.3$$
$$\approx 22.2 \text{ m}^2$$

**b** Area = area of rectangle − area of circle
$$= 7.8 \times 4.5 - \pi \times \left(\tfrac{2.1}{2}\right)^2 \text{ cm}^2$$
$$\approx 31.6 \text{ cm}^2$$

**4** Calculate the area of the following composite shapes. All measurements are given in cm.

**a**

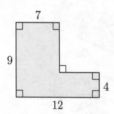

**b**

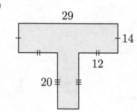

**c**

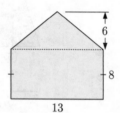

**5** Calculate the area of the following shaded regions. All measurements are given in cm.

**a**

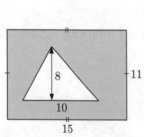

**b**

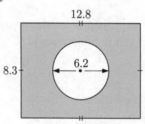

**c**

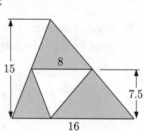

**6** Find a formula for the area $A$ of each shaded region:

**a**

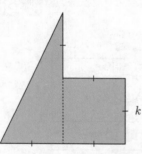

**b**

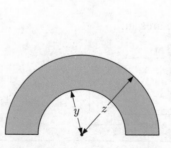

**c**

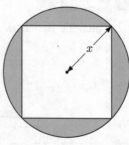

## PROBLEM SOLVING WITH AREA

**Example 9**                                                                                       ◀⑴ **Self Tutor**

A rectangular lawn is 12 m by 8 m.  A 3.2 m square garden bed is dug within it.
The remaining lawn is then reseeded with boxes of seed, each box costing $8.50 and
covering 18 m². Find:

a  the area of the lawn
b  the number of boxes of seed required
c  the total cost of the seed.

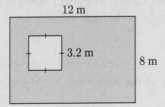

a    Area of lawn
    = area of rectangle − area of square
    $= (12 \times 8) - (3.2 \times 3.2)$ m²
    $= 85.76$ m²
    $\approx 85.8$ m²

b    Number of boxes

$= \dfrac{\text{area of lawn}}{\text{area covered by one box}}$

$= \dfrac{85.76 \text{ m}^2}{18 \text{ m}^2}$

$\approx 4.76$ boxes

∴  5 boxes of seeds are required.

c    Total cost
    = number of boxes × cost of 1 box
    $= 5 \times \$8.50$
    $= \$42.50$

## EXERCISE 11C.3

1  Concrete slabs suitable for a driveway are
sold in two sizes:

  Type A:   0.6 m by 0.6 m  or
  Type B:   0.6 m by 0.3 m.

Both types of slab cost $18.25 per square
metre.

A driveway is to be 2.4 m wide and 18 m
long.  The slabs are laid on sand which
costs $18 per tonne. A tonne of sand covers
17.5 m² to the required depth. Sand must be
purchased to a multiple of 0.2 of a tonne.

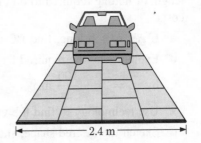

a  Calculate the area of the driveway.

b  Explain why you need 4 type B slabs for the pattern given in the diagram.

c  How many type A slabs are needed?

d  How much sand must be purchased?

e  Find the total cost of the slabs and sand.

**2** The third floor of an office building has the floorplan alongside. What is the usable floor space?

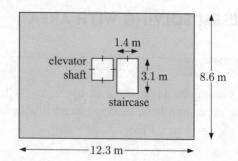

**3** Pete's Pizza Bar sells 3 sizes of circular pizza. The small pizza is 15 cm across and costs €4.20. The medium size is 30 cm across and costs €9.60. The super size has a diameter of 35 cm and costs €14.00. Which of the pizzas gives the best value?
**Hint:** Calculate the price per square centimetre.

**4** A cylindrical tank of base diameter 8 m and height 6 m is to have a non-porous lining on its circular base and curved walls. The lining of the base costs \$3.20 per $m^2$, and on the sides it costs \$4.50 per $m^2$.

   **a** Find the base radius.

   **b** Find the area of the base.

   **c** Find the cost of lining the base.

   **d** Explain why the area of the curved wall is given by $2\pi r \times h$ where $r$ is the radius and $h$ is the height.

   **e** Find the area of the curved wall.

   **f** Find the cost of lining the curved wall.

   **g** Find the total cost of the lining to the nearest \$10.

**5** Your task is to design a rectangular duck enclosure of area 100 $m^2$. Wire netting must be purchased for three of the sides, as the fourth side is an existing barn wall. Naturally you wish to minimise the length of netting required to do the job, thereby minimising your costs.

   **a** If AB is $x$ m long, find BC in terms of $x$.

   **b** Explain why the required length of netting is given by $L = 2x + \dfrac{100}{x}$ m.

   **c** Use technology to find the value of $x$ which will make $L$ a minimum.

   **d** Sketch the desired shape, showing the dimensions of the enclosure.

**6** An industrial shed is being constructed with a total floor space of 600 $m^2$. It is to be divided into three rectangular rooms of equal size. The walls will cost \$60 per metre to build.

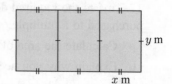

   **a** Calculate the area of the shed in terms of $x$ and $y$.

   **b** Explain why $y = \dfrac{200}{x}$.

**c** Show that the total cost of the walls is given by $C = 360x + \dfrac{48\,000}{x}$ dollars.

**d** Use technology to find $x$ (to the nearest cm) which will minimise the cost of the walls.

**e** Sketch the desired shape, showing all dimensions.

## SURFACE AREA

> The **surface area** of a three-dimensional figure with plane faces is the sum of the areas of the faces.

So, if we collapse the figure into its net, the surface area is the area of the net.

For example, the surface area of

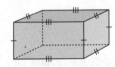    = the area of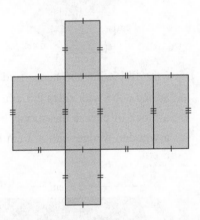

---

**Example 10**                                             ◀)) **Self Tutor**

Find the surface area of this square-based pyramid.

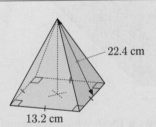

22.4 cm

13.2 cm

---

From the net of the pyramid shown alongside, we see that the figure has one square face with sides 13.2 cm, and four triangular faces with base 13.2 cm and height 22.4 cm

∴  the total surface area

$= 13.2^2 + 4 \times \left(\frac{1}{2} \times 13.2 \times 22.4\right)$ cm$^2$

$= 765.6$ cm$^2$

$\approx 766$ cm$^2$

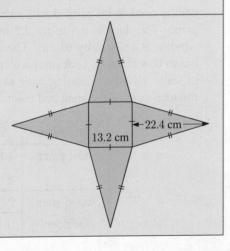

22.4 cm

13.2 cm

## EXERCISE 11C.4

**1** Find the total surface area of:

**a**                    **b**                    **c**

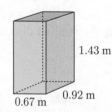

1.43 m

0.67 m    0.92 m

8.3 cm

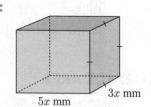

5x mm    3x mm

**2** Find the total surface area of:

**a**                                **b**

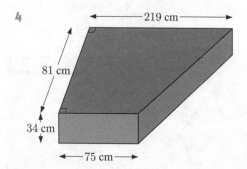

5 cm

4 cm

6 cm

3 cm

10 m

6 m

12 m

**3** Draw the following and hence find their surface areas:

  **a**   an ice cube with sides 2.5 cm

  **b**   a block of cheese measuring 14 cm by 8 cm by 3 cm

  **c**   a wooden wedge with a 3 cm by 4 cm by 5 cm triangular cross-section and length 8 cm.

**4**

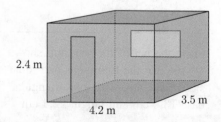

219 cm

81 cm

34 cm

75 cm

A harpsichord case has the dimensions shown.

  **a**   Find the area of the top surface.

  **b**   Find the area of each side of the case.

  **c**   If the timber costs $128 per square metre, find the cost of the timber to construct this case.

**5** The diagram shows a room whose walls and ceiling need to be painted with two coats of paint. The door is 0.8 m by 2.2 m and the window is 183 cm by 91 cm. The door also has to be stained on *both* sides with two coats of stain. Use the following table to calculate the total cost of the stain and paint:

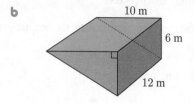

2.4 m

4.2 m    3.5 m

| Type of paint | Size | Area covered | Cost per tin |
|---|---|---|---|
| wall paint | 4 litres | 16 m² | $32.45 |
|  | 2 litres | 8 m² | $20.80 |
| wood stain | 2 litres | 10 m² | $23.60 |
| (for doors) | 1 litre | 5 m² | $15.40 |

**6**  The Taylor Prism is a clay hexagonal prism with a historical record written on its sides. It was found by archaeologist Colonel Taylor in 1830. If the ancient Assyrians had written on all the surfaces, what surface area was available to write on?

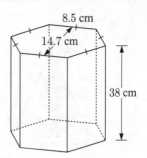

**Hint:** Divide the hexagonal top and bottom into triangles and find their area.

## CYLINDERS, SPHERES AND CONES

These objects have curved surfaces, but their surface area can still be calculated using formulae.

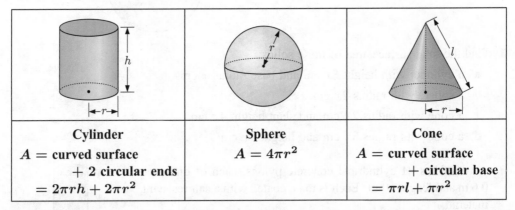

| Cylinder | Sphere | Cone |
|---|---|---|
| $A =$ **curved surface** $+$ **2 circular ends** $= 2\pi rh + 2\pi r^2$ | $A = 4\pi r^2$ | $A =$ **curved surface** $+$ **circular base** $= \pi rl + \pi r^2$ |

---

**Example 11**  ◀) **Self Tutor**

Find the outer surface area, to 1 decimal place, of:

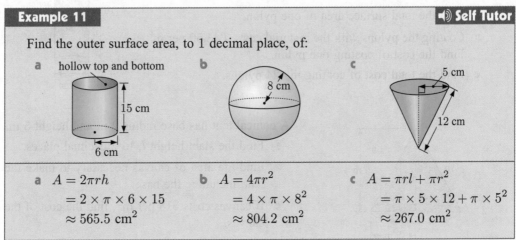

**a**  $A = 2\pi rh$
$= 2 \times \pi \times 6 \times 15$
$\approx 565.5 \text{ cm}^2$

**b**  $A = 4\pi r^2$
$= 4 \times \pi \times 8^2$
$\approx 804.2 \text{ cm}^2$

**c**  $A = \pi rl + \pi r^2$
$= \pi \times 5 \times 12 + \pi \times 5^2$
$\approx 267.0 \text{ cm}^2$

## EXERCISE 11C.5

**1**  Find, correct to one decimal place, the outer surface area of the following:

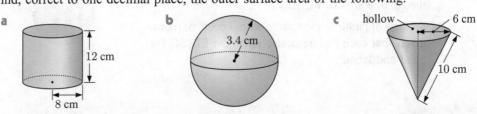

**d**

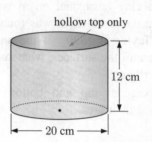

solid

18 m

14 m

**e**

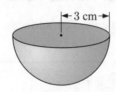

hollow top only

12 cm

20 cm

**f**

$r$

4.5 km

**2** Find the total surface area of the solid hemisphere shown.

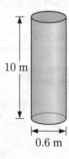

3 cm

**3** Find the total surface area of these solids:

**a** a cylinder with height $3x$ cm and base radius $x$ cm

**b** a sphere with radius $2x$ cm

**c** a cone with radius $2x$ cm and slant height $4x$ cm

**d** a cone with radius $3x$ cm and height $4x$ cm

**4** A wharf has 24 cylindrical concrete pylons, each of diameter 0.6 m and length 10 m. Each is to be coated with a salt resistant material.

**a** Find the total surface area of one pylon.

**b** Coating the pylons with the material costs £45.50 per m$^2$. Find the cost of coating one pylon.

**c** Find the total cost of coating the 24 pylons.

10 m

0.6 m

**5**

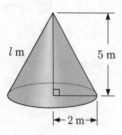

$l$ m    5 m

2 m

A conical tent has base radius 2 m and height 5 m.

**a** Find the slant height $l$, to 2 decimal places.

**b** Find the area of canvas necessary to make the tent, including the base.

**c** If canvas costs $18 per m$^2$, find the cost of the canvas.

**6** A spherical art piece has diameter 2 metres. Find:

**a** the surface area of the sphere

**b** the cost of painting the sphere with 3 coats of paint, given that each square metre will cost €13.50 for paint and labour.

### Example 12

◄)) **Self Tutor**

The length of a hollow pipe is three times its radius.

a Write an expression for its outer surface area.

b If its outer surface area is 301.6 m², find its radius.

a Let the radius be $x$ m, so
the length is $3x$ m.

Surface area $= 2\pi rh$

$\qquad = 2\pi x \times 3x$

$\qquad = 6\pi x^2 \text{ m}^2$

b The surface area is 301.6 m²

$\therefore\ 6\pi x^2 = 301.6$

$\therefore\ x^2 = \dfrac{301.6}{6\pi}$

$\therefore\ x = \sqrt{\dfrac{301.6}{6\pi}}$ {as $x > 0$}

$\therefore\ x \approx 4.00$

So, the radius of the pipe is 4 m.

7 The height of a hollow cylinder is the same as its diameter.

  a Write an expression for the outer surface area of the
cylinder in terms of its radius $r$.

  b Find the height of the cylinder if its surface area is
91.6 m².

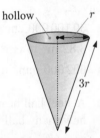

8 The slant height of a hollow cone is three times its radius.

  a Write an expression for its outer surface area in terms
of its radius $r$.

  b Find the slant height if its surface area is 21.2 cm².

  c Hence find its height.

# D                                   VOLUME

The **volume** of a solid is the amount of space it occupies. It is measured in cubic units.

## UNITS OF VOLUME

Just as for area, we can find relationships between different units of volume by investigating
the units of length.

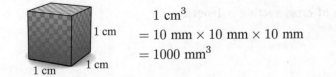

$1 \text{ cm}^3$

$= 10 \text{ mm} \times 10 \text{ mm} \times 10 \text{ mm}$

$= 1000 \text{ mm}^3$

$1 \text{ m}^3$

$= 100 \text{ cm} \times 100 \text{ cm} \times 100 \text{ cm}$

$= 1\,000\,000 \text{ cm}^3$

## CONVERSION DIAGRAM

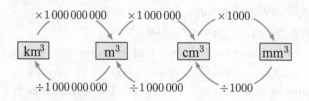

---

**Example 13**    ◀ッ **Self Tutor**

Convert  0.137 m$^3$ to cm$^3$.

$0.137 \text{ m}^3 = (0.137 \times 1\,000\,000) \text{ cm}^3$
$= 137\,000 \text{ cm}^3$

---

## EXERCISE 11D.1

1   Rohit was convinced that  1 m$^3$ = 1000 cm$^3$.  Sarat told Rohit to go back to basics. He
   said that 1 m$^3$ is the volume of a 1 m by 1 m by 1 m box and 1 m = 100 cm. Follow
   Sarat's instructions to show that  1 m$^3$ = 1\,000\,000 cm$^3$.

2   Convert:

   **a**  39\,100\,000 cm$^3$ to m$^3$     **b**  0.51 cm$^3$ to mm$^3$     **c**  469\,000 cm$^3$ to m$^3$

   **d**  3.82 m$^3$ to cm$^3$     **e**  5.27 mm$^3$ to cm$^3$     **f**  0.0179 m$^3$ to cm$^3$

   **g**  692\,000 mm$^3$ to cm$^3$     **h**  183\,460\,000 mm$^3$ to m$^3$     **i**  0.0051 m$^3$ to cm$^3$

3   **a**  A steel ball bearing has volume 0.27 cm$^3$. If the manufacturer has 1.35 m$^3$ of steel,
      how many ball bearings can be made?

   **b**  There is about 5.5 cm$^3$ of aluminium in a soft drink can. A recycling depot collects
      46\,291 cans and melts them down, losing 15% of the metal in the process. How
      many cubic metres of aluminium do they now have?

## UNIFORM SOLIDS

If the perpendicular cross-section of a solid is always the same shape and size, we call it a
**solid of uniform cross-section**.

For all solids of uniform cross-section,

**volume = area of cross-section × length**
*or*  **V = Al**

DEMO

In each of the following examples, $A$ is the cross-sectional area and $l$ is the length of the solid.

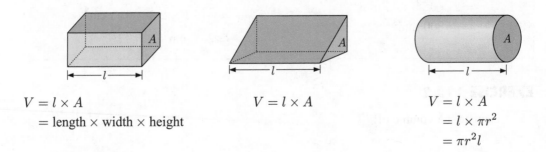

$V = l \times A$

= length × width × height

$V = l \times A$

$V = l \times A$

$= l \times \pi r^2$

$= \pi r^2 l$

## OTHER SOLIDS

The formulae for calculating the volume of some other common objects are shown below:

| Object | Figure | Volume |
|---|---|---|
| **Pyramids and cones** | height · base    height $h$ base | **Volume of a pyramid or cone** $= \frac{1}{3}(\text{area of base} \times \text{height})$  DEMO |
| **Spheres** | $r$ | **Volume of a sphere** $= \frac{4}{3}\pi r^3$ |

Find the volume of the following:

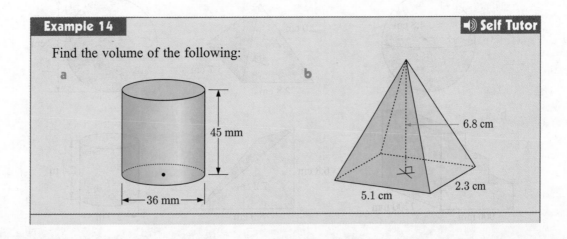

a

45 mm

36 mm

b

6.8 cm

2.3 cm

5.1 cm

> **a** $V$ = area of end × length
> $= \pi r^2 \times l$
> $= \pi \times 18^2 \times 45 \text{ mm}^3$
> $\approx 45\,800 \text{ mm}^3$
>
> **b** $V = \frac{1}{3}$(area of base × height)
> $= \frac{1}{3}$(length × width × height)
> $= \frac{1}{3}(5.1 \times 2.3 \times 6.8) \text{ cm}^3$
> $\approx 26.6 \text{ cm}^3$

## EXERCISE 11D.2

**1** Calculate the volume of:

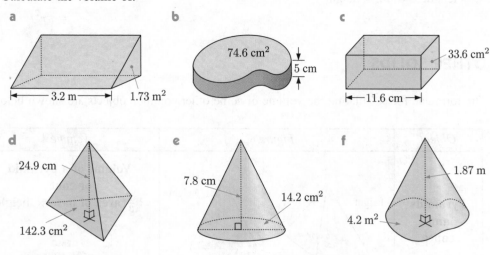

**a** 3.2 m, 1.73 m²

**b** 74.6 cm², 5 cm

**c** 33.6 cm², 11.6 cm

**d** 24.9 cm, 142.3 cm²

**e** 7.8 cm, 14.2 cm²

**f** 1.87 m, 4.2 m²

**2** Find the volume of:

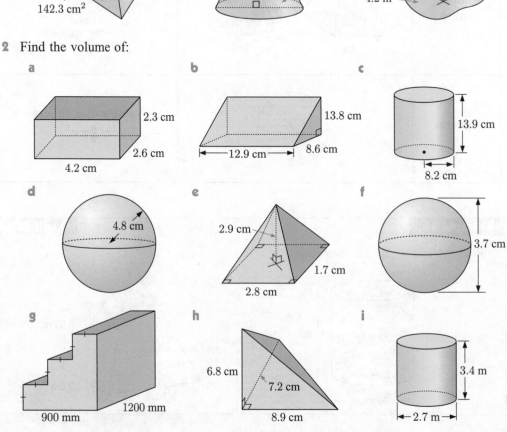

**a** 2.3 cm, 2.6 cm, 4.2 cm

**b** 13.8 cm, 12.9 cm, 8.6 cm

**c** 13.9 cm, 8.2 cm

**d** 4.8 cm

**e** 2.9 cm, 1.7 cm, 2.8 cm

**f** 3.7 cm

**g** 900 mm, 1200 mm

**h** 6.8 cm, 7.2 cm, 8.9 cm

**i** 3.4 m, 2.7 m

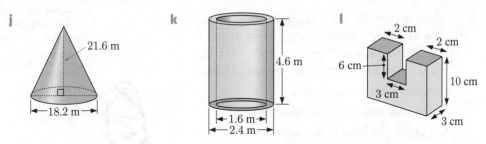

**j** 21.6 m, 18.2 m

**k** 4.6 m, 1.6 m, 2.4 m

**l** 2 cm, 2 cm, 6 cm, 3 cm, 10 cm, 3 cm

**3** For each solid, write down an expression for the volume $V$:

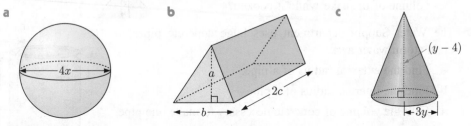

**a** $4x$

**b** $a$, $b$, $2c$

**c** $(y-4)$, $3y$

---

**Example 15**                                   ◀️)) **Self Tutor**

A box has a square base and its height is 12 cm. If the volume of the box is 867 cm$^3$, find its length.

Let the length be $x$ cm.

$\quad$ volume = length $\times$ width $\times$ height

$\therefore \quad 867 = x \times x \times 12$

$\therefore \quad 12x^2 = 867$

$\therefore \quad x^2 = \frac{867}{12}$

$\therefore \quad x = \sqrt{\frac{867}{12}} \quad \{\text{as } x > 0\}$

$\therefore \quad x = 8.5$

So, the length of the base is 8.5 cm.

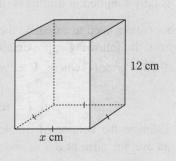

12 cm

$x$ cm

---

**4** **a** Find the length of the side of a cube if its volume is 2.52 cm$^3$.

$\quad$ **b** Find the height of a cylinder with base area 23.8 cm$^2$ and volume 142.8 cm$^3$.

**5** A concrete path 1 m wide and 10 cm deep is placed around a circular lighthouse of diameter 12 m.

$\quad$ **a** Draw a plan view of the situation.

$\quad$ **b** Find the surface area of the concrete.

$\quad$ **c** Find the volume of concrete required to lay the path.

**6** A circular cake tin has a radius of 20 cm and a height of 7 cm. When cake mix was added to the tin its height was 2 cm. After the cake was cooked it rose to 1.5 cm below the top of the tin.

Remember that percentage increase = $\dfrac{\text{increase}}{\text{original}} \times 100\%$

  **a** Sketch these two situations.

  **b** Find the volume of the cake mix.

  **c** Find the volume of the cooked cake.

  **d** What was the percentage increase in the volume of the cake while it cooked?

**7** The Water Supply department uses huge concrete pipes to drain storm water away.

  **a** Find the external radius of a pipe.

  **b** Find the internal radius of a pipe.

  **c** Find the volume of concrete necessary to make one pipe.

0.05 m

2.5 m

1 m

**8** A rectangular garage floor 9.2 m by 6.5 m is to be concreted to a depth of 120 mm.

  **a** What volume of concrete is required?

  **b** Concrete costs €135 per m$^3$. How much will it cost to concrete the floor if concrete is only supplied in multiples of 0.2 m$^3$?

**9** Timber cutters need to calculate the volume of usable timber in a tree. They use the following approximation for the tree's volume:

$$V \approx 0.06 \times g^2 \times l \quad \text{where} \quad V = \text{volume} \ (\text{in m}^3)$$
$$g = \text{approximate girth} \ (\text{in m})$$
$$\text{and} \ \ l = \text{usable length} \ (\text{in m}).$$

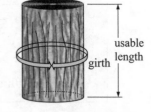

usable length

girth

  **a** Estimate the volume of usable timber in a tree with an average girth of 3.8 m and usable length 9.9 m.

  **b** For a cylinder with circumference $g$, show that $V = \frac{1}{4\pi} g^2 \times l$.

  **c** Find the percentage difference between the volumes predicted by these two formulae.

  **d** Explain this percentage difference.

**10** I want to build a new rectangular garden which is 8.6 m by 2.4 m, and 15 cm deep. I decide to get some soil from the local garden supplier, loading it into my trailer which measures 2.2 m × 1.8 m × 60 cm. I fill the trailer to within 20 cm from the top.

  **a** How many trailer loads of soil will I need?

  **b** Each load of soil costs $27.30. What is the total cost of the soil?

  **c** I decide to put bark on top of the soil in the garden. Each load covers 11 m$^2$ of garden bed. How many loads of bark will I need?

  **d** What is the total cost of the bark if it costs $17.95 per load?

  **e** Calculate the total cost of establishing the garden.

**11**  1000 km of black plastic cylindrical water piping with internal diameter 13 mm and walls of thickness 2 mm is required for a major irrigation project. The piping is made from bulk plastic which weighs 2.3 tonnes per cubic metre. How many tonnes of black plastic are required for the project?

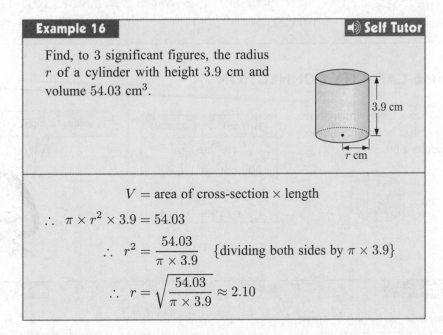

**Example 16**                                                                 ◄Ⴏ **Self Tutor**

Find, to 3 significant figures, the radius $r$ of a cylinder with height 3.9 cm and volume 54.03 cm$^3$.

$V$ = area of cross-section × length

$\therefore \ \pi \times r^2 \times 3.9 = 54.03$

$\therefore \ r^2 = \dfrac{54.03}{\pi \times 3.9}$   {dividing both sides by $\pi \times 3.9$}

$\therefore \ r = \sqrt{\dfrac{54.03}{\pi \times 3.9}} \approx 2.10$

**12**  Find:

**a**  the height of a rectangular prism with base 5 cm by 3 cm and volume 40 cm$^3$

**b**  the side length of a cube of butter with volume 34.01 cm$^3$

**c**  the height of a glass cone with base diameter 24.6 cm and volume 706 cm$^3$

**d**  the radius of a spherical weather balloon with volume 73.62 m$^3$

**e**  the radius of a steel cylinder with height 4.6 cm and volume 43.75 cm$^3$

**f**  the base radius of a conical bin with height 6.2 m and volume 203.9 m$^3$.

## E   CAPACITY

The **capacity** of a container is the quantity of fluid it is capable of holding.

**Capacity units**

1000 mL = 1 L
1000 L = 1 kL

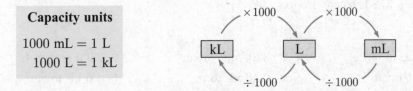

**Example 17**    ◀)) **Self Tutor**

Convert:    **a**  3.7 L to mL    **b**  57 620 L to kL

| | |
|---|---|
| **a**  3.7 L = (3.7 × 1000) mL | **b**  57 620 L = (57 620 ÷ 1000) kL |
| = 3700 mL | = 57.62 kL |

## VOLUME-CAPACITY CONNECTION

Alongside is a table which shows the connection between volume and capacity units.

| Volume | Capacity |
|---|---|
| 1 cm³ | ≡ 1 mL |
| 1000 cm³ | ≡ 1 L |
| 1 m³ | ≡ 1 kL |
| 1 m³ | ≡ 1000 L |

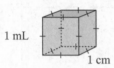

≡ means 'is equivalent to'

**Example 18**    ◀)) **Self Tutor**

Convert:    **a**  9.6 L to cm³    **b**  3240 L to m³

| | |
|---|---|
| **a**      9.6 L | **b**      3240 L |
| = (9.6 × 1000) cm³ | = (3240 ÷ 1000) m³ |
| = 9600 cm³ | = 3.24 m³ |

## EXERCISE 11E

**1**  Convert:

  **a**  4.21 L into mL      **b**  8.63 kL into L      **c**  4600 mL into L

  **d**  56 900 L into kL      **e**  3970 mL into kL      **f**  0.012 kL into mL

**2**  **a**  A petrol station begins the week with 143 kL of petrol in its storage tanks. During the week, 2856 people fill up their car tanks, using an average of 35.8 L each. How much petrol is left at the station?

  **b**  A citrus oil producer sells 200 mL bottles of oil. How many bottles can be filled from a 372 L batch of citrus oil?

**3**  Convert:

  **a**  83 kL to m³      **b**  3200 mL to cm³      **c**  2300 cm³ to L

  **d**  7154 m³ to L      **e**  0.46 kL to m³      **f**  4.6 kL to cm³

**Example 19**    ◀)) **Self Tutor**

Find how many kL of water it takes to fill a 2.6 m by 3.1 m by 1.45 m tank.

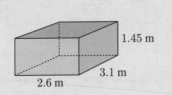

$V$ = area of cross-section × height
$$= 2.6 \times 3.1 \times 1.45 \text{ m}^3$$
$$= 11.687 \text{ m}^3$$
$$\approx 11.7 \text{ m}^3$$

The tank's capacity is approximately 11.7 kL.

**4**  Find the capacity (in kL) of the following tanks:

**a**

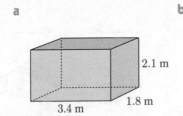

**b**

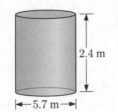

**c**

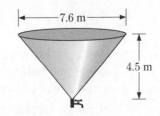

**5**  How much soup (in L) will fit in this hemispherical pot?

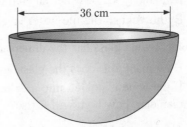

**6**  A dam wall is built at the narrow point of a river to create a small reservoir. When full, the reservoir has an average depth of 13 m and has the shape shown in the diagram. Find the capacity of the reservoir.

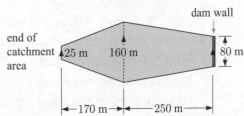

**Example 20**    ◀)) **Self Tutor**

17.3 mm of rain falls on a flat rectangular shed roof of length 10 m and width 6.5 m. All of the water goes into a cylindrical tank with base diameter 4 m. By how many millimetres does the water level in the tank rise?

*For the roof:*    The area is in m², so we convert 17.3 mm to metres.

17.3 mm = (17.3 ÷ 1000) m = 0.0173 m

The volume of water collected by the roof  = area of roof × depth
$$= 65 \text{ m}^2 \times 0.0173 \text{ m}$$
$$= 1.1245 \text{ m}^3$$

*For the tank:*    Area of base $= \pi r^2$

$$= \pi \times 2^2 \text{ m}^2$$

$$\approx 12.566 \text{ m}^2$$

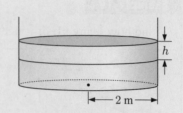

$\therefore$  the volume added to the tank

= area of base × height

$\approx 12.566 \times h \text{ m}^3$

So,    $12.566 \times h \approx 1.1245$        {volume added to tank = volume from roof}

$\therefore \quad h \approx \dfrac{1.1245}{12.566}$        {dividing both sides by 12.566}

$\therefore \quad h \approx 0.0895 \text{ m}$

$\therefore$  the water level rises by about 89.5 mm.

---

**7**  The base of a house has area 110 m$^2$. One night 12 mm of rain falls on the roof. All of the water goes into a tank of base diameter 4 m.

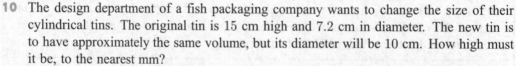

   **a**  Find the volume of water which fell on the roof.

   **b**  How many kL of water entered the tank?

   **c**  By how much did the water level in the tank rise?

**8**  A conical wine glass has the dimensions shown.

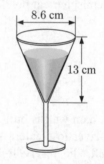

   **a**  How many mL does the glass hold if it is 75% full?

   **b**  If the wine is poured into a cylinder of the same diameter, how high will it rise?

**9**  Jam is packed into cylindrical tins which are 4.5 cm in radius and 15 cm high. The mixing vat is also cylindrical with a cross-section of 1.2 m$^2$ and height of 4.1 m.

   **a**  What is the capacity of jam in each tin?

   **b**  What is the capacity of the mixing vat?

   **c**  How many tins of jam could be filled from one vat?

   **d**  If the jam is sold at €2.05 per tin, what is the value of one vat of jam? Assume there is no spillage.

**10**  The design department of a fish packaging company wants to change the size of their cylindrical tins. The original tin is 15 cm high and 7.2 cm in diameter. The new tin is to have approximately the same volume, but its diameter will be 10 cm. How high must it be, to the nearest mm?

**11**  A fleet of trucks have containers with the shape illustrated. Wheat is to be transported in these containers, and its level must not exceed a mark 10 cm below the top. How many truck loads of wheat are necessary to fill a cylindrical silo with internal diameter 8 m and height 25 m?

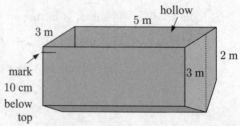

## INVESTIGATION                                     MINIMISING MATERIAL

Your boss, Pat, asks you to design a rectangular box-shaped container which is open at the top and contains exactly 1 litre of fluid. Pat intends manufacturing millions of these containers and wishes to keep manufacturing costs to a minimum. She therefore insists that the least amount of material is used. However, the base measurements must be in the ratio  2 : 1.

**What to do:**

**1** The base is to be in the ratio 2 : 1, so we let the dimensions be $x$ cm and $2x$ cm. The height is also unknown, so we let it be $y$ cm. As the values of $x$ and $y$ vary, the container changes size.

Explain why:

   **a**  the volume  $V = 2x^2y$          **b**  $2x^2y = 1000$          **c**  $y = \dfrac{500}{x^2}$.

**2** Show that the surface area is  $A = 2x^2 + 6xy$.

**3** You could design a **spreadsheet** which, for given values of $x = 1, 2, 3, 4, \ldots$, calculates $y$ then $A$

   *or*  use a **graphics calculator** to graph $A$ against $x$.

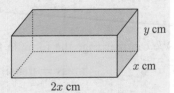

|   | A | B | C |
|---|---|---|---|
| 1 | x values | y values | A values |
| 2 | 1 | =500/A2^2 | =2*A2^2+6*A2*B2 |
| 3 | =A2+1 | | |
| 4 | ↓ | fill down ↓ | ↓ |

SPREADSHEET

**4** Find the smallest value of $A$ and the value of $x$ which produces it.

## F            DENSITY (EXTENSION)

Imagine two containers with capacity 1 kL. If one container was filled with concrete and the other container with feathers, which do you think would weigh more?

Obviously the container of concrete would have greater **mass** than the container of feathers. We say that concrete has a higher **density** than feathers.

> The **mass** of an object is the amount of matter it contains.

> **One gram** is the mass of one cubic centimetre of pure water at $4^oC$.

## DENSITY

> The **density** of a substance is its mass per unit volume.
>
> $$\text{density} = \frac{\text{mass}}{\text{volume}}$$

For example, the density of water is $1$ g per $1$ cm$^3$ or $\dfrac{1\text{ g}}{1\text{ cm}^3}$ or $1\text{ g cm}^{-3}$.

**Table of common densities:**

| Substance | Density $(g\,cm^{-3})$ |
|---|---|
| pine wood | 0.65 |
| paper | 0.93 |
| water | 1.00 |
| steel | 7.82 |
| lead | 11.37 |
| uranium | 18.97 |

We can rearrange the formula for density to obtain

$$\textbf{mass} = \textbf{density} \times \textbf{volume} \quad \text{and} \quad \textbf{volume} = \dfrac{\textbf{mass}}{\textbf{density}}.$$

---

**Example 21**  ◀) **Self Tutor**

Find the density of a metal with mass $25$ g and volume $4$ cm$^3$.

$$\begin{aligned}\text{Density} &= \dfrac{\text{mass}}{\text{volume}} \\ &= \dfrac{25\text{ g}}{4\text{ cm}^3} \\ &= 6.25\text{ g cm}^{-3}\end{aligned}$$

---

## EXERCISE 11F

**1** Find the density of:

   **a** a metal with mass $10$ g and volume $2$ cm$^3$

   **b** a substance with mass $2$ g and volume $1.5$ cm$^3$.

**2** Find the mass of a $5$ cm diameter sphere of a metal which has a density of $8.7$ g cm$^{-3}$.

**3** What volume is occupied by a lump of metal with a mass of $3.62$ kg and having a density of $11.6$ g cm$^{-3}$?

**4** Find the density of:

   **a** a cube of chocolate with sides $2$ cm and mass $18$ g

   **b** a $15$ cm by $8$ cm by $4$ cm rectangular block of metal with mass $9.6$ kg.

**5** A gold ingot with the dimensions shown has a mass of $12.36$ kg. Determine the density of gold.

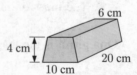

**6** A rectangular block of metal has base $7$ cm by $5$ cm. The block has total mass $1285$ g and the metal has density $7.5$ g cm$^{-3}$. How high is the block?

**7** Polystyrene spherical beads have an average diameter of $0.6$ cm. The density of polystyrene is $0.15$ g cm$^{-3}$. Estimate the total number of beads in a box of beads with total mass $8$ kg.

8   Determine the total mass of stone required to build a square-based pyramid in which all edges have length 200 m. The density of the stone is 2.25 tonnes per m³.

# G     HARDER APPLICATIONS

## EXERCISE 11G

1   A raised rectangular garden bed is to be built using clay bricks. The bricks measure 225 mm × 105 mm × 75 mm  and the mortar between them should be 10 mm thick. The garden bed will have approximate outside dimensions  2.6 m × 1 m,  and be approximately 0.65 m high.

   a   How many bricks are required for the first layer? How many layers are required? You may assume that no bricks will be cut. Show all calculations.

   b   Show the *actual* measurements of the garden bed, inside and outside, on a sketch.

   c   How many bricks should be ordered for the project? Explain your answer.

   d   What volume of soil will be needed to fill the bed? Explain what volume of soil you would probably order and why.

   e   Approximately how much mortar (in litres) will be required for the construction?

2   A feed silo is made out of sheet steel 3 mm thick using a hemisphere, a cylinder, and a cone.

   a   Explain why the height of the cone must be 70 cm and hence find the *slant height* of the conical section.

   b   Calculate the surface area of each of the three sections and hence show that the total amount of steel used is about 15.7 square metres.

   c   Show that the silo would hold about 5.2 cubic metres of grain when completely full.

   d   If grain has a density of 0.68 g cm⁻³ and the density of steel is 8 g cm⁻³, find the weight of the silo when it is full.

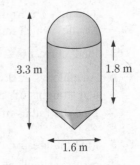

3   When work has to be done on underground telephone cables, workers often use a small tent over the opening. This shelters them from bad weather and stops passers-by from absent-mindedly falling in on top of them. The cover is constructed from canvas and this is supported by a tubular steel frame, as shown below.

Use the measurements from the diagram of the frame to calculate the following, showing all working:

   a   the length of steel tubing needed to make the frame

   b   the amount of room inside the tent in m³

   c   the amount of canvas in m² needed for the cover.

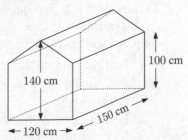

**4** A ready mixed concrete tanker is to be constructed of steel as a cylinder with conical ends.

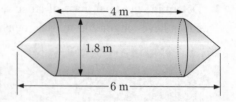

**a** Calculate the volume held in the tanker by working out the volume of the cylinder and the conical ends.

**b** How *long* would the tanker be if the ends were hemispheres instead of cones but the cylindrical section remained the same? Explain your reasoning.

**c** How much more or less concrete would fit in the tanker if the ends were hemispheres instead of cones?

**d** The surface area of the tanker with the conical ends is about 30 m². The tanker with hemispherical ends has surface area of nearly 33 m². Verify one of these figures by your own calculations.

**e** Using the figures you have from **a** to **d**, discuss the advantages of each design. Overall, which do you think is the better design for the tanker? Give reasons for your answer.

## REVIEW SET 11A

**1** Convert:    **a** 30.5 kg to t    **b** 0.093 kL to mL    **c** 8033 mm³ to cm³

**2** Moana tiles her bathroom floor with 12 cm by 12 cm tiles. The area of the floor is 4.96 m². Determine how many tiles she will need, assuming 10% extra are required for tiles which must be cut.

**3** Find, correct to 2 decimal places, the circumference of a circle of diameter 16.4 m.

**4** An athletics track is to have a perimeter of 400 m and straights of 78 m.
Find the radius of the circular 'bend'.

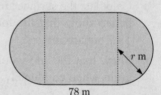

**5** Find the area of:

**a** a rectangular airport 3.4 km by 2.1 km

**b** a semi-circular garden bed with radius 5.64 m.

**6**

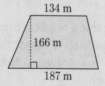

Find the area of the horse paddock shown alongside in:

**a** square metres    **b** hectares.

**7** A tool shed with the dimensions illustrated is to be painted with zinc-alum. Two coats are required with zinc-alum costing $8.25 per litre.

**a** Find the area to be painted including the roof. Reduce your answer by 5% to allow for windows.

**b** Find the total cost if the zinc-alum covers 5 m² per litre and must be bought in whole litres.

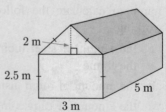

**8** A fish farm has six netted cylindrical cages open at one end. The cylinders have depth 17 m and diameter 7.5 m. Find the area of netting required.

**9** Calculate, correct to 3 significant figures, the volume of:

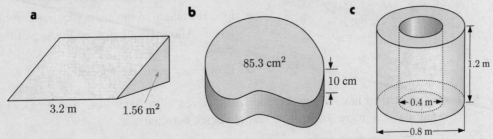

**a**   3.2 m   1.56 m$^2$

**b**   85.3 cm$^2$   10 cm

**c**   1.2 m   0.4 m   0.8 m

**10** Tom has just had a load of sand delivered. The pile of sand is in the shape of a cone of radius 1.6 m and height 1.2 m. Find the volume of sand that Tom has had delivered.

**11** A cylindrical drum for storing industrial waste has a capacity of 10 kL. If the height of the drum is 3 m, find its radius.

**12** Frank wants to have a large concrete F outside his shop for advertising. He designs one to the dimensions shown.
What volume of concrete will he need?

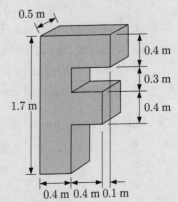

0.5 m   0.4 m   0.3 m   1.7 m   0.4 m   0.4 m  0.4 m  0.1 m

**13** Find:

**a** the density of a pebble with mass 19 g and volume 7 cm$^3$

**b** the volume of an oak log of density 710 kg m$^{-3}$ and mass 1150 kg.

## REVIEW SET 11B

**1** Convert:

**a** 23 L to m$^3$

**b** 5062 ha to km$^2$

**c** 0.534 g to mg

**2**

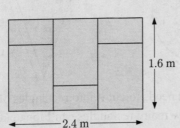

1.6 m   2.4 m

A window has the design alongside.
What length of wood is needed to build the frame?

**3**

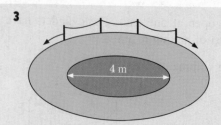

In the Cardone Gardens there is a 4 m diameter circular pond which is surrounded by a 1.5 m wide brick border. A chain fence is placed around the border with posts every 2 m.

**a** Find the length of the chain required for the fence. Allow 10% extra for the sag in the chain.

**b** How many posts are needed?

**4** Louise wanted to have a new outdoor patio paved with slate tiles. The area to be covered was 4.8 m by 3.6 m. She had to decide between:

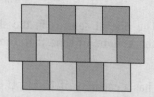

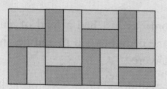

*Style 1:*   30 cm by 30 cm
                costing $4.55 per tile

*Style 2:*   40 cm by 20 cm
                costing $3.95 per tile

**a** Calculate the area to be paved.

**b** Find the area of a single slate tile of each style.

**c** Find the number of tiles needed for each style.

**d** Compare the total cost of using the different styles. Which would be cheaper?

**5** Find a formula for the area $A$ of each shaded region:

**a**

$y$

$x$

**b**

$r$

**c**

$a$

**6** Find the outer surface area, to 1 decimal place, of:

**a**

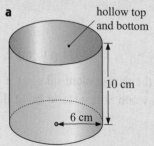

hollow top and bottom

10 cm

6 cm

**b**

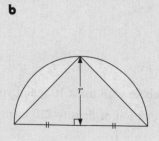

5.2 cm

**c**

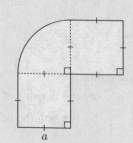

4 cm

12 cm

**7** Fiona purchased 400 m$^2$ of plastic sheeting and needs to cut it into rectangles of area 500 cm$^2$. This can be done with no waste. How many rectangles can Fiona cut out?

**8** The hexagonal gazebo shown has wood panelling for the roof, floor, and part of five of the walls.
What is the total surface area of wood panelling to be ordered?

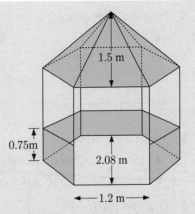

**9** A manufacturer of spikes has 0.245 kL of molten iron. If each spike contains 15 mL of iron, how many spikes can be made?

**10** A plastic beach ball has a radius of 27 cm. Find its volume.

**11**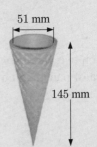
A gelateria sells gelato in cones with the dimensions opposite. Assuming the cone is filled completely, with a hemispherical scoop on top, how many cones can be sold from 10 L of gelato?

**12** A rectangular shed has a roof of length 12 m and width 5.5 m, which has water runoff to a cylindrical tank of base diameter 4.35 m. If 15.4 mm of rain falls, how many millimetres does the water level in the tank rise?

**13** At the top of the Washington Monument, there is an aluminium square-based pyramid with base length 14.2 cm and height 22.6 cm. Aluminium has density 2.7 $g\,cm^{-3}$.
  **a** Find the mass of the pyramid.
  **b** The pyramid actually weighs about 2.8 kg. Suggest a reason for the difference in mass.

## REVIEW SET 11C

**1** Convert:
  **a** 24.3 mm to m
  **b** 0.032 $m^3$ to $cm^3$
  **c** 845 mg to kg

**2** Half a tonne of rubber is to be turned into 20 g erasers. How many erasers can be made?

**3** A tourist walks all the way around the "Praça do Império", a large city square in Lisbon with sides 280 m long. How far did the tourist walk?

**4** Find the perimeter of:

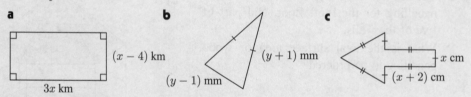

**a**

$(x-4)$ km

$3x$ km

**b**

$(y+1)$ mm

$(y-1)$ mm

**c**

$x$ cm

$(x+2)$ cm

**5** A rectangle measures 7.1 cm by 6.3 cm.

  **a** Find the radius of a circle with the same area.

  **b** Which has a shorter perimeter, and by how much?

**6** Find the volume of:

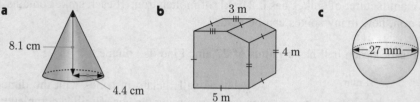

**a**

8.1 cm

4.4 cm

**b**

3 m

4 m

5 m

**c**

27 mm

**7**

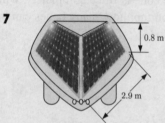

0.8 m

2.9 m

A solar powered car runs on two parallelogram-shaped solar panels. Find the area of panelling on the car.

**8** Find the volume of the igloo alongside.

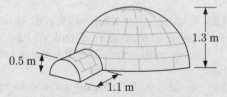

1.3 m

0.5 m

1.1 m

**9** A kitchen bench is a rectangular prism measuring 3845 mm by 1260 mm by 1190 mm. It contains a rectangular sink which is 550 mm wide, 750 mm long and 195 mm deep. Find the storage capacity of the bench in litres.

**10** I am sending some fragile objects to my sister, inside a postal cylinder which is 325 mm long with diameter 40 mm. What area of bubble wrap do I need to line the inside of the cylinder?

**11** 500 dozen bottles of wine, each of capacity 750 mL, are to be filled from tanks of capacity 1000 L. How many tanks are needed?

**12** Find:

  **a** the length of a triangular prism with end area 61 cm$^2$ and volume 671 cm$^3$

  **b** the radius of a circle of area 98 m$^2$

  **c** the height of a cone with base radius 5 cm and volume 288 cm$^3$.

**13** A set of plastic cubic dice contains six 16 mm dice. The set weighs 23 g. Find the density of the plastic in g cm$^{-3}$.

# Chapter 12

# Quadratic functions

**Syllabus reference:** 2.7, 4.3, 4.6

## OPENING PROBLEM

An athlete throws a javelin. Its height above the ground after it has travelled a horizontal distance of $x$ metres is given by $H(x) = -\frac{1}{60}x^2 + x$ metres.

**Things to think about:**

**a** What would the graph of $H$ against $x$ look like?

**b** How high is the javelin after it has travelled 20 metres?

**c** What is the maximum height reached by the javelin?

**d** How far did the javelin travel before it hit the ground?

The height function in the **Opening Problem** is an example of a **quadratic function**. In this chapter we will look at the properties of quadratic functions, and how to draw their graphs.

We will use the quadratic equation solving techniques studied in **Chapter 9** to solve problems involving quadratic functions.

## A          QUADRATIC FUNCTIONS

A **quadratic function** is a relationship between two variables which can be written in the form $y = ax^2 + bx + c$ where $x$ and $y$ are the variables and $a$, $b$ and $c$ represent constants, $a \neq 0$.

Using function notation, $y = ax^2 + bx + c$ can be written as $f(x) = ax^2 + bx + c$.

### FINDING $y$ GIVEN $x$

For any value of $x$, the corresponding value of $y$ can be found using substitution.

| Example 1 | ◀) Self Tutor |
|---|---|

If $y = 2x^2 + 4x - 5$ find the value of $y$ when: **a** $x = 0$  **b** $x = 3$.

**a** When $x = 0$,
$$y = 2(0)^2 + 4(0) - 5$$
$$= 0 + 0 - 5$$
$$= -5$$

**b** When $x = 3$,
$$y = 2(3)^2 + 4(3) - 5$$
$$= 2(9) + 12 - 5$$
$$= 18 + 12 - 5$$
$$= 25$$

We can test whether an ordered pair $(x, y)$ satisfies a quadratic function by substituting the $x$-coordinate into the function, and seeing whether the resulting value matches the $y$-coordinate.

**Example 2**    ◀)) **Self Tutor**

State whether the following quadratic functions are satisfied by the given ordered pairs:

a  $y = 3x^2 + 2x$    $(2, 16)$

b  $f(x) = -x^2 - 2x + 1$    $(-3, 1)$

a  When $x = 2$,
$$y = 3(2)^2 + 2(2)$$
$$= 12 + 4$$
$$= 16$$
So, when $x = 2$, $y = 16$
∴  $(2, 16)$ does satisfy
$y = 3x^2 + 2x$

b    $f(-3) = -(-3)^2 - 2(-3) + 1$
$$= -9 + 6 + 1$$
$$= -2$$
So, $f(-3) \neq 1$
∴  $(-3, 1)$ does not satisfy
$f(x) = -x^2 - 2x + 1$

When we substitute a value for $y$ into a quadratic function, we are left with a quadratic equation. Solving the quadratic equation gives us the values of $x$ corresponding to that $y$-value. Since the equation is quadratic, there may be 0, 1, or 2 values of $x$ for any one value of $y$.

**Example 3**    ◀)) **Self Tutor**

If  $y = x^2 - 6x + 8$  find the value(s) of $x$ when:  a  $y = 15$  b  $y = -1$

a  If $y = 15$ then
$$x^2 - 6x + 8 = 15$$
∴  $x^2 - 6x - 7 = 0$
∴  $(x + 1)(x - 7) = 0$
∴  $x = -1$ or $x = 7$
So, there are 2 solutions.

b  If $y = -1$ then
$$x^2 - 6x + 8 = -1$$
∴  $x^2 - 6x + 9 = 0$
∴  $(x - 3)^2 = 0$
∴  $x = 3$
So, there is only one solution.

# EXERCISE 12A

**1**  Which of the following are quadratic functions?

a  $y = 2x^2 - 4x + 10$
b  $y = 15x - 8$
c  $y = -2x^2$
d  $y = \frac{1}{3}x^2 + 6$
e  $3y + 2x^2 - 7 = 0$
f  $y = 15x^3 + 2x - 16$

**2**  For each of the following functions, find the value of $y$ for the given value of $x$:

a  $y = x^2 + 5x - 14$  when  $x = 2$
b  $y = 2x^2 + 9x$  when  $x = -5$
c  $y = -2x^2 + 3x - 6$  when  $x = 3$
d  $y = 4x^2 + 7x + 10$  when  $x = -2$

**3**  a  If  $f(x) = x^2 + 3x - 7$,  find $f(2)$ and $f(-1)$.
b  If  $f(x) = 2x^2 - x + 1$,  find $f(0)$ and $f(-3)$.
c  If  $g(x) = -3x^2 - 2x + 4$,  find $g(3)$ and $g(-2)$.

**4** State whether the following quadratic functions are satisfied by the given ordered pairs:

   **a** $f(x) = 6x^2 - 10$         $(0, 4)$        **b** $y = 2x^2 - 5x - 3$      $(4, 9)$

   **c** $y = -4x^2 + 6x$      $(-\frac{1}{2}, -4)$     **d** $y = -7x^2 + 9x + 11$    $(-1, -6)$

   **e** $f(x) = 3x^2 - 11x + 20$   $(2, -10)$     **f** $f(x) = -3x^2 + x + 6$    $(\frac{1}{3}, 4)$

**5** For each of the following quadratic functions, find any values of $x$ for the given value of $y$:

   **a** $y = x^2 + 6x + 10$ when $y = 1$       **b** $y = x^2 + 5x + 8$ when $y = 2$

   **c** $y = x^2 - 5x + 1$ when $y = -3$     **d** $y = 3x^2$ when $y = -3$.

**6** Find the value(s) of $x$ for which:

   **a** $f(x) = 3x^2 - 3x + 6$ takes the value 6

   **b** $f(x) = x^2 - 2x - 7$ takes the value $-4$

   **c** $f(x) = -2x^2 - 13x + 3$ takes the value $-4$

   **d** $f(x) = 2x^2 - 10x + 1$ takes the value $-11$.

---

**Example 4**                            ◀ **Self Tutor**

A stone is thrown into the air. Its height above the ground is given by the function $h(t) = -5t^2 + 30t + 2$ metres where $t$ is the time in seconds from when the stone is thrown.

   **a** How high is the stone above the ground at time $t = 3$ seconds?

   **b** From what height above the ground was the stone released?

   **c** At what time is the stone 27 m above the ground?

   **a** $h(3) = -5(3)^2 + 30(3) + 2$        **b** The stone was released when
           $= -45 + 90 + 2$                $t = 0$ s.
           $= 47$                    $\therefore$  $h(0) = -5(0)^2 + 30(0) + 2 = 2$

   $\therefore$ the stone is 47 m above the ground.     $\therefore$ the stone was released from 2 m
                                          above ground level.

   **c** When $h(t) = 27$,

          $-5t^2 + 30t + 2 = 27$

    $\therefore$  $-5t^2 + 30t - 25 = 0$

        $\therefore$  $t^2 - 6t + 5 = 0$   {dividing each term by $-5$}

      $\therefore$  $(t - 1)(t - 5) = 0$   {factorising}

             $\therefore$  $t = 1$ or $5$

   $\therefore$ the stone is 27 m above the ground after 1 second and after 5 seconds.

---

**7** An object is projected into the air with a velocity of 80 m s$^{-1}$. Its height after $t$ seconds is given by the function $h(t) = 80t - 5t^2$ metres.

   **a** Calculate the height after:  **i** 1 second   **ii** 3 seconds   **iii** 5 seconds.

   **b** Calculate the time(s) at which the height is:  **i** 140 m   **ii** 0 m.

   **c** Explain your answers to part **b**.

**8** A cake manufacturer finds that the profit from making $x$ cakes per day is given by the function

$$P(x) = -\tfrac{1}{2}x^2 + 36x - 40 \text{ dollars.}$$

**a** Calculate the profit if:  **i** 0 cakes  **ii** 20 cakes are made per day.

**b** How many cakes per day are made if the profit is $270?

## B | GRAPHS OF QUADRATIC FUNCTIONS

Consider the quadratic function $f(x) = x^2$.

The table below shows the values of $f(x)$ corresponding to $x$-values from $-3$ to 3.

| $x$ | $-3$ | $-2$ | $-1$ | 0 | 1 | 2 | 3 |
|-----|------|------|------|---|---|---|---|
| $f(x)$ | 9 | 4 | 1 | 0 | 1 | 4 | 9 |

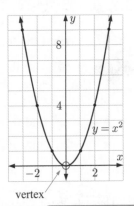

These points can be used to draw the graph of $f(x) = x^2$.

The shape formed is a **parabola**.   The graphs of quadratic functions all have this same basic shape.

Notice that the curve $y = x^2$:

- opens upwards
- is **symmetric** about the $y$-axis since, for example,

$$f(-2) = (-2)^2 = 4 \text{ and}$$
$$f(2) = 2^2 = 4, \text{ so } f(-2) = f(2).$$

- has a **vertex** or **turning point** at $(0, 0)$.

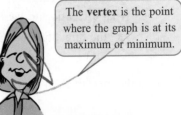

The **vertex** is the point where the graph is at its maximum or minimum.

---

**Example 5**                                  ◀) **Self Tutor**

Draw the graph of $y = x^2 - 2x - 5$ from a table of values.

Consider $f(x) = x^2 - 2x - 5$.
Now, $f(-3) = (-3)^2 - 2(-3) - 5$
$$= 9 + 6 - 5$$
$$= 10$$

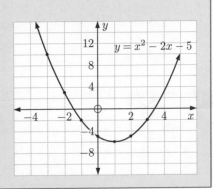

We can do the same for the other values of $x$.

The table of values is:

| $x$ | $-3$ | $-2$ | $-1$ | 0 | 1 | 2 | 3 |
|-----|------|------|------|---|---|---|---|
| $y$ | 10 | 3 | $-2$ | $-5$ | $-6$ | $-5$ | $-2$ |

## EXERCISE 12B.1

1 Construct a table of values for $x = -3, -2, -1, 0, 1, 2, 3$ for each of the following functions. Hence, draw the graph of each.

    **a** $y = x^2 + 2x - 2$      **b** $y = x^2 - 3$      **c** $y = x^2 - 2x$

    **d** $f(x) = -x^2 + x + 2$      **e** $y = x^2 - 4x + 4$      **f** $f(x) = -2x^2 + 3x + 10$

2 Use the **graphing package** or your **graphics calculator** to check your graphs in **1**.

 GRAPHING PACKAGE

---

## INVESTIGATION 1         GRAPHS OF THE FORM $y = ax^2$

**What to do:**

1 Use the **graphing package** or your **graphics calculator** to graph each pair of functions on the same set of axes.

 GRAPHING PACKAGE

    **a** $y = x^2$ and $y = 2x^2$      **b** $y = x^2$ and $y = 4x^2$

    **c** $y = x^2$ and $y = \frac{1}{2}x^2$      **d** $y = x^2$ and $y = -x^2$

    **e** $y = x^2$ and $y = -2x^2$      **f** $y = x^2$ and $y = -\frac{1}{2}x^2$

2 These functions are all members of the family $y = ax^2$.
What effect does $a$ have on:

    **a** the direction in which the graph opens      **b** the shape of the graph?

---

From the investigation we make the following observations:

> If $a > 0$, $y = ax^2$ opens upwards. It has the shape
>
> If $a < 0$, $y = ax^2$ opens downwards. It has the shape
>
> If $a < -1$ or $a > 1$, $y = ax^2$ is 'thinner' than $y = x^2$.
>
> If $-1 < a < 1$, $a \neq 0$, $y = ax^2$ is 'wider' than $y = x^2$.

---

### Example 6        ◀) Self Tutor

Sketch $y = x^2$ on a set of axes and hence sketch:

    **a** $y = 3x^2$                      **b** $y = -3x^2$

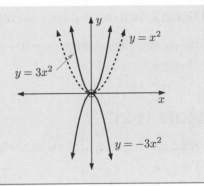

**a** $y = 3x^2$ is 'thinner' than $y = x^2$.

**b** $y = -3x^2$ has the same shape as $y = 3x^2$ but opens downwards.

## EXERCISE 12B.2

1 On separate sets of axes, sketch $y = x^2$ and each of the following. In each case comment on the direction in which the graph opens and the shape of the graph.

   **a** $y = 5x^2$             **b** $y = -5x^2$          **c** $y = \frac{1}{3}x^2$

   **d** $y = -\frac{1}{3}x^2$        **e** $y = -4x^2$         **f** $y = \frac{1}{4}x^2$

**GRAPHING PACKAGE**

2 Use your **graphics calculator** or **graphing package** to check your graphs in **1**.

## C                        AXES INTERCEPTS

The axes intercepts are an important property of quadratic functions. Knowing the axes intercepts helps us to graph the function.

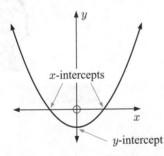

An **$x$-intercept** is a value of $x$ where the graph meets the $x$-axis. It is found by letting $y = 0$.

A **$y$-intercept** is a value of $y$ where the graph meets the $y$-axis. It is found by letting $x = 0$.

### INVESTIGATION 2         THE $y$-INTERCEPT OF A QUADRATIC

**What to do:**

1 Use the **graphing package** or your **graphics calculator** to find the $y$-intercept of:

**GRAPHING PACKAGE**

   **a** $y = x^2 + 3x - 5$         **b** $y = 2x^2 + x + 4$

   **c** $y = x^2 - 8$             **d** $y = x^2 - 6x$

   **e** $y = 3x^2 + 7x - 11$     **f** $y = 2x^2 - 5x + 17$

2 Use your observations in **1** to copy and complete:

   "The $y$-intercept of $y = ax^2 + bx + c$ is ....".

You should have found that the $y$-intercept of $y = ax^2 + bx + c$ is the constant term $c$.

We can see this since, letting $x = 0$,    $y = a(0)^2 + b(0) + c$
$$= 0 + 0 + c$$
$$= c$$

## EXERCISE 12C.1

1  State the $y$-intercept for the following functions:

a  $y = x^2 + 2x + 3$    b  $y = 2x^2 + 5x - 1$    c  $y = -x^2 - 3x - 4$

d  $f(x) = 3x^2 - 10x + 1$    e  $y = 3x^2 + 5$    f  $y = 4x^2 - x$

g  $y = 8 - x - 2x^2$    h  $f(x) = 2x - x^2 - 5$    i  $y = 6x^2 + 2 - 5x$

2  Find the $y$-intercept for the following functions:

a  $y = (x + 1)(x + 3)$    b  $y = (x - 2)(x + 3)$    c  $y = (x - 7)^2$

d  $y = (2x + 5)(3 - x)$    e  $y = x(x - 4)$    f  $y = -(x + 4)(x - 5)$

## THE $x$-INTERCEPTS

When a quadratic function is given in the form
$y = a(x - \alpha)(x - \beta)$, we can find the $x$-intercepts by
letting $y = 0$ and using the Null Factor law:

> The $x$-intercepts are
> also called the **zeros** of
> the function.

$$0 = a(x - \alpha)(x - \beta) \quad \text{where } a \neq 0$$
$$\therefore \quad x - \alpha = 0 \text{ or } x - \beta = 0 \quad \{\text{Null Factor law}\}$$
$$\therefore \quad x = \alpha \text{ or } \qquad x = \beta$$

The $x$-intercepts of $y = a(x - \alpha)(x - \beta)$ are $\alpha$ and $\beta$ for $a \neq 0$.

| Example 7 | ◀)) Self Tutor |
|---|---|

Find the $x$-intercepts of:

a  $y = 3(x - 4)(x + 2)$    b  $y = (x - 5)^2$

a  We let $y = 0$
   $\therefore \quad 3(x - 4)(x + 2) = 0$
   $\therefore \quad x = 4 \text{ or } x = -2$
   So, the $x$-intercepts are 4 and $-2$.

b  We let $y = 0$
   $\therefore \quad (x - 5)^2 = 0$
   $\therefore \quad x = 5$
   So, the only $x$-intercept is 5.

> The $x$-intercepts are
> easy to find when the
> quadratic is in
> **factorised** form.

## EXERCISE 12C.2

1 Find the $x$-intercepts of the following functions:

  **a** $y = (x - 2)(x - 5)$      **b** $y = (x - 3)(x + 4)$      **c** $y = 2(x + 6)(x + 3)$

  **d** $y = -(x - 7)(x + 1)$      **e** $y = x(x - 8)$      **f** $y = -3(x + 5)(x - 5)$

  **g** $y = (x + 4)^2$      **h** $y = 7(x - 2)^2$      **i** $y = -4(x + 1)^2$

## FINDING $x$-INTERCEPTS

For quadratic functions written in the expanded form $y = ax^2 + bx + c$, finding the $x$-intercepts is not so easy.

The $x$-intercepts are the **zeros** of the quadratic function, and we find them by solving the quadratic equation $ax^2 + bx + c = 0$.

In **Chapter 9** we saw that the quadratic equation can have two, one, or zero solutions. This means that quadratic functions can have two, one, or zero $x$-intercepts.

---

### INVESTIGATION 3            THE $x$-INTERCEPTS OF A QUADRATIC

 In this investigation you can use the **graphing package** or your graphics calculator to graph the quadratic functions.    GRAPHING PACKAGE

**What to do:**

1 Use technology to graph each quadratic function. Sketch each graph in your notebook and write down the $x$-intercepts.

  **a** $y = x^2 - x - 12$      **b** $y = x^2 - 6x + 9$      **c** $y = 3x^2 + 6x + 5$

  **d** $y = -x^2 + 5x - 6$      **e** $y = -2x^2 - 4x - 2$      **f** $y = -x^2 + 4x - 10$

2 How many zeros has the quadratic function which:

  **a** cuts the $x$-axis twice      **b** *touches* the $x$-axis

  **c** lies entirely below the $x$-axis?

3 Use technology to solve graphically:

  **a** $x^2 + 4x + 2 = 0$      **b** $x^2 + 6x - 2 = 0$      **c** $2x^2 - 3x - 7 = 0$

  **d** $x^2 + 2x + 5 = 0$      **e** $-x^2 - 4x - 6 = 0$      **f** $4x^2 - 4x + 1 = 0$

---

When you are given a quadratic function in expanded form, you should first look to see if it can be **factorised**. If it can, then you should do this to find the $x$-intercepts.

However, we saw in **Chapter 9** that many quadratic equations are not easily factorised, even those which have two solutions. To find the zeros or $x$-intercepts in these cases we can use technology to assist us.

### Example 8                                          ◀》 Self Tutor

Find the $x$-intercepts of these quadratic functions:

  **a** $y = x^2 - 2x - 15$                    **b** $y = x^2 + 2x + 1$

Check your answers using technology.

**a**  We let  $y = 0$

$\therefore \ x^2 - 2x - 15 = 0$

$\therefore \ (x + 3)(x - 5) = 0$

$\therefore \ x = -3 \text{ or } 5$

So, the $x$-intercepts are $-3$ and $5$.

**b**  We let  $y = 0$

$\therefore \ x^2 + 2x + 1 = 0$

$\therefore \ (x + 1)^2 = 0$

$\therefore \ x = -1$

So, the only $x$-intercept is $-1$.

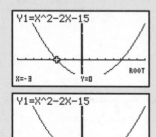

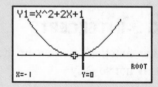

## EXERCISE 12C.3

**1**  Find the $x$-intercepts of the following functions:

> If you cannot factorise the function, use technology to graph the function and find any $x$-intercepts.

**a**  $y = x^2 - x - 6$

**b**  $y = x^2 - 16$

**c**  $y = x^2 + 5$

**d**  $y = 3x - x^2$

**e**  $y = x^2 - 12x + 36$

**f**  $y = x^2 + x - 7$

**g**  $y = -x^2 - 4x + 21$

**h**  $y = 2x^2 - 20x + 50$

**i**  $y = 2x^2 - 7x - 15$

**j**  $y = -2x^2 + x - 5$

**k**  $y = -6x^2 + x + 5$

**l**  $y = 3x^2 + x - 1$

**2**  Find the axes intercepts of the following functions:

**a**  $y = x^2 + x - 2$

**b**  $y = (x + 3)^2$

**c**  $y = (x + 5)(x - 2)$

**d**  $y = x^2 + x + 4$

**e**  $y = 3x^2 - 3x - 36$

**f**  $y = -x^2 - 8x - 16$

**g**  $y = x^2 - 7x$

**h**  $y = -2x^2 + 3x + 7$

**i**  $y = 2x^2 - 18$

**j**  $y = -x^2 + 2x - 9$

**k**  $y = 4x^2 - 4x - 3$

**l**  $y = 6x^2 - 11x - 10$

## GRAPHS FROM AXES INTERCEPTS

If we know the axes intercepts of a quadratic function, we can use them to draw its graph.

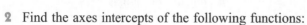

**Example 9**    ◆) **Self Tutor**

Sketch the graphs of the following functions by considering:

**i**  the value of $a$    **ii**  the $y$-intercept    **iii**  the $x$-intercepts.

**a**  $y = x^2 - 2x - 3$

**b**  $y = -2(x + 1)(x - 2)$

**a** $y = x^2 - 2x - 3$

   **i** Since $a = 1$ which is $> 0$, the parabola has shape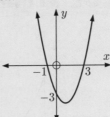

   **ii** The $y$-intercept occurs when $x = 0$, so the $y$-intercept is $-3$.

   **iii** $x$-intercepts occur when $y = 0$

     $\therefore\ x^2 - 2x - 3 = 0$

     $\therefore\ (x - 3)(x + 1) = 0$

     $\therefore\ x = 3$ or $x = -1$

     $\therefore$ the $x$-intercepts are 3 and $-1$.

*Sketch:*

**b** $y = -2(x + 1)(x - 2)$

   **i** Since $a = -2$ which is $< 0$, the parabola has shape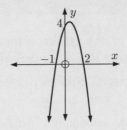

   **ii** The $y$-intercept occurs when $x = 0$

     $\therefore\ y = -2(0 + 1)(0 - 2)$

       $= -2 \times 1 \times -2$

       $= 4$

     $\therefore$ the $y$-intercept is 4

   **iii** $x$-intercepts occur when $y = 0$

     $\therefore\ -2(x + 1)(x - 2) = 0$

     $\therefore\ x = -1$ or $x = 2$

     $\therefore$ the $x$-intercepts are $-1$ and 2.

*Sketch:*

---

## Example 10

🔊 **Self Tutor**

Sketch the graph of $f(x) = 2(x - 3)^2$ by considering:

  **a** the value of $a$     **b** the $y$-intercept     **c** the $x$-intercepts.

$f(x) = 2(x - 3)^2$

  **a** Since $a = 2$ which is $> 0$, the parabola has shape

  **b** The $y$-intercept occurs when $x = 0$.

    Now $f(0) = 2(0 - 3)^2 = 18$

    $\therefore$ the $y$-intercept is 18.

  **c** $x$-intercepts occur when $f(x) = 0$

       $\therefore\ 2(x - 3)^2 = 0$

         $\therefore\ x = 3$

    $\therefore$ the $x$-intercept is 3.

There is only one $x$-intercept, which means the graph *touches* the $x$-axis.

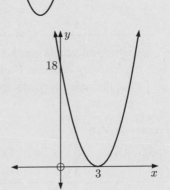

## EXERCISE 12C.4

1   Sketch the graph of the quadratic function with:

> If a quadratic function has only one $x$-intercept then its graph must *touch* the $x$-axis.

   **a**   $x$-intercepts $-1$ and 1,  and $y$-intercept $-1$

   **b**   $x$-intercepts $-3$ and 1,  and $y$-intercept 2

   **c**   $x$-intercepts 2 and 5,  and $y$-intercept $-4$

   **d**   $x$-intercept 2 and $y$-intercept 4.

2   Sketch the graphs of the following by considering:

   **i**   the value of $a$         **ii**   the $y$-intercept         **iii**   the $x$-intercepts.

   **a**   $y = x^2 - 4x + 4$         **b**   $f(x) = (x-1)(x+3)$         **c**   $y = 2(x+2)^2$

   **d**   $y = -(x-2)(x+1)$         **e**   $y = -3(x+1)^2$         **f**   $f(x) = -3(x-4)(x-1)$

   **g**   $y = 2(x+3)(x+1)$         **h**   $f(x) = 2x^2 + 3x + 2$         **i**   $y = -2x^2 - 3x + 5$

# D          AXIS OF SYMMETRY

The graph of any quadratic function is symmetric about a vertical line called the **axis of symmetry**.

Since the axis of symmetry is vertical, its equation will have the form $x = k$.

If a quadratic function has two $x$-intercepts, then the axis of symmetry lies halfway between them.

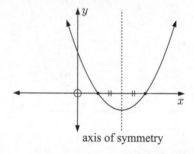

axis of symmetry

| Example 11 | ◀) Self Tutor |

Find the equation of the axis of symmetry for the following:

**a**
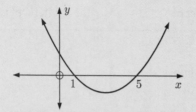

**b**
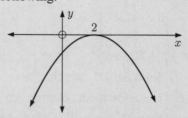

**a**   The $x$-intercepts are 1 and 5, and 3 is halfway between 1 and 5.
So, the axis of symmetry has equation $x = 3$.

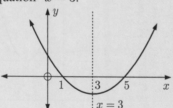

**b**   The only $x$-intercept is 2, so the axis of symmetry has equation $x = 2$.

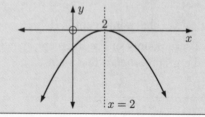

## EXERCISE 12D.1

**1** For each of the following, find the equation of the axis of symmetry:

**a**

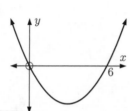

**b**

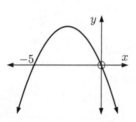

**c**

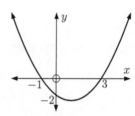

**d**

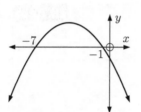

**e**

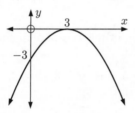

**f**

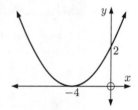

**2** Find the equation of the axis of symmetry for the following functions:

**a** $y = (x - 2)(x - 6)$      **b** $y = x(x + 4)$      **c** $y = -(x + 3)(x - 5)$

**d** $y = (x - 3)(x - 8)$      **e** $y = 2(x - 5)^2$      **f** $y = -3(x + 2)^2$

## AXIS OF SYMMETRY OF $y = ax^2 + bx + c$

We are often given quadratic functions in expanded form such as $y = 2x^2 + 9x + 4$, where we cannot easily identify the $x$-intercepts.

Other quadratic functions do not have any $x$-intercepts, such as the one illustrated alongside.

So, we need a method for finding the axis of symmetry of a function without using $x$-intercepts.

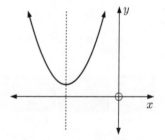

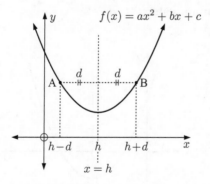

Consider the quadratic function $f(x) = ax^2 + bx + c$ alongside, with axis of symmetry $x = h$.

Suppose A and B are two points on $f(x)$, $d$ units either side of the axis of symmetry.

Thus, A and B have $x$-coordinates $h - d$ and $h + d$ respectively.

Since the function is *symmetric* about $x = h$, A and B will have the same $y$-coordinate.

So, $f(h - d) = f(h + d)$

$\therefore \ a(h - d)^2 + b(h - d) + \cancel{c} = a(h + d)^2 + b(h + d) + \cancel{c}$

$$\therefore \quad a(h^2 - 2hd + d^2) + bh - bd = a(h^2 + 2hd + d^2) + bh + bd$$

$$\therefore \quad -4ahd = 2bd$$

$$\therefore \quad h = \frac{-b}{2a}$$

So, the axis of symmetry has equation $\quad x = \frac{-b}{2a}$.

The equation of the axis of symmetry of $\;y = ax^2 + bx + c\;$ is $\;\boldsymbol{x = \dfrac{-b}{2a}}$.

---

**Example 12**                                        ◀) **Self Tutor**

Find the equation of the axis of symmetry of $\;y = 3x^2 + 4x - 5$.

$y = 3x^2 + 4x - 5\;$ has $\;a = 3, \;\; b = 4, \;\; c = -5$.

Now $\dfrac{-b}{2a} = \dfrac{-4}{2 \times 3} = -\tfrac{2}{3}$

So, the axis of symmetry has equation $\;x = -\tfrac{2}{3}$.

---

## EXERCISE 12D.2

1   Determine the equation of the axis of symmetry of:

    **a** $\;y = x^2 + 6x + 2$      **b** $\;y = x^2 - 8x - 1$      **c** $\;f(x) = 2x^2 + 5x - 3$

    **d** $\;y = -x^2 + 3x - 7$      **e** $\;y = 2x^2 - 5$      **f** $\;y = -5x^2 + 7x$

    **g** $\;f(x) = x^2 - 6x + 9$      **h** $\;y = 10x - 3x^2$      **i** $\;y = \tfrac{1}{8}x^2 + x - 1$

---

## E                                               VERTEX

The **vertex** or **turning point** of a parabola is the point at which the function has a **maximum value** for $\;a < 0\;$ ⌢ , or a **minimum value** for $\;a > 0\;$ ⌣ .

The vertex of a quadratic function always lies on the **axis of symmetry**.

So, the axis of symmetry gives us the $x$-coordinate of the vertex.

The $y$-coordinate can be found by substituting this value of $x$ into the function.

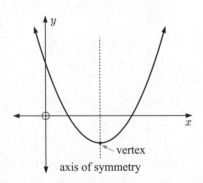
vertex
axis of symmetry

**Example 13**                                         ◀) **Self Tutor**

Determine the coordinates of the vertex of
$f(x) = x^2 + 6x + 4$.

> The vertex is either a maximum or minimum turning point.

$f(x) = x^2 + 6x + 4$ has $a = 1$, $b = 6$, $c = 4$.

Now $\dfrac{-b}{2a} = \dfrac{-6}{2 \times 1} = -3$

So, the axis of symmetry has equation $x = -3$.

$$f(-3) = (-3)^2 + 6(-3) + 4$$
$$= 9 - 18 + 4$$
$$= -5$$

So, the vertex is $(-3, -5)$.

## EXERCISE 12E

**1**   Find the vertex of each of the following quadratic functions:

**a** $y = x^2 - 4x + 7$    **b** $y = x^2 + 2x + 5$    **c** $f(x) = -x^2 + 6x - 1$

**d** $y = x^2 + 3$    **e** $f(x) = 2x^2 + 12x$    **f** $y = -3x^2 + 6x - 4$

**g** $y = x^2 - x - 1$    **h** $y = -2x^2 + 3x - 2$    **i** $y = -\frac{1}{4}x^2 + 3x - 2$

**2**   For each of the functions in **1**, state whether the vertex is a maximum or a minimum turning point.

**Example 14**                                         ◀) **Self Tutor**

Consider the quadratic function $y = -x^2 - 4x + 5$.

**a**   Find the axes intercepts.

**b**   Find the equation of the axis of symmetry.

**c**   Find the coordinates of the vertex.

**d**   Sketch the function, showing all important features.

**a**   When $x = 0$, $y = 5$
So, the $y$-intercept is 5.
When $y = 0$,
$$-x^2 - 4x + 5 = 0$$
$$\therefore\ x^2 + 4x - 5 = 0$$
$$\therefore\ (x + 5)(x - 1) = 0$$
$$\therefore\ x = -5 \text{ or } 1$$
So, the $x$-intercepts are $-5$ and 1.

**b**   $a = -1$, $b = -4$, $c = 5$
$$\therefore\ \frac{-b}{2a} = \frac{4}{-2} = -2$$
So, the axis of symmetry is $x = -2$.

**c**  When $x = -2$,

$$y = -(-2)^2 - 4(-2) + 5$$
$$= -4 + 8 + 5$$
$$= 9$$

So, the vertex is $(-2, 9)$.

**d**
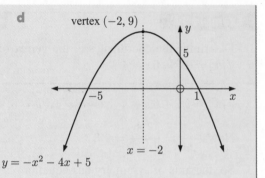

vertex $(-2, 9)$

$y = -x^2 - 4x + 5$

$x = -2$

**3**  For each of the following functions:

    **i**  find the axes intercepts      **ii**  find the equation of the axis of symmetry

    **iii**  find the coordinates of the vertex      **iv**  sketch the function.

  **a**  $y = x^2 - 4x + 3$      **b**  $y = -x^2 + 4x + 12$      **c**  $f(x) = x^2 + 2x$

  **d**  $y = (x + 5)(x - 3)$      **e**  $y = x^2 - 10x + 25$      **f**  $f(x) = -4x^2 - 8x - 3$

  **g**  $y = x^2 - 8x$      **h**  $y = 2x^2 - 2x - 12$      **i**  $f : x \mapsto -(x + 4)^2$

  **j**  $y = 9x^2 - 1$      **k**  $y = 3x^2 - 4x + 1$      **l**  $f : x \mapsto -\frac{1}{2}x^2 - x + 12$

## F      FINDING A QUADRATIC FROM ITS GRAPH

So far in this chapter we have learned how to draw a graph given an equation. Sometimes we wish to reverse this process.

If we are given sufficient information on or about a graph we can determine the quadratic equation that has that graph.

---

**Example 15**       🔊 **Self Tutor**

Find the equation of the quadratic with graph:

**a**
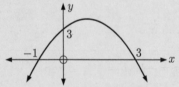

**b**
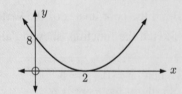

**a**  Since the $x$-intercepts are $-1$ and $3$,

  $y = a(x + 1)(x - 3)$,   $a < 0$.

But when $x = 0$,   $y = 3$

    ∴   $3 = a(1)(-3)$

    ∴   $a = -1$

So,   $y = -(x + 1)(x - 3)$.

**b**  Since it touches the $x$-axis at $2$,

  $y = a(x - 2)^2$,   $a > 0$.

But when $x = 0$,   $y = 8$

    ∴   $8 = a(-2)^2$

    ∴   $a = 2$

So,   $y = 2(x - 2)^2$.

**Example 16**                                    ◀ᴺ) **Self Tutor**

Find the equation of the quadratic
with graph:

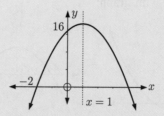

The axis of symmetry is $x = 1$, so the other $x$-intercept is 4

$$\therefore \quad y = a(x + 2)(x - 4)$$

But when $x = 0$, $y = 16$

$$\therefore \quad 16 = a(2)(-4)$$

$$\therefore \quad a = -2$$

$\therefore$ the quadratic is $y = -2(x + 2)(x - 4)$.

**Example 17**                                    ◀ᴺ) **Self Tutor**

Find, in the form $y = ax^2 + bx + c$, the equation of the quadratic whose graph cuts
the $x$-axis at 4 and $-3$ and passes through the point $(2, -20)$.

Since the $x$-intercepts are 4 and $-3$, the equation is
$$y = a(x - 4)(x + 3) \quad \text{where} \quad a \neq 0.$$

But when $x = 2$, $y = -20$ $\quad \therefore \quad -20 = a(2 - 4)(2 + 3)$

$$\therefore \quad -20 = a(-2)(5)$$

$$\therefore \quad a = 2$$

$\therefore$ the equation is $y = 2(x - 4)(x + 3)$ or $y = 2x^2 - 2x - 24$.

## EXERCISE 12F

1   Find the equation of the quadratic with graph:

a
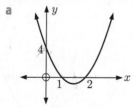

b
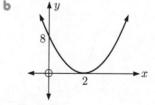

c
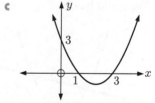

d
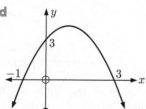

e
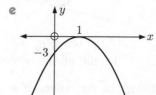

f
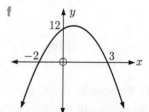

**2** Find the quadratic with graph:

**a**
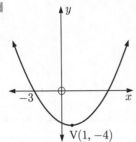

**b**
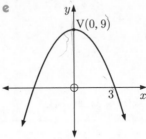

**c**
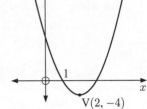

**d**
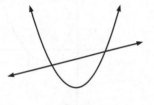

**e**
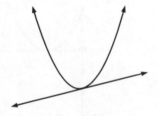

**f**
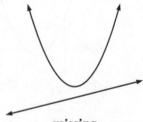

**3** Find, in the form  $y = ax^2 + bx + c$,   the equation of the quadratic whose graph:

  **a** cuts the $x$-axis at 5 and 1, and passes through $(2, -9)$

  **b** cuts the $x$-axis at 2 and $-\frac{1}{2}$, and passes through $(3, -14)$

  **c** touches the $x$-axis at 3 and passes through $(-2, -25)$

  **d** touches the $x$-axis at $-2$ and passes through $(-1, 4)$

  **e** cuts the $x$-axis at 3, passes through $(5, 12)$, and has axis of symmetry $x = 2$

  **f** cuts the $x$-axis at 5, passes through $(2, 5)$, and has axis of symmetry $x = 1$.

## G    WHERE FUNCTIONS MEET

Consider the graphs of a quadratic function and a linear function on the same set of axes.

We could have:

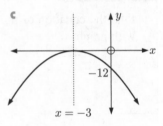

| **cutting** | **touching** | **missing** |
|:---:|:---:|:---:|
| 2 points of intersection | 1 point of intersection | no points of intersection |

If the graphs meet, the coordinates of the points of intersection of the graph of the two functions can be found by *solving the two equations simultaneously*.

**Example 18**                                                    ◀⑴ **Self Tutor**

Find the coordinates of the points of intersection of the graphs with equations
$y = x^2 - x - 18$  and  $y = x - 3$.

$y = x^2 - x - 18$  meets  $y = x - 3$  where

$$x^2 - x - 18 = x - 3$$
$$\therefore \ x^2 - 2x - 15 = 0 \qquad \{RHS = 0\}$$
$$\therefore \ (x - 5)(x + 3) = 0 \qquad \{factorising\}$$
$$\therefore \ x = 5 \text{ or } -3$$

Substituting into  $y = x - 3$,  when  $x = 5$,  $y = 2$  and when  $x = -3$,  $y = -6$.

$\therefore$  the graphs meet at  $(5, 2)$  and  $(-3, -6)$.

## EXERCISE 12G

1   Find the coordinates of the point(s) of intersection of the graphs with equations:

   a  $y = x^2 + x - 1$  and  $y = 2x - 1$      b  $y = -x^2 + 2x + 3$  and  $y = 2x - 1$

   c  $y = x^2 - 2x + 8$  and  $y = x + 6$      d  $y = -x^2 + 3x + 9$  and  $y = 2x - 3$

   e  $y = x^2 - 4x + 3$  and  $y = 2x - 6$      f  $y = -x^2 + 4x - 7$  and  $y = 5x - 4$

2   Use a **graphing package** or a **graphics calculator** to find the coordinates of the points
of intersection, to 3 significant figures, of the graphs with equations:

   a  $y = x^2 - 3x + 7$  and  $y = x + 5$

   b  $y = x^2 - 5x + 2$  and  $y = x - 7$

   c  $y = -x^2 - 2x + 4$  and  $y = x + 8$            GRAPHING

   d  $y = -x^2 + 4x - 2$  and  $y = 5x - 6$           PACKAGE

   e  $y = x^2 + 5x - 4$  and  $y = -\frac{1}{2}x - 3$

   f  $y = -x^2 + 7x + 1$  and  $y = -3x + 2$

   g  $y = 3x^2 - x - 2$  and  $y = 2x - \frac{11}{4}$

## H                   QUADRATIC MODELLING

There are many situations in the real world where the relationship between two variables is
a quadratic function.

The graph of such relationships will have shape 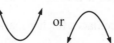  or  and the function will
have a minimum or maximum value.

For the quadratic function  $y = ax^2 + bx + c$,  we have already seen that the vertex or turning
point lies on the axis of symmetry.

- If $a > 0$,
  the **minimum**
  value of $y$ occurs
  at $x = -\dfrac{b}{2a}$.

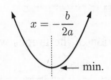

- If $a < 0$,
  the **maximum**
  value of $y$ occurs
  at $x = -\dfrac{b}{2a}$.

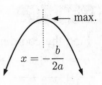

The process of finding the maximum or minimum value of a function is called **optimisation**.

---

**Example 19**    ◀)) **Self Tutor**

When a baseballer hits the ball straight up, its height above the ground $t$ seconds after being hit is $H(t) = 30t - 5t^2$ metres, $t \geqslant 0$.

a How long does it take for the ball to reach its maximum height?

b What is the maximum height reached by the ball?

c How long does it take for the ball to hit the ground?

---

a $H(t) = 30t - 5t^2$ has $a = -5$ which is $< 0$, so its shape is 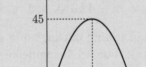.

The maximum height occurs when $t = \dfrac{-b}{2a} = \dfrac{-30}{2 \times (-5)} = 3$

So, the maximum height is reached after 3 seconds.

b $H(3) = 30(3) - 5(3)^2$

$\quad = 90 - 45$

$\quad = 45$

So, the maximum height reached is 45 metres.

c The ball hits the ground when $H(t) = 0$

$\therefore \quad 30t - 5t^2 = 0$

$\therefore \quad 5t^2 - 30t = 0$

$\therefore \quad 5t(t - 6) = 0$ \{factorising\}

$\therefore \quad t = 0$ or $6$

So, the ball hits the ground after 6 seconds.

---

## EXERCISE 12H

1 Andrew dives off a jetty. His height above the water $t$ seconds after diving is given by $H(t) = -4t^2 + 4t + 3$ metres, $t \geqslant 0$.

a How high above the water is the jetty?

b How long does it take for Andrew to reach the maximum height of his dive?

c How far is Andrew above the water at his highest point?

d How long does it take for Andrew to hit the water?

2 Jasmine makes necklaces for her market stall. Her daily profit from making $x$ necklaces is given by $P(x) = -x^2 + 20x$ dollars.

a How many necklaces should Jasmine make per day to maximise her profit?

b Find the maximum daily profit that Jasmine can make.

**3** The average cost of making $x$ televisions per week
is $C(x) = x^2 - 40x + 500$ dollars per television.

**a** How many televisions should be made per week
to minimise the average cost?

**b** Find the minimum average cost.

**c** How many televisions are made per week if the
average cost is $200 per television?

**4** Answer the questions in the **Opening Problem** on page **366**.

---

**Example 20**    ◀)) **Self Tutor**

A farmer has 20 metres of fencing to create a
rectangular enclosure next to his barn.

The two equal sides of the enclosure are $x$ metres
long.

**a** Show that the area of the enclosure is given
by $A = x(20 - 2x)$ m$^2$.

**b** Find the dimensions of the enclosure of
maximum area.

**a** The side XY has length $y = 20 - 2x$ m

The area of the enclosure $=$ length $\times$ width

$\therefore$ $A = x(20 - 2x)$ m$^2$

**b** $A = 20x - 2x^2 = -2x^2 + 20x$

which has $a = -2$, $b = 20$

Since $a < 0$, the shape is ⌢.

So, the maximum area occurs when

$$x = \frac{-b}{2a} = \frac{-20}{-4} = 5 \text{ m}$$

The area is maximised when YZ $= 5$ m and XY $= 20 - 2(5) = 10$ m.

---

**5** A rectangular plot is enclosed by 200 m of fencing and
has an area of $A$ square metres. Show that:

**a** $A = 100x - x^2$ where $x$ m is the length of one of
its sides

**b** the area is maximised when the rectangle is a square.

$x$ m

**6** A rectangular paddock to enclose horses is to be made, with one side being a straight
water drain. If 1000 m of fencing is available for the other 3 sides, what dimensions
should be used for the paddock so that it encloses the maximum possible area?

**7**  1800 m of fencing is available to fence six identical pens as shown in the diagram.

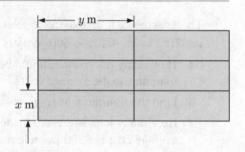

   **a**  Explain why $9x + 8y = 1800$.

   **b**  Show that the total area of each pen is given by $A = -\frac{9}{8}x^2 + 225x$ m$^2$.

   **c**  If the area enclosed is to be maximised, what is the shape of each pen?

**8**  500 m of fencing is available to make 4 rectangular pens of identical shape.

   Find the dimensions that maximise the area of each pen if the plan is:

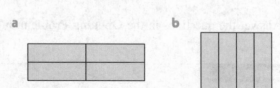

---

**Example 21**                                                  ◀⧽ **Self Tutor**

A manufacturer of pot-belly stoves has the following situation to consider.

If $x$ are made per week, each one will cost $\left(50 + \dfrac{400}{x}\right)$ dollars and the total income per week for selling them will be $(550x - 2x^2)$ dollars.

How many pot-belly stoves should be made per week to maximise the profit?

The total profit   $P = \text{income} - \text{costs}$

$$\therefore\ P = (550x - 2x^2) - \underbrace{\left(50 + \dfrac{400}{x}\right)}_{\substack{\uparrow \\ \text{cost for one}}} \underset{\substack{\uparrow \\ x \text{ of them}}}{x}$$

$$\therefore\ P = 550x - 2x^2 - 50x - 400$$
$$\therefore\ P = -2x^2 + 500x - 400 \text{ dollars}$$

This is a quadratic in $x$, with $a = -2$, $b = 500$, $c = -400$.

Since $a < 0$, the shape is

$P$ is maximised when $x = \dfrac{-b}{2a} = \dfrac{-500}{-4} = 125$

$\therefore$ 125 stoves should be made per week to maximise the profit.

---

**9**  The total cost of producing $x$ toasters per day is given by $C = (\frac{1}{10}x^2 + 20x + 25)$ euros, and the selling price of each toaster is $(44 - \frac{1}{5}x)$ euros. How many toasters should be produced each day in order to maximise the total profit?

**10** A manufacturer of barbecues knows that if $x$ of them are made each week then each one will cost $\left(60 + \dfrac{800}{x}\right)$ pounds and the total income per week will be $(1000x - 3x^2)$ pounds.

How many barbecues should be made per week for maximum profits?

---

**INVESTIGATION 4**                          **TUNNELS AND TRUCKS**

A tunnel is parabolic in shape with the dimensions shown.

A truck carrying a wide load is 4.8 m high and 3.9 m wide and needs to pass through the tunnel. Your task is to determine if the truck will fit through the tunnel.

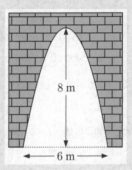

**What to do:**

**1** If a set of axes is fitted to the parabolic tunnel as shown, state the coordinates of points A, B and C.

**2** On your graphics calculator:

    **a** enter the $x$-coordinates of A, B and C into **List 1**

    **b** enter the $y$-coordinates of A, B and C into **List 2**.

**3** Draw a scatterplot of points A, B and C.

**4** Set your calculator to display 4 decimal places. By fitting a quadratic model to the data, determine the equation of the parabolic boundary of the tunnel in the form $y = ax^2 + bx + c$.

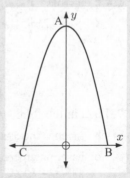

**5** What is the equation of the truck's roofline?

**6** Graph the equations from **4** and **5** on the same set of axes. Calculate the points of intersection of the graphs of these functions.

**7** Using the points of intersection found in **6**, will the truck pass through the tunnel? What is the maximum width of a truck that is 4.8 m high if it is to pass through the tunnel?

## REVIEW SET 12A

**1** If $f(x) = x^2 - 3x - 15$ find:

   **a** $f(0)$       **b** $f(1)$       **c** $x$ such that $f(x) = 3$.

**2** On the same set of axes, sketch $y = x^2$ and the function:

   **a** $y = 3x^2$       **b** $y = -\frac{1}{2}x^2$

**3** Consider the function $y = -2(x - 1)(x + 3)$.

   **a** Find the:

      **i** direction the parabola opens       **ii** $y$-intercept

      **iii** $x$-intercepts       **iv** equation of the axis of symmetry.

   **b** Sketch a graph of the function showing all of the above features.

**4** Consider the function $y = x^2 - 2x - 15$.

   **a** Find the:

      **i** $y$-intercept       **ii** $x$-intercepts

      **iii** equation of the axis of symmetry       **iv** coordinates of the vertex.

   **b** Sketch a graph of the function showing all of the above features.

**5** Find the $x$-intercepts of the following functions:

   **a** $y = 3x^2 - 12x$       **b** $y = 3x^2 - x - 10$       **c** $f(x) = x^2 - 11x - 60$

**6** Match the function with the correct graph:

   **a** $y = x^2$

   **b** $y = -\frac{1}{2}x^2$

   **c** $y = 3x^2$

   **d** $y = -2x^2$

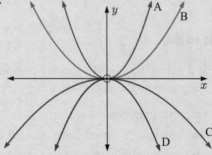

**7** Find, in the form $y = ax^2 + bx + c$, the equation of the quadratic whose graph:

   **a** touches the $x$-axis at 4 and passes through $(2, 12)$

   **b** has $x$-intercepts 3 and $-2$ and $y$-intercept 3.

**8** Find the maximum or minimum value of the relation $y = -2x^2 + 4x + 3$ and the value of $x$ for which the maximum or minimum occurs.

**9** A stone was thrown from the top of a cliff 60 metres above sea level. The height of the stone above sea level $t$ seconds after it was released is given by $H(t) = -5t^2 + 20t + 60$ metres.

   **a** Find the time taken for the stone to reach its maximum height.

   **b** What was the maximum height above sea level reached by the stone?

   **c** How long did it take before the stone struck the water?

## REVIEW SET 12B

**1** **a** Is $f(x) = -2x^2 + 13x - 4$ satisfied by the ordered pair $(1, 5)$?

  **b** Find the value(s) of $x$ for which $g(x) = x^2 - 5x - 9$ takes the value 5.

**2** Consider the function $y = 3(x - 2)^2$.

  **a** Find the:

     **i** direction the parabola opens      **ii** $y$-intercept

     **iii** $x$-intercepts      **iv** equation of the axis of symmetry.

  **b** Sketch a graph of the function showing all of the above features.

**3** Consider the function $y = -x^2 + 7x - 10$.

  **a** Find the:

     **i** $y$-intercept      **ii** $x$-intercepts

     **iii** equation of the axis of symmetry      **iv** coordinates of the vertex.

  **b** Sketch a graph of the function showing all of the above features.

**4** Find the equation of the axis of symmetry and the vertex of $y = -3x^2 + 8x + 7$.

**5** Find the equation of the quadratic relation with graph:

**a**      **b** 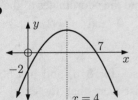     **c**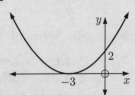

**6** Find the coordinates of the point(s) of intersection of the graphs with equations $y = x^2 + 13x + 15$ and $y = 2x - 3$.

**7** Determine the values of $a$ and $b$, given the diagram:

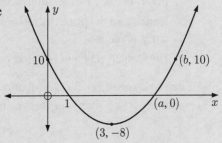

**8** A farmer has 2000 m of fencing to enclose two identical adjacent fields.

  **a** Find an expression for the total area of the fields in terms of $x$.

  **b** What is the maximum possible total area of the two fields?

  **c** What dimensions give this maximum total area?

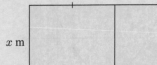

## REVIEW SET 12C

**1** If $g(x) = x^2 + 5x - 2$, find:

   **a** $g(-1)$             **b** $g(4)$             **c** $x$ if $g(x) = -6$

**2** Consider the quadratic function $y = 2x^2 + 6x - 3$.

   **a** Find the coordinates of the vertex.    **b** Find the $y$-intercept.

   **c** Sketch the graph of the function.

   **d** Use technology to check your answers.

**3** Draw the graph of $y = -x^2 + 2x$.

**4** Find the equation of the quadratic relation with graph:

   **a**

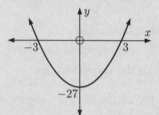

   **b**

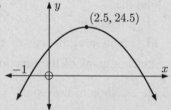

**5** Use your calculator to find the coordinates of the point(s) of intersection of the graphs with equations $y = 2x - 9$ and $y = 2x^2 - 3x - 8$.

**6** Find the vertex of $y = 2x^2 - 6x + 3$.

**7** A retailer sells sunglasses for \$15, and has 50 customers per day. From market research, the retailer discovers that for every dollar increase in the price of the sunglasses, he will lose 2 customers per day.

   **a** Given that revenue = (price) × (number of customers), show that the revenue collected by the retailer each day is $R = (15 + x)(50 - 2x)$, where $x$ is the price increase of the sunglasses in dollars.

   **b** Hence find the price the retailer should set for his sunglasses in order to maximise daily revenue.

   **c** How much revenue is made per day at this price?

**8** Find an expression for the quadratic which cuts the $x$-axis at 3 and $-2$ and has $y$-intercept 24. Give your answer in the form $y = ax^2 + bx + c$.

**9**

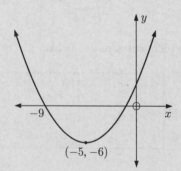

Find:

   **a** the axis of symmetry

   **b** the second $x$-intercept.

# Chapter 13

# Trigonometry

Syllabus reference: 5.3, 5.4, 5.5

Contents:

## OPENING PROBLEM

A triangular sail is to be cut from a section of cloth. Two of the sides must have lengths 4 m and 6 m as illustrated. The total area for the sail must be 11.6 m², the maximum allowed for the boat to race in its class.

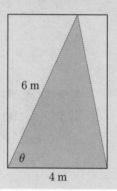

**Things to think about:**

**a** Can you find the size of the angle $\theta$ between the two sides of given length?

**b** Can you find the length of the third side?

# A    LABELLING RIGHT ANGLED TRIANGLES

The **hypotenuse (HYP)** of a right angled triangle is the side which is opposite the right angle. It is the longest side of the triangle.

For the angle marked $\theta$:

- BC is the side **opposite (OPP)** angle $\theta$
- AB is the side **adjacent (ADJ)** to angle $\theta$.

For the angle marked $\phi$:

- AB is the side **opposite (OPP)** angle $\phi$
- BC is the side **adjacent (ADJ)** to angle $\phi$.

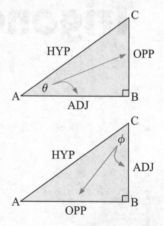

---

**Example 1**                                              ◀ɔ **Self Tutor**

For the triangle alongside, find the:

**a** hypotenuse
**b** side opposite $\alpha$
**c** side adjacent to $\alpha$
**d** side opposite $\beta$
**e** side adjacent to $\beta$.

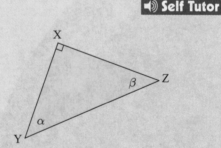

**a**  The hypotenuse is the side opposite the right angle, which is YZ.

**b**  The side opposite $\alpha$ is XZ.          **c**  The side adjacent to $\alpha$ is XY.

**d**  The side opposite $\beta$ is XY.          **e**  The side adjacent to $\beta$ is XZ.

## EXERCISE 13A

**1** For the triangles below, find the:

       **i** hypotenuse        **ii** side opposite $\alpha$        **iii** side adjacent to $\alpha$.

**a**       **b** 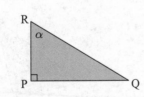      **c**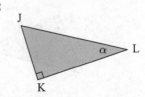

**2** For the triangle alongside, find the length of the:

     **a** hypotenuse

     **b** side opposite $\theta$

     **c** side adjacent to $\theta$

     **d** side opposite $\phi$

     **e** side adjacent to $\phi$.

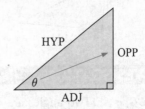

---

# B      THE TRIGONOMETRIC RATIOS

Consider a right angled triangle with an angle $\theta$. We label the sides OPP for the side opposite $\theta$, ADJ for the side adjacent to $\theta$, and HYP for the hypotenuse.

We define three **trigonometric ratios** which are the **sine**, **cosine**, and **tangent** of the angle $\theta$, in terms of the side lengths.

These ratios are:

$$\sin \theta = \frac{\textbf{OPP}}{\textbf{HYP}} \qquad \cos \theta = \frac{\textbf{ADJ}}{\textbf{HYP}} \qquad \tan \theta = \frac{\textbf{OPP}}{\textbf{ADJ}}$$

We use the trigonometric ratios as tools for finding side lengths and angles of right angled triangles.

## FINDING TRIGONOMETRIC RATIOS

| Example 2 | ◀)) Self Tutor |
|---|---|

For the following triangle, find:

     **a** $\sin \theta$     **b** $\cos \phi$     **c** $\tan \theta$

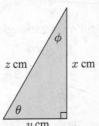

     **a** $\sin \theta = \dfrac{\text{OPP}}{\text{HYP}} = \dfrac{b}{c}$      **b** $\cos \phi = \dfrac{\text{ADJ}}{\text{HYP}} = \dfrac{b}{c}$      **c** $\tan \theta = \dfrac{\text{OPP}}{\text{ADJ}} = \dfrac{b}{a}$

## EXERCISE 13B.1

**1** For each of the following triangles, find:

  **i** $\sin\theta$   **ii** $\cos\theta$   **iii** $\tan\theta$

  **a** 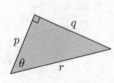   **b** 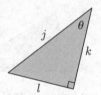   **c**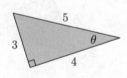

**2** For each of the following triangles, find:

  **i** $\sin\theta$   **ii** $\cos\theta$   **iii** $\tan\theta$   **iv** $\sin\phi$   **v** $\cos\phi$   **vi** $\tan\phi$

  **a** 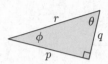   **b** 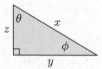   **c**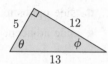

  **d** 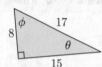   **e**    **f**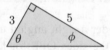

---

| INVESTIGATION 1 | COMPLEMENTARY ANGLES |
|---|---|

Two angles are **complementary** if their sum is $90^o$. We say that $\theta$ and $(90^o - \theta)$ are **complements** of each other.

**PRINTABLE WORKSHEET**

Your task is to determine if a relationship exists between the sines and cosines of an angle and its complement.

**What to do:**

**1** Use your calculator to complete a table like the one shown. Include some angles of your choice.

| $\theta$ | $\sin\theta$ | $\cos\theta$ | $90^o - \theta$ | $\sin(90^o - \theta)$ | $\cos(90^o - \theta)$ |
|---|---|---|---|---|---|
| $17^o$ | | | $73^o$ | | |
| $38^o$ | | | | | |
| $59^o$ | | | | | |
| | | | | | |
| | | | | | |

**2** Write down your observations from the tabled values.

**3** Use the figure alongside to prove that your observations are true for all angles $\theta$ where $0^o < \theta < 90^o$.

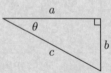

**4** Investigate possible connections between $\tan\theta$ and $\tan(90^o - \theta)$.

## FINDING SIDES

In a right angled triangle where we are given one other angle and the length of one of the sides, we can use the trigonometric ratios to find either of the remaining sides.

*Step 1:*   Redraw the figure and mark on it HYP, OPP, ADJ relative to the given angle.

*Step 2:*   Choose the correct trigonometric ratio and use it to set up an equation.

*Step 3:*   Solve the equation to find the unknown.

---

**Example 3**                                                              ◀) **Self Tutor**

Find, to 3 significant figures, the unknown length in the following triangles:

Make sure your calculator is set to **degrees** mode.

**a**

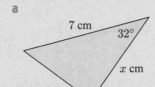

7 cm   32°   $x$ cm

**b**

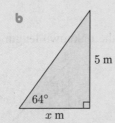

5 m   64°   $x$ m

---

**a**   The sides of interest are the *adjacent* side and the *hypotenuse*, so we use the cos ratio.

$$\cos 32^o = \frac{x}{7} \qquad \left\{ \cos \theta = \frac{\text{ADJ}}{\text{HYP}} \right\}$$

$$\therefore \ 7 \times \cos 32^o = x$$

$$\therefore \ x \approx 5.94 \quad \{7 \ \boxed{\times} \ \boxed{\text{COS}} \ 32 \ \boxed{\text{ENTER}} \}$$

So, the side is about 5.94 cm long.

HYP 7 cm   32°   $x$ cm ADJ   OPP

**b**   The sides of interest are the *adjacent* side and the *opposite* side, so we use the tan ratio.

$$\tan 64^o = \frac{5}{x} \qquad \left\{ \tan \theta = \frac{\text{OPP}}{\text{ADJ}} \right\}$$

$$\therefore \ x \times \tan 64^o = 5$$

$$\therefore \ x = \frac{5}{\tan 64^o}$$

$$\therefore \ x \approx 2.44 \quad \{5 \ \boxed{\div} \ \boxed{\text{tan}} \ 64 \ \boxed{\text{ENTER}} \}$$

So, the side is about 2.44 m long.

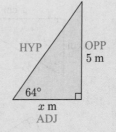

HYP   OPP 5 m   64°   $x$ m ADJ

---

## EXERCISE 13B.2

**1**   Set up a trigonometric equation connecting the given angle and sides:

**a**

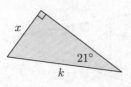

$x$   21°   $k$

**b**

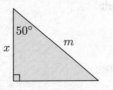

50°   $x$   $m$

**c**

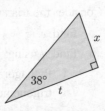

$x$   38°   $t$

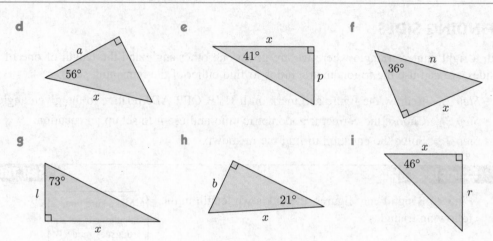

**d**

$a$ 56° $x$

**e**

$x$ 41° $p$

**f**

36° $n$ $x$

**g**

$l$ 73° $x$

**h**

$b$ 21° $x$

**i**

$x$ 46° $r$

**2** Find, to 3 significant figures, the unknown length in the following triangles:

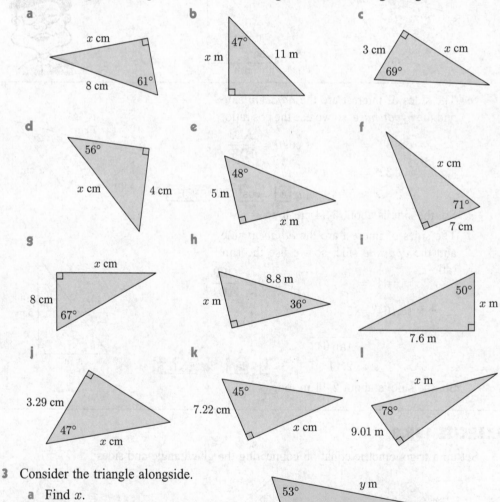

**a**

$x$ cm 8 cm 61°

**b**

47° $x$ m 11 m

**c**

3 cm $x$ cm 69°

**d**

56° $x$ cm 4 cm

**e**

48° 5 m $x$ m

**f**

$x$ cm 71° 7 cm

**g**

$x$ cm 8 cm 67°

**h**

8.8 m $x$ m 36°

**i**

50° $x$ m 7.6 m

**j**

3.29 cm 47° $x$ cm

**k**

45° 7.22 cm $x$ cm

**l**

$x$ m 78° 9.01 m

**3** Consider the triangle alongside.

**a** Find $x$.

**b** Find $y$ using:

  **i** Pythagoras' theorem

  **ii** trigonometry.

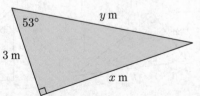

53° $y$ m 3 m $x$ m

**4**  Find, to 2 decimal places, *all* unknown sides of:

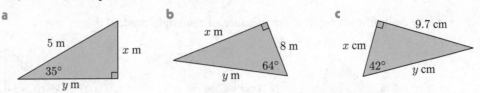

## FINDING ANGLES

If we know the lengths of two sides of a right angled triangle, we can find the size of its angles.

Suppose we want to find the size of angle $\theta$ in the triangle alongside.

We can see that $\sin\theta = \frac{2}{3}$, so we need to find the angle $\theta$ whose sine is $\frac{2}{3}$.

We say that $\theta$ is the **inverse sine** of $\frac{2}{3}$, and we write $\theta = \sin^{-1}\left(\frac{2}{3}\right)$.

We can use our graphics calculator to determine this value. For help, refer to the **graphics calculator instructions** at the start of the book.

The **inverse cosine** and **inverse tangent** functions work in a similar way.

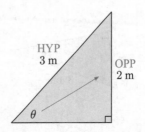

$\sin^{-1}(x)$ is the angle with a sine of $x$.

---

**Example 4**    ◀) **Self Tutor**

Find, to 3 significant figures, the measure of the angle marked $\theta$ in:

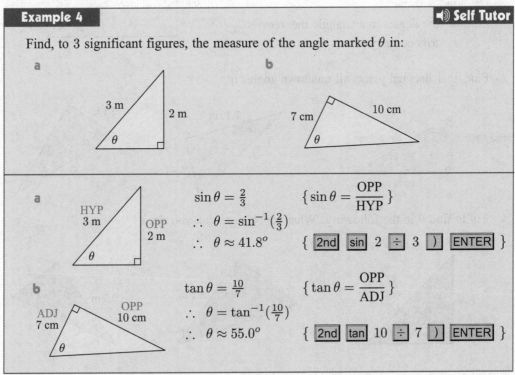

## EXERCISE 13B.3

**1** Find, to 3 significant figures, the measure of the angle marked $\theta$ in:

**a**

5 m  $\theta$  4 m

**b**

3 cm  $\theta$  4 cm

**c**

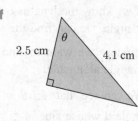

6 m  $\theta$  7 m

**d**

2.3 m  $\theta$  3.4 m

**e**

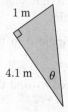

1 m  4.1 m  $\theta$

**f**

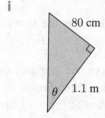

$\theta$  2.5 cm  4.1 cm

**g**

$\theta$  10.2 m  9.9 m

**h**

2 cm  $\theta$  4 cm

**i**

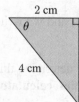

80 cm  $\theta$  1.1 m

**2** Consider the triangle alongside.

  **a** Find $\theta$, correct to 1 decimal place.

  **b** Find $\phi$ using:

    **i** the angles in a triangle theorem

    **ii** trigonometry.

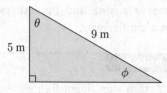

$\theta$  9 m  5 m  $\phi$

**3** Find, to 1 decimal place, all unknown angles in:

**a**

$\phi$  13 m  $\theta$  10 m

**b**

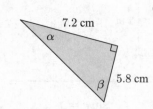

7.2 cm  $\alpha$  $\beta$  5.8 cm

**c**

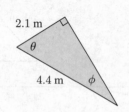

2.1 m  $\theta$  4.4 m  $\phi$

**4** Try to find $\theta$ in the following. What conclusions can you draw?

**a**

6 m  5 m  $\theta$

**b**

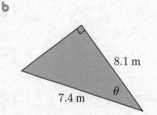

8.1 m  7.4 m  $\theta$

**c**

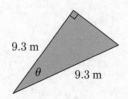

9.3 m  $\theta$  9.3 m

# C USING TRIGONOMETRY IN GEOMETRIC FIGURES

We can use trigonometry to find unknown lengths and angles in special geometric figures which contain right angled triangles.

## ISOSCELES TRIANGLES

To use trigonometry with isosceles triangles we draw the **perpendicular** from the apex to the base. This altitude **bisects** the base.

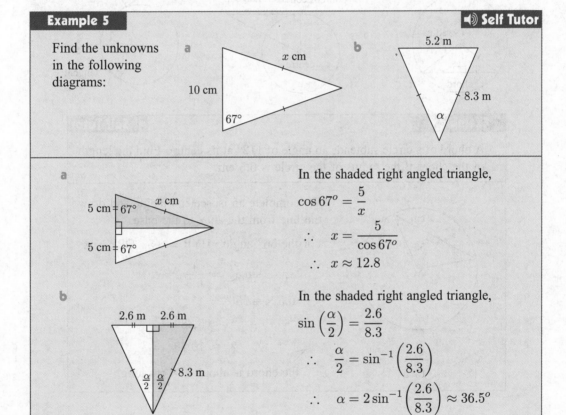

**Example 5**                                               ◀◗ **Self Tutor**

Find the unknowns in the following diagrams:

**a**

In the shaded right angled triangle,

$$\cos 67^o = \frac{5}{x}$$

$$\therefore \quad x = \frac{5}{\cos 67^o}$$

$$\therefore \quad x \approx 12.8$$

**b**

In the shaded right angled triangle,

$$\sin \left(\frac{\alpha}{2}\right) = \frac{2.6}{8.3}$$

$$\therefore \quad \frac{\alpha}{2} = \sin^{-1}\left(\frac{2.6}{8.3}\right)$$

$$\therefore \quad \alpha = 2\sin^{-1}\left(\frac{2.6}{8.3}\right) \approx 36.5^o$$

## EXERCISE 13C.1

1   Find, correct to 4 significant figures, the unknowns in the following:

**a**

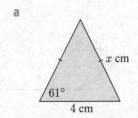

**b**

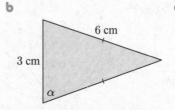

**c**

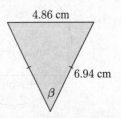

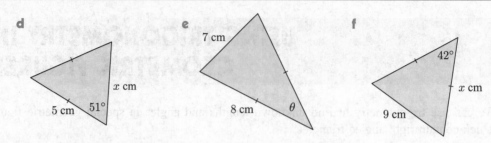

d

e

f

## CHORDS AND TANGENTS

Right angled triangles occur in chord and tangent problems.

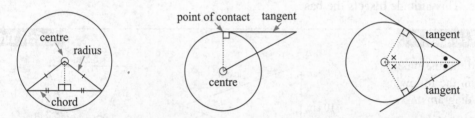

---

### Example 6

🔊 **Self Tutor**

A chord of a circle subtends an angle of $112^o$ at its centre. Find the length of the chord if the radius of the circle is 6.5 cm.

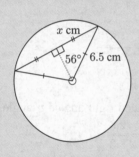

We complete an isosceles triangle and draw the line from the apex to the base.

For the $56^o$ angle,  HYP $= 6.5$,  OPP $= x$

$$\therefore \quad \sin 56^o = \frac{x}{6.5}$$

$$\therefore \quad 6.5 \times \sin 56^o = x$$

$$\therefore \quad x \approx 5.389$$

$$\therefore \quad 2x \approx 10.78$$

$\therefore$    the chord is about 10.8 cm long.

---

## EXERCISE 13C.2

1 Find the value of the unknown in:

a

b

c

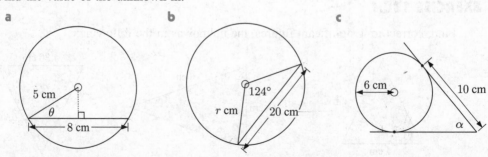

**2** A chord of a circle subtends an angle of $89°$ at its centre. Find the length of the chord given that the circle's diameter is 11.4 cm.

**3** A chord of a circle is 13.2 cm long and the circle's radius is 9.4 cm. Find the angle subtended by the chord at the centre of the circle.

**4** Point P is 10 cm from the centre of a circle of radius 4 cm. Tangents are drawn from P to the circle. Find the angle between the tangents.

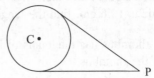

**5** A circular clock has dots on its boundary which indicate the numbers 1 to 12. The dots representing 10 and 2 are 24 cm apart. Find the radius of the clock.

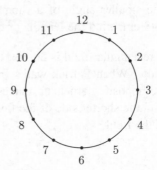

## OTHER FIGURES

Right angled triangles can also be found in other geometric figures such as rectangles, rhombi, and trapezia.

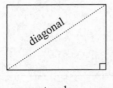

rectangle

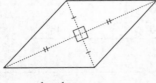

rhombus

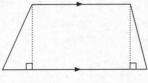

trapezium or trapezoid

---

| **Example 7** | ◀⑴ **Self Tutor** |

A rhombus has diagonals of length 10 cm and 6 cm respectively.
Find the smaller angle of the rhombus.

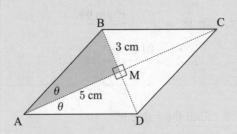

The diagonals bisect each other at right angles, so    AM = 5 cm and BM = 3 cm.

In $\triangle$ABM, $\theta$ will be the smallest angle as it is opposite the shortest side.

$$\tan \theta = \tfrac{3}{5}$$

$$\therefore \quad \theta = \tan^{-1}(\tfrac{3}{5})$$

$$\therefore \quad \theta \approx 30.964°$$

The required angle is $2\theta$ as the diagonals bisect the angles at each vertex.
So, the angle is about $61.9°$.

## EXERCISE 13C.3

**1** A rectangle is 9.2 m by 3.8 m. What angle does its diagonal make with its longer side?

**2** The diagonal and the longer side of a rectangle make an angle of $43.2°$. If the longer side is 12.6 cm, find the length of the shorter side.

**3** A rhombus has diagonals of length 12 cm and 7 cm respectively. Find the larger angle of the rhombus.

**4** The smaller angle of a rhombus measures $21.8°$ and the shorter diagonal has length 13.8 cm. Find the lengths of the sides of the rhombus.

**5** A rectangular field is 20 metres longer than it is wide. When Patrick walks from one corner to the opposite corner, he makes an angle of $55°$ with the shorter side of the field. Find the width of the field.

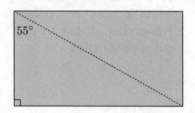

---

| **Example 8** | ◀ **Self Tutor** |

Find $x$ given:

10 cm / $x$ cm / $65°$ / $48°$

We draw perpendiculars AM and BN to DC, creating right angled triangles and the rectangle ABNM.

In $\triangle$ADM,  $\sin 65° = \dfrac{y}{10}$

$\therefore \; y = 10\sin 65°$

In  $\triangle$BCN,  $\sin 48° = \dfrac{y}{x} = \dfrac{10\sin 65°}{x}$

$\therefore \; x = \dfrac{10\sin 65°}{\sin 48°} \approx 12.2$

---

**6  a** Find the value of $x$ in:

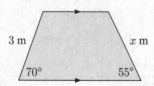

**b** Find the value of $\alpha$ in:

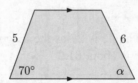

**7**  A stormwater drain is to have the shape illustrated. Determine the angle $\beta$ the left hand side makes with the bottom of the drain.

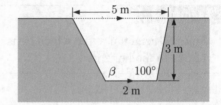

---

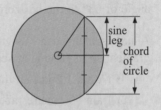
---

# D | PROBLEM SOLVING USING TRIGONOMETRY

Trigonometry is a very useful branch of mathematics. **Heights** and **distances** which are very difficult or even impossible to measure can often be found using trigonometry.

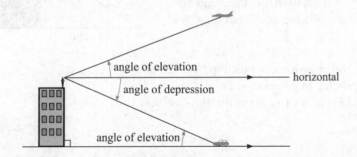

| Example 9 | ◀)) Self Tutor |
|---|---|

Find the height of a tree which casts a shadow of 12.4 m when the sun makes an angle of $52°$ to the horizon.

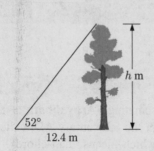

Let $h$ m be the tree's height.

For the $52°$ angle, OPP $= h$, ADJ $= 12.4$

$$\therefore \quad \tan 52° = \frac{h}{12.4}$$

$$\therefore \quad 12.4 \times \tan 52° = h$$

$$\therefore \quad h \approx 15.9$$

So, the tree is 15.9 m high.

## EXERCISE 13D

1  Find the height of a flagpole which casts a shadow of 9.32 m when the sun makes an angle of $63°$ to the horizontal.

2  A hill is inclined at $18°$ to the horizontal. It runs down to the beach with constant gradient so its base is at sea level.

   a  If I walk 1.2 km up the hill, what is my height above sea level?

   b  If I am 500 metres above sea level, how far have I walked up the hill?

3

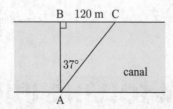

A surveyor standing at A notices two posts B and C on the opposite side of a canal. The posts are 120 m apart. If the angle of sight between the posts is $37°$, how wide is the canal?

4  A train must climb a constant gradient of 5.5 m for every 200 m of track. Find the angle of incline.

5  Find the angle of elevation to the top of a 56 m high building from point A which is 113 m from its base. What is the angle of depression from the top of the building to A?

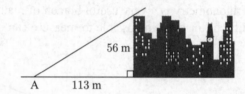

6  The angle of depression from the top of a 120 m high vertical cliff to a boat B is $16°$.
   Find how far the boat is from the base of the cliff.

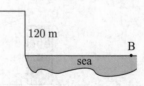

**7** Kylie measures the angle of elevation from a point on level ground to the top of a building 120 metres high to be $32°$. She walks towards the building until the angle of elevation is $45°$. How far does she walk?

---

**Example 10**  ◀》 **Self Tutor**

A builder has designed the roof structure illustrated. The pitch of the roof is the angle that the roof makes with the horizontal. Find the pitch of this roof.

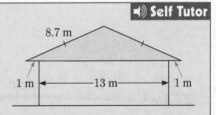

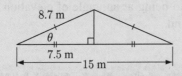

By constructing an altitude of the isosceles triangle, we form two right angled triangles. For angle $\theta$:

ADJ $= 7.5$,   HYP $= 8.7$

$\therefore \quad \cos\theta = \dfrac{7.5}{8.7}$

$\therefore \quad \theta = \cos^{-1}\left(\dfrac{7.5}{8.7}\right)$

$\therefore \quad \theta \approx 30.45°$

So, the pitch is approximately $30.5°$.

---

**8** Find $\theta$, the pitch of the roof.

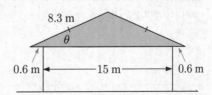

**9**

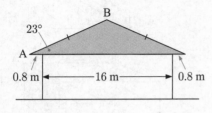

If the pitch of the given roof is $23°$, find the length of the timber beam AB.

**10** An open right-circular cone has a vertical angle measuring $40°$ and a base radius of 30 cm. Find:

**a** the height of the cone

**b** the capacity of the cone in litres.

**11** From an observer O, the angles of elevation to the bottom and the top of a flagpole are 36° and 38° respectively. Find the height of the flagpole.

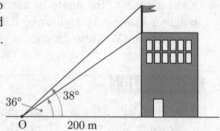

**12** The angle of depression from the top of a 150 m high cliff to a boat at sea is 7°. How much closer to the cliff must the boat move for the angle of depression to become 19°?

**13** A helicopter flies horizontally at 100 km h$^{-1}$. An observer notices that it takes 20 seconds for the helicopter to fly from directly overhead to being at an angle of elevation of 60°. Find the height of the helicopter above the ground.

# E    3-DIMENSIONAL PROBLEM SOLVING

We can use Pythagoras' theorem and trigonometry to find unknown angles and lengths in 3-dimensional figures.

### Example 11    ◀)) Self Tutor

A rectangular prism has the dimensions shown alongside. Find the angle between the diagonal AB and the edge BC.

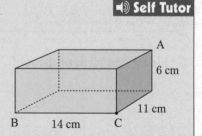

Consider the end of the prism containing A and C. Let AC be $x$ cm.

By Pythagoras,    $x^2 = 6^2 + 11^2$

$\therefore x^2 = 157$

$\therefore x = \sqrt{157}$

The points A, B and C form a triangle which is right angled at $\widehat{BCA}$.

$$\tan \theta = \frac{\text{OPP}}{\text{ADJ}} = \frac{\sqrt{157}}{14}$$

$\therefore \theta = \tan^{-1}\left(\frac{\sqrt{157}}{14}\right)$

$\therefore \theta \approx 41.8°$

So, the required angle is 41.8°.

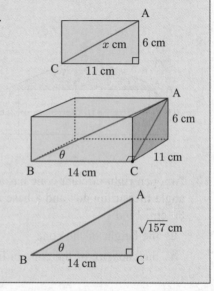

## EXERCISE 13E.1

**1**  The cube shown has sides of length 13 cm.  Find:

    **a**  BD       **b**  the angle FDB.

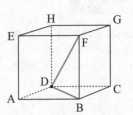

**2**  In the rectangular prism shown alongside, Z is the midpoint of XW.  Find:

    **a**  VX       **b**  the angle RXV

    **c**  YZ       **d**  the angle YZU

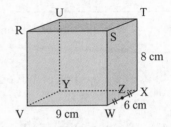

**3**  Elizabeth is terrified of spiders.  When she walks into the room, she notices one in the opposite corner of the room from where she is standing.

    **a**  If Elizabeth is 1.6 m tall, how far is the spider from her head?

    **b**  From the direction it is facing, this type of spider can see up to an angle of 42°.  This spider is facing a fly at F.  Can it see Elizabeth?

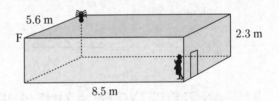

**4**  A wooden ramp is built as a triangular prism with supports DC and CE.  Find:

    **a**  the length of the supports

    **b**  the angle of the join between them.

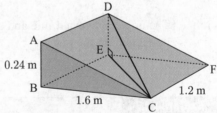

**5**  All edges of a square-based pyramid are 12 m in length.

    **a**  Find the angle between a slant edge and a base diagonal.

    **b**  Show that this angle is the same for any square-based pyramid with all edge lengths equal.

## SHADOW LINES (PROJECTIONS)

Consider a wire frame in the shape of a cube as shown in the diagram alongside.  Imagine a light source shining down directly onto this cube from above.

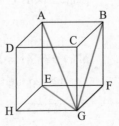

The shadow cast by wire AG would be EG.  This is called the **projection** of AG onto the base plane EFGH.

Similarly, the projection of BG onto the base plane is FG.

### Example 12

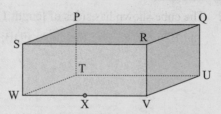

Find the shadow or projection of the following onto the base plane if a light is shone from directly above the figure:

**a** UP          **b** WP

**c** VP          **d** XP

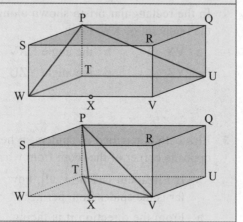

**a** The projection of UP onto the base plane is UT.

**b** The projection of WP onto the base plane is WT.

**c** The projection of VP onto the base plane is VT.

**d** The projection of XP onto the base plane is XT.

## THE ANGLE BETWEEN A LINE AND A PLANE

The angle between a line and a plane is the angle between the line and its projection on the plane.

### Example 13

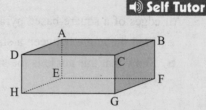

Name the angle between the following line segments and the base plane EFGH:

**a** AH          **b** AG.

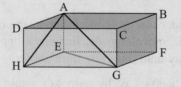

**a** The projection of AH onto the base plane EFGH is EH

∴   the required angle is $A\hat{H}E$.

**b** The projection of AG onto the base plane EFGH is EG

∴   the required angle is $A\hat{G}E$.

**Example 14**

Find the angle between the following line segments and the base plane EFGH:

**a** DG          **b** BH

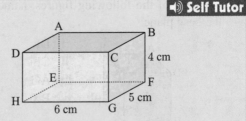

**a** The required angle is $\widehat{DGH}$.

$\therefore \quad \tan \theta = \dfrac{\text{OPP}}{\text{ADJ}} = \dfrac{4}{6}$

$\therefore \quad \theta = \tan^{-1}\left(\dfrac{4}{6}\right)$

$\therefore \quad \theta \approx 33.69°$

$\therefore$ the angle is about $33.7°$.

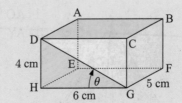

**b** The required angle is $\widehat{BHF}$.

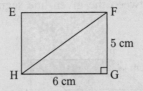

By Pythagoras,

$(HF)^2 = 6^2 + 5^2$ cm$^2$

$\therefore \quad (HF)^2 = 61$ cm$^2$

$\therefore \quad HF = \sqrt{61}$ cm

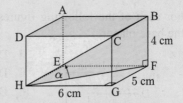

$\tan \alpha = \dfrac{\text{OPP}}{\text{ADJ}} = \dfrac{4}{\sqrt{61}}$

$\therefore \quad \alpha = \tan^{-1}\left(\dfrac{4}{\sqrt{61}}\right)$

$\therefore \quad \alpha \approx 27.12°$

$\therefore$ the angle is about $27.1°$.

## EXERCISE 13E.2

**1** Find the following projections onto the base planes of the given figures:

**a**

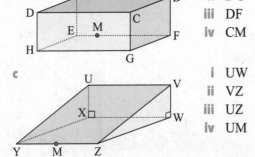

**i** CF
**ii** DG
**iii** DF
**iv** CM

**b**

**i** PC
**ii** PN

**c**

**i** UW
**ii** VZ
**iii** UZ
**iv** UM

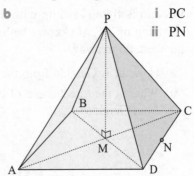

**2** For each of the following figures, name the angle between the given line segment and the base plane:

**a**

i   DE
ii  CE
iii AG
iv  BX

**b**

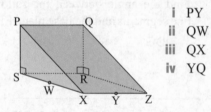

i   PY
ii  QW
iii QX
iv  YQ

**c**

i   AQ
ii  AY

**3** For each of the following figures, find the angle between the given line segments and the base plane:

**a**

i   DE
ii  DF
iii DX
iv  AX

**b**

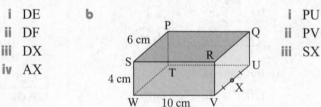

i   PU
ii  PV
iii SX

**c**

i   KO
ii  JX
iii KY

**d**

i   XD
ii  XY

**4** Roberto is flying his kite with the aid of a southerly wind. The kite is at an angle of elevation of 37°. He knows he has let out 54 m of string. His friend Geraldo stands to the west, 95 m away.

**a** How far is Geraldo from the kite?

**b** What is the kite's angle of elevation from Geraldo?

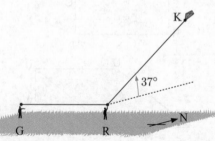

# F | AREAS OF TRIANGLES

If we know the base and height measurements of a triangle, we can calculate the area using
**area $= \frac{1}{2}$ base $\times$ height**.

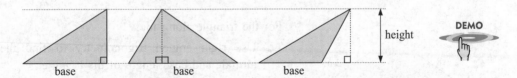

In many cases we do not know the height of the triangle. However, if we have sufficient
other information, we can find the area of the triangle using trigonometry.

## INVESTIGATION 2     THE AREA OF AN ISOSCELES TRIANGLE

In the diagram alongside, $\theta$ is the *included angle*
between the equal length sides.

In this investigation we seek a formula for the area
of an isosceles triangle which involves two side
lengths and the **included angle** between them.

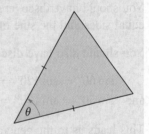

At the same time we will discover a useful property of **sine**.

**What to do:**

**1** Consider the equilateral triangle alongside.

  **a** Find the triangle's altitude using Pythagoras.

  **b** Find the area of the triangle using geometry.

  **c** Find the size of $\theta$.

  **d** Use your calculator to evaluate $1 \times 1 \times \sin\theta$.
    What do you notice?

**2** Now consider the isosceles triangle alongside.

  **a** Find the triangle's altitude using Pythagoras.

  **b** Find the area of the triangle using geometry.

  **c** Find the size of $\theta$ using right angled
    trigonometry.

  **d** Use your calculator to evaluate
    $1 \times 1 \times \sin\theta$.
    What do you notice?

  **e** Use your results from **1 d** and **2 d** to show that $\sin 120° = \sin 60°$.

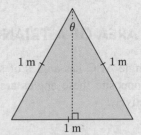
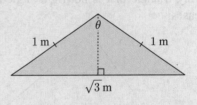

**3**

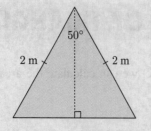

For the triangle alongside:

**a** Use right angled trigonometry to find the altitude and base length of the triangle.

**b** Find the area of the triangle using geometry.

**c** Use your calculator to evaluate $2 \times 2 \times \sin 50^o$. What do you notice?

**4**

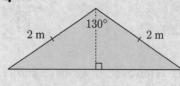

For the triangle alongside:

**a** Use right angled trigonometry to find the altitude and base length of the triangle.

**b** Find the area of the triangle using geometry.

**c** Use your calculator to evaluate $2 \times 2 \times \sin 130^o$. What do you notice?

**d** Use your results from **3 c** and **4 c** to show that $\sin 130^o = \sin 50^o$.

You should have discovered that the area of an isosceles triangle is half of the **product** of its equal sides and the sine of the included angle between them.

You should also have discovered that

$$\sin 60^o = \sin 120^o = \sin(180^o - 60^o)$$
$$\text{and} \quad \sin 50^o = \sin 130^o = \sin(180^o - 50^o).$$

Experiment using your calculator to satisfy yourself that this is true.

This leads us to the general conclusion

$$\sin \theta = \sin(180^o - \theta)$$

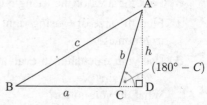

## THE AREA OF A TRIANGLE FORMULA

If triangle ABC has angles of size $A$, $B$ and $C$, the sides opposite these angles are labelled $a$, $b$ and $c$ respectively.

Any triangle that is not right angled must be either acute or obtuse. We will consider both cases:

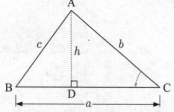

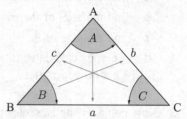

In both triangles a perpendicular is constructed from A to D on BC (extended if necessary).

$$\sin C = \frac{h}{b} \qquad\qquad \sin(180^o - C) = \frac{h}{b}$$

$$\therefore \quad h = b\sin C \qquad\qquad \therefore \quad h = b\sin(180^o - C)$$

$$\therefore \quad h = b\sin C$$

So,  area $= \frac{1}{2}ah$   gives   $\boxed{A = \frac{1}{2}ab\sin C.}$

Using different altitudes we can show that the area is also   $\frac{1}{2}bc\sin A$   or   $\frac{1}{2}ac\sin B$.

Given the lengths of two sides of a triangle and the included angle between them, the area of the triangle is

*a half of the product of two sides and the sine of the included angle.*

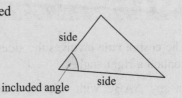

side

included angle    side

---

**Example 15**    ◀⑳ **Self Tutor**

Find the area of triangle ABC:

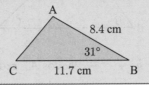

A

8.4 cm

$31^o$

C    11.7 cm    B

Area $= \frac{1}{2}ac\sin B$

$= \frac{1}{2} \times 11.7 \times 8.4 \times \sin 31^o$

$\approx 25.3$ cm$^2$

---

## EXERCISE 13F

**1** Find the area of:

**a**

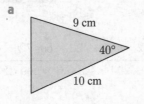

9 cm

$40^o$

10 cm

**b**

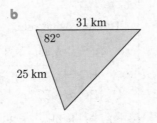

31 km

$82^o$

25 km

**c**

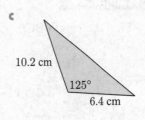

10.2 cm

$125^o$

6.4 cm

**2** If triangle ABC has area 150 cm$^2$, find the value of $x$:

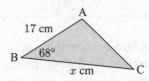

A

17 cm

B  $68^o$

$x$ cm    C

**3** A parallelogram has two adjacent sides of length 4 cm and 6 cm respectively. If the included angle measures $52^o$, find the area of the parallelogram.

**4** A rhombus has sides of length 12 cm and an angle of $72^o$. Find its area.

**5**

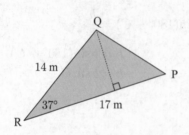

a Find the area of triangle PQR to 3 decimal places.

b Hence, find the length of the altitude from Q to RP.

# G    THE COSINE RULE

The **cosine rule** involves the sides and angles of any triangle. The triangle does not need to contain a right angle.

In any $\triangle ABC$ with sides $a$, $b$ and $c$ units in length, and opposite angles $A$, $B$ and $C$ respectively:

$$a^2 = b^2 + c^2 - 2bc \cos A$$
$$or \quad b^2 = a^2 + c^2 - 2ac \cos B$$
$$or \quad c^2 = a^2 + b^2 - 2ab \cos C$$

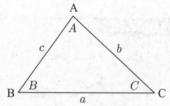

Note that if $A = 90^o$ then $\cos A = 0$ and $a^2 = b^2 + c^2 - 2bc \cos A$ reduces to $a^2 = b^2 + c^2$, which is Pythagoras' theorem.

The cosine rule can be used to solve triangles given:

- **two sides** and an **included angle**
- **three sides**.

---

### Example 16                                            ◀)) **Self Tutor**

Find the length BC:

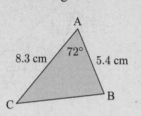

By the cosine rule,

$$BC^2 = 5.4^2 + 8.3^2 - 2 \times 5.4 \times 8.3 \times \cos 72^o$$
$$\therefore \quad BC = \sqrt{5.4^2 + 8.3^2 - 2 \times 5.4 \times 8.3 \times \cos 72^o}$$
$$\therefore \quad BC \approx 8.39 \text{ cm}$$

So, BC is about 8.39 cm long.

---

Rearrangement of the original cosine rule formulae can be used for finding angles if we know all three sides. The formulae for finding the angles are:

$$\cos A = \frac{b^2 + c^2 - a^2}{2bc} \qquad \cos B = \frac{c^2 + a^2 - b^2}{2ca} \qquad \cos C = \frac{a^2 + b^2 - c^2}{2ab}$$

We then need to use the **inverse** cosine ratio $\cos^{-1}$ to evaluate the angle.

**Example 17** ◀)) **Self Tutor**

In triangle ABC, if AB = 7 cm, BC = 5 cm and CA = 8 cm, find the measure of angle BCA.

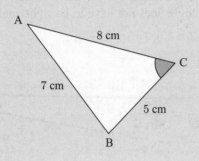

By the cosine rule:

$$\cos C = \frac{(5^2 + 8^2 - 7^2)}{(2 \times 5 \times 8)}$$

$$\therefore \quad C = \cos^{-1}\left(\frac{5^2 + 8^2 - 7^2}{2 \times 5 \times 8}\right)$$

$$\therefore \quad C = 60^o$$

So, angle BCA measures $60^o$.

## EXERCISE 13G

**1**  Find the length of the remaining side in the given triangle:

**a**

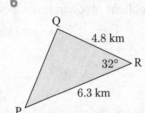

**b**

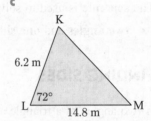

**c**

**2**  Find the measure of all angles of:

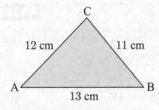

**3**  Find the measure of obtuse angle PQR.

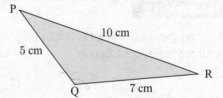

**4**  **a**  Find the smallest angle of a triangle with sides 11 cm, 13 cm and 17 cm.

**b**  Find the largest angle of a triangle with sides 4 cm, 7 cm and 9 cm.

The smallest angle is opposite the shortest side.

**5**  **a**  Find $\cos \theta$ but not $\theta$.

**b**  Find the value of $x$.

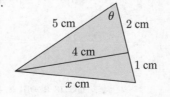

**THE SINE RULE**

The **sine rule** is a set of equations which connects the lengths of the sides of any triangle with the sines of the angles of the triangle. The triangle does not have to be right angled for the sine rule to be used.

In any triangle ABC with sides $a$, $b$ and $c$ units in length, and opposite angles $A$, $B$ and $C$ respectively,

$$\frac{\sin A}{a} = \frac{\sin B}{b} = \frac{\sin C}{c} \quad or \quad \frac{a}{\sin A} = \frac{b}{\sin B} = \frac{c}{\sin C}.$$

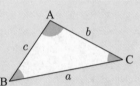

**Proof:**    The area of any triangle ABC is given by   $\frac{1}{2} bc \sin A = \frac{1}{2} ac \sin B = \frac{1}{2} ab \sin C$.

Dividing each expression by $\frac{1}{2} abc$ gives   $\dfrac{\sin A}{a} = \dfrac{\sin B}{b} = \dfrac{\sin C}{c}$.

The sine rule is used to solve problems involving triangles, given:

- **two angles** and **one side**
- **two sides** and a **non-included** angle.

## FINDING SIDES

If two angles of a triangle are known, we can easily find the third angle as the three angles must add to $180^o$. The sine rule can be used to determine the lengths of the other sides.

**Example 18**    ◀) **Self Tutor**

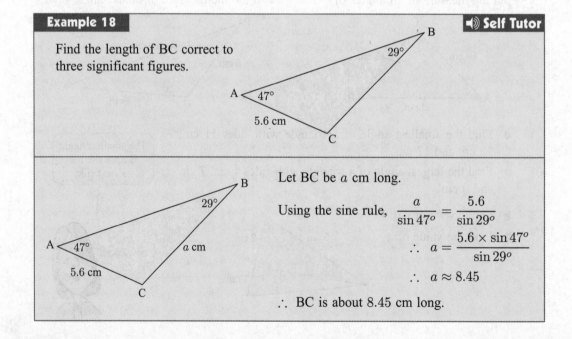

Find the length of BC correct to three significant figures.

Let BC be $a$ cm long.

Using the sine rule,   $\dfrac{a}{\sin 47^o} = \dfrac{5.6}{\sin 29^o}$

$$\therefore \quad a = \frac{5.6 \times \sin 47^o}{\sin 29^o}$$

$$\therefore \quad a \approx 8.45$$

$\therefore$  BC is about 8.45 cm long.

## EXERCISE 13H.1

1 Find the value of $x$:

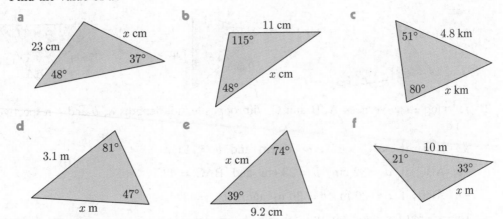

2 In triangle ABC, find:

  a  $a$ if $A = 63°$, $B = 49°$ and $b = 18$ cm

  b  $b$ if $A = 82°$, $C = 25°$ and $c = 34$ cm

  c  $c$ if $B = 21°$, $C = 48°$ and $a = 6.4$ cm.

## FINDING ANGLES

If two sides and a non-included angle are known in a triangle, the sine rule can be used to determine the size of the other angles.

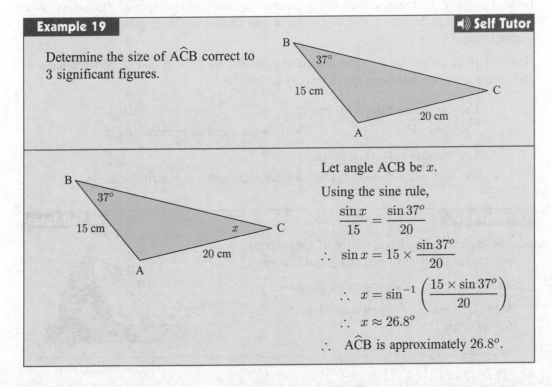

**Example 19**    ◀🔊 **Self Tutor**

Determine the size of $A\widehat{C}B$ correct to 3 significant figures.

Let angle ACB be $x$.

Using the sine rule,

$$\frac{\sin x}{15} = \frac{\sin 37°}{20}$$

$$\therefore \quad \sin x = 15 \times \frac{\sin 37°}{20}$$

$$\therefore \quad x = \sin^{-1}\left(\frac{15 \times \sin 37°}{20}\right)$$

$$\therefore \quad x \approx 26.8°$$

$$\therefore \quad A\widehat{C}B \text{ is approximately } 26.8°.$$

## EXERCISE 13H.2

**1** Find the value of $x$:

**a**

60 cm
30 cm
$x$
20°

**b**

58°
$x$
7 mm
9 mm

**c**

$x$
41°
17 km
14 km

**2** A triangle has vertices A, B and C with opposite side lengths $a$, $b$ and $c$ respectively. Find:

**a** $\hat{BAC}$ if $\hat{ABC} = 45°$, $a = 8$ cm and $b = 11$ cm

**b** $\hat{ABC}$ if $a = 32$ cm, $b = 23$ cm and $\hat{BAC} = 42°$

**c** $\hat{ACB}$ if $c = 30$ m, $b = 36$ m and $\hat{ABC} = 37°$.

**3** Unprepared for class, Mr Whiffen asks his students to determine the size of $x$ in the diagram shown.

**a** Show that Mr Whiffen's question cannot be solved.

**b** Explain what this means about the triangle Mr Whiffen created.

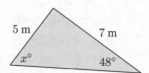

5 m
7 m
$x°$
48°

# I    USING THE SINE AND COSINE RULES

If we are given a problem involving a triangle, we must first decide which rule to use.

If the triangle is right angled then the trigonometric ratios or Pythagoras' Theorem can be used. For some problems we can add an extra line or two to the diagram to create a right angled triangle.

However, if we do not have a right angled triangle and we have to choose between the sine and cosine rules, the following checklist may be helpful:

> Use the **cosine rule** when given:
> - three sides
> - two sides and an included angle.
>
> Use the **sine rule** when given:
> - one side and two angles
> - two sides and a non-included angle.

---

| **Example 20** | ◀) **Self Tutor** |

The angles of elevation to the top of a mountain are measured from two beacons A and B at sea.

These angles are as shown on the diagram.

If the beacons are 1473 m apart, how high is the mountain?

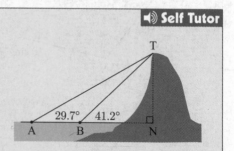

T
29.7°   41.2°
A      B      N

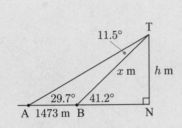

$\widehat{ATB} = 41.2^o - 29.7^o$ {exterior angle of $\Delta$}

$\quad\quad = 11.5^o$

We find $x$ in $\Delta ABT$ using the sine rule:

$$\frac{x}{\sin 29.7^o} = \frac{1473}{\sin 11.5^o}$$

$$\therefore \quad x = \frac{1473}{\sin 11.5^o} \times \sin 29.7^o$$

$$\approx 3660.62$$

Now, in $\Delta BNT$, $\quad \sin 41.2^o = \frac{h}{x} \approx \frac{h}{3660.62}$

$\therefore \quad h \approx \sin 41.2^o \times 3660.62$

$\therefore \quad h \approx 2410$

So, the mountain is about 2410 m high.

---

**Example 21**

Find the measure of angle RPV.

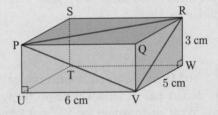

In $\Delta RVW$, $\quad RV = \sqrt{5^2 + 3^2} = \sqrt{34}$ cm. {Pythagoras}

In $\Delta PUV$, $\quad PV = \sqrt{6^2 + 3^2} = \sqrt{45}$ cm. {Pythagoras}

In $\Delta PQR$, $\quad PR = \sqrt{6^2 + 5^2} = \sqrt{61}$ cm. {Pythagoras}

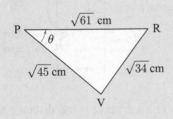

By rearrangement of the cosine rule,

$$\cos \theta = \frac{(\sqrt{61})^2 + (\sqrt{45})^2 - (\sqrt{34})^2}{2\sqrt{61}\sqrt{45}}$$

$$= \frac{61 + 45 - 34}{2\sqrt{61}\sqrt{45}}$$

$$= \frac{72}{2\sqrt{61}\sqrt{45}}$$

$$\therefore \quad \theta = \cos^{-1}\left(\frac{36}{\sqrt{61}\sqrt{45}}\right) \approx 46.6^o$$

$\therefore$ angle RPV measures about $46.6^o$.

## EXERCISE 13I

**1** Rodrigo wishes to determine the height of a flagpole. He takes a sighting to the top of the flagpole from point P. He then moves further away from the flagpole by 20 metres to point Q and takes a second sighting. The information is shown in the diagram alongside. How high is the flagpole?

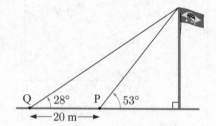

**2**

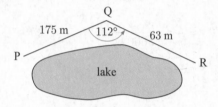

To get from P to R, a park ranger had to walk along a path to Q and then to R as shown. What is the distance in a straight line from P to R?

**3** A golfer played his tee shot a distance of 220 m to point A. He then played a 165 m six iron to the green. If the distance from tee to green is 340 m, determine the number of degrees the golfer was off line with his tee shot.

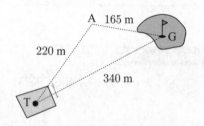

**4** Two yachts P and Q are anchored at different locations at sea. A beacon at B determines P and Q are 24 km and 21 km away respectively. The yacht at Q measures B and P to be 53° apart. What angle would the yacht at P measure between B and Q?

**5** A football goal is 5 metres wide. When a player is 26 metres from one goal post and 23 metres from the other, he shoots for goal. What is the angle of view of the goals that the player sees?

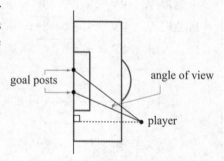

**6** A tower 42 metres high stands on top of a hill. From a point some distance from the base of the hill, the angle of elevation to the top of the tower is 13.2° and the angle of elevation to the bottom of the tower is 8.3°. Find the height of the hill.

**7** From the foot of a building I have to look upwards at an angle of 22° to sight the top of a tree. From the top of the building, 150 metres above ground level, I have to look down at an angle of 50° below the horizontal to sight the tree top.

    **a** How high is the tree?    **b** How far from the building is this tree?

**8**

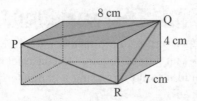
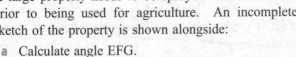

Find the measure of angle PQR in the rectangular box shown.

**9** A large property needs to be sprayed with insecticide prior to being used for agriculture. An incomplete sketch of the property is shown alongside:

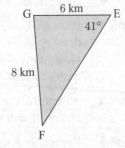

  **a** Calculate angle EFG.

  **b** Hence, determine the cost of spraying the property if insecticide costs £400 per square kilometre.

**10** Two observation posts are 12 km apart at A and B. A third observation post C is located such that angle CAB is 42° and angle CBA is 67°. Find the distance of C from both A and B.

**11** Stan and Olga are considering buying a sheep farm. A surveyor has supplied them with the given accurate sketch. Find the area of the property, giving your answer in:

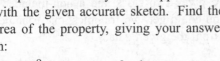

  **a** km²            **b** hectares.

**12** Thabo and Palesa start at point A. They each walk in a straight line at an angle of 120° to each other. Thabo walks at 6 km h⁻¹ and Palesa walks at 8 km h⁻¹. How far apart are they after 45 minutes?

**13** The cross-section design of the kerbing for a driverless-bus roadway is shown opposite. The metal strip is inlaid into the concrete and is used to control the direction and speed of the bus. Find the width of the metal strip.

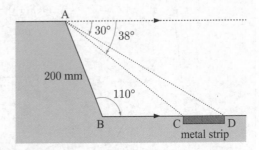

# J    THE AMBIGUOUS CASE (EXTENSION)

The problem of finding angles using the sine rule can be complicated because there may be two possible answers. We call this situation the **ambiguous case**.

DEMO

You can click on the icon to obtain an interactive demonstration of the ambiguous case, or else you can work through the following investigation.

## INVESTIGATION 3             THE AMBIGUOUS CASE

 You will need a blank sheet of paper, a ruler, a protractor, and a compass for the tasks that follow. In each task you will be required to construct triangles from given information. You could also do this using a computer package such as 'The Geometer's Sketchpad'.

**Task 1:**    Draw AB = 10 cm. At A construct an angle of 30°. Using B as the centre, draw an arc of a circle of radius 6 cm. Let the arc intersect the ray from A at C. How many different positions may C have, and therefore how many different triangles ABC may be constructed?

**Task 2:**    As before, draw AB = 10 cm and construct a 30° angle at A. This time draw an arc of radius 5 cm centred at B. How many different triangles are possible?

**Task 3:**    Repeat, but this time draw an arc of radius 3 cm centred at B. How many different triangles are possible?

**Task 4:**    Repeat with an arc of radius 12 cm from B. How many triangles are possible now?

You should have discovered that when you are given two sides and a non-included angle there are a number of different possibilities. You could get two triangles, one triangle, or it may be impossible to draw any triangles at all from the given data.

---

### Example 22        ◀) Self Tutor

Find the measure of angle $C$ in triangle ABC if AC = 7 cm, AB = 11 cm, and angle $B$ measures 25°.

Using the sine rule,

$$\frac{\sin C}{c} = \frac{\sin B}{b}$$

$$\therefore \ \frac{\sin C}{11} = \frac{\sin 25^o}{7}$$

$$\therefore \ \sin C = \frac{11 \times \sin 25^o}{7}$$

$$\therefore \ C = \sin^{-1}\left(\frac{11 \times \sin 25^o}{7}\right) \quad \text{or its supplement}$$

> Supplementary angles add up to 180°.

$$\therefore \ C \approx 41.6^o \ \text{or} \ 180^o - 41.6^o$$

$$\{\text{as } C \text{ may be obtuse}\}$$

$$\therefore \ C \approx 41.6^o \ \text{or} \ 138.4^o$$

$\therefore$   $C$ measures 41.6° if angle $C$ is acute, or 138.4° if angle $C$ is obtuse.

In this case there is insufficient information to determine the actual shape of the triangle.

---

Sometimes there is information in the question which enables us to **reject** one of the answers.

**Example 23**

◀) Self Tutor

Find the measure of angle $L$ in triangle KLM given that angle LKM measures $56^o$, LM = 16.8 m, and KM = 13.5 m.

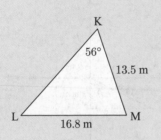

$$\frac{\sin L}{13.5} = \frac{\sin 56^o}{16.8} \qquad \text{\{by the sine rule\}}$$

$$\therefore \quad \sin L = \frac{13.5 \times \sin 56^o}{16.8}$$

$$\therefore \quad L = \sin^{-1}\left(\frac{13.5 \times \sin 56^o}{16.8}\right) \quad \text{or its supplement}$$

$$\therefore \quad L \approx 41.8^o \ \text{ or } \ 180^o - 41.8^o$$

$$\therefore \quad L \approx 41.8^o \ \text{ or } \ 138.2^o$$

We reject $L \approx 138.2^o$, since $138.2^o + 56^o > 180^o$ which is impossible.

$\therefore \quad L \approx 41.8^o$.

## EXERCISE 13J

1 Triangle ABC has angle $B = 40^o$, $b = 8$ cm, and $c = 11$ cm. Find the two possible values for angle $C$.

2 Find the measure of angle $P$ in triangle PQR given that angle $Q$ measures $34^o$, PR = 10 cm, and QR = 7 cm.

3 In triangle ABC, find the measure of:

   **a** angle $A$ if $a = 13.8$ cm, $b = 16.5$ cm and $A\widehat{B}C = 43^o$

   **b** angle $B$ if $b = 27.9$ m, $c = 20.4$ m and $A\widehat{C}B = 36^o$

   **c** angle $C$ if $a = 7.7$ km, $c = 8.1$ km and $B\widehat{A}C = 71^o$.

4 Is it possible to have a triangle with the measurements shown? Explain your answer.

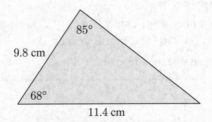

## BEARINGS (EXTENSION)

We have previously seen **true bearings** in **Chapter 6**, where we used Pythagoras' theorem to solve bearing problems which involved right angled triangles. We will now use trigonometry to solve more complicated bearing problems, including some involving non-right angled triangles.

### Example 24

◀) **Self Tutor**

A boat travels 30 km on a bearing 243°T. How far south of its starting point is it?

$\theta = 243° - 180° = 63°$

The distance we need to find is $x$.

Now $\cos 63° = \dfrac{x}{30}$

$\therefore \quad x = 30 \times \cos 63°$

$\therefore \quad x \approx 13.6$

So, the boat is 13.6 km south of its starting point.

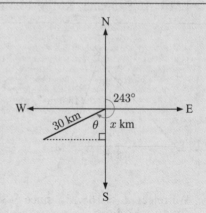

## EXERCISE 13K

**1** Richard cycles 10 km on a bearing 041°T. How far north of his starting point is he?

**2** An aeroplane flies 200 km on a course 137°T. How far east of its starting point is the aeroplane now?

**3** An athlete starts running in the direction 063°T. After 45 minutes he is 4300 m north of his starting point. Find the athlete's average speed in $km\,h^{-1}$.

**4** A train travels a distance of 15 km. It is now 9 km west and 12 km north of its starting point. Find the direction in which the train travelled.

### Example 25

◀) **Self Tutor**

Gus walks from camp S for 12.2 km in the direction 123°, then for 8.9 km in the direction 226° to camp F. Find:

**a** the distance from F to S   **b** the bearing of F from S.

**a**

```
        ▲N₁
        |
     123°|
    S ╲  |
    α°╲  12.2 km
       ╲      ▲N₂
        ╲     |
         ╲   θ°|
    x km  ╲  φ°|
           ╲   226°
            ╲8.9 km
             ╲|
              F
```

$\theta + 123 = 180$ {cointerior angles}

$\therefore \quad \theta = 57$

But $\phi + \theta + 226 = 360$ {angles at a point}

$\therefore \quad \phi + 57 + 226 = 360$

$\therefore \quad \phi = 77$

Using the cosine rule,

$x^2 = 8.9^2 + 12.2^2 - 2 \times 8.9 \times 12.2 \times \cos 77°$

$\therefore \quad x^2 \approx 179.199\,629$

$\therefore \quad x \approx 13.39$

The distance from F to S is about 13.4 km.

**b** We require angle $\alpha$.

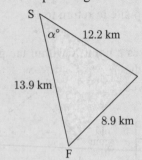

Using the cosine rule,

$$\therefore \cos\alpha^o = \frac{12.2^2 + 13.39^o - 8.9^2}{2 \times 12.2 \times 13.39}$$

$$\therefore \cos\alpha^o \approx 0.761891$$

$$\therefore \alpha \approx 40.4^o$$

and $\alpha + 123 \approx 163.4$

So, the bearing of F from S is $163^o$.

**5** In the diagram given, find the bearing of:

  **a** B from A     **b** B from C

  **c** A from B     **d** A from C.

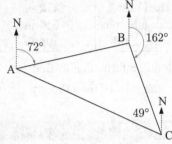

**6** A yacht sails 6 km in the direction $127^o$, then 4 km in the direction $068^o$. Find the:

  **a** distance of the yacht from its starting point

  **b** bearing of the yacht from its starting point.

**7** An aircraft takes off from an airport and flies 400 km in the direction $040^oT$. It then changes course and flies in the direction $160^oT$ until it is 500 km from the airport.

  **a** What is the direction of the airport from the aircraft's final position?

  **b** How far did it fly along the second leg of the journey?

**8** A man walks a distance of 8 km in the direction $236^oT$. He then walks due east for 20 km. What is the distance and bearing of the man from his starting point?

**9** Two cyclists depart from the same point. One travels due east at $18 \text{ km h}^{-1}$ while the other travels north west at $20 \text{ km h}^{-1}$. How long, to the nearest minute, will it be before they are 80 km apart?

**10** Hikers Ritva and Esko leave point P at the same time. Ritva walks 4 km on a bearing of $040^o$ and then walks a further 6 km on a bearing of $155^o$. Esko hikes directly from P to the camp site.

  **a**  **i** How far does Esko hike?

     **ii** In which direction does Esko hike?

  **b** Ritva hikes at $10 \text{ km h}^{-1}$ and Esko hikes at $6 \text{ km h}^{-1}$.

     **i** Who will arrive at the camp site first?

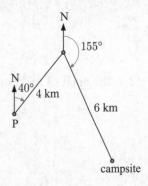

ii How long will this person need to wait before the other person arrives?

c On what bearing should they walk from the camp site to return to P?

11 Anna has her property surveyed. The surveyor chooses a point X within the property and uses his laser device to measure the distances of the boundary corners from X. The surveyor also gives bearings of the corner points from X.

| Corner | Distance from X | Bearing from X |
|--------|-----------------|----------------|
| pine corner | 368 m | 048 |
| road post 2 | 439 m | 132 |
| road post 1 | 412 m | 213 |
| old gum tree | 516 m | 280 |
| windmill | 508 m | 343 |

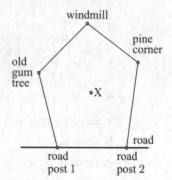

Use this information to find:

a the area of the property

b the perimeter of the property.

## REVIEW SET 13A

**1**

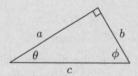

For the triangle alongside, find:

a the hypotenuse

b the side adjacent to $\phi$

c $\sin \theta$

d $\tan \phi$

**2** Find the value of $x$:

a

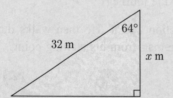

b

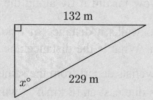

**3** Find the measure of all unknown sides and angles in triangle CDE:

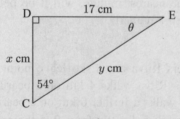

**4** Find $\theta$, the pitch of the roof.

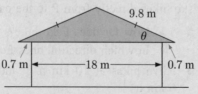

**5**  A ship sails 40 km on the bearing 056°. How far is it north of its starting point?

**6**  Two identical buildings stand opposite each other, as shown alongside. Find the angle of depression from A to B.

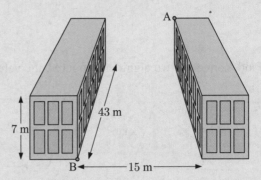

**7**  Determine the area of:

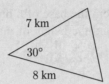

**8**  Determine the value of $x$:

**a**

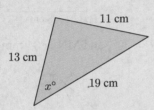

**b**

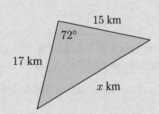

**9**  Find the unknown side and angles:

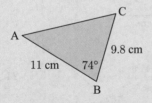

**10**  Find the area of quadrilateral ABCD:

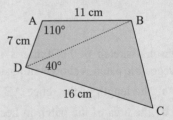

**11**  Peter, Sue and Alix are sea-kayaking. Peter is 430 m from Sue on a bearing of 113°, while Alix is on a bearing of 210° and a distance 310 m from Sue. Find the distance and bearing of Peter from Alix.

## REVIEW SET 13B

**1**  Find $\sin \theta$, $\cos \theta$ and $\tan \theta$ for the triangle:

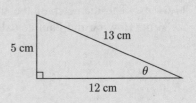

**2**  Find the lengths of the unknown sides:

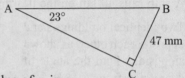

**3**  Find, correct to two significant figures, the value of $x$ in:

**a**

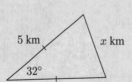

**b**

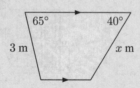

**c**

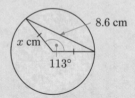

**4**  From a point 120 m horizontally from the base of a building, the angle of elevation to the top of the building is $34°$. Find the height of the building.

**5**  Find the angle that:

   **a**  AH makes with HG.

   **b**  DF makes with the base plane EFGH.

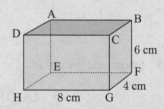

**6**  Triangle LMN has area 184 mm$^2$, angle LMN $= 20°$, and MN is 34 mm long. Find the length of LM.

**7**  Find the measure of angle RST.

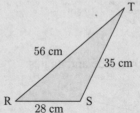

**8**  Jason's sketch of his father's triangular vegetable patch is shown alongside. Find:

   **a**  the length of the fence AB.

   **b**  the area of the patch in hectares.

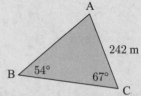

**9**  Paul 'puts' a shot put from the front of the throwing circle. It only just lands inside the $40°$ throwing boundaries.

The official measurement goes from the shot to the nearest point of the throwing circle, and reads 17.64 m. The diameter of the throwing circle is 2.135 m. How far did Paul actually put the shot?

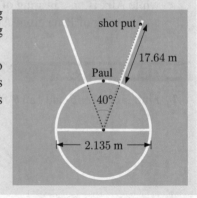

**10**  A vertical tree is growing on the side of a hill with gradient $10°$ to the horizontal. From a point 50 m downhill from the tree, the angle of elevation to the top of the tree is $18°$. Find the height of the tree.

**11**  Find the measure of:

    **a**  angle $D$ in triangle DEF if $d = 35$ m, $e = 40$ m, and $\widehat{DEF} = 61°$

    **b**  angle $J$ in triangle IJK if $i = 5.9$ cm, $j = 8.2$ cm, and $\widehat{JIK} = 37°$.

## REVIEW SET 13C

**1**  Use your calculator to find, correct to 4 decimal places:

    **a**  $\cos 74°$           **b**  $\sin 132°$           **c**  $\tan 97°$.

**2**  Find the value of $x$ in the following:

    **a** 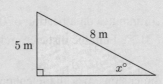         **b**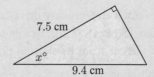

**3**  Find the measure of all unknown sides and angles in triangle KLM:

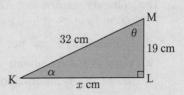

**4**  A sports cone has a vertical angle of $28°$. A tennis ball of diameter 65.5 mm is dropped into the cone. How far up the side of the cone does it sit?

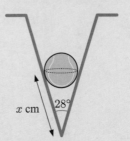

**5**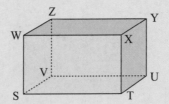

Name:

    **a**  the projection of ZS onto the base plane STUV

    **b**  the angle between XS and the base plane

    **c**  the angle between UW and the base plane.

**6**  The figure alongside is a square-based pyramid. Find:

    **a**  $\widehat{ADM}$         **b**  $\widehat{ACD}$.

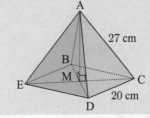

**7** Anke and Lucas are considering buying a block of land. The land agent supplies them with the given accurate sketch. Find the area of the property, giving your answer in:

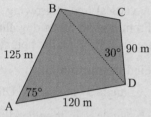

**a**  m$^2$                **b**  hectares.

**8** From point A, the angle of elevation to the top of a tall building is 20°. On walking 80 m towards the building, the angle of elevation is now 23°. How tall is the building?

**9** Find the measure of angle EDG:

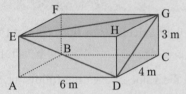

**10** A family in Germany drives at 140 km h$^{-1}$ for 45 minutes on a bearing of 032° and then 180 km h$^{-1}$ for 40 minutes on a bearing of 317°. Find the distance and bearing of the car from its starting point.

**11** Soil contractor Frank was given the following dimensions over the telephone:
The triangular garden plot ABC has angle CAB measuring 44°, AC is 8 m long, and BC is 6 m long. Soil to a depth of 10 cm is required.

**a** Explain why Frank needs extra information from his client.

**b** What is the maximum volume of soil needed if his client is unable to supply the necessary information?

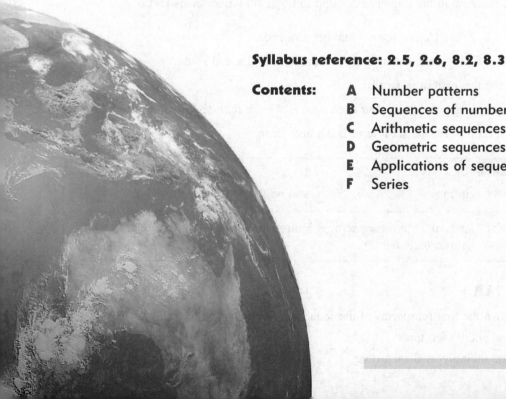

# Chapter **14**

# Sequences and series

**Syllabus reference:** 2.5, 2.6, 8.2, 8.3

**Contents:**    **A**    Number patterns
             **B**    Sequences of numbers
             **C**    Arithmetic sequences
             **D**    Geometric sequences
             **E**    Applications of sequences
             **F**    Series

## OPENING PROBLEM

Vicki has 30 days to train for a swimming competition.

She swims 20 laps on the first day, then each day after that she swims two more laps than the previous day. So, she swims 22 laps on the second day, 24 laps on the third day, and so on.

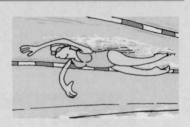

**Things to think about:**

**a**  How many laps does Vicki swim on:    **i**  the tenth day    **ii**  the final day?

**b**  How many laps does Vicki swim in total?

To solve problems like the **Opening Problem** and many others, we need to study **sequences** and their sums which are called **series**.

## A | NUMBER PATTERNS

In mathematics it is important that we can:
- **recognise** a pattern in a set of numbers
- **describe** the pattern in words, and
- **continue** the pattern.

A list of numbers where there is a pattern is called a **number sequence**.
The numbers in the sequence are said to be its **members** or its **terms**.

For example,   3, 7, 11, 15, ....  form a number sequence.

The first term is 3, the second term is 7, the third term is 11, and so on.

We can describe this pattern in words:

"*The sequence starts at 3 and each term is 4 more than the previous one.*"

Thus, the fifth term is 19, the sixth term is 23, and so on.

| Example 1 | ◀ Self Tutor |
|---|---|

Describe the sequence:   14, 17, 20, 23, ....  and write down the next two terms.

The sequence starts at 14 and each term is 3 more than the previous term.
The next two terms are 26 and 29.

## EXERCISE 14A

**1**  Write down the first four terms of the sequence if you start with:

**a**  4 and add 9 each time

**b**  45 and subtract 6 each time

**c**  2 and multiply by 3 each time

**d**  96 and divide by 2 each time.

**2** For each of the following write a description of the sequence and find the next 2 terms:

    **a** 8, 16, 24, 32, ....        **b** 2, 5, 8, 11, ....        **c** 36, 31, 26, 21, ....

    **d** 96, 89, 82, 75, ....     **e** 1, 4, 16, 64, ....       **f** 2, 6, 18, 54, ....

    **g** 480, 240, 120, 60, ....   **h** 243, 81, 27, 9, ....    **i** 50 000, 10 000, 2000, 400, ....

**3** Describe the following number patterns and write down the next 3 terms:

    **a** 1, 4, 9, 16, ....        **b** 1, 8, 27, 64, ....     **c** 2, 6, 12, 20, ....

**4** Find the next two terms of:

    **a** 95, 91, 87, 83, ....     **b** 5, 20, 80, 320, ....   **c** 1, 16, 81, 256, ....

    **d** 16, 8, 4, 2, ....       **e** 2, 3, 5, 7, 11, ....    **f** 2, 4, 7, 11, ....

# B    SEQUENCES OF NUMBERS

A **number sequence** is a set of numbers defined by a rule that is valid for positive integers.

A number sequence is a function whose domain is the set of positive integers.

Sequences may be defined in one of the following ways:

- listing the first few terms and assuming that the pattern represented continues indefinitely
- giving a description in words
- using a formula which represents the **general term** (or $n$**th term**).

Consider the illustrated tower of bricks. The first row has three bricks, the second row has four bricks, and the third row has five bricks.

If $u_n$ represents the number of bricks in row $n$ (from the top) then $u_1 = 3$, $u_2 = 4$, $u_3 = 5$, $u_4 = 6$, ....

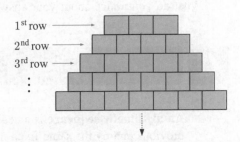

This sequence can be specified by:

- **listing terms**             3, 4, 5, 6, ....

- **using words**            "The top row has three bricks and each successive row under it has one more brick."

- **using an explicit formula**   $u_n = n + 2$ is the **general term** or $n$**th term** formula for  $n = 1, 2, 3, 4, 5, ....$

                          *Check:*  $u_1 = 1 + 2 = 3$ ✓    $u_2 = 2 + 2 = 4$ ✓

                                      $u_3 = 3 + 2 = 5$ ✓

- **a pictorial or graphical representation**

    Early members of a sequence can be graphed with each represented by a dot.

    The dots *must not* be joined because $n$ must be an integer.

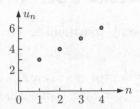

## THE GENERAL TERM

$u_n$, $T_n$, $t_n$, $A_n$, and so on can all be used to represent the **general term** or **$n$th term** of a sequence. The general term is defined for $n = 1, 2, 3, 4, 5, 6, \ldots$.

$\{u_n\}$ represents the sequence that can be generated by using $u_n$ as the **$n$th term**.

For example, $\{2n + 1\}$ represents the sequence $3, 5, 7, 9, 11, \ldots$.

## EXERCISE 14B

**1** List the first *five* terms of the sequence:

    **a** $\{2n\}$         **b** $\{2n + 2\}$         **c** $\{2n - 1\}$         **d** $\{2n - 3\}$

    **e** $\{2n + 3\}$         **f** $\{2n + 11\}$        **g** $\{3n + 1\}$         **h** $\{4n - 3\}$

**2** List the first *five* terms of the sequence:

    **a** $\{2^n\}$         **b** $\{3 \times 2^n\}$         **c** $\{6 \times (\tfrac{1}{2})^n\}$        **d** $\{(-2)^n\}$

**3** List the first *five* terms of the sequence $\{15 - (-2)^n\}$.

**4** List the terms of these sequences:

    **a** start with 5 and add 3 each time           **b** $\{2 + 3n\}$

    **c** start with 100 and take 7 each time       **d** $\{107 - 7n\}$

    **e** start with 5 and multiply successively by 2    **f** $\{5 \times 2^{n-1}\}$

    **g** start with 48 and multiply successively by $\tfrac{1}{2}$   **h** $\{48 \times (\tfrac{1}{2})^{n-1}\}$

    What do you notice about your answers?

## C     ARITHMETIC SEQUENCES

An **arithmetic sequence** is a sequence in which each term differs from the previous one by the same fixed number.

For example:

- the tower of bricks in the previous section forms an arithmetic sequence where the difference between terms is 1
- $2, 5, 8, 11, 14, \ldots$ is arithmetic as $5 - 2 = 8 - 5 = 11 - 8 = 14 - 11 \ldots$
- $31, 27, 23, 19, \ldots$ is arithmetic as $27 - 31 = 23 - 27 = 19 - 23 \ldots$

## ALGEBRAIC DEFINITION

$\{u_n\}$ is **arithmetic** $\Leftrightarrow$ $u_{n+1} - u_n = d$   for all positive integers $n$ where $d$ is a constant called the **common difference**.

The symbol $\Leftrightarrow$ is read as 'if and only if'. It implies that if $\{u_n\}$ is arithmetic then $u_{n+1} - u_n$ is a constant *and* if $u_{n+1} - u_n$ is a constant then $\{u_n\}$ is arithmetic.

## THE NAME 'ARITHMETIC'

If $a$, $b$ and $c$ are any consecutive terms of an arithmetic sequence then

$$b - a = c - b \qquad \text{\{equating common differences\}}$$
$$\therefore \quad 2b = a + c$$
$$\therefore \quad b = \frac{a + c}{2}$$

So, the middle term is the **arithmetic mean** of the terms on either side of it.

## THE GENERAL TERM FORMULA

Suppose the first term of an arithmetic sequence is $u_1$ and the common difference is $d$.

Then $\quad u_2 = u_1 + d, \quad u_3 = u_1 + 2d, \quad u_4 = u_1 + 3d, \quad$ and so on.

$$\text{Hence} \quad u_n = u_1 + \underbrace{(n - 1)}d$$

The *coefficient* of $d$ is one less than the *term number*.

> For an **arithmetic sequence** with **first term $u_1$** and **common difference $d$**
> the **general term** or **$n$th term** is $\qquad u_n = u_1 + (n - 1)d$.

---

**Example 2**    ◀)) **Self Tutor**

Consider the sequence    $2, 9, 16, 23, 30, \, ....$

a  Show that the sequence is arithmetic.

b  Find the formula for the general term $u_n$.

c  Find the 100th term of the sequence.

d  Is   i   828   ii   2341   a member of the sequence?

---

a $\quad 9 - 2 = 7 \qquad$ So, assuming that the pattern continues,

$\quad 16 - 9 = 7 \qquad$ consecutive terms differ by 7.

$\quad 23 - 16 = 7 \qquad \therefore \quad$ the sequence is arithmetic with $u_1 = 2, \quad d = 7$.

$\quad 30 - 23 = 7$

b $\quad u_n = u_1 + (n - 1)d \qquad \therefore \quad u_n = 2 + 7(n - 1)$
$\qquad\qquad\qquad\qquad\qquad\quad \therefore \quad u_n = 7n - 5$

c  If $\quad n = 100, \quad u_{100} = 7(100) - 5 = 695$.

d  i $\quad$ Let $\quad u_n = 828 \qquad\qquad$ ii $\quad$ Let $\quad u_n = 2341$

$\qquad \therefore \quad 7n - 5 = 828 \qquad\qquad\qquad \therefore \quad 7n - 5 = 2341$

$\qquad \therefore \quad 7n = 833 \qquad\qquad\qquad\qquad \therefore \quad 7n = 2346$

$\qquad \therefore \quad n = 119 \qquad\qquad\qquad\qquad \therefore \quad n = 335\tfrac{1}{7}$

$\qquad \therefore \quad$ 828 is a term of the sequence. $\qquad$ which is not possible as $n$ must

$\qquad$ In fact it is the 119th term. $\qquad\qquad$ be an integer.

$\qquad\qquad\qquad\qquad\qquad\qquad\qquad\qquad \therefore \quad$ 2341 cannot be a term.

## EXERCISE 14C

**1** Find the 10th term of each of the following arithmetic sequences:

    **a**   19, 25, 31, 37, ....      **b**   101, 97, 93, 89, ....      **c**   $8, 9\frac{1}{2}, 11, 12\frac{1}{2}$, ....

**2** Find the 15th term of each of the following arithmetic sequences:

    **a**   31, 36, 41, 46, ....                  **b**   5, −3, −11, −19, ....

    **c**   $a, a + d, a + 2d, a + 3d$, ....

**3** Consider the sequence   6, 17, 28, 39, 50, ....

    **a**   Show that the sequence is arithmetic.    **b**   Find the formula for its general term.

    **c**   Find its 50th term.                     **d**   Is 325 a member?

    **e**   Is 761 a member?

**4** Consider the sequence 87, 83, 79, 75, ....

    **a**   Show that the sequence is arithmetic.    **b**   Find the formula for its general term.

    **c**   Find the 40th term.                  **d**   Which term of the sequence is −297?

**5** A sequence is defined by   $u_n = 3n - 2$.

    **a**   Prove that the sequence is arithmetic.   **Hint:**   Find   $u_{n+1} - u_n$.

    **b**   Find $u_1$ and $d$.                  **c**   Find the 57th term.

    **d**   What is the least term of the sequence which is greater than 450?

**6** A sequence is defined by   $u_n = \dfrac{71 - 7n}{2}$.

    **a**   Prove that the sequence is arithmetic.    **b**   Find $u_1$ and $d$.    **c**   Find   $u_{75}$.

    **d**   For what values of $n$ are the terms of the sequence less than −200?

---

| **Example 3** | ◀ᴺ **Self Tutor** |
|---|---|

Find $k$ given that $3k + 1$, $k$ and $-3$ are consecutive terms of an arithmetic sequence.

Since the terms are consecutive,   $k - (3k + 1) = -3 - k$      {equating differences}

$$\therefore \quad k - 3k - 1 = -3 - k$$
$$\therefore \quad -2k - 1 = -3 - k$$
$$\therefore \quad -1 + 3 = -k + 2k$$
$$\therefore \quad k = 2$$

---

**7** Find $k$ given the consecutive arithmetic terms:

    **a**   32, $k$, 3           **b**   $k$, 7, 10           **c**   $k + 1, 2k + 1, 13$

    **d**   $k - 1, 2k + 3, 7 - k$    **e**   $2k + 7, 3k + 5, 5k - 4$    **f**   $2k + 18, -2 - k, 2k + 2$

**8** Find $k$ given the following consecutive terms of an arithmetic sequence:

    **a**   $k, k^2, k^2 + 6$         **b**   $4k - k^2, 3k, 3$         **c**   $5, k, k^2 - 8$

**Example 4**    ◀) **Self Tutor**

Find the general term $u_n$ for an arithmetic sequence with $u_3 = 8$ and $u_8 = -17$.

$u_3 = 8$ $\qquad \therefore \quad u_1 + 2d = 8$ $\qquad$ .... (1) $\qquad$ {using $u_n = u_1 + (n-1)d$}

$u_8 = -17$ $\quad \therefore \quad u_1 + 7d = -17$ $\qquad$ .... (2)

We now solve (1) and (2) simultaneously:

$-u_1 - 2d = -8$ $\qquad$ {multiplying both sides of (1) by $-1$}

$\underline{u_1 + 7d = -17}$

$\therefore \quad 5d = -25$ $\qquad$ {adding the equations}

$\therefore \quad d = -5$

So, in (1):

$u_1 + 2(-5) = 8$ $\qquad\qquad$ *Check:*

$\therefore \quad u_1 - 10 = 8$ $\qquad\qquad u_3 = 23 - 5(3)$

$\therefore \quad u_1 = 18$ $\qquad\qquad\qquad = 23 - 15$

Now $\quad u_n = u_1 + (n-1)d$ $\qquad\quad = 8$ ✓

$\therefore \quad u_n = 18 - 5(n-1)$ $\qquad u_8 = 23 - 5(8)$

$\therefore \quad u_n = 18 - 5n + 5$ $\qquad\qquad = 23 - 40$

$\therefore \quad u_n = 23 - 5n$ $\qquad\qquad\quad = -17$ ✓

> To solve simultaneous equations, use substitution, elimination, or technology.

**9** Find the general term $u_n$ for an arithmetic sequence given that:

**a** $u_7 = 41$ and $u_{13} = 77$ $\qquad\qquad$ **b** $u_5 = -2$ and $u_{12} = -12\frac{1}{2}$

**c** the seventh term is 1 and the fifteenth term is $-39$

**d** the eleventh and eighth terms are $-16$ and $-11\frac{1}{2}$ respectively.

**Example 5**    ◀) **Self Tutor**

Insert four numbers between 3 and 12 so that all six numbers are in arithmetic sequence.

If the numbers are $\quad 3, \ 3+d, \ 3+2d, \ 3+3d, \ 3+4d, \ 12$

then $\quad 3 + 5d = 12$

$\therefore \quad 5d = 9$

$\therefore \quad d = \frac{9}{5} = 1.8$

So, we have $\quad 3, 4.8, 6.6, 8.4, 10.2, 12.$

**10** **a** Insert three numbers between 5 and 10 so that all five numbers are in arithmetic sequence.

**b** Insert six numbers between $-1$ and 32 so that all eight numbers are in arithmetic sequence.

**11** Consider the finite arithmetic sequence $36, 35\frac{1}{3}, 34\frac{2}{3}, ...., -30.$

**a** Find $u_1$ and $d$. $\qquad\qquad$ **b** How many terms does the sequence have?

**12**  An arithmetic sequence starts  23, 36, 49, 62, ....   What is the first term of the sequence to exceed 100 000?

# D          GEOMETRIC SEQUENCES

A sequence is **geometric** if each term can be obtained from the previous one by multiplying by the same non-zero constant.

For example:   2, 10, 50, 250, ....  is a geometric sequence as

$$2 \times 5 = 10 \quad \text{and} \quad 10 \times 5 = 50 \quad \text{and} \quad 50 \times 5 = 250.$$

Notice that  $\frac{10}{2} = \frac{50}{10} = \frac{250}{50} = 5$,  so each term divided by the previous one gives the same constant.

## ALGEBRAIC DEFINITION

$\{u_n\}$ is **geometric**  $\Leftrightarrow$  $\dfrac{u_{n+1}}{u_n} = r$   for all positive integers $n$

where $r$ is a **constant** called the **common ratio**.

For example:   • 2, 10, 50, 250, ....      is geometric with  $r = 5$.
              • 2, $-10$, 50, $-250$, ....  is geometric with  $r = -5$.

## THE NAME 'GEOMETRIC'

If $a$, $b$ and $c$ are any consecutive terms of a geometric sequence then  $\dfrac{b}{a} = \dfrac{c}{b}$.

$\therefore$  $b^2 = ac$  and so  $b = \pm\sqrt{ac}$  where $\sqrt{ac}$ is the **geometric mean** of $a$ and $c$.

## THE GENERAL TERM

Suppose the first term of a geometric sequence is $u_1$ and the common ratio is $r$.

Then  $u_2 = u_1 r$,   $u_3 = u_1 r^2$,   $u_4 = u_1 r^3$,   and so on.

Hence  $u_n = u_1 r^{n-1}$

The *power* of $r$ is one less than the *term number*.

For a **geometric sequence** with **first term** $u_1$ and **common ratio** $r$,
the **general term** or $n$th **term** is      $u_n = u_1 r^{n-1}$.

### Example 6                                                   ◀) Self Tutor

For the sequence   8, 4, 2, 1, $\frac{1}{2}$, ....

 **a**  Show that the sequence is geometric.       **b**  Find the general term $u_n$.
 **c**  Hence, find the 12th term as a fraction.

a   $\dfrac{4}{8} = \dfrac{1}{2}$    $\dfrac{2}{4} = \dfrac{1}{2}$    $\dfrac{1}{2} = \dfrac{1}{2}$    $\dfrac{\frac{1}{2}}{1} = \dfrac{1}{2}$

So, assuming the pattern continues, consecutive terms have a common ratio of $\frac{1}{2}$.

∴  the sequence is geometric with  $u_1 = 8$  and  $r = \frac{1}{2}$.

b   $u_n = u_1 r^{n-1}$    ∴  $u_n = 8 \left(\frac{1}{2}\right)^{n-1}$  $or$  $u_n = 2^3 \times (2^{-1})^{n-1}$
$$= 2^3 \times 2^{-n+1}$$
$$= 2^{3+(-n+1)}$$
$$= 2^{4-n}$$

c   $u_{12} = 8 \times \left(\frac{1}{2}\right)^{11}$
$$= \frac{1}{256}$$

---

### Example 7    ◄⑴ Self Tutor

$k - 1$, $2k$  and  $21 - k$  are consecutive terms of a geometric sequence. Find $k$.

Since the terms are geometric,        $\dfrac{2k}{k-1} = \dfrac{21-k}{2k}$        {equating $rs$}

$$\therefore \quad 4k^2 = (21-k)(k-1)$$
$$\therefore \quad 4k^2 = 21k - 21 - k^2 + k$$
$$\therefore \quad 5k^2 - 22k + 21 = 0$$
$$\therefore \quad (5k-7)(k-3) = 0 \quad \text{and so} \quad k = \tfrac{7}{5} \text{ or } 3$$

*Check:*        If  $k = \frac{7}{5}$  the terms are:  $\frac{2}{5}, \frac{14}{5}, \frac{98}{5}$.  ✓  $\{r = 7\}$

If  $k = 3$  the terms are:  2, 6, 18.  ✓    $\{r = 3\}$

---

### Example 8    ◄⑴ Self Tutor

A geometric sequence has  $u_2 = -6$  and  $u_5 = 162$.  Find its general term.

$$u_2 = u_1 r = -6 \quad \text{.... (1)}$$
$$\text{and} \quad u_5 = u_1 r^4 = 162 \quad \text{.... (2)}$$
$$\text{So,} \quad \dfrac{u_1 r^4}{u_1 r} = \dfrac{162}{-6} \quad \{(2) \div (1)\}$$
$$\therefore \quad r^3 = -27$$
$$\therefore \quad r = \sqrt[3]{-27}$$
$$\therefore \quad r = -3$$
$$\text{and so in (1)} \quad u_1(-3) = -6$$
$$\therefore \quad u_1 = 2$$
$$\text{Thus} \quad u_n = 2 \times (-3)^{n-1}.$$

### Example 9

◀ Self Tutor

Find the first term of the sequence $6, 6\sqrt{2}, 12, 12\sqrt{2}, ....$ which exceeds 1400.

The sequence is geometric with    $u_1 = 6$ and $r = \sqrt{2}$

$$\therefore \quad u_n = 6 \times (\sqrt{2})^{n-1}.$$

Next we need to find $n$ such that $u_n > 1400$.

Using a graphics calculator with $Y_1 = 6 \times (\sqrt{2})^{\wedge}(X - 1)$, we view a *table of values*:

| X | Y$_1$ |
|----|--------|
| 15 | 768 |
| 16 | 1086.1 |
| 17 | 1536 |
| 18 | 2172.2 |
| 19 | 3072 |
| 20 | 4344.5 |
| 21 | 6144 |

X=15

So, the first term to exceed 1400 is $u_{17} = 1536$.

## EXERCISE 14D

**1**  For the geometric sequence with first two terms given, find $b$ and $c$:

    **a**  $2, 6, b, c, ....$         **b**  $10, 5, b, c, ....$         **c**  $12, -6, b, c, ....$

**2**  Find the 6th term in each of the following geometric sequences:

    **a**  $3, 6, 12, 24, ....$         **b**  $2, 10, 50, ....$         **c**  $512, 256, 128, ....$

**3**  Find the 9th term in each of the following geometric sequences:

    **a**  $1, 3, 9, 27, ....$   **b**  $12, 18, 27, ....$   **c**  $\frac{1}{16}, -\frac{1}{8}, \frac{1}{4}, -\frac{1}{2}, ....$   **d**  $a, ar, ar^2, ....$

**4**  **a**  Show that the sequence $5, 10, 20, 40, ....$ is geometric.

    **b**  Find $u_n$ and hence find the 15th term.

**5**  **a**  Show that the sequence $12, -6, 3, -\frac{3}{2}, ....$ is geometric.

    **b**  Find $u_n$ and hence find the 13th term (as a fraction).

**6**  Show that the sequence $8, -6, 4.5, -3.375, ....$ is geometric. Hence find the 10th term in decimal form.

**7**  Show that the sequence $8, 4\sqrt{2}, 4, 2\sqrt{2}, ....$ is geometric. Hence find, in simplest form, the general term $u_n$.

**8**  Find $k$ given that the following are consecutive terms of a geometric sequence:

    **a**  $7, k, 28$         **b**  $k, 3k, 20 - k$         **c**  $k, k + 8, 9k$

**9**  Find the general term $u_n$ of the geometric sequence which has:

    **a**  $u_4 = 24$ and $u_7 = 192$         **b**  $u_3 = 8$ and $u_6 = -1$

    **c**  $u_7 = 24$ and $u_{15} = 384$         **d**  $u_3 = 5$ and $u_7 = \frac{5}{4}$.

**10**  **a**  Find the first term of the sequence $2, 6, 18, 54, ....$ which exceeds 10 000.

    **b**  Find the first term of the sequence $4, 4\sqrt{3}, 12, 12\sqrt{3}, ....$ which exceeds 4800.

    **c**  Find the first term of the sequence $12, 6, 3, 1.5, ....$ which is less than 0.0001.

## E  APPLICATIONS OF SEQUENCES

### SIMPLE INTEREST

Suppose you invest \$1000 in the bank. You leave the money in the bank for 3 years, and are paid a *simple* interest rate of 10% per annum.

This means that the interest earned each year does not accumulate, and is fixed at 10% of the original principal. This is 10% of \$1000, or \$100.

So, your initial investment is \$1000.
After one year it is worth   \$1000 + \$100 = \$1100.
After 2 years it is worth   \$1000 + \$200 = \$1200.
After 3 years it is worth   \$1000 + \$300 = \$1300.

If we write the yearly totals as a sequence of numbers, we have:

$$\$1000, \quad \$1100, \quad \$1200, \quad \$1300, \quad ....$$

We label these:   $u_1, \quad u_2, \quad u_3, \quad u_4, \quad ....$

This sequence is arithmetic with first term  $u_1 = \$1000$  and common difference  $d = \$100$.

The value of the investment in dollars is:

$$u_1 = 1000$$
$$u_2 = u_1 + 1 \times 100 \qquad \text{after 1 year}$$
$$u_3 = u_1 + 2 \times 100 \qquad \text{after 2 years}$$
$$u_4 = u_1 + 3 \times 100 \qquad \text{after 3 years}$$
$$\vdots$$
$$u_{n+1} = u_1 + n \times 100 \qquad \text{after } n \text{ years.}$$

An investment with simple interest $r$% p.a. for $n$ years will have value

$$u_{n+1} = u_1 + n \times f$$

where  $u_1 =$ initial investment, and
$f = r\%$ of $u_1$ is the fixed amount of interest earned each year.

---

#### Example 10 ◀) Self Tutor

€6000 is invested at 5% p.a. simple interest for 15 years.
Calculate the value of the investment at the end of this period.

Now   $u_{n+1} = u_1 + n \times f$  where  $u_1 = €6000$,  $r = 5\%$,  $n = 15$,
and  $f = 5\%$ of €6000 = €300

So, the value of the investment after 15 years is

$$u_{16} = 6000 + 15 \times 300$$
$$= €10\,500$$

## EXERCISE 14E.1

**1** Calculate the final value of:

a $2000 invested at 10% p.a. simple interest for 4 years

b $5000 invested at 5% p.a. simple interest for 6 years

c £3500 invested at 7% p.a. simple interest for 9 years

d €4800 invested at 3.9% p.a. simple interest for 10 years.

**2** Calculate the total amount to repay for a simple interest loan of:

a $3000 at 5% p.a. over 10 years

b £12 000 at 3.5% p.a. over 12 years

c €20 000 at 8.75% p.a. over 7 years

d £500 at 22% p.a. over 6 years.

## COMPOUND INTEREST

Suppose once again you invest $1000 in the bank for 3 years, but this time you are paid a *compound* interest rate of 10% p.a. The interest is added to your investment each year, and now you are paid *interest on the interest*.

The percentage increase each year is 10%, so at the end of the year you will have $100\% + 10\% = 110\%$ of the value at its start. This corresponds to a *multiplier* of 1.1 .

After one year your investment is worth   $1000 \times 1.1 = \$1100$.

| After two years it is worth | After three years it is worth |
|---|---|
| $1100 \times 1.1$ | $1210 \times 1.1$ |
| $= \$1000 \times 1.1 \times 1.1$ | $= \$1000 \times (1.1)^2 \times 1.1$ |
| $= \$1000 \times (1.1)^2 = \$1210$ | $= \$1000 \times (1.1)^3 = \$1331$ |

This suggests that if the money is left in your account for $n$ years it would amount to $1000 \times (1.1)^n$.

Observe that:    $u_1 = \$1000$        = initial investment

$u_2 = u_1 \times 1.1$        = amount after 1 year

$u_3 = u_1 \times (1.1)^2$    = amount after 2 years

$u_4 = u_1 \times (1.1)^3$    = amount after 3 years

$\vdots$

$u_{n+1} = u_1 \times (1.1)^n$    = amount after $n$ years

> We can use the **compound interest formula**    $u_{n+1} = u_1 \times r^n$
>
> where        $u_1$ = initial investment        $n$ = number of years
>
>              $r$ = growth multiplier        $u_{n+1}$ = amount after $n$ years.

**Example 11**    ◄)) Self Tutor

$5000 is invested for 4 years at 7% p.a. compound interest, compounded annually.
What will it amount to at the end of this period? Give your answer to the nearest cent.

$u_5 = u_1 \times r^4$        is the amount after 4 years

$\quad = 5000 \times (1.07)^4$    {for a 7% increase 100% becomes 107%}

$\quad \approx 6553.98$      {5000 $\boxed{\times}$ 1.07 $\boxed{\wedge}$ 4 $\boxed{\text{ENTER}}$ }

So, it amounts to $6553.98.

**Example 12**    ◄)) Self Tutor

How much should I invest now if I want the maturing value to be €10 000 in 4 years' time, if I am able to invest at 8.5% p.a. compounded annually? Give your answer to the nearest cent.

$u_1 = ?, \quad u_5 = 10\,000, \quad r = 1.085$

$\qquad u_5 = u_1 \times r^4$       {using $u_{n+1} = u_1 \times r^n$}

$\therefore \quad 10\,000 = u_1 \times (1.085)^4$

$\therefore \quad u_1 = \dfrac{10\,000}{(1.085)^4}$

$\therefore \quad u_1 = 7215.74$     {10 000 $\boxed{\div}$ 1.085 $\boxed{\wedge}$ 4 $\boxed{\text{ENTER}}$ }

So, I should invest €7215.74 now.

## EXERCISE 14E.2

1   a   What will an investment of £3000 at 10% p.a. compound interest amount to after 3 years?

    b   What part of this is interest?

2   How much compound interest is earned by investing €20 000 at 12% p.a. if the investment is over a 4 year period?

3   a   What will an investment of ¥30 000 at 8% p.a. compound interest amount to after 4 years?

    b   What part of this is interest?

4   How much compound interest is earned by investing $80 000 at 9% p.a., if the investment is over a 3 year period?

5   Joachim can earn 5.2% p.a. compounded annually on a 3 year investment. How much does he need to invest now to have a maturing investment of €55 000 in 3 years' time?

## ARITHMETIC SEQUENCE PROBLEMS

**Example 13**    ◀ᴗ) **Self Tutor**

Ryan is a cartoonist. His comic strip has just been bought by a newspaper, so he sends them the 28 comic strips he has drawn so far. Each week after the first he mails 3 more comic strips to the newspaper.

a   Find the total number of comic strips sent after 1, 2, 3 and 4 weeks.

b   Show that the total number of comic strips sent after $n$ weeks forms an arithmetic sequence.

c   Find the number of comic strips sent after 15 weeks.

d   When does Ryan send his 120th comic strip?

a   *Week 1:*            28   comic strips
   *Week 2:*   $28 + 3 = 31$   comic strips
   *Week 3:*   $31 + 3 = 34$   comic strips
   *Week 4:*   $34 + 3 = 37$   comic strips

b   Every week, Ryan sends 3 comic strips, so the difference between successive weeks is always 3. We have an arithmetic sequence with $u_1 = 28$ and common difference $d = 3$.

c   $u_n = u_1 + (n-1)d$
   $\quad = 28 + (n-1) \times 3$        $\therefore \ u_{15} = 25 + 3 \times 15$
   $\quad = 25 + 3n$                              $= 70$

So, after 15 weeks Ryan has sent 70 comic strips.

d   We want to find $n$ such that        $u_n = 120$
   $\therefore \ 25 + 3n = 120$
   $\therefore \ 3n = 95$
   $\therefore \ n = 31\frac{2}{3}$

So, Ryan sends the 120th comic strip in the 32nd week.

## EXERCISE 14E.3

1   A luxury car maker sets up a factory for a new model. In the first month only 5 cars are produced. After this, 13 cars are assembled every month.

   a   List the total number of cars that have been made in the factory by the end of each of the first six months.

   b   Explain why the total number of cars made after $n$ months forms an arithmetic sequence.

   c   How many cars are made in the first year?

   d   How long is it until the 250th car is manufactured?

2   Valéria joins a social networking website. After 1 week she has 34 online friends. At the end of 2 weeks she has 41 friends, after 3 weeks she has 48 friends, and after 4 weeks she has 55 friends.

**a** Show that Valéria's number of friends forms an arithmetic sequence.

**b** Find the number of online friends Valéria will have after 12 weeks, assuming the pattern continues.

**c** After how many weeks will Valéria have 150 online friends?

**3** A farmer feeds his cattle herd with hay every day in July. The amount of hay in his barn at the end of day $n$ is given by the arithmetic sequence $u_n = 100 - 2.7n$ tonnes.

**a** Write down the amount of hay in the barn on the first three days of July.

**b** Find and interpret the common difference.

**c** Find and interpret $u_{25}$.

**d** How much hay is in the barn at the beginning of August?

## GEOMETRIC SEQUENCE PROBLEMS

Problems of **growth and decay** involve repeated multiplications by a constant number. We can therefore use geometric sequences to model the situations.

---

**Example 14**                                                    ◀)) **Self Tutor**

The initial population of rabbits on a farm was 50.
The population increased by 7% each week.

**a** How many rabbits were present after:

   **i** 15 weeks        **ii** 30 weeks?

**b** How long would it take for the population to reach 500?

---

There is a fixed percentage increase each week, so the population forms a geometric sequence.

$u_1 = 50$    and    $r = 1.07$

$u_2 = 50 \times 1.07 =$ the population after 1 week

**a**  **i**   $u_{n+1} = u_1 \times r^n$           **ii**  $u_{31} = 50 \times (1.07)^{30}$

      $\therefore$  $u_{16} = 50 \times (1.07)^{15}$                 $\approx 380.61$

               $\approx 137.95$           There were 381 rabbits.

       There were 138 rabbits.

**b**  $u_{n+1} = u_1 \times (1.07)^n$   after $n$ weeks

   So, we need to find when   $50 \times (1.07)^n = 500$.

   **Trial and error** on your calculator gives  $n \approx 34$ weeks.

   *or*   by finding the **point of intersection**
   of  $Y_1 = 50 \times 1.07^{\wedge}X$  and  $Y_2 = 500$
   on a graphics calculator, the solution is
   $\approx 34.0$ weeks.

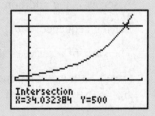

## EXERCISE 14E.4

1   A nest of ants initially contains 500 individuals.
    The population is increasing by 12% each week.

    **a**  How many ants will there be after

        **i**  10 weeks              **ii**  20 weeks?

    **b**  Use technology to find how many weeks it will
        take for the ant population to reach 2000.

2   The animal *Eraticus* is endangered. Since 1995 there has only been one colony remaining,
    and in 1995 the population of the colony was 555. Since then the population has been
    steadily decreasing at 4.5% per year. Find:

    **a**  the population in the year 2010

    **b**  the year in which we would expect the population to have declined to 50.

3

    A herd of 32 deer is to be left unchecked on a large
    island off the coast of Alaska. It is estimated that
    the size of the herd will increase each year by 18%.

    **a**  Estimate the size of the herd after:

        **i**  5 years              **ii**  10 years.

    **b**  How long will it take for the herd size to reach
        5000?

4   A population of rodents was initially 400, but increased by 54% per month.

    **a**  Find the expected population size after 18 months.

    **b**  How long will it take for the population to reach 1 000 000?

5   An endangered species of marsupials has a population of 178. However, with a successful
    breeding program it is expected to increase by 32% each year.

    **a**  Find the expected population size after:    **i**  10 years    **ii**  25 years.

    **b**  How long will it take for the population to reach 10 000?

## F          SERIES

A **series** is the addition of the terms of a sequence.

For the sequence $\{u_n\}$ the corresponding series is $u_1 + u_2 + u_3 + .... + u_n$.

The **sum** of a series is the result when we perform the addition.

Given a series which includes the first $n$ terms of a sequence, its sum is
$S_n = u_1 + u_2 + u_3 + .... + u_n$.

**Example 15**    ◄ᴺ **Self Tutor**

Consider the sequence    1, 4, 9, 16, 25, ....

  **a** Write down an expression for $S_n$.   **b** Find $S_n$ for $n = 1, 2, 3, 4$ and $5$.

  **a** $S_n = 1^2 + 2^2 + 3^2 + 4^2 + .... + n^2$
     {all terms are perfect squares}

  **b** $S_1 = 1$
     $S_2 = 1 + 4 = 5$
     $S_3 = 1 + 4 + 9 = 14$
     $S_4 = 1 + 4 + 9 + 16 = 30$
     $S_5 = 1 + 4 + 9 + 16 + 25 = 55$

## SIGMA NOTATION (EXTENSION)

$u_1 + u_2 + u_3 + u_4 + .... + u_n$ can be written more compactly using **sigma notation**.

$\sum$, which is called **sigma**, is the equivalent of capital S in the Greek alphabet.

We write $u_1 + u_2 + u_3 + u_4 + .... + u_n$ as $\displaystyle\sum_{k=1}^{n} u_k$.

$\displaystyle\sum_{k=1}^{n} u_k$ reads "the sum of all numbers of the form $u_k$ where $k = 1, 2, 3, ...., $ up to $n$".

**Example 16**    ◄ᴺ **Self Tutor**

Expand and evaluate:   **a** $\displaystyle\sum_{k=1}^{7} (k+1)$   **b** $\displaystyle\sum_{k=1}^{5} \frac{1}{2^k}$

  **a**  $\displaystyle\sum_{k=1}^{7} (k+1)$
     $= 2 + 3 + 4 + 5 + 6 + 7 + 8$
     $= 35$

  **b**  $\displaystyle\sum_{k=1}^{5} \frac{1}{2^k}$
     $= \frac{1}{2} + \frac{1}{4} + \frac{1}{8} + \frac{1}{16} + \frac{1}{32}$
     $= \frac{31}{32}$

## EXERCISE 14F.1

**1** For the following sequences:

    **i** write down an expression for $S_n$        **ii** find $S_5$.

  **a** 3, 11, 19, 27, ....     **b** 42, 37, 32, 27, ....     **c** $12, 6, 3, 1\frac{1}{2}, ....$

  **d** $2, 3, 4\frac{1}{2}, 6\frac{3}{4}, ....$     **e** $1, \frac{1}{2}, \frac{1}{4}, \frac{1}{8}, ....$     **f** 1, 8, 27, 64, ....

**2** Expand and evaluate:

  **a** $\displaystyle\sum_{k=1}^{4} 2k$     **b** $\displaystyle\sum_{k=1}^{5} (k+1)$     **c** $\displaystyle\sum_{k=1}^{4} (10 - k)$     **d** $\displaystyle\sum_{k=1}^{4} (3k - 5)$

  **e** $\displaystyle\sum_{k=1}^{5} (11 - 2k)$     **f** $\displaystyle\sum_{k=1}^{5} 2$     **g** $\displaystyle\sum_{k=1}^{7} k(k+1)$     **h** $\displaystyle\sum_{k=1}^{5} (10 \times 2^{k-1})$

**3** For $u_n = 3n - 1$, write $u_1 + u_2 + u_3 + .... + u_{20}$ using sigma notation and evaluate the sum.

# ARITHMETIC SERIES

An **arithmetic series** is the addition of successive terms of an arithmetic sequence.

For example:    $21, 23, 25, 27, ...., 49$   is an arithmetic sequence.

so   $21 + 23 + 25 + 27 + .... + 49$   is an arithmetic series.

If the first term of an arithmetic series is $u_1$ and the common difference is $d$, the terms are $u_1, u_1 + d, u_1 + 2d, u_1 + 3d,$ and so on.

Suppose that $u_n$ is the final term of the series.

So,  $S_n = u_1 + (u_1 + d) + (u_1 + 2d) + .... + (u_n - 2d) + (u_n - d) + u_n$

But  $S_n = u_n + (u_n - d) + (u_n - 2d) + .... + (u_1 + 2d) + (u_1 + d) + u_1$   {reversing them}

Adding these two expressions vertically we get

$$2S_n = \underbrace{(u_1 + u_n) + (u_1 + u_n) + (u_1 + u_n) + .... + (u_1 + u_n) + (u_1 + u_n) + (u_1 + u_n)}_{n \text{ of these}}$$

$\therefore$  $2S_n = n(u_1 + u_n)$

$\therefore$  $S_n = \dfrac{n}{2}(u_1 + u_n)$   where   $u_n = u_1 + (n-1)d$

So,    $\boxed{S_n = \dfrac{n}{2}(u_1 + u_n) \quad or \quad S_n = \dfrac{n}{2}(2u_1 + (n-1)d)}$

---

**Example 17**    ◀⑴ **Self Tutor**

Find the sum of  $4 + 7 + 10 + 13 + ....$  to 50 terms.

The series is arithmetic with  $u_1 = 4$,  $d = 3$  and  $n = 50$.

Now  $S_n = \dfrac{n}{2}(2u_1 + (n-1)d)$

$\therefore$  $S_{50} = \frac{50}{2}(2 \times 4 + 49 \times 3)$

$= 3875$

---

**Example 18**    ◀⑴ **Self Tutor**

Find the sum of  $-6 + 1 + 8 + 15 + .... + 141$.

The series is arithmetic with  $u_1 = -6$,  $d = 7$  and  $u_n = 141$.
First we need to find $n$.

Now  $u_n = 141$

$\therefore$  $u_1 + (n-1)d = 141$          Using  $S_n = \frac{n}{2}(u_1 + u_n)$,

$\therefore$  $-6 + 7(n-1) = 141$              $S_{22} = \frac{22}{2}(-6 + 141)$

$\therefore$  $7(n-1) = 147$                  $= 11 \times 135$

$\therefore$  $n - 1 = 21$                    $= 1485$

$\therefore$  $n = 22$

## EXERCISE 14F.2

**1** Find the sum $1 + 5 + 9 + 13 + 17 + 21 + 25$

   **a** by simple addition          **b** using $S_n = \dfrac{n}{2}(u_1 + u_n)$

   **c** using $S_n = \dfrac{n}{2}(2u_1 + (n-1)d)$

**2** Find the sum of:

   **a** $3 + 7 + 11 + 15 + ....$ to 20 terms      **b** $\frac{1}{2} + 3 + 5\frac{1}{2} + 8 + ....$ to 50 terms

   **c** $100 + 93 + 86 + 79 + ....$ to 40 terms    **d** $50 + 48\frac{1}{2} + 47 + 45\frac{1}{2} + ....$ to 80 terms.

**3** Find the sum of:

   **a** $5 + 8 + 11 + 14 + .... + 101$      **b** $50 + 49\frac{1}{2} + 49 + 48\frac{1}{2} + .... + (-20)$

   **c** $8 + 10\frac{1}{2} + 13 + 15\frac{1}{2} + .... + 83$

**4** Evaluate these arithmetic series:

   **a** $\displaystyle\sum_{k=1}^{10}(2k+5)$      **b** $\displaystyle\sum_{k=1}^{15}(k-50)$      **c** $\displaystyle\sum_{k=1}^{20}\left(\dfrac{k+3}{2}\right)$

   **Hint:** List the first 3 terms and the last term.

**5** An arithmetic series has seven terms. The first term is 5 and the last term is 53. Find the sum of the series.

**6** An arithmetic series has eleven terms. The first term is 6 and the last term is $-27$. Find the sum of the series.

**7** 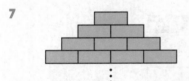 A bricklayer builds a triangular wall with layers of bricks as shown. If the bricklayer uses 171 bricks, how many layers did he build?

**8** Each section of a soccer stadium has 44 rows with 22 seats in the first row, 23 in the second row, 24 in the third row, and so on. How many seats are there in:

   **a** row 44      **b** each section      **c** the stadium which has 25 sections?

**9** Find the sum of:

   **a** the first 50 multiples of 11

   **b** the multiples of 7 between 0 and 1000

   **c** the integers between 1 and 100 which are not divisible by 3.

**10** Find the first two terms of an arithmetic sequence if the sixth term is 21 and the sum of the first seventeen terms is 0.

**11** Three consecutive terms of an arithmetic sequence have a sum of 12 and a product of $-80$. Find the terms.   **Hint:** Let the terms be $x - d$, $x$ and $x + d$.

**12** Five consecutive terms of an arithmetic sequence have a sum of 40. The product of the first, middle and last terms is 224. Find the terms of the sequence.

## GEOMETRIC SERIES

A **geometric series** is the addition of successive terms of a geometric sequence.

For example:    $1, 2, 4, 8, 16, ...., 1024$   is a geometric sequence.

so    $1 + 2 + 4 + 8 + 16 + .... + 1024$   is a geometric series.

If the first term of a geometric series is $u_1$ and the common ratio is $r$, then the terms are: $u_1, u_1r, u_1r^2, u_1r^3, ....$

So,    $S_n = u_1 + \underset{\underset{u_2}{\uparrow}}{u_1r} + \underset{\underset{u_3}{\uparrow}}{u_1r^2} + \underset{\underset{u_4}{\uparrow}}{u_1r^3} + .... + \underset{\underset{u_{n-1}}{\uparrow}}{u_1r^{n-2}} + \underset{\underset{u_n}{\uparrow}}{u_1r^{n-1}}$

and for   $r \neq 1$,    $$S_n = \frac{u_1(r^n - 1)}{r - 1} \quad or \quad S_n = \frac{u_1(1 - r^n)}{1 - r}.$$

**Proof:**        If   $S_n = u_1 + u_1r + u_1r^2 + u_1r^3 + .... + u_1r^{n-2} + u_1r^{n-1}$    .... (1)

then   $rS_n = (u_1r + u_1r^2 + u_1r^3 + u_1r^4 + .... + u_1r^{n-1}) + u_1r^n$

$\therefore$   $rS_n = (S_n - u_1) + u_1r^n$      {from (1)}

$\therefore$   $rS_n - S_n = u_1r^n - u_1$

$\therefore$   $S_n(r - 1) = u_1(r^n - 1)$  and so  $S_n = \dfrac{u_1(r^n - 1)}{r - 1}$  or  $\dfrac{u_1(1 - r^n)}{1 - r}$  for  $r \neq 1$.

In the case  $r = 1$  we have a sequence in which all terms are the same, and  $S_n = u_1n$.

---

### Example 19 ◀) Self Tutor

Find the sum of   $2 + 6 + 18 + 54 + ....$   to 12 terms.

The series is geometric with  $u_1 = 2$,  $r = 3$  and  $n = 12$.

$S_n = \dfrac{u_1(r^n - 1)}{r - 1}$

$\therefore S_{12} = \dfrac{2(3^{12} - 1)}{3 - 1} = 531\,440$

---

### Example 20 ◀) Self Tutor

Find a formula for  $S_n$  for the first $n$ terms of
$9 - 3 + 1 - \frac{1}{3} + ....$

> This answer cannot be simplified as we do not know if $n$ is odd or even.

The series is geometric with  $u_1 = 9$  and  $r = -\frac{1}{3}$

So,   $S_n = \dfrac{u_1(1 - r^n)}{1 - r} = \dfrac{9(1 - (-\frac{1}{3})^n)}{\frac{4}{3}}$

$\therefore$   $S_n = \frac{27}{4}(1 - (-\frac{1}{3})^n)$

## EXERCISE 14F.3

1   Find the sum  $3 + 6 + 12 + 24 + 48$

    **a**  by simple addition
                          **b**  using  $S_n = \dfrac{u_1(r^n - 1)}{r - 1}$

2   Find the sum of the following series:

    **a**  $12 + 6 + 3 + 1.5 + \dots$  to 10 terms
    **b**  $\sqrt{7} + 7 + 7\sqrt{7} + 49 + \dots$  to 12 terms
    **c**  $6 - 3 + 1\frac{1}{2} - \frac{3}{4} + \dots$  to 15 terms
    **d**  $1 - \frac{1}{\sqrt{2}} + \frac{1}{2} - \frac{1}{2\sqrt{2}} + \dots$  to 20 terms

3   Find a formula for $S_n$ for the first $n$ terms of:

    **a**  $\sqrt{3} + 3 + 3\sqrt{3} + 9 + \dots$
    **b**  $12 + 6 + 3 + 1\frac{1}{2} + \dots$
    **c**  $0.9 + 0.09 + 0.009 + 0.0009 + \dots$
    **d**  $20 - 10 + 5 - 2\frac{1}{2} + \dots$

4   Evaluate these geometric series:

    **a**  $\displaystyle\sum_{k=1}^{5} 4 \times 2^{k-1}$
    **b**  $\displaystyle\sum_{k=1}^{12} 40 \times \left(\tfrac{1}{2}\right)^{k-1}$
    **c**  $\displaystyle\sum_{k=1}^{25} 6 \times (-2)^{k}$

**Hint:**  List the first three terms.

5   Each year a salesperson is paid a bonus of \$2000 which is banked into the same account. It earns a fixed rate of interest of 6% p.a. with interest being paid annually. The total amount in the account at the end of each year is calculated as follows:

$$A_0 = 2000$$
$$A_1 = A_0 \times 1.06 + 2000$$
$$A_2 = A_1 \times 1.06 + 2000 \quad \text{and so on.}$$

    **a**  Show that  $A_2 = 2000 + 2000 \times 1.06 + 2000 \times (1.06)^2$.
    **b**  Show that  $A_3 = 2000[1 + 1.06 + (1.06)^2 + (1.06)^3]$.
    **c**  Find the total bank balance after 10 years, assuming there are no fees or charges.

6   Consider  $S_n = \frac{1}{2} + \frac{1}{4} + \frac{1}{8} + \frac{1}{16} + \dots + \dfrac{1}{2^n}$.

    **a**  Find  $S_1, S_2, S_3, S_4$ and $S_5$  in fractional form.
    **b**  From **a** guess the formula for $S_n$.
    **c**  Find $S_n$ using  $S_n = \dfrac{u_1(1 - r^n)}{1 - r}$.
    **d**  What do you suspect happens to $S_n$ as $n$ gets very large? Use the diagram alongside to help.

## REVIEW SET 14A

**1** Identify the following sequences as arithmetic, geometric, or neither:

    **a** $7, -1, -9, -17, ....$    **b** $9, 9, 9, 9, ....$    **c** $4, -2, -1, -\frac{1}{2}, ....$

    **d** $1, 1, 2, 3, 5, 8, ....$    **e** the set of all multiples of 4 in ascending order.

**2** Find $k$ if $3k$, $k-2$ and $k+7$ are consecutive terms of an arithmetic sequence.

**3** Show that $28, 23, 18, 13, ....$ is arithmetic. Hence find $u_n$ and the sum $S_n$ of the first $n$ terms in simplest form.

**4** Find $k$ given that $4$, $k$ and $k^2 - 1$ are consecutive terms of a geometric sequence.

**5** Determine the general term of a geometric sequence given that its sixth term is $\frac{16}{3}$ and its tenth term is $\frac{256}{3}$.

**6** Insert six numbers between 23 and 9 so that all eight numbers are in arithmetic sequence.

**7** Find the 8th term of each of the following sequences:

    **a** $5, 1, \frac{1}{5}, ....$    **b** $-11, -8\frac{1}{2}, -6, ....$    **c** $a, a-d, a-2d, ....$

**8** At the start of the dry season, Yafiah's 3000 L water tank is full. She uses 183 L of water each week to water her garden.

    **a** Find the amount of water left in the tank after 1, 2, 3 and 4 weeks.

    **b** Explain why the amount of water left in the tank after $n$ weeks forms an arithmetic sequence.

    **c** When does Yafiah's tank run out of water?

**9** Write down the expansion of:    **a** $\displaystyle\sum_{k=1}^{7} k^2$    **b** $\displaystyle\sum_{k=1}^{8} \frac{k+3}{k+2}$

**10** Find the sum of:

    **a** $14 + 11 + 8 + .... + (-55)$    **b** $3 + 15 + 75 + .... + 5\,859\,375$

## REVIEW SET 14B

**1** A sequence is defined by $u_n = 6(\frac{1}{2})^{n-1}$.

    **a** Prove that the sequence is geometric.

    **b** Find $u_1$ and $r$.

    **c** Find the 16th term to 3 significant figures.

**2**    **a** Determine the number of terms in the sequence $24, 23\frac{1}{4}, 22\frac{1}{2}, ...., -36$.

    **b** Find the value of $u_{35}$ for the sequence in **a**.

    **c** Find the sum of the terms of the sequence in **a**.

**3** Find the sum of:

    **a** $3 + 9 + 15 + 21 + ....$ to 23 terms    **b** $24 + 12 + 6 + 3 + ....$ to 12 terms.

**4** List the first five terms of the sequence:

   **a** $\left\{(\tfrac{1}{3})^n\right\}$     **b** $\{12 + 5n\}$     **c** $\left\{\dfrac{4}{n+2}\right\}$

**5** **a** What will an investment of €6000 at 7% p.a. compound interest amount to after 5 years?

   **b** What part of this is interest?

**6** The $n$th term of a sequence is given by the formula $u_n = 4n - 7$.

   **a** Find the value of $u_{10}$.

   **b** Write down an expression for $u_{n+1} - u_n$ and simplify it.

   **c** Use **b** to explain why the sequence is arithmetic.

   **d** Evaluate $u_{15} + u_{16} + u_{17} + .... + u_{30}$.

**7** A geometric sequence has $u_6 = 24$ and $u_{11} = 768$. Determine the general term of the sequence and hence find:

   **a** $u_{17}$     **b** the sum of the first 15 terms.

**8** Find the first term of the sequence $24, 8, \tfrac{8}{3}, \tfrac{8}{9}, ....$ which is less than $0.001$.

**9** **a** Determine the number of terms in the sequence $128, 64, 32, 16, ...., \tfrac{1}{512}$.

   **b** Find the sum of these terms.

**10** Sandy wants to break the world record for holding his breath. Each day he can hold his breath for 14 seconds longer than the previous day, starting at 37 seconds on the first day.

   **a** How long does Sandy hold his breath for on the tenth day?

   **b** Assuming he keeps improving at this rate, when does Sandy break the 2009 world record of 11 minutes and 35 seconds?

## REVIEW SET 14C

**1** A sequence is defined by $u_n = 68 - 5n$.

   **a** Prove that the sequence is arithmetic.     **b** Find $u_1$ and $d$.

   **c** Find the 37th term.

   **d** State the first term of the sequence less than $-200$.

**2** **a** Show that the sequence $3, 12, 48, 192, ....$ is geometric.

   **b** Find $u_n$ and hence find $u_9$.

**3** Find the general term of the arithmetic sequence with $u_7 = 31$ and $u_{15} = -17$. Hence, find the value of $u_{34}$.

**4** Calculate the total amount owed on a simple interest loan of $5900 at 5.8% p.a. for 6 years.

**5** Evaluate:    **a** $\displaystyle\sum_{k=1}^{8} \left(\frac{31-3k}{2}\right)$    **b** $\displaystyle\sum_{k=1}^{15} 50(0.8)^{k-1}$

**Hint:**  List some of the terms.

**6** In 2006 there were 3000 koalas on Koala Island. Since then, the population of koalas on the island has increased by 5% each year.

  **a** How many koalas were on the island in 2009?

  **b** In what year will the population first exceed 5000?

**7** Find the formula for $u_n$, the general term of:

  **a**  86, 83, 80, 77, ....    **b**  $\frac{3}{4}$, 1, $\frac{7}{6}$, $\frac{9}{7}$, ....    **c**  100, 90, 81, 72.9, ....

**Hint:**  One of these sequences is neither arithmetic nor geometric.

**8** Find the first term of the sequence  5, 10, 20, 40, ....  which exceeds 10 000.

**9** $-1$, $k$, $k^2 - 7$  are consecutive terms of an arithmetic sequence. Find $k$.

**10** Each year, a school manages to use only 90% as much paper as the previous year. In the year 2000, they used 700 000 sheets of paper.

  **a** Find how much paper the school used in the years 2001 and 2002.

  **b** How much total paper did the school use in the decade from 2000 to 2009?

# Chapter 15

# Financial mathematics

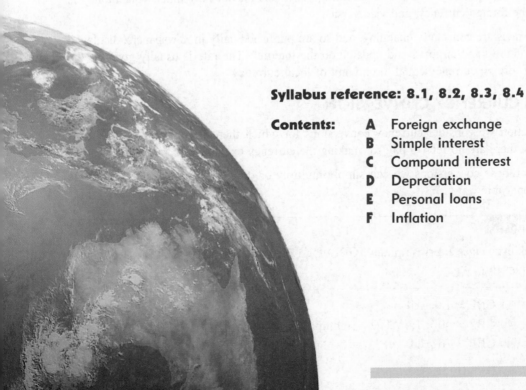

**Syllabus reference: 8.1, 8.2, 8.3, 8.4**

Contents:

## OPENING PROBLEM

Hassan wants a break from living in London, so he decides to take an overseas working holiday. He visits Spain, the United Arab Emirates, and New Zealand. He sets aside £10 000 for his holiday expenses. Before he leaves, Hassan also invests £4500 for his return.

**Things to think about:**

**a** How much is Hassan's money worth in the local currencies of the places he visits?

**b** Is it better value to exchange his money from currency to currency to currency, or to only exchange his English money as he needs it?

**c** What investment options does Hassan have for his £4500? How can he compare these different options?

**d** How does inflation affect the value of Hassan's money?

The **Opening Problem** illustrates some of the many questions about money that people face. An understanding of the mathematical processes involved is vital for making good financial decisions. It is also important to research current interest rates, fees, and other conditions when dealing with money, as these change over time and are not the same in every country.

# A    FOREIGN EXCHANGE

If you visit another country or buy products from overseas, you usually have to use the **currency** of that country. We use an **exchange rate** to find out how much your money is worth in the foreign currency, and vice versa.

Exchange rates are constantly changing, and so are published daily in newspapers, displayed in bank windows and airports, and updated on the internet. The rate is usually given as the amount of foreign currency equal to one unit of local currency.

## SIMPLE CURRENCY CONVERSION

In this section we consider currency conversions for which there is **no commission**. This means that there are no fees to pay for making the currency exchange.

To perform these conversions we can simply multiply or divide by the currency **exchange rate** as applicable.

### Example 1
◄》 **Self Tutor**

A bank exchanges 1 British pound (GBP) for 1.9 Australian dollars (AUD). Convert:

**a**  40 GBP to AUD

**b**  500 AUD to GBP.

**a**      1 GBP = 1.9 AUD

∴   40 GBP = 40 × 1.9 AUD    {multiplying by 40}

∴   40 GBP = 76 AUD

b
$$1 \text{ GBP} = 1.9 \text{ AUD}$$

$$\therefore \ \frac{1}{1.9} \text{ GBP} = 1 \text{ AUD} \quad \{\text{dividing by } 1.9\}$$

$$\therefore \ 500 \times \frac{1}{1.9} \text{ GBP} = 500 \text{ AUD} \quad \{\text{multiplying by } 500\}$$

$$\therefore \ 500 \text{ AUD} \approx 263 \text{ GBP}$$

Sometimes the exchange rates between currencies are presented in a table. In this case we select the row by the currency we are converting *from*, and the column by the currency we are converting *to*.

currency converting to

|  | Hong Kong (HKD) | China (CNY) | Japan (JPY) |
|---|---|---|---|
| Hong Kong (HKD) | 1 | 0.873 | 11.599 |
| China (CNY) | 1.146 | 1 | 13.290 |
| Japan (JPY) | 0.086 | 0.075 | 1 |

currency converting from

For example, to convert 2000 Chinese yuan to Japanese yen, we choose the row for CNY and the column for JPY.

So, $\quad 2000 \text{ CNY} = 13.290 \times 2000 \text{ JPY}$
$$= 26\,580 \text{ JPY}$$

---

**Example 2**   ◀)) **Self Tutor**

The table alongside shows the transfer rates between US dollars (USD), Swiss francs (CHF), and British pounds (GBP).

|  | USD | GBP | CHF |
|---|---|---|---|
| USD | 1 | 0.625 | 1.03 |
| GBP | 1.60 | 1 | 1.67 |
| CHF | 0.97 | 0.60 | 1 |

a  Write down the exchange rate from:
  i  CHF to USD        ii  USD to CHF.

b  Convert:
  i  3000 USD to GBP        ii  10 000 francs to pounds.

a  i  $1 \text{ CHF} = 0.97 \text{ USD}$        ii  $1 \text{ USD} = 1.03 \text{ CHF}$

b  i  $\qquad 1 \text{ USD} = 0.625 \text{ GBP}$        ii  $\qquad 1 \text{ CHF} = 0.6 \text{ GBP}$

$\therefore \ 3000 \text{ USD} = 3000 \times 0.625 \text{ GBP}$        $\therefore \ 10\,000 \text{ CHF} = 10\,000 \times 0.6 \text{ GBP}$

$\therefore \ 3000 \text{ USD} = 1875 \text{ GBP}$        $\therefore \ 10\,000 \text{ CHF} = 6000 \text{ GBP}$

---

## EXERCISE 15A.1

1  A currency exchange will convert 1 Singapore dollar (SGD) to 5.4 South African rand (ZAR).

a  Convert the following into South African rand:   i  3000 SGD   ii  450 SGD.

b  Convert the following into Singapore dollars:   i  21 000 ZAR   ii  1.35 ZAR.

**2** Exchange rates for the US dollar are shown in the table alongside.

| Currency | 1 USD |
|---|---|
| Taiwan Dollar (TWD) | 31.9632 |
| Norwegian Kroner (NOK) | 5.8818 |
| Chinese Yuan (CNY) | 6.8268 |

  **a** Convert 200 USD into:

    **i** TWD    **ii** NOK    **iii** CNY

  **b** Convert 5000 NOK into:    **i** USD    **ii** CNY.

  **c** Convert 100 TWD into:    **i** USD    **ii** CNY.

**3** A bank offers the following currency exchanges:

$$\text{1 Indian rupee (INR)} = 0.1473 \text{ Chinese yuan (CNY)}$$
$$\text{1 Indian rupee (INR)} = 0.6554 \text{ Russian rubles (RUB)}$$

  **a** Convert 15 750 INR to:    **i** CNY    **ii** RUB.

  **b** Calculate the exchange rate from:

    **i** Chinese yuan to Indian rupee      **ii** Russian rubles to Chinese yuan.

  **c** How much are 30 000 Russian rubles worth in Chinese yuan?

**4** The table alongside shows the conversion rates between Mexican pesos (MXN), Russian rubles (RUB), and South African rand (ZAR).

| | MXN | RUB | ZAR |
|---|---|---|---|
| MXN | 1 | 2.322 | 0.5820 |
| RUB | 0.4307 | 1 | 0.2506 |
| ZAR | $p$ | $q$ | $r$ |

  **a** Convert 5000 rubles into:    **i** rand    **ii** pesos.

  **b** How many Russian rubles can be bought for 20 000 Mexican pesos?

  **c** Calculate the values of:    **i** $p$    **ii** $q$    **iii** $r$

  **d** Which is worth more in rand, 1 peso or 1 ruble?

---

**Example 3**            ◀ৈ **Self Tutor**

The graph alongside shows the relationship between Australian dollars and English pounds on a particular day. Find:

  **a** the number of dollars in 250 pounds

  **b** the number of pounds in 480 dollars

  **c** whether a person with 360 AUD could afford to buy an item valued at 200 pounds.

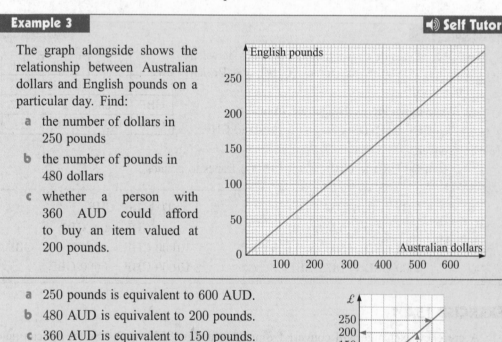

  **a** 250 pounds is equivalent to 600 AUD.

  **b** 480 AUD is equivalent to 200 pounds.

  **c** 360 AUD is equivalent to 150 pounds.

    ∴ the person cannot afford to buy the item.

**5** Use the currency conversion graph of **Example 3** to estimate:

   **a** the number of dollars in    **i** 130 pounds    **ii** 240 pounds

   **b** the number of pounds in    **i** 400 AUD     **ii** 560 AUD.

---

**ACTIVITY 1**                      **CURRENCY TRENDS**

Over a period of a month, collect from the daily newspaper or internet the currency conversions which compare your currency to the currency of another country. Graph your results, updating the graph each day. You could use *www.x-rates.com/calculator.html* or *www.xe.com/ucc* .

## COMMISSION ON CURRENCY EXCHANGE

When a currency trader (such as a bank) exchanges currency for a customer, a commission is often paid by the customer for this service. The commission could vary from $\frac{1}{2}\%$ to $3\%$, or could be a constant amount or 'flat fee'. Some traders charge no commission but offer worse exchange rates instead.

Suppose you live in the United States of America. The table below shows how much one American dollar (USD) is worth in some other currencies.

| Country | Currency name | Code | Buys | Sells |
|---|---|---|---|---|
| Europe | Euro | EUR | 0.6819 | 0.6547 |
| United Kingdom | Pounds | GBP | 0.6064 | 0.5821 |
| Australia | Dollars | AUD | 1.0883 | 1.0601 |
| Canada | Dollars | CAD | 1.0681 | 1.0253 |
| China | Yuan | CNY | 6.8465 | 6.8017 |
| Denmark | Kroner | DKK | 5.0593 | 4.8569 |
| Hong Kong | Dollars | HKD | 7.8443 | 7.5308 |
| Japan | Yen | JPY | 90.99 | 87.36 |
| New Zealand | Dollars | NZD | 1.3644 | 1.3098 |
| Norway | Kroner | NOK | 5.5248 | 5.3038 |
| Saudi Arabia | Riyals | SAR | 3.6927 | 3.5450 |
| Singapore | Dollars | SGD | 1.4047 | 1.3485 |
| South Africa | Rand | ZAR | 7.3608 | 7.0663 |
| Sweden | Kronor | SEK | 6.8075 | 6.5352 |
| Switzerland | Francs | CHF | 1.0281 | 0.9869 |
| Thailand | Baht | THB | 32.159 | 30.873 |

Tables such as this one often show different rates for buying and selling. This lets the currency dealer make a profit on all money exchanges.

The 'buy' and 'sell' rates are listed relative to the currency broker (bank or exchange) and are in terms of the foreign currency.

So, the foreign currency EUR will be bought by a currency broker at the rate 1 USD = 0.6819 EUR,   and sold by the broker at the rate   1 USD = 0.6547 EUR.

**Example 4**    ◀)) Self Tutor

Use the currency conversion table above to perform the following conversions:

a  Convert 400 USD into euros.

b  How much does it cost in US dollars to buy 5000 yen?

c  How many US dollars can you buy for 2000 Swedish kronor?

---

a  Euros are sold at the rate

$$1 \text{ USD} = 0.6547 \text{ EUR}$$
$$\therefore \quad 400 \text{ USD} = 400 \times 0.6547 \text{ EUR}$$
$$= 261.88 \text{ EUR}$$

b  The currency broker sells yen at the rate

$$1 \text{ USD} = 87.36 \text{ JPY}$$
$$\therefore \quad \frac{1}{87.36} \text{ USD} = 1 \text{ JPY}$$
$$\therefore \quad 5000 \times \frac{1}{87.36} \text{ USD} = 5000 \text{ JPY}$$
$$\therefore \quad 5000 \text{ JPY} = 57.23 \text{ USD}$$

c  The currency broker buys kronor at the rate

$$1 \text{ USD} = 6.8075 \text{ SEK}$$
$$\therefore \quad \frac{1}{6.8075} \text{ USD} = 1 \text{ SEK}$$
$$\therefore \quad 2000 \times \frac{1}{6.8075} \text{ USD} = 2000 \text{ SEK}$$
$$\therefore \quad 2000 \text{ SEK} = 293.79 \text{ USD}$$

## EXERCISE 15A.2

For questions **1** to **4**, suppose you are a citizen of the USA and use the currency table on page **459**.

1  On holiday you set aside 300 USD to spend in each country you visit. How much local currency can you buy in:

    a  Europe (euros)

    b  the United Kingdom

    c  Singapore

    d  Australia?

2  Find the cost in USD of:

    a  400 Canadian dollars

    b  730 Swiss francs

    c  ¥12 430

    d  4710 DKK.

3  Find the price in American dollars of:

    a  a computer worth 7000 Hong Kong dollars

    b  a rugby ball worth 35 NZD

    c  a watch worth 949 SAR.

4  Find how many US dollars you could buy for:

    a  €2500

    b  57 000 rand

    c  £165

    d  86 370 baht.

**Example 5**   ◀ঠ) **Self Tutor**

A currency exchange service exchanges 1 euro for Japanese yen with the buy rate 135.69, and sell rate 132.08. Cedric wishes to exchange 800 euros for yen.

a  How many yen will he receive?

b  If the yen in a were exchanged immediately back to euros, how many euros would they be worth?

c  What is the resultant commission on the double transaction?

a  Cedric receives  $800 \times 132.08 \approx 105\,700$ yen

   {using the selling rate as the bank is selling currency}

b  Cedric receives  $\dfrac{105\,700}{135.69} \approx €779$

   {using the buying rate as the bank is buying currency}

c  The resultant commission is  $€800 - €779 = €21$.

---

**5**  A currency exchange service exchanges 1 Mexican peso for Thai baht using a buy rate of 2.584 and a sell rate of 2.4807.  Sergio wishes to exchange 400 peso for Thai baht.

a  How many baht will he receive?

b  If he immediately exchanges the baht back to pesos, how many will he get?

c  What is the resultant commission for the double transaction?

**6**  A currency exchange service exchanges 1 Chinese yuan to Indian rupees with buy rate 6.8086 and sell rate 6.5641.  Lili wishes to exchange 425 yuan for rupees.

a  How much will he receive?

b  If he immediately exchanges the rupees back to yuan, how many will he get?

c  What is the resultant commission for the double transaction?

**7**  A bank exchanges 1 Botswana pula to Angolan kwanza with buy rate 13.527 and sell rate 13.068.  Kefilwe wishes to exchange 3200 pula to kwanza.

a  How much will he receive?

b  If he immediately exchanges the kwanza back to pula, how many will he get?

c  What is the resultant commission for the double transaction?

## FIXED COMMISSION ON CURRENCY EXCHANGE

**Example 6**   ◀ঠ) **Self Tutor**

A banker changes South African rand to other currencies at a fixed commission of 1.5%.  Wendy wishes to convert R800 to rubles where R1 buys 3.86 Russian rubles.

a  What commission is charged?           b  How much does Wendy receive?

a  Commission $= $ R800 $\times 1.5\%$            b  Wendy receives   $788 \times 3.86$ rubles

   $= $ R800 $\times 0.015$                               $\approx 3042$ rubles

   $= $ R12

## EXERCISE 15A.3

1   A bank exchanges UK pounds for a commission of 1.5%. For the following transactions, calculate:

     **i**   the commission charged    **ii**   how much the customer receives

  **a**   converting 500 UK pounds to US dollars where £1 UK buys 1.8734 USD

  **b**   converting 350 UK pounds to euros where £1 UK buys €1.5071

  **c**   converting £1200 UK to New Zealand dollars where £1 UK buys \$2.8424 NZ.

2   A bank exchanges Singapore dollars for a commission of 1.8%. For the following transactions, calculate:

     **i**   the commission charged    **ii**   how much the customer receives

  **a**   converting 250 SGD to UK pounds if 1 SGD buys £0.429 88

  **b**   converting 700 SGD to AUD if 1 SGD buys 0.7745 AUD

  **c**   converting 1500 SGD to euros if 1 SGD buys €0.483 28.

## TRAVELLERS CHEQUES (EXTENSION)

When travelling overseas some people carry their money as **travellers cheques**. These are more convenient than carrying large amounts of cash. They provide protection in case of accidental loss or theft. If necessary, travellers cheques may be quickly replaced.

Travellers cheques are usually purchased from a bank before you leave your country. You should take cheques in the currency of the country you are visiting, or a widely accepted currency like euro. Usually banks who provide travellers cheques charge 1% of the value of the cheques when they are issued.

$$\textbf{cost of travellers cheques} = \frac{\textbf{amount of foreign currency}}{\textbf{selling exchange rate}} \times \textbf{101\%}$$

It is also possible to buy foreign currency using a credit card that is accepted internationally, such as Visa or Mastercard. Currency can be purchased using your credit card at banks and automatic teller machines (ATMs) in most countries.

| Example 7 | ◀ﾟ Self Tutor |
|---|---|

You want to buy 2000 UK pounds worth of travellers cheques. What will it cost in Australian dollars, if 1 AUD = 0.4032 pounds?

$$\text{cost} = \frac{2000}{0.4032} \times 1.01 = 5009.90 \text{ AUD}$$

## EXERCISE 15A.4

1   Calculate the cost of purchasing travellers cheques worth:

  **a**   1000 euros, using US dollars, if  1 USD = €0.6684

b  130 000 yen, using Canadian dollars, if  1 CAD $=$ ¥84.5976

c  2700 Swiss francs, using Saudi Arabian riyals, if 1 riyal $=$ 0.269 53 Swiss francs

d  8400 rand, using UK pounds, if 1 UK pound $=$ 12.487 rand.

# B        SIMPLE INTEREST

When money is lent, the **borrower** must repay the original amount to the **lender**, usually within a certain amount of time. The initial amount is called the **principal** or **capital**. The borrower usually must also pay a charge for borrowing the money, called **interest**.

The amount of interest depends on the size of the capital, the length of time the loan is for, and the interest rate. Nearly all interest is calculated using one of two methods: **simple interest** or **compound interest**.

## SIMPLE INTEREST

In this method, interest is only charged on the capital and not on any interest already owed.

For example, suppose €2000 is borrowed at 8% p.a. for 3 years.

$$\text{The interest owed after 1 year} = 8\% \text{ of } \text{€}2000$$
$$= \tfrac{8}{100} \times \text{€}2000$$
$$\therefore \quad \text{the interest owed after 3 years} = \tfrac{8}{100} \times \text{€}2000 \times 3$$

From examples like this one we construct the **simple interest formula**:

$$I = \frac{Crn}{100} \quad \text{where} \quad I \text{ is the \textbf{simple interest}}$$

$C$ is the **capital** or amount borrowed

$r$ is the **flat rate of interest per annum** as a percentage

$n$ is the **time** or **duration** of the loan in **years**.

| **Example 8** | ◀) **Self Tutor** |
|---|---|

Calculate the simple interest on a loan of $8000 at a rate of 7% p.a. over 18 months.

$C = 8000, \quad r = 7\%, \quad n = \frac{18}{12} = 1.5$ years

Now $I = \dfrac{Crn}{100} = \dfrac{8000 \times 7 \times 1.5}{100} = 840$

$\therefore$  the simple interest is $840.

p.a. stands for *per annum*.

The simple interest formula can also be used to find the other variables $C$, $r$ and $n$.

## EXERCISE 15B.1

**1** Find the simple interest on a loan of:

   **a** £3000 at a rate of 7% p.a. over 3 years

   **b** $6100 at a rate of 5.9% p.a. over 15 months

   **c** ¥800 000 at a rate of $6\frac{1}{2}$% p.a. over 4 years 7 months

   **d** €250 000 at a rate of 4.8% p.a. over a 134 day period.

**2** Which loan for $130 000 works out cheaper overall:

   **A** 8.2% simple interest for 5 years      **B** 7.7% simple interest for $5\frac{1}{2}$ years?

---

| Example 9 | ◄⟩ Self Tutor |
|---|---|

How much money has been borrowed if the flat rate of interest is 8% p.a. and the simple interest owed after 4 years is $1600?

A **flat rate** is a simple interest rate.

$$I = \frac{C \times r \times n}{100} \qquad \text{where} \quad I = 1600,$$
$$\therefore \quad 1600 = \frac{C \times 8 \times 4}{100} \qquad \qquad r = 8,$$
$$\qquad \qquad \qquad \qquad \qquad \qquad n = 4$$
$$\therefore \quad 1600 = 0.32C$$
$$\therefore \quad \frac{1600}{0.32} = C$$
$$\therefore \quad C = 5000 \qquad \text{So, } \$5000 \text{ was borrowed.}$$

---

**3** A loan at a flat rate of 7% p.a. results in an interest charge of $910 after 5 years. How much money was borrowed?

**4** How much was borrowed if a flat rate of 8% p.a. results in an interest charge of £3456 after 3 years?

**5** An investor wants to earn €2300 in 21 months. If the current simple interest rate is 6.5% p.a., how much does he need to invest?

---

| Example 10 | ◄⟩ Self Tutor |
|---|---|

What flat rate of interest does a bank need to charge so that €5000 will earn €900 simple interest in 18 months?

$$I = \frac{Crn}{100} \qquad \text{where} \quad C = 5000, \quad I = 900, \quad n = 18 \text{ months}$$
$$\therefore \quad 900 = \frac{5000 \times r \times 1.5}{100} \qquad \qquad \qquad = \frac{18}{12}$$
$$\therefore \quad 900 = 75r \qquad \qquad \qquad \qquad \qquad = 1.5 \text{ years}$$
$$\therefore \quad \frac{900}{75} = r \qquad \{\text{dividing both sides by 75}\}$$
$$\therefore \quad 12 = r \qquad \therefore \quad \text{the bank needs to charge 12\% flat rate.}$$

**6** What flat rate of interest must a bank charge if it wants to earn

    **a** $900 in 3 years on $4500         **b** ¥32 000 after 2 years on ¥170 000?

**7** What rate of simple interest needs to be charged on a loan of $9000 in order to earn $700 interest after 8 months?

**8** Anne has saved up £2600 in a flat rate bank account. Her dream holiday costs £3200 and she would like to go in 18 months' time. What flat rate of interest must the account pay for Anne to reach her target?

---

**Example 11**      ◀) Self Tutor

How long will it take $2000 invested at a flat rate of $12\frac{1}{2}\%$ p.a. to amount to $3000?

The interest earned must be $3000 - \$2000 = \$1000$

$$I = \frac{Crn}{100} \qquad \text{where} \quad I = 1000$$
$$\qquad\qquad\qquad\qquad\qquad\qquad C = 2000$$
$$\therefore \quad 1000 = \frac{2000 \times 12.5 \times n}{100} \qquad r = 12.5$$
$$\therefore \quad 1000 = 250n$$
$$\therefore \quad n = 4 \qquad \therefore \quad \text{it will take 4 years}$$

---

**9** How long will it take to earn interest of:

    **a** $5000 on a loan of $20 000 at a flat rate of 7% p.a.

    **b** €487 on a loan of €1200 at $6\frac{3}{4}\%$ p.a. simple interest?

**10** You have £9400 in the bank. If your account pays interest at a flat rate of 6.75% p.a., how long will it take to earn £1800 in interest?

---

**ACTIVITY 2**         **SIMPLE INTEREST CALCULATOR**

 Click on the icon to obtain a simple interest calculator.     **SIMPLE INTEREST**

**What to do:**

Check the answers to **Examples 8** to **11**.

## CALCULATING REPAYMENTS FOR SIMPLE INTEREST LOANS

When a loan is taken out, it must be repaid within the allotted time, along with the interest charges. To help the borrower, the repayments are often made in regular (usually equal) payments over the length of the loan. These may be weekly, fortnightly, monthly, or at other time intervals.

The size of one of these regular payments is found by dividing the total amount to be repaid (capital plus interest) by the number of repayment periods:

$$\text{regular payment} = \frac{\textbf{total to be repaid}}{\textbf{number of repayments}}$$

### Example 12

◀)) **Self Tutor**

Calculate the monthly repayments on a loan of $23 000 at 8% p.a. flat rate over 6 years.

*Step 1:*   Calculate the interest on the loan.

$C = 23\,000$        Now   $I = \dfrac{Crn}{100} = \dfrac{23\,000 \times 8 \times 6}{100}$

$r = 8\%$        $\therefore$   interest $= \$11\,040$

$n = 6$

*Step 2:*   Calculate the total amount to be repaid

total repayment = capital + interest

$= \$23\,000 + \$11\,040$

$= \$34\,040$

*Step 3:*   Calculate the total number of payments.
Repayments are made each month.
In 6 years we have  $6 \times 12 = 72$ months.

*Step 4:*   Determine the size of the regular payment.

Monthly repayment $= \dfrac{\$34\,040}{72} \approx \$472.78$

## EXERCISE 15B.2

1   Calculate the monthly repayments on a loan of $6800 at $8\frac{1}{2}\%$ p.a. simple interest over $2\frac{1}{2}$ years.

2   If a loan of 10 000 baht at a simple interest rate of $5\frac{3}{4}\%$ p.a. for 10 years is to be repaid with half-yearly repayments, how much should each repayment be?

3   A young couple obtained a loan from friends for €15 000 for 36 months at a simple interest rate of $4\frac{1}{2}\%$ p.a.  Calculate the quarterly repayments they must make on this loan.

4   Justine arranges a loan of £8000 from her parents and repays £230 per month for $3\frac{1}{2}$ years. How much interest does she pay on the loan?

5   Eric approaches two friends for a loan and receives the following offers:
*Rachel* will lend $12 000 at $5\frac{1}{4}\%$ p.a. simple interest repayable monthly for $3\frac{1}{2}$ years.
*Lesley* can lend $12 000 at $4\frac{3}{4}\%$ p.a. simple interest repayable monthly for $4\frac{1}{2}$ years.
Eric can only afford a maximum repayment of $300 per month.
Which loan should he accept?

# C COMPOUND INTEREST

**Compound interest** is a method of calculating interest in which the *interest is added to the capital each period*. This means that the interest generated in one period then earns interest itself in the next period.

Each time the interest is calculated, we use the formula $I = \dfrac{Crn}{100}$ where $C$ is the present capital, $r$ is the interest rate per annum, and $n$ is the proportion of a year over which the interest compounds.

### Example 13 🔊 Self Tutor

Calculate the interest paid on a deposit of $6000 at 8% p.a. compounded annually for 3 years.

The interest is compounded annually, so we need to calculate interest each year.

| Year | Capital (1) | $Interest = \dfrac{Crn}{100}$ (2) | Balance (1) + (2) |
|------|-------------|-----------------------------------|-------------------|
| 1 | $6000.00 | $6000.00 × $\frac{8}{100}$ × 1 = $480.00 | $6480.00 |
| 2 | $6480.00 | $6480.00 × $\frac{8}{100}$ × 1 = $518.40 | $6998.40 |
| 3 | $6998.40 | $6998.40 × $\frac{8}{100}$ × 1 = $559.87 | $7558.27 |

Thus, the $6000.00 grows to $7558.27 after 3 years,

∴ $7558.27 − $6000.00 = $1558.27 is interest.

We can see that:

- the amount of interest paid increases from one period to the next since the capital is increasing
- the total interest earned = the final balance − the initial capital.

## EXERCISE 15C.1

1 Find the final value of a compound interest investment of:

    **a** €4500 after 3 years at 7% p.a. with interest calculated annually

    **b** $6000 after 4 years at 5% p.a. with interest calculated annually

    **c** £7400 after 3 years at 6.5% p.a. with interest calculated annually.

2 Find the total interest earned for the following compound interest investments:

    **a** 950 euro after 2 years at 5.7% p.a. with interest calculated annually

    **b** £4180 after 3 years at 5.75% p.a. with interest calculated annually

    **c** ¥237 000 after 4 years at 7.3% p.a. with interest calculated annually.

**3** Luisa invests $15 000 into an account which pays 8% p.a. compounded annually. Find:

  **a** the value of her account after 2 years

  **b** the total interest earned after 2 years.

**4** Yumi places 888 000 yen in a fixed term investment account which pays 6.5% p.a. compounded annually.

  **a** How much will she have in her account after 3 years?

  **b** What interest has she earned over this period?

## DIFFERENT COMPOUNDING PERIODS

Interest can be compounded more than once per year. Interest is commonly compounded:

- half-yearly   (two times per year)
- quarterly   (four times per year)
- monthly   (12 times per year)
- daily   (365 or 366 times a year)

---

**Example 14**    ◀) **Self Tutor**

Calculate the final balance of a $10 000 investment at 6% p.a. where interest is compounded quarterly for one year.

We need to calculate the interest generated each quarter.

| Quarter | Capital (1) | Interest $= \dfrac{Crn}{100}$ (2) | Balance (1) + (2) |
|:---:|:---:|:---:|:---:|
| 1 | $10 000.00 | $10 000.00 $\times \frac{6}{100} \times \frac{1}{4} = $150.00$ | $10 150.00 |
| 2 | $10 150.00 | $10 150.00 $\times \frac{6}{100} \times \frac{1}{4} = $152.25$ | $10 302.25 |
| 3 | $10 302.25 | $10 302.25 $\times \frac{6}{100} \times \frac{1}{4} = $154.53$ | $10 456.78 |
| 4 | $10 456.78 | $10 456.78 $\times \frac{6}{100} \times \frac{1}{4} = $156.85$ | $10 613.63 |

Thus, the final balance would be $10 613.63.

---

## EXERCISE 15C.2

**1** Mac places $8500 in a fixed deposit account that pays interest at the rate of 6% p.a. compounded quarterly. How much will Mac have in his account after 1 year?

**2** Michaela invests her savings of €24 000 in an account that pays 5% p.a. compounded monthly. How much interest will she earn in 3 months?

**3** Compare the interest paid on $45 000 at 8.5% p.a. over 2 years if the interest is:

  **a** simple interest       **b** compounded $\frac{1}{2}$ yearly       **c** compounded quarterly.

## COMPOUND INTEREST FORMULAE

Instead of using a geometric sequence as in **Chapter 14**, we can now use these compound interest formulae:

For interest compounding annually,   $A = C \times \left(1 + \frac{r}{100}\right)^n$

where:   $A$  is the **future value** (or **final balance**)
         $C$  is the **present value** or **capital** (the amount originally invested)
         $r$  is the **interest rate per year**
         $n$  is the **number of years**

For interest compounding with $k$ periods in a single year,   $A = C \times \left(1 + \frac{r}{100k}\right)^{kn}$

In either case the interest   $I = A - C$.

### Example 15                                                    ◄) Self Tutor

Calculate the final balance of a $10\,000$ investment at $6\%$ p.a. where interest is compounded quarterly for one year.

> Compare this method with the method in **Example 14**.

$C = 10\,000, \ r = 6, \ n = 1, \ k = 4$

Now   $A = C \times \left(1 + \frac{r}{100k}\right)^{kn}$

$\therefore \ A = 10\,000 \times \left(1 + \frac{6}{400}\right)^4$

$\therefore \ A = 10\,613.64$

So, the final balance is   $\$10\,613.64$.

### Example 16                                                    ◄) Self Tutor

How much interest is earned if €8800 is placed in an account that pays $4\frac{1}{2}\%$ p.a. compounded monthly for $3\frac{1}{2}$ years?

$C = 8800$                                 Now   $A = C \times \left(1 + \frac{r}{100k}\right)^{kn}$

$r = 4.5, \ n = 3.5$                       $\therefore \ A = 8800 \times \left(1 + \frac{4.5}{1200}\right)^{42}$

$k = 12$                                   $\therefore \ A = 10\,298.08$

$\therefore \ kn = 12 \times 3\frac{1}{2} = 42$     So,   $I = A - C = 10\,298.08 - 8800$

$= 1498.08$

The interest earned is   €1498.08.

## EXERCISE 15C.3

1   Ali places £9000 in a savings account that pays $8\%$ p.a. compounded quarterly. How much will she have in the account after 5 years?

2   How much interest would be earned on a deposit of $2500 at $5\%$ p.a. compounded half yearly for 4 years?

**3** Compare the interest earned on 35 000 yuan left for 3 years in an account paying $4\frac{1}{2}\%$ p.a. where the interest is:

 **a** simple interest    **b** compounded annually  **c** compounded half yearly

 **d** compounded quarterly  **e** compounded monthly.

**4** Jai recently inherited $92 000. He decides to invest it for 10 years before he spends any of it. The two banks in his town offer the following terms:

  *Bank A:*   $5\frac{1}{2}\%$ p.a. compounded yearly.

  *Bank B:*   $5\frac{1}{4}\%$ p.a. compounded monthly.

 Which bank offers Jai the greater interest on his inheritance?

**5** Mimi has €28 000 to invest. She can place it in an account that pays $8\%$ p.a. simple interest or one that pays $7\frac{1}{2}\%$ p.a. compounded monthly. Which account will earn her more interest over a 4 year period, and how much more will it be?

## USING A GRAPHICS CALCULATOR FOR COMPOUND INTEREST PROBLEMS

Most graphics calculators have an in-built **finance program** that can be used to investigate financial scenarios. This is called a **TVM Solver**, where **TVM** stands for **time value of money**. The TVM Solver can be used to find any variable if all the other variables are given. For the **TI-84 plus**, the abbreviations used are:

- $N$  represents the **number of time periods**
- $I\%$  represents the **interest rate per year**
- $PV$  represents the **present value** of the investment
- $PMT$  represents the **payment each time period**
- $FV$  represents the **future value** of the investment
- $P/Y$  is the **number of payments per year**
- $C/Y$  is the **number of compounding periods per year**
- $PMT$ : END BEGIN  lets you choose between the payments at the end of a time period or at the beginning of a time period. Most interest payments are made at the end of the time periods.

The abbreviations used by the other calculator models are similar, and can be found in the **graphics calculator instructions** at the start of the book.

## INVESTIGATION 1         DOUBLING TIME

Many investors pose the question: "How long will it take to double my money?"

**What to do:**

**1** Use the in-built finance program on your graphics calculator to find the amount that investments of $10 000 grow to if interest is compounded *annually* at:

 **a** $8\%$ p.a. for 9 years  **b** $6\%$ p.a. for 12 years  **c** $4\%$ p.a. for 18 years.

**2** You should notice that each investment approximately *doubles* in value. Can you see a pattern involving the interest rate and time of the investment?

**3** Suggest a rule that would tell an investor:

**a** how long they need to invest their money at a given annual compound rate for it to double in value

**b** the annual compound rate they need to invest at for a given time period for it to double in value.

**4** Use your rule to estimate the time needed for a $6000 investment to double in value at the following annual compound rates:

**a** 2% p.a.     **b** 5% p.a.     **c** 10% p.a.     **d** 18% p.a.

Check your estimations using a graphics calculator.

**5** Use your rule to estimate the annual compound interest rate required for a $50 000 investment to double in value in:

**a** 20 years     **b** 10 years     **c** 5 years     **d** 2 years

Check your estimations using a graphics calculator.

---

| Example 17 | ◀) Self Tutor |
|---|---|

Holly invests 15 000 UK pounds in an account that pays 4.25% p.a. compounded monthly. How much is her investment worth after 5 years?

To answer this using the TVM function on the calculator, first set up the TVM screen. Note that the initial investment is considered as an outgoing and is entered as a negative value.

Casio fx-9860g            TI-84 plus            TI-*n*spire

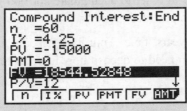 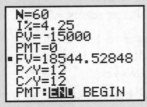 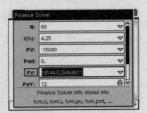

Holly has 18 544.53 UK pounds after 5 years.

---

## EXERCISE 15C.4

Use a graphics calculator to answer the following questions:

**1** If I deposit £6000 in a bank account that pays 5% p.a. compounded daily, how much will I have in my account after 2 years?

**2** When my child was born I deposited $2000 in a bank account paying 4% p.a. compounded half-yearly. How much will my child receive on her 18th birthday?

**3** Calculate the compound interest earned on an investment of €13 000 for 4 years if the interest rate is 7% p.a. compounded quarterly.

---

**Example 18**                                                              ◀ᴑ) **Self Tutor**

How much does Halena need to deposit into an account to collect $50 000 at the end of 3 years if the account is paying 5.2% p.a. compounded quarterly?

*Formula solution:*

Given  $A = 50\,000$

$\quad\quad r = 5.2$

$\quad\quad n = 3, \ k = 4$

$\therefore \ kn = 4 \times 3 = 12$

Using  $A = C \times \left(1 + \frac{r}{100k}\right)^{kn}$

$\therefore \ 50\,000 = C \times \left(1 + \frac{5.2}{400}\right)^{12}$

$\therefore \ C = 42\,820.99 \quad$ {using solver}

$\therefore \ \$42\,821$ needs to be deposited.

*Graphics Calculator Solution:*

To answer this using the TVM function, set up the TVM screen as shown.
There are  $3 \times 4 = 12$  quarter periods.

| Casio fx-9860g | TI-84 plus | TI-*n*spire |
|----------------|------------|-------------|
| 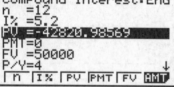 |  | 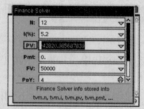 |

Thus,  $42\,821$ needs to be deposited.

---

**4** Calculate the amount you would need to invest now in order to accumulate 250 000 yen in 5 years' time, if the interest rate is 4.5% p.a. compounded monthly.

**5** You would like to buy a car costing $23 000 in two years' time. Your bank account pays 5% p.a. compounded half-yearly. How much do you need to deposit now in order to be able to buy your car in two years?

**6** You have just won the lottery and decide to invest the money. Your accountant advises you to deposit your winnings in an account that pays 5% p.a. compounded daily. After two years your winnings have grown to €88 413.07. How much did you win in the lottery?

**7** Before leaving Italy for a three year trip to India, I deposit a sum of money in an account that pays 6% p.a. compounded quarterly. When I return from the trip, the balance in my account is now €9564.95. How much interest has been added while I have been away?

**Example 19**   ◀ Self Tutor

For how long must Magnus invest €4000 at 6.45% p.a. compounded half-yearly for it to amount to €10 000?

*Formula solution:*

Given  $A = 10\,000$  

$C = 4000$  

$r = 6.45$  

$k = 2$

Using  $A = C \times \left(1 + \frac{r}{100k}\right)^{kn}$

$\therefore\ 10\,000 = 4000 \times \left(1 + \frac{6.45}{200}\right)^{2n}$

$\therefore\ 10\,000 = 4000 \times (1.032\,25)^{2n}$

$\therefore\ n \approx 14.43$   {using solver}

Thus, 14.5 years are required (rounding to next half-year).

*Graphics calculator:*

To answer this using the TVM function, set up the TVM screen as shown. We then need to find the number of periods $n$ required (which is distinct from the variable $n$ which gives the number of years used in the formula above).

**Casio fx-9860g**    **TI-84 plus**    **TI-*n*spire**

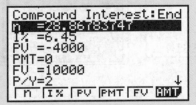    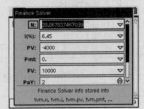

$n = 28.9$, so 29 half-years are required, or 14.5 years.

When using a TVM solver, we find the number of compounding periods and need to convert to the time units required.

**8**  Your parents give you $8000 to buy a car but the car you want costs $9200. You deposit the $8000 into an account that pays 6% p.a. compounded monthly. How long will it be before you have enough money to buy the car you want?

**9**  A couple inherited €40 000 and deposited it in an account paying $4\frac{1}{2}$% p.a. compounded quarterly. They withdrew the money as soon as they had over €45 000. How long did they keep the money in that account?

**10**  A business deposits £80 000 in an account that pays $5\frac{1}{4}$% p.a. compounded monthly. How long will it take before they double their money?

**11**  An investor deposits $12 000 in an account paying 5% p.a. compounded daily. How long will it take the investor to earn $5000 in interest?

**Example 20**                                                     ◄)) **Self Tutor**

If Iman deposits $5000 in an account that compounds interest monthly, and 2.5 years later the account totals $6000, what annual rate of interest was paid?

*Formula solution:*

Given  $A = 6000$          Using  $A = C \left(1 + \frac{r}{100k}\right)^{kn}$

$\quad\quad C = 5000$          $\therefore\ 6000 = 5000 \times \left(1 + \frac{r}{1200}\right)^{30}$

$\quad\quad n = 2.5$

$\quad\quad k = 12$             $\therefore\ r \approx 7.32\%$  per year

$\therefore\ kn = 12 \times 2.5 = 30$     So,  7.32% p.a. is required.

*Graphics calculator:*

To answer this using the TVM function on the calculator, set up the TVM screen as shown. In this case  $n = 2.5 \times 12 = 30$ months.

| Casio fx-9860g | TI-84 plus | TI-*n*spire |
|:---:|:---:|:---:|
| 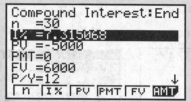 | 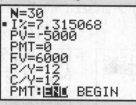 |  |

An annual interest rate of 7.32% p.a. is required.

**12** An investor purchases rare medals for $10 000 and hopes to sell them 3 years later for $15 000. What must the annual increase in the value of the medals be over this period, in order for the investor's target to be reached?

**13** If I deposited €5000 into an account that compounds interest monthly, and $3\frac{1}{2}$ years later the account totals €6165, what annual rate of interest did the account pay?

**14** A young couple invests their savings of 900 000 yen in an account where the interest is compounded annually. Three years later the account balance is 1 049 322 yen. What interest rate has been paid?

**15** An investor purchased a parcel of shares for £15 000 and sold them 4 years later for £24 500. He also purchased a house for £105 000 and sold it 7 years later for £198 000. Which investment had the greater average annual percentage increase in value?

## FIXED TERM DEPOSITS

As the name suggests, deposits can be locked away for a fixed time period (from one month to ten years) at a fixed interest rate.

The interest is calculated on the daily balance and can be paid monthly, quarterly, half-yearly, or annually.

The interest can be compounded so that the capital increases during the fixed term. However, the interest can also be paid out. Many retirees live off interest that fixed term deposits generate.

Generally, the interest rate offered increases if the money is locked away for a longer period of time. We will consider scenarios where the interest is compounded as an application of **compound interest**.

Below is a typical schedule of rates offered by a financial institution, for deposits of $5000 to $25 000, and $25 000 to $100 000. All interest rates given are per annum.

For terms of 12 months or more, interest must be paid at least annually.

| Term (months) | Interest at Maturity | | Monthly Interest | | Quarterly Interest | | Half-yearly Interest | |
|---|---|---|---|---|---|---|---|---|
| | $5k - $25k | $25k - $100k | $5k - $25k | $25k - $100k | $5k - $25k | $25k - $100k | $5k - $25k | $25k - $100k |
| 1 | 3.80% | 4.50% | | | | | | |
| 2 | 4.15% | 4.75% | | | | | | |
| 3 | 5.20% | 5.20% | | | | | | |
| 4 | 5.40% | 6.00% | | | | | | |
| 5* | 5.45%* | 6.25%* | | | | | | |
| 6 | 5.45% | 5.50% | | | | | 5.45% | 5.50% |
| 7 - 8* | 6.10%* | 6.35%* | | | | | 6.05%* | 6.30%* |
| 9 - 11 | 5.65% | 5.90% | | | | | 5.65% | 5.90% |
| 12 - 17* | 6.30%* | 6.40%* | 6.15%* | 6.20%* | 6.15%* | 6.25%* | 6.20%* | 6.30%* |
| 18 - 23 | 6.10% | 6.40% | 5.95% | 6.20% | 5.95% | 6.25% | 6.00% | 6.30% |
| 24 - 120 | 6.20% | 6.40% | 6.05% | 6.20% | 6.05% | 6.25% | 6.10% | 6.30% |

\* indicates special offers

---

### Example 21                                    ◀ Self Tutor

For the institution with interest rates given above, compare the interest offered if $45 000 is deposited for 15 months with interest compounded:   **a** monthly   **b** quarterly.

**a**  $45 000 deposited for 15 months with interest compounded monthly receives 6.2% p.a. Using a graphics calculator, we solve for $FV$.

| Casio fx-9860g | TI-84 plus | TI-*n*spire |
|---|---|---|
| 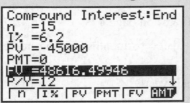 | N=15<br>I%=6.2<br>PV=-45000<br>PMT=0<br>•FV=48616.49946<br>P/Y=12<br>C/Y=12<br>PMT:**END** BEGIN |  |

Interest = $48 616.50 − $45 000 = $3616.50

**b** $45\,000$ deposited for 15 months with interest compounded quarterly receives 6.25% p.a. Using a graphics calculator, we solve for $FV$.

| Casio fx-9860g | TI-84 plus | TI-*n*spire |
|---|---|---|
| 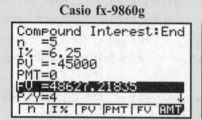 | 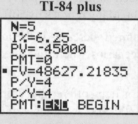 |  |

Interest $= \$48\,627.22 - \$45\,000 = \$3627.22$

So, the quarterly option earns $10.72 more interest.

---

### Example 22

$10\,000$ is invested in a fixed term deposit for 24 months, with interest paid monthly at the rate given in the table. Find the effective return on the investment if the investor must pay 48.5 cents tax out of every dollar they earn.

From the interest rate table, $10\,000$ deposited for 24 months with the interest compounded monthly receives 6.05% p.a.

Using a graphics calculator, we solve for $FV$.

| Casio fx-9860g | TI-84 plus | TI-*n*spire |
|---|---|---|
|  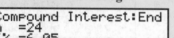  | 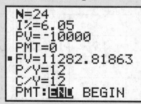 | 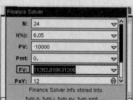 |

$$\text{Interest} = \$11\,282.82 - \$10\,000$$
$$= \$1282.82$$
$$\text{Tax} = 48.5\% \text{ of } \$1282.82$$
$$= \$622.17$$
$$\therefore \quad \text{the effective return} = \$1282.82 - \$622.17$$
$$= \$660.65 \quad \text{(which is an average of 3.30\% p.a.)}$$

---

## EXERCISE 15C.5

In the questions below, refer to the Fixed Term deposit rates on page **475**:

**1** Compare the interest offered if $18\,000$ is deposited for 18 months and the interest is compounded:

    **a** monthly                    **b** half-yearly.

**2** Calculate the effective return after tax for the investments in **1** if the tax rate is:

    **a** 48.5 cents in the dollar           **b** 31.5 cents in the dollar.

**3** Derk wins $50 000 and decides to deposit it in a fixed term deposit for one year.

    **a** What option would you advise Derk to invest in?

    **b** How much interest would he earn?

    **c** What is Derk's effective return after tax if Derk's tax rate is 44.5%?

## THE EFFECTIVE INTEREST RATE ON AN INVESTMENT (EXTENSION)

Because interest rates are applied in different ways, comparing them can be misleading.

Consider €10 000 invested at 6% compounded annually.

Now consider €10 000 invested at 5.85% compounded monthly.

After 1 year,

$$C = €10\,000 \times \left(1 + \tfrac{6}{100}\right)^1$$
$$= €10\,000 \times (1.06)^1$$
$$= €10\,600$$

After 1 year,

$$C = €10\,000 \times \left(1 + \tfrac{5.85}{1200}\right)^{12}$$
$$= €10\,000 \times (1.004\,875)^{12}$$
$$= €10\,600.94$$

Hence, 5.85% p.a. compounded monthly is equivalent to 6% p.a. compounded annually.

We say 5.85% p.a. compounded monthly is a **nominal rate** (the named rate) and it is equivalent to an **effective rate** of 6% p.a. compounded on an annual basis.

> The **effective rate** is the **equivalent annualised rate** or **equivalent interest rate compounded annually**.

To convert a nominal compound rate to an effective rate:

$$\frac{r}{100} = \left(1 + \frac{i}{100}\right)^c - 1 \quad \text{where} \quad r \text{ is the \textbf{effective rate}}$$

$i$ is the **rate per compound interest period**

$c$ is the **number of compound periods per annum**.

### Example 23
    ◀) **Self Tutor**

Which is the better rate offered:

    4% p.a. compounded monthly   or   4.2% p.a. compounded quarterly?

Given $i = \tfrac{4}{12} \approx 0.333$, $c = 12$

$$\frac{r}{100} = \left(1 + \frac{i}{100}\right)^c - 1$$
$$\approx (1.003\,33)^{12} - 1$$
$$\approx 0.040\,74$$
$$\therefore \ r \approx 4.07$$

Given $i = \tfrac{4.2}{4} = 1.05$, $c = 4$

$$\frac{r}{100} = \left(1 + \frac{i}{100}\right)^c - 1$$
$$= (1.0105)^4 - 1$$
$$\approx 0.042\,66$$
$$\therefore \ r \approx 4.27$$

∴ the effective rate is 4.07% p.a.      ∴ the effective rate is 4.27% p.a.

The better rate for an investment is 4.2% p.a. compounded quarterly.

## EXERCISE 15C.6

**1**  Which is the better rate offered:
    5.4% p.a. compounded half-yearly  or  5.3% p.a. compounded quarterly?

**2**  Which is the better rate offered:
    7.6% p.a. compounded monthly  or  7.75% p.a. compounded half-yearly?

**3**  **a**  Find the effective rate of interest on an investment where the nominal rate is:
        **i**  4.95% p.a. compounded annually    **ii**  4.9% p.a. compounded monthly.
    **b**  Which investment option would you choose?

**4**  **a**  Find the effective rate of interest on an investment where the nominal rate is:
        **i**  7.75% p.a. compounded daily    **ii**  7.95% p.a. compounded half-yearly.
    **b**  Which investment option would you choose?

**5**  A bank offers an investment rate of 6.8% p.a. They claim the account will effectively
    yield 7.02% p.a. How many times is the interest compounded per annum?

**6**  Suppose you have $40 000 to invest in a fixed term deposit for one year.
    **a**  Consult the rates on page **475** and calculate the effective rate of interest if it is paid:
        **i**  monthly        **ii**  quarterly        **iii**  half-yearly        **iv**  at maturity.
    **b**  Which option would you take and how much interest would you receive?

## D          DEPRECIATION

Assets such as computers, cars, and furniture lose value as time passes. This is due to wear
and tear, technology becoming old, fashions changing, and other reasons. We say that they
**depreciate** over time.

> **Depreciation** is the loss in value of an item over time.

In many countries, the Taxation Office will allow a business to claim a **tax deduction** on
depreciating assets that are necessary for the business to run.

Different countries use different systems to calculate depreciation. One common way is the
**reducing balance method**, where an item is depreciating by a fixed percentage each year of
its useful life.

The table below shows the depreciation on a pickup truck over a three year period. The truck
was bought for $36 000 and loses value at 25% each year.

The depreciated value is also called the **book value** of the item.

| Age (years) | Depreciation | Book value |
|---|---|---|
| 0 | | $36 000.00 |
| 1 | 25% of $36 000.00 = $9000.00 | $36 000.00 − $9000.00 = $27 000.00 |
| 2 | 25% of $27 000.00 = $6750.00 | $27 000.00 − $6750.00 = $20 250.00 |
| 3 | 25% of $20 250.00 = $5062.50 | $20 250.00 − $5062.50 = $15 187.50 |

The annual depreciation decreases each year as it is calculated from the previous year's (reduced) book value.

We can also use our knowledge of geometric sequences to find the book value of the pickup truck after 3 years.

Each year, the truck is worth $100\% - 25\% = 75\%$ of its previous value.

This is a constant ratio of 0.75.

$$\therefore \quad \text{the value after 3 years} = \$36\,000 \times (0.75)^3$$
$$= \$15\,187.50$$

When calculating depreciation, the **annual multiplier** is $\left(1 + \dfrac{r}{100}\right)$, where $r$ is the *negative* annual depreciation rate as a percentage.

Recall that instead of using a geometric sequence to find compound interest, we used a formula. We can do the same thing here, using the same formula but note that $r$ is negative for depreciation.

> The **depreciation formula** is   $A = C \times \left(1 + \dfrac{r}{100}\right)^n$
>
> where   $A$ is the **future value** after $n$ time periods
>   $C$ is the **original purchase price**
>   $r$ is the **depreciation rate per period** and $r$ is **negative**
>   $n$ is the **number of periods**.

### Example 24                                    ◄ Self Tutor

An industrial dishwasher was purchased for £2400 and depreciated at 15% each year.

a Find its value after six years.        b By how much did it depreciate?

a   $A = C \times \left(1 + \frac{r}{100}\right)^n$ where $C = 2400$, $r = -15$, $n = 6$
$\therefore \quad A = 2400 \times (1 - 0.15)^6$
$\quad\quad = 2400 \times (0.85)^6$
$\quad\quad \approx 905.16$        So, after 6 years the value is £905.16.

b Depreciation $= £2400 - £905.16 = £1494.84$

## EXERCISE 15D

1 a A lathe, purchased by a workshop for €2500, depreciates by 15% each year. Copy and complete the table to find the value of the lathe after 3 years.

| Age (years) | Depreciation | Book Value |
|---|---|---|
| 0 | | €2500 |
| 1 | 15% of €2500 = €375 | |
| 2 | | |
| 3 | | |

b How much depreciation can be claimed as a tax deduction by the workshop in:

   i Year 1        ii Year 2        iii Year 3?

**2  a**  A tractor, purchased for €110 000, depreciates at 25% p.a. for 5 years. Find its book value at the end of this period.

  **b**  By how much did it depreciate?

**3  a**  I buy a laptop for ¥87 500 and keep it for 3 years, during which time it depreciates at an annual rate of 30%. What will its value be at the end of this period?

  **b**  By how much has the laptop depreciated?

---

**Example 25**    ◀ɔ) **Self Tutor**

A vending machine bought for $15 000 is sold 3 years later for $9540. Calculate its annual rate of depreciation.

*Formula solution:*    $A = 9540, \ C = 15\,000, \ n = 3$

$$A = C \left(1 + \tfrac{r}{100}\right)^n$$

$$\therefore \ 9540 = 15\,000 \times \left(1 + \tfrac{r}{100}\right)^3$$

$$\therefore \ r \approx -14.0025 \quad \{\text{using solver}\}$$

So, the annual rate of depreciation is 14.0%.

*Graphics calculator solution:*

To answer this using the TVM function, set up the TVM screen with $N = 3$, $PV = -15\,000$, $PMT = 0$, $FV = 9540$, $P/Y = 1$, $C/Y = 1$.

| **Casio fx-9860g** | **TI-84 plus** | **TI-*n*spire** |
|:---:|:---:|:---:|
| 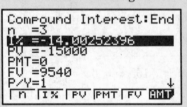 |  | 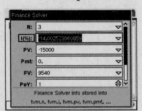 |

Thus, the annual depreciation rate is 14.0%.

---

**4**  A printing press costing £250 000 was sold 4 years later for £80 000. At what yearly rate did it depreciate in value?

**5**  A 4-wheel-drive vehicle was purchased for $45 000 and sold for $28 500 after 2 years and 3 months. Find its annual rate of depreciation.

**6**  The Taxation Office allows industrial vehicles to be depreciated at $7\tfrac{1}{2}\%$ each 6 months.

  **a**  What would be the value in 2 years' time of vehicles currently worth $240 000?

  **b**  By how much have they depreciated?

# PERSONAL LOANS

Many people take out a **personal loan** to finance purchases such as cars, boats, renovations, overseas holidays, education expenses, or share portfolios.

Different loans have different terms, conditions, fees, and interest rates, so it is important to shop around. Personal loans can be obtained from banks, credit unions, and finance companies.

Personal loans are usually **short term** (6 months to 7 years) and can be either **secured** or **unsecured**. Car loans are usually **secured**. This means the car acts as **security** in the event that the borrower fails to make the payments. The bank has the right to sell the car and take the money owed to them. A loan to pay for an overseas holiday may be **unsecured**. Such loans will usually charge higher interest rates than secured loans.

Interest is calculated on the **reducing balance** of the loan, so the interest reduces as the loan is repaid. Borrowers can usually choose between **fixed** or **variable** interest rates.

**Fixed rate loans** have fixed repayments for the entire loan period. This may appeal to people on a tight budget.

**Variable rate loans** have interest rates that fluctuate with economic changes and thus repayments may vary.

For some loans, higher repayments than the minimum may be allowed if you want to pay the loan off sooner.

## INTEREST

Interest is an important factor to consider in the repayment of loans. For long term loans the interest may amount to more than the original amount borrowed. So, when selecting a loan, the borrower will be given an indication of the regular repayment amount based on the loan amount, the time of the loan, and the interest rate charged.

A table of monthly repayments follows and is based on borrowing 1000 units of currency.

| Table of Monthly Repayments per 1000 units of currency | | | | | | | |
|---|---|---|---|---|---|---|---|
| Loan term | Annual interest rate | | | | | | |
| (months) | 6% | 7% | 8% | 9% | 10% | 11% | 12% |
| 12 | 86.0664 | 86.5267 | 86.9884 | 87.4515 | 87.9159 | 88.3817 | 88.8488 |
| 18 | 58.2317 | 58.6850 | 59.1403 | 59.5977 | 60.0571 | 60.5185 | 60.9820 |
| 24 | 44.3206 | 44.7726 | 45.2273 | 45.6847 | 46.1449 | 46.6078 | 47.0735 |
| 30 | 35.9789 | 36.4319 | 36.8883 | 37.3482 | 37.8114 | 38.2781 | 38.7481 |
| 36 | 30.4219 | 30.8771 | 31.3364 | 31.7997 | 32.2672 | 32.7387 | 33.2143 |
| 42 | 26.4562 | 26.9142 | 27.3770 | 27.8445 | 28.3168 | 28.7939 | 29.2756 |
| 48 | 23.4850 | 23.9462 | 24.4129 | 24.8850 | 25.3626 | 25.8455 | 26.3338 |
| 54 | 21.1769 | 21.6416 | 22.1124 | 22.5894 | 23.0724 | 23.5615 | 24.0566 |
| 60 | 19.3328 | 19.8012 | 20.2764 | 20.7584 | 21.2470 | 21.7424 | 22.2444 |

In decimal currencies, the resulting monthly instalments are usually rounded off to the **next 10 cents**. For example, $485.51 becomes $485.60.

---

### Example 26

🔊 Self Tutor

Isabelle buys a car using a €9200 personal loan. The bank charges 12% p.a. interest over a $3\frac{1}{2}$ year term. Find the:

**a** monthly repayments    **b** total repayments    **c** interest charged.

---

**a** The loan is for 42 months at an interest rate of 12% p.a.
From the table, the monthly repayments on each €1000 are €29.2756

∴ the repayments on €9200 = €29.2756 × 9.2    {9.2 lots of €1000}

$\phantom{∴ the repayments on €9200} = €269.335\,52$

$\phantom{∴ the repayments on €9200} ≈ €269.40$    {next 10 cents}

∴ the repayments are €269.40 per month.

**b** Total repayments = monthly repayment × number of months

$\phantom{Total repayments} = €269.40 × 42$

$\phantom{Total repayments} = €11\,314.80$

∴ €11 314.80 is repaid in total.

**c** Interest = total repayments − amount borrowed

$\phantom{Interest} = €11\,314.80 − €9200$

$\phantom{Interest} = €2114.80$

So, €2114.80 is paid in interest.

---

The in-built finance program on a **graphics calculator** can also be used to calculate the monthly repayments on a loan.

For example, to calculate the monthly repayments for **Example 26** the following information is entered:

**Casio fx-9860g**        **TI-84 plus**        **TI-*n*spire**

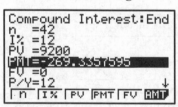
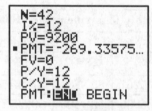
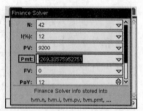

We solve for *PMT* to find the monthly repayments, then round off the monthly repayment of €269.34 to the next 10 cents, which is €269.40.

## EXERCISE 15E

**1** Raphael wants to go overseas on holidays. He takes out a personal loan for $1200, which he will repay over 5 years at 8% p.a. Calculate the:

**a** monthly repayments    **b** total repayments    **c** interest charged.

**2** Pepe takes out a personal loan of $14 000 to buy an oboe. He will repay it over 4 years at 11% p.a. Calculate the:

   **a** monthly repayments    **b** total repayments    **c** interest charged.

**3** Dave and Maddie need £21 000 to pay for house renovations. Their bank offers them a personal loan at 9% p.a. Calculate the total interest they will pay if they repay it over:

   **a** 2 years       **b** 5 years.

**4** Carla wants to borrow €25 000 to invest in an olive plantation. Calculate the total interest charged for the following options:

   **A** Northwest Bank offers 6% over 4 years

   **B** County Credit Union offers 8% over $2\frac{1}{2}$ years.

What would you recommend for Carla?

## INVESTIGATION 2                      BUYING A CAR

Use the skills and knowledge you have built up in this chapter to **investigate** the following scenario. You could possibly set up a **spreadsheet** to help you.

Alma is considering buying a new car. She wants to spend about $20 000. She has $5000 in savings and a spare $500 per month to either save or use on repayments.

**What to do:**

**1** Suppose Alma invests the $5000 in a 6 month Term Deposit Account. She also opens a Cash Management Account and saves $500 per month in it. Investigate how long it will take her to have $20 000 saved. You could investigate the interest rates offered by your local banks, or make a reasonable estimate of the rates and fees. Detail your assumptions and calculations, including interest earned. You may or may not want to consider tax.

**2** Now suppose Alma wants to buy a $20 000 car now. She has two choices:

   • **Personal Loan**: available at 11% p.a. over 3 years

   • **Paying on terms**: the dealer will accept a 10% deposit and $420 per month over 5 years.

Investigate the costs involved in each option. Detail any assumptions you make, such as the size of the personal loan, and calculate the total costs and interest paid. Which option would you recommend and why?

**3** Investigate a combination of saving and borrowing. For example, what would happen if Alma saved for 6 months or a year and then borrowed money? Detail any assumptions you make and set out all calculations.

**4** Based on your investigations in **1**, **2** and **3**, how would **you** advise Alma to buy the car? Clearly explain your reasons.

## F  INFLATION

The **Consumer Price Index (CPI)** measures the increase in price of a general 'basket' of goods and services over time, and is an accepted method of measuring **inflation**. Inflation effectively reduces the purchasing power of money since over time, a fixed amount of money will not be able to purchase the same amount of goods and services.

For example, you may have €15 000 ready to purchase a new car. If you delay buying the car now, a similar new car may cost €17 000 in a few years. Your €15 000 has lost some of its purchasing power due to inflation. Of course, the €15 000 could be invested at a rate greater than that of inflation to counter this.

Many investors take the effects of inflation into account when they access the returns received from investments. The **real rate of return** takes into account the effect of inflation.

### Example 27                                              ◀) Self Tutor

£10 000 is deposited in a fixed term account for 3 years with interest of 5.4% p.a. compounded monthly. Inflation over the period averages 2.5% p.a.

  **a** Calculate the value of the investment after three years.

  **b** What is the value of the £10 000 indexed for inflation?

  **c** What is the real increase in value of the investment?

  **d** Calculate the real average annual percentage increase in the investment.

---

  **a** Using a graphics calculator, we solve for $FV$.

    $N = 36$, $I\% = 5.4$, $PV = -10\,000$, $PMT = 0$, $P/Y = 12$, $C/Y = 12$

    The investment is worth £11 754.33 after three years.

  **b** Inflation increases at 2.5% p.a. on a compound basis.

    Indexed value $= £10\,000 \times 1.025 \times 1.025 \times 1.025$

                  $= £10\,000 \times (1.025)^3$

                  $= £10\,768.91$

  **c** Real increase in value of the investment $= £11\,754.33 - £10\,768.91 = £985.42$

  **d** Using a graphics calculator we find the real average percentage increase in the investment, by solving for $I\%$.

    $N = 3$, $PV = -10\,768.91$, $PMT = 0$, $FV = 11\,754.33$, $P/Y = 1$, $C/Y = 1$

    After inflation there is effectively a 2.96% p.a. increase in the investment.

## EXERCISE 15F.1

**1** Ian requires £1000 per week to maintain his lifestyle. If inflation averages 3% p.a., how much will Ian require per week to maintain his current lifestyle in:

  **a** 10 years         **b** 20 years         **c** 30 years?

**2** Addie deposited 50 000 Swiss francs in a fixed term account for five years with interest of 5.7% p.a. compounded quarterly. Inflation over the period averages 2.3% p.a.

  **a** Find the value of her investment after five years.

    **b**  Calculate the value of the 50 000 francs indexed for inflation.

    **c**  Find the real increase in value of her investment.

    **d**  What is the real average annual percentage increase in her investment?

**3**  Gino invested €20 000 in a fixed term deposit for three years with interest of 3.85% p.a. compounded monthly. Inflation over the period averages 3.4% p.a.

    **a**  What is the value of Gino's investment after three years?

    **b**  Index the €20 000 for inflation.

    **c**  Calculate the real increase in value of Gino's investment.

    **d**  Find the real average annual percentage increase in the investment.

**4**  Jordan leaves $5000 in an account paying 4.15% p.a. compounded annually for 2 years. Inflation runs at 3.5% p.a. in year 1 and 5.2% p.a. in year 2. Has the real value of the $5000 increased or decreased?

# DISCOUNTING VALUES BY INFLATION

A loaf of bread is a regular purchase for many families. Imagine a loaf of bread costs $2.30 and that the cost of the loaf has risen by the average inflation rate of 3.8% in the last 20 years.

To find what a loaf of bread would have cost 20 years ago, we first suppose this value was $x$.

$$\text{So,} \quad x \times (1.038)^{20} = \$2.30$$

$$\therefore \quad x = \frac{\$2.30}{(1.038)^{20}} = \$1.09$$

So, the loaf of bread may have cost around $1.09 twenty years ago.

Notice that when we want to discount a value by the inflation rate we *divide*.

---

**Example 28**   ◀⑳ **Self Tutor**

In 2004, £4000 was invested in a term deposit for 5 years at 5.3% p.a. interest compounded monthly. Inflation over the same period averaged 3.6% p.a.

    **a**  Calculate the amount in the account after 5 years.

    **b**  What is the value of the deposit in 2004 pounds?

    **a**  Using a graphics calculator,

        $N = 60, \quad I\% = 5.3, \quad PV = -4000, \quad PMT = 0, \quad P/Y = 12, \quad C/Y = 12$

        There is £5210.68 in the account in 2009.

    **b**  The value of the deposit in 2004 pounds $= \dfrac{£5210.68}{(1.036)^5} = £4366.12$

## EXERCISE 15F.2

1 Thirty years ago your father purchased some land in the country which is now worth 1 130 000 francs. If inflation over that period averaged 3.5% p.a., what was the original cost of the property?

2 Mandy invested $15 000 in 2005 in a term deposit for three years at 6.15% p.a., with interest compounded quarterly. Inflation over the three year period averages 4.3% p.a.

   a Calculate the amount in the account after three years.

   b What is the value of the deposit in 2005 dollars?

3 Frances deposited €8000 in a term deposit account at the start of 2006. She received 4.8% p.a. interest compounded monthly.

   a What amount will be in the account after ten years?

   b What will be the value of the investment in 2006 euros if inflation is expected to average:   i 2.5% p.a.   ii 3.5% p.a.   iii 4.5% p.a.?

4 Christianne invested £25 000 in five year bonds paying 6.25% p.a. simple interest in 2004.

   a How much interest will she receive over the five years?

   b What is the value of her capital invested in 2004 pounds, if inflation averages:

     i 3.5% p.a.     ii 5.5% p.a.?

5 At the start of 2008, Marcin left €3000 in a savings account paying 0.5% p.a. interest compounded annually. He travels overseas for the next 4 years.

   a How much will there be in Marcin's account when he returns from overseas in 2012?

   b If inflation averages 4.2% p.a. for the four year period, what will the value of the account in 2008 euros be?

   c At what interest rate did Marcin need to invest to make a real return on his money?

## REVIEW SET 15A

1 Currency exchange rates for the Canadian dollar (CAD), European euro (EUR), and Tajikstani somoni (TJS) are given in the table alongside.

| | CAD | EUR | TJS |
|---|---|---|---|
| CAD | 1 | 0.675 | 4.069 |
| EUR | 1.481 | 1 | 6.029 |
| TJS | 0.246 | 0.166 | 1 |

   a Convert 300 EUR into:

     i CAD     ii TJS.

   b How many somoni can be bought for 1780 Canadian dollars?

   c 1 euro is worth 3.088 Sudanese pounds (SDG). What are 2500 Sudanese pounds worth in somoni?

2 Roger has 640 Swiss francs. A currency exchange service exchanges 1 Swiss franc for Danish krone at a buying rate of 5.202 krone and a selling rate of 4.987 krone.

   a How many krone can Roger buy?

   b If Roger immediately sells the krone back for Swiss francs, how many will he now have?

**c** Find the commission for the double transaction.

**3** Josie places $9600 in an account paying $5\frac{3}{4}\%$ simple interest. How long will it take the account to earn $3000 in interest?

**4** Mary borrowed 13 000 euro from Wally and over 3 years repaid 15 250 euro. What simple interest rate was Mary being charged?

**5** Sven sells his stamp collection and deposits the proceeds of $8700 in a term deposit account for nine months. The account pays $9\frac{3}{4}\%$ p.a. compounded monthly. How much interest will he earn over this period?

**6** Val receives a $285 000 superannuation payment when she retires. She finds the following investment rates are offered:

> *Bank A:*   $6\frac{1}{2}\%$ p.a. simple interest
>
> *Bank B:*   6% p.a. compounded quarterly
>
> *Bank C:*   $5\frac{3}{4}\%$ p.a. compounded monthly.

Compare the interest that would be received from these banks over a ten year period. In which bank should Val deposit her superannuation?

**7** **a** Find the future value of a truck which is purchased for $135 000 if it depreciates at 15% p.a. for 5 years.

**b** By how much did it depreciate?

**8** Ena currently has £7800, and wants to buy a car valued at £9000. She puts her money in an account paying 4.8% p.a. compounded quarterly. When will she be able to buy the car?

**9** Manuel deposited $25 000 in a fixed term account for 3 years with 5.4% p.a. interest compounded quarterly. Inflation over the period averages 2.1% p.a.

**a** Find the value of his investment after 3 years.

**b** Calculate the value of the $25 000 indexed for inflation.

**c** Find the real increase in value of his investment.

**d** What is the real average annual percentage increase in his investment?

## REVIEW SET 15B

**1** A bank exchanges 5500 Chinese yuan to Japanese yen for a commission of 1.8%.

**a** What commission is charged?

**b** What does the customer receive for the transaction if 1 Chinese yuan = 13.1947 Japanese yen?

**2**  Tia deposits her lottery winnings into an account that pays 5.5% p.a. simple interest. After 18 months she has earned \$32 600 in interest. How much did she win in the lottery?

**3**  Pieter has £28 000 to invest. He places it in an account that pays $4\frac{1}{2}$% p.a. interest compounded monthly. After 18 months he withdraws all of the money from that account and places it in another account that pays $4\frac{3}{4}$% p.a. interest compounded quarterly. How much does he have in the account after a further 15 months?

**4**  Before leaving overseas on a three year trip to India, I leave a sum of money in an account that pays 6% p.a. compounded half-yearly. When I return from the trip, there is €5970.26 in my account. How much interest has been added since I've been away?

**5**  Megan deposits £3700 in a 2 year term deposit paying interest compounded monthly. She ends up with £4072.

  **a**  What rate of interest did Megan receive?

  **b**  Calculate the effective return if the tax rate was 36.5 pence in the pound.

**6**  Alberto takes out a personal loan for €17 000 at 12% p.a. over 5 years to buy a piano. Find:

  **a**  his monthly repayments        **b**  the total cost of the piano

  **c**  the interest charged.

**7**  Mirna is about to purchase a car for \$18 500 and is considering the following options:

  *Option 1:*  Buy on terms from a car dealer. The terms are 10% deposit and \$117.90 per week for 48 months.

  *Option 2:*  Borrow the full amount from the bank and repay the loan at \$445.10 per month for 5 years.

  **a**  Calculate the total cost of the car for each option.

  **b**  Calculate the amount of interest charged for each option.

  **c**  Which option would you recommend for Mirna? Explain your answer.

**8**  Ian obtains a personal loan of \$25 000 for renovating his home. The loan is to be repaid monthly over 5 years, at a compound interest rate of 8% p.a.

  **a**  What monthly repayments will Ian have to make?

  **b**  How much interest will Ian pay?

**9**  Retief invested £10 000 in 2004, in a term deposit for 3 years at 6.45% p.a. interest compounded quarterly. Inflation over the three year period averaged 3.1% p.a.

  **a**  Calculate the amount in the account after 3 years.

  **b**  What was the amount worth in 2004 pounds?

# Chapter **16**

# Probability

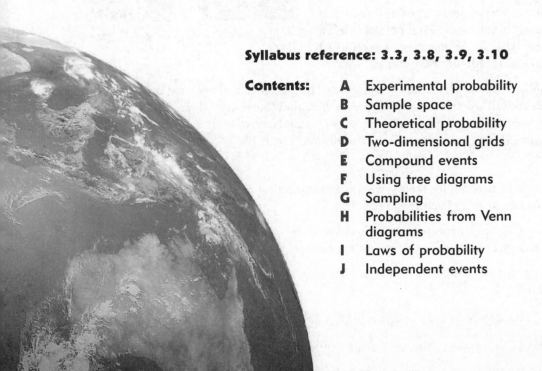

## OPENING PROBLEM

Consider the following game:

You first roll a die. If the result is less than 3, you randomly select a ball from bag A.

Otherwise, you randomly select a ball from bag B.

You win if the ball is red, and lose if the ball is blue.

Bag A          Bag B

**Things to think about:**

**a** What is the probability that the die will give a result less than 3?

**b** If bag B is selected, what is the probability the ball selected will be red?

**c** Are you more likely to win or lose this game?

## HISTORICAL NOTE

The development of modern probability theory began in 1653 when gambler Chevalier de Mere contacted mathematician **Blaise Pascal** with a problem on how to divide the stakes when a gambling game is interrupted during play.    Pascal involved **Pierre de Fermat**, a lawyer and amateur mathematician, and together they solved the problem. In the process they laid the foundations upon which the laws of probability were formed.

*Blaise Pascal*          *Pierre de Fermat*

In the late 17th century, English mathematicians compiled and analysed mortality tables which showed the number of people who died at different ages. From these tables they could estimate the probability that a person would be alive at a future date. This led to the establishment of the first life-insurance company in 1699.

In the field of **probability theory** we use a mathematical method to describe the **chance** or **likelihood** of an event happening.

This theory has important applications in physical and biological sciences, economics, politics, sport, insurance, quality control, production planning, and a host of other areas.

We assign to every event a number which lies between 0 and 1 inclusive. We call this number a **probability**.

An **impossible** event which has 0% chance of happening is assigned a probability of 0.

A **certain** event which has 100% chance of happening is assigned a probability of 1.

All other events can be assigned a probability between 0 and 1.

The number line below shows how we could interpret different probabilities:

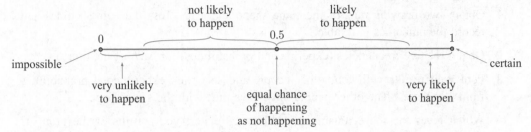

The assigning of probabilities is usually based on either:

- observing the results of an experiment (experimental probability),    or
- using arguments of symmetry (theoretical probability).

<h1>A | EXPERIMENTAL PROBABILITY</h1>

In experiments involving chance we use the following terms to talk about what we are doing and the results we obtain:

- The **number of trials** is the total number of times the experiment is repeated.
- The **outcomes** are the different results possible for one trial of the experiment.
- The **frequency** of a particular outcome is the number of times that this outcome is observed.
- The **relative frequency** of an outcome is the frequency of that outcome expressed as a fraction or percentage of the total number of trials.

When a small plastic cone was tossed into the air 279 times it fell on its *side* 183 times and on its *base* 96 times.

The relative frequencies of *side* and *base* are $\frac{183}{279} \approx 0.656$  and  $\frac{96}{279} \approx 0.344$  respectively.

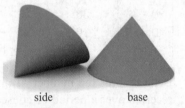

side          base

In the absence of any further data, the relative frequency of each event is our best estimate of the probability of that event occurring.

> **Experimental probability = relative frequency**

In this case:  Experimental  P(side) = 0.656  and  Experimental  P(base) = 0.344.

<h2>INVESTIGATION 1                    TOSSING DRAWING PINS</h2>

If a drawing pin tossed in the air finishes ⊥ we say it has finished

on its *back*. If it finishes ⋏ we say it has finished on its *side*.

If two drawing pins are tossed simultaneously the possible results are:

*two backs*        *back and side*        *two sides*

**What to do:**

1 Obtain two drawing pins of the same shape and size. Toss the pair 80 times and record the outcomes in a table.

2 Obtain relative frequencies (experimental probabilities) for each of the three events.

3 Pool your results with four other people and so obtain experimental probabilities from 400 tosses. The other people must have pins with the same shape.

4 Which gives the more reliable probability estimates, your results or the group's? Why?

5 Keep your results as they may be useful later in this chapter.

In some situations, for example in the investigation above, experimentation is the only way of obtaining probabilities.

## EXERCISE 16A.1

1 When a batch of 145 paper clips was dropped onto 6 cm by 6 cm squared paper it was observed that 113 fell completely inside squares and 32 finished up on the grid lines. Find, to 2 decimal places, the experimental probability of a clip falling:

    **a** inside a square     **b** on a line.

2

| Length | Frequency |
|--------|-----------|
| 0 - 19 | 17 |
| 20 - 39 | 38 |
| 40 - 59 | 19 |
| 60+ | 4 |

Jose surveyed the length of TV commercials (in seconds). Find, to 3 decimal places, the experimental probability that a randomly chosen TV commercial will last:

    **a** 20 to 39 seconds     **b** more than a minute

    **c** between 20 and 59 seconds (inclusive).

3 Betul records the number of phone calls she receives over a period of consecutive days.

    **a** For how many days did the survey last?

    **b** Estimate Betul's chance of receiving:

        **i** no phone calls on one day

        **ii** 5 or more phone calls on a day

        **iii** less than 3 phone calls on a day.

4 Pat does a lot of travelling in her car and she keeps records on how often she fills her car with petrol. The table alongside shows the frequencies of the number of days between refills. Estimate the likelihood that:

    **a** there is a four day gap between refills

    **b** there is at least a four day gap between refills.

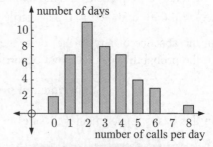

| Days between refills | Frequency |
|----------------------|-----------|
| 1 | 37 |
| 2 | 81 |
| 3 | 48 |
| 4 | 17 |
| 5 | 6 |
| 6 | 1 |

# EXPERIMENTS WITH COINS AND DICE

## INVESTIGATION 2 — COIN TOSSING EXPERIMENTS

The coins of most currencies have two distinct faces, usually referred to as 'heads' and 'tails'. When we toss a coin in the air, we expect it to finish on a head or tail with equal likelihood.

In this investigation the coins do not have to be all the same type.

**What to do:**

**1** Toss *one coin* 40 times. Record the number of heads resulting in each trial, in a table:

| Result | Tally | Frequency | Relative frequency |
|--------|-------|-----------|--------------------|
| 1 head |       |           |                    |
| 0 head |       |           |                    |

**2** Toss *two coins* 60 times. Record the number of heads resulting in each trial, in a table.

| Result | Tally | Frequency | Relative frequency |
|---------|-------|-----------|--------------------|
| 2 heads |       |           |                    |
| 1 head  |       |           |                    |
| 0 head  |       |           |                    |

**3** Toss *three coins* 80 times. Record the number of heads resulting in each trial, in a table.

| Result | Tally | Frequency | Relative frequency |
|---------|-------|-----------|--------------------|
| 3 heads |       |           |                    |
| 2 heads |       |           |                    |
| 1 head  |       |           |                    |
| 0 head  |       |           |                    |

**4** Share your results to **1**, **2** and **3** with several other students. Comment on any similarities and differences.

**5** Pool your results and find new relative frequencies for tossing one coin, two coins, and three coins.

**6** Click on the icon to examine a coin tossing simulation.
Set it to toss one coin 10 000 times.
Run the simulation ten times, each time recording the % frequency for each possible result. Comment on these results. Do your results agree with what you expected?

**COIN TOSSING**

**7** Repeat **6** but this time with *two coins* and then with *three coins*.

From the previous investigation you should have observed that, when tossing two coins, there are roughly twice as many 'one head' results as there are 'no heads' or 'two heads'. The explanation for this is best seen using two different coins where you could get:

two heads          one head          one head          no heads

This shows that we should expect the ratio  two heads : one head : no heads  to be  1 : 2 : 1. However, due to chance, there will be variations from this when we look at experimental results.

## INVESTIGATION 3                    DICE ROLLING EXPERIMENTS

**You will need:**

At least one normal six-sided die with numbers 1 to 6 on its faces. Several dice would be useful to speed up the experimentation.

WORKSHEET

**What to do:**

**1**  List the possible outcomes for the uppermost face when the die is rolled.

**2**  Consider the possible outcomes when the die is rolled 60 times.

Copy and complete the following table of your **expected results**:

| Outcomes | Expected frequency | Expected rel. frequency |
|----------|--------------------|--------------------------|
| ⋮ | | |

**3**  Roll the die 60 times.  Record the results in a table like the one shown:

| Outcome | Tally | Frequency | Relative frequency |
|---------|-------|-----------|---------------------|
| 1 | | | |
| 2 | | | |
| ⋮ | | | |
| 6 | | | |
| | Total | 60 | |

**4**  Pool as much data as you can with other students.

SIMULATION

  **a**  Look at similarities and differences from one set to another.

  **b**  Summarise the overall pooled data in one table.

  **c**  Compare your results with your expectation in **2**.

**5**  Use the die rolling simulation on the CD to roll the die 10 000 times.  Repeat this 10 times.  On each occasion, record your results in a table like that in **3**.  Do your results further confirm your expected results?

**6**  The different possible results when a pair of dice is rolled are shown alongside.

There are 36 possible outcomes.

Notice that three of the outcomes, {1, 3}, {2, 2} and {3, 1}, give a sum of 4.

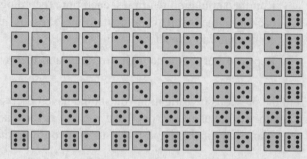

Using the illustration above, copy and complete the table of **expected results**:

| Sum | 2 | 3 | 4 | 5 | ⋯ | 12 |
|-----|---|---|---|---|---|----|
| Fraction of total | | | $\frac{3}{36}$ | | | |
| Fraction as decimal | | | 0.083 | | | |

**7**  If a pair of dice is rolled 150 times, how many of each result (2, 3, 4, ...., 12) would you expect to get? Extend the table in **6** by adding another row and writing your **expected frequencies** within it.

**8**  Toss two dice 150 times. Record the *sum of the two numbers* for each toss in a table.

WORKSHEET

| Sum | Tally | Frequency | Rel. Frequency |
|-----|-------|-----------|----------------|
| 2 | | | |
| 3 | | | |
| 4 | | | |
| ⋮ | | | |
| 12 | | | |
| Total | | 150 | 1 |

**9**  Pool as much data as you can with other students and find the overall relative frequency of each sum.

**10**  Use the two dice simulation on the CD to roll the pair of dice 10 000 times. Repeat this 10 times and on each occasion record your results in a table like that in **8**. Are your results consistent with your expectations?

SIMULATION

## ESTIMATING PROBABILITIES FROM DATA

Statistical information can be used to calculate probabilities in many situations.

---

**Example 1**   ◀ᴗ) **Self Tutor**

### Short-Term Visitors to Australia

| Main reason for journey | April 2003 '000 | May 2003 '000 | June 2003 '000 |
|-------------------------|-----------------|---------------|----------------|
| Convention/conference | 8.3 | 14.8 | 8.8 |
| Business | 27.2 | 33.9 | 32.0 |
| Visiting friends/relatives | 77.5 | 52.7 | 59.9 |
| Holiday | 159.3 | 119.3 | 156.5 |
| Employment | 4.2 | 4.3 | 5.5 |
| Education | 9.8 | 7.9 | 12.5 |
| Other | 35.2 | 28.0 | 33.2 |
| *Total* | 321.5 | 260.9 | 308.3 |

The table shows the number of short-term visitors coming to Australia in the period April - June 2003, and the main reason for their visit.

**a**  What is the probability that a person who visited in June was on holiday?

**b**  What is the probability that a person coming to Australia arrived in May?

**c**  Lars arrived in Australia in April, May or June 2003. He came to visit his brother. What is the probability that he arrived in April?

a   $P(\text{on holiday in June}) = \dfrac{156.5}{308.3} \leftarrow$ number on holiday in June
            $\leftarrow$ total number for June

$\approx 0.508$

b   There were $321.5 + 260.9 + 308.3 = 890.7$ thousand short-term visitors during the three months.

$\therefore$   $P(\text{arrived in May}) = \dfrac{260.9}{890.7} \approx 0.293$

c   $77.5 + 52.7 + 59.9 = 190.1$ thousand people came to Australia to visit friends or relatives during this period.

$\therefore$   $P(\text{arrived in April}) = \dfrac{77.5}{190.1} \approx 0.408$

## EXERCISE 16A.2

1   The table shows data from a survey conducted at five schools on the rate of smoking amongst 15 year old students.

   a   Find the probability that a randomly chosen female 15 year old student at school **C** is a smoker.

   b   Find the probability that a randomly chosen 15 year old student at school **E** is *not* a smoker.

| School | No. of 15 year olds | | No. of smokers | |
|--------|------|--------|------|--------|
|        | Male | Female | Male | Female |
| A | 45 | 51 | 10 | 11 |
| B | 36 | 42 | 9 | 6 |
| C | 52 | 49 | 13 | 13 |
| D | 28 | 33 | 9 | 10 |
| E | 40 | 39 | 7 | 4 |
| Total | 201 | 214 | 48 | 44 |

   c   If a 15 year old is chosen at random from the five schools, what is the probability that he or she is a smoker?

2   The given table shows complaints received by the Telecommunications Ombudsman concerning internet services over a four year period.

| Reason | 2006/07 | 2007/08 | 2008/09 | 2009/10 |
|--------|---------|---------|---------|---------|
| Access | 585 | 1127 | 2545 | 1612 |
| Billing | 1822 | 2102 | 3136 | 3582 |
| Contracts | 242 | 440 | 719 | 836 |
| Credit control | 3 | 44 | 118 | 136 |
| Customer Service | 12 | 282 | 1181 | 1940 |
| Disconnection | n/a | n/a | n/a | 248 |
| Faults | 86 | 79 | 120 | 384 |
| Privacy | 93 | 86 | 57 | 60 |
| Provision | 173 | 122 | 209 | 311 |
| Total | 3015 | 4282 | 8085 | 9109 |

   a   What is the probability that a complaint received in 2008/09 was about customer service?

   b   What is the probability that a complaint received at any time during the 4 year period was related to billing?

   c   What is the probability that a complaint received in 2009/10 did *not* relate to either billing or faults?

**3**  The table provides data on the average daily maximum temperatures in Auburn during summer. You may assume that there are 28 days in February.

| Summer Temperatures in Auburn | Month | | |
|---|---|---|---|
| | *Dec* | *Jan* | *Feb* |
| Mean days max. $\geqslant 40^\circ$ C | 0.3 | 1.2 | 0.7 |
| Mean days max. $\geqslant 35^\circ$ C | 3.0 | 5.8 | 5.3 |
| Mean days max. $\geqslant 30^\circ$ C | 9.4 | 12.3 | 12.6 |

  **a**  Find the probability that on a February day in Auburn, the maximum temperature will:

  **i**  be 35°C or higher   **ii**  not exceed 30°C.

  **b**  Find the probability that on any summer day in Auburn, the temperature will be 30°C or higher.

  **c**  It is a 40°C summer day in Auburn. Find the probability that the month is January.

# B          SAMPLE SPACE

> A **sample space** $U$ is the set of all possible outcomes of an experiment. It is also referred to as the **universal set** $U$.

There are a variety of ways of representing or illustrating sample spaces, including:

- lists
- 2-dimensional grids
- tree diagrams
- Venn diagrams

## LISTING OUTCOMES

**Example 2**                                               ◀⑴ **Self Tutor**

List the sample space for:

  **a**  tossing a coin                          **b**  rolling a die.

  **a**  When a coin is tossed, there are two possible outcomes.

  $\therefore$  sample space $= \{H, T\}$

  **b**  When a die is rolled, there are 6 possible outcomes.

  $\therefore$  sample space $= \{1, 2, 3, 4, 5, 6\}$

## 2-DIMENSIONAL GRIDS

When an experiment involves more than one operation we can still use listing to illustrate the sample space. However, a grid can often be more efficient.

These grids are also known as **lattice diagrams**. Each point on the grid represents one of the outcomes.

**Example 3**                                               ◀⑴ **Self Tutor**

Illustrate the possible outcomes when 2 coins are tossed by using a 2-dimensional grid.

Each of the points on the grid represents one of the possible outcomes:

$\{HH, HT, TH, TT\}$

# TREE DIAGRAMS

The sample space in **Example 3** could also be represented by a tree diagram. The advantage of tree diagrams is that they can be used when more than two operations are involved.

**Example 4** ◀》 **Self Tutor**

Illustrate, using a tree diagram, the possible outcomes when:

**a** tossing two coins

**b** drawing three marbles from a bag containing many red and yellow marbles.

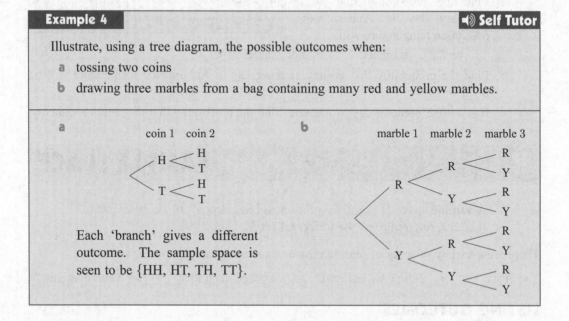

Each 'branch' gives a different outcome. The sample space is seen to be {HH, HT, TH, TT}.

# EXERCISE 16B

1 List the sample space for the following:
   **a** twirling a square spinner labelled A, B, C, D
   **b** the sexes of a 2-child family
   **c** the order in which 4 blocks A, B, C and D can be lined up
   **d** the 8 different 3-child families.

2 Illustrate on a 2-dimensional grid the sample space for:
   **a** rolling a die and tossing a coin simultaneously
   **b** rolling two dice
   **c** rolling a die and spinning a spinner with sides A, B, C, D
   **d** twirling two square spinners, one labelled A, B, C, D and the other 1, 2, 3, 4.

3 Illustrate on a tree diagram the sample space for:
   **a** tossing a 5-cent and a 10-cent coin simultaneously
   **b** tossing a coin and twirling an equilateral triangular spinner labelled A, B and C
   **c** twirling two equilateral triangular spinners labelled 1, 2 and 3 and X, Y and Z
   **d** drawing three tickets from a hat containing a number of pink and white tickets.

# C | THEORETICAL PROBABILITY

Consider the **octagonal spinner** alongside.

Since the spinner is symmetrical, when it is spun the arrowed marker could finish with equal likelihood on each of the sections marked 1 to 8.

The likelihood of obtaining a particular number, for example 4, would be:

$$1 \text{ chance in } 8, \qquad \tfrac{1}{8}, \qquad 12\tfrac{1}{2}\% \qquad \text{or} \qquad 0.125.$$

This is a **mathematical** or **theoretical** probability and is based on what we theoretically expect to occur. It is the chance of that event occurring in any trial of the experiment.

If we are interested in the event of getting a result of *6 or more* from one spin of the octagonal spinner, there are three favourable results (6, 7 or 8) out of the eight possibilities. Since each of these is equally likely to occur,   $P(6 \text{ or more}) = \tfrac{3}{8}$.

> We read $\tfrac{3}{8}$ as "3 chances in 8".

In general, when each of the outcomes of an experiment are **equally likely**, the probability of an event $A$ occurring is

$$P(A) = \frac{\text{the number of outcomes in the event } A}{\text{the total number of possible outcomes}} = \frac{n(A)}{n(U)}.$$

---

### Example 5 | ◀) Self Tutor

A ticket is *randomly selected* from a basket containing 3 green, 4 yellow and 5 blue tickets. Determine the probability of getting:

| | |
|---|---|
| **a**  a green ticket | **b**  a green or yellow ticket |
| **c**  an orange ticket | **d**  a green, yellow or blue ticket. |

The sample space is   $\{G_1, G_2, G_3, Y_1, Y_2, Y_3, Y_4, B_1, B_2, B_3, B_4, B_5\}$
which has   $3 + 4 + 5 = 12$   outcomes.

| **a** | $P(G)$ | **b** | $P(G \text{ or } Y)$ | **c** | $P(O)$ | **d** | $P(G, Y \text{ or } B)$ |
|---|---|---|---|---|---|---|---|
| | $= \tfrac{3}{12}$ | | $= \tfrac{3+4}{12}$ | | $= \tfrac{0}{12}$ | | $= \tfrac{3+4+5}{12}$ |
| | $= \tfrac{1}{4}$ | | $= \tfrac{7}{12}$ | | $= 0$ | | $= 1$ |

---

In **Example 5** notice that in **c** an orange result cannot occur. The calculated probability is 0 because the event has *no chance of occurring*.

In **d** we see that a green, yellow or blue result is certain to occur. It is 100% likely so the theoretical probability is 1.

Events which have *no chance of occurring* (probability 0), or events which are *certain to occur* (probability 1), are two extremes.

Consequently, for any event $A$,        $\mathbf{0 \leqslant P(A) \leqslant 1.}$

---

**Example 6**    ◀)) **Self Tutor**

An ordinary 6-sided die is rolled once. Determine the chance of:

a getting a 6                          b not getting a 6

c getting a 1 or 2                     d not getting a 1 or 2

---

The sample space of possible outcomes is    $\{1, 2, 3, 4, 5, 6\}$

a      $P(6)$          b   $P(\text{not a } 6)$       c      $P(1 \text{ or } 2)$       d   $P(\text{not a } 1 \text{ or } 2)$

$= \frac{1}{6}$              $= P(1, 2, 3, 4 \text{ or } 5)$     $= \frac{2}{6}$          $= P(3, 4, 5, \text{ or } 6)$

$= \frac{5}{6}$                              $= \frac{4}{6}$

## COMPLEMENTARY EVENTS

In **Example 6** notice that                  $P(6) + P(\text{not getting a } 6) = 1$   and that

$P(1 \text{ or } 2) + P(\text{not getting a } 1 \text{ or } 2) = 1.$

This is no surprise as *getting a 6* and *not getting a 6* are **complementary events** where one of them **must occur**.

> Two events are **complementary** if exactly one of the events must occur.
> If $A$ is an event, then $A'$ is the complementary event of $A$, or 'not $A$'.
>
> So,    $\mathbf{P}(A) + \mathbf{P}(A') = 1$    or    $\mathbf{P}(A') = 1 - \mathbf{P}(A).$

## EXERCISE 16C

**1** A marble is randomly selected from a box containing 5 green, 3 red and 7 blue marbles. Determine the probability that the marble is:

a red                       b green                     c blue

d not red                   e neither green nor blue    f green or red.

**2** A carton of a dozen eggs contains eight brown eggs. The rest are white.

a How many white eggs are there in the carton?

b What is the probability that an egg selected at random is:    i white    ii brown?

**3** A dart board has 36 sectors labelled 1 to 36. Determine the probability that a dart thrown at the centre of the board hits:

a a multiple of 4

b a number between 6 and 9 inclusive

c a number greater than 20

d 9        e a multiple of 13

f an odd number that is a multiple of 3

g a multiple of 4 and 6        h not a multiple of 4 or 6.

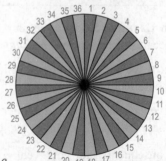

**4** What is the probability that a randomly chosen person has his or her next birthday:

   **a** on a Tuesday   **b** on a weekend   **c** in July   **d** in January or February?

**5** **a** List the six different orders in which Antti, Kai and Neda may sit in a row.

   **b** If the three of them sit randomly in a row, determine the probability that:

   **i** Antti sits in the middle   **ii** Antti sits at the left end

   **iii** Antti does *not* sit at the left end   **iv** Kai and Neda are seated together.

**6** **a** List the 8 possible 3-child families according to the gender of the children. For example, GGB means *"the first is a girl, the second is a girl, the third is a boy"*.

   **b** Assuming that each of these is equally likely to occur, determine the probability that a randomly selected 3-child family consists of:

   **i** all boys   **ii** all girls   **iii** boy then girl then girl

   **iv** two girls and a boy   **v** a girl for the eldest   **vi** at least one boy.

**7** **a** List, in systematic order, the 24 different arrangements in which four people A, B, C and D may sit in a row.

   **b** Determine the probability that when the four people sit at random in a row:

   **i** A sits on one of the end seats   **ii** B sits on one of the two middle seats

   **iii** A and B are seated together   **iv** A and B are *not* seated together

   **v** A, B and C are seated together, not necessarily in that order.

**8** List the possible outcomes when four coins are tossed simultaneously. Hence determine the probability of getting:

   **a** all heads   **b** two heads and two tails   **c** more tails than heads

   **d** at least one tail   **e** exactly one head.

# D           TWO-DIMENSIONAL GRIDS

**Two-dimensional grids** can give us excellent visual displays of sample spaces. We can use them to count favourable outcomes and so calculate probabilities.

This point represents 'a tail from coin A' and 'a tail from coin B'.

This point represents 'a tail from coin A' and 'a head from coin B'. There are four members of the sample space.

| Example 7 | ◄)) Self Tutor |
|---|---|

Use a two-dimensional grid to illustrate the sample space for tossing a coin and rolling a die simultaneously. From this grid determine the probability of:

   **a** tossing a head   **b** getting a tail and a 5   **c** getting a tail or a 5.

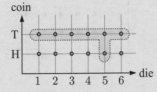

There are 12 members in the sample space.

**a** P(head) $= \frac{6}{12} = \frac{1}{2}$   **b** P(tail and a '5') $= \frac{1}{12}$

**c** P(tail or a '5') $= \frac{7}{12}$   {the enclosed points}

**Example 8**

◄) **Self Tutor**

Two square spinners, each with 1, 2, 3 and 4 on their edges, are twirled simultaneously. Draw a two-dimensional grid of the possible outcomes. Use your grid to determine the probability of getting:

**a** a 3 with each spinner         **b** a 3 and a 1

**c** an even result with each spinner.

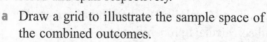

There are 16 members in the sample space.

**a** P(a 3 with each spinner) $= \frac{1}{16}$

**b** P(a 3 and a 1) $= \frac{2}{16}$ {crossed points}

$= \frac{1}{8}$

**c** P(an even result with each spinner)

$= \frac{4}{16}$ {circled points}

$= \frac{1}{4}$

## EXERCISE 16D.1

**1** Draw the grid of the sample space when a 5-cent and a 10-cent coin are tossed simultaneously. Hence determine the probability of getting:

**a** two heads                      **b** two tails

**c** exactly one head              **d** at least one head.

**2** A coin and a pentagonal spinner with sectors 1, 2, 3, 4 and 5 are tossed and spun respectively.

**a** Draw a grid to illustrate the sample space of the combined outcomes.

**b** How many combined outcomes are possible?

**c** Use your grid to determine the chance of getting:

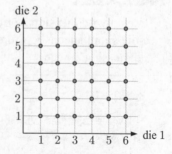

**i** a tail and a 3                 **ii** a head and an even number

**iii** an odd number              **iv** a head or a 5.

**3** A pair of dice is rolled. The 36 different possible results are illustrated in the 2-dimensional grid.

Use the grid to determine the probability of getting:

**a** two 3s              **b** a 5 and a 6

**c** a 5 or a 6         **d** at least one 6

**e** exactly one 6     **f** no sixes.

## DISCUSSION

**Read and discuss:**

Three children have been experimenting with a coin, tossing it in the air and recording the outcomes. They have done this 10 times and have recorded 10 tails. Before the next toss they make the following statements:

**Jackson:** "It's got to be a head next time!"

**Sally:** "No, it always has an equal chance of being a head or a tail. The coin cannot remember what the outcomes have been."

**Amy:** "Actually, I think it will probably be a tail again, because I think the coin must be biased. It might be weighted so it is more likely to give a tail."

## TABLES OF OUTCOMES

In many board games, the players are required to roll two dice simultaneously. The results of the rolls are added together to determine how many squares the player moves.

We can represent the possible outcomes of a player's turn using a two-dimensional grid in which the sum of the dice is written at each grid-point. We call this a **table of outcomes**.

| Example 9 | ◀》 Self Tutor |
|---|---|

Draw a table of outcomes to display the possible results when two dice are rolled and the scores are added together.

Hence, determine the probability that the sum of the dice is 7.

```
die 2
 6    7  8  9 10 11 12
 5    6  7  8  9 10 11
 4    5  6  7  8  9 10
 3    4  5  6  7  8  9
 2    3  4  5  6  7  8
 1    2  3  4  5  6  7
                        die 1
      1  2  3  4  5  6
```

Of the 36 possible combinations of scores from the two dice, six have the sum 7.

$\therefore$   the probability $= \frac{6}{36} = \frac{1}{6}$

## EXERCISE 16D.2

1  **a**  Draw a table of outcomes to display the possible results when two dice are rolled and the scores are added together.

   **b**  Hence determine the probability that the sum of the dice is:

   **i**  11          **ii**  8 or 9          **iii**  less than 6.

**2  a** Draw a table of outcomes to display the possible results when two dice are rolled, and the smaller number is subtracted from the larger number.

**b** Hence determine the probability that the resulting value is:

    **i** 0           **ii** 2           **iii** greater than 3.

**3** Suppose the spinners alongside are spun, and the scores are multiplied together.

**a** Draw a table of outcomes to display the possible results.

**b** Hence determine the probability that the result is:

    **i** 6     **ii** less than 5     **iii** odd.

# E                COMPOUND EVENTS

Consider the following problem:

Box X contains 2 blue and 2 green balls. Box Y contains 1 white and 3 red balls. A ball is randomly selected from each of the boxes. Determine the probability of getting "a blue ball from X and a red ball from Y".

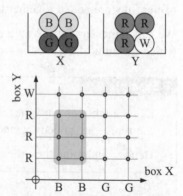

By illustrating the sample space on the two-dimensional grid shown, we can see that 6 of the 16 possibilities are blue from X and red from Y. Each of the outcomes is equally likely, so P(blue from X **and** red from Y) $= \frac{6}{16}$.

In this section we look for a quicker method for finding the probability of two events both occurring.

## INVESTIGATION 4     PROBABILITIES OF COMPOUND EVENTS

The purpose of this investigation is to find a rule for calculating P($A$ and $B$) for two events $A$ and $B$.

Suppose a coin is tossed and a die is rolled at the same time. The result of the coin toss will be called outcome $A$, and the result of the die roll will be outcome $B$.

**What to do:**

**1** Copy and complete, using a 2-dimensional grid if necessary:

|  | P($A$ and $B$) | P($A$) | P($B$) |
|---|---|---|---|
| P(a head and a 4) |  |  |  |
| P(a head and an odd number) |  |  |  |
| P(a tail and a number larger than 1) |  |  |  |
| P(a tail and a number less than 3) |  |  |  |

**2** What is the connection between P($A$ and $B$), P($A$), and P($B$)?

## INVESTIGATION 5                    REVISITING DRAWING PINS

We cannot find by theoretical argument the probability that a drawing pin will land on its back ⊥ . We can only find this probability by experimentation.

So, when tossing *two* drawing pins can we use the rule for compound events:
$$P(\text{back } and \text{ back}) = P(\text{back}) \times P(\text{back})?$$

**What to do:**

**1** From **Investigation 1** on page **491**, what is your estimate of P(back *and* back)?

**2** **a** Count the number of drawing pins in a full packet. They must be identical to each other and the same ones that you used in **Investigation 1**.

**b** Drop the whole packet onto a solid surface and count the number of *backs* and *sides*. Repeat this several times. Pool results with others and finally estimate P(back).

**3** Find P(back) × P(back) using **2 b**.

**4** Is P(back *and* back) ≈ P(back) × P(back)?

From **Investigations 4** and **5**, it seems that:

If $A$ and $B$ are two events for which the occurrence of each one does not affect the occurrence of the other, then $P(A \textbf{ and } B) = P(A) \times P(B)$.

Before we can formalise this as a rule, however, we need to distinguish between **independent** and **dependent** events.

## INDEPENDENT EVENTS

Events are independent if the occurrence of each of them does not affect the probability that the others occur.

Consider again the example on the previous page. Suppose we happen to choose a blue ball from box X. This does not affect the outcome when we choose a ball from box Y. So, the two events "a blue ball from X" and "a red ball from Y" are independent.

If $A$ and $B$ are **independent events** then $P(A \textbf{ and } B) = P(A) \times P(B)$.

This rule can be extended for any number of independent events.

For example, if $A$, $B$ and $C$ are all independent events, then
$P(A \textbf{ and } B \textbf{ and } C) = P(A) \times P(B) \times P(C)$.

### Example 10                                             ◀)) Self Tutor

A coin and a die are tossed simultaneously. Determine the probability of getting a head and a 3 without using a grid.

$P(\text{a head and a 3}) = P(H) \times P(3)$     {events are clearly physically independent}
$= \frac{1}{2} \times \frac{1}{6} = \frac{1}{12}$

## EXERCISE 16E.1

**1** Rob and Kerry each roll a die. Determine the probability that:

   **a** Rob rolls a 4 and Kerry rolls a 2.

   **b** Rob rolls an odd number and Kerry rolls a number greater than 4.

   **c** they both roll a number greater than 1.

**2** A coin is tossed 3 times. Determine the probability of getting the following sequences of results:  **a** head then head then head  **b** tail then head then tail.

**3** A school has two photocopiers. On any one day, machine A has an 8% chance of malfunctioning and machine B has a 12% chance of malfunctioning. Determine the probability that on any one day both machines will:

   **a** malfunction                           **b** work effectively.

**4** A couple decide that they want 4 children, none of whom will be adopted. They will be unhappy if the children are not born in the order boy, girl, boy, girl. Determine the probability that they will be:

   **a** happy with the order of arrival       **b** unhappy with the order of arrival.

**5** Two marksmen fire at a target simultaneously. Jiri hits the target 70% of the time and Benita hits it 80% of the time. Determine the probability that:

   **a** they both hit the target

   **b** they both miss the target

   **c** Jiri hits but Benita misses

   **d** Benita hits but Jiri misses.

**6**

An archer hits the bullseye on average 2 out of every 5 shots. If 3 arrows are shot at the target, determine the probability that the bullseye is hit:

   **a** every time

   **b** the first two times, but not on the third shot

   **c** on no occasion.

## DEPENDENT EVENTS

Suppose a hat contains 5 red and 3 blue tickets. One ticket is randomly chosen, its colour is noted, and it is then put aside. A second ticket is then randomly selected. What is the chance that it is red?

If the first ticket was red,    $P(\text{second is red}) = \frac{4}{7}$      4 reds remaining

                                                    7 to choose from

If the first ticket was blue,    $P(\text{second is red}) = \frac{5}{7}$      5 reds remaining

                                                    7 to choose from

So, the probability of the second ticket being red *depends* on what colour the first ticket was. We therefore have **dependent events**.

Two or more events are **dependent** if they are **not independent**.

**Dependent** events are events for which the occurrence of one of the events *does affect* the occurrence of the other event.

For compound events which are dependent, a similar product rule applies to that for independent events:

If $A$ and $B$ are dependent events then

$$\text{P}(A \textbf{ then } B) = \text{P}(A) \times \text{P}(B \text{ given that } A \text{ has occurred}).$$

---

**Example 11**                                                                    ◀)) **Self Tutor**

A box contains 4 red and 2 yellow tickets. Two tickets are randomly selected from the box one by one *without* replacement. Find the probability that:

  **a**  both are red             **b**  the first is red and the second is yellow.

---

  **a**    P(both red)

      = P(first selected is red *and* second is red)

      = P(first selected is red) $\times$ P(second is red given that the first is red)

      = $\frac{4}{6} \times \frac{3}{5}$ ◀—— If a red is drawn first, 3 reds remain out of a total of 5.

      = $\frac{2}{5}$ —— 4 reds out of a total of 6 tickets

  **b**    P(first is red *and* second is yellow)

      = P(first is red) $\times$ P(second is yellow given that the first is red)

      = $\frac{4}{6} \times \frac{2}{5}$ ◀—— If a red is drawn first, 2 yellows remain out of a total of 5.

      = $\frac{4}{15}$ —— 4 reds out of a total of 6 tickets

---

**Example 12**                                                                    ◀)) **Self Tutor**

A hat contains tickets with the numbers 1, 2, 3, ...., 19, 20 printed on them. If 3 tickets are drawn from the hat, without replacement, determine the probability that all are prime numbers.

> In each fraction the numerator is the number of outcomes in the event. The denominator is the total number of possible outcomes.

---

$\{2, 3, 5, 7, 11, 13, 17, 19\}$ are primes.

$\therefore$ there are 20 numbers of which 8 are primes.

$\therefore$  P(3 primes)

    = P(1st drawn is prime *and* 2nd is prime *and* 3rd is prime)

    = $\frac{8}{20} \times \frac{7}{19} \times \frac{6}{18}$

                 —— 8 primes out of 20 numbers

                 —— 7 primes out of 19 numbers after a successful first draw

                 —— 6 primes out of 18 numbers after two successful draws

    $\approx 0.0491$

## EXERCISE 16E.2

1   A bin contains 12 identically shaped chocolates of which 8 are strawberry creams.  If 3 chocolates are selected simultaneously from the bin, determine the probability that:

Drawing three chocolates *simultaneously* implies there is no replacement.

  a   they are all strawberry creams

  b   none of them are strawberry creams.

2   A box contains 7 red and 3 green balls.  Two balls are drawn one after another from the box without replacement.  Determine the probability that:

  a   both are red                              b   the first is green and the second is red

  c   a green and a red are obtained.

3   A lottery has 100 tickets which are placed in a barrel.  Three tickets are drawn at random from the barrel, without replacement, to decide 3 prizes.  If John has 3 tickets in the lottery, determine his probability of winning:

  a   first prize    b   first and second prize    c   all 3 prizes    d   none of the prizes.

4   A hat contains 7 names of players in a tennis squad including the captain and the vice captain.  If a team of 3 is chosen at random by drawing the names from the hat, determine the probability that it does *not* contain:

  a   the captain                               b   the captain or the vice captain.

# F          USING TREE DIAGRAMS

Tree diagrams can be used to illustrate sample spaces if the alternatives are not too numerous. Once the sample space is illustrated, the tree diagram can be used for determining probabilities.

Consider two archers firing simultaneously at a target.

Li has probability $\frac{3}{4}$ of hitting a target and Yuka has probability $\frac{4}{5}$.

The tree diagram for this information is:

H = hit   M = miss

| | Yuka's results | outcome | probability |
|---|---|---|---|
| Li's results | | | |
| H $\frac{3}{4}$ | H $\frac{4}{5}$ | H and H | $\frac{3}{4} \times \frac{4}{5} = \frac{12}{20}$ |
| | M $\frac{1}{5}$ | H and M | $\frac{3}{4} \times \frac{1}{5} = \frac{3}{20}$ |
| M $\frac{1}{4}$ | H $\frac{4}{5}$ | M and H | $\frac{1}{4} \times \frac{4}{5} = \frac{4}{20}$ |
| | M $\frac{1}{5}$ | M and M | $\frac{1}{4} \times \frac{1}{5} = \frac{1}{20}$ |
| | | total | 1 |

Notice that:

  •  The probabilities for hitting and missing are marked on the branches.

  •  There are *four* alternative branches, each showing a particular outcome.

  •  All outcomes are represented.

  •  The probability of each outcome is obtained by **multiplying** the probabilities along its branch.

**Example 13**    ◀》 **Self Tutor**

Carl is not having much luck lately.  His car will only start 80% of the time and his motorbike will only start 60% of the time.

**a** Draw a tree diagram to illustrate this situation.

**b** Use the tree diagram to determine the chance that:

   **i**  both will start          **ii** Carl can only use his car.

**a**  C = car starts

    M = motorbike starts

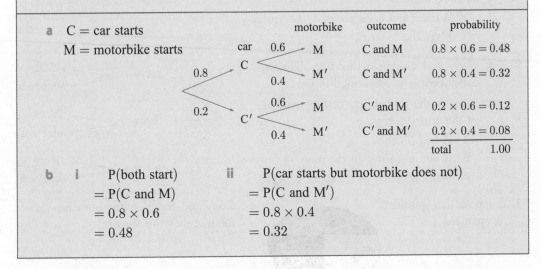

| | | outcome | probability |
|---|---|---|---|
| | M | C and M | $0.8 \times 0.6 = 0.48$ |
| | M′ | C and M′ | $0.8 \times 0.4 = 0.32$ |
| | M | C′ and M | $0.2 \times 0.6 = 0.12$ |
| | M′ | C′ and M′ | $0.2 \times 0.4 = 0.08$ |
| | | total | 1.00 |

**b**  **i**     P(both start)

     = P(C and M)

     = $0.8 \times 0.6$

     = 0.48

**ii**    P(car starts but motorbike does not)

     = P(C and M′)

     = $0.8 \times 0.4$

     = 0.32

If there is more than one outcome in an event then we need to **add** the probabilities of these outcomes.

**Example 14**    ◀》 **Self Tutor**

Two boxes each contain 6 petunia plants that are not yet flowering. Box A contains 2 plants that will have purple flowers and 4 plants that will have white flowers. Box B contains 5 plants that will have purple flowers and 1 plant that will have white flowers. A box is selected by tossing a coin, and one plant is removed at random from it. Determine the probability that it will have purple flowers.

Box A

| P | W | W |
|---|---|---|
| W | P | W |

Box B

| P | P | P |
|---|---|---|
| W | P | P |

P(purple flowers)

= P(A and P) + P(B and P)

= $\frac{1}{2} \times \frac{2}{6} + \frac{1}{2} \times \frac{5}{6}$   {branches marked ✓}

= $\frac{7}{12}$

flower

box

$\frac{2}{6}$  P ✓

A

$\frac{4}{6}$  W

$\frac{1}{2}$

$\frac{5}{6}$  P ✓

$\frac{1}{2}$  B

$\frac{1}{6}$  W

## EXERCISE 16F

1   Of the students in a class playing musical instruments, 60% are female. 20% of the females and 30% of the males play the violin.

   **a** Copy and complete the tree diagram.

   **b** What is the probability that a randomly selected student:

   **i** is male and does not play the violin

   **ii** plays the violin?

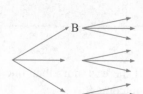

2   **a** Copy and complete this tree diagram about people in the armed forces.

   **b** What is the probability that a member of the armed forces:

   **i** is an officer

   **ii** is not an officer in the navy

   **iii** is not an army or air force officer?

3   Suppose this spinner is spun twice.

   **a** Copy and complete the branches on the tree diagram shown.

   **b** Find the probability that black appears on both spins.

   **c** Find the probability that yellow appears on both spins.

   **d** Find the probability that different colours appear on the two spins.

   **e** Find the probability that black appears on either spin.

4   The probability of rain tomorrow is estimated to be $\frac{1}{5}$. If it does rain, Mudlark will start favourite in the horse race, with probability $\frac{1}{2}$ of winning. If it does not rain, he only has a 1 in 20 chance of winning. Display the sample space of possible results of the horse race on a tree diagram. Hence determine the probability that Mudlark will win tomorrow.

5   Machine A makes 40% of the bottles produced at a factory. Machine B makes the rest. Machine A spoils 5% of its product, while Machine B spoils only 2%. Using an appropriate tree diagram, determine the probability that the next bottle inspected at this factory is spoiled.

6   Jar A contains 2 white and 3 red discs. Jar B contains 3 white and 1 red disc. A jar is chosen at random by the flip of a coin, and one disc is taken at random from it. Determine the probability that the disc is red.

7   The English Premier League consists of 20 teams. Tottenham is currently in 8th place on the table. It has 20% chance of winning and 50% chance of losing against any team placed above it. If a team is placed below it, Tottenham has a 50% chance of winning and a 30% chance of losing. Find the probability that Tottenham will draw its next game.

**8** Three bags contain different numbers of red and blue marbles. A bag is selected using a die which has three A faces, two B faces, and one C face.

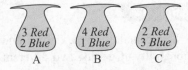

One marble is then selected randomly from the bag. Determine the probability that it is:

**a** blue                    **b** red.

# G                                                            SAMPLING

Suppose we have a large group of objects. The process of **sampling** is when we select one of the objects at random and inspect it for particular features.

If the object is put back in the group before another is chosen, we call it **sampling with replacement**.

If the object is put to one side, we call it **sampling without replacement**.

Sampling is commonly used in the quality control of industrial processes.

Sometimes the inspection process makes it impossible to return the object to the large group. For example:

- To see if a chocolate is hard or soft-centred, we need to bite it or squeeze it.
- To see if an egg contains one or two yolks, we need to break it open.
- To see if an object is correctly made, we may need to pull it apart.

Consider a box containing 3 red, 2 blue and 1 yellow marble. If we sample two marbles, we can do this either:

- **with replacement** of the first before the second is drawn, or
- **without replacement** of the first before the second is drawn.

Examine how the tree diagrams differ:

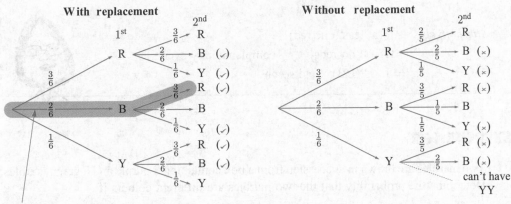

This branch represents a blue marble with the first draw and a red marble with the second draw. We write this as BR.

Notice that:        • with replacement              • without replacement

$$P(\text{two reds}) = \tfrac{3}{6} \times \tfrac{3}{6} = \tfrac{1}{4} \qquad P(\text{two reds}) = \tfrac{3}{6} \times \tfrac{2}{5} = \tfrac{1}{5}$$

**Example 15**    ◄⧅ **Self Tutor**

A box contains 3 red, 2 blue and 1 yellow marble. Find the probability of getting two different colours:

   **a**  if replacement occurs  **b**  if replacement does not occur.

Notice that in **b**
P(2 different colours)
$= 1 - $ P(2 the same)
$= 1 - $ P(RR or BB)
$= 1 - (\frac{3}{6} \times \frac{2}{5} + \frac{2}{6} \times \frac{1}{5})$
$= \frac{11}{15}$

To answer this question we use the tree diagram on page **511**.

**a**  P(two different colours)

$= $ P(RB or RY or BR or BY or YR or YB)  {ticked ones ✓ }

$= \frac{3}{6} \times \frac{2}{6} + \frac{3}{6} \times \frac{1}{6} + \frac{2}{6} \times \frac{3}{6} + \frac{2}{6} \times \frac{1}{6} + \frac{1}{6} \times \frac{3}{6} + \frac{1}{6} \times \frac{2}{6}$

$= \frac{11}{18}$

**b**  P(two different colours)

$= $ P(RB or RY or BR or BY or YR or YB)  {crossed ones ✗ }

$= \frac{3}{6} \times \frac{2}{5} + \frac{3}{6} \times \frac{1}{5} + \frac{2}{6} \times \frac{3}{5} + \frac{2}{6} \times \frac{1}{5} + \frac{1}{6} \times \frac{3}{5} + \frac{1}{6} \times \frac{2}{5}$

$= \frac{11}{15}$

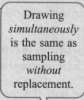

**Example 16**    ◄⧅ **Self Tutor**

A bag contains 5 red and 3 blue marbles. Two marbles are drawn simultaneously from the bag. Determine the probability that at least one is red.

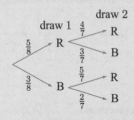

P(at least one red)

$= $ P(RR or RB or BR)

$= \frac{5}{8} \times \frac{4}{7} + \frac{5}{8} \times \frac{3}{7} + \frac{3}{8} \times \frac{5}{7}$

$= \frac{20+15+15}{56}$

$= \frac{25}{28}$

Drawing *simultaneously* is the same as sampling *without* replacement.

*Alternatively,*   P(at least one red)

$= 1 - $ P(no reds)  {complementary events}

$= 1 - $ P(BB)  and so on.

## EXERCISE 16G

**1**  Two marbles are drawn in succession from a box containing 2 purple and 5 green marbles. Determine the probability that the two marbles are different colours if:

  **a**  the first is replaced         **b**  the first is *not* replaced.

**2**  5 tickets numbered 1, 2, 3, 4 and 5 are placed in a bag. Two are taken from the bag without replacement. Determine the probability that:

  **a**  both are odd    **b**  both are even    **c**  one is odd and the other even.

**3** Jar A contains 3 red and 2 green tickets. Jar B contains 3 red and 7 green tickets. A die has 4 faces showing A, and 2 faces showing B. When rolled, the die is used to select either jar A or jar B. Once a jar has been selected, two tickets are randomly selected from it, the first being replaced before the second is selected. Determine the probability that:

   **a** both are green      **b** they are different in colour.

**4** Marie has a bag of sweets which are all identical in shape. The bag contains 6 orange drops and 4 lemon drops. She selects one sweet at random, eats it, and then takes another at random. Determine the probability that:

   **a** both sweets were orange drops

   **b** both sweets were lemon drops

   **c** the first was an orange drop and the second was a lemon drop

   **d** the first was a lemon drop and the second was an orange drop.

Add your answers to **a**, **b**, **c** and **d**. Explain why the total must be 1.

**5** A bag contains four red and two blue marbles. Three marbles are selected simultaneously. Determine the probablity that:

   **a** all are red      **b** only two are red      **c** at least two are red.

**6** Bag A contains 3 red and 2 white marbles. Bag B contains 4 red and 3 white marbles. One marble is randomly selected from A and its colour noted. If it is red, 2 reds are added to B. If it is white, 2 whites are added to B. A marble is then selected from B. What is the chance that the marble selected from B is white?

**7** A man holds two tickets in a 100-ticket lottery in which there are two winning tickets. If no replacement occurs, determine the probability that he will win:

   **a** both prizes      **b** neither prize      **c** at least one prize.

**8** A container holds 3 red, 7 white, and 2 black balls. A ball is chosen at random from the container and is replaced. A second ball is then chosen. Find the probability of choosing one white and one black ball in any order.

## INVESTIGATION 6            SAMPLING SIMULATION

 When balls enter the 'sorting' chamber shown they hit a metal rod and may go left or right. This movement continues as the balls fall from one level of rods to the next. The balls finally come to rest in collection chambers at the bottom of the sorter.

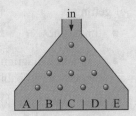

This sorter looks very much like a tree diagram rotated through $90°$.

Click on the icon to open the simulation. Notice that the sliding bar will alter the probabilities of balls going to the left or right at each rod.

**What to do:**

1   To simulate the results of tossing two coins, set the bar to 50% and the sorter to show:

   Run the simulation 200 times and repeat this four more times. Record each set of results.

2   A bag contains 7 blue and 3 red marbles. Two marbles are randomly selected from the bag, the first being *replaced* before the second is drawn.

   Since   $P(\text{blue}) = \frac{7}{10} = 70\%$,   set the bar to 70%.

   The sorter should show:

   Run the simulation a large number of times. Use the results to estimate the probability of getting:   **a**  two blues   **b**  one blue   **c**  no blues.

3   The tree diagram representation of the marble selection in **2** gives us theoretical probabilities for the different outcomes:

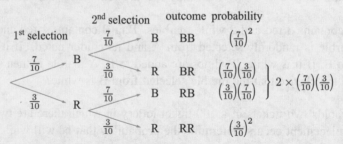

   **a**  Do the theoretical probabilities agree with the experimental results obtained in **2**?

   **b**  Write down the algebraic expansion of  $(a + b)^2$.

   **c**  Substitute  $a = \frac{7}{10}$  and  $b = \frac{3}{10}$  in the  $(a + b)^2$  expansion. What do you notice?

4   From the bag of 7 blue and 3 red marbles, *three* marbles are randomly selected *with replacement*. Set the sorter to 3 levels and the bar to 70%.

   Run the simulation a large number of times to obtain the experimental probabilities of getting:

   **a**  three blues   **b**  two blues   **c**  one blue   **d**  no blues.

5   **a**  Use a tree diagram showing 1st selection, 2nd selection and 3rd selection to find theoretical probabilities for getting the outcomes in **4**.

   **b**  Show that  $(a + b)^3 = a^3 + 3a^2b + 3ab^2 + b^3$  and use this expansion with  $a = \frac{7}{10}$  and  $b = \frac{3}{10}$  to also check the results of **4** and **5a**.

# H PROBABILITIES FROM VENN DIAGRAMS

**Venn diagrams**, which we encountered in **Chapter 3**, are a useful way of representing the events in a sample space. They can also be used to solve certain types of probability questions.

The Venn diagram alongside shows the sample space for rolling a die.

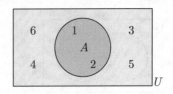

We can write the universal set $U = \{1, 2, 3, 4, 5, 6\}$ since the sample space consists of the numbers from 1 to 6.

The event $A$ is "*a number less than* 3". There are two outcomes which satisfy event $A$, and we can write $A = \{1, 2\}$.

Since 2 out of the 6 outcomes satisfy $A$, $P(A) = \dfrac{n(A)}{n(U)} = \dfrac{2}{6}$.

---

**Example 17**  ◀)) **Self Tutor**

The Venn diagram alongside represents the set $U$ of all children in a class. Each dot represents a student. The event $A$ shows all those students with blue eyes. Determine the probability that a randomly selected child:

  **a** has blue eyes   **b** does not have blue eyes.

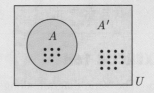

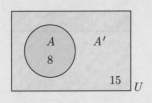

$n(U) = 23$,  $n(A) = 8$

**a** $P(\text{blue eyes}) = \dfrac{n(A)}{n(U)} = \dfrac{8}{23}$

**b** $P(\text{not blue eyes}) = \dfrac{n(A')}{n(U)} = \dfrac{15}{23}$

*or*   $P(\text{not blue})$
$= 1 - P(\text{blue eyes})$   {complementary events}
$= 1 - \frac{8}{23} = \frac{15}{23}$

---

**Example 18**  ◀)) **Self Tutor**

In a class of 30 students, 19 study Physics, 17 study Chemistry, and 15 study both of these subjects. Display this information on a Venn diagram and hence determine the probability that a randomly selected class member studies:

  **a** both subjects
  **b** at least one of the subjects
  **c** Physics but not Chemistry
  **d** exactly one of the subjects
  **e** neither subject
  **f** Chemistry if it is known that the student studies Physics.

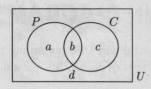

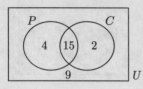

Let $P$ represent the event of 'studying Physics' and $C$ represent the event of 'studying Chemistry'.

Now    $a + b = 19$    {as 19 study Physics}
       $b + c = 17$    {as 17 study Chemistry}
       $b = 15$        {as 15 study both}
       $a + b + c + d = 30$    {as there are 30 in the class}

$\therefore$  $b = 15$, $a = 4$, $c = 2$, $d = 9$.

**a**  P(studies both)
$= \frac{15}{30}$ or $\frac{1}{2}$

**b**  P(studies at least one subject)
$= \frac{4+15+2}{30} = \frac{7}{10}$

**c**  P($P$ but not $C$)
$= \frac{4}{30} = \frac{2}{15}$

**d**  P(studies exactly one)
$= \frac{4+2}{30} = \frac{1}{5}$

**e**  P(studies neither)
$= \frac{9}{30} = \frac{3}{10}$

**f**  P($C$ given $P$)
$= \frac{15}{15+4} = \frac{15}{19}$

## EXERCISE 16H

**1**  The Venn diagram alongside represents the set $U$ of sheep in a pen. Each dot represents a sheep. The event $B$ shows the sheep with black wool.
Determine the probability that a randomly selected sheep:

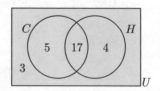

**a**  has black wool

**b**  does not have black wool.

**2**  The Venn diagram alongside illustrates the number of students in a particular class who study Chemistry ($C$) and History ($H$). Determine the probability that a randomly chosen student studies:

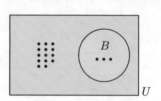

**a**  both subjects

**b**  at least one of the subjects

**c**  only Chemistry.

**3**  In a survey at an alpine resort, people were asked whether they liked skiing ($S$) or snowboarding ($B$). Use the Venn diagram to determine the probability that a randomly chosen person:

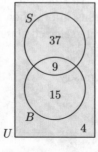

**a**  liked both activities

**b**  liked neither activity

**c**  liked exactly one activity.

**4**  In a class of 40 students, 19 play tennis, 20 play netball, and 8 play neither of these sports. A student is randomly chosen from the class. Determine the probability that the student:

  **a**  plays tennis  **b**  does not play netball

  **c**  plays at least one of the sports  **d**  plays one and only one of the sports

  **e**  plays netball but not tennis  **f**  plays tennis given he or she plays netball.

**5**  50 married men were asked whether they gave their wife flowers or chocolates for her last birthday. The results were: 31 gave chocolates, 12 gave flowers, and 5 gave both chocolates and flowers. If one of the married men was chosen at random, determine the probability that he gave his wife:

  **a**  chocolates or flowers  **b**  chocolates but not flowers

  **c**  neither chocolates nor flowers

  **d**  flowers if it is known that he did not give her chocolates.

**6**  The medical records for a class of 30 children showed that 24 had previously had measles, 12 had previously had measles and mumps, and 26 had previously had at least one of measles or mumps. If one child from the class is selected at random, determine the probability that he or she has had:

  **a**  mumps  **b**  mumps but not measles  **c**  neither mumps nor measles.

**7**

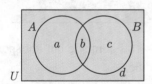

From the Venn diagram,   $P(A) = \dfrac{a+b}{a+b+c+d}$ .

  **a**  Use the Venn diagram to find:
   **i**  $P(B)$   **ii**  $P(A \text{ and } B)$   **iii**  $P(A \text{ or } B)$   **iv**  $P(A) + P(B) - P(A \text{ and } B)$

  **b**  What is the connection between  $P(A \text{ or } B)$  and  $P(A) + P(B) - P(A \text{ and } B)$?

**8**  In the Venn diagram, $U$ is the set of all 60 members of a club.

The members indicate their liking for Chinese ($C$), Italian ($I$), and Thai ($T$) takeaway food.

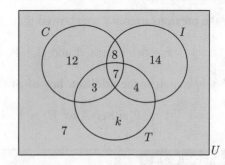

  **a**  Find the value of $k$.

  **b**  If a randomly chosen member is asked about their preference, what is the probability that the member likes:

   **i**  only Italian  **ii**  Italian and Thai

   **iii**  none of these choices  **iv**  at least one of these choices

   **v**  all of the choices  **vi**  Chinese and Italian, but not Thai

   **vii**  Thai or Italian  **viii**  exactly one of the three choices of takeaway food.

**9** As a group bonding project, 50 delegates at a European conference were asked what languages they had conversations in at lunch time. The data collected is summarised alongside:

| Languages | Delegates |
|---|---|
| English only | 17 |
| French only | 7 |
| Spanish only | 12 |
| English and French only | 3 |
| English and Spanish only | 6 |
| French and Spanish only | 4 |
| English, French and Spanish | 1 |

  **a** Construct a Venn diagram to display the information.

  **b** Determine the probability that a randomly selected delegate had a conversation in:

  **i** English    **ii** French    **iii** Spanish, but not one in English

  **iv** French, but not one in Spanish    **v** French, and also one in English.

**10** The Venn diagram opposite indicates the types of program a group of 40 individuals watched on television last night.

  $M$ represents movies, $S$ represents sport, and $D$ represents drama.

  **a** Given that 10 people watched a movie last night, calculate $a$ and $b$.

  **b** Find the probability that one of these individuals, selected at random, watched:

  **i** sport    **ii** drama and sport    **iii** a movie but not sport

  **iv** drama but not a movie    **v** drama or a movie.

# LAWS OF PROBABILITY

## THE ADDITION LAW

In the previous exercise we showed that:

> For two events $A$ and $B$, $P(A \cup B) = P(A) + P(B) - P(A \cap B)$.

This is known as the **addition law of probability**, and can be written as

> P(**either** $A$ **or** $B$) = P($A$) + P($B$) − P(**both** $A$ **and** $B$).

---

**Example 19**    ◀) **Self Tutor**

If $P(A) = 0.6$, $P(A \cup B) = 0.7$ and $P(A \cap B) = 0.3$, find $P(B)$.

$P(A \cup B) = P(A) + P(B) - P(A \cap B)$

$\therefore \quad 0.7 = 0.6 + P(B) - 0.3$

$\therefore \quad P(B) = 0.4$

| *or* | Using a Venn diagram with the probabilities on it, |
|---|---|
| 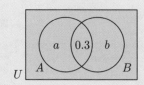 | $a + 0.3 = 0.6$ and $a + b + 0.3 = 0.7$ <br> $\therefore \quad a = 0.3$ $\qquad \therefore \quad a + b = 0.4$ <br> $\qquad\qquad\qquad\qquad \therefore \quad 0.3 + b = 0.4$ <br> $\qquad\qquad\qquad\qquad \therefore \quad b = 0.1$ <br> $\therefore \quad P(B) = 0.3 + b = 0.4$ |

## MUTUALLY EXCLUSIVE OR DISJOINT EVENTS

If $A$ and $B$ are **mutually exclusive** events then $P(A \cap B) = 0$
and so the addition law becomes $P(A \cup B) = P(A) + P(B)$.

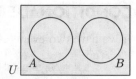

---

**Example 20** ◀)) **Self Tutor**

Of the 31 people on a bus tour, 7 were born in Scotland ($S$), and 5 were born in Wales ($W$).

**a** Are $S$ and $W$ mutually exclusive events?

**b** If a member of the tour is chosen at random, find the probability that he or she was born in:

   **i** Scotland          **ii** Wales          **iii** Scotland or Wales

---

**a** A person cannot be born in both Scotland and Wales.
So, $S$ and $W$ are mutually exclusive.

**b**  **i** $P(S) = \frac{7}{31}$      **ii** $P(W) = \frac{5}{31}$

   **iii** $P(S \cup W) = P(S) + P(W)$     {mutually exclusive events}

                $= \frac{7}{31} + \frac{5}{31}$

                $= \frac{12}{31}$

## EXERCISE 16I.1

**1** If $P(A) = 0.4$, $P(A \cup B) = 0.9$ and $P(A \cap B) = 0.1$, find $P(B)$.

**2** If $P(X) = 0.6$, $P(Y) = 0.5$ and $P(X \cup Y) = 0.9$, find $P(X \cap Y)$.

**3** $A$ and $B$ are mutually exclusive events.
If $P(B) = 0.45$ and $P(A \cup B) = 0.8$, find $P(A)$.

**4** Tickets numbered 1 to 15 are placed in a hat, and one ticket is chosen at random. Let $A$ be the event that the number drawn is greater than 11, and $B$ be the event that the number drawn is less than 8.

  **a** Are $A$ and $B$ mutually exclusive?

  **b** Find:   **i** $P(A)$   **ii** $P(B)$   **iii** $P(A \cup B)$.

**5** A class consists of 25 students.

      11 students are fifteen years old ($F$).

      12 students are sixteen years old ($S$).

      8 students own a dog ($D$).

      7 students own a cat ($C$).

      4 students do not own any pets ($N$).

A student is chosen at random. If possible, find:

  **a** $P(F)$     **b** $P(S)$     **c** $P(D)$     **d** $P(C)$     **e** $P(N)$

  **f** $P(F \cup S)$   **g** $P(F \cup D)$   **h** $P(C \cup N)$   **i** $P(C \cup D)$   **j** $P(D \cup N)$

## CONDITIONAL PROBABILITY

If we have two events $A$ and $B$, then

> $A \mid B$ is used to represent that '$A$ occurs knowing that $B$ has occurred'.
> $A \mid B$ is read as "$A$ given $B$".

---

**Example 21**        ◀) **Self Tutor**

In a class of 25 students, 14 like pizza and 16 like iced coffee. One student likes neither and 6 students like both. One student is randomly selected from the class. What is the probability that the student:

  **a** likes pizza         **b** likes pizza given that he or she likes iced coffee?

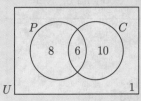

The Venn diagram of the situation is shown.

  **a** $P(\text{pizza}) = \frac{14}{25}$   {of the 25 students, 14 like pizza}

  **b** $P(\text{pizza} \mid \text{iced coffee}) = \frac{6}{16}$

      {of the 16 who like iced coffee, 6 like pizza}

---

> If $A$ and $B$ are events then $\mathbf{P}(A \mid B) = \dfrac{\mathbf{P}(A \cap B)}{\mathbf{P}(B)}$.

**Proof:**

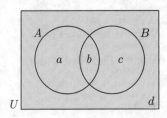

$$P(A \mid B) = \frac{b}{b+c} \quad \text{\{Venn diagram\}}$$

$$= \frac{\dfrac{b}{(a+b+c+d)}}{\dfrac{b+c}{(a+b+c+d)}}$$

$$= \frac{P(A \cap B)}{P(B)}$$

It follows that    $\mathbf{P}(A \cap B) = \mathbf{P}(A \mid B)\,\mathbf{P}(B)$  or  $\mathbf{P}(A \cap B) = \mathbf{P}(B \mid A)\,\mathbf{P}(A)$.

### Example 22                                                        ◀) Self Tutor

In a class of 40 students, 34 like bananas, 22 like pineapple, and 2 dislike both fruits.
If a student is randomly selected, find the probability that the student:

**a**  likes both fruits                       **b**  likes at least one fruit

**c**  likes bananas given that he or she likes pineapple

**d**  dislikes pineapple given that he or she likes bananas.

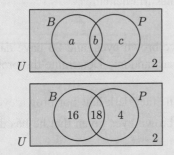

$B$ represents students who like bananas.
$P$ represents students who like pineapple.

We are given that   $a + b = 34$
$$b + c = 22$$
$$a + b + c = 38$$

$\therefore$   $c = 38 - 34$     and so   $b = 18$
$$= 4 \qquad \text{and} \quad a = 16$$

**a**   P(likes both)     **b**   P(likes at least one)   **c**   $P(B \mid P)$   **d**   $P(P' \mid B)$

$= \frac{18}{40}$       $= \frac{38}{40}$       $= \frac{18}{22}$       $= \frac{16}{34}$

$= \frac{9}{20}$       $= \frac{19}{20}$       $= \frac{9}{11}$       $= \frac{8}{17}$

### Example 23                                                        ◀) Self Tutor

The top shelf in a cupboard contains 3 cans of pumpkin soup and 2 cans of chicken
soup. The bottom shelf contains 4 cans of pumpkin soup and 1 can of chicken soup.

Lukas is twice as likely to take a can from the bottom shelf as he is from the top shelf.
If he takes one can without looking at the label, determine the probability that it:

**a**  is chicken                       **b**  was taken from top shelf given that it is chicken.

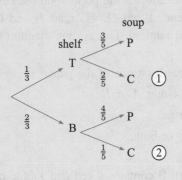

**a**   P(soup is chicken)

$= \frac{1}{3} \times \frac{2}{5} + \frac{2}{3} \times \frac{1}{5}$   {path ① + path ②}

$= \frac{4}{15}$

**b**   P(top shelf | chicken)

$= \dfrac{\text{P(top shelf and chicken)}}{\text{P(chicken)}}$

$= \dfrac{\frac{1}{3} \times \frac{2}{5}}{\frac{4}{15}}$   ◀—— path ①

$= \frac{1}{2}$

## EXERCISE 16I.2

1   In a group of 50 students, 40 study Mathematics, 32 study Physics, and each student studies at least one of these subjects.

   **a**  Use a Venn diagram to find how many students study both subjects.

   **b**  If a student from this group is randomly selected, find the probability that he or she:

   **i**  studies Mathematics but not Physics

   **ii**  studies Physics given that he or she studies Mathematics.

2   In a group of 40 boys, 23 have dark hair, 18 have brown eyes, and 26 have dark hair, brown eyes or both. One of the boys is selected at random. Determine the probability that he has:

   **a**  dark hair and brown eyes

   **b**  neither dark hair nor brown eyes

   **c**  dark hair but not brown eyes

   **d**  brown eyes given that he has dark hair.

3   50 students went bushwalking. 23 were sunburnt, 22 were bitten by ants, and 5 were both sunburnt and bitten by ants. Determine the probability that a randomly selected student:

   **a**  escaped being bitten

   **b**  was either bitten or sunburnt

   **c**  was neither bitten nor sunburnt

   **d**  was bitten, given that he or she was sunburnt

   **e**  was sunburnt, given that he or she was not bitten.

4   400 families were surveyed. It was found that 90% had a TV set and 60% had a computer. Every family had at least one of these items. If one of these families is randomly selected, find the probability it has a TV set given that it has a computer.

5   In a certain town three newspapers are published. 20% of the population read $A$, 16% read $B$, 14% read $C$, 8% read $A$ and $B$, 5% read $A$ and $C$, 4% read $B$ and $C$, and 2% read all 3 newspapers. A person is selected at random. Use a Venn diagram to help determine the probability that the person reads:

   **a**  none of the papers

   **b**  at least one of the papers

   **c**  exactly one of the papers

   **d**  either $A$ or $B$

   **e**  $A$, given that the person reads at least one paper

   **f**  $C$, given that the person reads either $A$ or $B$ or both.

6   Urn A contains 2 red and 3 blue marbles, and urn B contains 4 red and 1 blue marble. Peter selects an urn by tossing a coin, and takes a marble from that urn.

   **a**  Determine the probability that it is red.

   **b**  Given that the marble is red, what is the probability that it came from B?

**7** The probability that Greta's mother takes her shopping is $\frac{2}{5}$. When Greta goes shopping with her mother she gets an icecream 70% of the time. When Greta does not go shopping with her mother she gets an icecream 30% of the time. Determine the probability that:

    **a** Greta's mother buys her an icecream when shopping

    **b** Greta went shopping with her mother, given that her mother buys her an icecream.

**8** On a given day, machine A has a 10% chance of malfunctioning and machine B has a 7% chance of the same. Given that at least one of the machines malfunctioned today, what is the chance that machine B malfunctioned?

**9** On any day, the probability that a boy eats his prepared lunch is 0.5. The probability that his sister eats her lunch is 0.6. The probability that the girl eats her lunch given that the boy eats his is 0.9. Determine the probability that:

    **a** both eat their lunch    **b** the boy eats his lunch given that the girl eats hers

    **c** at least one of them eats their lunch.

**10** The probability that a randomly selected person has cancer is 0.02. The probability that he or she reacts positively to a test which detects cancer is 0.95 if he or she has cancer, and 0.03 if he or she does not. Determine the probability that a randomly tested person:

    **a** reacts positively    **b** has cancer given that he or she reacts positively.

**11** A group of teenagers were surveyed on which of three types of computer games they play. The results are shown in the Venn diagram on the right, where:

A represents those who play arcade games
S represents those who play sports games
R represents those who play role-playing games.

Find the probability that a randomly selected member of the group plays:

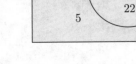

    **a** arcade games but not role-playing games

    **b** sports games and arcade games    **c** role-playing games or sports games

    **d** sports games, given that he or she plays arcade games

    **e** role-playing games, given that he or she plays arcade games

    **f** arcade games, given that he or she does *not* play sports games.

**12** In a team of 30 judo players, 13 have won a match by throwing ($T$), 12 have won by hold-down ($H$), and 13 have won by points decision ($P$). 2 have won matches by all three methods. 5 have won matches by throwing and hold-down. 4 have won matches by hold-down and points decision. 3 have won matches by throwing and points decision.

    **a** Draw a Venn diagram to display this information.

    **b** Find:

        **i** $P(T \cap H)$        **ii** $P(P)$        **iii** $P(H \mid P)$

        **iv** $P(T \cup P)$        **v** $P(T \mid H')$        **vi** $P((T \cap P) \mid H)$

## J            INDEPENDENT EVENTS

$A$ and $B$ are **independent events** if the occurrence of each one of them does not affect the probability that the other occurs.

This means that   $P(A \mid B) = P(A \mid B') = P(A)$.

So, as   $P(A \cap B) = P(A \mid B) P(B)$,

$A$ and $B$ are **independent events** $\Leftrightarrow$ $P(A \cap B) = P(A) P(B)$.

$\Leftrightarrow$ means 'if and only if'.

---

### Example 24                                          ◀)) Self Tutor

$P(A) = \frac{1}{2}$,  $P(B) = \frac{1}{3}$  and  $P(A \cup B) = p$.  Find $p$ if:

  **a**   $A$ and $B$ are mutually exclusive       **b**   $A$ and $B$ are independent.

**a**  If $A$ and $B$ are mutually exclusive, $A \cap B = \varnothing$  and so  $P(A \cap B) = 0$
   But   $P(A \cup B) = P(A) + P(B) - P(A \cap B)$
   $\therefore$   $p = \frac{1}{2} + \frac{1}{3} - 0 = \frac{5}{6}$

**b**  If $A$ and $B$ are independent,        $P(A \cap B) = P(A) P(B)$
                                              $= \frac{1}{2} \times \frac{1}{3} = \frac{1}{6}$
   $\therefore$  $P(A \cup B) = \frac{1}{2} + \frac{1}{3} - \frac{1}{6}$
         and hence  $p = \frac{2}{3}$.

---

### Example 25                                          ◀)) Self Tutor

Given  $P(A) = \frac{2}{5}$,  $P(B \mid A) = \frac{1}{3}$  and  $P(B \mid A') = \frac{1}{4}$  find:   **a**   $P(B)$   **b**   $P(A \cap B')$

$P(B \mid A) = \dfrac{P(B \cap A)}{P(A)}$   so  $P(B \cap A) = P(B \mid A) P(A) = \frac{1}{3} \times \frac{2}{5} = \frac{2}{15}$

Similarly,   $P(B \cap A') = P(B \mid A') P(A') = \frac{1}{4} \times \frac{3}{5} = \frac{3}{20}$

$\therefore$   the Venn diagram is:

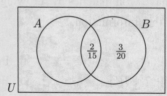

**a**  $P(B) = \frac{2}{15} + \frac{3}{20} = \frac{17}{60}$

**b**  $P(A \cap B') = P(A) - P(A \cap B)$
      $= \frac{2}{5} - \frac{2}{15}$
      $= \frac{4}{15}$

## EXERCISE 16J

1 If $P(R) = 0.4$, $P(S) = 0.5$ and $P(R \cup S) = 0.7$, are $R$ and $S$ independent events?

2 If $P(A) = \frac{2}{5}$, $P(B) = \frac{1}{3}$ and $P(A \cup B) = \frac{1}{2}$, find:

   a $P(A \cap B)$                      b $P(B \mid A)$                      c $P(A \mid B)$

   Are $A$ and $B$ independent events?

3 If $P(X) = 0.5$, $P(Y) = 0.7$ and $X$ and $Y$ are independent events, determine the probability of the occurrence of:

   a both $X$ and $Y$       b $X$ or $Y$           c neither $X$ nor $Y$

   d $X$ but not $Y$       e $X$ given that $Y$ occurs.

4 The probabilities that A, B and C can solve a particular problem are $\frac{3}{5}$, $\frac{2}{3}$ and $\frac{1}{2}$ respectively. If they all try, determine the probability that at least one of the group solves the problem.

5 $A$ and $B$ are independent events. Prove that $A'$ and $B'$ are also independent events.

6 Suppose $P(A \cap B) = 0.1$ and $P(A \cap B') = 0.4$. Find $P(A \cup B')$ given that $A$ and $B$ are independent.

## REVIEW SET 16A

1   a List the different orders in which 4 people A, B, C and D could line up.

   b If they line up at random, determine the probability that:

     i A is next to C     ii there is exactly one person between A and C.

2 A coin is tossed and a square spinner labelled A, B, C, D is twirled. Determine the probability of obtaining:

   a a head and consonant    b a tail and C       c a tail or a vowel.

3 The probability that a man will be alive in 25 years is $\frac{3}{5}$, and the probability that his wife will be alive is $\frac{2}{3}$. Determine the probability that in 25 years:

   a both will be alive           b at least one will be alive

   c only the wife will be alive.

4 Given $P(Y) = 0.35$ and $P(X \cup Y) = 0.8$, and that $X$ and $Y$ are mutually exclusive events, find:

   a $P(X \cap Y)$              b $P(X)$

   c the probability that $X$ occurs or $Y$ occurs, but not both $X$ and $Y$.

5 What is meant by:    a independent events    b disjoint events?

6 Graph the sample space of all possible outcomes when a pair of dice is rolled. Hence determine the probability of getting:

   a at least one 4           b both numbers greater than 3.

**7** In a group of 40 students, 22 study Economics, 25 study Law, and 3 study neither of these subjects. Determine the probability that a randomly chosen student studies:

    **a** both Economics and Law         **b** at least one of these subjects

    **c** Economics given that he or she studies Law.

**8** The probability that a particular salesman will leave his sunglasses behind in any store is $\frac{1}{5}$. Suppose the salesman visits two stores in succession and leaves his sunglasses behind in one of them. What is the probability that the salesman left his sunglasses in the first store?

## REVIEW SET 16B

**1** A group of businesses were asked whether they had increased or decreased the number of employees in the last year.

| Number of employees | Decreased | Stayed the same | Increased |
|---|---|---|---|
| 1-4 | 26 | 168 | 25 |
| 5-9 | 19 | 41 | 3 |
| 10-19 | 23 | 9 | 7 |
| 20-99 | 20 | 2 | 14 |
| 100-499 | 6 | 0 | 6 |
| 500+ | 14 | 0 | 19 |
| Total | 108 | 220 | 74 |

    **a** Using this data, find the probability that a business with 10-19 employees grew in the previous year.

    **b** What is the probability that a business that increased in size had 10-99 employees?

    **c** Find the probability that a randomly selected business decreased in size over the previous year.

**2** Two dice are rolled and the results are multiplied together.

    **a** Draw a table of outcomes to display the possible results.

    **b** Hence determine the probability that the resulting value is:

        **i** 12              **ii** greater than 17         **iii** a square number.

**3** Niklas and Rolf play tennis with the winner being the first to win two sets. Niklas has a 40% chance of beating Rolf in any set. Draw a tree diagram showing the possible outcomes and hence determine the probability that Niklas will win the match.

**4** I buy 4 tickets in a 500 ticket lottery, and the prizes are drawn without replacement. Determine the probability that I will win:

    **a** the first 3 prizes         **b** at least one of the first 3 prizes.

**5** The students in a school are all vaccinated against measles. 48% of the students are males, of whom 16% have an allergic reaction to the vaccine. 35% of the girls also have an allergic reaction. If a student is randomly chosen from the school, what is the probability that the student:

    **a** has an allergic reaction

    **b** is female given that a reaction occurs?

**6** On any one day it could rain with 25% chance and be windy with 36% chance. Draw a tree diagram showing the possibilities with regard to wind and rain on a particular day. Hence determine the probability that on a particular day there will be:

    **a** rain and wind            **b** rain or wind.

**7** Divers A, B and C have a 10%, 20% and 30% chance of successfully finding an artefact in a shipwreck. If they all try independently of one another, what is the probability that the artefact is found?

**8** Today there were 42 staff members in the common room at morning tea. Their selection of biscuits is illustrated in the Venn diagram alongside.
$A$ is the set of staff who ate a chocolate biscuit.
$B$ is the set of staff who ate a cookie.
$C$ is the set of staff who ate a cream biscuit.

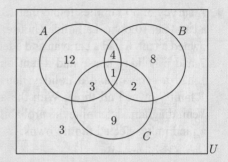

Find the probability that a randomly selected staff member ate:

  **a** a chocolate biscuit          **b** a chocolate biscuit and a cookie

  **c** a chocolate biscuit or a cookie    **d** exactly one type of biscuit

  **e** exactly two types of biscuit     **f** a cream biscuit but not a cookie

  **g** a cookie given that he or she ate a chocolate biscuit

  **h** a cream biscuit given that he or she ate a cookie.

## REVIEW SET 16C

**1** Systematically list the possible sexes of a 4-child family. Hence determine the probability that a randomly selected 4-child family has two children of each sex.

**2** A bag contains 3 red, 4 yellow and 5 blue marbles. Two marbles are randomly selected from the bag without replacement. What is the probability that:

  **a** both are blue            **b** they have the same colour

  **c** at least one is red        **d** exactly one is yellow?

**3** An art gallery has 25 rooms. 17 contain sculptures, 19 contain paintings and the cloak room has neither. If a visitor enters a room at random, determine the probability that it contains:

  **a** both paintings and sculptures     **b** only one type of art

  **c** paintings given there are no sculptures.

**4** An urn contains three red balls and six blue balls.

  **a** A ball is drawn at random and found to be blue. What is the probability that a second draw with no replacement will also produce a blue ball?

  **b** Two balls are drawn without replacement and the second is found to be red. What is the probability that the first ball was also red?

**5**  An automatic gate has a 95% chance of working on any particular day. Find the probability that it will be working on at least one of the next two days.

**6**  Jon goes cycling on three random mornings of each week. When he goes cycling he has eggs for breakfast 70% of the time. When he does not go cycling he has eggs for breakfast 25% of the time. Determine the probability that he:

   **a**  has eggs for breakfast   **b**  goes cycling given that he has eggs for breakfast.

**7**  If  $P(X) = \frac{1}{4}$,  $P(Y') = \frac{1}{6}$  and  $P(X \cup Y) = \frac{7}{8}$,  are $X$ and $Y$ independent?

**8**  A survey of 50 families found that 13 owned a caravan, 10 owned a holiday house, and 30 owned a tent. 6 had a caravan and a tent only, 7 had a holiday house and a tent only, and 1 had a caravan and a holiday house only. 1 family owned all three. With the aid of a Venn diagram, determine the probability that a randomly selected family owns:

   **a**  a caravan only

   **b**  exactly two types of holiday accommodation

   **c**  none of these things.

# Chapter 17

# Logic

## OPENING PROBLEM

On Saint Patrick's Day, the students in a class are all encouraged to wear green clothes to school.

Brogan        Eamonn        Padraig        Sean

### Things to think about:

For each of these statements, list the students for which the statement is true:

**a** I am wearing a green shirt.

**b** I am not wearing a green shirt.

**c** I am wearing a green shirt and green pants.

**d** I am wearing a green shirt or green pants.

**e** I am wearing a green shirt or green pants, but not both.

**Mathematical logic** deals with the conversion of worded statements into symbols, and how we can apply rules of deduction to them. The concept was originally suggested by **G W Leibniz** (1646-1716).

**George Boole** (1815-1864) introduced the symbolism which provided the tools for the analysis. Other people who made important contributions to the field include Bertrand Russell, Augustus DeMorgan, David Hilbert, John Venn, Giuseppe Peano, and Gottlob Frege.

Mathematical arguments require basic **definitions** and **axioms**, which are simple statements that we accept without proof. Logical reasoning is then essential to building clear rules based upon these definitions.

**G W Leibniz**

## A                                    PROPOSITIONS

**Propositions** are statements which may be true or false.

Questions are not propositions.

Comments or opinions that are subjective, for example, 'Green is a nice colour' are also not propositions since they are not definitely true or false.

Propositions may be **indeterminate**. For example, 'your father is 177 cm tall' would not have the same answer (true or false) for all people.

The **truth value** of a proposition is whether it is true or false.

### Example 1

🔊 **Self Tutor**

Which of the following statements are propositions? If they are propositions, are they true, false, or indeterminate?

a   $20 \div 4 = 80$

b   $25 \times 8 = 200$

c   Where is my pen?

d   Your eyes are blue.

a   This is a proposition. It is false as $20 \div 4 = 5$.

b   This is a proposition and is true.

c   This is a question, so is not a proposition.

d   This is a proposition. It is indeterminate, as the statement is true for some people and false for other people.

## NOTATION USED FOR PROPOSITIONS

We represent propositions by letters such as $p$, $q$ and $r$.

For example,   $p$: It always rains on Tuesdays.

$q$: $37 + 9 = 46$

$r$: $x$ is an even number.

## NEGATION

The **negation** of a proposition $p$ is "not $p$", and is written as $\neg p$.
The truth value of $\neg p$ is the opposite of the truth value of $p$.

For example:

The negation of  $p$: It is raining  is  $\neg p$: It is not raining.

The negation of  $p$: Tim has brown hair  is  $\neg p$: Tim does not have brown hair.

From these examples, we can see that $\neg p$ is $\begin{cases} \text{false when } p \text{ is true} \\ \text{true when } p \text{ is false.} \end{cases}$

This information can be represented in a **truth table**. The first column contains the possible truth values for $p$, and the second column contains the corresponding values for $\neg p$.

| $p$ | $\neg p$ |
|---|---|
| T | F |
| F | T |

## EXERCISE 17A.1

1   Which of the following statements are propositions? If they are propositions, are they true, false or indeterminate?

a   $11 - 5 = 7$

b   $12 \in \{\text{odd numbers}\}$

c   $\frac{3}{4} \in \mathbb{Q}$

d   $2 \notin \mathbb{Q}$

e   A hexagon has 6 sides.

f   $37 \in \{\text{prime numbers}\}$

g   How tall are you?

h   All squares are rectangles.

i   Is it snowing?

j   A rectangle is not a parallelogram.

**k**  Your brother is 13.

**l**  Do you like dramatic movies?

**m**  Joan sings loudly.

**n**  You were born in China.

**o**  Alternate angles are equal.

**p**  Parallel lines eventually meet.

**2**  For each of the following propositions:

  **i**  write down the negation    **ii**  indicate if the proposition or its negation is true.

  **a**  $p$:  All rectangles are parallelograms.

  **b**  $m$:  $\sqrt{5}$ is an irrational number.

  **c**  $r$:  7 is a rational number.

  **d**  $q$:  $23 - 14 = 12$

  **e**  $r$:  $52 \div 4 = 13$

  **f**  $s$:  The difference between any two odd numbers is even.

  **g**  $t$:  The product of consecutive integers is always even.

  **h**  $u$:  All obtuse angles are equal.

  **i**  $p$:  All trapeziums are parallelograms.

  **j**  $q$:  If a triangle has two equal angles it is isosceles.

**3**  Find the negation of these propositions for $x, y \in \mathbb{R}$:

  **a**  $x < 5$        **b**  $x \geqslant 3$        **c**  $y < 8$        **d**  $y \leqslant 10$

**4**  For the two propositions $r$ and $s$ given:

  **i**  Is $s$ the negation of $r$?

  **ii**  If $s$ is not the negation of $r$, give the correct negation of $r$.

  **a**  $r$:  Kania scored more than 60%.    $s$:  Kania scored less than 60%.

  **b**  $r$:  Dea has less than two sisters.    $s$:  Dea has at least two sisters.

  **c**  $r$:  Fari is at soccer practice.    $s$:  Fari is at music practice.

  **d**  $r$:  I have been to Canada.    $s$:  I have never been to Canada.

  **e**  $r$:  I drank black tea today.    $s$:  I drank white tea today.

| Example 2 | ◀⁾ Self Tutor |
|---|---|
| Find the negation of: <br> **a**  $x$ is a dog  for  $x \in \{\text{dogs, cats}\}$ <br> **b**  $x \geqslant 2$  for  $x \in \mathbb{N}$ <br> **c**  $x \geqslant 2$  for  $x \in \mathbb{Z}$. | **a**  $x$ is a cat. <br> **b**  $x \in \{0, 1\}$ <br> **c**  $x < 2$  for  $x \in \mathbb{Z}$ |

**5**  Find the negation of:

  **a**  $x \geqslant 5$  for  $x \in \mathbb{Z}^+$

  **b**  $x$ is a cow for  $x \in \{\text{horses, sheep, cows, goats, deer}\}$

  **c**  $x \geqslant 0$  for  $x \in \mathbb{Z}$

  **d**  $x$ is a male student for  $x \in \{\text{students}\}$

  **e**  $x$ is a female student for  $x \in \{\text{females}\}$.

## NEGATION AND VENN DIAGRAMS

Many propositions contain a variable.

The proposition may be true for some values of the variable, and false for others.

We can use a **Venn diagram** to represent these propositions and their negations.

For example, consider  $p$: $x$ is greater than 10.

$U$  is the **universal set** of all the values that the
variable $x$ may take.

$P$  is the **truth set** of the proposition $p$, or the set
of values of  $x \in U$  for which $p$ is true.

$P'$  is the truth set of  $\neg p$.

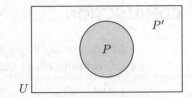

| | |
|---|---|

---

**Example 3**                                          ◄◙ **Self Tutor**

For  $U = \{x \mid 0 < x < 10, \ x \in \mathbb{N}\}$  and proposition  $p$: $x$ is a prime number,
find the truth sets of $p$ and $\neg p$.

If $P$ is the truth set of $p$ then  $P = \{2, 3, 5, 7\}$.

The truth set of  $\neg p$  is  $P' = \{1, 4, 6, 8, 9\}$

The Venn diagram representation is:

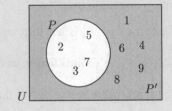

## EXERCISE 17A.2

1  **a**  Find the truth sets of these statements:

    **i**  $p$: $x$ is a multiple of 3,  for  $U = \{x \mid 20 < x < 30\}$

    **ii**  $p$: $x$ is an even number,  for  $U = \{x \mid 1 < x \leqslant 10\}$

    **iii**  $p$: $x$ is a factor of 42,  for  $U = \mathbb{Z}$.

  **b**  Draw Venn diagrams to represent  **a i**  and  **a ii**.

2  Suppose  $U = \{$students in Year 11$\}$,  $M = \{$students who study music$\}$,  and
$O = \{$students who play in the orchestra$\}$.

Draw a Venn diagram to represent the statements:

  **a**  All music students play in the school orchestra.

  **b**  None of the orchestral students study music.

  **c**  No-one in the orchestra does not study music.

3  **a**  **i**  Represent  $U = \{x \mid 5 < x < 15, \ x \in \mathbb{N}\}$  and  $p$: $x < 9$  on a Venn diagram.

    **ii**  List the truth set of  $\neg p$.

  **b**  **i**  Represent  $U = \{x \mid x < 10, \ x \in \mathbb{N}\}$  and  $p$: $x$ is a multiple of 2
on a Venn diagram.

    **ii**  List the truth set of  $\neg p$.

# B  COMPOUND PROPOSITIONS

Compound propositions are statements which are formed using connectives such as **and** and **or**.

## CONJUNCTION

When two propositions are joined using the word **and**, the new proposition is the **conjunction** of the original propositions.

If $p$ and $q$ are propositions, $p \wedge q$ is used to denote their conjunction.

For example, if  $p$: Eli had soup for lunch

$\phantom{For example, if  p:}$ $q$: Eli had a pie for lunch

then  $p \wedge q$: Eli had soup and a pie for lunch.

We see that  $p \wedge q$  is only true if Eli had both soup *and* a pie for lunch, which means that both $p$ and $q$ are true.

If either of $p$ or $q$ is not true, or both $p$ and $q$ are not true, then  $p \wedge q$  is not true.

A conjunction is true only when both original propositions are true.

The **truth table** below shows the conjunction "$p$ and $q$".

| $p$ | $q$ | $p \wedge q$ |
|---|---|---|
| T | T | T |
| T | F | F |
| F | T | F |
| F | F | F |

$p \wedge q$ is true when both $p$ and $q$ are true.

$p \wedge q$  is false whenever one or both of $p$ and $q$ are false.

The first 2 columns list the possible combinations for $p$ and $q$.

We can use Venn diagrams to represent conjunctions.

Suppose  $P$ is the truth set of $p$,  and

$\phantom{Suppose  }$ $Q$ is the truth set of $q$.

The truth set of  $p \wedge q$  is  $P \cap Q$,  the region where both $p$ **and** $q$ are true.

$P \cap Q$

## EXERCISE 17B.1

1  Write  $p \wedge q$  for the following pairs of propositions:

  a  $p$: Ted is a doctor, $q$: Shelly is a dentist.

  b  $p$: $x$ is greater than 15, $q$: $x$ is less than 30.

  c  $p$: It is windy, $q$: It is raining.

  d  $p$: Kim has brown hair, $q$: Kim has blue eyes.

**2** For the following pairs of propositions $p$ and $q$, determine whether $p \wedge q$ is true or false:

    **a** $p$: 5 is an odd number,   $q$: 5 is a prime number.

    **b** $p$: A square has four sides,   $q$: A triangle has five sides.

    **c** $p$: $39 < 27$,   $q$: $16 > 23$

    **d** $p$: 3 is a factor of 12,   $q$: 4 is a factor of 12.

    **e** $p$: $5 + 8 = 12$,   $q$: $6 + 9 = 15$.

**3** For $U = \{x \mid 1 \leqslant x \leqslant 12, \ x \in \mathbb{Z}\}$, consider the propositions $p$: $x$ is even and $q$: $x$ is less than 7.

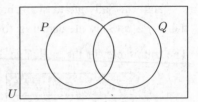

    **a** Illustrate the truth sets for $p$ and $q$ on a Venn diagram like the one alongside.

    **b** Use your Venn diagram to find the truth set of $p \wedge q$.

# DISJUNCTION

When two propositions are joined by the word **or**, the new proposition is the **disjunction** of the original propositions.

If $p$ and $q$ are propositions, $p \vee q$ is used to denote their disjunction.

For example, if   $p$: Frank played tennis today

         and   $q$: Frank played golf today

     then   $p \vee q$: Frank played tennis or golf today.

$p \vee q$ is true if Frank played tennis or golf or both today.

So, $p \vee q$ is true if $p$ or $q$ or both are true.

> A disjunction is true when one or both propositions are true.

Alternatively, we can say that

> A disjunction is only false if both propositions are false.

The truth table for the disjunction "$p$ or $q$" is:

| $p$ | $q$ | $p \vee q$ |
|---|---|---|
| T | T | T |
| T | F | T |
| F | T | T |
| F | F | F |

$p \vee q$ is true if $p$ or $q$ or both are true.

$p \vee q$ is only false if both $p$ and $q$ are false.

If $P$ and $Q$ are the truth sets for propositions $p$ and $q$ respectively, then the truth set for $p \vee q$ is $P \cup Q$, the region where $p$ or $q$ or both are true.

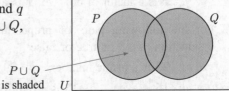

$P \cup Q$
is shaded   $U$

## EXCLUSIVE DISJUNCTION

> The **exclusive disjunction** is true when **only one** of the propositions is true.
>
> The exclusive disjunction of $p$ and $q$ is written $p \veebar q$.

We can describe $p \veebar q$ as "$p$ or $q$, but not both", or "exactly one of $p$ and $q$".

So, if    $p$: Sally ate cereal for breakfast

and    $q$: Sally ate toast for breakfast

then    $p \veebar q$: Sally ate cereal or toast, but not both, for breakfast.

The truth table for the exclusive disjunction $p \veebar q$ is:

| $p$ | $q$ | $p \veebar q$ |
|-----|-----|-----|
| T | T | F |
| T | F | T |
| F | T | T |
| F | F | F |

$p \veebar q$ is true if exactly one of $p$ and $q$ is true.

$p \veebar q$ is false if $p$ and $q$ are both true or both false.

If $P$ and $Q$ are the truth sets for propositions $p$ and $q$ respectively, then the truth set for $p \veebar q$ is the region shaded, where exactly one of $p$ and $q$ is true.

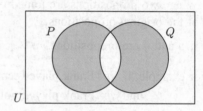

## EXERCISE 17B.2

1  Write the disjunction $p \vee q$ for the following pairs of propositions:

   **a** $p$: Tim owns a bicycle,   $q$: Tim owns a scooter.

   **b** $p$: $x$ is a multiple of 2,   $q$: $x$ is a multiple of 5.

   **c** $p$: Dana studies Physics,   $q$: Dana studies Chemistry.

2  For the following propositions, determine whether $p \vee q$ is true or false:

   **a** $p$: 24 is a multiple of 4,   $q$: 24 is a multiple of 6.

   **b** $p$: There are $100°$ in a right angle,   $q$: There are $180°$ on a straight line.

   **c** $p$: $-8 > -5$,   $q$: $5 < 0$

   **d** $p$: The mean of 5 and 9 is 7,   $q$: The mean of 8 and 14 is 10.

3  Write the exclusive disjunction $p \veebar q$ for the following pairs of propositions:

   **a** $p$: Meryn will visit Japan next year,   $q$: Meryn will visit Singapore next year.

   **b** $p$: Ann will invite Kate to her party,   $q$: Ann will invite Tracy to her party.

   **c** $p$: $x$ is a factor of 56,   $q$: $x$ is a factor of 40.

4  For the following pairs of propositions $a$ and $b$, determine whether the exclusive disjunction $a \veebar b$ is true or false:

   **a** $a$: 23 is a prime number,   $b$: 29 is a prime number.

   **b** $a$: 15 is even,   $b$: 15 is a multiple of 3.

   **c** $a$: $4.5 \in \mathbb{Z}$,   $b$:  $-8 \in \mathbb{N}$

   **d** $a$: $2^3 \times 2^4 = 2^7$,   $b$: $(2^8)^6 = 2^{42}$

**5** Consider $r$: Kelly is a good driver,  and   $s$: Kelly has a good car.

   Write in symbolic form:

   **a** Kelly is not a good driver

   **b** Kelly is a good driver and has a good car

   **c** Kelly does not have a good car and is not a good driver

   **d** Kelly has a good car or Kelly is a good driver.

**6** Consider $x$:  Sergio would like to go swimming tomorrow, and

                $y$:  Sergio would like to go bowling tomorrow.

   Write in symbolic form:

   **a** Sergio would not like to go swimming tomorrow

   **b** Sergio would like to go swimming and bowling tomorrow

   **c** Sergio would like to go swimming or bowling tomorrow

   **d** Sergio would not like to go both swimming and bowling tomorrow

   **e** Sergio would like either to go swimming or go bowling tomorrow, but not both.

**7** For each of the following, define appropriate propositions and then write in symbolic form:

   **a** Phillip likes icecream and jelly.

   **b** Phillip likes icecream or Phillip does not like jelly.

   **c** $x$ is both greater than 10 and a prime number.

   **d** Tuan can go to the mountains or the beach, but not both.

   **e** The computer is not on.

   **f** Angela does not have a watch but does have a mobile phone.

   **g** Maya studied one of Spanish or French.

   **h** I can hear thunder or an aeroplane.

**8** If $p \vee q$ is true and $p \veebar q$ is false, determine the truth values of:

   **a** $p$            **b** $q$

**9** For $U = \{x \mid 1 \leqslant x \leqslant 20,\ x \in \mathbb{Z}\}$,  consider the propositions

      $p$: $x$ is a multiple of 3,  and  $q$: $x$ is an odd number.

   **a** Illustrate the truth sets for $p$ and $q$ on a Venn diagram.

   **b** Use your Venn diagram to find the truth set for:

        **i** $\neg q$          **ii** $p \vee q$         **iii** $p \wedge q$        **iv** $p \veebar q$

**10** **a** For $U = \{x \mid 1 \leqslant x \leqslant 12,\ x \in \mathbb{Z}\}$, use a Venn diagram to illustrate the truth sets for   $p$: $x$ is prime,  and  $q$: $x$ is a factor of 12.

   **b** Write down the meaning of:

        **i** $p \wedge q$          **ii** $p \vee q$         **iii** $p \veebar q$

   **c** Use your Venn diagram to find the truth sets for:

        **i** $p \wedge q$          **ii** $p \vee q$         **iii** $p \veebar q$

**11** Read the description of Ed's day:

"Ed slept in, then had pancakes for breakfast. He went to the gym in the morning, then ate a sandwich for lunch. He played golf in the afternoon, and had steak for dinner."

Consider the following propositions:

| | | | |
|---|---|---|---|
| $p$: | Ed got out of bed early | $q$: | Ed ate pancakes for breakfast |
| $r$: | Ed ate steak for lunch | $s$: | Ed ate steak for dinner |
| $t$: | Ed ate fish for dinner | $u$: | Ed went to the gym |
| $v$: | Ed went to the movies | $w$: | Ed played golf. |

Determine whether the following are true or false:

**a** $p$    **b** $s$    **c** $q \wedge u$    **d** $p \vee w$    **e** $r \vee s$    **f** $r \wedge s$    **g** $r \veebar s$    **h** $t \vee v$

---

**Example 4**

Let $P$ be the truth set of proposition $p$ and $Q$ be the truth set of proposition $q$.
Use mathematical logic to express the following shaded regions in terms of $p$ and $q$:

**a** 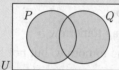    **b**     **c**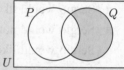

**a** The shaded region is $P \cup Q$, which is the region in $P$ or $Q$ or both.
So, $p$ or $q$ or both are true, which is $p \vee q$.

**b** The shaded region is $Q'$, which is the region not in $Q$.
So, $q$ is not true, which is $\neg q$.

**c** The shaded region is $P' \cap Q$, which is the region in $Q$ but not in $P$.
So, $p$ is not true and $q$ is true, which is $\neg p \wedge q$.

---

**12** Let $P$ be the truth set of proposition $p$ and $Q$ be the truth set of proposition $q$. Use mathematical logic to express the following shaded regions in terms of $p$ and $q$:

**a** 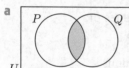    **b** 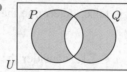    **c**

**13** For each of the following propositions:

    **i** write down the corresponding set notation    **ii** illustrate on a Venn diagram.

**a** $p \vee q$        **b** $\neg p \vee q$        **c** $p \veebar q$        **d** $\neg p \wedge \neg q$

**14** Consider $a$: The captain is male  and  $b$: The captain is old.

Let $A$ be the truth set of $a$ and $B$ be the truth set of $b$.

Interpret each of the following Venn diagrams:

**a** 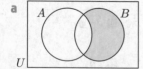    **b** 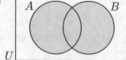    **c**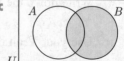

# C TRUTH TABLES AND LOGICAL EQUIVALENCE

The truth tables for negation, conjunction, disjunction, and exclusive disjunction can be summarised in one table.

| $p$ | $q$ | Negation $\neg p$ | Conjunction $p \wedge q$ | Disjunction $p \vee q$ | Exclusive disjunction $p \veebar q$ |
|---|---|---|---|---|---|
| T | T | F | T | T | F |
| T | F | F | F | T | T |
| F | T | T | F | T | T |
| F | F | T | F | F | F |

We can use these rules to construct truth tables for more complicated propositions.

---

**Example 5**  ◀ Self Tutor

Construct a truth table for $p \vee \neg q$.

To construct a truth table for $p \vee \neg q$, we use the negation rule on $q$ to find $\neg q$, then use the disjunction rule on $p$ and $\neg q$ to find $p \vee \neg q$.

We start by listing all the possible combinations for $p$ and $q$:

| $p$ | $q$ | $\neg q$ | $p \vee \neg q$ |
|---|---|---|---|
| T | T | | |
| T | F | | |
| F | T | | |
| F | F | | |

We then use the negation rule on the $q$ column to find $\neg q$:

| $p$ | $q$ | $\neg q$ | $p \vee \neg q$ |
|---|---|---|---|
| T | T | F | |
| T | F | T | |
| F | T | F | |
| F | F | T | |

Finally, we use the disjunction rule on the $p$ and $\neg q$ columns to find $p \vee \neg q$:

| $p$ | $q$ | $\neg q$ | $p \vee \neg q$ |
|---|---|---|---|
| T | T | F | T |
| T | F | T | T |
| F | T | F | F |
| F | F | T | T |

---

## TAUTOLOGY AND LOGICAL CONTRADICTION

A compound proposition is a **tautology** if all the values in its truth table column are **true**.

A compound proposition is a **logical contradiction** if all the values in its truth table column are **false**.

**Example 6**    ◀ⁱ) **Self Tutor**

Show that  $p \lor \neg p$  is a tautology.

The truth table is:

| $p$ | $\neg p$ | $p \lor \neg p$ |
|---|---|---|
| T | F | T |
| F | T | T |

All the values in the  $p \lor \neg p$  column are true, so
$p \lor \neg p$  is a tautology.

For any proposition $p$,
either $p$ is true or  $\neg p$
is true. So,  $p \lor \neg p$  is
**always** true.

## LOGICAL EQUIVALENCE

Two propositions are **logically equivalent** if they have the same truth table column.

**Example 7**    ◀ⁱ) **Self Tutor**

Show that  $\neg(p \land q)$  and  $\neg p \lor \neg q$  are logically equivalent.

The truth table for  $\neg(p \land q)$  is:

| $p$ | $q$ | $p \land q$ | $\neg(p \land q)$ |
|---|---|---|---|
| T | T | T | F. |
| T | F | F | T |
| F | T | F | T |
| F | F | F | T |

The truth table for  $\neg p \lor \neg q$  is:

| $p$ | $q$ | $\neg p$ | $\neg q$ | $\neg p \lor \neg q$ |
|---|---|---|---|---|
| T | T | F | F | F |
| T | F | F | T | T |
| F | T | T | F | T |
| F | F | T | T | T |

As the truth table columns for  $\neg(p \land q)$  and  $\neg p \lor \neg q$  are identical,
$\neg(p \land q)$  and  $\neg p \lor \neg q$  are logically equivalent.

So,  $\neg(p \land q) = \neg p \lor \neg q$.

## EXERCISE 17C.1

**1** Construct a truth table for the following propositions:

    **a**  $\neg p \land q$      **b**  $\neg(p \veebar q)$      **c**  $\neg p \lor \neg q$      **d**  $p \lor p$

**2** For the following propositions:

    **i** construct a truth table for the proposition

    **ii** determine whether the proposition is a tautology, a logical contradiction, or
    neither.

    **a**  $\neg p \land \neg q$      **b**  $(p \lor q) \lor \neg p$      **c**  $p \land (p \veebar q)$      **d**  $(p \land q) \land (p \veebar q)$

**3**  **a** Explain why  $p \land \neg p$  is always false.

    **b** Use a truth table to show that  $p \land \neg p$  is a logical contradiction.

4   Use truth tables to establish the following logical equivalences:

   a   $\neg(\neg p) = p$           b   $p \wedge p = p$                     c   $p \vee (\neg p \wedge q) = p \vee q$

   d   $\neg(p \veebar q) = p \veebar \neg q$    e   $\neg(q \vee \neg p) = \neg q \wedge (p \vee q)$    f   $\neg p \veebar (p \vee q) = p \vee \neg q$

5   a   Construct a truth table for  $(\neg p \wedge q) \vee (p \wedge \neg q)$.

   b   Use the truth table summary at the start of this section to identify a proposition logically equivalent to  $(\neg p \wedge q) \vee (p \wedge \neg q)$.

6   a   Consider the propositions  $p$: I like apples  and  $q$: I like bananas.
       Write the meaning of:

       i   $p \vee q$            ii   $\neg(p \vee q)$            iii   $\neg p$                iv   $\neg p \wedge \neg q$

   b   Use truth tables to show that  $\neg(p \vee q)$  and  $\neg p \wedge \neg q$  are logically equivalent.

7   a   Complete the truth table below:

| $p$ | $q$ | $p \veebar q$ | $q \wedge (p \veebar q)$ | $(p \veebar q) \vee p$ |
|---|---|---|---|---|
| T | T |  |  |  |
| T | F |  |  |  |
| F | T |  |  |  |
| F | F |  |  |  |

   b   Consider the propositions  $p$: $-3 \leqslant x \leqslant 7$  and  $q$: $x \geqslant 2$.
       Find the values of $x$ which make the following propositions true:

       i   $p \veebar q$                    ii   $q \wedge (p \veebar q)$                iii   $(p \veebar q) \vee p$

8   Explain why:

   a   any two tautologies are logically equivalent

   b   any two logical contradictions are logically equivalent.

9   What can be said about:

   a   the negation of a logical contradiction

   b   the negation of a tautology

   c   the disjunction of a tautology and any other statement?

## TRUTH TABLES FOR THREE PROPOSITIONS

When three propositions are under consideration, we usually denote them $p$, $q$ and $r$.

The possible combinations of the truth values for $p$, $q$ and $r$ are listed systematically in the table alongside.

| $p$ | $q$ | $r$ |
|---|---|---|
| T | T | T |
| T | T | F |
| T | F | T |
| T | F | F |
| F | T | T |
| F | T | F |
| F | F | T |
| F | F | F |

### Example 8

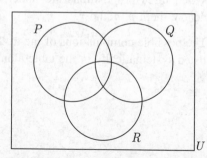  Self Tutor

Construct a truth table for the compound proposition $(p \lor q) \land r$.

To find $(p \lor q) \land r$, we must first find $p \lor q$. We then find the conjunction of $p \lor q$ and $r$.

| $p$ | $q$ | $r$ | $p \lor q$ | $(p \lor q) \land r$ |
|---|---|---|---|---|
| T | T | T | T | T |
| T | T | F | T | F |
| T | F | T | T | T |
| T | F | F | T | F |
| F | T | T | T | T |
| F | T | F | T | F |
| F | F | T | F | F |
| F | F | F | F | F |

## EXERCISE 17C.2

1 Construct truth tables for these compound statements:

   **a** $\neg p \lor (q \land r)$       **b** $(p \lor \neg q) \land r$       **c** $(p \lor q) \lor (p \land \neg r)$

2 Determine whether the following propositions are tautologies, logical contradictions, or neither:

   **a** $(p \lor q) \lor \neg(r \land p)$       **b** $(p \veebar r) \land \neg q$       **c** $(q \land r) \land \neg(p \lor q)$

3  **a** Consider the propositions     $p$: Jake owns a phone
                                   $q$: Jake owns a TV
                                   $r$: Jake owns a laptop.

     Write down the meaning of:

     **i** $p \land q$      **ii** $(p \land q) \land r$      **iii** $q \land r$      **iv** $p \land (q \land r)$

   **b** Use truth tables to show that $(p \land q) \land r = p \land (q \land r)$.

4 Use truth tables to show that $(p \lor q) \lor r$ and $p \lor (q \lor r)$ are logically equivalent.

5  **a** Consider the propositions     $p$: Mary will study Mathematics next year
                                     $q$: Mary will study French next year
                                   $r$: Mary will study German next year.

     Write down the meaning of:

     **i** $q \lor r$   **ii** $p \land (q \lor r)$   **iii** $p \land q$   **iv** $p \land r$   **v** $(p \land q) \lor (p \land r)$

   **b** Use truth tables to show that $p \land (q \lor r) = (p \land q) \lor (p \land r)$.

6  **a** Use truth tables to show that $p \lor (q \land r) = (p \lor q) \land (p \lor r)$.

   **b** Consider the Venn diagram alongside, where $P$, $Q$, and $R$ are the truth sets of $p$, $q$, and $r$ respectively.

     On separate Venn diagrams, shade the truth set for:

     **i** $p \lor (q \land r)$

     **ii** $(p \lor q) \land (p \lor r)$

   Comment on your results.

# D | IMPLICATION AND EQUIVALENCE

## IMPLICATION

If two propositions can be linked with "If ...., then ....",  then we have an **implication**.

The implicative statement "if $p$ then $q$" is written  $p \Rightarrow q$  and reads "$p$ implies $q$".

$p$ is called the **antecedent**  and  $q$ is called the **consequent**.

For example, if  $p$:  Kato has a TV set,  and  $q$:  Kato can watch TV,

then we have  $p \Rightarrow q$:  If Kato has a TV set, then Kato can watch TV.

### THE TRUTH TABLE FOR IMPLICATION

Consider  $p$:  It will rain on Saturday,  and  $q$:  The Falcons will win.

The implicative statement is  $p \Rightarrow q$:  If it rains on Saturday, then the Falcons will win.

To establish the truth table for  $p \Rightarrow q$,  we will consider each of the possible combinations for $p$ and $q$ in turn:

| $p$ | $q$ | Scenario | $p \Rightarrow q$ |
|---|---|---|---|
| T | T | It rains on Saturday, and the Falcons win. This is consistent with the implicative statement. | T |
| T | F | It rains on Saturday, but the Falcons do not win. This is inconsistent with the implicative statement. | F |
| F | T | It does not rain on Saturday, and the Falcons win. This is consistent with the implicative statement, as no claim has been made regarding the outcome if it does not rain. | T |
| F | F | It does not rain on Saturday, and the Falcons do not win. Again, this is consistent with the implicative statement as no claim has been made regarding the outcome if it does not rain. | T |

So, the truth table for  $p \Rightarrow q$  is:

| $p$ | $q$ | $p \Rightarrow q$ |
|---|---|---|
| T | T | T |
| T | F | F |
| F | T | T |
| F | F | T |

$p \Rightarrow q$  is only false if $p$ is true but $q$ is false.

## EQUIVALENCE

If two propositions are linked with ".... if and only if ....",  then we have an **equivalence**.

The equivalence  "$p$ if and only if $q$"  is written  $p \Leftrightarrow q$.

$p \Leftrightarrow q$ is logically equivalent to the conjunction of the implications $p \Rightarrow q$ and $q \Rightarrow p$.

Consider $p$: I will pass the exam, and $q$: The exam is easy.

We have $p \Rightarrow q$: *If* I pass the exam, *then* the exam is easy.

$q \Rightarrow p$: *If* the exam is easy, *then* I will pass it.

$p \Leftrightarrow q$: I will pass the exam *if and only if* the exam is easy.

## THE TRUTH TABLE FOR EQUIVALENCE

We can find the truth table for $p \Leftrightarrow q$ by constructing the truth table of its logical equivalent $(p \Rightarrow q) \wedge (q \Rightarrow p)$:

| $p$ | $q$ | $p \Rightarrow q$ | $q \Rightarrow p$ | $(p \Rightarrow q) \wedge (q \Rightarrow p)$ |
|---|---|---|---|---|
| T | T | T | T | T |
| T | F | F | T | F |
| F | T | T | F | F |
| F | F | T | T | T |

So, the truth table for **equivalence** $p \Leftrightarrow q$ is:

| $p$ | $q$ | $p \Leftrightarrow q$ |
|---|---|---|
| T | T | T |
| T | F | F |
| F | T | F |
| F | F | T |

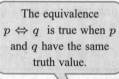

The equivalence $p \Leftrightarrow q$ is true when $p$ and $q$ have the same truth value.

## EXERCISE 17D

1 In the following implicative statements, state the antecedent and the consequent.

**a** If I miss the bus, then I will walk to school.

**b** If the temperature is low enough, then the lake will freeze.

**c** If $x > 20$, then $x > 10$.

**d** If you jump all 8 hurdles, then you may win the race.

2 For the following propositions, write down the implicative statement $p \Rightarrow q$:

**a** $p$: The sun is shining, $q$: I will go swimming

**b** $p$: $x$ is a multiple of 6, $q$: $x$ is even

**c** $p$: There are eggs in the fridge, $q$: Jan will bake a cake.

3 For the following propositions $p$ and $q$:

**i** write down the equivalence $p \Leftrightarrow q$

**ii** state whether the equivalence is true or false.

**a** $p$: Rome is the capital of Italy, $q$: Paris is the capital of France

**b** $p$: $2x + 3 = 10$ is an expression, $q$: $2x + 3$ is an expression

**c** $p$: Cows have nine legs, $q$: Horses have five heads.

**4** Consider the propositions   $p$: It is raining  and  $q$: There are puddles forming.
Write the following statements in symbols:

   **a** If it is raining then puddles are forming.

   **b** If puddles are forming then it is raining.

   **c** Puddles are not forming.

   **d** It is not raining.

   **e** If it is not raining, then puddles are not forming.

   **f** If it is raining, then puddles are not forming.

   **g** If there are no puddles, then it is raining.

   **h** It is raining if and only if there are puddles forming.

**5** Construct truth tables for:

   **a** $p \Rightarrow \neg q$     **b** $\neg q \Rightarrow \neg p$     **c** $(p \wedge q) \Rightarrow p$     **d** $q \wedge (p \Rightarrow q)$

   **e** $p \Leftrightarrow \neg q$     **f** $(p \Leftrightarrow q) \wedge \neg p$    **g** $p \Rightarrow (p \wedge \neg q)$    **h** $(p \Rightarrow q) \Rightarrow \neg p$

**6** By examining truth tables, show that:

   **a** $p \veebar q = \neg(p \Leftrightarrow q)$             **b** $\neg p \Rightarrow q = p \vee q$

   **c** $q \Rightarrow (p \veebar q) = \neg(p \wedge q)$        **d** $p \Leftrightarrow q = (p \wedge q) \vee (\neg p \wedge \neg q)$

**7** Which of these forms are logically equivalent to the negation of  $q \Rightarrow p$?

   **A** $p \Rightarrow q$      **B** $\neg q \Rightarrow p$      **C** $q \Rightarrow \neg p$      **D** $\neg(\neg p \Rightarrow \neg q)$

**8** Determine whether the following are logical contradictions, tautologies, or neither:

   **a** $p \Rightarrow (\neg p \wedge q)$     **b** $(p \wedge q) \Rightarrow (p \vee q)$    **c** $(p \Rightarrow \neg q) \vee (\neg p \Rightarrow q)$

# E    CONVERSE, INVERSE AND CONTRAPOSITIVE

## THE CONVERSE

The **converse** of the statement  $p \Rightarrow q$  is the statement  $q \Rightarrow p$.

The converse has truth table:

| $p$ | $q$ | $q \Rightarrow p$ |
|:---:|:---:|:---:|
| T | T | T |
| T | F | T |
| F | T | F |
| F | F | T |

---

**Example 9**          ◄ঠ **Self Tutor**

For  $p$: the triangle is isosceles,  and  $q$: two angles of the triangle are equal,
state  $p \Rightarrow q$  and its converse  $q \Rightarrow p$.

$p \Rightarrow q$:  If the triangle is isosceles, then two of its angles are equal.

$q \Rightarrow p$:  If two angles of the triangle are equal, then the triangle is isosceles.

## THE INVERSE

> The **inverse** statement of $p \Rightarrow q$ is the statement $\neg p \Rightarrow \neg q$.

The inverse has truth table:

| $p$ | $q$ | $\neg p$ | $\neg q$ | $\neg p \Rightarrow \neg q$ |
|-----|-----|----------|----------|------------------------------|
| T   | T   | F        | F        | T                            |
| T   | F   | F        | T        | T                            |
| F   | T   | T        | F        | F                            |
| F   | F   | T        | T        | T                            |

This is the same truth table as $q \Rightarrow p$.

So, the converse and inverse of an implication are logically equivalent.

## THE CONTRAPOSITIVE

> The **contrapositive** of the statement $p \Rightarrow q$ is the statement $\neg q \Rightarrow \neg p$.

The **contrapositive** has truth table:

| $p$ | $q$ | $\neg q$ | $\neg p$ | $\neg q \Rightarrow \neg p$ |
|-----|-----|----------|----------|------------------------------|
| T   | T   | F        | F        | T                            |
| T   | F   | T        | F        | F                            |
| F   | T   | F        | T        | T                            |
| F   | F   | T        | T        | T                            |

The truth table for $\neg q \Rightarrow \neg p$ is the same as that for $p \Rightarrow q$.

So, the implication and its contrapositive are logically equivalent.

For example, consider $p$: Sam is in the library and $q$: Sam is reading.

| Implication $p \Rightarrow q$ | If Sam is in the library, then Sam is reading. |
|-------------------------------|-----------------------------------------------|
| Converse $q \Rightarrow p$ | If Sam is reading, then Sam is in the library. |
| Inverse $\neg p \Rightarrow \neg q$ | If Sam is not in the library, then Sam is not reading. |
| Contrapositive $\neg q \Rightarrow \neg p$ | If Sam is not reading, then Sam is not in the library. |

logically equivalent

The implication and the converse are *not* logically equivalent since, for example, the implication allows for the possibility that Sam is reading in the classroom, but the converse does not.

## EXERCISE 17E

1 Write the converse and inverse for:

  a If Nicole is wearing a jumper, then she is warm.

  b If two triangles are similar, then they are equiangular.

  c If $2x^2 = 12$, then $x = \pm\sqrt{6}$.

**d**  If Alex is in the playground, then he is having fun.

**e**  If a triangle is equilateral, then its three sides are equal in length.

---

**Example 10**                                             ◀) **Self Tutor**

Write down the contrapositive of: "All teachers drive blue cars".

This statement is the same as "if a person is a teacher, then he or she drives a blue car".

This has the form $p \Rightarrow q$ with $p$: A person is a teacher and $q$: A person drives a blue car.

The contrapositive $\neg q \Rightarrow \neg p$ is "If a person does not drive a blue car, then the person is not a teacher."

---

**2**  Write down the contrapositives of these statements:
   **a**  All rose bushes have thorns.
   **b**  All umpires make correct decisions all the time.
   **c**  All good soccer players have good kicking skills.
   **d**  Liquids always take the shape of the container in which they are placed.
   **e**  If a person is fair and clever then the person is a doctor.

**3**  **a**  State the contrapositive of: "All high school students study Mathematics."
   **b**  Suppose the statement in **a** is true. What, if anything, can be deduced about:
      **i**  Keong, who is a high school student
      **ii**  Tamra, who does not study Mathematics
      **iii**  Eli, who studies English and Mathematics?

**4**  Write down the contrapositive of:
   **a**  $x$ is divisible by 3  $\Rightarrow$  $x^2$ is divisible by 9
   **b**  $x$ is a number ending in 2  $\Rightarrow$  $x$ is even
   **c**  PQRS is a rectangle  $\Rightarrow$  PQ $\parallel$ SR  and  PS $\parallel$ QR
   **d**  KLM is an equilateral triangle  $\Rightarrow$  K$\widehat{M}$L measures $60°$.

**5**  Consider $p$: A house has at least 3 windows  and  $q$: A house has a chimney.
   The implication is  $p \Rightarrow q$: If a house has at least 3 windows, then it has a chimney.
   **a**  For this implication, write down the:
      **i**  converse             **ii**  inverse             **iii**  contrapositive.
   **b**  Determine the truth values for the implication, converse, inverse, and contrapositive for each of these houses:

   **i**    **ii**    **iii**

**6** $W$ represents all weak students and $E$ represents all Year 11 students.

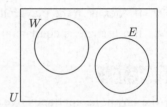

   **a** Copy and complete:

      **i** No weak students are ....

      **ii** No Year 11 students are ....

   **b** Copy and complete:

      **i** If $x \in W$ then ....

      **ii** If $x \in E$ then ....

   **c** What is the relationship between the implications in **b**?

# F    VALID ARGUMENTS (EXTENSION)

An **argument** is made up of a set of propositions, called the **premise**, that leads to a conclusion.
An argument is usually indicated by the words 'therefore' or 'hence'.

A simple example of an argument is:

> If George is at the beach, then he is getting sunburnt.
> George is at the beach.
> *Therefore*, George is getting sunburnt.

We set out arguments by separating the premise and the conclusion with a horizontal line.

$$\left.\begin{array}{r}\text{If George is at the beach, then he is getting sunburnt.}\\\text{George is at the beach.}\end{array}\right\}\text{premise}$$

$$\overline{\hspace{6cm}}$$

$$\text{George is getting sunburnt.} \;\}\,\text{conclusion}$$

We can test whether the logic applied in our argument is valid by expressing the argument in terms of propositions.

If we have $p$: George is at the beach, and $q$: George is getting sunburnt, then the argument becomes:

$$\left.\begin{array}{r}p \Rightarrow q\\p\end{array}\right\}\text{premise}$$

$$\overline{\hspace{3cm}}$$

$$q \;\}\,\text{conclusion}$$

So, from the propositions $p \Rightarrow q$ and $p$, we are implying the conclusion $q$. We can write this argument in logical form as $(p \Rightarrow q) \wedge p \Rightarrow q$.

To determine whether this argument is valid, we construct a truth table for this proposition, and see whether it is a tautology.

| $p$ | $q$ | $p \Rightarrow q$ | $(p \Rightarrow q) \wedge p$ | $(p \Rightarrow q) \wedge p \Rightarrow q$ |
|---|---|---|---|---|
| T | T | T | T | T |
| T | F | F | F | T |
| F | T | T | F | T |
| F | F | T | F | T |

Since we have a tautology, we can say that our argument is valid. This means that the conclusion we have made follows logically from the premise.

**Example 11**　　　　　　　　　　　　　　　　　　　　　◀) **Self Tutor**

Determine the validity of the following argument:

If a triangle has three sides, then $2 + 4 = 7$.
$2 + 4 = 7$
Hence, a triangle has three sides.

We have $p$: A triangle has three sides and $q$: $2 + 4 = 7$

The argument is:　　　$\left.\begin{array}{c} p \Rightarrow q \\ q \end{array}\right\}$ premise

　　　　　　　　　　　$p$ }conclusion

We can write this in logical form as $(p \Rightarrow q) \wedge q \Rightarrow p$.

| $p$ | $q$ | $p \Rightarrow q$ | $(p \Rightarrow q) \wedge q$ | $(p \Rightarrow q) \wedge q \Rightarrow p$ |
|-----|-----|-------------------|------------------------------|--------------------------------------------|
| T | T | T | T | T |
| T | F | F | F | T |
| F | T | T | T | F |
| F | F | T | F | T |

Since we do **not** have a tautology, the argument is not valid.

**IMPORTANT:**　Proposition $q$ is clearly false. However, this does not affect the validity of the argument. Logic is not concerned with whether the premise is true or false, but rather with what can be validly concluded from the premise.

> The validity of an argument is not related to the actual truth values of the propositions within it.

# EXERCISE 17F.1

1　Consider the following argument:

　　Lucy will have to work if and only if Paul is sick.
　　Paul is not sick.
　　Therefore, Lucy will not have to work today.

　a　Write down the premise and conclusion of this argument in terms of the propositions
　　$p$: Lucy will have to work today　and　$q$: Paul is sick.

　b　Write the argument in logical form.

　c　Construct a truth table to show that the argument is valid.

**2**  **a**  Write the following arguments in logical form:

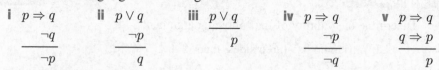

    **i** $p \Rightarrow q$     **ii** $p \lor q$    **iii** $p \lor q$    **iv** $p \Rightarrow q$    **v** $p \Rightarrow q$

       $\dfrac{\neg q}{\neg p}$     $\dfrac{\neg p}{q}$     $\dfrac{\ }{p}$     $\dfrac{\neg p}{\neg q}$     $\dfrac{q \Rightarrow p}{p}$

  **b**  Construct truth tables for each part in **a**. Which of the arguments are valid?

**3**  Determine the validity of the following arguments written in logical form:

  **a**  $(p \land q) \Rightarrow p$               **b**  $(p \Rightarrow q) \land \neg q \Rightarrow p$

  **c**  $(p \Rightarrow q) \land (q \Rightarrow p) \Rightarrow (p \Leftrightarrow q)$     **d**  $(p \land \neg q) \Rightarrow (\neg p \lor q)$

**4**  Use  $p$: $x$ is prime  and  $q$: $x$ is odd  to show that the following are valid arguments:

  **a**  If $x$ is prime, then $x$ is odd.        **b**  $x$ is prime or odd, but not both.
      $x$ is prime or odd.                  $x$ is not odd.
      Hence, $x$ is odd.                   Therefore, $x$ is prime.

**5**  Consider the following argument:    Don has visited Australia or New Zealand.
                                   Don has visited New Zealand.
                                   Therefore, Don has not visited Australia.

  **a**  Use a truth table to show that this argument is invalid.

  **b**  Describe the scenario which demonstrates that the argument is invalid.

**6**  Determine the validity of the following arguments:

  **a**  Tan went to the movies or the theatre last night, but not both.
      Tan did not go to the movies.
      Therefore, Tan went to the theatre.

  **b**  If $x$ is a multiple of 4, then $x$ is even.
      Hence, if $x$ is even, then $x$ is a multiple of 4.

  **c**  London is in China if and only if 20 is a multiple of 5.
      20 is a multiple of 5.
      Therefore, London is in China.

  **d**  $x$ is a factor of 30 or 50.
      Hence, $x$ is a factor of 50.

  **e**  If the sequence is not geometric, then the sequence is arithmetic.
      Therefore, the sequence is arithmetic or geometric.

  **f**  All students like chips.
      Melanie likes chips.
      Hence, Melanie is a student.

## INVESTIGATION                                             SYLLOGISMS

 A **syllogism** is an argument consisting of three lines.  The third line is supposed to be the logical conclusion from the first two lines.

*Example 1:*

If I had wings like a seagull I could fly.
I have wings like a seagull.
Therefore, I can fly.

*Example 2:*

If I had wings like a seagull I could fly.
I can fly.
Therefore, I have wings like a seagull.

The arguments in these examples can be written as:

*Example 1:*  $p \Rightarrow q$

$$\frac{p}{q}$$

*Example 2:*  $p \Rightarrow q$

$$\frac{q}{p}$$

**What to do:**

1  Use truth tables to show that the first example is a valid argument, and the second is invalid.

2  Consider this syllogism:    All cows have four legs.
                                Wendy is not a cow.
                                Hence, Wendy does not have four legs.

We see it is comprised of two propositions,  $p$: $x$ is a cow,  and
                                             $q$: $x$ has four legs.

Write the argument in logical form and show that it is invalid.

3  Test the validity of the following syllogisms:

   **a**  All prime numbers greater than two are odd. 15 is odd.
       Hence, 15 is a prime number.

   **b**  All mathematicians are clever. Jules is not clever.
       Therefore, Jules is not a mathematician.

   **c**  All rabbits eat grass. Peter is a rabbit.
       Therefore, Peter eats grass.

4  Give the third line of the following syllogisms to reach a correct conclusion.

   **a**  All cats have fur.
       Jason is a cat.
       Therefore, ......

   **b**  Students who waste
       time fail.
       Takuma wastes time.
       Hence, ......

   **c**  All emus cannot fly.
       Fred can fly.
       Therefore, ......

## ARGUMENTS WITH THREE PROPOSITIONS

**Example 12** ◀)) **Self Tutor**

Determine the validity of the following argument:

If $x$ is a natural number, then $x$ is an integer.
If $x$ is an integer, then $x$ is rational.
Therefore, if $x$ is a natural number, then $x$ is rational.

We have $p$: $x$ is a natural number, $q$: $x$ is an integer, and $r$: $x$ is rational.

The argument is written as

$$p \Rightarrow q$$
$$q \Rightarrow r$$
$$\overline{p \Rightarrow r}$$

We can write this in logical form as $(p \Rightarrow q) \wedge (q \Rightarrow r) \Rightarrow (p \Rightarrow r)$.

| $p$ | $q$ | $r$ | $p \Rightarrow q$ | $q \Rightarrow r$ | $(p \Rightarrow q) \wedge (q \Rightarrow r)$ | $p \Rightarrow r$ | $(p \Rightarrow q) \wedge (q \Rightarrow r)$ $\Rightarrow (p \Rightarrow r)$ |
|---|---|---|---|---|---|---|---|
| T | T | T | T | T | T | T | T |
| T | T | F | T | F | F | F | T |
| T | F | T | F | T | F | T | T |
| T | F | F | F | T | F | F | T |
| F | T | T | T | T | T | T | T |
| F | T | F | T | F | F | T | T |
| F | F | T | T | T | T | T | T |
| F | F | F | T | T | T | T | T |

The logical form of the argument is a tautology, so the argument is valid.

## EXERCISE 17F.2

1 Consider the propositions $p$: It is sunny, $q$: I am warm, and $r$: I feel happy.
Write the following arguments in words.

   a $(p \wedge q) \Rightarrow r$            b $p \wedge \neg q \Rightarrow \neg r$         c $q \wedge r \Rightarrow p$

2 Which, if any, of the following arguments are valid?

   **A** $p \Rightarrow q$            **B** $(p \wedge q) \vee r$        **C** $(p \wedge q) \Rightarrow r$
        $\dfrac{q \Rightarrow r}{(q \wedge r)}$              $\dfrac{\phantom{(p \wedge q) \vee r}}{p \vee r}$         $\dfrac{\phantom{(p \wedge q) \Rightarrow r}}{r}\ \ p$

3   a Show that the argument $\begin{array}{c} p \Rightarrow q \\ q \Rightarrow r \\ \hline p \Rightarrow \neg r \end{array}$ is invalid.

   b What truth values of $p$, $q$ and $r$ lead to an invalid argument?

**4** If I do not like a subject, I do not work hard. If I do not work hard I fail. I passed, therefore I must like the subject.

   **a** Identify the propositions $p$, $q$ and $r$.

   **b** Write the above argument in logical form.

   **c** Is the conclusion a result of valid reasoning?

**5** Determine the validity of this argument:

     If Jeremy is on the basketball team, then he is tall and fast.

     Jeremy is tall and he is not on the basketball team.

     Therefore, Jeremy is not fast.

## REVIEW SET 17A

**1** Which of the following are propositions? If they are propositions, state whether they are true, false or indeterminate.

   **a** Sheep have four legs.      **b** Do giraffes have four legs?

   **c** Alicia is good at Mathematics.      **d** I think my favourite team will win.

   **e** Vicki is very clever.      **f** There are 7 days in a week.

   **g** Put your shoes on.      **h** All cows are brown.

   **i** $a^2 + b^2 = c^2$

   **j** The opposite sides of a parallelogram are equal.

**2** Consider the propositions $p$: $x$ is an even number, and $q$: $x$ is divisible by 3. Write the following in words:

   **a** $\neg p$     **b** $p \vee q$     **c** $p \veebar q$     **d** $p \Rightarrow q$

   **e** $\neg p \wedge q$     **f** $\neg p \veebar q$     **g** $p \Rightarrow \neg q$     **h** $\neg p \Rightarrow \neg q$

**3** Consider the propositions $p$: $x$ is a prime number, and $q$: $x$ is a multiple of 7. Write the following in symbolic language:

   **a** If $x$ is a prime number then $x$ is a multiple of 7.

   **b** $x$ is not a prime number.

   **c** $x$ is a multiple of 7 and not a prime number.

   **d** $x$ is either a prime number or a multiple of 7 but not both.

   **e** $x$ is neither a prime number nor a multiple of 7.

In each case, write down a number that satisfies the statement.

**4** Write the implication $p \Rightarrow q$, the inverse, converse and contrapositive of the following propositions in both words and symbols.

   **a** $p$: I love swimming.      **b** $p$: I like food.

     $q$: I live near the sea.      $q$: I eat a lot.

**5** Represent the truth sets of the following on Venn diagrams:

   **a** $p \veebar q$     **b** $\neg(p \vee q)$     **c** $\neg p \wedge q$

   **d** $\neg p$     **e** $\neg p \vee q$     **f** $\neg(p \wedge q \wedge r)$

**6** For the propositions $p$: $x$ is a factor of 12, and $q$: $x$ is an odd number $< 10$, list the truth sets of:

    **a** $p$                **b** $q$                 **c** $p \wedge q$            **d** $p \vee q$

**7** Use truth tables to determine the validity of the following arguments:

    **a** $\dfrac{p \Rightarrow q}{\qquad \neg p \qquad}$         **b** $\dfrac{p \vee q}{\qquad \neg q \qquad}$         **c** $\begin{array}{c} p \Rightarrow q \\ \dfrac{q \Rightarrow r}{\quad r \vee q \quad} \end{array}$

        $\neg q$                     $\neg p$

## REVIEW SET 17B

**1** Consider the propositions $p$: $x$ is a multiple of 4, $18 < x < 30$

                                    $q$: $x$ is a factor of 24,

                  and $r$: $x$ is an even number, $18 < x < 30$.

    **a** List the truth sets of $p$, $q$, $r$, and $p \wedge q \wedge r$.

    **b** List the truth sets of:   **i** $p \wedge q$   **ii** $q \wedge r$   **iii** $p \wedge r$

**2** Find negations for the following:

    **a** Eddy is good at football.

    **b** The maths class includes more than 10 boys.

    **c** The writing is illegible.         **d** Ali owns a new car.

**3** Write the following statements as implications:

    **a** All birds have two legs.         **b** Snakes are not mammals.

    **c** No rectangle has five sides.       **d** This equation has no real solutions.

**4** 'Positive' and 'negative' are defined as follows:

              $x$ is positive $\Leftrightarrow$ $x > 0$      $x$ is negative $\Leftrightarrow$ $x < 0$

    **a** Is zero positive or negative?

    **b** What is the negation of '$x$ is negative' when $x \in \{$rational numbers$\}$?

**5** Let $P$, $Q$ and $R$ be the truth sets of propositions $p$, $q$ and $r$ respectively. Write the following as compound propositions in terms of $p$, $q$ and $r$:

    **a** 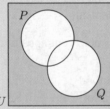     **b** 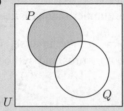     **c**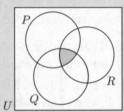

**6** Which of the following pairs are logically equivalent?

    **a** $p \Rightarrow q$ and $\neg q \Rightarrow \neg p$         **b** $\neg(p \wedge q)$ and $\neg p \vee \neg q$

    **c** $p \Leftrightarrow q$ and $(p \wedge q) \wedge \neg q$     **d** $\neg p \Rightarrow \neg q$ and $q \Rightarrow p$

**7** Express the following in logical form. Determine whether or not the argument is valid.

   **a** If the sun is shining I will wear my shorts. The sun is shining. Therefore, I wear shorts.

   **b** All teachers work hard. Marty is not a teacher. Therefore Marty does not work hard.

## REVIEW SET 17C

**1** Find the negation of:
   **a** $x \leqslant 3$ for $x \in \mathbb{Z}$
   **b** $x$ is a comb, for $x \in \{$brush, comb, hairclip, bobby pin$\}$
   **c** $x$ is a tall woman for $x \in \{$women$\}$

**2** For $U = \{x \mid 1 \leqslant x \leqslant 20\}$, consider the propositions
   $p$: $x$ is an even number, and $q$: $x$ is a square number.
   **a** Illustrate the truth sets for $p$ and $q$ on a Venn diagram.
   **b** Use your Venn diagram to find the truth set for:
      **i** $p \wedge q$        **ii** $\neg p \vee q$        **iii** $\neg(p \veebar q)$

**3** Write down, in words, the inverse, converse and contrapositive for the implication: "The diagonals of a rhombus are equal."

**4** Consider the propositions $p$: cakes are sweet, and $q$: cakes are full of sultanas. Write each of the following using logic symbols:
   **a** If cakes are not sweet they are not full of sultanas.
   **b** If cakes are not sweet they are full of sultanas.
   **c** Cakes are full of sultanas and they are not sweet.
   **d** Cakes are not sweet or they are full of sultanas.

**5** Consider the propositions:
   $p$: The plane leaves from gate 5.        $q$: The plane leaves from gate 2.
   $r$: The plane does not leave this morning.
   **a** Write the following logic statement in words: $p \Rightarrow (\neg r \wedge \neg q)$
   **b** Write in symbols: The plane leaves this morning if and only if it leaves from gate 2 or from gate 5.

**6** Construct truth tables for the following and state whether the statements are tautologies, logical contradictions or neither:
   **a** $(p \Rightarrow q) \wedge q \Rightarrow p$     **b** $(p \wedge q) \wedge \neg(p \vee q)$     **c** $\neg p \Leftrightarrow q$
   **d** $(p \vee \neg q) \Rightarrow q$     **e** $(\neg p \vee q) \Rightarrow r$     **f** $p \wedge q \Rightarrow q$

**7** Express the following in logical form.  Determine whether or not the argument is valid.

    **a** If Fred is a dog he has fur. If Fred has fur he has a cold nose.

      Fred is a dog. Hence, Fred has a cold nose.

    **b** If Viv is a judge, she wears a robe or a wig.

      Viv does not wear a wig, nor is she a judge.

      Therefore, Viv does not wear a robe.

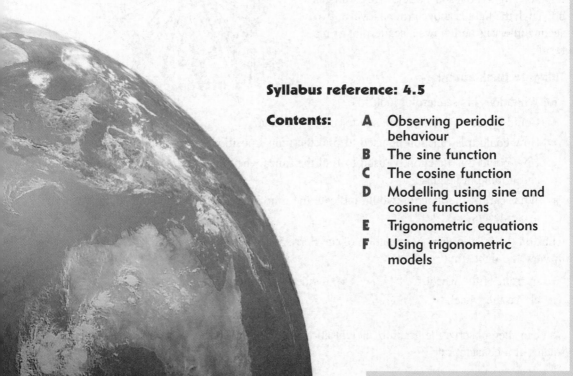

# Chapter 18

# Trigonometric functions

Syllabus reference: 4.5

Contents:
- **A** Observing periodic behaviour
- **B** The sine function
- **C** The cosine function
- **D** Modelling using sine and cosine functions
- **E** Trigonometric equations
- **F** Using trigonometric models

**Periodic phenomena** occur all the time in the physical world. For example, in:

- seasonal variations in our climate
- variations in average maximum and minimum monthly temperatures
- the number of daylight hours at a particular location
- tidal variations in the depth of water in a harbour
- the phases of the moon
- animal populations.

These phenomena illustrate variable behaviour which is repeated over time. The repetition may be called **periodic**, **oscillatory**, or **cyclic** in different situations.

In this chapter we will consider how trigonometric functions can be used to model periodic phenomena. We will then extend our knowledge of the trigonometric functions by considering formulae that connect them.

## OPENING PROBLEM

 A Ferris wheel rotates at a constant speed. The wheel's radius is 10 m and the bottom of the wheel is 2 m above ground level. From a point in front of the wheel, Andrew is watching a green light on the perimeter of the wheel. Andrew notices that the green light moves in a circle. He estimates how high the light is above ground level at two second intervals and draws a scatterplot of his results.

**Things to think about:**

- What does his scatterplot look like?
- Could a known function be used to model the data?
- How could this function be used to find the light's position at any point in time?
- How could this function be used to find the times when the light is at its maximum and minimum heights?
- What part of the function would indicate the time interval over which one complete cycle occurs?

Click on the icon to visit a simulation of the Ferris wheel. You will be able to view the light from:

- in front of the wheel
- above the wheel.
- a side-on position

DEMO

You can then observe the graph of height above or below the wheel's axis as the wheel rotates at a constant rate.

**A** ## OBSERVING PERIODIC BEHAVIOUR

Consider the table below which shows the mean monthly maximum temperature for Cape Town, South Africa.

| Month | Jan | Feb | Mar | Apr | May | Jun | Jul | Aug | Sep | Oct | Nov | Dec |
|---|---|---|---|---|---|---|---|---|---|---|---|---|
| Temp (°C) | 28 | 27 | $25\frac{1}{2}$ | 22 | $18\frac{1}{2}$ | 16 | 15 | 16 | 18 | $21\frac{1}{2}$ | 24 | 26 |

On the scatterplot alongside we plot the temperature $T$ on the vertical axis. We assign January as $t = 1$ month, February as $t = 2$ months, and so on for the 12 months of the year.

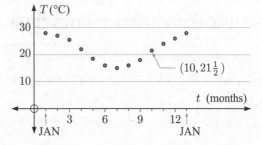

The temperature shows a variation from an average of 28°C in January through a range of values across the months. The cycle will repeat itself for the next 12 month period. By the end of the chapter we will be able to establish a function which approximately fits this set of points.

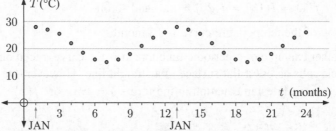

### HISTORICAL NOTE

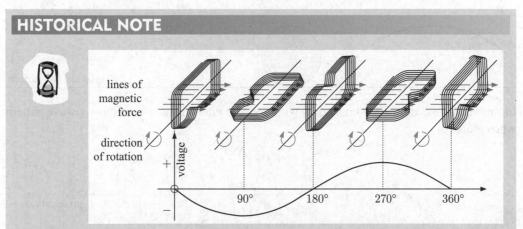

In 1831 **Michael Faraday** discovered that an electric current was generated by rotating a coil of wire in a magnetic field. The electric current produced showed a voltage which varied between positive and negative values as the coil rotated through 360°.

Graphs with this basic shape where the cycle is repeated over and over are called **sine waves**.

## GATHERING PERIODIC DATA

Data on a number of periodic phenomena can be found online or in other publications. For example:

- Maximum and minimum monthly temperatures can be found at
  *http://www.bom.gov.au/silo/*

- Tidal details can be obtained from daily newspapers or internet sites such as
  *http://tidesandcurrents.noaa.gov*   or   *http://www.bom.gov.au/oceanography*

## TERMINOLOGY USED TO DESCRIBE PERIODICITY

A **periodic function** is one which repeats itself over and over in a horizontal direction.

The **period** of a periodic function is the length of one repetition or cycle.

$f(x)$ is a periodic function with period $p$   $\Leftrightarrow$   $f(x + p) = f(x)$  for all $x$,
and $p$ is the smallest positive value for this to be true.

For example, for the temperature graph on page **559**, we see that   $f(x + 12) = f(x)$   for all $x$ on the curve.

This means that   $f(0) = f(12) = f(24) = ....$
$\phantom{This means that}$ $f(1) = f(13) = f(25) = ....$   and so on.

We say the *period* of the temperature curve is 12 months.

A **cycloid** is another example of a periodic function. It is the curve traced out by a point on a circle as the circle rolls across a flat surface in a straight line. However, the cycloid function cannot be written as a Cartesian equation in the form  $y = ......$   or   $f(x) = ......$

**DEMO**

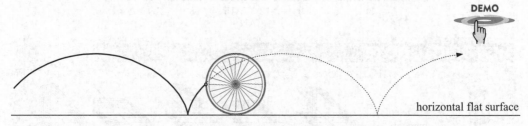

horizontal flat surface

In this course we are mainly concerned with periodic phenomena which show a wave pattern when graphed.

the wave

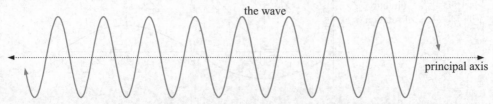

principal axis

The wave oscillates about a horizontal line called the **principal axis** or **mean line**.

A **maximum point** occurs at the top of a crest, and a **minimum point** at the bottom of a trough.

The **amplitude** of a periodic function is the distance between a maximum (or minimum) point and the principal axis.

$$\text{amplitude} = \frac{\text{max} - \text{min}}{2} \qquad\qquad \text{principal axis} \quad y = \frac{\text{max} + \text{min}}{2}$$

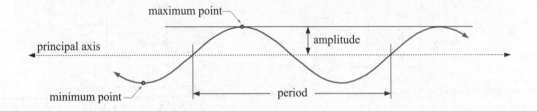

## EXERCISE 18A

**1** For each set of data below, draw a scatterplot and decide whether or not the data exhibits approximately periodic behaviour.

**a**

| $x$ | 0 | 1 | 2 | 3 | 4 | 5 | 6 | 7 | 8 | 9 | 10 | 11 | 12 |
|---|---|---|---|---|---|---|---|---|---|---|---|---|---|
| $y$ | 0 | 1 | 1.4 | 1 | 0 | −1 | −1.4 | −1 | 0 | 1 | 1.4 | 1 | 0 |

**b**

| $x$ | 0 | 1 | 2 | 3 | 4 |
|---|---|---|---|---|---|
| $y$ | 4 | 1 | 0 | 1 | 4 |

**c**

| $x$ | 0 | 0.5 | 1.0 | 1.5 | 2.0 | 2.5 | 3.0 | 3.5 |
|---|---|---|---|---|---|---|---|---|
| $y$ | 0 | 1.9 | 3.5 | 4.5 | 4.7 | 4.3 | 3.4 | 2.4 |

**d**

| $x$ | 0 | 2 | 3 | 4 | 5 | 6 | 7 | 8 | 9 | 10 | 12 |
|---|---|---|---|---|---|---|---|---|---|---|---|
| $y$ | 0 | 4.7 | 3.4 | 1.7 | 2.1 | 5.2 | 8.9 | 10.9 | 10.2 | 8.4 | 10.4 |

**2** The following tabled values show the height above the ground of a point on a bicycle wheel as the bicycle is wheeled along a flat surface.

| Distance travelled (cm) | 0 | 20 | 40 | 60 | 80 | 100 | 120 | 140 | 160 | 180 | 200 |
|---|---|---|---|---|---|---|---|---|---|---|---|
| Height above ground (cm) | 0 | 6 | 23 | 42 | 57 | 64 | 59 | 43 | 23 | 7 | 1 |

| Distance travelled (cm) | 220 | 240 | 260 | 280 | 300 | 320 | 340 | 360 | 380 | 400 |
|---|---|---|---|---|---|---|---|---|---|---|
| Height above ground (cm) | 5 | 27 | 40 | 55 | 63 | 60 | 44 | 24 | 9 | 3 |

**a** Plot the graph of height against distance.

**b** Is the data periodic? If so, estimate:
   **i** the equation of the principal axis    **ii** the maximum value
   **iii** the period    **iv** the amplitude.

**c** Is it reasonable to fit a curve to this data, or should we leave it as discrete points?

**3**  Which of these graphs show periodic behaviour?

**a**
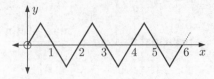

**b**
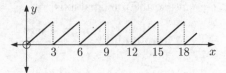

**c**
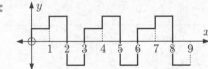

**d**
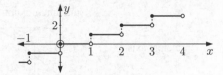

**e**
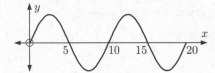

**f**
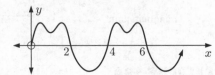

**4**
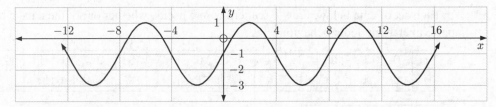

For the given periodic function:

**a**  state its amplitude

**b**  state its period.

**c**  State the coordinates of the first maximum point such that $x > 0$.

**d**  What is the distance between successive maxima?

**e**  What is the equation of the principal axis?

## B    THE SINE FUNCTION

In previous studies of trigonometry we have only considered right angled triangles, or static situations where an angle $\theta$ is fixed. However, when an object moves around a circle, the situation is dynamic. The angle between the radius OP and the horizontal axis continually changes with time.

Consider again the **Opening Problem** in which a Ferris wheel of radius 10 m revolves at constant speed.

The height of P, the point representing the green light on the wheel relative to the principal axis O, can be determined using right angled triangle trigonometry.

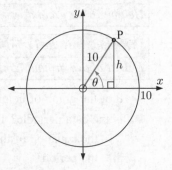

$$\sin \theta = \frac{h}{10}, \quad \text{so} \quad h = 10 \sin \theta.$$

As time goes by, $\theta$ changes and so does $h$.

So, $h$ is a function of $\theta$, but more importantly $h$ is a function of time $t$.

Suppose the Ferris wheel observed by Andrew takes 100 seconds for a full revolution. The graph below shows the height of the light above or below the principal axis against the time in seconds.

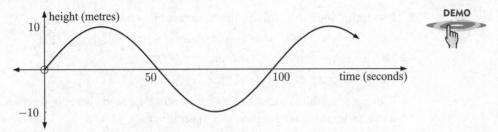

We observe that the amplitude is 10 metres and the period is 100 seconds.

## THE BASIC SINE CURVE

Suppose the point P moves around a circle of radius 1 unit centred at the origin O, so the *angle* OP makes with the horizontal axis is $x$. In this case the $y$-coordinate of P will be $\sin x$.

If we project the values of $\sin x$ from the unit circle onto a set of axes on the right, we obtain the graph of $y = \sin x$.

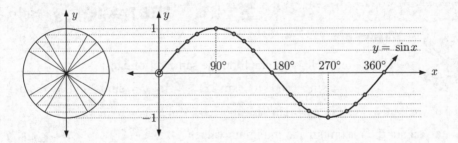

The wave of course can be continued beyond $0° \leqslant x \leqslant 360°$ as shown:

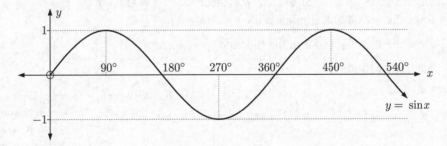

We expect the *period* to be $360°$, since the point P returns to its starting point after one full revolution.

The *maximum* value is 1 and the *minimum* is $-1$.

The *amplitude* is 1.

**GRAPHING PACKAGE**

Use your **graphics calculator** or **graphing package** to obtain the graph of $y = \sin x$ to check these features.

## INVESTIGATION 1                    THE FAMILY  $y = a \sin x$

**What to do:**

1  Use technology to graph on the same set of axes:

GRAPHING
PACKAGE

   **a**  $y = \sin x$  and  $y = 2\sin x$

   **b**  $y = \sin x$  and  $y = 0.5\sin x$

   **c**  $y = \sin x$  and  $y = -\sin x$

   If using a graphics calculator, make sure that the mode is set in **degrees** and that your viewing window is appropriate.

2  For each of  $y = \sin x$,  $y = 2\sin x$,  $y = 0.5\sin x$,  and  $y = -\sin x$:

   **a**  record the maximum and minimum values

   **b**  state the period and amplitude.

3  Describe the effect of  $a$  in the function  $y = a\sin x$.

4  State the amplitude of:

   **a**  $y = 3\sin x$            **b**  $y = \sqrt{7}\sin x$            **c**  $y = -2\sin x$

## INVESTIGATION 2                    THE FAMILY  $y = \sin bx$

**What to do:**

1  Use technology to graph on the same set of axes:

   **a**  $y = \sin x$  and  $y = \sin 2x$        **b**  $y = \sin x$  and  $y = \sin(\frac{1}{2}x)$

2  For each of  $y = \sin x$,  $y = \sin 2x$,  and  $y = \sin(\frac{1}{2}x)$:

   **a**  record the maximum and minimum values

   **b**  state the period and amplitude.

GRAPHING
PACKAGE

3  On the same set of axes, sketch  $y = \sin x$  and  $y = \sin(-x)$.
   State the period and amplitude of  $y = \sin(-x)$.

4  Describe the effect of  $b$  in the function  $y = \sin bx$.

5  State the period of:

   **a**  $y = \sin 3x$        **b**  $y = \sin(\frac{1}{3}x)$        **c**  $y = \sin(1.2x)$

   **d**  $y = \sin(-2x)$      **e**  $y = \sin(-\frac{1}{2}x)$      **f**  $y = \sin bx$

> $|a|$ is the **modulus** of $a$. It is the *size* of $a$, and cannot be negative.

From the previous investigations you should have observed that:

- In  $y = a\sin x$,  $|a|$  determines the amplitude.
  The graph of  $y = \sin x$  is vertically stretched
  if  $|a| > 1$,  or compressed if  $|a| < 1$,  to obtain
  the graph of  $y = a\sin x$.
  We call this a **vertical dilation**.
  If  $a < 0$  the graph is also reflected in the  $x$-axis.

- In $y = \sin bx$, $b \neq 0$, $b$ affects the period and the period is $\dfrac{360^o}{|b|}$.

  The graph of $y = \sin x$ is horizontally stretched if $0 < |b| < 1$, or compressed if $|b| > 1$, to obtain the graph of $y = \sin bx$.
  We call this a **horizontal dilation**.
  If $b < 0$ the graph is also reflected in the $x$-axis.

---

| **Example 1** | ◀) Self Tutor |
| --- | --- |

Without using technology, sketch the graphs of:

**a** $y = 2 \sin x$          **b** $y = -2 \sin x$   for $0^o \leqslant x \leqslant 360^o$.

**a** The amplitude is 2 and the period is $360^o$.

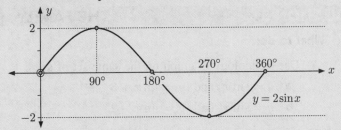

We place the 5 points as shown and fit the sine wave to them.

**b** The amplitude is 2, the period is $360^o$, and $y = -2 \sin x$ is the reflection of $y = 2 \sin x$ in the $x$-axis.

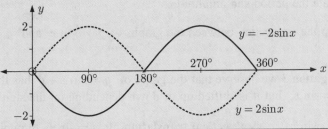

---

| **Example 2** | ◀) Self Tutor |
| --- | --- |

Without using technology, sketch the graph of $y = \sin 2x$ for $0^o \leqslant x \leqslant 360^o$.

The period is $\frac{360^o}{2} = 180^o$.

The maximum values are therefore $180^o$ apart.

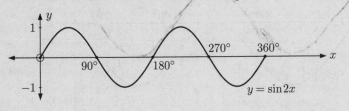

As $\sin 2x$ has half the period of $\sin x$, the first maximum is at $45^o$ not $90^o$.

## EXERCISE 18B.1

**1** Without using technology, sketch the graphs of the following for $0^o \leqslant x \leqslant 360^o$:

   **a** $y = 3 \sin x$      **b** $y = -3 \sin x$      **c** $y = \frac{3}{2} \sin x$      **d** $y = -\frac{3}{2} \sin x$

**2** Without using technology, sketch the graphs of the following for $0^o \leqslant x \leqslant 540^o$:

   **a** $y = \sin 3x$      **b** $y = \sin\left(\frac{x}{2}\right)$      **c** $y = \sin(-2x)$

**3** State the period of:

   **a** $y = \sin 4x$      **b** $y = \sin(-4x)$      **c** $y = \sin\left(\frac{x}{3}\right)$      **d** $y = \sin(0.6x)$

**4** Find $b$ given that the function $y = \sin bx$, $b > 0$ has period:

   **a** $900^o$      **b** $120^o$      **c** $2160^o$

---

**INVESTIGATION 3**                    **THE FAMILY** $y = \sin x + c$

**What to do:**

GRAPHING PACKAGE

**1** Use technology to graph on the same set of axes:

   **a** $y = \sin x$ and $y = \sin x + 3$

   **b** $y = \sin x$ and $y = \sin x - 2$

**2** For each of $y = \sin x$, $y = \sin x + 3$ and $y = \sin x - 2$:

   **a** record the maximum and minimum values

   **b** calculate the equation of the principal axis

   **c** state the period and amplitude.

**3** Explain the connection between the graphs of $y = \sin x$ and $y = \sin x + c$.

---

From **Investigation 3** we observe that the graph of $y = \sin x + c$ has the same shape as the graph of $y = \sin x$, but it is shifted up or down depending on the sign of $c$. We say:

> $y = \sin x + c$ is a **vertical translation** of $y = \sin x$ through $c$ units.
>
> Its principal axis has equation $y = c$.

---

**Example 3**                                             ◀ᴺ **Self Tutor**

On the same set of axes graph for $0 \leqslant x \leqslant 720^o$:   $y = \sin x$ and $y = \sin x - 1$

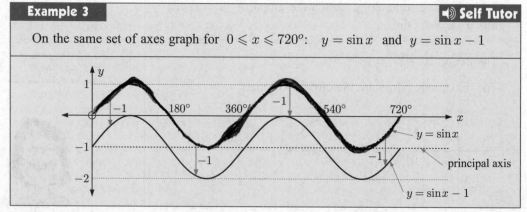

## THE GENERAL SINE FUNCTION

$y = a \sin bx + c$   is called the **general sine function**.

affects **amplitude**    affects **period**    affects **principal axis**

The **principal axis** of the general sine function is  $y = c$.

The **period** of the general sine function is  $\dfrac{360^o}{|b|}$.

Consider  $y = 2 \sin 3x + 1$.

So, starting with  $y = \sin x$  we would:

- double the amplitude to produce      $y = 2 \sin x$,   then
- divide the period by 3 to produce    $y = 2 \sin 3x$,   then
- translate upwards 1 unit to produce  $y = 2 \sin 3x + 1$.

## EXERCISE 18B.2

1   Find a formula in the form  $y = a \sin bx + c$  which produces the following graphs:

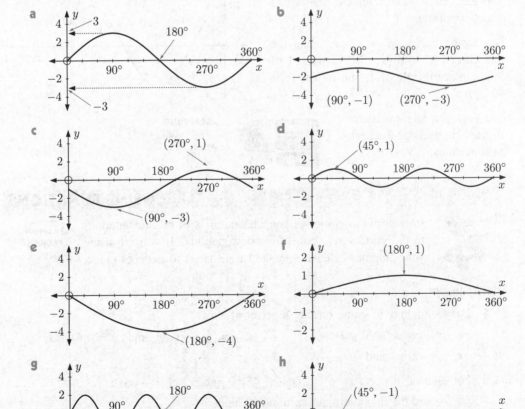

**2**  Without using technology, sketch the graphs of the following for $0° \leqslant x \leqslant 360°$:

   **a**  $y = \sin x + 1$       **b**  $y = \sin x - 2$       **c**  $y = 1 - \sin x$

   **d**  $y = 2\sin x - 1$     **e**  $y = \sin 3x + 1$    **f**  $y = 1 - \sin 2x$

GRAPH PAPER

Click on the icon to obtain printable graph paper for the above question.

# C  THE COSINE FUNCTION

DEMO

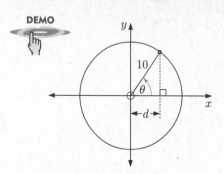

We return to the Ferris wheel to see the cosine function being generated.

Click on the icon to inspect a simulation of the view from above the wheel.

The graph being generated over time is a **cosine function**.

This is no surprise as $\cos \theta = \dfrac{d}{10}$ and so $d = 10 \cos \theta$.

The graph alongside shows the horizontal displacement of the light on the Ferris wheel over time.

The cosine curve $y = \cos x$, like the sine curve $y = \sin x$, has a **period** of $360°$, an **amplitude** of 1, and its **range** is $-1 \leqslant y \leqslant 1$.

Use your graphics calculator or graphing package to check these features.

GRAPHING PACKAGE

## INVESTIGATION 4                    COSINE FUNCTIONS

In this investigation we consider families of cosine functions in the same way we did for sine functions. If you are using your graphics calculator, make sure it is set to **degrees** mode.

GRAPHING PACKAGE

**What to do:**

**1**  Use technology to graph on the same set of axes:

   **a**  $y = \cos x$ and $y = 2\cos x$      **b**  $y = \cos x$ and $y = 0.5\cos x$

   **c**  $y = \cos x$ and $y = -\cos x$

**2**  For each of $y = \cos x$, $y = 2\cos x$, $y = 0.5\cos x$, $y = -\cos x$:

   **a**  record the maximum and minimum values

   **b**  state the period and amplitude.

**3**  Describe the effect of $a$ in the function $y = a\cos x$.

**4** State the amplitude of:

    **a** $y = 3\cos x$         **b** $y = \sqrt{7}\cos x$         **c** $y = -2\cos x$

**5** Use technology to graph on the same set of axes:

    **a** $y = \cos x$ and $y = \cos 2x$         **b** $y = \cos x$ and $\cos(\frac{1}{2}x)$

**6** For each of $y = \cos x$, $y = \cos 2x$, $y = \cos(\frac{1}{2}x)$, $y = \cos(-2x)$:

    **a** record the maximum and minimum values

    **b** state the period and amplitude.

**7** Describe the effect of $b$ in the function $y = \cos bx$.

**8** State the period of:

    **a** $y = \cos 3x$         **b** $y = \cos(\frac{1}{3}x)$         **c** $y = \cos(1.2x)$

    **d** $y = \cos(-x)$         **e** $y = \cos(-3x)$         **f** $y = \cos bx$

**9** Use technology to graph on the same set of axes:

    **a** $y = \cos x$ and $y = \cos x + 3$         **b** $y = \cos x$ and $y = \cos x - 2$

**10** For each of $y = \cos x$, $y = \cos x + 3$ and $y = \cos x - 2$:

    **a** record the maximum and minimum values

    **b** find the equation of the principal axis

    **c** state the period and amplitude.

**11** Explain the connection between the graphs of $y = \cos x$ and $y = \cos x + c$.

You should have observed that:

- in $y = a\cos x$, $|a|$ determines the amplitude
- in $y = \cos bx$, $b$ affects the period and the period is $\dfrac{360^o}{|b|}$
- in $y = \cos x + c$, $c$ affects the principal axis.

---

**Example 4**             ◀)) **Self Tutor**

Without using technology, sketch the graph of $y = 2\cos 2x$ for $0^o \leqslant x \leqslant 360^o$.

$a = 2$, so the amplitude is $|2| = 2$.

$b = 2$, so the period is

$$\frac{360^o}{|b|} = \frac{360^o}{2} = 180^o.$$

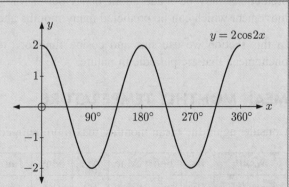

## EXERCISE 18C

**1** Given the graph of $y = \cos x$, sketch the graphs of:

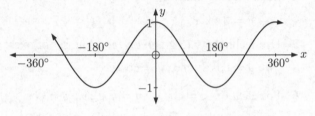

GRAPH PAPER

  **a** $y = \cos x + 2$            **b** $y = \cos x - 1$            **c** $y = \frac{2}{3}\cos x$

  **d** $y = \frac{3}{2}\cos x$            **e** $y = -\cos x$              **f** $y = \cos 2x$

  **g** $y = \cos\left(\frac{x}{2}\right)$          **h** $y = 3\cos 2x$

**2** Without graphing them, state the periods of:

  **a** $y = \cos 3x$              **b** $y = \cos\left(\frac{x}{3}\right)$           **c** $y = \cos\left(\frac{x}{2}\right)$

**3** The general cosine function is $y = a\cos bx + c$.
State the geometrical significance of $a$, $b$ and $c$.

**4** For the following graphs, find the cosine function representing them:

  **a** 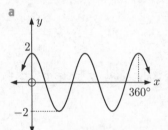     **b** 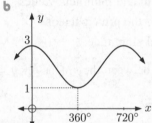     **c**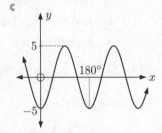

## D    MODELLING USING SINE AND COSINE FUNCTIONS

When patterns of variation can be identified and quantified in terms of a formula or equation, predictions may be made about behaviour in the future. Examples of this include tidal movement which can be predicted many months ahead, and the date of a future full moon.

In this section we use sine and cosine functions to model certain biological and physical phenomena that are periodic in nature.

### MEAN MONTHLY TEMPERATURE

Consider again the mean monthly maximum temperature for Cape Town:

| Month | Jan | Feb | Mar | Apr | May | Jun | Jul | Aug | Sep | Oct | Nov | Dec |
|-------|-----|-----|-----|-----|-----|-----|-----|-----|-----|-----|-----|-----|
| Temp (°C) | 28 | 27 | $25\frac{1}{2}$ | 22 | $18\frac{1}{2}$ | 16 | 15 | 16 | 18 | $21\frac{1}{2}$ | 24 | 26 |

The graph over a two year period is shown below:

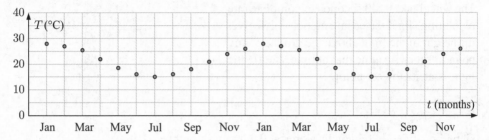

Since the maximum is at the start of the year, we attempt to model this data using the general cosine function $y = a \cos bx + c$, or in this case $T = a \cos bt + c$.

The period is 12 months, so $\dfrac{360^o}{|b|} = 12$ months.

$$\therefore \quad b = \dfrac{360^o}{12} = 30^o \text{ per month.}$$

The amplitude $= \dfrac{\max - \min}{2} \approx \dfrac{28 - 15}{2} \approx 6.5, \quad$ so $\quad a \approx 6.5$.

The principal axis is midway between the maximum and minimum,

so $\quad c \approx \dfrac{28 + 15}{2} \approx 21.5$.

So, the model is $T \approx 6.5 \cos(30t) + 21.5$ and is superimposed on the graph which follows:

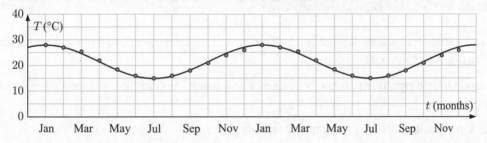

## EXERCISE 18D

1   At the Mawson base in Antarctica, the mean monthly temperatures for the last 30 years are as follows:

| Month | Jan | Feb | Mar | Apr | May | Jun | July | Aug | Sept | Oct | Nov | Dec |
|---|---|---|---|---|---|---|---|---|---|---|---|---|
| Temperature (°C) | 0 | −4 | −10 | −15 | −16 | −17 | −18 | −19 | −17 | −13 | −6 | −1 |

Find a cosine model for this data without using technology.

2   Some of the largest tides in the world are observed in Canada's Bay of Fundy. The difference between high and low tides is 14 metres and the average time difference between high tides is about 12.4 hours.

   a   Find a sine model for the height of the tide $H$ in terms of the time $t$ hours after mean tide.

   b   Sketch the graph of the model over one period.

**3**  Revisit the **Opening Problem** on page **558**.
The wheel takes 100 seconds to complete one
revolution. Find the cosine model which gives
the height of the light above the ground at any
point in time. Assume that at time $t = 0$, the
light is at its lowest point.

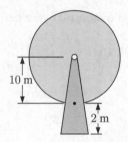

**4**  Geraldine rides her bicycle along a flat road at night.
Ian can clearly see a reflector on the spoke of her wheel
rotating. He measures the height of the reflector above
the ground at different times using a video.

| Time ($t$ s) | 0.1 | 0.2 | 0.3 | 0.4 | 0.5 | 0.6 | 0.7 | 0.8 | 0.9 |
|---|---|---|---|---|---|---|---|---|---|
| Height ($H$ cm) | 19 | 17 | 38 | 62 | 68 | 50 | 24 | 15 | 31 |

  **a**  Find a sine model for $H$ in terms of $t$.
  **b**  Sketch the graph of the model over one period.
  **c**  Find the diameter of Geraldine's wheel.
  **d**  How fast was Geraldine travelling?

reflector

# E     TRIGONOMETRIC EQUATIONS

Linear equations such as $2x + 3 = 11$ have exactly one solution. Quadratic equations have
up to two real solutions.

**Trigonometric equations** generally have infinitely many solutions unless a restrictive domain
such as $0^o \leqslant x \leqslant 540^o$ is given.

We will examine solving trigonometric equations using:

- pre-prepared graphs
- technology.

For the Ferris wheel **Opening Problem** the model is $H = -10\cos(3.6t) + 12$.

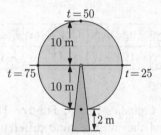

We can easily check this by substituting $t = 0, 25, 50, 75$

$$H(0) = -10\cos 0^o + 12 = -10 + 12 = 2 \quad \checkmark$$

$$H(25) = -10\cos 90^o + 12 = 12 \quad \checkmark$$

$$H(50) = -10\cos 180^o + 12 = 22 \quad \checkmark$$

$$H(75) = -10\cos 270^o + 12 = 12 \quad \checkmark$$

However, we may be interested in the times when the light is some other height above the
ground, for example 16 m. We would then need to solve the equation

$$-10\cos(3.6t) + 12 = 16.$$

# GRAPHICAL SOLUTION OF TRIGONOMETRIC EQUATIONS

Sometimes simple trigonometric graphs are available on grid paper. In such cases we can estimate solutions straight from the graph.

For example, we could use a graph to find approximate solutions for trigonometric equations such as $\cos x = 0.4$ for $0^o \leqslant x \leqslant 540^o$.

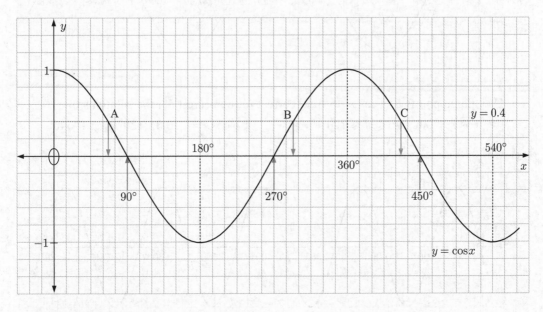

$y = 0.4$ meets $y = \cos x$ at A, B and C.

Hence, to the nearest degree, $x \approx 66^o$, $294^o$ or $426^o$.

So, the solutions of $\cos x = 0.4$ for $0^o \leqslant x \leqslant 540^o$ are $66^o$, $294^o$ and $426^o$.

## EXERCISE 18E.1

**1**

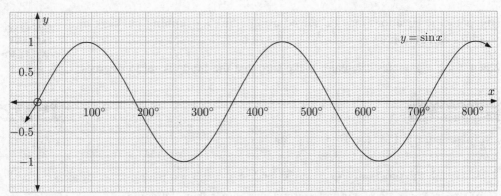

Use the graph of $y = \sin x$ to find, correct to the nearest $5^o$, the solutions of:

   **a** $\sin x = 0.3$ for $0^o \leqslant x \leqslant 720^o$       **b** $\sin x = -0.4$ for $180^o \leqslant x \leqslant 360^o$.

**2**

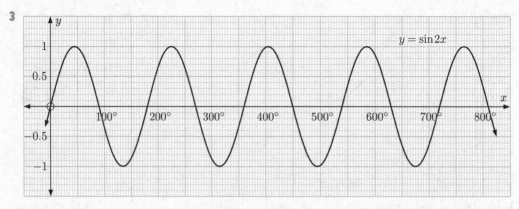

Use the graph of $y = \cos x$ to find, correct to the nearest $5^o$, the solutions of:

**a**  $\cos x = 0.6$, $0^o \leqslant x \leqslant 720^o$        **b**  $\cos x = -0.3$, $180^o \leqslant x \leqslant 540^o$.

**3**

Use the graph of $y = \sin 2x$ to find, correct to the nearest $5^o$, the solutions of:

**a**  $\sin 2x = 0.7$, $0^o \leqslant x \leqslant 540^o$        **b**  $\sin 2x = -0.3$, $0^o \leqslant x \leqslant 540^o$.

# SOLVING TRIGONOMETRIC EQUATIONS USING TECHNOLOGY

Trigonometric equations may be solved using either a **graphing package** or a **graphics calculator**.

GRAPHING
PACKAGE

When using a graphics calculator make sure that the **mode** is set to **degrees**.

| **Example 5** | ◀)) **Self Tutor** |
|---|---|

Solve $\sin x = 0.3$ for $0^o \leqslant x \leqslant 360^o$.

We graph the functions $Y_1 = \sin X$ and $Y_2 = 0.3$ on the same set of axes.
We need to use **view-window** settings just larger than the domain.
In this case, $X\min = -30^o$, $X\max = 390^o$, $X\text{scale} = 30^o$.

The grid facility on the graphics calculator can also be helpful, particularly when a sketch is required.

Using the appropriate function on the calculator gives the solutions $x \approx 17.5^o$, $163^o$.

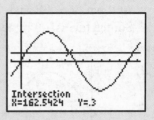

## EXERCISE 18E.2

1 Solve each of the following for $0^o \leqslant x \leqslant 360^o$:

   a $\sin x = 0.414$        b $\sin x = -0.673$        c $\cos x = 1.289$

   d $\sin(2x) = 0.162$     e $\cos\left(\dfrac{x}{2}\right) = 0.606$     f $\sin\left(\dfrac{2x}{3}\right) = 0.9367$

# F    USING TRIGONOMETRIC MODELS

In this section we apply our knowledge of trigonometric functions and equations to different modelling situations.

### Example 6      ◀))) Self Tutor

The height $h(t)$ metres of the tide above mean sea level on January 24th at Cape Town is modelled approximately by $h(t) = 3\sin(30t)$ where $t$ is the number of hours after midnight.

   a Graph $y = h(t)$ for $0 \leqslant t \leqslant 24$.

   b When is high tide and what is the maximum height?

   c What is the height at 2 pm?

   d If a ship can cross the harbour provided the tide is at least 2 m above mean sea level, when is crossing possible on January 24?

   a $h(t) = 3\sin(30t)$ has period $= \dfrac{360}{30} = 12$ hours and $h(0) = 0$

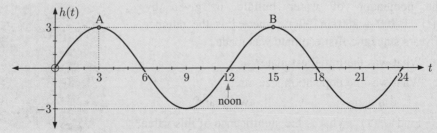

   b High tide is at 3 am and 3 pm. The maximum height is 3 m above the mean as seen at points A and B.

**c** At 2 pm, $t = 14$ and $h(14) = 3\sin(30 \times 14) \approx 2.60$ m

So, the tide is 2.6 m above the mean.

**d**

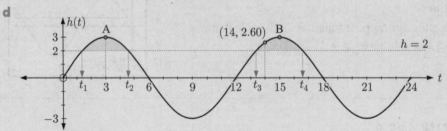

We need to solve $h(t) = 2$, so $3\sin(30t) = 2$.

Using a graphics calculator with $Y_1 = 3\sin(30X)$ and $Y_2 = 2$

we obtain $t_1 = 1.39$, $t_2 = 4.61$, $t_3 = 13.39$, $t_4 = 16.61$

Now 1.39 hours = 1 hour 23 minutes, and so on.

So, the ship can cross between 1:23 am and 4:37 am or 1:23 pm and 4:37 pm.

## EXERCISE 18F

**1** The population of grasshoppers after $t$ weeks where $0 \leqslant t \leqslant 12$ is estimated by
$P(t) = 7500 + 3000\sin(90t)$.

  **a** Find: **i** the initial estimate   **ii** the estimate after 5 weeks.

  **b** What is the greatest population size over this interval and when does it occur?

  **c** When is the population: **i** 9000   **ii** 6000?

  **d** During what time interval(s) does the population size exceed 10 000?

**2** The model for the height of a light on a Ferris wheel is $H(t) = 20 - 19\sin(120t)$,
where $H$ is the height in metres above the ground, and $t$ is in minutes.

  **a** Where is the light at time $t = 0$?

  **b** At what time is the light at its lowest in the first revolution of the wheel?

  **c** How long does the wheel take to complete one revolution?

  **d** Sketch the graph of the function $H(t)$ over one revolution.

**3** The population of water buffalo is given by
$P(t) = 400 + 250\sin(90t)$ where $t$ is the number
of years since the first estimate was made.

  **a** What was the initial estimate?

  **b** What was the population size after:

    **i** 6 months       **ii** two years?

  **c** Find $P(1)$. What is the significance of this value?

  **d** Find the smallest population size and when it first
occurred.

  **e** Find the first time when the herd exceeded 500.

**4** Over a 28 day period, the cost per litre of petrol was modelled by
$C(t) = 9.2\cos(25.7t) + 107.8$ cents $L^{-1}$.

   **a** True or false?

     **i** "The cost per litre oscillates about 107.8 cents with maximum price $1.17."

     **ii** "Every 14 days, the cycle repeats itself."

   **b** What was the cost of petrol on day 4, to the nearest tenth of a cent per litre?

   **c** On what days was the petrol priced at $1.10 per litre?

   **d** What was the minimum cost per litre and when did it occur?

## REVIEW SET 18A

**1** For each set of data below, draw a scatterplot and state if the data exhibits approximately periodic behaviour.

   **a**

| $x$ | 0 | 1 | 2 | 3 | 4 | 5 | 6 | 7 | 8 | 9 | 10 | 11 | 12 |
|---|---|---|---|---|---|---|---|---|---|---|---|---|---|
| $y$ | 2.7 | 0.8 | -1.7 | -3 | -2.1 | 0.3 | 2.5 | 2.9 | 1.3 | -1.3 | -2.9 | -2.5 | -0.3 |

   **b**

| $x$ | 0 | 1 | 2 | 3 | 4 | 5 | 6 | 7 | 8 | 9 |
|---|---|---|---|---|---|---|---|---|---|---|
| $y$ | 5 | 3.5 | 6 | -1.5 | 4 | -2.5 | -0.8 | 0.9 | 2.6 | 4.3 |

**2** Draw the graph of $y = 4\sin x$ for $0^o \leqslant x \leqslant 360^o$.

**3** State the minimum and maximum values of:

   **a** $y = 1 + \sin x$                **b** $y = -2\cos(3x)$

   **c** $y = 5\sin x - 3$              **d** $y = \frac{1}{3}\cos x + 1$

**4**

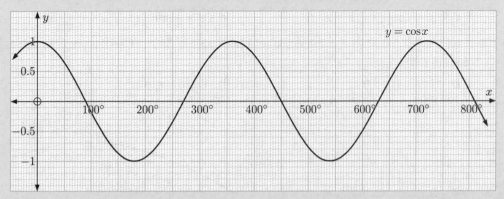

   Use the graph of $y = \cos x$ to find, correct to the nearest $5^o$, solutions of:

   **a** $\cos x = -0.4$, $\quad 0^o \leqslant x \leqslant 720^o$      **b** $\cos x = 0.9$, $\quad 0^o \leqslant x \leqslant 540^o$

**5** Use technology to solve for $0^o \leqslant x \leqslant 360^o$:

   **a** $\cos x = 0.3$           **b** $2\sin(3x) = \sqrt{2}$          **c** $43 + 8\sin x = 50.1$

**6** An ecologist studying a species of water beetle estimates the population of a colony over an eight week period. If $t$ is the number of weeks after the initial estimate is made, then the population in thousands can be modelled by

$P(t) = 5 + 2\sin(60t)$  where  $0 \leqslant t \leqslant 8$.

   **a** What was the initial population?

   **b** What were the smallest and largest populations?

   **c** During what time interval(s) did the population exceed 6000?

## REVIEW SET 18B

**1** Which of the following graphs display periodic behaviour?

**a**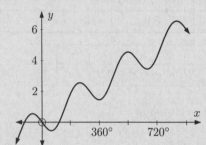

**b**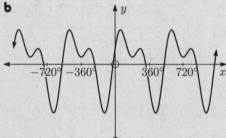

**2** Draw the graph of $y = \sin 3x$ for $0^o \leqslant x \leqslant 360^o$.

**3** State the period of:

   **a** $y = 4\sin(\frac{x}{5})$

   **b** $y = -2\cos(4x)$

   **c** $y = 4\cos(\frac{x}{2}) + 4$

   **d** $y = \frac{1}{2}\sin(3x)$

**4** Consider $y = \sin(\frac{x}{3})$ on the domain $-360^o \leqslant x \leqslant 360^o$. Use the graph to solve, correct to the nearest $5^o$:

   **a** $\sin(\frac{x}{3}) = -0.9$

   **b** $\sin(\frac{x}{3}) = \frac{1}{4}$

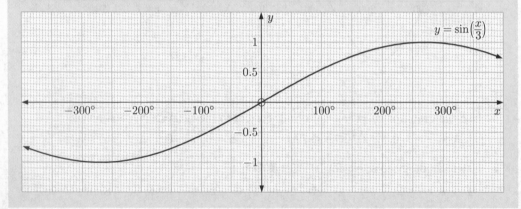

**5** On the same set of axes, for the domain $0° \leqslant x \leqslant 360°$, sketch:

    **a** $y = \cos x$ and $y = \cos x - 3$    **b** $y = \cos x$ and $y = -\frac{1}{2}\cos x$

    **c** $y = \sin x$ and $y = 3\sin(2x)$    **d** $y = \cos x$ and $y = 2\cos(\frac{x}{2}) + 3$

**6** A robot on Mars records the temperature every Mars day. A summary series, showing every one hundredth Mars day, is shown in the table below.

| Number of Mars days | 0 | 100 | 200 | 300 | 400 | 500 | 600 | 700 | 800 | 900 | 1000 | 1100 | 1200 | 1300 |
|---|---|---|---|---|---|---|---|---|---|---|---|---|---|---|
| Temp. (°C) | −43 | −15 | −5 | −21 | −59 | −79 | −68 | −50 | −27 | −8 | −15 | −70 | −78 | −68 |

    **a** Find the maximum and minimum temperatures recorded by the robot.

    **b** Find a sine model for the temperature $T$ in terms of the number of Mars days $d$.

    **c** Use this information to estimate the length of a Mars year.

## REVIEW SET 18C

**1** For each of the following functions, find the:

    **i** amplitude        **ii** vertical translation.

    **a** $y = 2\sin x + 1$    **b** $f(x) = -3\cos x + \frac{1}{2}$    **c** $g(x) = \sin(4x) - 5$

**2**  **a** Without using technology, draw the graph of $f(x) = \sin(\frac{x}{3}) + 2$.

    **b** For what values of $k$ will $f(x) = k$ have solutions?

**3** Find the cosine function represented in the following graphs:

    **a**                                      **b**

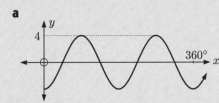
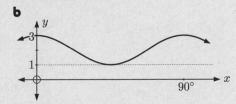

**4** Use technology to solve for $0° \leqslant x \leqslant 1000°$:

    **a** $\sin x = 0.382$        **b** $\cos(\frac{x}{2}) = -0.458$

**5** For the following graphs, state the:

    **i** equation of the principal axis    **ii** amplitude    **iii** period

    **a**                                        **b**

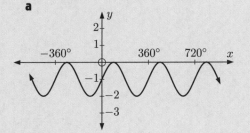
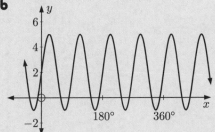

**6** In an industrial city, the amount of pollution in the air becomes greater during the working week when factories are operating, and lessens over the weekend. The number of milligrams of pollutants in a cubic metre of air is given by

$$P(t) = 40 - 12\sin(51.4t)$$

where $t$ is the number of days after midnight on Saturday night.

**a** What is the minimum level of pollution?

**b** At what time during the week does this minimum level occur?

# Chapter **19**

# Exponential functions

**Syllabus reference: 4.4**

**Contents:**   **A**   Evaluating exponential functions

**B**   Graphs of exponential functions

**C**   Growth and decay

## OPENING PROBLEM

Bacteria reproduce by dividing themselves in two to create two 'daughter' cells. A Petri dish contains a colony of 10 million bacteria. It takes one hour for each of these bacteria to divide into two bacteria, so every hour the total number of bacteria doubles. We can make a table which shows the population $b$ million bacteria over time $t$ hours.

| $t$ (hours) | 0 | 1 | 2 | 3 | 4 |
|---|---|---|---|---|---|
| $b$ (millions) | 10 | 20 | 40 | 80 | 160 |

**Things to think about:**

**a**  What type of series do these values form?

**b**  If $b$ is plotted against $t$, what shape do these points form on a graph?

**c**  Is it reasonable to connect the points with a smooth curve?

**d**  What function can be used to model the bacteria population over time?

The growth pattern in the **Opening Problem** can be shown on a graph like the one alongside.

Since not all the bacteria will divide at the same time, but rather throughout the hour, it is reasonable to join the points with a smooth curve. This allows us to estimate how many bacteria are alive at times other than on the hour. For example, at $1\frac{1}{2}$ hours there are about 28 million bacteria present.

However, drawing a curve on a graph and then reading off values is not a very precise way to investigate the colony. It would be better to have an equation linking $t$ and $b$.

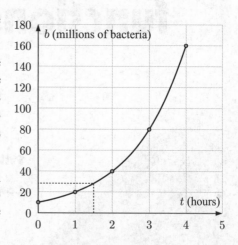

Using our knowledge from **Chapter 14**, we see that the population after each hour forms a geometric sequence with common ratio 2. The general term of the sequence is $b_t = 20 \times 2^{t-1}$.

However, we are also interested in what happens when $t$ is not an integer.

We therefore use the function
$$\begin{aligned} b(t) &= 20 \times 2^{t-1} \\ &= 2 \times 10 \times 2^{t-1} \\ &= 10 \times 2^t \end{aligned}$$

Functions of this form are called **exponential functions** because the variable appears in an **exponent**.

# A  EVALUATING EXPONENTIAL FUNCTIONS

### Example 1

◀) **Self Tutor**

For the function $f(x) = 3^x + 5$, find:

  **a** $f(6)$         **b** $f(0)$         **c** $f(-2)$

| | | |
|---|---|---|
| **a** $f(6) = 3^6 + 5$ | **b** $f(0) = 3^0 + 5$ | **c** $f(-2) = 3^{-2} + 5$ |
| $\quad = 729 + 5$ | $\quad = 1 + 5$ | $\quad = \dfrac{1}{3^2} + 5$ |
| $\quad = 734$ | $\quad = 6$ | $\quad = 5\frac{1}{9}$ |

## EXERCISE 19A

**1** If $f(x) = 2^x - 3$, find:

  **a** $f(2)$     **b** $f(1)$     **c** $f(0)$     **d** $f(-1)$     **e** $f(-2)$

**2** If $f(x) = 5 \times 3^x$, find:

  **a** $f(1)$     **b** $f(3)$     **c** $f(0)$     **d** $f(-4)$     **e** $f(-1)$

**3** If $f(x) = 2^{x+1}$, find:

  **a** $f(4)$     **b** $f(0)$     **c** $f(1)$     **d** $f(-1)$     **e** $f(-5)$

**4** If $g(x) = 5^{-x}$, find:

  **a** $g(1)$     **b** $g(3)$     **c** $g(0)$     **d** $g(-2)$     **e** $g(-3)$

**5** If $h(x) = 3 \times (1.1)^x$, use your calculator to evaluate the following:

  **a** $h(0)$     **b** $h(1)$     **c** $h(5)$     **d** $h(-2)$     **e** $h(3.8)$

# B   GRAPHS OF EXPONENTIAL FUNCTIONS

The simplest **exponential functions** have the form $y = a^x$ where $a > 0$, $a \neq 1$.

For example, $y = 2^x$ is an exponential function.

We construct a table of values from which we graph the function:

| $x$ | $-3$ | $-2$ | $-1$ | $0$ | $1$ | $2$ | $3$ |
|---|---|---|---|---|---|---|---|
| $y$ | $\frac{1}{8}$ | $\frac{1}{4}$ | $\frac{1}{2}$ | $1$ | $2$ | $4$ | $8$ |

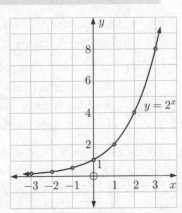

We notice that when $x = -10$, $y = 2^{-10} \approx 0.001$ and when $x = -50$, $y = 2^{-50} \approx 8.88 \times 10^{-16}$.

As $x$ becomes large and negative, the graph of $y = 2^x$ approaches the $x$-axis from above it.

We say that $y = 2^x$ is 'asymptotic to the $x$-axis' or '$y = 0$ is a horizontal asymptote'.

We use the notation $x \to a$ to say that $x$ approaches the value $a$. We also write $x \to \infty$ to show that $x$ becomes infinitely large.

In this example, as $x \to \infty$, $y \to \infty$, and as $x \to -\infty$, $y \to 0$.

## INVESTIGATION 1                    EXPONENTIAL GRAPHS

The object of this investigation is to examine the graphs of various families of exponential functions.

GRAPHING PACKAGE

**What to do:**

1  **a** On the same set of axes, use a **graphing package** or **graphics calculator** to graph the functions:  $y = 2^x$, $y = 3^x$, $y = 10^x$, $y = (1.3)^x$.

   **b** The functions in **a** are all members of the family $y = a^x$.
   
   **i** What effect does changing $a$ have on the shape of the graph?
   
   **ii** What is the $y$-intercept of each graph?
   
   **iii** What is the horizontal asymptote of each graph?

2  **a** On the same set of axes, use a **graphing package** or **graphics calculator** to graph the functions:  $y = 2^x$, $y = 2^x + 1$, $y = 2^x - 2$.

   **b** The functions in **a** are all members of the family $y = 2^x + c$ where $c$ is a constant.
   
   **i** What effect does changing $c$ have on the position of the graph?
   
   **ii** What effect does changing $c$ have on the shape of the graph?
   
   **iii** What is the horizontal asymptote of each graph?
   
   **iv** What is the horizontal asymptote of $y = 2^x + c$?

   **c** To graph $y = 2^x + c$ from $y = 2^x$, what transformation is used?

3  **a** On the same set of axes, use a **graphing package** or **graphics calculator** to graph the functions $y = 2^x$ and $y = 2^{-x}$.

   **b** **i** What is the $y$-intercept of each graph?
   
   **ii** What is the horizontal asymptote of each graph?
   
   **iii** Describe how the graphs of $y = 2^x$ and $y = 2^{-x}$ are related.

4  **a** On the same set of axes, use a **graphing package** or **graphics calculator** to graph the functions:  $y = 2^x$, $y = 2^{2x}$, $y = 2^{-x}$, $y = 2^{\frac{1}{2}x}$ and $y = 2^{-3x}$.

   **b** The functions in **a** are all members of the family $y = 2^{\lambda x}$.
   
   **i** What effect does changing $\lambda$ have on the shape of the graph?
   
   **ii** What is the $y$-intercept of each graph?
   
   **iii** What is the horizontal asymptote of each graph?

5  **a** On the same set of axes, use a **graphing package** or **graphics calculator** to graph the following sets of functions:

   **i** $y = 2^x$, $y = 3 \times 2^x$, $y = \frac{1}{2} \times 2^x$

**ii** $y = -2^x$, $y = -3 \times 2^x$, $y = -\frac{1}{2} \times 2^x$

**b** The functions in **a** are all members of the family $y = k \times 2^x$ where $k$ is a constant. Comment on the effect on the graph when   **i** $k > 0$   **ii** $k < 0$.

**c** What is the horizontal asymptote of each graph? Explain your answer.

From your investigation you should have discovered that:

For the general exponential function $y = ka^{\lambda x} + c$

- $a$ and $\lambda$ control how steeply the graph increases or decreases
- $c$ controls vertical translation and $y = c$ is the equation of the horizontal asymptote.

  ▸ if $k > 0$, $a^\lambda > 1$ the function is increasing.

  ▸ if $k > 0$, $0 < a^\lambda < 1$ the function is decreasing.

  ▸ if $k < 0$, $a^\lambda > 1$ the function is decreasing.

  ▸ if $k < 0$, $0 < a^\lambda < 1$ the function is increasing.

We can sketch reasonably accurate graphs of exponential functions using:

- the horizontal asymptote
- the $y$-intercept
- two other points, for example, when $x = 2$, $x = -2$

All exponential graphs are similar in shape and have a horizontal asymptote.

---

**Example 2**                                    ◀ッ **Self Tutor**

Sketch the graph of $y = 2^{-x} - 3$.

For $y = 2^{-x} - 3$,
the horizontal asymptote is $y = -3$.

When $x = 0$, $y = 2^0 - 3$
$\qquad\qquad\quad = 1 - 3$
$\qquad\qquad\quad = -2$

∴ the $y$-intercept is $-2$

When $x = 2$, $y = 2^{-2} - 3$
$\qquad\qquad\quad = \frac{1}{4} - 3$
$\qquad\qquad\quad = -2\frac{3}{4}$

When $x = -2$, $y = 2^2 - 3 = 1$

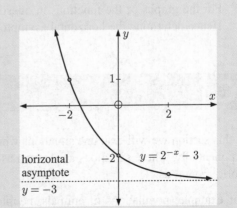

horizontal asymptote

$y = -3$

$y = 2^{-x} - 3$

## EXERCISE 19B

**1** Given the graph of $y = 2^x$ we can estimate values of $2^x$ for various values of $x$.

For example:

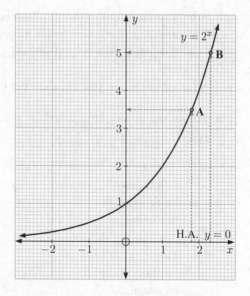

- $2^{1.8} \approx 3.5$      (point A)
- $2^{2.3} \approx 5$      (point B)

Use the graph to determine approximate values of:

  **a** $2^{\frac{1}{2}}$ $(= \sqrt{2})$     **b** $2^{0.8}$

  **c** $2^{1.5}$     **d** $2^{-1.6}$

  **e** $2^{\sqrt{2}}$     **f** $2^{-\sqrt{2}}$

**2** Draw freehand sketches of the following pairs of graphs using your observations from the previous investigation:

**GRAPHING PACKAGE**

  **a** $y = 2^x$ and $y = 2^x - 2$     **b** $y = 2^x$ and $y = 2^{-x}$

  **c** $y = 2^x$ and $y = 2^{2x}$     **d** $y = 2^x$ and $y = 2(2^x)$

**3** Draw freehand sketches of the following pairs of graphs:

  **a** $y = 3^x$ and $y = 3^{-x}$        **b** $y = 3^x$ and $y = 3^x + 1$

  **c** $y = 3^x$ and $y = -3^x$        **d** $y = 3^x$ and $y = 3^{-2x}$

**4** Sketch the graphs of:

  **a** $y = 2^x + 1$     **b** $y = 2 - 2^x$     **c** $y = 2^{-x} + 3$     **d** $y = 3 - 2^{-x}$

**5** Use your graphics calculator to graph the functions in question **4**. In each case find the value of $y$ when $x = \sqrt{2}$.

**6** For the graphs of the functions in question **4**, discuss the behaviour of $y$ as $x \to \pm\infty$. Hence determine the horizontal asymptotes for each graph.

## C      GROWTH AND DECAY

In this section we will examine situations where quantities are either increasing or decreasing exponentially. These situations are known as **growth** and **decay**, and occur frequently in the world around us.

For example, populations of animals, people, and bacteria usually *grow* in an exponential way. Radioactive substances, and items that depreciate in value, usually *decay* exponentially.

# GROWTH

Consider a population of 100 mice which under favourable conditions is increasing by 20% each week. To increase a quantity by 20%, we multiply it by 120% or 1.2.

If $P_n$ is the population after $n$ weeks, then

$P_0 = 100$          {the original population}

$P_1 = P_0 \times 1.2 = 100 \times 1.2$

$P_2 = P_1 \times 1.2 = 100 \times (1.2)^2$

$P_3 = P_2 \times 1.2 = 100 \times (1.2)^3$,  and so on.

From this pattern we see that   $P_n = 100 \times (1.2)^n$.

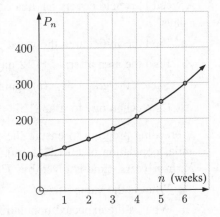

**Alternatively:**

This is an example of a *geometric sequence* and we could find the rule to generate it. Clearly $P_0 = 100$  and  $r = 1.2$,  so  $P_n = P_0 r^n = 100 \times (1.2)^n$  for  $n = 0, 1, 2, 3, ....$

---

**Example 3**                                                                ◀)) **Self Tutor**

An entomologist monitoring a grasshopper plague notices that the area affected by the grasshoppers is given by $A_n = 1000 \times 2^{0.2n}$ hectares, where $n$ is the number of weeks after the initial observation.

a   Find the original affected area.

b   Find the affected area after:   i  5 weeks    ii  10 weeks.

c   Find the affected area after 12 weeks.

d   Draw the graph of $A_n$ against $n$.

a   $A_0 = 1000 \times 2^0$

$= 1000 \times 1$

$= 1000$        $\therefore$  the original affected area was 1000 ha.

b   i  $A_5 = 1000 \times 2^1$                    ii  $A_{10} = 1000 \times 2^2$

$= 2000$                                $= 4000$

The affected area is 2000 ha.        The affected area is 4000 ha.

c   $A_{12} = 1000 \times 2^{0.2 \times 12}$

$= 1000 \times 2^{2.4}$        {*Press:*   1000 $\boxed{\times}$ 2 $\boxed{\wedge}$ 2.4 $\boxed{\text{ENTER}}$ }

$\approx 5280$

$\therefore$   after 12 weeks, the area affected is about 5280 ha.

d

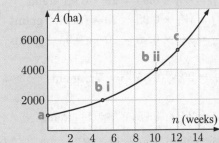

## EXERCISE 19C.1

1 A weed in a field covers an area of $A(t) = 3 \times 2^{0.1t}$ square metres after $t$ days.

**GRAPHING PACKAGE**

 a Find the initial area the weed covered.

 b Find the area after:  i 2 days  ii 10 days  iii 30 days.

 c Sketch the graph of $A(t)$ against $t$ using the results of a and b only.

 d Use technology to graph $Y_1 = 3 \times 2^{0.1X}$ and check your answers to a, b and c.

2 A breeding program to ensure the survival of pygmy possums was established with an initial population of 50 (25 pairs). From a previous program, the expected population $P_n$ in $n$ years' time is given by $P_n = P_0 \times 1.23^n$.

 a What is the value of $P_0$?

 b What is the expected population after:  i 2 years  ii 5 years  iii 10 years?

 c Sketch the graph of $P_n$ against $n$ using a and b only.

 d Use technology to graph $Y_1 = 50 \times 1.23^X$ and check your answers to b.

3 The speed $V_t$ of a chemical reaction is given by $V_t = V_0 \times 2^{0.05t}$ where $t$ is the temperature in $^{\circ}C$. Find:

 a the speed at $0^{\circ}C$    b the speed at $20^{\circ}C$

 c the percentage increase in speed at $20^{\circ}C$ compared with the speed at $0^{\circ}C$.

 d Find $\left(\dfrac{V_{50} - V_{20}}{V_{20}}\right) \times 100\%$. What does this calculation represent?

4 Six pairs of bears were introduced in 1998 to a large island off Alaska where previously there were no bears. It is expected that the population will increase according to $B_t = B_0 \times 2^{0.18t}$ where $t$ is the time since the introduction.

 a Find $B_0$.    b Find the expected bear population in 2018.

 c Find the expected percentage increase from 2008 to 2018.

## DECAY

Consider a radioactive substance with original weight 20 grams. It *decays* or reduces by 5% each year. The multiplier is thus 95% or 0.95.

If $W_n$ is the weight after $n$ years, then:

$W_0 = 20$ grams

$W_1 = W_0 \times 0.95 = 20 \times 0.95$ grams

$W_2 = W_1 \times 0.95 = 20 \times (0.95)^2$ grams

$W_3 = W_2 \times 0.95 = 20 \times (0.95)^3$ grams

$\vdots$

$W_{20} = 20 \times (0.95)^{20} \approx 7.2$ grams

$\vdots$

$W_{100} = 20 \times (0.95)^{100} \approx 0.1$ grams

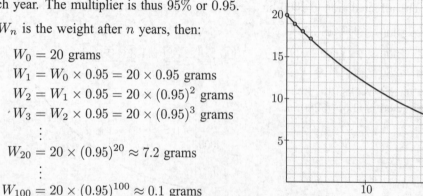

From this pattern we see that $W_n = 20 \times (0.95)^n$.

**Alternatively:**

Once again we have a *geometric sequence.*

In this case $W_0 = 20$ and $r = 0.95$, so $W_n = 20 \times (0.95)^n$ for $n = 0, 1, 2, 3, ....$

---

**Example 4**                                                            ◀ᅴ**Self Tutor**

When medication is taken by a patient, it is slowly used by their body. After $t$ hours, the amount of drug remaining in the body is given by $D(t) = 120 \times (0.9)^t$ mg.

a  Find $D(t)$ when $t = 0, 4, 12$ and 24 hours.

b  What was the original drug dose?

c  Graph $D(t)$ against $t$ for $t \geqslant 0$ using the information from a.

d  Use the graph or technology to find when there is only 25 mg of the drug left in the body.

---

a  $D(t) = 120 \times (0.9)^t$ mg

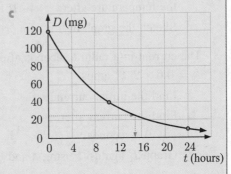

| | |
|---|---|
| $D(0)$ | $D(4)$ |
| $= 120 \times (0.9)^0$ | $= 120 \times (0.9)^4$ |
| $= 120$ mg | $\approx 78.7$ mg |
| $D(12)$ | $D(24)$ |
| $= 120 \times (0.9)^{12}$ | $= 120 \times (0.9)^{24}$ |
| $\approx 33.9$ mg | $\approx 9.57$ mg |

b  $D(0) = 120$, so the original dose was 120 mg.

d  From the graph, the time to reach 25 mg is about 15 hours.

*or*

By finding the point of intersection of $Y_1 = 120 \times (0.9)^X$ and $Y_2 = 25$ on a graphics calculator, the solution is $\approx 14.9$ hours.

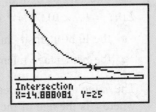

---

**Example 5**                                                            ◀ᅴ**Self Tutor**

The weight of radioactive material remaining after $t$ years is given by $W_t = W_0 \times 2^{-0.001t}$ grams.

a  Find the original weight.        b  Find the percentage remaining after 200 years.

---

a  When $t = 0$, $W_t = W_0 \times 2^0 = W_0$

∴ $W_0$ is the original weight.

b  When $t = 200$, $W_{200} = W_0 \times 2^{-0.001 \times 200}$

$= W_0 \times 2^{-0.2}$

$\approx W_0 \times 0.8706$

$\approx 87.06\%$ of $W_0$        ∴ $87.1\%$ remains.

## EXERCISE 19C.2

1 The weight of a radioactive substance $t$ years after being buried is given by $W(t) = 250 \times (0.998)^t$ grams.

  a How much radioactive substance was initially buried?

  b Determine the weight of the substance after:

    i 400 years               ii 800 years               iii 1200 years.

  c Sketch the graph of $W(t)$ for $t \geqslant 0$, using the above information.

  d Use your graph or graphics calculator to find how long it takes for the substance to decay to 125 grams.

2 The temperature $T$ of a liquid which has been placed in a refrigerator is given by $T(t) = 100 \times 2^{-0.02t}$ °C where $t$ is the time in minutes. Find:

  a the initial temperature

  b the temperature after:    i 15 minutes    ii 20 minutes    iii 78 minutes.

  c Sketch the graph of $T(t)$ for $t \geqslant 0$ using a and b only.

3 The current in a radio $t$ seconds after it is switched off is given by $I_t = 0.6 \times 2^{-5t}$ amps.

  a Find the initial current.

  b Find the current after:

    i 0.1 seconds             ii 0.5 seconds             iii 1 second.

  c Graph $I_t$ against $t$ using a and b only.

4 The intensity of light in the ocean $d$ metres below the surface is given by $L(d) = L_0 \times (0.9954)^d$ candelas. Find:

  a the light intensity at sea level

  b the percentage intensity decrease at 1000 metres.

5 The value of a car depreciates according to the formula $C_t = 4500 \times 0.68^t + 500$ euros, where $t$ is the age of the car in years.

  a Sketch a graph of $C_t$ against $t$.        b What was the initial cost of the car?

  c How much is the car worth after $4\frac{1}{2}$ years?

  d State the equation of the horizontal asymptote of $C_t$. What does this mean?

6 The population of turtles in a lake decreases each year to 93% of the previous year. In 2005 there were 340 turtles in the lake.

  a Find a model for the number of turtles $T$ in the lake, $n$ years after 2005. Your model should have the form $T = T_0 \times a^n$.

  b Graph your model from a.

  c How many turtles were in the lake in 2010?

  d If the population falls as low as 10, conservationists will not be able to save the turtle colony. According to your model, when will this occur?

## INVESTIGATION 2        CONTINUOUS COMPOUND INTEREST

In **Chapter 15** we used the compund interest formula $A = C\left(1 + \frac{r}{100k}\right)^{kn}$

where    $A$  is the final amount,      $C$  is the initial amount,
$r$  is the interest rate per annum,
$k$  is the number of times interest is compounded per year,
$n$  is the number of years.

We can see now that this is an exponential function.

In this investigation we look at the final value of an investment for various values of $k$, and allow $k$ to get extremely large.

**What to do:**

**1**  Suppose \$1000 is invested for one year at a fixed rate of 6% per annum. Use your calculator to find the final amount or *maturing value* if the interest is paid:

  **a**  annually                **b**  quarterly              **c**  monthly

  **d**  daily                    **e**  by the second          **f**  by the millisecond.

  Comment on your answers.

**2**  If we let  $a = \dfrac{100k}{r}$,  show that  $A = C\left[\left(1 + \dfrac{1}{a}\right)^{a}\right]^{\frac{r}{100}n}$.

**3**  For *continuous* compound growth, the number of interest payments per year $k$ gets very large.

  **a**  Explain why $a$ gets very large as $k$ gets very large.

  **b**  Copy and complete, giving your answers as accurately as technology permits:

| $a$ | 10 | 100 | 1000 | 10 000 | 100 000 |
|---|---|---|---|---|---|
| $\left(1 + \dfrac{1}{a}\right)^{a}$ | | | | | |

**4**  You should have found that for very large values of $a$,

$$\left(1 + \frac{1}{a}\right)^{a} \approx 2.718\,281\,828\,459\ldots$$

This is a special number in mathematics called $e$. $e$ is an irrational number like $\pi$. Use the  $\boxed{e^x}$  key of your calculator to find the value of $e^1$.

**5**  For continuous growth,  $A = Ce^{\frac{r}{100}n}$ where  $C$ is the initial amount
$r$  is the annual percentage rate
$n$  is the number of years

Use this formula to find the final value if \$1000 is invested for 4 years at a fixed rate of 6% per annum, where the interest is calculated continuously.

## REVIEW SET 19A

**1** If $f(x) = 3 \times 2^x$, find the value of:

   **a** $f(0)$                 **b** $f(3)$                 **c** $f(-2)$

**2**   **a** Graph $y = 3^x$, $y = 3^{-x}$ and $y = 3^x + 1$ on the same set of axes.

     **b** Discuss the behaviour of $y$ as $x \to \pm\infty$ for each of these graphs.

**3** An autograph by Marilyn Monroe had value $V = 20 \times 1.12^t$ dollars, where $t$ is the number of years after 1960.

   **a** Find the original value of the autograph.

   **b** How much was the autograph worth in:    **i** 1970    **ii** 1990    **iii** 2010?

   **c** Draw the graph of $V$ against $t$.

   **d** When was the autograph worth $1000?

**4** The graph opposite shows the temperature of a pie put in the fridge immediately after it is cooked. The temperature $T$ after $t$ minutes is given by $T_t = T_0 \times 2^{-0.133t}$ °C.

   **a** Find $T_0$.

   **b** What is the temperature of the pie after 20 minutes?

   **c** The pie is to be served at 5°C. How long after cooking can it be served?

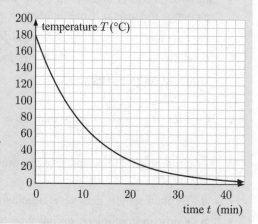

## REVIEW SET 19B

**1** If $f(x) = 5^{x+1}$, find:    **a** $f(2)$         **b** $f(0)$         **c** $f(-4)$

**2** On the same set of axes draw the graphs of:    **a** $y = 2^x$    **b** $y = 2^x - 4$.
In each case state the $y$-intercept and the equation of the horizontal asymptote.

**3** The weight of a lump of radioactive plutonium after $t$ years is given by $W_t = W_0 \times 2^{-0.07t}$ grams.

   **a** Find the original weight of the plutonium.

   **b** Find the percentage remaining after:    **i** 10 years    **ii** 50 years.

   **c** When has the weight remaining decayed to 1% of the original level?

**4** 8 pairs of rhinoceroses are introduced onto an Indonesian island. The expected population $P_n$ after $n$ years is given by $P_n = P_0 \times 1.03^n$.

   **a** Find $P_0$.

   **b** Find the expected population after 25 years.

   **c** Once there are 40 pairs of rhinoceroses, a new colony can be formed. When is this expected to occur?

# Chapter 20

# Two variable statistics

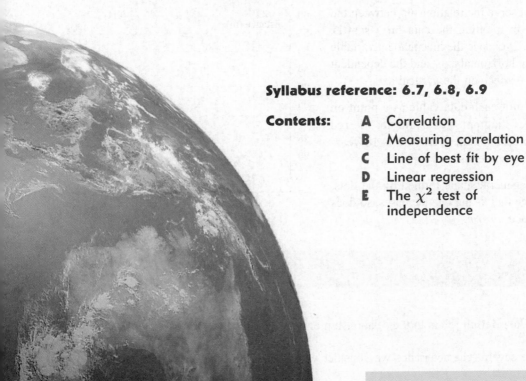

## OPENING PROBLEM

At a junior tournament, a group of young athletes throw a discus. The *age* and *distance thrown* are recorded for each athlete.

| Athlete | A | B | C | D | E | F | G | H | I | J | K | L |
|---|---|---|---|---|---|---|---|---|---|---|---|---|
| Age (years) | 12 | 16 | 16 | 18 | 13 | 19 | 11 | 10 | 20 | 17 | 15 | 13 |
| Distance thrown (m) | 20 | 35 | 23 | 38 | 27 | 47 | 18 | 15 | 50 | 33 | 22 | 20 |

**Things to think about:**

- Do you think the distance an athlete can throw is related to the person's age?
- What happens to the distance thrown as the age of the athlete increases?
- How could you graph the data to more clearly see the relationship between the variables?
- How can we *measure* the relationship between the variables?

Statisticians are often interested in how two variables are **related**.

For example, in the **Opening Problem**, we want to know how a change in the *age* of the athlete will affect the *distance* the athlete can throw.

We can observe the relationship between the variables by plotting the data on a **scatter diagram**. We place the independent variable *age* on the horizontal axis, and the dependent variable *distance* on the vertical axis.

We then plot each data value as a point on the scatter diagram. For example, the red point represents athlete H, who is 10 years old and threw the discus 15 metres.

From the general shape formed by the dots, we can see that as the *age* increases, so does the *distance thrown*.

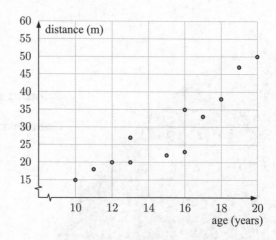

## A                    CORRELATION

> **Correlation** refers to the relationship or association between two variables.

There are several characteristics we consider when describing the correlation between two variables.

Firstly, we can describe the **direction** of the correlation.

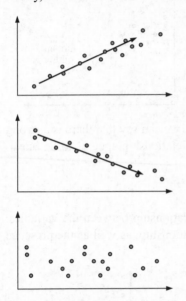

For a generally *upward* trend, we say that the correlation is **positive**. An increase in the independent variable means that the dependent variable generally increases.

For a generally *downward* trend, we say that the correlation is **negative**. An increase in the independent variable means that the dependent variable generally decreases.

For *randomly scattered* points, with no upward or downward trend, we say there is **no correlation**.

Secondly, we can describe the **strength** of the correlation, or how closely the data follows a pattern or trend. The strength of correlation is usually described as either strong, moderate, or weak.

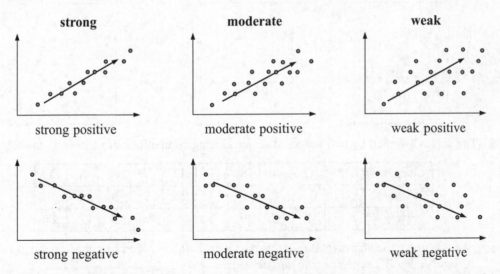

Thirdly, we can determine whether the points follow a **linear** trend, which means they approximately form a straight line.

These points are roughly linear.

These points do not follow a linear trend.

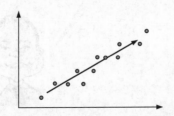

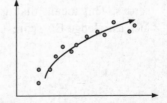

Finally we can observe and investigate any **outliers**. These are isolated points which do not follow the trend formed by the main body of data.

If an outlier is the result of a recording or graphing error, it should be discarded. However, if the outlier proves to be a genuine piece of data, it should be kept.

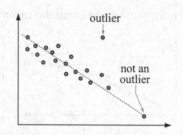

For the scatter diagram for the data in the **Opening Problem**, we can say that there is a strong positive correlation between *age* and *distance thrown*. The relationship appears to be linear, with no outliers.

## EXERCISE 20A

1   For each of the scatter diagrams below, describe the relationship between the variables. Consider the direction, strength, and linearity of the relationship, as well as the presence of outliers.

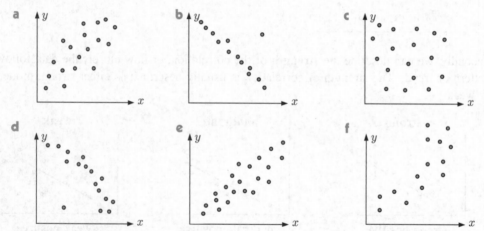

2   The scores awarded by two judges at an ice skating competition are shown in the table.

| Competitor | P | Q | R | S | T | U | V | W | X | Y |
|---|---|---|---|---|---|---|---|---|---|---|
| Judge A | 5 | 6.5 | 8 | 9 | 4 | 2.5 | 7 | 5 | 6 | 3 |
| Judge B | 6 | 7 | 8.5 | 9 | 5 | 4 | 7.5 | 5 | 7 | 4.5 |

a   Construct a scatter diagram for this data with Judge A's scores on the horizontal axis and Judge B's scores on the vertical axis.

b   Copy and complete the following comments about the scatter diagram:

There appears to be ...., .... correlation between Judge A's scores and Judge B's scores. This means that as Judge A's scores increase, Judge B's scores ....

> You can use technology to draw scatter diagrams. Consult the **graphics calculator instructions**.

**3** The results of a group of students for a Maths test and an Art essay are compared:

This data is called **bivariate** data because *two* variables are recorded for each individiual.

| Student | A | B | C | D | E | F | G | H | I | J |
|---|---|---|---|---|---|---|---|---|---|---|
| Maths test | 64 | 67 | 69 | 70 | 73 | 74 | 77 | 82 | 84 | 85 |
| Art essay | 85 | 82 | 80 | 82 | 72 | 71 | 70 | 71 | 62 | 66 |

**a** Construct a scatter diagram for the data. Make the scales on both axes from 60 to 90.

**b** Describe the relationship between the Mathematics and Art marks.

**4** For the following pairs of variables, choose the scatter diagram which would best illustrate the relationship between the variables.

**a** $x$ = the number of apples bought by customers, $y$ = the total cost of apples

**b** $x$ = the number of pushups a student can perform in one minute,
$y$ = the time taken for the student to run 100 metres

**c** $x$ = the height of people, $y$ = the weight of people

**d** $x$ = the distance a student travels to school, $y$ = the height of the student's uncle

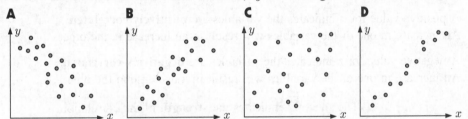

**5** The scatter diagram alongside shows the marks obtained by students in a test out of 50 marks, plotted against the number of hours each student studied for the test.

**a** Describe the correlation between the variables.

**b** How should the outlier be treated? Explain your answer.

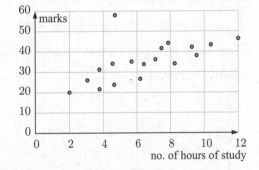

## B         MEASURING CORRELATION

In the previous section, we classified the strength of the correlation between two variables as either strong, moderate, or weak. We observed the points on a scatter diagram, and made a judgement as to how clearly the points formed a linear relationship.

To give a more precise measure of the strength of linear correlation, we can use **Pearson's product-moment correlation coefficient** $r$.

Given a set of $n$ pairs of data values for the variables $X$ and $Y$, Pearson's correlation coefficient is

| $X$ | $x_1$ | $x_2$ | $x_3$ | .... | $x_n$ |
|---|---|---|---|---|---|
| $Y$ | $y_1$ | $y_2$ | $y_3$ | .... | $y_n$ |

$$r = \frac{s_{xy}}{s_x s_y}$$

where $s_{xy} = \dfrac{\sum(x - \overline{x})(y - \overline{y})}{n} = \dfrac{\sum xy}{n} - \overline{x}\,\overline{y}$ is the **covariance** of $X$ and $Y$

$s_x = \sqrt{\dfrac{\sum(x - \overline{x})^2}{n}} = \sqrt{\dfrac{\sum x^2}{n} - \overline{x}^2}$ is the **standard deviation** of $X$

$s_y = \sqrt{\dfrac{\sum(y - \overline{y})^2}{n}} = \sqrt{\dfrac{\sum y^2}{n} - \overline{y}^2}$ is the **standard deviation** of $Y$.

So, $r = \dfrac{\sum(x - \overline{x})(y - \overline{y})}{\sqrt{\sum(x - \overline{x})^2}\sqrt{\sum(y - \overline{y})^2}}$ or $\dfrac{\sum xy - n\overline{x}\,\overline{y}}{\sqrt{\sum x^2 - n\overline{x}^2}\sqrt{\sum y^2 - n\overline{y}^2}}$

The values of $r$ range from $-1$ to $+1$.

> The **sign** of $r$ indicates the **direction** of the correlation.

A positive value for $r$ indicates the variables are **positively correlated**.
An increase in one of the variables will result in an increase in the other.

A negative value for $r$ indicates the variables are **negatively correlated**.
An increase in one of the variables will result in a decrease in the other.

> The **size** of $r$ indicates the **strength** of the correlation.

A value of $r$ close to $+1$ or $-1$ indicates strong correlation between the variables.

A value of $r$ close to zero indicates weak correlation between the variables.

Here are some scatter diagrams showing various values of $r$:

**Positive correlation:**

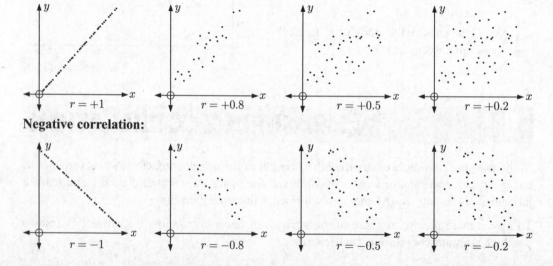

$r = +1$    $r = +0.8$    $r = +0.5$    $r = +0.2$

**Negative correlation:**

$r = -1$    $r = -0.8$    $r = -0.5$    $r = -0.2$

**Example 1** Self Tutor

The Department of Road Safety wants to know if there is any association between *average speed* in the metropolitan area and the *age of drivers*. They commission a device to be fitted in cars of drivers of different ages.

The results are shown in the scatter diagram. The $r$-value for this association is $+0.027$. Describe the association.

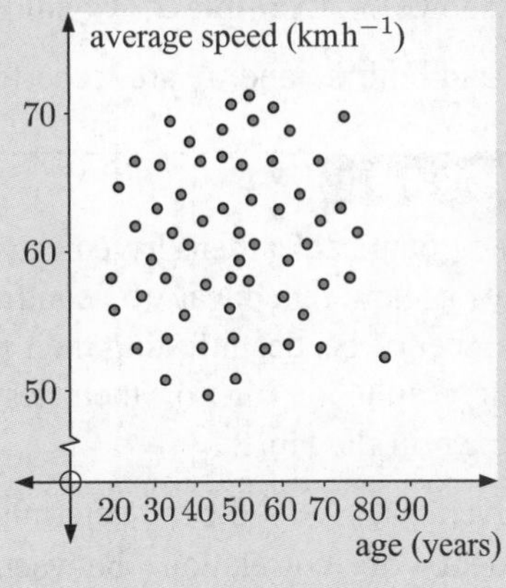


As $r$ is close to zero, there is no correlation between the two variables.

We observe this in the graph as the points are randomly scattered.

**Example 2** Self Tutor

Sue investigates how the volume of water in a pot affects how long it takes to boil on the stove. The results are given in the table.

Find Pearson's correlation coefficient between the two variables.

| Pot | *Volume* ($x$ L) | *Time to boil* ($y$ min) |
|---|---|---|
| A | 1 | 3 |
| B | 2 | 4 |
| C | 4 | 6 |
| D | 5 | 8 |

| | $x$ | $y$ | $xy$ | $x^2$ | $y^2$ |
|---|---|---|---|---|---|
| | 1 | 3 | 3 | 1 | 9 |
| | 2 | 4 | 8 | 4 | 16 |
| | 4 | 6 | 24 | 16 | 36 |
| | 5 | 8 | 40 | 25 | 64 |
| Totals: | 12 | 21 | 75 | 46 | 125 |

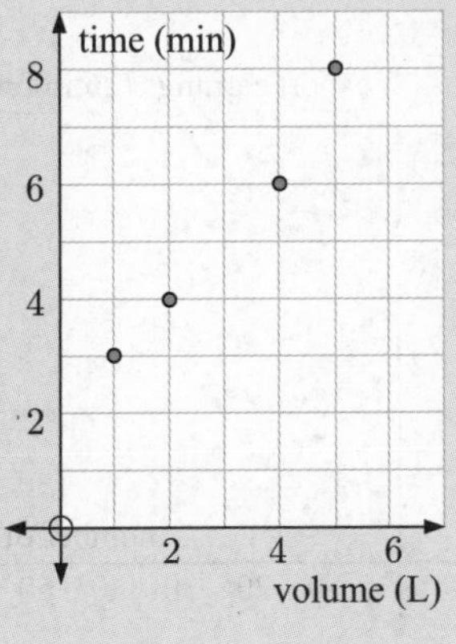


There are 4 pairs of data values, so $n = 4$.

$$\overline{x} = \frac{\sum x}{n} = \frac{12}{4} = 3$$

$$\overline{y} = \frac{\sum y}{n} = \frac{21}{4} = 5.25$$

$$r = \frac{\sum xy - n\overline{x}\,\overline{y}}{\sqrt{\sum x^2 - n\overline{x}^2}\sqrt{\sum y^2 - n\overline{y}^2}}$$

$$= \frac{75 - 4 \times 3 \times 5.25}{\sqrt{46 - 4 \times 3^2}\sqrt{125 - 4 \times 5.25^2}}$$

$$= \frac{12}{\sqrt{10}\sqrt{14.75}}$$

$$\approx 0.988$$

Positive $r$ means that as the volume of water increases, so does the time to boil the water. Since $r$ is close to 1, there is a strong positive correlation.

In examinations, candidates will not be required to find $r$ using the formulae for $s_{xy}$, $s_x$ and $s_y$ as shown in **Example 2**. Candidates may be required to use $r = \dfrac{s_{xy}}{s_x s_y}$ where $s_{xy}$ is given and both $s_x$ and $s_y$ are to be found using technology.

---

**Example 3**　　　◀) **Self Tutor**

The Botanical Gardens have been trying out a new chemical to control the number of beetles infesting their plants. The results of one of their tests are shown in the table.

Given $s_{xy} = -5.81$, determine the extent of correlation between the *quantity of chemical* and the *number of surviving beetles* in the test sample.

| Sample | Quantity of chemical (g) | Number of surviving beetles |
|--------|--------------------------|------------------------------|
| A | 2 | 11 |
| B | 5 | 6 |
| C | 6 | 4 |
| D | 3 | 6 |
| E | 9 | 3 |

Using technology, $s_x \approx 2.45$ and $s_y \approx 2.76$

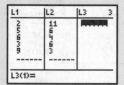 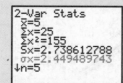 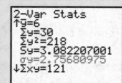

> We use the population standard deviations $\sigma_x$ and $\sigma_y$ since the data given is the population of values we are interested in.

$$\therefore\ r = \frac{s_{xy}}{s_x s_y} = \frac{-5.81}{2.45 \times 2.76} \approx -0.859$$

There is a moderate negative correlation between the *amount of chemical used* and the *number of surviving beetles*.

In general, the more chemical that is used, the fewer beetles that survive.

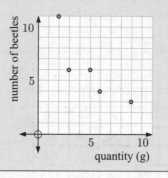 

---

## EXERCISE 20B.1

**1** In a recent survey, the Department of International Commerce compared the *size of a company* with its *export earnings*. A scatter diagram of their data is shown alongside. The corresponding value of $r$ is $0.556$.

Describe the association between the variables.

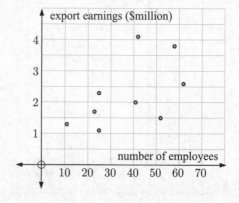

**2** For each of the following graphs, evaluate $r = \dfrac{\sum xy - n\overline{x}\,\overline{y}}{\sqrt{\sum x^2 - n\overline{x}^2}\sqrt{\sum y^2 - n\overline{y}^2}}$ and comment on its value.

**a**
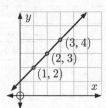

**b**
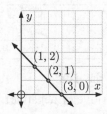

**c**
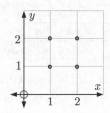

**3** Match each scatter diagram with the correct value of $r$.

**a**
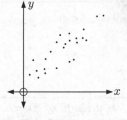

**b**
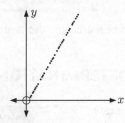

**c**
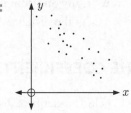

**d**
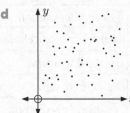

**e**
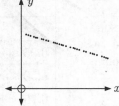

**A** $r = 1$    **B** $r = 0.6$    **C** $r = 0$    **D** $r = -0.7$    **E** $r = -1$

**4** Find Pearson's correlation coefficient for random variables $X$ and $Y$ where:

**a** $s_x = 14.7$, $s_y = 19.2$, $s_{xy} = 136.8$

**b** the standard deviation of $X$ is 8.71, the standard deviation of $Y$ is 13.23, and the covariance of $X$ and $Y$ is $-9.26$.

**5** The scores awarded by two judges at a diving competition are shown in the table.

| Competitor | P | Q | R | S | T | U | V | W |
|---|---|---|---|---|---|---|---|---|
| Judge A | 7 | 6 | 8.5 | 8 | 5 | 5 | 6 | 7.5 |
| Judge B | 6 | 5 | 9 | 8 | 4.5 | 3.5 | 6.5 | 7 |

**a** Construct a scatter diagram for this data, with Judge A's scores on the horizontal axis and Judge B's scores on the vertical axis.

**b** Copy and complete the following:
There appears to be a ...., .... correlation between Judge A's scores and Judge B's scores. This means that as Judge A's scores increase, Judge B's scores ....

**c** Given $s_{AB} \approx 2.008$, calculate and interpret Pearson's correlation coefficient $r$.

**6**  A basketballer takes 20 shots from each of ten different positions marked on the court. The table below shows how far each position is from the goal, and how many shots were successful:

| Position | A | B | C | D | E | F | G | H | I | J |
|---|---|---|---|---|---|---|---|---|---|---|
| Distance from goal ($x$ m) | 2 | 5 | 3.5 | 6.2 | 4.5 | 1.5 | 7 | 4.1 | 3 | 5.6 |
| Successful shots ($y$) | 17 | 6 | 10 | 5 | 8 | 18 | 6 | 8 | 13 | 9 |

**a**  Draw a scatter diagram of the data.

**b**  Do you think $r$ will be positive or negative?

**c**  Given $s_{xy} = -6.68$, calculate the value of $r$.

**d**  Copy and complete:

As the distance from goal increases, the number of successful shots generally ....

## THE COEFFICIENT OF DETERMINATION $r^2$

To help describe the *strength* of correlation we calculate the **coefficient of determination** $r^2$. This is simply the square of Pearson's correlation coefficient $r$, and as such the direction of correlation is eliminated.

The table alongside is a guide for describing the strength of linear correlation using the coefficient of determination.

| value | strength of correlation |
|---|---|
| $r^2 = 0$ | no correlation |
| $0 < r^2 < 0.25$ | very weak correlation |
| $0.25 \leqslant r^2 < 0.50$ | weak correlation |
| $0.50 \leqslant r^2 < 0.75$ | moderate correlation |
| $0.75 \leqslant r^2 < 0.90$ | strong correlation |
| $0.90 \leqslant r^2 < 1$ | very strong correlation |
| $r^2 = 1$ | perfect correlation |

## USING TECHNOLOGY TO CALCULATE $r$ AND $r^2$

Given a set of bivariate data, you can use your calculator to find the values of $r$ and $r^2$. For help, consult the **graphics calculator instructions** at the front of the book.

STATISTICS PACKAGE

Alternatively, you can use the statistics package on your CD.

---

**Example 4**                                                     ◀╗ **Self Tutor**

At a father-son camp, the heights of the fathers and their sons were measured.

| Father's height ($x$ cm) | 175 | 183 | 170 | 167 | 179 | 180 | 183 | 185 | 170 | 181 | 185 |
|---|---|---|---|---|---|---|---|---|---|---|---|
| Son's height ($y$ cm) | 167 | 178 | 158 | 162 | 171 | 167 | 180 | 177 | 152 | 164 | 172 |

**a**  Draw a scatter diagram of the data.    **b**  Calculate $r$ and $r^2$ for the data.

**c**  Describe the correlation between the variables.

**a**

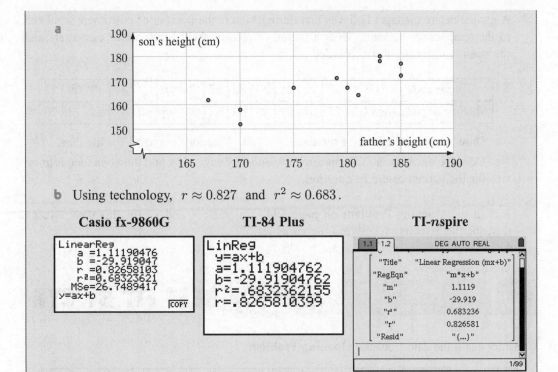

**b** Using technology, $r \approx 0.827$ and $r^2 \approx 0.683$.

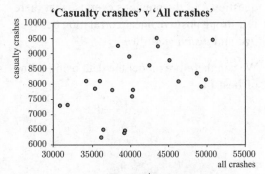

**c** There is a moderate positive correlation between the heights of the fathers and the heights of their sons.

## EXERCISE 20B.2

**1** The scatter diagram alongside shows the number of car crashes in which a casualty occurred, compared with the total number of car crashes in each year from 1972 to 1994. The $r$ value is 0.494.

**a** Find $r^2$.

**b** Describe the correlation between these variables.

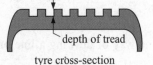

'Casualty crashes' v 'All crashes'

**2** A sample of 8 tyres was taken to examine the association between the *tread depth* and the *number of kilometres travelled*.

depth of tread

tyre cross-section

| Kilometres ($x$ thousand) | 14 | 17 | 24 | 34 | 35 | 37 | 38 | 39 |
|---|---|---|---|---|---|---|---|---|
| Tread depth ($y$ mm) | 5.7 | 6.5 | 4.0 | 3.0 | 1.9 | 2.7 | 1.9 | 2.3 |

**a** Draw a scatter diagram of the data.      **b** Calculate $r$ and $r^2$ for the data.

**c** Describe the correlation between the *tread depth* and the *number of kilometres travelled*.

**3**   A garden centre manager believes that during March, the number of customers is related to the temperature at noon. Over a period of a fortnight the number of customers and the noon temperature were recorded.

| Temperature ($x$ °C) | 23 | 25 | 28 | 30 | 30 | 27 | 25 | 28 | 32 | 31 | 33 | 29 | 27 |
|---|---|---|---|---|---|---|---|---|---|---|---|---|---|
| Number of customers ($y$) | 57 | 64 | 62 | 75 | 69 | 58 | 61 | 78 | 80 | 67 | 84 | 73 | 76 |

   **a**  Draw a scatter diagram of the data.    **b**  Calculate $r$ and $r^2$ for the data.

   **c**  Describe the association between the *number of customers* and the *noon temperature* for the garden centre in question.

**4**   Revisit the **Opening Problem** on page **594**. Calculate $r$ and $r^2$ for this data. Hence describe the association between the variables.

# C    LINE OF BEST FIT BY EYE

Consider again the data from the **Opening Problem**:

| Athlete | A | B | C | D | E | F | G | H | I | J | K | L |
|---|---|---|---|---|---|---|---|---|---|---|---|---|
| Age (years) | 12 | 16 | 16 | 18 | 13 | 19 | 11 | 10 | 20 | 17 | 15 | 13 |
| Distance thrown (m) | 20 | 35 | 23 | 38 | 27 | 47 | 18 | 15 | 50 | 33 | 22 | 20 |

We can see from the scatter diagram and question **4** of the previous exercise that there is a strong positive linear correlation between *age* and *distance thrown*.

We can therefore model the data using a **line of best fit**.

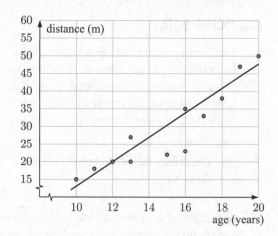

One way of drawing a line of best fit connecting variables $X$ and $Y$ is as follows:

*Step 1:*   Calculate the mean of the $X$ values $\overline{x}$, and the mean of the $Y$ values $\overline{y}$.

*Step 2:*   Mark the **mean point** $(\overline{x}, \overline{y})$ on the scatter diagram.

*Step 3:*   Draw a line through the mean point such that about the same number of data points are above the line as below it.

The line formed is called a **line of best fit by eye**. This line will vary from person to person.

For the **Opening Problem**, the mean point is (15, 29). So, we draw our line of best fit through (15, 29).

We can use the line of best fit to estimate the value of $y$ for any given value of $x$, and vice versa.

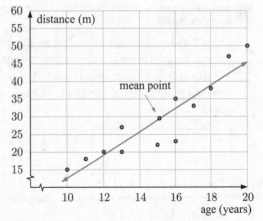

## INTERPOLATION AND EXTRAPOLATION

Consider the data in the scatter diagram alongside. A line of best fit has been drawn so we can predict the value of one variable for a given value of the other.

If we predict a $y$ value for an $x$ value **in between** the smallest and largest values that were supplied, we say we are **interpolating** in between the poles.

If we predict a $y$ value for an $x$ value **outside** the smallest and largest $x$ values that were supplied, we say we are **extrapolating** outside the poles.

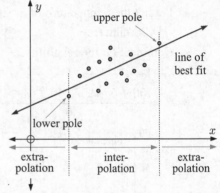

The accuracy of an interpolation depends on how linear the original data was. This can be gauged by the correlation coefficient and by ensuring that the data is randomly scattered around the line of best fit.

The accuracy of an extrapolation depends not only on how linear the original data was, but also on the assumption that the linear trend will continue past the poles. The validity of this assumption depends greatly on the situation under investigation.

For example, using our line of best fit from the **Opening Problem** data, the age of 14 is within the range of ages already supplied. So, it is reasonable to predict that a 14 year old will be able to throw the discus 26 m.

However, it is unreasonable to predict that a 30 year old will throw the discus 78 m. The age of 30 is outside the range of values already supplied, and it is unlikely that the linear trend shown in the data will continue up to the age of 30.

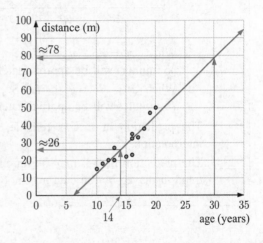

**Example 5**    ◀⬤ **Self Tutor**

On a hot day, six cars were left in the sun for various lengths of time. The length of time each car was left in the sun was recorded, as well as the temperature inside the car at the end of the period.

| Car | A | B | C | D | E | F |
|---|---|---|---|---|---|---|
| Time ($x$ min) | 50 | 5 | 25 | 40 | 15 | 45 |
| Temperature ($y$ °C) | 47 | 28 | 36 | 42 | 34 | 41 |

**a** Calculate $\overline{x}$ and $\overline{y}$.

**b** Draw a scatter diagram for the data.

**c** Plot the mean point $(\overline{x}, \overline{y})$ on the scatter diagram and draw a line of best fit through the mean point.

**d** Predict the temperature of a car which has been left in the sun for:
   **i** 35 minutes          **ii** 75 minutes.

**e** Comment on the reliability of your predictions in **d**.

**a** $\overline{x} = \dfrac{50 + 5 + 25 + 40 + 15 + 45}{6} = 30$,    $\overline{y} = \dfrac{47 + 28 + 36 + 42 + 34 + 41}{6} = 38$

**b, c**

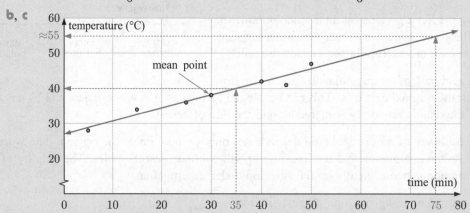

**d**  **i** When $x = 35$, $y \approx 40$. So, the temperature of a car left in the sun for 35 minutes will be approximately 40°C.

   **ii** When $x = 75$, $y \approx 55$. So, the temperature of a car left in the sun for 75 minutes will be approximately 55°C.

**e** The prediction in **d i** is reliable, as the data appears linear, and this is an interpolation.

The prediction in **d ii** may be unreliable, as it is an extrapolation, and the linear trend displayed by the data may not apply over 75 minutes.

## EXERCISE 20C

1   Fifteen students were weighed, and their pulse rates were measured:

| Weight ($x$ kg) | 61 | 52 | 47 | 72 | 62 | 79 | 57 | 45 | 67 | 71 | 80 | 58 | 51 | 43 | 55 |
|---|---|---|---|---|---|---|---|---|---|---|---|---|---|---|---|
| Pulse rate ($y$ beats per min) | 65 | 59 | 54 | 74 | 69 | 87 | 61 | 59 | 70 | 69 | 75 | 60 | 56 | 53 | 58 |

    **a**  Draw a scatter diagram for the data.    **b**  Calculate $r$ and $r^2$.

    **c**  Describe the relationship between *weight* and *pulse rate*.

    **d**  Calculate the mean point $(\overline{x},\ \overline{y})$.

    **e**  Plot the mean point on the scatter diagram, and draw a line of best fit through the mean point.

    **f**  Estimate the pulse rate of a student who weighs 65 kg. Comment on the reliability of your estimate.

2   To investigate whether speed cameras have an impact on road safety, data was collected from several cities. The number of speed cameras in operation was recorded for each city, as well as the number of accidents over a 7 day period.

| Number of speed cameras ($x$) | 7 | 15 | 20 | 3 | 16 | 17 | 28 | 17 | 24 | 25 | 20 | 5 | 16 | 25 | 15 | 19 |
|---|---|---|---|---|---|---|---|---|---|---|---|---|---|---|---|---|
| Number of car accidents ($y$) | 48 | 35 | 31 | 52 | 40 | 35 | 28 | 30 | 34 | 19 | 29 | 42 | 31 | 21 | 37 | 32 |

    **a**  Construct a scatter diagram to display the data.

    **b**  Calculate $r$ and $r^2$ for the data.

    **c**  Describe the relationship between the *number of speed cameras* and the *number of car accidents*.

    **d**  Plot the mean point $(\overline{x},\ \overline{y})$ on the scatter diagram, and draw a line of best fit through the mean point.

    **e**  Where does your line cut the $y$-axis? Interpret what this answer means.

3   The trunk widths and heights of the trees in a garden were recorded:

| Trunk width ($x$ cm) | 35 | 47 | 72 | 40 | 15 | 87 | 20 | 66 | 57 | 24 | 32 |
|---|---|---|---|---|---|---|---|---|---|---|---|
| Height ($y$ m) | 11 | 18 | 24 | 12 | 3 | 30 | 22 | 21 | 17 | 5 | 10 |

    **a**  Draw a scatter diagram of the data.

    **b**  Which of the points is an outlier?

    **c**  How would you describe the tree represented by the outlier?

    **d**  Calculate the mean point $(\overline{x},\ \overline{y})$.

    **e**  Plot the mean point on the scatter diagram, and draw a line of best fit through the mean point.

    **f**  Predict the height of a tree with trunk width 120 cm. Comment on the reliability of your prediction.

# D                    LINEAR REGRESSION

The problem with drawing a line of best fit by eye is that the line drawn will vary from one person to another.

Instead, mathematicians use a method known as **linear regression** to find the equation of the line which best fits the data. The most common method is the method of 'least squares'.

## THE LEAST SQUARES REGRESSION LINE

Consider the set of points alongside.

For any line we draw to model the points, we can find the vertical distances $d_1$, $d_2$, $d_3$, .... between each point and the line.

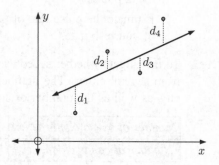

We can then square each of these distances, and find their sum $d_1^2 + d_2^2 + d_3^2 + ....$

If the line is a good fit for the data, most of the distances will be small, and so the sum of their squares will also be small.

The **least squares regression line** is the line which makes this sum as small as possible.

The demonstration alongside allows you to experiment with various data sets. Use trial and error to find the least squares line of best fit for each set.

## THE LEAST SQUARES REGRESSION FORMULA

The **least squares regression line** for a set of data $(x, y)$ is

$$y - \overline{y} = \frac{s_{xy}}{s_x{}^2}(x - \overline{x}).$$

The value $\dfrac{s_{xy}}{s_x{}^2}$ is the **gradient** of the line of best fit.

**Note:** In examinations, the value of $s_{xy}$ will be given. The value of $s_x$ should be found using technology.

---

| Example 6 | | | | | | | 🔊 Self Tutor |
|---|---|---|---|---|---|---|---|

Consider the data alongside.

a Given $s_{xy} \approx -14.3$, find the equation of the least squares line of best fit connecting $x$ and $y$.

| $x$ | 2 | 5 | 9 | 7 | 9 | 10 | 7 |
|---|---|---|---|---|---|---|---|
| $y$ | 25 | 17 | 11 | 10 | 8 | 7 | 13 |

b Estimate the value of $y$ when $x = 6$. Comment on the reliability of your estimate.

**a**  $\bar{x} = \dfrac{2 + 5 + 9 + 7 + 9 + 10 + 7}{7} = 7$

$\bar{y} = \dfrac{25 + 17 + 11 + 10 + 8 + 7 + 13}{7} = 13$

Using technology, $s_x \approx 2.56$, so $s_x{}^2 \approx 6.57$.
The least squares line of best fit has equation

$$y - \bar{y} = \frac{s_{xy}}{s_x{}^2}(x - \bar{x})$$

$$\therefore \quad y - 13 \approx \frac{-14.3}{6.57}(x - 7)$$

$$\therefore \quad y - 13 \approx -2.18x + 15.2$$

$$\therefore \quad y \approx -2.18x + 28.2$$

**b**  When $x = 6$, $y \approx -2.18(6) + 28.2$

$$\therefore \quad y \approx 15.2$$

This is an interpolation, and the data appears linear, so the estimate is likely to be reliable.

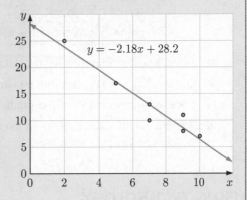

# EXERCISE 20D.1

**1**  Consider the data alongside.

| $x$ | 8 | 2 | 5 | 4 | 6 |
|---|---|---|---|---|---|
| $y$ | 4 | 14 | 6 | 9 | 7 |

   **a**  Calculate $\bar{x}$ and $\bar{y}$.

   **b**  Use technology to find $s_x$.

   **c**  Given $s_{xy} = -6.4$, find the equation of the least squares line of best fit.

   **d**  Does this line pass through the mean point $(\bar{x}, \bar{y})$?

**2**  Find the least squares regression line for a set of data $(x, y)$ if:

   **a**  $\bar{x} = 6.12$, $\bar{y} = 5.94$, $s_{xy} = -4.28$, $s_x = 2.32$

   **b**  $\bar{x} = 21.6$, $\bar{y} = 45.9$, $s_{xy} = 12.28$, $s_x = 8.77$

**3**  A craft shop sells canvasses in a variety of sizes. The table below shows the area and price of each canvas type.

| Area ($x$ cm$^2$) | 100 | 225 | 300 | 625 | 850 | 900 |
|---|---|---|---|---|---|---|
| Price ($\$y$) | 6 | 12 | 13 | 24 | 30 | 35 |

   **a**  Construct a scatter diagram for the data.

   **b**  Describe the correlation between *area* and *price*.

   **c**  Given $s_{xy} = 3200$, find the equation of the least squares regression line.

   **d**  Draw the line of best fit on your scatter diagram.

   **e**  Estimate the price of a canvas with area $1200$ cm$^2$. Is your estimate likely to be reliable?

**4** Two variables $X$ and $Y$ are such that $\overline{x} = 12.4$, $\overline{y} = 21.5$, $s_{xy} = -7.84$, $s_x = 3.91$.

    **a** Find the equation of the least squares regression line.

    **b** Estimate the value of $y$ when $x = 11$.

    **c** Comment on the likely accuracy of your estimate.

**5** A group of children were asked the number of hours they spent exercising and watching television each week.

| Exercise ($x$ hours per week) | 4 | 1 | 8 | 7 | 10 | 3 | 3 | 2 |
|---|---|---|---|---|---|---|---|---|
| Television ($y$ hours per week) | 12 | 24 | 5 | 9 | 1 | 18 | 11 | 16 |

    **a** Draw a scatter diagram for the data.

    **b** Given $s_{xy} = -19$, find the equation of the least squares line of best fit.

    **c** Give an interpretation of the gradient and the $y$-intercept of this line.

    **d** Another child exercises for 5 hours each week. Estimate how long he spends watching television each week.

## USING TECHNOLOGY

We can use technology to find the equation of the line of best fit. For help, consult the **graphics calculator instructions** at the start of the book.

---

**Example 7**　　　　　　　　　　　　　　　　　　　　　🔊 **Self Tutor**

The table below shows the annual income and average weekly grocery bill for a selection of families.

| Income ($x$ thousand pounds) | 55 | 36 | 25 | 47 | 60 | 64 | 42 | 50 |
|---|---|---|---|---|---|---|---|---|
| Grocery bill ($y$ pounds) | 120 | 90 | 60 | 160 | 190 | 250 | 110 | 150 |

    **a** Construct a scatter diagram to illustrate the data.

    **b** Use technology to find the line of best fit.

    **c** Estimate the weekly grocery bill for a family with an annual income of £95 000. Comment on whether this estimate is likely to be reliable.

    **a**

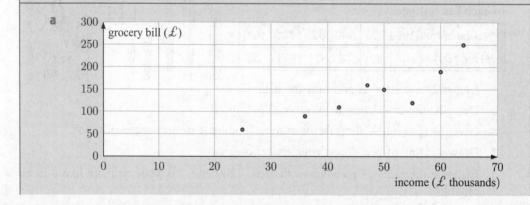

> **b**  Using technology, the line of best fit is  $y \approx 4.18x - 56.7$
>
> | Casio fx-9860G | TI-84 Plus | TI-*n*spire |
> |:---:|:---:|:---:|
> | 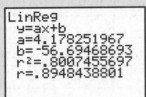 | | 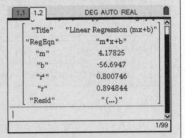 |
>
> **c**  When  $x = 95$,  $y \approx 4.18(95) - 56.7 \approx 340$
>
> So, we expect a family with an income of £95 000 to have a weekly grocery bill of approximately £340.
>
> This is an extrapolation, however, so the estimate may not be reliable.

## EXERCISE 20D.2

**1**  A newspaper reports starting salaries for recently graduated university students which depend on whether they hold a Bachelor degree or a PhD.

| Field | Bachelor degree ($x$) | PhD ($y$) |
|:---|:---:|:---:|
| Chemical engineer | 38 250 | 48 750 |
| Computer coder | 41 750 | 68 270 |
| Electrical engineer | 38 250 | 56 750 |
| Sociologist | 32 750 | 38 300 |
| Applied mathematician | 43 000 | 72 600 |
| Accountant | 38 550 | 46 000 |

  **a**  Draw a scatter diagram for the data.

  **b**  Determine $r$ and $r^2$.

  **c**  Describe the association between *starting salaries for Bachelor degrees* and *starting salaries for PhDs*.

  **d**  Find the equation of the line of best fit.

  **e**  Interpret the gradient of this line.

  **f**  The starting salary for an economist with a Bachelor degree is $40 000.

   **i**  Predict the starting salary for an economist with a PhD.

   **ii**  Comment on the reliability of your prediction.

**2**  Steve wanted to see whether there was any relationship between the temperature when he leaves for work in the morning, and the time it takes to get to work.

He collected data over a 14 day period:

| Temperature ($x$ °C) | 25 | 19 | 23 | 27 | 32 | 35 | 29 | 27 | 21 | 18 | 16 | 17 | 28 | 34 |
|:---|:--:|:--:|:--:|:--:|:--:|:--:|:--:|:--:|:--:|:--:|:--:|:--:|:--:|:--:|
| Time ($y$ min) | 35 | 42 | 49 | 31 | 37 | 33 | 31 | 47 | 42 | 36 | 45 | 33 | 48 | 39 |

  **a**  Draw a scatter diagram of the data.

  **b**  Calculate $r$ and $r^2$.

  **c**  Describe the relationship between the variables.

  **d**  Is it reasonable to try to find a line of best fit for this data?

3   The table below shows the price of petrol and the number of customers per hour for
sixteen petrol stations.

| Petrol price ($x$ cents per litre) | 105.9 | 106.9 | 109.9 | 104.5 | 104.9 | 111.9 | 110.5 | 112.9 |
|---|---|---|---|---|---|---|---|---|
| Number of customers ($y$) | 45 | 42 | 25 | 48 | 43 | 15 | 19 | 10 |

| Petrol price ($x$ cents per litre) | 107.5 | 108.0 | 104.9 | 102.9 | 110.9 | 106.9 | 105.5 | 109.5 |
|---|---|---|---|---|---|---|---|---|
| Number of customers ($y$) | 30 | 23 | 42 | 50 | 12 | 24 | 32 | 17 |

a   Calculate $r$ and $r^2$ for the data.

b   Describe the relationship between the *petrol price* and the *number of customers*.

c   Use technology to find the line of best fit.

d   Interpret the gradient of this line.

e   Estimate the number of customers per hour for a petrol station which sells petrol at
115.9 cents per litre.

f   Comment on the validity of your estimate in e.

4   The table below contains information on the *maximum speed* and *maximum altitude
obtainable* (ceiling) for nineteen World War II fighter planes. The maximum speed is
given in thousands of $km\,h^{-1}$, and the ceiling is given in km.

| max. speed | ceiling | max. speed | ceiling | max. speed | ceiling |
|---|---|---|---|---|---|
| 0.46 | 8.84 | 0.68 | 10.66 | 0.67 | 12.49 |
| 0.42 | 10.06 | 0.72 | 11.27 | 0.57 | 10.66 |
| 0.53 | 10.97 | 0.71 | 12.64 | 0.44 | 10.51 |
| 0.53 | 9.906 | 0.66 | 11.12 | 0.67 | 11.58 |
| 0.49 | 9.448 | 0.78 | 12.80 | 0.70 | 11.73 |
| 0.53 | 10.36 | 0.73 | 11.88 | 0.52 | 10.36 |
| 0.68 | 11.73 | | | | |

a   Draw a scatter diagram for this data.    b   Determine the $r$ and $r^2$ values.

c   Describe the association between *maximum speed* ($x$) and *ceiling* ($y$).

d   Use technology to find the line of best fit.

e   Estimate the ceiling for a fighter plane with a maximum speed of 600 $km\,h^{-1}$.

5   The yield of pumpkins on a farm depends on the quantity of fertiliser used.

| Fertiliser ($x$ $g\,m^{-2}$) | 4 | 13 | 20 | 26 | 30 | 35 | 50 |
|---|---|---|---|---|---|---|---|
| Yield ($y$ kg) | 1.8 | 2.9 | 3.8 | 4.2 | 4.7 | 5.7 | 4.4 |

a   Draw a scatter diagram of the data and identify the outlier.

b   Calculate the correlation coefficient:
  i   with the outlier included         ii   without the outlier.

c   Calculate the equation of the least squares regression line:
  i   with the outlier included         ii   without the outlier.

d   If you wish to estimate the yield when 15 $g\,m^{-2}$ of fertiliser is used, which regression
line from c should be used?

e   Can you explain what may have caused the outlier?

## INVESTIGATION    SPEARMAN'S RANK ORDER CORRELATION COEFFICIENT (EXTENSION)

 Suppose we wish to test the degree of agreement between two judges, for example, wine tasting judges at a vintage festival, or judges at a diving competition.

To do this we use **Spearman's rank order correlation coefficient**

$$t = 1 - \frac{6 \sum d^2}{n(n^2 - 1)}$$

where    $t$ is **Spearman's rank order correlation coefficient**
$d$ is the **difference in the ranking**
$n$ is the **number of rankings**
and $\sum d^2$ is the **sum of the squares of the differences**.

**What to do:**

1 Amy and Lee are two wine judges. They are considering six red wines: A, B, C, D, E and F. They taste each wine and rank them in order, with 1 being the best and 6 the worst. The results of their judging are shown in the table which follows:

| Wine | A | B | C | D | E | F |
|------|---|---|---|---|---|---|
| Amy's order | 3 | 1 | 6 | 2 | 4 | 5 |
| Lee's order | 6 | 5 | 2 | 1 | 3 | 4 |

Notice that
for wine A,   $d = 6 - 3 = 3$
and for wine C,   $d = 6 - 2 = 4$

  **a** Find Spearman's rank order correlation coefficient for the wine tasting data.

  **b** Graph the data with Amy's order on one axis and Lee's order on the other axis.

  **c** Comment on the degree of agreement between their rankings of the wine.

  **d** What is the significance of the sign of $t$?

2 Amy and Lee then taste six white wines. Their rankings are:

| Wine | A | B | C | D | E | F |
|------|---|---|---|---|---|---|
| Amy's order | 1 | 2 | 4 | 3 | 5 | 6 |
| Lee's order | 2 | 1 | 3 | 4 | 6 | 5 |

  **a** Find Spearman's rank order correlation coefficient for the wine tasting data.

  **b** Graph the data with Amy's order on one axis and Lee's order on the other axis.

  **c** Comment on the degree of agreement between their rankings of the wine.

  **d** What is the significance of the sign of $t$?

3 Find $t$ for:    **a** perfect agreement    **b** completely opposite order.

4 Construct some examples of your own for the following cases:

  **a** $t$ being close to $+1$    **b** $t$ being close to $-1$    **c** $t$ being close to 0

  **d** $t$ being positive    **e** $t$ being negative.

As a consequence of your investigation, comment on these five categories.

5 Arrange some competitions of your own choosing and test for rank agreement between the views of two friends. Record all data and show all calculations. You could examine preferences in food tasting, or sports watched on TV.

## E    THE $\chi^2$ TEST OF INDEPENDENCE

This table shows the results of a sample of 400 randomly selected adults classified according to *gender* and *regular exercise*.

We call this a 2 × 2 **contingency table**.

|  | Regular exercise | No regular exercise | sum |
|---|---|---|---|
| *Male* | 110 | 106 | 216 |
| *Female* | 98 | 86 | 184 |
| *sum* | 208 | 192 | 400 |

We may be interested in how the variables *gender* and *regular exercise* are related. The variables may be **dependent**, for example females may be more likely to exercise regularly than males. Alternatively, the variables may be **independent**, which means the gender of a person has no effect on whether they exercise regularly.

The **chi-squared** or $\chi^2$ **test** is used to determine whether two variables from the same sample are independent.

### CALCULATING $\chi^2$

To test whether *gender* and *regular exercise* are independent, we first consider only the sum values of the contingency table. We then calculate the values we would *expect* to obtain if the variables were independent.

|  | Regular exercise | No regular exercise | sum |
|---|---|---|---|
| *Male* | | | 216 |
| *Female* | | | 184 |
| *sum* | 208 | 192 | 400 |

For example, if *gender* and *regular exercise* were independent, then

$$\text{P}(male \cap regular\ exercise) = \text{P}(male) \times \text{P}(regular\ exercise)$$
$$= \tfrac{216}{400} \times \tfrac{208}{400}$$

So, in a sample of 400 adults, we would expect

$$400 \times \left( \tfrac{216}{400} \times \tfrac{208}{400} \right) = \tfrac{216 \times 208}{400} = 112.32 \text{ to be male and exercise regularly.}$$

We can perform similar calculations for each cell to obtain an **expected frequency table** of values we would expect to obtain if the variables were independent.

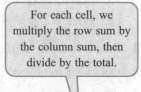

For each cell, we multiply the row sum by the column sum, then divide by the total.

| | Regular exercise | No regular exercise | sum |
|---|---|---|---|
| *Male* | $\frac{216 \times 208}{400} = 112.32$ | $\frac{216 \times 192}{400} = 103.68$ | 216 |
| *Female* | $\frac{184 \times 208}{400} = 95.68$ | $\frac{184 \times 192}{400} = 88.32$ | 184 |
| *sum* | 208 | 192 | 400 |

The $\chi^2$ test examines the difference between the **observed** values we obtained from our sample, and the **expected** values we have calculated.

$$\chi^2_{calc} = \sum \frac{(f_o - f_e)^2}{f_e} \qquad \text{where } f_o \text{ is an observed frequency} \\ \text{and } f_e \text{ is an expected frequency.}$$

If the variables are independent, the observed and expected values will be very similar. This means that the values of $(f_o - f_e)$ will be small, and so $\chi^2_{calc}$ will be small.

If the variables are not independent, the observed values will differ significantly from the expected values. The values of $(f_o - f_e)$ will be large, and hence $\chi^2_{calc}$ will be large.

For our example on *gender* and *regular exercise*, our $\chi^2$ calculation is

| $f_o$ | $f_e$ | $f_o - f_e$ | $(f_o - f_e)^2$ | $\dfrac{(f_o - f_e)^2}{f_e}$ |
|---|---|---|---|---|
| 110 | 112.32 | −2.32 | 5.3824 | 0.0479 |
| 106 | 103.68 | 2.32 | 5.3824 | 0.0519 |
| 98 | 95.68 | 2.32 | 5.3824 | 0.0563 |
| 86 | 88.32 | −2.32 | 5.3824 | 0.0609 |
| | | | *Total* | $\approx 0.2170$ |

In this case, $\chi^2_{calc} \approx 0.217$, which is very small.

This indicates that *gender* and *regular exercise* are independent.

## EXERCISE 20E.1

**1** Find $\chi^2_{calc}$ for the following contingency tables:

**a**

| | Likes football | Dislikes football | sum |
|---|---|---|---|
| *Male* | 21 | 5 | 26 |
| *Female* | 7 | 17 | 24 |
| *sum* | 28 | 22 | 50 |

**b**

| | $M_1$ | $M_2$ | sum |
|---|---|---|---|
| $N_1$ | 31 | 22 | 53 |
| $N_2$ | 20 | 27 | 47 |
| *sum* | 51 | 49 | 100 |

**c**

| | $S_1$ | $S_2$ | sum |
|---|---|---|---|
| $R_1$ | 28 | 17 | |
| $R_2$ | 52 | 41 | |
| *sum* | | | |

**d**

| | Left handed | Right handed | sum |
|---|---|---|---|
| *Employed* | 8 | 62 | |
| *Unemployed* | 4 | 26 | |
| *sum* | | | |

**e**

| | $A_1$ | $A_2$ |
|---|---|---|
| $B_1$ | 24 | 11 |
| $B_2$ | 16 | 18 |
| $B_3$ | 25 | 12 |

**f**

| | $T_1$ | $T_2$ | $T_3$ | $T_4$ |
|---|---|---|---|---|
| $D_1$ | 31 | 22 | 21 | 16 |
| $D_2$ | 23 | 19 | 22 | 13 |

**2** Use a calculator to check your answers to question **1**. Consult the **graphics calculator instructions** at the start of the book if you need assistance. Your answers may differ slightly from the calculator's answers if you have rounded the expected values.

# FORMAL TEST FOR INDEPENDENCE

We have seen that a small value of $\chi^2$ indicates that two variables are independent, while a large value of $\chi^2$ indicates that the variables are not independent.

We will now consider a more formal test which determines how large $\chi^2$ must be for us to conclude the variables are not independent.

## DEGREES OF FREEDOM

In a $\chi^2$ table the number of **degrees of freedom (df)** is the number of values which are free to vary.

Consider the $2 \times 2$ contingency table alongside, with the sum values given.

|       | $A_1$ | $A_2$ | sum |
|-------|-------|-------|-----|
| $B_1$ |       |       | 12  |
| $B_2$ |       |       | 8   |
| sum   | 15    | 5     | 20  |

The value in the top left corner is free to vary, as it can take many possible values, one of which is 9. However, once we set this value, the remaining values are *not* free to vary, as they are determined by the row and column sums.

So, the number of degrees of freedom is 1, which is $(2-1) \times (2-1)$.

|       | $A_1$ | $A_2$ | sum |
|-------|-------|-------|-----|
| $B_1$ | 9     | 3     | 12  |
| $B_2$ | 6     | 2     | 8   |
| sum   | 15    | 5     | 20  |

In a $3 \times 3$ contingency table, we can choose $(3-1) \times (3-1) = 4$ values before the remaining values are not free to vary.

|       | $C_1$ | $C_2$ | $C_3$ | sum |
|-------|-------|-------|-------|-----|
| $D_1$ |       |       |       | 12  |
| $D_2$ |       |       |       | 8   |
| $D_3$ |       |       |       | 13  |
| sum   | 13    | 9     | 11    | 33  |

|       | $C_1$ | $C_2$ | $C_3$ | sum |
|-------|-------|-------|-------|-----|
| $D_1$ | 5     | 3     | 4     | 12  |
| $D_2$ | 2     | 4     | 2     | 8   |
| $D_3$ | 6     | 2     | 5     | 13  |
| sum   | 13    | 9     | 11    | 33  |

For a contingency table which is $r \times c$ in size, $\mathbf{df} = (r-1)(c-1)$.

Our original *gender* and *regular exercise* contingency table is $2 \times 2$, so the number of degrees of freedom is $df = (2-1) \times (2-1) = 1$.

## TABLE OF CRITICAL VALUES

The $\chi^2$ distribution graph is:

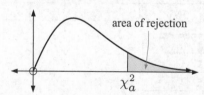

area of rejection

$\chi_a^2$

The values 0.10, 0.05, 0.01, or 10%, 5%, 1%, are called **significance levels** and these are the ones which are commonly used to test for independence.

| Degrees of freedom (df) | Area right of table value | | |
|---|---|---|---|
|   | 0.10 | 0.05 | 0.01 |
| 1 | 2.71 | 3.84 | 6.63 |
| 2 | 4.61 | 5.99 | 9.21 |
| 3 | 6.25 | 7.81 | 11.34 |
| 4 | 7.78 | 9.49 | 13.28 |
| 5 | 9.24 | 11.07 | 15.09 |
| 6 | 10.64 | 12.59 | 16.81 |
| 7 | 12.02 | 14.07 | 18.48 |
| 8 | 13.36 | 15.51 | 20.09 |
| 9 | 14.68 | 16.92 | 21.67 |
| 10 | 15.99 | 18.31 | 23.21 |

For a given significance level and degrees of freedom, the table gives the **critical value** of $\chi^2$, above which we conclude the variables are not independent.

For example, at a 5% significance level with $df = 1$, $\chi^2_{0.05} = 3.84$. This means that at a 5% significance level, the departure between the observed and expected values is too great if $\chi^2_{calc} > 3.84$.

Likewise, at a 1% significance level with $df = 7$, the departure between the observed and expected values is too great if $\chi^2_{calc} > 18.48$.

**Important:** In order for $\chi^2$ to be distributed approximately as shown in the graph, the sample size $n$ must be sufficiently large. Generally, $n$ is sufficiently large if no more than 20% of values in the expected value table are less than 5, and none of the expected values is less than 1.

## THE $p$-VALUE

When finding $\chi^2$ on your calculator, a **$p$-value** is also provided. This can be used, together with the $\chi^2$ value and the critical value, to determine whether or not to accept that the variables are independent.

For a given contingency table, the **$p$-value** is the probability of obtaining observed values as far or further from the expected values, assuming the variables are independent.

If the $p$-value is smaller than the significance level, then it is sufficiently unlikely that we would have obtained the observed results if the variables had been independent. We therefore conclude that the variables are not independent.

It is not always essential to use the $p$-value when testing for independence, as we can perform the test by simply comparing $\chi^2_{calc}$ with the critical value. However, the $p$-value does give a more meaningful measure of how likely it is that the variables are independent.

## THE FORMAL TEST FOR INDEPENDENCE

*Step 1:*   State $H_0$ called the **null hypothesis**. This is a statement that the two variables being considered are independent.
State $H_1$ called the **alternative hypothesis**. This is a statement that the two variables being considered are not independent.

*Step 2:*   Calculate $df = (r - 1)(c - 1)$.

*Step 3:*   Quote the **significance level** required, 10%, 5% or 1%.

*Step 4:*   State the **rejection inequality** $\chi^2_{calc} > k$ where $k$ is obtained from the **table of critical values**.

*Step 5:*   From the contingency table, find $\chi^2_{calc} = \sum \dfrac{(f_o - f_e)^2}{f_e}$.

*Step 6:*   We either reject $H_0$ or do not reject $H_0$, depending on the result of the rejection inequality.

*Step 7:*   We could also use a **$p$-value** to help us with our decision making.
For example, at a 5% significance level:   If $p < 0.05$, we reject $H_0$.
If $p > 0.05$, we do not reject $H_0$.

We write 'we do not reject $H_0$' rather than 'we accept $H_0$' because if we perform the test again with a tighter level of significance, we may then have reason to reject $H_0$.

Returning to our original *gender* and *regular exercise* example:

*Step 1:*   $H_0$ is that *gender* and *regular exercise* are independent.
          $H_1$ is that *gender* and *regular exercise* are not independent.

*Step 2:*   df $= (2-1)(2-1) = 1$

*Step 3:*   The significance level is 5%.

*Step 4:*   We reject $H_0$ if $\chi^2_{calc} > 3.84$.

*Step 5:*   $\chi^2_{calc} \approx 0.2170$

*Step 6:*   As $\chi^2_{calc} < 3.84$, we do not reject $H_0$.

*Step 7:*   $p \approx 0.641$ which is $> 0.05$, providing further evidence to not reject $H_0$.

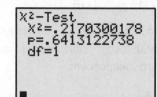

We conclude that at a 5% significance level, *gender* and *regular exercise* are independent.

---

**Example 8**                                                                      ◄)) **Self Tutor**

A survey was given to randomly chosen high school students from years 9 to 12 on possible changes to the school's canteen.

The contingency table shows the results.

|          | Year group | | | |
|----------|---|----|----|----|
|          | 9 | 10 | 11 | 12 |
| *change*    | 7 | 9 | 13 | 14 |
| *no change* | 14 | 12 | 9 | 7 |

At a 5% level, test whether the proportion of students wanting a change depends on the year group.

---

$H_0$ is that *year group* and *change* are independent.
$H_1$ is that *year group* and *change* are not independent.

df $= (2-1)(4-1) = 3$       The significance level is 5% or 0.05.

We reject $H_0$ if $\chi^2_{calc} > 7.81$.    {from the table of critical values}

The $2 \times 4$ contingency table is:

|      | Year group | | | | sum |
|------|----|----|----|----|-----|
|      | 9 | 10 | 11 | 12 |    |
| $C$  | 7 | 9 | 13 | 14 | 43 |
| $C'$ | 14 | 12 | 9 | 7 | 42 |
| *sum* | 21 | 21 | 22 | 21 | 85 |

The expected frequency table is:

|      | Year group | | | |
|------|------|------|------|------|
|      | 9 | 10 | 11 | 12 |
| $C$  | 10.6 | 10.6 | 11.1 | 10.6 |
| $C'$ | 10.4 | 10.4 | 10.9 | 10.4 |

| $f_o$ | $f_e$ | $f_o - f_e$ | $(f_o - f_e)^2$ | $\dfrac{(f_o - f_e)^2}{f_e}$ |
|---|---|---|---|---|
| 7 | 10.6 | −3.6 | 12.96 | 1.223 |
| 9 | 10.6 | −1.6 | 2.56 | 0.242 |
| 13 | 11.1 | 1.9 | 3.61 | 0.325 |
| 14 | 10.6 | 3.4 | 11.56 | 1.091 |
| 14 | 10.4 | 3.6 | 12.96 | 1.246 |
| 12 | 10.4 | 1.6 | 2.56 | 0.246 |
| 9 | 10.9 | −1.9 | 3.61 | 0.331 |
| 7 | 10.4 | −3.4 | 11.56 | 1.112 |
| | | | Total | 5.816 |

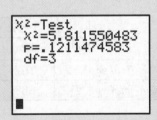

Using technology, $\chi^2_{calc} \approx 5.81$, which is $< 7.81$.

Therefore, we do not reject $H_0$.

$p \approx 0.121$ which is $> 0.05$, providing further evidence to not reject $H_0$.

We conclude that at a 5% level of significance, the variables *year group* and *change* are independent.

## EXERCISE 20E.2

**1** A random sample of people is taken to find if there is a relationship between *smoking marijuana as a teenager* and *suffering schizophrenia within the next 15 years*. The results are given in the table below:

| | Schizophrenic | Non-Schizophrenic |
|---|---|---|
| *Smoker* | 58 | 735 |
| *Non-smoker* | 269 | 6248 |

Test at a 5% level whether there is a relationship between *smoking marijuana as a teenager* and *suffering schizophrenia within the next 15 years*.

**2** Examine the following contingency tables for the independence of variables $P$ and $Q$. Use a $\chi^2$ test at:

   **i** a 5% level of significance       **ii** a 10% level of significance.

**a**

| | $Q_1$ | $Q_2$ |
|---|---|---|
| $P_1$ | 11 | 17 |
| $P_2$ | 21 | 23 |
| $P_3$ | 28 | 19 |
| $P_4$ | 17 | 28 |

**b**

| | $Q_1$ | $Q_2$ | $Q_3$ | $Q_4$ |
|---|---|---|---|---|
| $P_1$ | 6 | 11 | 14 | 18 |
| $P_2$ | 9 | 12 | 21 | 17 |
| $P_3$ | 13 | 24 | 16 | 10 |

**3** The table opposite shows the way in which a random sample of people intend to vote in the next election.

Test at a 5% level whether there is any association between the *age of a voter* and the *party they wish to vote for*.

| | Age of voter | | |
|---|---|---|---|
| | 18 to 35 | 36 to 59 | 60+ |
| Party A | 85 | 95 | 131 |
| Party B | 168 | 197 | 173 |

**4**

| | Income level | | | |
|---|---|---|---|---|
| | low | average | high | very high |
| Smoker | 82 | 167 | 74 | 31 |
| Non-smoker | 212 | 668 | 428 | 168 |

The table shows the results of a random sample of people comparing *annual income* and *cigarette smoking*.

Test at a 10% level whether income is associated with smoking.

**5** This contingency table shows the responses of a randomly chosen sample of adults regarding the person's weight and whether they have *diabetes*.

Test at a 1% level whether there is a link between *weight* and suffering *diabetes*.

| | Weight | | | |
|---|---|---|---|---|
| | light | medium | heavy | obese |
| Diabetic | 11 | 19 | 21 | 38 |
| Non-diabetic | 79 | 68 | 74 | 53 |

## COMBINING DATA

$\chi^2$ tests can be unreliable if more than 20% of the expected values are less than 5.

Consider the following contingency table:

| | $P_1$ | $P_2$ |
|---|---|---|
| $Q_1$ | 42 | 28 |
| $Q_2$ | 50 | 15 |
| $Q_3$ | 3 | 4 |

The chi-squared calculated value for this data is 6.28, with 2 degrees of freedom.

At a 5% significance level, the critical value is 5.99.

Since $6.28 > 5.99$ we would conclude that, at a 5% significance level, the two events were not independent.

Now consider the expected values for this table:

| | $P_1$ | $P_2$ |
|---|---|---|
| $Q_1$ | 46.8 | 23.2 |
| $Q_2$ | 43.5 | 21.5 |
| $Q_3$ | 4.68 | 2.32 |

There are 2 cells in the table with values $< 5$, so $33\frac{1}{3}\%$ of the expected values are $< 5$.

This means that the conclusion drawn above may not be reliable.

We can improve the reliability of the test by combining rows or columns so that there are no cells which have expected values $< 5$. In this case we combine rows $Q_2$ and $Q_3$ to produce

| | $P_1$ | $P_2$ |
|---|---|---|
| $Q_1$ | 42 | 28 |
| $Q_2$ and $Q_3$ | 53 | 19 |

which has expected values

| | $P_1$ | $P_2$ |
|---|---|---|
| $Q_1$ | 46.8 | 23.2 |
| $Q_2$ and $Q_3$ | 48.2 | 23.8 |

Having done this, $\chi^2_{calc} \approx 2.97$ with df $= 1$, and at a 5% significance level the critical value is 3.84. Since $2.97 < 3.84$, we conclude that, at a 5% significance level, the two variables are independent. Thus, the original conclusion was incorrect.

## EXERCISE 20E.3

1 Consider the contingency table alongside:

a Calculate the expected values.

b What percentage of the expected values are less than 5?

|       | $P_1$ | $P_2$ | $P_3$ | $P_4$ |
|-------|-------|-------|-------|-------|
| $Q_1$ | 4     | 7     | 15    | 19    |
| $Q_2$ | 5     | 12    | 10    | 11    |

c Combine the data so that none of the cells have an expected value less than 5.

2 The following table is a result of a major investigation considering the two factors of *intelligence level* and *cigarette smoking*.

|                     | Intelligence level | | | |
|---------------------|-----|---------|------|-----------|
|                     | *low* | *average* | *high* | *very high* |
| *Non smoker*        | 279 | 386     | 96   | 2         |
| *Medium level smoker* | 123 | 201   | 58   | 5         |
| *Heavy smoker*      | 100 | 147     | 64   | 2         |

a Test at a 1% level whether there is a link between *intelligence level* and *cigarette smoking*.

b Observe the expected values. Combine appropriate columns to reduce the number of cells with expected values $< 5$.

c Perform this test again at the 1% level. Is your conclusion the same as in part a?

## REVIEW SET 20A

1 Thomas rode for an hour each day for eleven days. He recorded the number of kilometres he rode along with the temperature that day.

| Temperature, $T$ °C | 32.9 | 33.9 | 35.2 | 37.1 | 38.9 | 30.3 | 32.5 | 31.7 | 35.7 | 36.3 | 34.7 |
|---------------------|------|------|------|------|------|------|------|------|------|------|------|
| Distance, $d$ km    | 26.5 | 26.7 | 24.4 | 19.8 | 18.5 | 32.6 | 28.7 | 29.4 | 23.8 | 21.2 | 29.7 |

a Using technology, construct a scatter diagram of the data.

b Find and interpret Pearson's correlation coefficient for the two variables.

c Calculate the equation of the least squares regression line. How hot must it get before Thomas does not ride at all?

2 The contingency table below shows the results of motor vehicle accidents in relation to whether the traveller was wearing a seat belt.

|                    | *Serious injury* | *Permanent disablement* | *Death* |
|--------------------|------------------|--------------------------|---------|
| *Wearing a belt*   | 189              | 104                      | 58      |
| *Not wearing a belt* | 83             | 67                       | 46      |

Find $\chi^2$ and test at a 5% level whether the *wearing of a seat belt* and *severity of injury* are independent factors.

**3** A clothing store recorded the length of time customers were in the store and the amount they spent.

| Time (min) | 8 | 18 | 5 | 10 | 17 | 11 | 2 | 13 | 18 | 4 | 11 | 20 | 23 | 22 | 17 |
|---|---|---|---|---|---|---|---|---|---|---|---|---|---|---|---|
| Money (€) | 40 | 78 | 0 | 46 | 72 | 86 | 0 | 59 | 33 | 0 | 0 | 122 | 90 | 137 | 93 |

  **a** Draw a scatter diagram of the data.    **b** Calculate the mean point.

  **c** Plot the mean point on your diagram and draw a line of best fit through the mean point.

  **d** Describe the relationship between *time in the store* and *money spent*.

**4** A drinks vendor varies the price of Supa-fizz on a daily basis. He records the number of sales of the drink as shown:

| Price (p) | $2.50 | $1.90 | $1.60 | $2.10 | $2.20 | $1.40 | $1.70 | $1.85 |
|---|---|---|---|---|---|---|---|---|
| Sales (s) | 389 | 450 | 448 | 386 | 381 | 458 | 597 | 431 |

  **a** Produce a scatter diagram for the data.

  **b** Are there any outliers? If so, should they be included in the analysis?

  **c** Calculate the least squares regression line.

  **d** Do you think the least squares regression line would give an accurate prediction of sales if Super-fizz was priced at 50 cents? Explain your answer.

**5** Eight identical flower beds contain petunias. The different beds were watered different numbers of times each week, and the number of flowers each bed produced was recorded in the table below:

| Number of waterings (n) | 0 | 1 | 2 | 3 | 4 | 5 | 6 | 7 |
|---|---|---|---|---|---|---|---|---|
| Flowers produced (f) | 18 | 52 | 86 | 123 | 158 | 191 | 228 | 250 |

  **a** Which is the independent variable?

  **b** Calculate the equation of the least squares regression line.

  **c** Plot the least squares regression line on a scatter diagram of the data.

  **d** Violet has two beds of petunias. One she waters five times a fortnight ($2\frac{1}{2}$ times a week), and the other ten times a week.

   **i** How many flowers can she expect from each bed?

   **ii** Which is the more reliable estimate?

**6** Examine the following contingency table for the independence of factors $P$ and $Q$.

Use a $\chi^2$ test:    **a** at a 5% level of significance

   **b** at a 1% level of significance.

|  | $Q_1$ | $Q_2$ | $Q_3$ | $Q_4$ |
|---|---|---|---|---|
| $P_1$ | 19 | 23 | 27 | 39 |
| $P_2$ | 11 | 20 | 27 | 35 |
| $P_3$ | 26 | 39 | 21 | 30 |

## REVIEW SET 20B

**1** A homebuyer makes a table of the prices of 2 bedroom flats in Greater Bristol, and their distances from the city centre.

| Distance (km) | 17 | 4 | 16 | 8 | 6 | 10 | 11 | 5 | 2 | 5 |
|---|---|---|---|---|---|---|---|---|---|---|
| Price (1000s of pounds) | 100 | 216 | 135 | 150 | 177 | 120 | 130 | 140 | 209 | 170 |

  **a** Draw a scatter diagram of the data.
  **b** Given $s_{xy} = -141.08$, find $r$ and $r^2$.
  **c** Comment on the relationship between a flat's distance from the centre of Bristol, and its price.

**2** The following table gives the average number of children for different family incomes.

| Income ($I$ thousand $) | 20 | 25 | 30 | 35 | 40 | 50 | 60 | 70 | 90 |
|---|---|---|---|---|---|---|---|---|---|
| Number of children, $n$ | 4.2 | 3.4 | 3.2 | 2.9 | 2.7 | 2.5 | 2.3 | 2.1 | 1.9 |

  **a** Construct an appropriate graph to display the data.
  **b** Find $r$ and $r^2$.
  **c** Find the equation of the line of best fit.
  **d** Alina and Vera examine the data. Alina thinks that the value for a $20\,000 income is an outlier. Vera disagrees, saying that the data is non-linear. Who do you think is right, and why?

**3** The table shows the responses to a survey about whether the city speed limit should be increased.
Test at a 5% level whether there is any association between the *age of a driver* and *increasing the speed limit*.

| | Age of driver | | |
|---|---|---|---|
| | 18 to 30 | 31 to 54 | 55+ |
| Increase | 234 | 169 | 134 |
| No increase | 156 | 191 | 233 |

**4** The following table shows the results from a major investigation considering the two factors *intelligence level* and *business success*.

| | | Intelligence level | | | |
|---|---|---|---|---|---|
| | | low | average | high | very high |
| | No success | 35 | 30 | 41 | 25 |
| Business | Low success | 28 | 41 | 26 | 29 |
| success | Success | 35 | 24 | 41 | 56 |
| | High success | 52 | 38 | 63 | 72 |

Test at a 1% level whether there is a link between *intelligence level* and *business success*.

**5** Safety authorities advise drivers to travel three seconds behind the car in front of them. This provides the driver with a greater chance of avoiding a collision if the car in front has to brake quickly or is itself involved in an accident.

A test was carried out to find out how long it would take a driver to bring a car to rest from the time a red light was flashed. The following results are for one driver in the same car under the same test conditions.

| Speed ($v$ km h$^{-1}$) | 10 | 20 | 30 | 40 | 50 | 60 | 70 | 80 | 90 |
|---|---|---|---|---|---|---|---|---|---|
| Stopping time ($t$ s) | 1.23 | 1.54 | 1.88 | 2.20 | 2.52 | 2.83 | 3.15 | 3.45 | 3.83 |

**a** Produce a scatter diagram of the data and indicate its most likely model type.

**b** Find the linear model which best fits the data.

**c** Use the model to estimate the stopping time for a speed of:

    **i** 55 km h$^{-1}$        **ii** 110 km h$^{-1}$

**d** Interpret the vertical intercept of the model.

**6** Two supervillains, Silent Predator and the Furry Reaper, terrorise Metropolis by abducting fair maidens (most of whom happen to be journalists). The superhero Superman believes that they are collaborating, alternatively abducting fair maidens so as not to compete with each other for ransom money. He plots their abduction rate below, in dozens of maidens.

| Silent Predator ($p$) | 4 | 6 | 5 | 9 | 3 | 5 | 8 | 11 | 3 | 7 | 7 | 4 |
|---|---|---|---|---|---|---|---|---|---|---|---|---|
| Furry Reaper ($r$) | 13 | 10 | 11 | 8 | 11 | 9 | 6 | 6 | 12 | 7 | 10 | 8 |

**a** Plot the data on a scatter diagram with Silent Predator on the horizontal axis.

**b** Find the least squares regression line.

**c** Calculate $r$ and $r^2$, and hence describe the strength of Silent Predator and Furry Reaper's relationship. Is there any evidence to support Superman's suspicions?

**d** Estimate the number of the Furry Reaper's abductions when the Silent Predator's were 6 dozen.

**e** Why is the model inappropriate when the Furry Reaper abducts more than 20 dozen maidens?

**f** Calculate the $p$- and $r$-intercepts of the regression line. What do these values represent?

**g** If Superman is faced with a choice of capturing one supervillain but not the other, which should he choose?

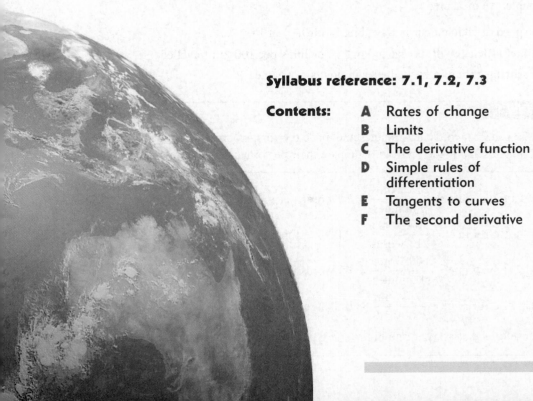

# Chapter **21**

# Differential calculus

**Syllabus reference:** 7.1, 7.2, 7.3

## OPENING PROBLEM

Valentino is riding his motorbike around a racetrack. A computer chip on his bike measures the distance Valentino has travelled as time goes on. This data is used to plot a graph of Valentino's progress.

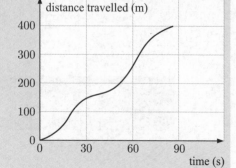

**Things to think about:**

a   What is meant by a *rate*?

b   What do we call the rate at which Valentino is travelling?

c   What is the difference between an *instantaneous* rate and an *average* rate?

d   How can we read a rate from a graph?

e   Which is the fastest part of the racetrack?

# A        RATES OF CHANGE

A **rate** is a comparison between two quantities of different kinds.

Rates are used every day to measure performance.

For example, we measure:

- the **speed** at which a car is travelling in $km\,h^{-1}$ or $m\,s^{-1}$.
- the **fuel efficiency** of the car in $km\,L^{-1}$ or litres per 100 km travelled.
- the **scoring rate** of a basketballer in points per game.

### Example 1                                             ◀) Self Tutor

Josef typed 213 words in 3 minutes and made 6 errors, whereas Marie typed 260 words in 4 minutes and made 7 errors. Compare their performance using rates.

$$\text{Josef's typing rate} = \frac{213 \text{ words}}{3 \text{ minutes}} = 71 \text{ words per minute.}$$

$$\text{Josef's error rate} = \frac{6 \text{ errors}}{213 \text{ words}} \approx 0.0282 \text{ errors per word.}$$

$$\text{Marie's typing rate} = \frac{260 \text{ words}}{4 \text{ minutes}} = 65 \text{ words per minute.}$$

$$\text{Marie's error rate} = \frac{7 \text{ errors}}{260 \text{ words}} \approx 0.0269 \text{ errors per word.}$$

∴  Josef typed at a faster rate but Marie typed with greater accuracy.

## EXERCISE 21A.1

**1** Karsten's pulse rate was measured at 67 beats per minute.

   **a** Explain exactly what this rate means.

   **b** How many heart beats would Karsten expect to have each hour?

**2** Jana typed a 14 page document and made eight errors. If an average page of typing has 380 words, find Jana's error rate in:

   **a** errors per word                  **b** errors per 100 words.

**3** Niko worked 12 hours for $148.20 whereas Marita worked 13 hours for $157.95. Who worked for the better hourly rate of pay?

**4** New tyres have a tread depth of 8 mm. After driving for 32 178 km, the tread depth on Joanne's tyres was reduced to 2.3 mm. What was the wearing rate of the tyres in:

   **a** mm per km travelled             **b** mm per 10 000 km travelled?

**5** We left Kuala Lumpur at 11.43 am and travelled to Penang, a distance of 350 km. We arrived there at 3.39 pm. What was our average speed in:   **a** $km\,h^{-1}$   **b** $m\,s^{-1}$?

## INVESTIGATION 1                                   CONSTANT AND VARIABLE RATES OF CHANGE

When water is added at a **constant rate** to a cylindrical container, the depth of water in the container is a linear function of time. This is because the volume of water added is directly proportional to the time taken to add it. If water was not added at a constant rate the direct proportionality would not exist.

The depth-time graph for a cylindrical container is shown alongside.

In this investigation we explore the changes in the graph for different shaped containers such as the conical vase.

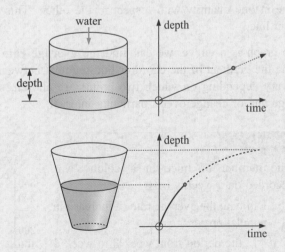

DEMO

**What to do:**

**1** What features of the graph indicate a rate of change in water level that is:

   **a** constant                **b** variable?

**2** For each of the following containers, draw a depth-time graph as water is added:

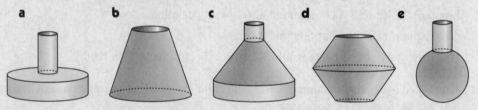

**a**      **b**      **c**      **d**      **e**

**3** Use the water filling demonstration to check your answers to question **2**.

**4** Write a brief report on the connection between the shape of a vessel and the corresponding shape of its depth-time graph. You may wish to discuss this in parts. For example, first examine cylindrical containers, then conical, then other shapes. Gradients of curves must be included in your report.

**5** Draw possible containers as in question **2** which have the following depth-time graphs:

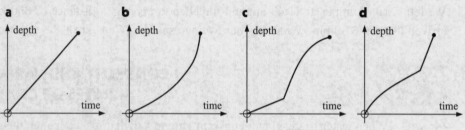

**a**      **b**      **c**      **d**

## AVERAGE RATE OF CHANGE

If the graph which compares two quantities is a **straight line**, there is a constant rate of change in one quantity with respect to the other. This constant rate is the gradient of the straight line.

If the graph is a **curve**, we can find the **average rate of change** between two points by finding the gradient of the chord or line segment between them. The average rate of change will vary depending on which two points are chosen, so it makes sense to talk about the average rate of change over a particular interval.

---

**Example 2**      ◀» **Self Tutor**

The number of mice in a colony was recorded on a weekly basis.

**a** Estimate the average rate of increase in population for:

   **i** the period from week 3 to week 6

   **ii** the seven week period.

**b** What is the overall trend with regard to population increase over this period?

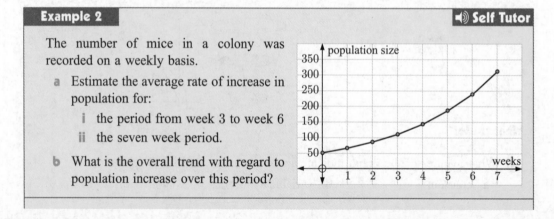

> **a**   **i**   population growth rate
>
> $= \dfrac{\text{increase in population}}{\text{increase in time}}$
>
> $= \dfrac{(240 - 110) \text{ mice}}{(6 - 3) \text{ weeks}}$
>
> $\approx 43$ mice per week
>
>   **ii**   population growth rate
>
> $= \dfrac{(315 - 50) \text{ mice}}{(7 - 0) \text{ weeks}}$
>
> $\approx 38$ mice per week

The **average rate of change** between two points on the graph is the **gradient of the chord** between them.

> **b**   The graph is increasing over the period by larger and larger amounts, so the population is increasing at an ever increasing rate.

## EXERCISE 21A.2

**1**   For the travel graph given alongside, estimate the average speed:

  **a**   in the first 4 seconds

  **b**   in the last 4 seconds

  **c**   in the 8 second interval.

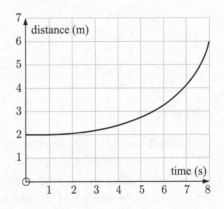

**2**   The numbers of lawn beetles per $m^2$ of lawn which are left surviving after various doses of poison are shown in the graph alongside.

  **a**   Estimate the rate of beetle decrease when:

    **i**   the dose increases from 0 to 10 g

    **ii**   the dose increases from 4 to 8 g.

  **b**   Describe the effect on the rate of beetle decline as the dose goes from 0 to 14 g.

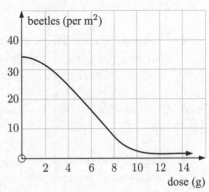

## INSTANTANEOUS RATES OF CHANGE

The speed of a moving object such as a motor car, an aeroplane, or a runner, will vary over time. The speed of the object at a particular instant in time is called its **instantaneous speed**. To examine this concept in greater detail, consider the following investigation.

## INVESTIGATION 2                                    INSTANTANEOUS SPEED

When a ball bearing is dropped from the top of a tall building, the distance it has fallen after $t$ seconds is recorded, and the following graph of distance against time obtained.

In this investigation we will try to measure the speed of the ball at the instant when $t = 2$ seconds.

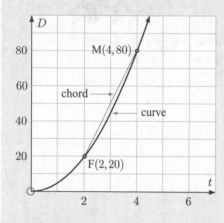

The *average* speed in the time interval $2 \leqslant t \leqslant 4$ is

$$= \frac{\text{distance travelled}}{\text{time taken}}$$

$$= \frac{(80 - 20) \text{ m}}{(4 - 2) \text{ s}}$$

$$= \frac{60}{2} \text{ m s}^{-1}$$

$$= 30 \text{ m s}^{-1}$$

DEMO

### What to do:

**1** Click on the icon to start the demonstration. F is the point where $t = 2$ seconds, and M is another point on the curve. To start with M is at $t = 4$ seconds.

The number in the box marked *gradient* is the gradient of the chord FM. This is the *average speed* of the ball bearing in the interval from F to M. For M at $t = 4$ seconds, you should see the average speed is $30 \text{ m s}^{-1}$.

**2** Click on M and drag it slowly towards F. Copy and complete the table alongside with the gradient of the chord when M is at various times $t$.

| $t$ | gradient of FM |
|------|----------------|
| 3    |                |
| 2.5  |                |
| 2.1  |                |
| 2.01 |                |

**3** Observe what happens as M reaches F. Explain why this is so.

**4** When $t = 2$ seconds, what do you suspect the instantaneous speed of the ball bearing is?

**5** Move M to the origin, and then slide it towards F from the left. Copy and complete the table alongside with the gradient of the chord when M is at various times $t$.

| $t$ | gradient of FM |
|------|----------------|
| 0    |                |
| 1.5  |                |
| 1.9  |                |
| 1.99 |                |

**6** Do your results agree with those in **4**?

From the investigation you should have discovered that:

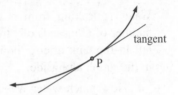

The **instantaneous rate of change** of a variable at a particular instant is given by the **gradient of the tangent** to the graph at that point.

For example, the graph alongside shows how a cyclist accelerates away from an intersection.

The average speed over the first 8 seconds is

$$\frac{100 \text{ m}}{8 \text{ sec}} = 12.5 \text{ m s}^{-1}.$$

Notice that the cyclist's early speed is quite small, but it increases as time goes by.

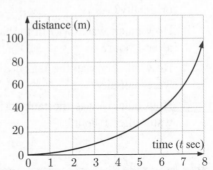

To find the instantaneous speed at any time instant, for example $t = 4$, we draw the tangent at the point and find its gradient.

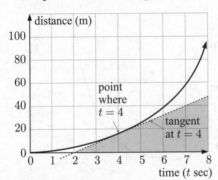

This tangent passes through $(2, 0)$ and $(7, 40)$.

$\therefore$ the instantaneous speed at $t = 4$

$= $ gradient of tangent

$= \dfrac{(40 - 0) \text{ m}}{(7 - 2) \text{ s}}$

$= \frac{40}{5} \text{ m s}^{-1}$

$= 8 \text{ m s}^{-1}$

## EXERCISE 21A.3

PRINTABLE GRAPHS

**1** For each of the following graphs, estimate the rate of change at the point shown by the arrow. Make sure your answer has the correct units.

**a**

distance (m), $t = 1$, time (s)

**b**

distance (km), $t = 3$, time (h)

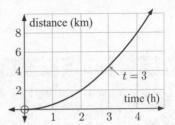

**c**

profit ($ thousands), $x = 30$, number of items sold

**d**

population of bat colony, $t = 5$, time (weeks)

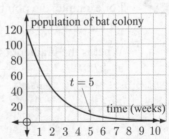

**2** Water is leaking from a tank. The number of thousands of litres of water left in the tank after $x$ hours is given in the graph alongside.

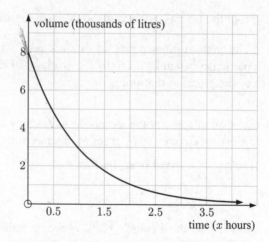

volume (thousands of litres)

time ($x$ hours)

a How much water was in the tank originally?

b How much water was in the tank after 1 hour?

c How quickly was the tank losing water initially?

d How quickly was the tank losing water after 1 hour?

## B          LIMITS

We have seen that the gradient of the **chord** AB measures the average rate of change of the function for the given change in $x$-values.

The gradient of the **tangent** at point A measures the instantaneous rate of change of the function at point A.

We say that in the **limit** as B approaches A, the gradient of the chord AB will be the gradient of the tangent at A.

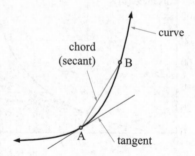

curve

chord (secant)

B

A

tangent

The **gradient of the tangent** at $x = a$ is defined as the **gradient of the curve** at the point where $x = a$, and is the instantaneous rate of change in $f(x)$ with respect to $x$ at that point.

## INVESTIGATION 3          THE GRADIENT OF A TANGENT

Given a curve $f(x)$, we wish to find the gradient of the tangent at the point $(a,\ f(a))$.

For example, the point A(1, 1) lies on the curve $f(x) = x^2$.

What is the gradient of the tangent at A?

DEMO

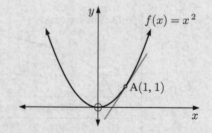

$y$

$f(x) = x^2$

A(1, 1)

$x$

**What to do:**

**1**

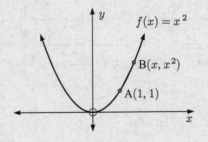

Suppose B lies on $f(x) = x^2$ and B has coordinates $(x, x^2)$.

**a** Show that the chord AB has gradient

$$\frac{f(x) - f(1)}{x - 1} \quad \text{or} \quad \frac{x^2 - 1}{x - 1}.$$

**b** Copy and complete the table alongside:

| $x$ | Point B | gradient of AB |
|-----|---------|----------------|
| 5   | (5, 25) | 6              |
| 3   |         |                |
| 2   |         |                |
| 1.5 |         |                |
| 1.1 |         |                |
| 1.01|         |                |
| 1.001|        |                |

**2** Comment on the gradient of AB as $x$ gets closer to 1.

**3** Repeat the process as $x$ gets closer to 1, but from the left of A.

**4** Click on the icon to view a demonstration of the process.

**5** What do you suspect is the gradient of the tangent at A?

Fortunately we do not have to use a graph and table of values each time we wish to find the gradient of a tangent. Instead we can use an algebraic and geometric approach which involves **limits**.

## LIMIT ARGUMENT

From the investigation, the gradient of AB $= \dfrac{x^2 - 1}{x - 1}$

$$\therefore \quad \text{the gradient of AB} = \frac{(x + 1)(x - 1)}{x - 1} = x + 1 \quad \text{provided that} \quad x \neq 1$$

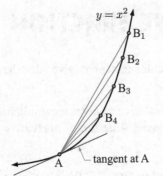

In the limit as B approaches A, $x \to 1$ and the gradient of AB $\to$ the gradient of the tangent at A.

So, the gradient of the tangent at the point A is

$$m_T = \lim_{x \to 1} \frac{x^2 - 1}{x - 1}$$
$$= \lim_{x \to 1} x + 1, \quad x \neq 1$$
$$= 2$$

As B approaches A, the gradient of AB approaches or **converges** to 2.

Limit arguments like that above form the foundation of **differential calculus**. However, formal treatment of limits is beyond the scope of this course.

**Example 3**                                          ◀ **Self Tutor**

Evaluate:    a  $\lim\limits_{x \to 2} x^2$    b  $\lim\limits_{x \to 0} \dfrac{5x + x^2}{x}$    c  $\lim\limits_{x \to 3} \dfrac{x^2 - 9}{x - 3}$

a  $x^2$ can be made as close as we like to 4 by making $x$ sufficiently close to 2.

$\therefore \quad \lim\limits_{x \to 2} x^2 = 4.$

b  $\lim\limits_{x \to 0} \dfrac{5x + x^2}{x}$

$= \lim\limits_{x \to 0} \dfrac{x(5 + x)}{x}$

$= \lim\limits_{x \to 0} 5 + x \quad \text{provided } x \neq 0$

$= 5$

c  $\lim\limits_{x \to 3} \dfrac{x^2 - 9}{x - 3}$

$= \lim\limits_{x \to 3} \dfrac{(x + 3)(x - 3)}{x - 3}_{1}$

$= \lim\limits_{x \to 3} (x + 3) \quad \text{provided } x \neq 3$

$= 3 + 3$

$= 6$

## EXERCISE 21B

1  Evaluate:

a  $\lim\limits_{x \to 3} (x + 4)$

b  $\lim\limits_{x \to -1} (5 - 2x)$

c  $\lim\limits_{x \to 4} (3x - 1)$

d  $\lim\limits_{x \to 2} 5x^2 - 3x + 2$

e  $\lim\limits_{h \to 0} h^2(1 - h)$

f  $\lim\limits_{x \to -1} \dfrac{1 - 2x}{x^2 + 1}$

g  $\lim\limits_{x \to 0} (x^2 + 5)$

h  $\lim\limits_{x \to -2} \dfrac{4}{x}$

2  Evaluate the following limits by looking for a common factor in the numerator and denominator:

a  $\lim\limits_{x \to 0} \dfrac{x^2 - 3x}{x}$

b  $\lim\limits_{h \to 0} \dfrac{2h^2 + 6h}{h}$

c  $\lim\limits_{h \to 0} \dfrac{h^3 - 8h}{h}$

## C    THE DERIVATIVE FUNCTION

We have seen how the rate of change of a function at a particular instant is given by the gradient of the tangent at that point.

We can hence describe a **gradient function** which, for any given value of $x$, gives the gradient of the tangent at that point. We call this gradient function the **derived function** or **derivative function** of the curve.

If we are given $y$ in terms of $x$, we represent the derivative function by $\dfrac{dy}{dx}$. We say this as 'dee $y$ by dee $x$'.

If we are given the function $f(x)$, we represent the derivative function by $f'(x)$. We say this as '$f$ dashed $x$'.

## INVESTIGATION 4                    THE DERIVATIVE OF $y = x^2$

The graphs below show $y = x^2$ with tangents drawn at the points where $x = -3, -2, ...., 3$.

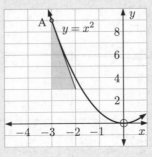
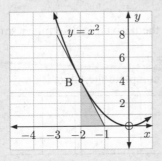
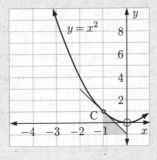

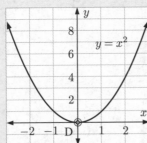
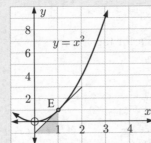
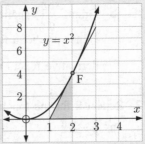

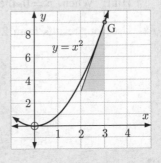

### What to do:

**1** Use the shaded triangles to find the gradients of the tangents to $y = x^2$ at the seven different points. Hence complete the following table:

| $x$-coordinate | $-3$ | | | | | | |
|---|---|---|---|---|---|---|---|
| gradient of tangent | | | | | | | |

**2** Use your table to help complete:
"the gradient of the tangent to $y = x^2$ at $(x, y)$ is $m = ....$"

**DEMO**

**3** Click on the icon to check the validity of your statement in **2**.
Click on the bar at the top to drag the point of contact of the tangent along the curve.

You should have found that the gradient of the tangent to $y = x^2$ at the point $(x, y)$ is given by $2x$.

So, $y = x^2$ has the derivative function $\dfrac{dy}{dx} = 2x$,

or alternatively, if $f(x) = x^2$ then $f'(x) = 2x$.

## INVESTIGATION 5                    THE DERIVATIVE OF $y = x^n$

In this investigation we seek derivative functions for other functions of the form $y = x^n$ where $n \in \mathbb{Z}$.

DERIVATIVE
DETERMINER

**What to do:**

**1** Click on the icon to run the derivative determiner software.

**2** Choose the function $y = x$.

   **a** Use the software to complete the table:

| $x$ | $-3$ | $-2$ | $-1$ | $0$ | $1$ | $2$ | $3$ |
|---|---|---|---|---|---|---|---|
| $\dfrac{dy}{dx}$ | | | | | | | |

   **b** Graph $\dfrac{dy}{dx}$ against $x$.

   Hence predict a formula for the derivative function $\dfrac{dy}{dx}$.

**3** Repeat **2** for the functions:

   **a** $y = x^3$       **b** $y = x^4$       **c** $y = x^{-1}$       **d** $y = x^{-2}$

**Hint:** When $x = 0$, the derivatives of both $y = x^{-1}$ and $y = x^{-2}$ are undefined.

**4** Use your results from **2** and **3** to complete:

| Function | Derivative function |
|---|---|
| $x$ | |
| $x^2$ | $2x$ |
| $x^3$ | |
| $x^4$ | |
| $x^{-1}$ | |
| $x^{-2}$ | |

**5** Predict the form of $\dfrac{dy}{dx}$ where $y = x^n$.

You should have discovered that:    If $y = x^n$ then $\dfrac{dy}{dx} = nx^{n-1}$.

## DISCUSSION

Does the rule "if $y = x^n$ then $\dfrac{dy}{dx} = nx^{n-1}$" work when $n = 0$?

# FINDING THE DERIVATIVE FUNCTION USING LIMITS

Consider a general function $y = f(x)$ where A is $(x, f(x))$ and B is $(x + h, f(x + h))$.

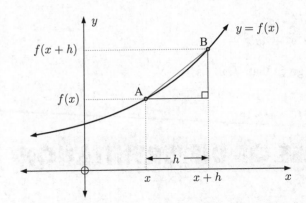

The chord AB has gradient

$$= \frac{f(x + h) - f(x)}{x + h - x}$$

$$= \frac{f(x + h) - f(x)}{h}.$$

If we now let B approach A, then the gradient of AB approaches the gradient of the tangent at A.

So, the gradient of the tangent at the variable point $(x, f(x))$ is the limiting value of

$$\frac{f(x + h) - f(x)}{h} \quad \text{as } h \text{ approaches } 0, \text{ or } \quad \lim_{h \to 0} \frac{f(x + h) - f(x)}{h}.$$

This formula gives the gradient of the tangent for any value of the variable $x$. Since there is only one value of the gradient for each value of $x$, the formula is actually a function.

The **gradient** or **derivative function** is defined as $f'(x) = \lim\limits_{h \to 0} \dfrac{f(x + h) - f(x)}{h}$.

When we evaluate this limit to find the derivative function, we call this the **method of first principles**.

| Example 4 | ◄⑴ Self Tutor |
|---|---|

Use the definition of $f'(x)$ to find the gradient function of $f(x) = x^2$.

$f'(x) = \lim\limits_{h \to 0} \dfrac{f(x + h) - f(x)}{h}$

$\quad = \lim\limits_{h \to 0} \dfrac{(x + h)^2 - x^2}{h}$

$\quad = \lim\limits_{h \to 0} \dfrac{x^2 + 2hx + h^2 - x^2}{h}$

$\quad = \lim\limits_{h \to 0} \dfrac{h(2x + h)}{h}$

$\quad = \lim\limits_{h \to 0} (2x + h) \quad \{\text{as } h \neq 0\}$

$\quad = 2x$

## EXERCISE 21C

**1** Find, from first principles, the gradient function of $f(x)$ where $f(x)$ is:

    **a** $x$                  **b** $5$                  **c** $x^3$                **d** $x^4$

    **Hint:** $(a + b)^3 = a^3 + 3a^2b + 3ab^2 + b^3$

               $(a + b)^4 = a^4 + 4a^3b + 6a^2b^2 + 4ab^3 + b^4$

**2** Find, from first principles, $f'(x)$ given that $f(x)$ is:

    **a** $2x + 5$          **b** $-x + 4$          **c** $x^2 - 3x$         **d** $2x^2 + x - 1$

# D    SIMPLE RULES OF DIFFERENTIATION

> **Differentiation** is the process of finding a derivative or gradient function.

There are a number of rules associated with differentiation. These rules can be used to differentiate more complicated functions without having to resort to the tedious method of first principles.

## INVESTIGATION 6      SIMPLE RULES OF DIFFERENTIATION

In this investigation we attempt to differentiate functions of the form $cx^n$ where $c$ is a constant, and functions which are a sum or difference of terms of the form $cx^n$.

**What to do:**

**1** Find, from first principles, the derivatives of:

    **a** $x^2$            **b** $4x^2$           **c** $x^3$            **d** $2x^3$

    Hence copy and complete:     "If $f(x) = cx^n$, then $f'(x) = ....$"

**2** Use first principles to find $f'(x)$ for:

    **a** $f(x) = x^2 + 3x$                **b** $f(x) = x^3 - 2x^2$

    Hence copy and complete:     "If $f(x) = u(x) + v(x)$ then $f'(x) = ....$"

We have now determined the following rules for differentiating:

| Function | $f(x)$ | $f'(x)$ |
|:---:|:---:|:---:|
| a constant | $a$ | $0$ |
| $x^n$ | $x^n$ | $nx^{n-1}$ |
| a constant multiple of $x^n$ | $ax^n$ | $anx^{n-1}$ |
| multiple terms | $u(x) + v(x)$ | $u'(x) + v'(x)$ |

Using the rules we have now developed we can differentiate sums of powers of $x$.

For example,   if   $f(x) = 3x^4 + 2x^3 - 5x^2 + 7x + 6$   then

$$f'(x) = 3(4x^3) + 2(3x^2) - 5(2x) + 7(1) + 0$$
$$= 12x^3 + 6x^2 - 10x + 7$$

---

**Example 5**                                             ◀)) **Self Tutor**

Find $f'(x)$ for $f(x)$ equal to:

**a** $5x^3 + 6x^2 - 3x + 2$  **b** $7x - \dfrac{4}{x} + \dfrac{3}{x^3}$  **c** $\dfrac{x^2 + 4x - 5}{x}$

**a** $\quad f(x) = 5x^3 + 6x^2 - 3x + 2$

$\therefore \quad f'(x) = 5(3x^2) + 6(2x) - 3(1)$
$\qquad\quad = 15x^2 + 12x - 3$

**b** $\quad f(x) = 7x - \dfrac{4}{x} + \dfrac{3}{x^3}$

$\qquad\quad = 7x - 4x^{-1} + 3x^{-3}$

$\therefore \quad f'(x) = 7(1) - 4(-1x^{-2}) + 3(-3x^{-4})$
$\qquad\quad = 7 + 4x^{-2} - 9x^{-4}$
$\qquad\quad = 7 + \dfrac{4}{x^2} - \dfrac{9}{x^4}$

Remember that $\dfrac{1}{x^n} = x^{-n}$.

**c** $\quad f(x) = \dfrac{x^2 + 4x - 5}{x}$

$\qquad\quad = \dfrac{x^2}{x} + 4 - \dfrac{5}{x}$

$\qquad\quad = x + 4 - 5x^{-1}$

$\therefore \quad f'(x) = 1 + 5x^{-2}$

---

**Example 6**                                             ◀)) **Self Tutor**

Find the gradient function of $f(x) = x^2 - \dfrac{4}{x}$.

Hence find the gradient of the tangent to the function at the point where $x = 2$.

$\qquad f(x) = x^2 - \dfrac{4}{x}$

$\qquad\quad = x^2 - 4x^{-1}$

$\therefore \quad f'(x) = 2x - 4(-1x^{-2})$

$\qquad\quad = 2x + 4x^{-2}$                Now $f'(2) = 4 + 1 = 5$.

$\qquad\quad = 2x + \dfrac{4}{x^2}$          So, the tangent has gradient $= 5$.

## EXERCISE 21D

**1** Find $f'(x)$ given that $f(x)$ is:

   **a** $x^3$                   **b** $2x^3$                 **c** $7x^2$

   **d** $x^2 + x$            **e** $4 - 2x^2$           **f** $x^2 + 3x - 5$

   **g** $x^3 + 3x^2 + 4x - 1$     **h** $5x^4 - 6x^2$      **i** $3 - 6x^{-1}$

   **j** $\dfrac{2x - 3}{x^2}$          **k** $\dfrac{x^3 + 5}{x}$        **l** $\dfrac{x^3 + x - 3}{x}$

**2** Suppose $f(x) = 4x^3 - x$. Find:

   **a** $f'(x)$               **b** $f'(2)$              **c** $f'(0)$

**3** Suppose $g(x) = \dfrac{x^2 + 1}{x}$. Find:

   **a** $g'(x)$             **b** $g'(3)$             **c** $g'(-2)$

**4** Find the gradient of the tangent to:

   **a** $y = x^2$ at $x = 2$            **b** $y = \dfrac{8}{x^2}$ at $x = 9$

   **c** $y = 2x^2 - 3x + 7$ at $x = -1$     **d** $y = 2x - 5x^{-1}$ at $x = 2$

   **e** $y = \dfrac{x^2 - 4}{x^2}$ at $x = 4$        **f** $y = \dfrac{x^3 - 4x - 8}{x^2}$ at $x = -1$

**5** Find $\dfrac{dy}{dx}$ for $y = (3x + 1)^2$.

   **Hint:** Start by expanding the brackets.

---

**Example 7**                             ◀)) **Self Tutor**

If $y = 3x^2 - 4x$, find $\dfrac{dy}{dx}$ and interpret its meaning.

As $y = 3x^2 - 4x$, $\dfrac{dy}{dx} = 6x - 4$.

$\dfrac{dy}{dx}$ is: • the gradient function or derivative function of $y = 3x^2 - 4x$, from which the gradient at any point can be found

             • the instantaneous rate of change in $y$ as $x$ changes.

---

**6**  **a** If $y = 4x - \dfrac{3}{x}$, find $\dfrac{dy}{dx}$ and interpret its meaning.

   **b** The position of a car moving along a straight road is given by $S = 2t^2 + 4t$ metres where $t$ is the time in seconds. Find $\dfrac{dS}{dt}$ and interpret its meaning.

   **c** The cost of producing and selling $x$ toasters each week is given by

      $C = 1785 + 3x + 0.002x^2$ dollars. Find $\dfrac{dC}{dx}$ and interpret its meaning.

# E     TANGENTS TO CURVES

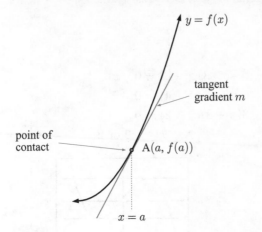

Consider a curve $y = f(x)$.

If A is the point with $x$-coordinate $a$, then the gradient of the tangent at this point is $f'(a) = m$.

The equation of the tangent is

$$\frac{y - f(a)}{x - a} = f'(a) \quad \text{\{equating gradients\}}$$

$$or \quad y - f(a) = f'(a)(x - a).$$

Alternatively, the equation of the tangent at the point A$(a, b)$ is

$$\frac{y - b}{x - a} = f'(a) \qquad or \qquad y - b = f'(a)(x - a).$$

The equation can also be written in the form $y = mx + c$.

For example:   If $f(x) = x^2$ then $f'(x) = 2x$.

At $x = 3$, $m = f'(3) = 6$, so the tangent has gradient 6.

Since $f(3) = 9$, the tangent has equation $y - 9 = 6(x - 3)$

$$or \quad y = 6x - 9.$$

You can also find the equations of tangents at a given point using your graphics calculator. For assistance with this, consult the **graphics calculator instructions** at the start of the book.

---

**Example 8**            ◀》 **Self Tutor**

Find the equation of the tangent to $f(x) = x^2 + 1$ at the point where $x = 1$.

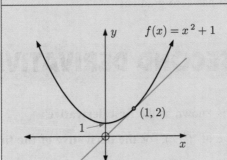

Since $f(1) = 1 + 1 = 2$, the point of contact is $(1, 2)$.

Now $f'(x) = 2x$, so $m = f'(1) = 2$

$\therefore$   the tangent has equation

$$\frac{y - 2}{x - 1} = 2$$

which is   $y - 2 = 2x - 2$

$$or \quad y = 2x.$$

**Example 9**                                                    ◀》 **Self Tutor**

Find the equations of any horizontal tangents to $y = x^3 - 12x + 2$.

Since $y = x^3 - 12x + 2$, $\dfrac{dy}{dx} = 3x^2 - 12$

Horizontal tangents have gradient 0,        so   $3x^2 - 12 = 0$

$$\therefore \quad 3(x^2 - 4) = 0$$
$$\therefore \quad 3(x + 2)(x - 2) = 0$$
$$\therefore \quad x = -2 \text{ or } 2$$

When $x = 2$, $y = 8 - 24 + 2 = -14$

When $x = -2$, $y = -8 + 24 + 2 = 18$

$\therefore$ the points of contact are

$(2, -14)$ and $(-2, 18)$

$\therefore$ the tangents are $y = -14$ and $y = 18$.

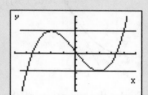

## EXERCISE 21E

**1** Find the equation of the tangent to:

**a** $y = x^2$ at $x = 4$

**b** $y = x^3$ at $x = -2$

**c** $y = 3x^{-1}$ at $x = -1$

**d** $y = \dfrac{4}{x^3}$ at $x = 2$

**e** $y = x^2 + 5x - 4$ at $x = 1$

**f** $y = 2x^2 + 5x + 3$ at $x = -2$

**g** $y = x^3 + 2x$ at $x = 0$

**h** $y = x^2 + x^{-1}$ at $x = 0$

**i** $y = x + 2x^{-1}$ at $x = 2$

**j** $y = \dfrac{x^2 + 4}{x}$ at $x = -1$

**2** Find the coordinates of the point(s) on:

**a** $f(x) = x^2 + 3x + 5$ where the tangent is horizontal

**b** $f(x) = x^3 + x^2 - 1$ where the tangent has gradient 1

**c** $f(x) = x^3 - 3x + 1$ where the tangent has gradient 9

**d** $f(x) = ax^2 + bx + c$ where the tangent has zero gradient.

# F        THE SECOND DERIVATIVE

Given a function $f(x)$, the derivative $f'(x)$ is known as the **first derivative**.

The **second derivative** of $f(x)$ is the derivative of $f'(x)$, or **the derivative of the first derivative**.

We use $f''(x)$ or $y''$ or $\dfrac{d^2y}{dx^2}$ to represent the second derivative.

$f''(x)$ is read as "$f$ *double dashed of $x$*".

$\dfrac{d^2y}{dx^2} = \dfrac{d}{dx}\left(\dfrac{dy}{dx}\right)$ is read as "*dee two $y$ by dee $x$ squared*".

## THE SECOND DERIVATIVE IN CONTEXT

Michael rides up a hill and down the other side to his friend's house. The dots on the graph show Michael's position at various times $t$.

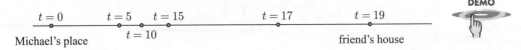

The distance Michael has travelled at various times is given in the following table:

| Time (t min) | 0 | 2.5 | 5 | 7.5 | 10 | 12.5 | 15 | 17 | 19 |
|---|---|---|---|---|---|---|---|---|---|
| Distance travelled (s m) | 0 | 498 | 782 | 908 | 989 | 1096 | 1350 | 1792 | 2500 |

The model $s \approx 1.18t^3 - 30.47t^2 + 284.52t - 16.08$ metres fits this data well, although the model gives $s(0) \approx -16.08$ m whereas the actual data gives $s(0) = 0$. This sort of problem often occurs when modelling from data.

A graph of the data points and the model is given below:

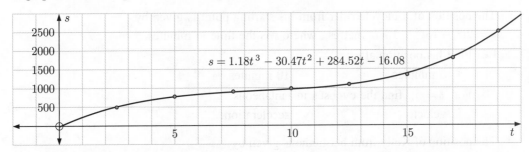

$$s = 1.18t^3 - 30.47t^2 + 284.52t - 16.08$$

Now $\dfrac{ds}{dt} \approx 3.54t^2 - 60.94t + 284.52$ metres per minute is the instantaneous rate of change in displacement per unit of time, or instantaneous velocity.

The instantaneous rate of change in velocity at any point in time is Michael's **acceleration**,

so $\dfrac{d}{dt}\left(\dfrac{ds}{dt}\right) = \dfrac{d^2s}{dt^2}$ is the instantaneous acceleration.

In this case $\dfrac{d^2s}{dt^2} \approx 7.08t - 60.94$ metres per minute per minute.

We see that when $t = 12$, $s \approx 1050$ m,

$$\dfrac{ds}{dt} \approx 63 \text{ metres per minute,}$$

and $\dfrac{d^2s}{dt^2} \approx 24$ metres per minute per minute.

**Example 10**                                          ◀» **Self Tutor**

Find $f''(x)$ given that $f(x) = x^3 - \dfrac{3}{x}$.

Now   $f(x) = x^3 - 3x^{-1}$

$\therefore \quad f'(x) = 3x^2 + 3x^{-2}$

$\therefore \quad f''(x) = 6x - 6x^{-3}$

$\qquad\qquad = 6x - \dfrac{6}{x^3}$

## EXERCISE 21F

**1** Find $f''(x)$ given that:

     **a** $f(x) = 3x^2 - 6x + 2$           **b** $f(x) = 2x^3 - 3x^2 - x + 5$

     **c** $f(x) = \dfrac{2 - 3x}{x^2}$           **d** $f(x) = \dfrac{2x - x^3}{x^2}$

**2** Find $\dfrac{d^2y}{dx^2}$ given that:

     **a** $y = x - x^3$        **b** $y = x^2 - \dfrac{5}{x^2}$        **c** $y = \dfrac{4 - x}{x}$

**3** The position of a bicycle rider from his starting point is given by
$s = 2t^3 - 15t^2 + 100t$ metres, where $t$ is the time in minutes.

     **a** Find his position after:

         **i** 5 minutes          **ii** 10 minutes.

     **b** For $t = 5$, find the cyclist's instantaneous:

         **i** velocity          **ii** acceleration.

**4** The position of Kelly from her home is given by
$s = 10t^3 - 100t^2 + 200t$ metres, where $t$ is the
time in minutes, $0 \leqslant t \leqslant 7.24$.

     **a** When is Kelly at home?

     **b** When is Kelly furthermost from her home?
How far is she from home at this time?

     **c** For $t = 4$, find Kelly's:

         **i** position

         **ii** instantaneous velocity

         **iii** instantaneous acceleration.

     Explain what these results mean.

## REVIEW SET 21A

**1** The total number of televisions sold over many months is shown on the graph alongside.

Estimate the rate of sales:

   **a** from 40 to 50 months

   **b** from 0 to 50 months

   **c** at 20 months.

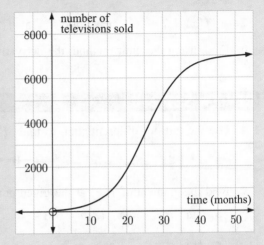

**2** Use the rules of differentiation to find $f'(x)$ for $f(x)$ equal to:

   **a** $7x^3$        **b** $3x^2 - x^3$        **c** $(2x - 3)^2$        **d** $\dfrac{7x^3 + 2x^4}{x^2}$

**3** Consider $f(x) = x^4 - 3x - 1$. Find:    **a** $f'(x)$    **b** $f'(2)$    **c** $f'(0)$.

**4** Find the equation of the tangent to $y = -2x^2$ at the point where $x = -1$.

**5** Find $f''(x)$ for:    **a** $f(x) = 3x^2 - \dfrac{1}{x}$     **b** $f(x) = (x + 4)^2$

**6** Find the derivative of $f(x) = 3x - 1$ from first principles.

## REVIEW SET 21B

**1** Consider the function $f(x) = x^2 + 2x$, with graph shown alongside.

   **a** Find the gradient of the line through $(1, 3)$ and the point on $f(x)$ with $x$-coordinate:

      **i** 2       **ii** 1.5       **iii** 1.1

   **b** Find $f'(x)$.

   **c** Find the gradient of the tangent to $f(x)$ at $(1, 3)$. Compare this with your answers to **a**.

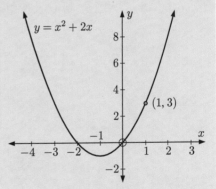

**2** Find $\dfrac{dy}{dx}$ for:

   **a** $y = 3x^2 - x^4$        **b** $y = \dfrac{x^3 - x}{x^2}$        **c** $y = 2x + x^{-1} - 3x^{-2}$

**3** Find the equation of the tangent to $y = x^3 - 3x + 5$ at the point where $x = 2$.

**4** Find all points on the curve $y = 2x + x^{-1}$ which have a tangent parallel to the $x$-axis.

**5** If $f(x) = 7 + x - 3x^2$, find:    **a** $f(3)$    **b** $f'(3)$    **c** $f''(3)$.

**6** Find, using the limit method, the derivative function of $f(x) = x^3 - 2x$.

## REVIEW SET 21C

**1** Use the rules of differentiation to find $f'(x)$ for $f(x)$ equal to:

    **a** $x^4 + 2x^3 + 3x^2 - 5$    **b** $2x^{-3} + x^{-4}$    **c** $\dfrac{1}{x} - \dfrac{4}{x^2}$

**2** Find the gradient of $f(x)$ at the given point for the following functions:

    **a** $f(x) = x^2 - 3x$, at $x = -1$    **b** $f(x) = -3x^2 + 4$, at $x = 2$

    **c** $f(x) = x + \dfrac{2}{x}$, at $x = 3$    **d** $f(x) = x^3 - x^2 - x - 2$, at $x = 0$

**3** Find the equation of the tangent to $y = \dfrac{12}{x^2}$ at the point $(1,\ 12)$.

**4** Sand is poured into a bucket for 30 seconds. After $t$ seconds, the weight of sand is $S(t) = 0.3t^3 - 18t^2 + 550t$ grams.
Find and interpret $S'(t)$.

**5** Find $\dfrac{d^2y}{dx^2}$ for:    **a** $y = 7x^3 - 4x$    **b** $y = 2x^2 + \dfrac{5}{x}$

**6** Evaluate:

    **a** $\displaystyle\lim_{x \to 1} x^2 + 3$    **b** $\displaystyle\lim_{x \to -4} \dfrac{3-x}{x}$    **c** $\displaystyle\lim_{h \to 0} \dfrac{h^2 - 3h}{h}$

**7** Find, from first principles, the derivative of $f(x) = x^2 + 2x$.

# Chapter 22

# Applications of differential calculus

Syllabus reference: 7.4, 7.5

Contents:   A   Properties of curves
            B   Rates of change
            C   Optimisation

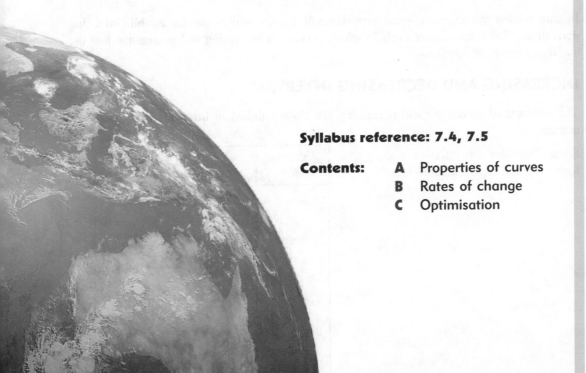

## OPENING PROBLEM

A skatepark designer proposes to build a bowl with cross-section given by
$h(x) = 0.014x^4 - 0.196x^3 + 1.039x^2 - 2.471x + 2.225$ metres, $0 \leqslant x \leqslant 7$.

**Things to think about:**

**a** How high is the wall of the bowl?

**b** Is the lowest point exactly in the middle of the bowl?

**c** How steep are the sides? What units could we use to measure this?

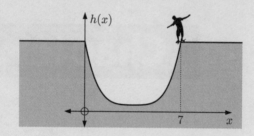

We saw in the previous chapter how differential calculus can be used to help find the equation of a tangent to a curve. There are many other uses, however, including the following which we now consider:

- properties of curves (decreasing and increasing, stationary points)
- rates of change
- optimisation (maxima and minima)

# A          PROPERTIES OF CURVES

In this section we consider some properties of curves which can be established using derivatives. These include intervals in which curves are increasing and decreasing, and the stationary points of functions.

## INCREASING AND DECREASING INTERVALS

The concepts of increasing and decreasing are closely linked to **intervals** of a function's domain.

Some examples of intervals and their graphical representations are:

| Algebraic form | Geometric form |
|---|---|
| $x \geqslant 2$ | ●——→ $x$  (2) |
| $x > 2$ | ○——→ $x$  (2) |
| $x \leqslant 4$ | ←——● $x$  (4) |
| $x < 4$ | ←——○ $x$  (4) |
| $2 \leqslant x \leqslant 4$ | ●——● $x$  (2, 4) |
| $2 \leqslant x < 4$ | ●——○ $x$  (2, 4) |

On an interval which is **increasing**, an increase in $x$ produces an **increase** in $y$.

On an interval which is **decreasing**, an increase in $x$ produces a **decrease** in $y$.

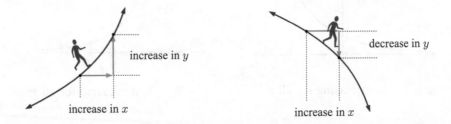

Suppose $S$ is an interval in the domain of $f(x)$, so $f(x)$ is defined for all $x$ in $S$.

- $f(x)$ is **increasing** on $S$ if $f(a) < f(b)$ for all $a, b \in S$ such that $a < b$.
- $f(x)$ is **decreasing** on $S$ if $f(a) > f(b)$ for all $a, b \in S$ such that $a < b$.

For example:

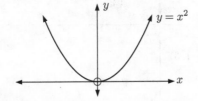

$y = x^2$ is decreasing for $x \leqslant 0$ and increasing for $x \geqslant 0$.

**Important:**

People often get confused about the point $x = 0$. They wonder how the curve can be both increasing and decreasing at the same time when it is clear that the tangent is horizontal. The answer is that increasing and decreasing are associated with *intervals*, not particular values for $x$. We must clearly state that $y = x^2$ is decreasing *on the interval* $x \leqslant 0$ and increasing *on the interval* $x \geqslant 0$.

We can deduce when a curve is increasing or decreasing by considering $f'(x)$ on the interval in question.

For the functions that we deal with in this course:

- $f(x)$ is **increasing** on $S$ if $f'(x) \geqslant 0$ for all $x$ in $S$.
- $f(x)$ is **strictly increasing** if $f'(x) > 0$ for all $x$ in $S$.
- $f(x)$ is **decreasing** on $S$ if $f'(x) \leqslant 0$ for all $x$ in $S$.
- $f(x)$ is **strictly decreasing** if $f'(x) < 0$ for all $x$ in $S$.

## INCREASING AND DECREASING FUNCTIONS

Many functions are either increasing or decreasing for all $x \in \mathbb{R}$. We say these are either **increasing functions** or **decreasing functions**.

For example:

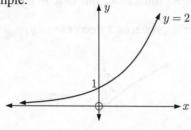 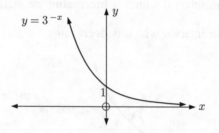

$y = 2^x$ is increasing for all $x$.      $y = 3^{-x}$ is decreasing for all $x$.

---

**Example 1**                                              ◀⟩ **Self Tutor**

Find intervals where $f(x)$ is:
a  increasing
b  decreasing.

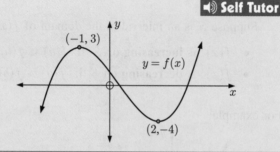

a  $f(x)$ is increasing for $x \leqslant -1$
   and for $x \geqslant 2$ since $f'(x) \geqslant 0$
   on these intervals.
b  $f(x)$ is decreasing for
   $-1 \leqslant x \leqslant 2$.

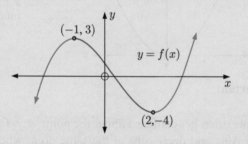

---

**Sign diagrams** for the derivative are extremely useful for determining intervals where a function is increasing or decreasing.

The critical values for $f'(x)$ are the values of $x$ for which $f'(x) = 0$ or $f'(x)$ is undefined. When $f'(x) = 0$, the critical values are shown on a number line using tick marks. When $f'(x)$ is undefined, the critical values are shown with a vertical dotted line.

We complete the sign diagram by marking positive or negative signs, depending on whether $f'(x)$ is positive or negative, in the intervals between the critical values.

Consider the following examples:

- $f(x) = x^2$                    $f'(x) = 2x$                which has sign diagram

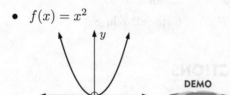

DEMO

$\therefore$  $f(x) = x^2$  is  decreasing for $x \leqslant 0$
                         and  increasing for $x \geqslant 0$.

- $f(x) = -x^2$

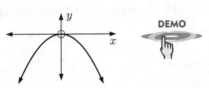

$f'(x) = -2x$      which has sign diagram

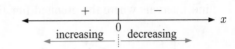

$\therefore \quad f(x) = -x^2$  is  increasing for  $x \leqslant 0$

and  decreasing for  $x \geqslant 0$.

- $f(x) = x^3$

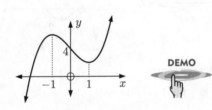

$f'(x) = 3x^2$      which has sign diagram

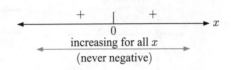

$\therefore \quad f(x)$  is increasing for all  $x$.

- $f(x) = x^3 - 3x + 4$

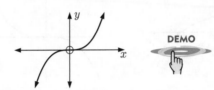

$f'(x) = 3x^2 - 3$
$\qquad = 3(x^2 - 1)$
$\qquad = 3(x + 1)(x - 1)$

which has sign diagram

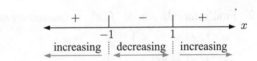

$\therefore \quad f(x)$  is increasing for  $x \leqslant -1$  and for  $x \geqslant 1$,  and decreasing for  $-1 \leqslant x \leqslant 1$.

---

### Example 2 | ◄» Self Tutor

Find the intervals where  $f(x) = -x^3 + 3x^2 + 5$  is increasing or decreasing.

$$f(x) = -x^3 + 3x^2 + 5$$
$$\therefore \quad f'(x) = -3x^2 + 6x$$
$$\therefore \quad f'(x) = -3x(x - 2)$$
$$f'(x) = 0 \quad \text{when} \quad x = 0 \text{ or } 2$$

So $f'(x)$ has sign diagram

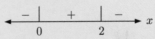

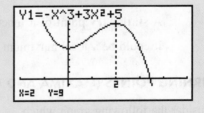

So, $f(x)$ is decreasing for  $x \leqslant 0$  and for  $x \geqslant 2$,  and increasing for  $0 \leqslant x \leqslant 2$.

---

Remember that $f(x)$ must be defined for all $x$ on an interval before we can classify the interval as increasing or decreasing. We must exclude points where a function is undefined, and need to take care with vertical asymptotes.

## EXERCISE 22A.1

**1** Find intervals where the graphed function is:    **i** increasing    **ii** decreasing:

**a**

**b**

**c**

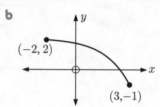
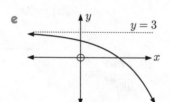

**d**

**e**

**f**

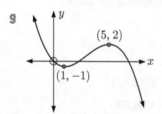
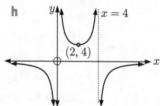
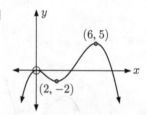

**g**

**h**

**i**

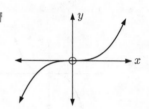

**2** Find intervals where $f(x)$ is increasing or decreasing:

**a** $f(x) = 2x + 1$

**b** $f(x) = -3x + 2$

**c** $f(x) = x^2$

**d** $f(x) = -x^3$

**e** $f(x) = 2x^2 + 3x - 4$

**f** $f(x) = x^3 - 6x^2$

**g** $f(x) = -2x^3 + 4x$

**h** $f(x) = -4x^3 + 15x^2 + 18x + 3$

**i** $f(x) = 2x^3 + 9x^2 + 6x - 7$

**j** $f(x) = x^3 - 6x^2 + 3x - 1$

## STATIONARY POINTS

A **stationary point** of a function is a point such that $f'(x) = 0$.

It could be a local maximum, local minimum, or horizontal inflection.

### TURNING POINTS (MAXIMA AND MINIMA)

Consider the following graph which has a restricted domain of $-5 \leqslant x \leqslant 6$.

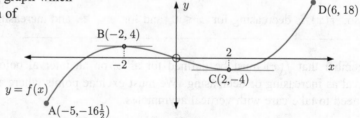

A is a **global minimum** as it is the minimum value of $y$ on the entire domain.

B is a **local maximum** as it is a turning point where the curve has shape ⌢ and $f'(x) = 0$ at that point.

C is a **local minimum** as it is a turning point where the curve has shape ⌣ and $f'(x) = 0$ at that point.

D is a **global maximum** as it is the maximum value of $y$ on the entire domain.

For many functions, a local maximum or minimum is also the global maximum or minimum.

For example, for $y = x^2$ the point $(0, 0)$ is a local minimum and is also the global minimum.

## HORIZONTAL OR STATIONARY POINTS OF INFLECTION

It is not always true that whenever we find a value of $x$ where $f'(x) = 0$ we have a local maximum or minimum.

For example, $f(x) = x^3$ has $f'(x) = 3x^2$
and $f'(x) = 0$ when $x = 0$.

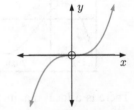

The $x$-axis is a tangent to the curve which actually crosses over the curve at O$(0, 0)$. This tangent is horizontal but O$(0, 0)$ is neither a local maximum nor a local minimum.

It is called a **horizontal inflection** (or **inflexion**) as the curve changes its curvature or shape.

## SIGN DIAGRAMS

Consider the graph alongside.

The sign diagram of its gradient function is shown directly beneath it.

We can use the sign diagram to describe the stationary points of the function.

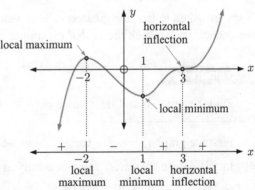

| Stationary point | Sign diagram of $f'(x)$ near $x = a$ | Shape of curve near $x = a$ |
|---|---|---|
| local maximum | $\xleftarrow{\quad + \;\mid\; - \quad} x$ <br> $a$ | ⌢ $x = a$ |
| local minimum | $\xleftarrow{\quad - \;\mid\; + \quad} x$ <br> $a$ | ⌣ $x = a$ |
| horizontal inflection or stationary inflection | $\xleftarrow{+ \mid +} x$ <br> $a$ or $\xleftarrow{- \mid -} x$ <br> $a$ | $x = a$ or $x = a$ |

**Example 3**    ◀ঙ Self Tutor

Find and classify all stationary points of   $f(x) = x^3 - 3x^2 - 9x + 5$.

$$f(x) = x^3 - 3x^2 - 9x + 5$$
$$\therefore \quad f'(x) = 3x^2 - 6x - 9$$
$$= 3(x^2 - 2x - 3)$$
$$= 3(x - 3)(x + 1) \quad \text{which has sign diagram:}$$

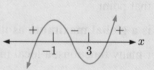

So, we have a local maximum at $x = -1$ and a local minimum at $x = 3$.

$$f(-1) = (-1)^3 - 3(-1)^2 - 9(-1) + 5 \qquad f(3) = 3^3 - 3 \times 3^2 - 9 \times 3 + 5$$
$$= 10 \qquad\qquad\qquad\qquad\qquad\qquad = -22$$

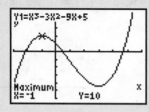

There is a local maximum at $(-1, 10)$.    There is a local minimum at $(3, -22)$.

If we are asked to find the greatest or least value on an interval, then we should always check the endpoints. We seek the *global* maximum or minimum on the given domain.

**Example 4**    ◀ঙ Self Tutor

Find the greatest and least value of   $x^3 - 6x^2 + 5$   on the interval   $-2 \leqslant x \leqslant 5$.

First we graph   $y = x^3 - 6x^2 + 5$   on   $-2 \leqslant x \leqslant 5$.

In this case the greatest value is clearly at the

local maximum when   $\dfrac{dy}{dx} = 0$.

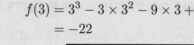

Now   $\dfrac{dy}{dx} = 3x^2 - 12x$

$\qquad\qquad = 3x(x - 4)$

and   $\dfrac{dy}{dx} = 0$   when   $x = 0$ or 4.

So, the greatest value is   $f(0) = 5$   when   $x = 0$.

The least value is either   $f(-2)$   or   $f(4)$,   whichever is smaller.

Now   $f(-2) = -27$   and   $f(4) = -27$

$\therefore$   least value is $-27$ when $x = -2$ *and* when $x = 4$.

## EXERCISE 22A.2

**1** The tangents at points A, B and C are horizontal.

a Classify points A, B and C.

b Draw a sign diagram for the gradient function $f'(x)$ for all $x$.

c State intervals where $y = f(x)$ is:

　i increasing　ii decreasing.

d Draw a sign diagram for $f(x)$ for all $x$.

e Comment on the differences between the sign diagrams found above.

**2** Consider the quadratic function $f(x) = 2x^2 - 5x + 1$.

a Use quadratic theory to find the equation of the axis of symmetry.

b Find $f'(x)$ and hence find $x$ such that $f'(x) = 0$. Explain your result.

**3** For each of the following functions, find and classify the stationary points, and hence sketch the function showing all important features.

a $f(x) = x^2 - 2$　　　b $f(x) = x^3 + 1$　　　　　　　c $f(x) = x^3 - 3x + 2$

d $f(x) = x^4 - 2x^2$　　e $f(x) = x^3 - 6x^2 + 12x + 1$　　f $f(x) = 4x - x^3$

**4** At what value of $x$ does the quadratic function $f(x) = ax^2 + bx + c$, $a \neq 0$, have a stationary point? Under what conditions is the stationary point a local maximum or a local minimum?

**5** $f(x) = 2x^3 + ax^2 - 24x + 1$ has a local maximum at $x = -4$. Find $a$.

**6** $f(x) = x^3 + ax + b$ has a stationary point at $(-2, 3)$. Find:

a $a$ and $b$　　　　b the position and nature of all stationary points.

**7** Find the greatest and least value of:

a $x^3 - 12x - 2$ for $-3 \leqslant x \leqslant 5$　　　b $4 - 3x^2 + x^3$ for $-2 \leqslant x \leqslant 3$

**8** A manufacturing company makes door hinges. They have a standing order filled by producing 50 each hour, but production of more than 150 per hour is useless as they will not sell. The cost function for making $x$ hinges per hour is:

$C(x) = 0.0007x^3 - 0.1796x^2 + 14.663x + 160$ dollars where $50 \leqslant x \leqslant 150$.

Find the minimum and maximum hourly costs, and the production levels when each occurs.

## B　　　　　　　　　　　　　　　　　RATES OF CHANGE

When we first introduced derivative functions, we discussed how

> $\dfrac{dy}{dx}$ gives the **rate of change in $y$ with respect to $x$**.
>
> If $y$ increases as $x$ increases, then $\dfrac{dy}{dx}$ will be positive.
>
> If $y$ decreases as $x$ increases, then $\dfrac{dy}{dx}$ will be negative.

# TIME RATES OF CHANGE

There are countless quantities in the real world that vary with time.

For example:
- temperature varies continuously
- the height of a tree varies as it grows
- the prices of stocks and shares vary with each day's trading.

Varying quantities can be modelled using functions of time.

For example, we could use:

- $s(t)$   to model the distance travelled by a runner

  $\dfrac{ds}{dt}$ or $s'(t)$ is the instantaneous *speed* of the runner.

  It might have units metres per second or $m\,s^{-1}$.

- $H(t)$   to model the height of a person riding in a Ferris wheel

  $\dfrac{dH}{dt}$ or $H'(t)$ is the instantaneous rate of ascent of the person in the Ferris wheel.

  It might also have units metres per second or $m\,s^{-1}$.

- $C(t)$   to model the capacity of a person's lungs, which changes when the person breathes.

  $\dfrac{dC}{dt}$ or $C'(t)$ is the person's instantaneous rate of change in lung capacity.

  It might have units litres per second or $L\,s^{-1}$.

# EXERCISE 22B.1

1  Find:

   **a**  $\dfrac{dM}{dt}$  if  $M = t^3 - 3t^2 + 1$      **b**  $\dfrac{dR}{dt}$  if  $R = (2t + 1)^2$

2  **a**  If $A$ is measured in $cm^2$ and $t$ is measured in seconds, what are the units for $\dfrac{dA}{dt}$?

   **b**  If $V$ is measured in $m^3$ and $t$ is measured in minutes, what are the units for $\dfrac{dV}{dt}$?

---

**Example 5**                                                          ◀ᴺ **Self Tutor**

The volume of air in a hot air balloon after $t$ minutes is given by
$V = 2t^3 - 3t^2 + 10t + 2$ $m^3$  where  $0 \leqslant t \leqslant 8$.

Find:

  **a**  the initial volume of air in the balloon

  **b**  the volume when  $t = 8$  minutes

  **c**  $\dfrac{dV}{dt}$          **d**  the rate of increase in volume when  $t = 4$  minutes.

**a** When $t = 0$, $V(0) = 2$ m$^3$
So, initially there was 2 m$^3$ of air in the balloon.

**b** When $t = 8$, $V(8) = 2(8)^3 - 3(8)^2 + 10(8) + 2$
$$= 914 \text{ m}^3 \text{ in the balloon.}$$

After 8 minutes there was 914 m$^3$ in the balloon.

**c** $\dfrac{dV}{dt} = 6t^2 - 6t + 10$  m$^3$ min$^{-1}$

**d** When $t = 4$, $\dfrac{dV}{dt} = 6(4)^2 - 6(4) + 10$
$$= 82 \text{ m}^3 \text{ min}^{-1}$$

Since $\dfrac{dV}{dt} > 0$, $V$ is increasing.

Hence, $V$ is increasing at 82 m$^3$ min$^{-1}$ when $t = 4$.

---

**3** The number of bacteria in a dish is modelled by $B(t) = 0.3t^2 + 30t + 150$ thousand, where $t$ is in days, and $0 \leqslant t \leqslant 10$.

  **a** Find $B'(t)$ and state its meaning.

  **b** Find $B'(3)$ and state its meaning.

  **c** Explain why $B(t)$ is increasing over the first 10 days.

**4** The estimated future profits of a small business are given by $P(t) = 2t^2 - 12t + 118$ thousand dollars, where $t$ is the time in years from now.

  **a** What is the current annual profit?      **b** Find $\dfrac{dP}{dt}$ and state its units.

  **c** What is the significance of $\dfrac{dP}{dt}$?

  **d** For what values of $t$ will the profit:

   **i** decrease       **ii** increase      on the previous year?

  **e** What is the minimum profit and when does it occur?

  **f** Find $\dfrac{dP}{dt}$ when $t = 4$, 10 and 25. What do these figures represent?

**5** Water is draining from a swimming pool such that the remaining volume of water after $t$ minutes is $V = 200(50 - t)^2$ m$^3$. Find:

  **a** the average rate at which the water leaves the pool in the first 5 minutes

  **b** the instantaneous rate at which the water is leaving at $t = 5$ minutes.

**6** When a ball is thrown, its height above the ground is given by
$s(t) = 1.2 + 28.1t - 4.9t^2$ metres, where $t$ is the time in seconds.

  **a** From what distance above the ground was the ball released?

  **b** Find $s'(t)$ and state what it represents.

  **c** Find $t$ when $s'(t) = 0$. What is the significance of this result?

  **d** What is the maximum height reached by the ball?

e Find the ball's speed:    i when released    ii at $t = 2$ s.    iii at $t = 5$ s.
State the significance of the sign of the derivative at these values.

f How long will it take for the ball to hit the ground?

**7** The height of a palm tree is given by $H = 20 - \dfrac{18}{t}$ metres, where $t$ is the number of years after the tree was planted from an established potted juvenile tree, $t \geqslant 1$.

a How high was the palm after 1 year?

b Find the height of the palm at $t = 2, 3, 5, 10$, and 50 years.

c Find $\dfrac{dH}{dt}$ and state its units.

d At what rate is the tree growing at $t = 1, 3$, and 10 years?

e Explain why $\dfrac{dH}{dt} > 0$ for all $t \geqslant 1$. What does this mean in terms of the tree's growth?

## GENERAL RATES OF CHANGE

Other rate problems can be treated in the same way as those involving time. However, we must always pay careful attention to the *units* of the quantities involved.

For example:

- the cost of manufacturing $x$ items has a **cost function** $C(x)$ dollars associated with it.
  $\dfrac{dC}{dx}$ or $C'(x)$ is the **instantaneous rate of change in cost** with respect to the number of items made.

  In this case $\dfrac{dC}{dx}$ has the units dollars per item.

- the **profit** $P(x)$ in making and selling $x$ items is given by
  $P(x) = R(x) - C(x)$ where $R(x)$ is the **revenue function** and $C(x)$ is the **cost function**.
  $\dfrac{dP}{dx}$ or $P'(x)$ represents the rate of change in profit with respect to the number of items sold.

---

**Example 6**  ◀) **Self Tutor**

The cost of producing $x$ items in a factory each day is given by

$$C(x) = \underbrace{0.000\,13x^3 + 0.002x^2}_{\substack{\text{cost of} \\ \text{labour}}} + \underset{\substack{\uparrow \\ \text{raw material} \\ \text{costs}}}{5x} + \underset{\substack{\uparrow \\ \text{fixed or overhead costs such as} \\ \text{heating, cooling, maintenance, rent}}}{2200}$$

a Find $C'(x)$.

b Find $C'(150)$. Interpret this result.

c Find $C(151) - C(150)$. Compare this with the answer in b.

**a** $C'(x) = 0.000\,39x^2 + 0.004x + 5$

**b** $C'(150) = \$14.38$ per item

This is the rate at which the costs are increasing with respect to the production level $x$ when 150 items are made per day.

**c** $C(151) - C(150) \approx \$3448.19 - \$3433.75$
$$\approx \$14.44$$

This is the actual cost of making the 151st item each week, and is similar to the answer from **b**.

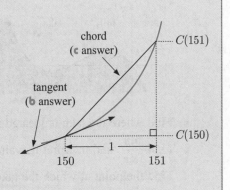

## EXERCISE 22B.2

**1** Find:

**a** $\dfrac{dT}{dr}$ if $T = r^2 - \dfrac{100}{r}$    **b** $\dfrac{dA}{dh}$ if $A = 2\pi h + \frac{1}{4}h^2$

**2** If $C$ is measured in pounds and $x$ is the number of items produced, what are the units for $\dfrac{dC}{dx}$?

**3** The total cost of running a train from Paris to Marseille is given by

$$C(v) = \tfrac{1}{5}v^2 + \dfrac{200\,000}{v} \text{ euros } \text{ where } v \text{ is the average speed of the train in } \mathrm{km\,h^{-1}}.$$

**a** Find the total cost of the journey if the average speed is:

   **i** $50\ \mathrm{km\,h^{-1}}$    **ii** $100\ \mathrm{km\,h^{-1}}$.

**b** Find the rate of change in the cost of running the train at speeds of:

   **i** $30\ \mathrm{km\,h^{-1}}$    **ii** $90\ \mathrm{km\,h^{-1}}$.

**4** The cost function for producing $x$ items each day is

$$C(x) = 0.000\,072x^3 - 0.000\,61x^2 + 0.19x + 893 \text{ dollars.}$$

**a** Find $C'(x)$ and explain what it represents.

**b** Find $C'(300)$ and explain what it estimates.

**c** Find the actual cost of producing the 301st item.

**5** Seablue make denim jeans. The cost model for making $x$ pairs per day is

$$C(x) = 0.0003x^3 + 0.02x^2 + 4x + 2250 \text{ dollars.}$$

**a** Find $C'(x)$.

**b** Find $C'(220)$. What does it estimate?

**c** Find $C(221) - C(220)$. What does this represent?

**d** Find $C''(x)$ and the value of $x$ when $C''(x) = 0$. What is the significance of this value?

**6**

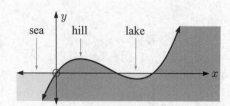

Alongside is a land and sea profile where the $x$-axis is sea level. The function $y = \frac{1}{10}x(x - 2)(x - 3)$ km gives the height of the land or sea bed relative to sea level.

**a** Find where the lake is located relative to the shore line of the sea.

**b** Find $\dfrac{dy}{dx}$ and interpret its value when $x = \frac{1}{2}$ and when $x = 1\frac{1}{2}$ km.

**c** Find the point at which the lake floor is level, and the depth at this point.

**7** The resistance to the flow of electricity in a metal is given by
$R = 20 + \frac{1}{10}T - \frac{1}{200}T^2$ ohms, where $T$ is the temperature in $^\circ$C of the metal.

**a** Find the resistance $R$, at temperatures of $0^\circ$C, $20^\circ$C and $40^\circ$C.

**b** Find the rate of change in the resistance at any temperature $T$.

**c** For what values of $T$ does the resistance increase as the temperature increases?

**8** The profit made in selling $x$ items is given by $P(x) = 5x - 2000 - \dfrac{x^2}{10\,000}$ dollars.

**a** Graph $P(x)$ using technology and determine the sales levels which produce a profit.

**b** Find $P'(x)$ and hence find $x$ such that the profit is increasing.

**9** The cost of producing $x$ items is given by $C(x) = 0.002x^3 + 0.04x^2 + 10x + 3000$ dollars. If each item sells for $30, find:

**a** the revenue function $R(x)$

**b** the profit function $P(x)$

**c** $P'(x)$

**d** $P'(50)$ and explain the significance of this result.

## C — OPTIMISATION

There are many problems for which we need to find the **maximum** or **minimum** value for a function. We can solve such problems using differential calculus techniques. The solution is often referred to as the **optimum** solution and the process is called **optimisation**.

### WARNING

The maximum or minimum value does not always occur when the first derivative is zero. It is essential to also examine the values of the function at the endpoint(s) of the domain for global maxima and minima.

For example:

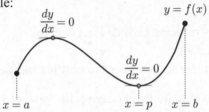

The maximum value of $y$ occurs at the endpoint $x = b$.

The minimum value of $y$ occurs at the local minimum $x = p$.

## TESTING OPTIMAL SOLUTIONS

If one is trying to optimise a function $f(x)$ and we find values of $x$ such that $f'(x) = 0$, there are several tests we can use to see whether we have a maximum or a minimum solution:

### SIGN DIAGRAM TEST

If near to $x = a$ where $f'(a) = 0$ the sign diagram of $f'(x)$ is:

-  we have a **local maximum**
-  we have a **local minimum**.

### GRAPHICAL TEST

If the graph of $y = f(x)$ shows:

- ⌢ we have a **local maximum**
- ⌣ we have a **local minimum**.

## OPTIMISATION PROBLEM SOLVING METHOD

*Step 1:* Draw a large, clear diagram of the situation.

*Step 2:* Construct a formula with the variable to be **optimised** (maximised or minimised) as the subject. It should be written in terms of **one** convenient **variable**, $x$ say. You should write down what restrictions there are on $x$.

*Step 3:* Find the **first derivative** and find the values of $x$ when it is **zero**.

*Step 4:* If there is a restricted domain such as $a \leqslant x \leqslant b$, the maximum or minimum may occur either when the derivative is zero or else at an endpoint.

Show using the **sign diagram test** or the **graphical test**, that you have a maximum or a minimum situation.

Use **calculus techniques** to answer the following problems.

In cases where finding the zeros of the derivatives is difficult you may use a **graphics calculator** or **graphing package** to help you.

GRAPHING PACKAGE

## EXERCISE 22C

**1** The cost per racquet of making $x$ tennis racquets each day is given by
$C(x) = x^2 - 20x + 120$ dollars per racquet.
How many racquets should be made per day to minimise the cost per racquet?

**2** When a stone is thrown vertically upwards its height above the ground is given by
$h(t) = 49t - 9.8t^2$ metres. Find the maximum height reached.

**3** A small business which employs $x$ workers earns profit given by
$P(x) = -x^3 + 300x + 1000$ pounds.
How many workers should be employed to maximise the profit?

**4** A manufacturer can produce $x$ fittings per day where $0 \leqslant x \leqslant 10\,000$. The production costs are:

- €1000 per day for the workers
- €$\dfrac{5000}{x}$ per day for running costs and maintenance.
- €2 per day per fitting

How many fittings should be produced daily to minimise costs?

**5** For the cost function $C(x) = 720 + 4x + 0.02x^2$ dollars and revenue function
$R(x) = 15x - 0.002x^2$ dollars, find the production level that will maximise profits.

**6** The total cost of producing $x$ blankets per day is $\frac{1}{4}x^2 + 8x + 20$ dollars, and for this production level each blanket may be sold for $(23 - \frac{1}{2}x)$ dollars.
How many blankets should be produced per day to maximise the total profit?

**7** The cost of running a boat is $\pounds\dfrac{v^2}{10}$ per hour where $v$ km h$^{-1}$ is the speed of the boat.
All other costs amount to £62.50 per hour. Find the speed which will minimise the total cost per kilometre.

| **Example 7** | ◀) **Self Tutor** |
|---|---|

A 4 litre container must have a square base, vertical sides, and an open top. Find the most economical shape which minimises the surface area of material needed.

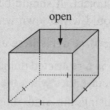
open

*Step 1:*

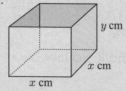

$y$ cm

$x$ cm

$x$ cm

Let the base lengths be $x$ cm and the depth be $y$ cm. The volume

$$V = \text{length} \times \text{width} \times \text{depth}$$
$$\therefore \quad V = x^2 y$$
$$\therefore \quad 4000 = x^2 y \quad \text{.... (1)} \quad \{\text{as 1 litre} \equiv 1000 \text{ cm}^3\}$$

*Step 2:*   The total surface area

$A$ = area of base + 4(area of one side)

$= x^2 + 4xy$

$= x^2 + 4x \left( \dfrac{4000}{x^2} \right)$   {using (1)}

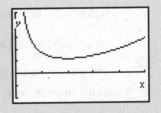

$\therefore \ A(x) = x^2 + 16\,000x^{-1}$   where $x > 0$

*Step 3:*   $A'(x) = 2x - 16\,000x^{-2}$

$\therefore \ A'(x) = 0$   when   $2x = \dfrac{16\,000}{x^2}$

$\therefore \quad 2x^3 = 16\,000$

$\therefore \quad x = \sqrt[3]{8000} = 20$

*Step 4:*   **Sign diagram test**

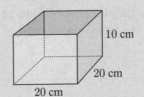

If $x = 10$,

$A'(10) = 20 - \frac{16\,000}{100}$

$= 20 - 160$

$= -140$

If $x = 30$,

$A'(30) = 60 - \frac{16\,000}{900}$

$\approx 60 - 17.8$

$\approx 42.2$

The minimum material is used to make the container when $x = 20$ and

$y = \dfrac{4000}{20^2} = 10.$

So,

is the most economical shape.

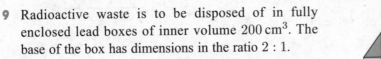

---

**8**  An open rectangular box has a square base and a fixed inner surface area of 108 cm².

   **a**  Explain why $x^2 + 4xy = 108$.

   **b**  Hence show that $y = \dfrac{108 - x^2}{4x}$.

   **c**  Find a formula for the capacity $C$ of the container, in terms of $x$ only.

   **d**  Find $\dfrac{dC}{dx}$. Hence find $x$ when $\dfrac{dC}{dx} = 0$.

   **e**  What size must the base be in order to maximise the capacity of the box?

**9**  Radioactive waste is to be disposed of in fully enclosed lead boxes of inner volume 200 cm³. The base of the box has dimensions in the ratio 2 : 1.

   **a**  What is the inner length of the box?

   **b**  Explain why $x^2h = 100$.

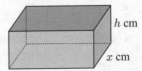

**c** Explain why the inner surface area of the box is given by $A(x) = 4x^2 + \dfrac{600}{x}$ cm$^2$.

**d** Use *technology* to help sketch the graph of $y = 4x^2 + \dfrac{600}{x}$.

**e** Find the minimum inner surface area of the box and the corresponding value of $x$.

**f** Sketch the optimum box shape showing all dimensions.

**10** Consider the manufacture of cylindrical tin cans of 1 L capacity where the cost of the metal used is to be minimised. This means that the surface area must be as small as possible.

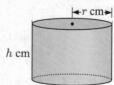

**a** Explain why the height $h$ is given by $h = \dfrac{1000}{\pi r^2}$ cm.

**b** Show that the total surface area $A$ is given by
$A = 2\pi r^2 + \dfrac{2000}{r}$ cm$^2$.

**c** Use *technology* to help you sketch the graph of $A$ against $r$.

**d** Find the value of $r$ which makes $A$ as small as possible.

**e** Sketch the can of smallest surface area.

---

**Example 8**  ◀)) **Self Tutor**

A square sheet of metal 12 cm × 12 cm has smaller squares cut from its corners as shown.

What sized square should be cut out so that when the sheet is bent into an open box it will hold the maximum amount of liquid?

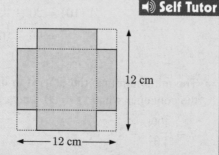

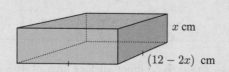

Let $x$ cm by $x$ cm squares be cut out.

Volume = length × width × depth
$$= (12 - 2x) \times (12 - 2x) \times x$$
$$= x(12 - 2x)^2$$
$$= x(144 - 48x + 4x^2)$$
$$= 4x^3 - 48x^2 + 144x$$

$\therefore \quad V'(x) = 12x^2 - 96x + 144$
$$= 12(x^2 - 8x + 12)$$
$$= 12(x - 2)(x - 6)$$

$\therefore \quad V'(x) = 0$ when $x = 2$ or $6$

However, $12 - 2x$ must be $> 0$ and so $x < 6$

$\therefore \quad x = 2$ is the only value in $0 < x < 6$ with $V'(x) = 0$.

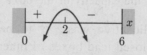

*Conclusion:*   The resulting container has maximum capacity when 2 cm × 2 cm squares are cut from its corners.

**11** Sam has sheets of metal which are 36 cm by 36 cm square. He wants to cut out identical squares which are $x$ cm by $x$ cm from the corners of each sheet. He will then bend the sheets along the dashed lines to form an open container.

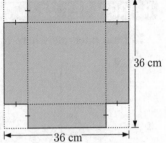

**a** Show that the capacity of the container is given by $V(x) = x(36 - 2x)^2$ cm$^3$.

**b** What sized squares should be cut out to produce the container of greatest capacity?

**12** An athletics track has two 'straights' of length $l$ m and two semi-circular ends of radius $x$ m. The perimeter of the track is 400 m.

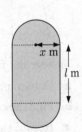

**a** Show that $l = 200 - \pi x$ and hence write down the possible values that $x$ may have.

**b** Show that the area inside the track is $A = 400x - \pi x^2$.

**c** What values of $l$ and $x$ produce the largest area inside the track?

**13** Answer the **Opening Problem** on page **648**.

**14**

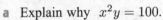

A beam with rectangular cross-section is to be cut from a log of diameter 1 m.

The strength of the beam is given by $S = kwd^2$, where $w$ is the width and $d$ is the depth.

**a** Show that $d^2 = 1 - w^2$ using the rule of Pythagoras.

**b** Find the dimensions of the strongest beam that can be cut.

**15** A water tank has the dimensions shown. The capacity of the tank is 300 kL.

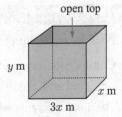

**a** Explain why $x^2 y = 100$.

**b** Use **a** to find $y$ in terms of $x$.

**c** Show that the area of plastic used to make the tank is given by $A = 3x^2 + 800x^{-1}$ m$^2$.

**d** Find the value of $x$ which minimises the surface area $A$.

**e** Sketch the tank, showing the dimensions which minimise $A$.

## REVIEW SET 22A

**1** Find intervals where the graphed function is increasing or decreasing.

**a**

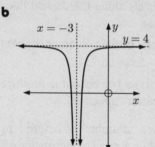

**b**

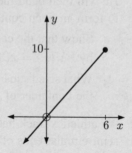

**c**

**2** Consider the function $f(x) = x^3 - 3x$.

**a** Determine the $y$-intercept.

**b** Find the coordinates of any local maxima, local minima or horizontal inflections.

**c** Hence, sketch the graph of the function.

**3** Consider the function $f(x) = x^3 - 4x^2 + 4x$.

**a** Find all axes intercepts.    **b** Find and classify all stationary points.

**c** Sketch the graph of $y = f(x)$ showing features from **a** and **b**.

**4** An open box is made by cutting squares out of the corners of a 24 cm by 24 cm square sheet of tinplate. What size squares should be removed to maximise the volume of the box?

**5** A factory makes $x$ thousand chopsticks per day with a cost of $C(x) = 0.4x^2 + 1.6x + 150$ dollars. Packs of 1000 chopsticks sell for \$28. Find the production level that maximises daily profit, and the profit at that production level.

## REVIEW SET 22B

**1** Find the maximum and minimum values of $x^3 - 3x^2 + 5$ for $-1 \leqslant x \leqslant 4$.

**2** Consider the function $f(x) = 2x^3 - 3x^2 - 36x + 7$.

**a** Find and classify all stationary points.

**b** Find intervals where the function is increasing and decreasing.

**c** Sketch the graph of $y = f(x)$, showing all important features.

**3** An astronaut standing on the moon throws a ball into the air. The ball's height above the surface of the moon is given by $H(t) = 1.5 + 19t - 0.8t^2$ metres, where $t$ is the time in seconds.

**a** Find $H'(t)$ and state its units.

**b** Calculate $H'(0)$, $H'(10)$ and $H'(20)$. Interpret these values, including their sign.

**c** How long is the ball in the 'air' for?

**4** For the function shown opposite, draw a
sign diagram of:

**a** $f(x)$         **b** $f'(x)$.

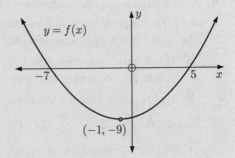

**5**   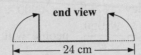    A rectangular gutter is formed by bending a 24 cm wide
sheet of metal as illustrated. Where must the bends be
made to maximise the capacity of the gutter?

**6** A 200 m fence is to be placed around a lawn which has
the shape of a rectangle with a semi-circle on one of its
sides and dimensions as shown.

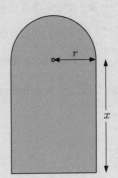

**a** Find the expression for the perimeter of the lawn in
terms of $r$ and $x$.

**b** Find $x$ in terms of $r$.

**c** Show that the area of the lawn $A$ can be written as
$A = 200r - r^2 \left(2 + \frac{\pi}{2}\right)$.

**d** Find the dimensions of the lawn which maximise
the area of the lawn.

## REVIEW SET 22C

**1** $f(x) = x^3 + Ax + B$   has a stationary point at $(1, 5)$.

**a** Find $A$ and $B$.         **b** Find the nature of all the stationary points of $f(x)$.

**2** Consider the function   $f(x) = x^3 + x^2 + 2x - 4$.

**a** State the $y$-intercept.

**b** State where the function is increasing or decreasing.

**c** Find the position and nature of any stationary points.

**d** Sketch the cubic, showing the features found in **a**, **b** and **c**.

**3** The cost per hour of running a barge up the Rhein is given by   $C(v) = 10v + \dfrac{90}{v}$

euros,   where $v$ is the average speed of the barge.

**a** Find the cost of running the barge for:

**i** two hours at 15 km h$^{-1}$         **ii** 5 hours at 24 km h$^{-1}$.

**b** Find the rate of change in the cost of running the barge at speeds of:

**i** 10 km h$^{-1}$         **ii** 6 km h$^{-1}$.

**c** At what speed will the cost per hour be a minimum?

**4** A manufacturer of open steel boxes has to make one with a square base and a volume of 1 m$^3$. The steel costs \$2 per square metre.

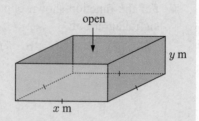

  **a** If the base measures $x$ m by $x$ m and the height is $y$ m, find $y$ in terms of $x$.

  **b** Hence, show that the total cost of the steel is $C(x) = 2x^2 + \dfrac{8}{x}$ dollars.

  **c** Find the dimensions which minimise the cost of the box.

**5** The cost of running an advertising campaign for $x$ days is $C(x) = 6900 + 950x$ pounds. Research shows that after $x$ days, $7500 - \dfrac{98\,000}{x}$ people will have responded, bringing an average profit of £17 per person.

  **a** Show that the profit from running the campaign for $x$ days is
  $$P(x) = 120\,600 - \dfrac{1\,666\,000}{x} - 950x \text{ pounds.}$$

  **b** Find how long the campaign should last to maximise profit.

**6** Find the maximum and minimum values of $y = \frac{1}{3}x^3 + x^2 - 3x$ for $-4 \leqslant x \leqslant 4$.

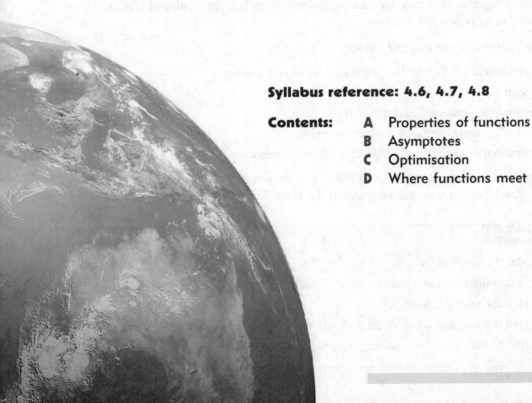

# Chapter 23

# Unfamiliar functions

Syllabus reference: 4.6, 4.7, 4.8

Contents:  A  Properties of functions
           B  Asymptotes
           C  Optimisation
           D  Where functions meet

## OPENING PROBLEM

During an earthquake, the shockwaves shaking the earth are measured using a **seismometer**.

The readings on the Richter scale for a particularly large earthquake were given by the function

$$y(t) = 8\cos(50t) \times 2^{-\frac{2}{5}(t-4)^2}$$

where $t$ is the time in minutes, $t > 0$.

An alarm rings in the local weather station whenever there is a reading above 2.

**Things to think about:**

**a** What is the general shape of the graph?

**b** What is the highest Richter scale measurement taken for this earthquake?

**c** Between what times will the alarm be ringing for this earthquake?

# A    PROPERTIES OF FUNCTIONS

Many real world situations are modelled by mathematical functions which are difficult to analyse using algebra. However, we can use technology to help us graph and investigate the key features of an unfamiliar function.

The main features we are interested in are:

- the axes intercepts (where the graph cuts the $x$ and $y$-axes)
- gradients
- turning points (maxima and minima)
- values of $x$ where the function does not exist
- the presence of asymptotes (lines that the graph approaches).

When graphing a function using technology, it is important to start with a large viewing window. This ensures we do not miss any of the features of the function.

### Example 1                                                    ◀ᴺ Self Tutor

Consider the function $y = 2x^3 - 17x^2 + 42x - 30$.

**a** Sketch the function without plotting actual points.

**b** Find the axes intercepts.

**c** Find the coordinates and nature of any turning points.

**d** Add to your graph in **a** all key features found in **b** and **c**.

**a**

Using technology, we can sketch the graph:

**b** When $x = 0$, $y = -30$. So, the $y$-intercept is $-30$.

So, the $x$-intercepts are $1.27$, $2.5$ and $4.73$.

**c**

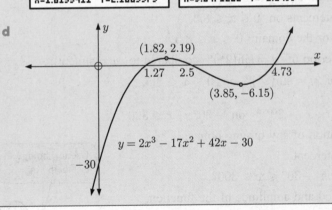

So, we have a local maximum at $(1.82, 2.19)$ and a local minimum at $(3.85, -6.15)$.

When using technology, always start with a large viewing window.

**d**

$(1.82, 2.19)$

$1.27 \quad 2.5$

$4.73$

$(3.85, -6.15)$

$y = 2x^3 - 17x^2 + 42x - 30$

$-30$

# EXERCISE 23A

**1** For each of the following:

    **i** sketch the function without plotting actual points

    **ii** find the axes intercepts

    **iii** find any local maxima or minima

    **iv** add to your graph in **i** all key features found in **ii** and **iii**.

**a** $y = \frac{1}{2}x(x - 4)(x + 3)$

**b** $y = -3x^3 - 24x^2 - 48x$

**c** $y = \frac{4}{5}x^4 + 5x^3 + 5x^2 + 2$

**d** $y = 3x^3 - 7x^2 - 28x + 10$

**e** $y = 4(x - 1)^3(2x + 3)$

**f** $y = -x(x + 2)(x - 1)(x - 4)$

**2**  For each of the following:

  **i**   sketch the function without plotting actual points
  **ii**  find the axes intercepts
  **iii** find any local maxima or minima
  **iv**  find the global maximum and minimum
  **v**   add to your graph in **i** all key features found in **ii**, **iii** and **iv**.

  **a**  $y = 2x^4 - 8x^3 + 7x + 2$  on the domain  $-1 \leqslant x \leqslant 4$

  **b**  $y = -x^3 + \frac{7}{2}x^2 + \frac{7}{2}x - 6$  on the domain  $-3 \leqslant x \leqslant 5$

  **c**  $y = (x+4)(x+1)(x-2)(x-3)$  on the domain  $-4.2 \leqslant x \leqslant 3.5$

  **d**  $y = 2x^2(x-3)$  on the domain  $-1 \leqslant x \leqslant 2.5$

**3**  Find the maximum value of:

  **a**  $y = -x^4 + 2x^3 + 5x^2 + x + 2$  on the interval  $0 \leqslant x \leqslant 4$

  **b**  $y = -2x^4 + 5x^2 + x + 2$  on the interval:

  **i**  $-2 \leqslant x \leqslant 2$         **ii**  $-2 \leqslant x \leqslant 0$         **iii**  $0 \leqslant x \leqslant 2$.

**4**  Find the minimum value of  $f(x) = x^4 + 3x^3 + x^2 + x + 4$  on the interval  $-3 \leqslant x \leqslant 0$.

**5**  Consider the function  $f : x \mapsto \sin(2^x)^o$  on  $0 \leqslant x \leqslant 8.5$.

  **a**  Determine the location of any turning points.

  **b**  Determine the $x$-intercepts on  $0 \leqslant x \leqslant 8.5$.

  **c**  Specify the range for the domain  $0 \leqslant x \leqslant 8.5$.

  **d**  Comment on the period of  $y = \sin(2^x)^o$  compared to  $y = \sin(2x)^o$.

  **e**  Sketch the graph of  $y = \sin(2^x)^o$  on  $0 \leqslant x \leqslant 8.5$.

**6**  Consider the function  $f : x \mapsto 2^{\cos x}$  on  $-30^o \leqslant x \leqslant 390^o$.

  **a**  Determine the location of any turning points.

  **b**  Determine the $y$-intercept.

Use technology to help you.

  **c**  Specify the range on  $-30^o \leqslant x \leqslant 390^o$.

  **d**  Determine the period and amplitude of the function.

  **e**  Sketch the graph of  $y = 2^{\cos x}$  on  $-30^o \leqslant x \leqslant 390^o$.

**7**  Consider the function  $f : x \mapsto x^{\sin x}$.

  **a**  Find the first three local maxima on  $0^o \leqslant x \leqslant 1000^o$.

  **b**  **i**  Try to find the $y$-intercept by 'zooming in' close to the $y$-axis.

  **ii**  Explain why the technology cannot find where the graph *appears* to touch the $y$-axis.  **Hint:** Evaluate  $f(0)$  and comment on your result.

  **c**  Does  $f(x) = x^{\sin x}$  have any $x$-intercepts on  $0^o \leqslant x \leqslant 1000^o$?

  **d**  Sketch  $y = f(x)$  on  $0^o \leqslant x \leqslant 1000^o$.

# B                                ASYMPTOTES

An **asymptote** is a line which a function gets closer and closer to but never quite reaches.

In this course we consider asymptotes which are **horizontal** or **vertical**.

## HORIZONTAL ASYMPTOTES

In **Chapter 19** we observed exponential functions such as $f(x) = 2^x$.

We saw that as $x \to -\infty$, $f(x) \to 0$ from above.

Since $f(x)$ approaches, but never quite reaches, the line $y = 0$, we say that $y = 0$ is a **horizontal asymptote** of the function.

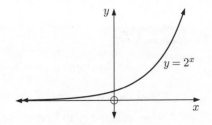

In general, to determine the equation of a horizontal asymptote, we must consider the behaviour of the function as $x \to \pm\infty$. To do this on a calculator, we adjust the viewing window to show a very wide domain. We then use the **trace** feature to investigate $y$ for extreme values of $x$.

For example, consider the function $g(x) = \dfrac{x}{2 - x}$.

Using a graphics calculator, we can obtain this graph for the domain $-100 \leqslant x \leqslant 100$.

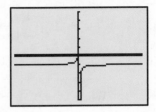

Using the trace feature, we observe:

- as $x \to -\infty$, $g(x) \to -1$ from above
- as $x \to \infty$, $g(x) \to -1$ from below.

So, $g(x)$ has the horizontal asymptote $y = -1$.

## VERTICAL ASYMPTOTES

The graph of $y = \dfrac{x}{2 - x}$ is now given for the domain $-5 \leqslant x \leqslant 5$.

We observe there is a 'jump' or *discontinuity* in the graph when $x = 2$.

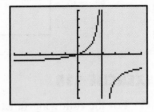

This occurs because $g(2) = \dfrac{2}{2 - 2} = \dfrac{2}{0}$ which is undefined.

As $x \to 2$ from the left, $g(x) \to \infty$. As $x \to 2$ from the right, $g(x) \to -\infty$.

Since $g(x)$ approaches, but never reaches, the line $x = 2$, we say that $x = 2$ is a **vertical asymptote** of the function.

For **rational functions**, or functions which are fractions, vertical asymptotes occur when the denominator is zero.

We can now display a complete graph of the function $g(x) = \dfrac{x}{2-x}$, including both horizontal and vertical asymptotes.

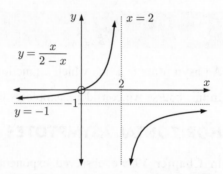

---

**Example 2**    ◄)) **Self Tutor**

Consider the function $y = \dfrac{6}{x-2} + 4$.

a   Find the asymptotes of the function.    b   Find the axes intercepts.

c   Use technology to help sketch the function, including the features from a and b.

---

a   The vertical asymptote is $x = 2$.
    The horizontal asymptote is $y = 4$.

b   When $y = 0$, $\dfrac{6}{x-2} = -4$

$\therefore \ -4(x-2) = 6$

$\therefore \ -4x + 8 = 6$

$\therefore \ -4x = -2$

$\therefore \ x = \frac{1}{2}$

When $x = 0$, $y = \dfrac{6}{-2} + 4 = 1$

So, the $x$-intercept is $\frac{1}{2}$ and the $y$-intercept is 1.

c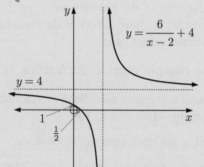

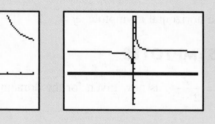

---

## EXERCISE 23B

1   For the following functions:

   i   use technology to help sketch the function

   ii  find any asymptotes    iii   find the axes intercepts

   iv  add to your graph the features found in ii and iii.

a   $y = \dfrac{3}{x-1} + 2$    b   $y = 5 - 2 \times 3.1^{0.4x}$    c   $y = \dfrac{x-6}{x+3}$

d   $y = \dfrac{-5x+1}{2x-1}$    e   $y = \dfrac{6}{x+2} - 4$    f   $y = 7 \times (0.2)^x - 3$

**Example 3**                                                      ◀)) **Self Tutor**

Consider the function $f(x) = \dfrac{x-4}{x^2+3x-10}$.

  **a**  Find the vertical asymptotes.

  **b**  Use technology to sketch the graph, checking your answers to **a**.

  **c**  Determine the positions of any axes intercepts and turning points.

  **a**  We need to find where the denominator is 0.

$$\therefore \; x^2 + 3x - 10 = 0$$
$$\therefore \; (x+5)(x-2) = 0 \qquad \text{\{factorising\}}$$
$$\therefore \; x = -5 \text{ or } 2 \quad \text{\{Null Factor law\}}$$

So, the vertical asymptotes are $x = -5$ and $x = 2$.

  **b**

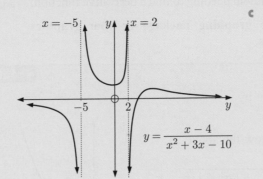

$$y = \frac{x-4}{x^2+3x-10}$$

  **c**  Using technology:

- the $x$-intercept is $x = 4$
- the $y$-intercept is $y = 0.4$
- there is a local minimum at $(-0.243,\ 0.398)$
- there is a local maximum at $(8.24,\ 0.0513)$

**2** For each of the following functions:

    **i**  find the vertical asymptotes      **ii**  sketch the graph of the function.

  **a**  $y = \dfrac{3x+1}{x+2}$

  **b**  $y = \dfrac{2x+1}{3x+4}$

  **c**  $y = \dfrac{x+3}{(x+4)(x-1)}$

  **d**  $y = \dfrac{2x+1}{(2x+5)(x-3)}$

  **e**  $y = \dfrac{-7}{x^2+4x-12}$

  **f**  $y = \dfrac{5-x}{2x^2-x-21}$

**3** Sketch a graph of each function, labelling all asymptotes, axes intercepts, and turning points.

  **a**  $y = \dfrac{x+1}{x^2-4}$

  **b**  $y = 3^{x+4}$

  **c**  $y = \dfrac{x^2+9}{x^2-4x-11}$

  **d**  $y = \dfrac{6}{x^3-3x-3}$

  **e**  $y = 9 - 2^{\frac{1}{2}(x-4)}$

  **f**  $y = \dfrac{-x^2-9x+11}{x-5}$

**4** Use technology to help graph $y = \dfrac{2^x}{x}$. Your graph should include any axes intercepts, turning points, and asymptotes.

**5** Consider the function $f : x \mapsto 3x \times 2^x$ on $-6 \leqslant x \leqslant 1$.

   **a** Using technology, find:

      **i** the $y$-intercept          **ii** $f(-6)$ and $f(1)$

      **iii** the minimum value of $f(x)$ on $-6 \leqslant x \leqslant 1$

      **iv** the equation of the horizontal asymptote.

   **b** Sketch a graph of $y = f(x)$ on $-6 \leqslant x \leqslant 1$, showing *all* of the features found above.

# C    OPTIMISATION

In the calculus chapter we learnt to differentiate only a limited number of function types. However, the use of technology enables us to solve more complicated optimisation problems without needing to find a derivative function.

GRAPHING PACKAGE

In the following exercise, use the **graphing package** or your **graphics calculator** to help solve the problems.

---

**Example 4**    🔊 **Self Tutor**

The distance from A to P is given by
$D = \sqrt{(5-x)^2 + (y-1)^2}$ units.

  **a** Show, using triangle PQA, how the above formula was obtained.

  **b** Explain why $D = \sqrt{(5-x)^2 + (x^2-1)^2}$.

  **c** Sketch the graph of $D$ against $x$ for $0 \leqslant x \leqslant 6$.

  **d** Find the smallest value of $D$ and the value of $x$ where it occurs.

  **e** Interpret the results of **d**.

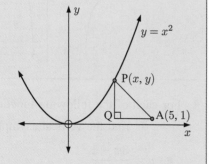

---

**a**

$QA = 5 - x$ and $PQ = y - 1$

$\therefore \ D^2 = (5-x)^2 + (y-1)^2$

$\therefore \ D = \sqrt{(5-x)^2 + (y-1)^2}$

**b** Since P is on the curve $y = x^2$, $D = \sqrt{(5-x)^2 + (x^2-1)^2}$.

**c**

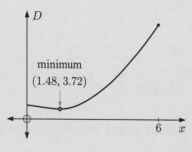

**d** Using technology, the coordinates of the turning point are $(1.48, \ 3.72)$.
So, the smallest value of $D$ is $3.72$ units when $x \approx 1.48$.

**e** The shortest distance from A(5, 1) to the graph of $y = x^2$ is $3.72$ units. The closest point on the graph to A(5, 1) is when $x \approx 1.48$.

## EXERCISE 23C

**1**  The distance from A to P can be found using triangle ABP.

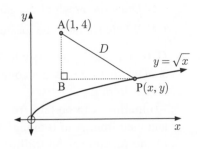

  **a**  Show that  $D = \sqrt{(x-1)^2 + (y-4)^2}$  units.

  **b**  Explain why  $D = \sqrt{(x-1)^2 + (\sqrt{x}-4)^2}$.

  **c**  Sketch the graph of $D$ against $x$ for  $0 \leqslant x \leqslant 8$.

  **d**  Find the smallest value of $D$ and the value of $x$ where it occurs.

  **e**  Interpret the results of **d**.

**2**

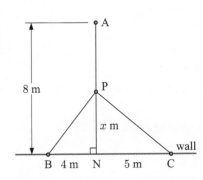

A, B and C are computers.  A printer P is networked to each computer as shown.

  **a**  Find, in terms of $x$, the lengths of AP, BP and CP.

  **b**  Let  $D = AP + BP + CP$  be the total length of cable needed to connect the three computers to the printer.  Use **a** to write $D$ in terms of $x$.

  **c**  Draw the graph of $D$ against $x$.

  **d**  Where should the printer be placed so that the total cable length used is minimised?

**3**  A closed pizza box is folded from a sheet of cardboard 64 cm by 40 cm.  To do this, equal squares of side length $x$ cm are cut from two corners of the short side, and two equal rectangles of width $x$ cm are cut from the long side as shown.

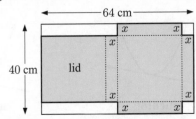

  **a**  Find the dimensions of the lid and the base of the box in terms of $x$.

  **b**  Find the volume of the box in terms of $x$.

  **c**  What is the maximum possible volume of the box?

  **d**  What are the dimensions of the box which has the maximum volume?

**4**  Three towns and their grid references are marked on the diagram alongside.  A pumping station is to be located at P on the pipeline, to pump water to the three towns.  The grid units are kilometres.

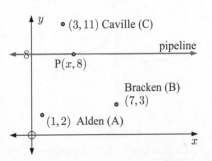

  **a**  The distance PC is found using the distance formula.   So,  $PC = \sqrt{(x-3)^2 + (8-11)^2}$

           $\therefore \ PC = \sqrt{(x-3)^2 + 9}$

  Find formulae for the distances PA and PB.

**b** Write a formula for the sum of the distances $S = PA + PB + PC$ in terms of $x$.

**c** Draw the graph of $S$ against $x$.

**d** Where should P be located to minimise the total length of connecting pipe needed?

**5** G is a natural gas rig which is 7 km from the straight shore PB. B is a collection station which is 13 km from P.

A pipeline is to be laid from G underwater to A, and then from A to B along the shoreline. The cost of the pipeline is $6 million per km underwater, and $4 million per km along the shore.

We are to locate point A on the shoreline so that the cost of the pipeline will be minimised.

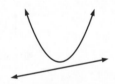

**a** Explain why the distance AG is $\sqrt{x^2 + 49}$ km.

**b** Find the distance from A to B in terms of $x$.

**c** Explain why the total cost of the pipeline is $C = 6\sqrt{x^2 + 49} + 52 - 4x$ million dollars.

**d** Graph $C$ against $x$ and find the minimum turning point.

**e** Where should A be located to minimise the cost?

# D   WHERE FUNCTIONS MEET

When a quadratic function and a linear function are graphed on the same set of axes, there are three situations which could occur:

    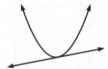

| **cutting** | **touching** | **missing** |
|:---:|:---:|:---:|
| (2 points of intersection) | (1 point of intersection) | (no points of intersection) |

Similarly, when the function $y = \dfrac{1}{x}$ is graphed on the same set of axes as a linear function, there may be two, one, or zero points of intersection:

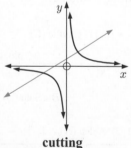    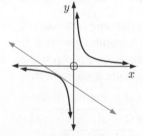    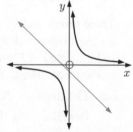

| **cutting** | **touching** | **missing** |
|:---:|:---:|:---:|
| (2 points of intersection) | (1 point of intersection) | (no points of intersection) |

For other combinations of functions there may be three, four, or even infinitely many points of intersection.

For example, consider these different lines and how many times they intersect with $y = \sin x$.

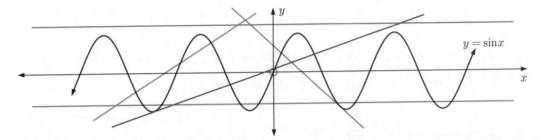

**Example 5**                                                                    ◀ )) **Self Tutor**

Find where the line $y = x - 3$ meets $y = \dfrac{4}{x}$.

Using technology, we graph the two functions and then solve for their intersection.

$y = x - 3$ meets $y = \dfrac{4}{x}$ at

$(4, 1)$ and $(-1, -4)$.

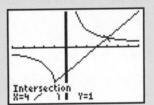

## EXERCISE 23D

1 Use technology to find where the line:

 **a** $y = 2x - 3$ meets $y = \dfrac{4}{x}$

 **b** $y = 4x + 3$ meets $y = -\dfrac{10}{x}$

 **c** $y = 3x - 2$ meets $y = \dfrac{6}{x}$

 **d** $y = 3x + 5$ meets $y = \dfrac{12}{x}$

 **e** $3x - 5y = 10$ meets $y = \dfrac{5}{x}$

 **f** $3x + 2y = 6$ meets $y = \dfrac{10}{x}$

2  **a** Use your calculator to draw, on the same set of axes, the graphs of $y = \dfrac{10}{x}$ and $y = -2x - 9$.

 **b** Is the line a tangent to the curve?

 **c** Confirm your answer using technology.

3 Find the points of intersection of the following functions using a graphics calculator:

 **a** $y = (x + 1)^2$ and $y = -x^2 + x + 4$

 **b** $y = 6\left(x - \dfrac{1}{x}\right)$ and $y = 5$

 **c** $y = 6x - 1$ and $y = \dfrac{10}{x - 2}$

**4** Find the points of intersection between:

    **a** $y = 5^{-x}$ and $y = 5x + 10$         **b** $y = 3^x$ and $y = 2x + 1$

    **c** $y = 2^{-x}$ and $y = x^2 - 2x - 3$     **d** $y = -3^x$ and $y = -x^4$

    **e** $y = 5^x$ and $y = \dfrac{1}{x}$           **f** $y = 4^x$ and $y = \dfrac{x}{2x - 1}$

**5**   **a** Using the 'solver' mode of your calculator, find a solution to $x^3 = \dfrac{2}{x}$.

    **b** Using the 'graph' mode of your calculator, find the points of intersection between

      $y = x^3$ and $y = \dfrac{2}{x}$.

    **c** Comment on the advantages and disadvantages of using 'graph' mode compared to 'solver' mode.

**6** Find the points of intersection between $y = \cos x$ and the line:

    **a** $y = \dfrac{x}{20}$                **b** $y = \dfrac{x}{200}$

**7** Find the points of intersection between $y = \sin x$ and the line:

    **a** $y = \dfrac{x}{20}$                **b** $y = \dfrac{x}{90}$

**8** Solve:

    **a** $x^2 \times 2^x = -(x - 3)(x + 2)$     **b** $\dfrac{3^x}{x} = 5 - x$

    **c** $\dfrac{x + 1}{(x - 1)(x + 3)} = 2^x$       **d** $2x - 2^x = x - 3$

    **e** $\sin x = \cos 2x$, on $0° \leqslant x \leqslant 360°$

## REVIEW SET 23A

**1** For each of the following:

    **i** use technology to observe the function

    **ii** sketch the graph of $y = f(x)$ without plotting points from a table of values

    **iii** find the $y$-intercept and include it on your graph.

    **a** $y = x^3 + 3$           **b** $y = -2x^2(x + 4)$

**2** For each of the following:

    **i** sketch a graph without plotting actual points

    **ii** find the axes intercepts

    **iii** find any local maxima or local minima

    **iv** add to your graph in **i** the key features found in **ii** and **iii**.

    **a** $y = (x - 2)^2(x + 1)(x - 3)$     **b** $y = 3x^3 - x^2 + 2x - 1$

**3** Find the minimum value of $y = x^4 - x^3 - 3x^2 + x + 2$ on the interval:

    **a** $-2 \leqslant x \leqslant 2$     **b** $-1 \leqslant x \leqslant 1$     **c** $0 \leqslant x \leqslant 2$

**4** For the function $\quad y = \dfrac{x-1}{(x+3)(x-2)}$ :

   **a** use technology to help sketch the function

   **b** find any asymptotes

   **c** find the axes intercepts

   **d** find any turning points

   **e** add to your graph in **a** all key features.

**5** The height of a seedling $t$ days after planting is given by

$$H(t) = \dfrac{10}{1 + 4 \times (1.5)^{-1.2t}} \text{ cm}, \quad t \geqslant 0.$$

   **a** Sketch the graph of $H(t)$ for $0 \leqslant t \leqslant 15$.

   **b** How high was the seedling when it was planted?

   **c** How high was the seedling after 1 week?

   **d** How long did it take for the seedling to reach a height of 5 cm?

   **e** Is there a limit to how high the seedling can grow? If so, what is it?

**6** The volume of usable wood produced by a forest is given by $V(t) = 178 \times 2^{1-\frac{80}{t}}$ thousand cubic metres, where $t$ is the time in years since the forest was planted, $0 < t \leqslant 80$.

   **a** Graph $V(t)$ against $t$.

   **b** What is the volume of wood after   **i** 20 years   **ii** 40 years?

   **c** Find the percentage increase in the volume of usable wood from $t = 40$ to $t = 50$.

   **d** At what time does the volume of usable wood reach $100\,000$ m$^3$?

**7** Solve:

   **a** $\dfrac{3}{x} = 2x + 5$                     **b** $2^x = -\frac{1}{2}x^2 - 4x$

## REVIEW SET 23B

**1** For each of the following:

     **i** use technology to observe the function

    **ii** sketch the function without plotting actual points

   **iii** find the axes intercepts

    **iv** find any local maxima or local minima

     **v** add to your graph in **ii** all key features.

   **a** $y = -(x-1)(x+1)(x-3)^2$      **b** $y = x^4 - 4x^3 + 6x^2 - 4x + 1$

**2** Find the minimum value of $y = x^4 - x^3 + 2x^2 + 3x - 1$ on $-2 \leqslant x \leqslant 2$.

**3** Use technology to find the coordinates of the points of intersection of the graphs with equations $y = x^2 - 5x + 6$ and $y = 2x - 1$.

**4** Consider the function $y = \dfrac{2}{x+1} - 3$.

   **a** What is the vertical asymptote?      **b** What is the horizontal asymptote?

   **c** What is the $x$-intercept?           **d** What is the $y$-intercept?

   **e** Using only **a** to **d**, sketch the graph of the function.

**5** Consider the function $f : x \mapsto x \times 2^x$.

   **a** Using technology, find:

   **i** the $y$-intercept

   **ii** the equation of the horizontal asymptote

   **iii** the minimum value of $f(x)$ on $-4 \leqslant x \leqslant 1$

   **iv** $f(-4)$ and $f(1)$.

   **b** Sketch $y = f(x)$ on the domain $-4 \leqslant x \leqslant 1$, showing all of the features calculated above.

**6** The number of people infected with a virus $t$ days after an outbreak is given by $N(t) = 100t \times (1.3)^{-t}$ for $t \geqslant 0$.

   **a** Sketch the graph of $N(t)$ for $0 \leqslant t \leqslant 20$.

   **b** How many people were infected after 1 day?

   **c** At what time was the outbreak greatest? How many people were infected at this time?

   **d** How long did it take before the outbreak was contained to 15 people?

**7** At time $t$ years after mining begins on a mountain of iron ore, the rate of mining is given by $R(t) = \dfrac{100 \times 3^{0.03t}}{25 + 3^{0.05t-10}}$ million tonnes per year, $t \geqslant 0$.

   **a** Graph $R(t)$ against $t$ for $0 \leqslant t \leqslant 800$.

   **b** At what rate will the ore be mined after $t = 200$ years?

   **c** What will be the maximum rate of mining, and at what time will it occur?

   **d** When will the rate of mining be 6000 million tonnes per year?

**8** Max throws a stone into the air. It lands 5.9 seconds later. The distance of the stone from Max is given by $D(t) = \sqrt{24.01t^4 - 294t^3 + 936t^2}$ metres, where $t$ is the time in seconds.

   **a** What is the maximum distance of the stone?

   **b** How far away does it land?

# Chapter 24

# Miscellaneous problems

**Contents:**   **A**   Short questions
              **B**   Long questions

# A                                              SHORT QUESTIONS

## EXERCISE 24A

**1**  Calculate the value of $\dfrac{(1.2 \times 10^{-1})^2}{4.72 \times 10^{-2}}$, giving your answer:

    **a**  correct to two decimal places        **b**  correct to 3 significant figures

    **c**  in scientific notation correct to 6 significant figures.

**2**  Two propositions $p$ and $q$ are defined as follows:

    $p$: Farouk studies for the test.      $q$: Farouk scores a good mark.

    **a**  Write in words:     **i**  $p \Rightarrow q$        **ii**  the inverse of $p \Rightarrow q$.

    **b**  Write in symbols:     **i**  the converse of $p \Rightarrow q$     **ii**  the contrapositive of $p \Rightarrow q$.

    **c**  Use a truth table to show that the contrapositive of $p \Rightarrow q$ is equivalent to the original statement $p \Rightarrow q$.

**3**  The function $g$ is defined as $g : x \mapsto \cos(30x)^{\circ}$ for the domain $\{x \mid 0 \leqslant x \leqslant 4, \ x \in \mathbb{N}\}$.

    **a**  Write down the values of $a$, $b$, and $c$ in the mapping diagram representing the function $g$.

    **b**  Write down the range for the function $g$.

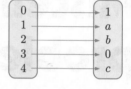

**4**  The graph shows the line $3x + 2y = 18$. The axes intercepts are A and B, and M is the midpoint of the line segment AB.

    **a**  Find the coordinates of A and B.

    **b**  Find the coordinates of point M.

    **c**  Find the gradient of the line AB.

    **d**  Find the equation of the perpendicular bisector of AB in the form $ax + by = c$, where $a, b \in \mathbb{Z}$ and $a > 0$.

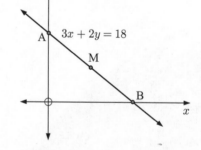

**5**  The lengths of a random sample of 200 fish caught one day from the local jetty are displayed in the cumulative frequency curve.

    **a**  Write down the median length of fish caught.

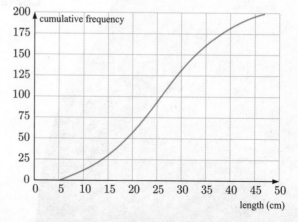

**b**  Complete the following table of values for the lengths of fish.
Give your answers to the nearest 5 fish.

| Length (cm) | $0 < x \leqslant 10$ | $10 < x \leqslant 20$ | $20 < x \leqslant 30$ | $30 < x \leqslant 40$ | $40 < x \leqslant 50$ |
|---|---|---|---|---|---|
| Frequency | 15 | $55-15=40$ | $130-55=75$ | | |

**c**  Use your table in **b** to estimate the mean length of fish caught from the jetty.

**6**  Consider the function $f(x) = 2x^5 - 5x^2 + 1$.

**a**  Find $f'(x)$.                              **b**  Find $f''(x)$.

**c**  Find the equation of the tangent to $y = f(x)$ at the point $(1, -2)$.

**7**  Romeo has $12 000 which he would like to invest for four years until he finishes his University degree. The following options are available:

> Option A:  5.8% p.a. interest compounding monthly.
> Option B:  6.3% p.a. simple interest.

**a**  For each option, calculate the value of the investment after four years.

**b**  Which option is better, and by how much?

**8**  A *light-year* (ly) is the distance light travels in a vacuum in one year.

**a**  Light travels at $2.998 \times 10^5$ km s$^{-1}$. Assuming there are 365.25 days in a year, calculate the distance light travels in 1 year. Write your answer correct to 3 significant figures, in the form $a \times 10^k$ km where $1 \leqslant a < 10$ and $k \in \mathbb{Z}$.

**b**  The Andromeda Galaxy is approximately $2.2 \times 10^5$ ly wide. Write this distance in kilometres, in the form $a \times 10^k$ where $1 \leqslant a < 10$ and $k \in \mathbb{Z}$.

**9**  Let $U$ be the universal set $\{x \mid 1 \leqslant x \leqslant 10, \ x \in \mathbb{Z}\}$.
$P$ and $Q$ are subsets of $U$, and contain the elements shown in the Venn diagram alongside.
Let $p$ and $q$ be the propositions:

> $p$:  $x$ is an element of $P$.
> $q$:  $x$ is an element of $Q$.

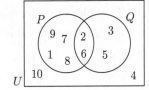

**a**  For what values of $x$ are the following statements true:

  **i**  $\neg p$            **ii**  $\neg p \wedge q$            **iii**  $p \veebar q$?

**b**  Complete the truth table:

| $p$ | $q$ | $\neg p$ | $\neg p \wedge q$ | $p \veebar q$ |
|---|---|---|---|---|
| T | T | | | |
| T | F | | | |
| F | T | | | |
| F | F | | | |

**10**  The function $f : x \mapsto 4 - 2x$ is illustrated in the mapping diagram opposite.

**a**  Determine the value of:

  **i**  $a$            **ii**  $b$

**b**  Hence, write down the:

  **i**  domain of $f$        **ii**  range of $f$.

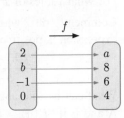

**11** Line $V$ is vertical and passes through A(5, 6) as shown.

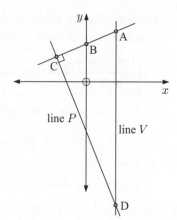

  **a** Write down the equation of line $V$.

  **b** B(0, 4) is the midpoint of line segment AC. Write down the coordinates of point C.

  **c** Line $P$ passes through C and is perpendicular to AC. Write down the equation of line $P$, giving your answer in the form $ax + by + d = 0$.

  **d** Write down the coordinates of D, the point of intersection of lines $P$ and $V$.

**12** A high school principal believes that academic success is related to the degree to which students are involved with co-curricular activities. To investigate this further, the principal compiled the following information.

| Grade average | Total time spent on co-curricular activities | | |
|:---:|:---:|:---:|:---:|
| | *Less than 2 hours* | *From 2 to 5 hours* | *More than 5 hours* |
| 1 or 2 | 15 | 14 | 17 |
| 3, 4 or 5 | 31 | 26 | 18 |
| 6 or 7 | 22 | 24 | 31 |

The principal performs a $\chi^2$ test on the data at a 1% significance level.

  **a** For this $\chi^2$ test:

    **i** write down the null hypothesis $H_0$

    **ii** explain why there are 4 degrees of freedom

    **iii** calculate the value of the $\chi^2$ test statistic.

  **b** Given $\chi^2_{crit} \approx 13.3$ at a 1% significance level, comment on whether $H_0$ is rejected.

  **c** Comment on whether this $\chi^2$ test at a 1% significance level supports the principal's belief.

**13** Consider the graph of $y = f(x)$ shown opposite. B is a local minimum, D is a local maximum and the tangent at C is horizontal.

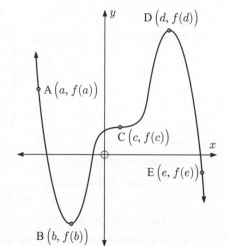

  **a** Write down the equation of the tangent at C.

  **b** Write down all solutions to $f'(x) = 0$.

  **c** For what values of $x$ is $f(x)$ decreasing?

  **d** Comment on whether the following expression is positive, negative, or zero:

$$\frac{f(b) - f(a)}{b - a}$$

  **e** What can be said about the tangent lines at A and E if $f'(a) = f'(e)$?

**14** Mr Bond receives 2 million pounds in retirement money. He decides to spend £100 000 on an 18 month holiday to France, leaving the remainder of his retirement fund in the bank.

    **a** When Mr Bond converts his holiday money from British pounds (GBP) to euros (EUR), the exchange rate is 1 GBP = 1.12 EUR. Given that a 3% commission fee is required on this transaction, calculate the amount of money Mr Bond receives in euros.

    **b** For the period when Mr Bond is on holiday, he leaves the remainder of his retirement money in an account offering 5.6% p.a. interest, compounding monthly. Calculate the value of his retirement fund at the end of the holiday period.

    **c** Did Mr Bond spend more on his holiday than he earned in interest over this period?

**15** A rectangular field is 91.4 m long and 68.5 m wide.

    **a** Calculate the exact area of the field in m$^2$.

    **b** Round your answer in **a** to two significant figures.

    **c** Calculate the percentage error of your answer in **b**.

**16** Suppose $U = \{x \mid 1 \leqslant x \leqslant 11, \ x \in \mathbb{Z}\}$, $p$: $x$ is a prime number, and $q$: $x$ is an even number.

    **a** Represent the information on a Venn diagram.

    **b** Write down the truth set for:   **i** $p \wedge q$   **ii** $p \vee \neg q$.

**17** The graph alongside shows $y = x^2 - 3x - 18$. It cuts the $x$-axis at A, and its vertex is at B.

    **a** Factorise $x^2 - 3x - 18$.

    **b** Write down the coordinates of:

        **i** A               **ii** B.

    **c** Find the coordinates of the points where the curve $y = x^2 - 3x - 18$ meets the line $y = -8$.

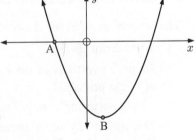

**18** The height of a radio tower is 190 m. The angle of elevation from a house to the top of the tower is 16°. The house is $x$ metres from the bottom of the tower.

    **a** Draw a diagram to show this information.    **b** Calculate the value of $x$.

    **c** Find the straight line distance from the top of the tower to the house.

**19** The histogram shows the amounts of time a group of students spent travelling to school in the morning.

    **a** Construct a frequency table for this data.

    **b** Estimate the mean and standard deviation for the travel time.

    **c** Find the percentage of students who spend more than 40 minutes travelling to school in the morning.

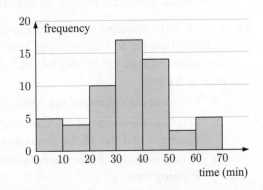

**20**  **a** Expand the expression $2(x-1)(x+5)$.

    **b** Differentiate $f(x) = 2(x-1)(x+5)$ with respect to $x$.

    **c** The tangent to $y = f(x)$ at the point where $x = a$ has gradient $-5$.

      **i** Find the value of $a$.

      **ii** Hence, find the coordinates of the point on the curve where the gradient is $-5$.

**21** The table alongside shows exchange rates for the Malaysian ringgit (MYR).

| Currency | 1 MYR |
|---|---|
| Euro (EUR) | 0.196 193 |
| Chinese yuan (CNY) | 1.955 30 |

    **a** Calculate how many Chinese yuan can be exchanged for 1000 MYR.

    **b** If the transaction is subject to a 1.5% commission, calculate the amount of yuan received by the purchaser. Give your answer correct to the nearest yuan.

    **c** A tourist exchanges 5000 CNY into Malaysian ringgit, and then changes that money into euros. Commission applies to each transaction. Determine the amount of euros received, giving your answer correct to the nearest cent.

**22** A ball is dropped from a height of 4 metres. After each bounce, the ball reaches 80% of its previous height.

    **a** Find the height reached by the ball after the:   **i** first bounce   **ii** second bounce.

    **b** Assuming this trend continues, write an expression for the height reached by the ball after the $n$th bounce.

    **c** Determine the height reached by the ball after the 20th bounce. Write your answer correct to the nearest millimetre.

**23** The probability of event $A$ occurring in any given trial of an experiment is $P(A) = a$.

    **a** Write down $P(A')$.

    **b** Suppose two trials of the experiment are performed independently. Find, in terms of $a$, the probability of:

      **i** $A$ occurring exactly once         **ii** $A$ occurring exactly twice.

    **c** The probability of $A$ occurring at least once in two independent trials is 0.94. Determine the value of $a$.

**24** Consider the equation $y = -2 \times 3^x + 6$, where $x \in \mathbb{R}$.

    **a** Find:   **i** the $x$-intercept   **ii** the $y$-intercept.

    **b** Determine the equation of the horizontal asymptote.

    **c** Sketch $y = -2 \times 3^x + 6$, clearly showing the features found in **a** and **b**.

**25** A solid metal spinning top is constructed by joining a hemispherical top to a cone-shaped base.
The radius of both the hemisphere and the base of the cone is 3 cm.

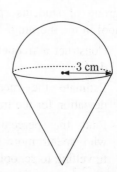

    **a** Calculate the volume of the hemispherical top.

    **b** Calculate the height of the cone-shaped base if its volume is half that of the hemisphere.

    **c** Hence, calculate the total outer surface area of the spinning top.

**26** The relationship between two variables $x$ and $y$ is such that $r = +0.93$, $s_{xy} = 12.1$, $s_x = 3.94$, and $(\overline{x}, \overline{y}) = (10.8, 11.9)$.

    **a** In terms of strength and direction, describe the correlation between $x$ and $y$.

    **b** Determine the least squares regression line for $y$ in terms of $x$. Give your answer in the form $y = ax + b$.

    **c** Calculate the value of $s_y$ and interpret its meaning.

**27** A small confectionery company produces $x$ candy bars per day, where $x \leqslant 1500$. For a given day, the cost per candy bar $C$ depends on $x$, such that
$C(x) = 0.000\,004x^2 - 0.008x + 5$ dollars.

    **a** Calculate $C(1500)$ and interpret this value.

    **b** Find $C'(x)$.            **c** Solve $C'(x) = 0$.

    **d** Determine the minimum daily cost per candy bar.

**28** The current cost of 1 kg of rice is $2.99.

    **a** If the rate of inflation is forecast to be 3.8% per year, how much will 1 kg of rice cost:

        **i** 1 year from now         **ii** 5 years from now?

    **b** The average rate of inflation of the past 10 years has been 4.1% per year. How much did 1 kg of rice cost 10 years ago?

**29** The speed of sound in dry air at 20°C is $343$ m s$^{-1}$. Calculate how many metres sound travels in one hour. Give your answer:

    **a** correct to two significant figures         **b** in scientific notation.

**30** Propositions $p$ and $q$ are defined as follows:   $p$: Antonio plays football.
                                                   $q$: Antonio is good at kicking a ball.

    **a** Write the following in words:

        **i** $p \wedge \neg q$         **ii** $\neg q \Rightarrow p$

    **b** Write the following in symbolic language:

        **i** Antonio plays football or is good at kicking a ball, but does not do both.

        **ii** If Antonio does not play football, then he is not good at kicking a ball.

    **c** Use a truth table to show that the implication in **a ii** is not a tautology.

**31** Alongside is a graph of
$$y = p\sin(qx) + r$$
where $p$, $q$ and $r$ are positive integers, and $x$ is measured in degrees.

    **a** Find the values of $p$, $q$ and $r$.

    **b** Find, to the nearest degree, the value of $x$ when $y = 4.5$ and $0° \leqslant x \leqslant 90°$.

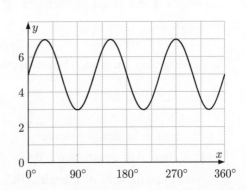

**32** A sail in the shape of a rhombus has sides of length 8 metres, and the longer diagonal has length 13 metres.

  **a** Draw a diagram and label the given information.

  **b** Find:    **i** the length of the shorter diagonal
             **ii** the measure of the smaller angle in the rhombus.

**33** The ages in months of 20 students are:

  198, 192, 195, 194, 205, 208, 210, 200, 206, 203,
  196, 198, 196, 201, 194, 198, 197, 195, 220, 204.

  **a** Find:
    **i** the median age              **ii** the interquartile range.

  **b** Determine whether the 220 month old student is an outlier.

  **c** Draw a box and whisker plot for the ages of the students. Represent any outliers with an asterisk.

**34** Consider the function $f(x) = 2x^3 - 3x^{-2} - 24x + \frac{3}{4}$.

  **a** Find $f'(x)$.              **b** Write down the value of $f'(2)$.

  **c** Given $f(2) = -32$, find the equation of the tangent to $y = f(x)$ at the point where $x = 2$. Write your answer in the form $ax + by = c$, where $a > 0$.

**35** Last Tuesday, 48.47 Indian rupee (INR) was equivalent to 90.83 Japanese yen (JPY).

  **a** If the exchange rate of INR to JPY was $1 : a$, find the value of $a$. Give your answer correct to 5 significant figures.

  **b** Calculate the value of 2000 rupees in yen, correct to the nearest yen.

  **c** Calculate the value of 15 000 yen in rupees, correct to 2 decimal places.

**36** The set $X = \{\frac{2}{7}, \sqrt{7}, 0, 2^{-4}, 0.\overline{1}, -1.2 \times 10^4\}$ is a subset of $\mathbb{R}$.

The Venn diagram alongside shows subsets of the real numbers.

Place each element of $X$ in the correct position on the Venn diagram.

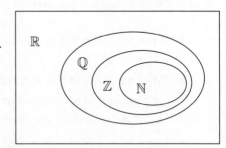

**37** Two events $A$ and $B$ are independent. $P(A) = 0.1$ and $P(B) = 0.5$.

  **a** Calculate:
    **i** $P(A \cap B)$              **ii** $P(A \cup B)$              **iii** $P((A \cup B)')$

  **b** State, giving a reason, whether events $A$ and $B$ are mutually exclusive.

**38** Triangle ABC has $\widehat{ACB} = 35°$, $AC = 14$ cm, and $AB = 17$ cm.

  **a** Sketch triangle ABC, showing all of the information provided. Your diagram does not need to be drawn to scale.

  **b** Calculate $\widehat{ABC}$ correct to 2 decimal places.

  **c** Determine the area of triangle ABC, correct to the nearest cm$^2$.

**39** A group of students participate in an IQ test to measure their intelligence. The results were:

119, 102, 89, 84, 85, 120, 90, 104, 95, 94, 89, 132

    **a** For this data, calculate the:

        **i** range          **ii** mean          **iii** standard deviation.

    **b** A result of two standard deviations above the mean is classified as "superior intelligence". What proportion of the students within this group have superior intelligence?

**40** The graph of $y = f(x)$ is shown opposite, where $f(x) = ax^2 + bx + c$.

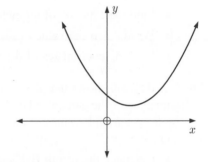

    **a** Copy and complete the table below by filling in either *positive*, *negative* or *zero*.

| Constant | $a$ | $b$ | $c$ |
|---|---|---|---|
| Value | | | |

    **b** How many real zeros does $f(x)$ possess?

    **c** Another function $g(x)$ has the form $g(x) = px^2 + qx + r$, where $p$, $q$ and $r$ are real constants with signs as outlined in the table below:

| Constant | $p$ | $q$ | $r$ |
|---|---|---|---|
| Value | negative | positive | negative |

Given that $g(x)$ has exactly one real zero, sketch a possible graph of $y = g(x)$.

**41** A drug in the bloodstream of a patient $t$ hours after being administered has concentration $C(t) = 2t \times 3^{-t}$, where $0 \leqslant t \leqslant 8$.

    **a** Using your calculator, sketch the graph of $C(t)$ for the domain specified. Clearly show the coordinates of the local maximum.

    **b** For what time interval is the concentration of the drug:

        **i** decreasing          **ii** greater than 0.5?

**42** £20 000 is to be invested for 4 years.

    **a** Calculate the final value of this investment if interest is offered at:

        **i** 5% p.a. compounded annually         **ii** 5% p.a. compounded daily.

    **b** What is the percentage increase in the final value of the investment when the interest is compounded on a daily basis, rather than annually?

**43** Consider the Venn diagram opposite.

    **a** List the letters in:

        **i** $A \cap B$         **ii** $(A \cup B)'$

        **iii** $A \cup B'$         **iv** $A' \cap B$

    **b** Determine:

        **i** $n(A \cup B)$         **ii** $n(A \cap B')$

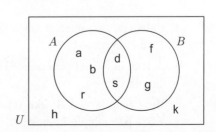

**44** A bag contains 5 red, 3 yellow, and 2 green balloons. Without looking, Mary takes one balloon out of the bag and blows it up. She then takes out a second balloon.

   **a** Find the probability of Mary selecting a red balloon and then a yellow balloon.

   **b** Find the probability that the second balloon is green, given that the first balloon chosen is green.

   **c** Find the probability that the first balloon is not red and the second balloon is red.

**45** A quadratic function has $x$-intercepts $-2$ and $3$, and the graph of the function passes through $(-3, 18)$.

   **a** Find the equation of the function. Write your answer in the form $y = ax^2 + bx + c$.

   **b** Write down the value of the $y$-intercept.

   **c** Find the coordinates of the vertex of the graph algebraically.

**46** The diagram shows the plan of a triangular garden bed. The garden bed will be enclosed by a 50 cm high wall and then filled with soil.

   **a** Calculate the length BC.

   **b** Calculate the area of the garden bed.

   **c** Find the volume of soil needed to fill the garden bed.

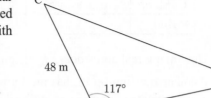

**47** The following results were recorded in a recent Mathematical Studies test.

| Score (%) | $50 \leqslant S < 60$ | $60 \leqslant S < 70$ | $70 \leqslant S < 80$ | $80 \leqslant S < 90$ | $90 \leqslant S < 100$ |
|---|---|---|---|---|---|
| Frequency | 6 | 15 | 20 | 10 | 4 |

   **a** Draw a table of cumulative frequencies.

   **b** Draw a cumulative frequency curve for this information.

   **c** Find:

       **i** the number of student scores in the 80th percentile or above

       **ii** the score required to be in the 80th percentile or above.

**48** A and B are points on the curve $f(x) = 2x^3 - 5x^2 - 4x + 3$ at which the tangents to the curve are parallel to the $x$-axis.

   **a** Write down the gradient of the tangent at A.

   **b** Find the gradient function of the curve.

   **c** Find the exact $x$-coordinates of points A and B.

**49** **a** Calculate the interest on a loan of $7000 at 7.5% p.a. simple interest over an 18 month period.

   **b** A loan of $7000 generates $1000 interest over an 18 month period. Find the rate of simple interest.

   **c** How long would it take for $1000 interest to accumulate on a loan of $7000 at 7.5% p.a. simple interest?

**50** A running track consists of two straight segments joined by semi-circular ends, as shown.

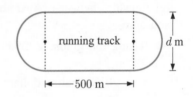

running track

$d$ m

←——500 m——→

  **a** If the total perimeter of the track is 1600 metres, determine the diameter of the semi-circular ends.

  **b** Jason takes 4 minutes and 25 seconds to complete a single lap of the track. Calculate Jason's average speed in $m\,s^{-1}$.

**51** A group of 250 students of ages 13, 14 and 15 were asked to choose which of Art and Music they preferred. The results are shown in the table alongside.

|  | 13 | 14 | 15 | Total |
|---|---|---|---|---|
| Music | 35 | $p$ | 65 | 120 |
| Art | 55 | $q$ | $r$ | 130 |
| Total | 90 | 50 | 110 |  |

  **a** Calculate the values of $p$, $q$ and $r$.

  **b** A student is selected at random. Calculate the probability that this student:

    **i** is 13 years old

    **ii** is not 13 years old and Music is their preferred subject

    **iii** is not 15 given that their preferred subject is Art.

**52** The vertex of a quadratic function is $(2, -25)$, and one of the $x$-intercepts is $-3$.

  **a** Sketch this quadratic function, clearly showing the information provided.

  **b** Write down the other $x$-intercept.

  **c** The quadratic function can be written in the form $y = a(x - p)(x - q)$. Determine the values of:

    **i** $p$ and $q$, if $p < q$     **ii** $a$.

**53** Triangle ACH is isosceles with altitude 25 cm and base angles $H\widehat{A}C = H\widehat{C}A = 65°$.

  **a** Calculate the length of:

    **i** AH     **ii** AC

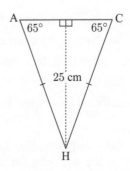

  **b** Triangle ACH lies within the square-based rectangular prism shown. Determine the volume of this square-based prism.

**54** The curve with equation $y = x^3 - 4x^2 + 3x + 1$ passes through $A(3, 1)$.

  **a** Find $\dfrac{dy}{dx}$.

  **b** Determine the equation of the tangent to this curve at A.

**55** The straight line graph shows the relationship between Australian dollars and euros.

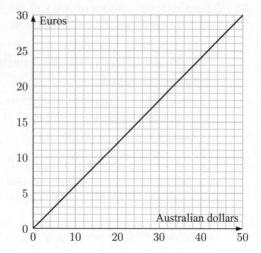

  **a** Using the graph, estimate the value of:

   **i** 20 Australian dollars in euros

   **ii** 25 euros in Australian dollars.

  **b** Write down the exchange rate from Australian dollars to euros.

  **c** The sum of 75 000 AUD is converted into euros. If the transaction is charged 2% commission, how many euros are received?

**56** During a darts competition, players record their best 3-dart score out of 180. The results of a competition are shown in the stem and leaf plot.

  **a** Determine the median score.

  **b** Calculate the interquartile range.

  **c** Draw a box and whisker plot to display the results of the competition.

| Stem | Leaf |
|------|------|
| 10 | 2 |
| 11 | 3 5 7 |
| 12 | 1 2 6 6 |
| 13 | 2 3 5 7 8 |
| 14 | 0 2 6 6 8 |
| 15 | 4 6 9 |
| 16 | 1 8 |
| 17 | 0 |

*Scale:* $10 \,|\, 2 = 102$ points

**57** A sequence is specified by the formula $t_n = 7n - 12$.

  **a** List the first three terms of the sequence.

  **b** Determine whether these terms form an arithmetic or geometric sequence.

  **c** Find the 100th term of the sequence.

  **d** Hence, or otherwise, find the sum of the first 100 terms.

**58** Use Venn diagrams like the one alongside to illustrate the truth set for the given compound propositions.

  **a** $p \wedge q$    **b** $\neg(p \vee q)$    **c** $p \veebar q$

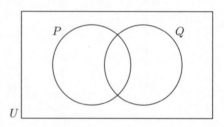

**59** **a** For $y = -3\cos 0.5x$, find:

   **i** the amplitude    **ii** the period.

  **b** Find the value of $x$ on $0° \leqslant x \leqslant 270°$ when:

   **i** $y = 1$    **ii** $y = -3$

**60** A child's toy is made by combining a hemisphere of radius 3.5 cm with a cone of slant height $l = 10$ cm as shown.

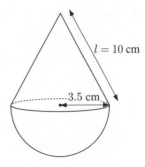

   **a** Calculate the volume of the hemisphere.

   **b** Calculate the volume of the cone.

   **c** Calculate the total surface area of the toy.

**61** Nunu performs a chi-squared test to see if there is any association between the *time taken to travel to work* in the morning (short time or long time) and the *quality of work* she accomplishes in a day (good or poor). She performs this test at the 5% level of significance.

   **a** Write down the null and alternate hypotheses.

   **b** Determine the number of degrees of freedom for this test.

   **c** The $p$-value for her test is 0.082. What conclusion can be drawn? Justify your answer.

**62** Consider $f(x) = x^3 - \dfrac{3}{x}, \ 0 < x \leqslant 3$.

   **a** Find $f''(x)$.

   **b** Solve $f''(x) = 0$.

   **c** Write down the coordinates of the point in the given domain where the gradient function is a minimum.

   **d** Write down the interval in the given domain for which the graph is increasing.

**63** Josie takes out a consumer loan for €4500 at a simple interest rate of 8.3% p.a. She will repay the loan in equal monthly installments over 3 years.

   **a** Find the total amount to be repaid.

   **b** Calculate the amount of each repayment.

   **c** Determine the amount Josie would save if the loan was taken over 2 years instead.

**64** Triangle LMO has $\hat{LMO} = 120°$, LM $= 3$ cm, LO $= 21$ cm and MO $= x$ cm.

   **a** Evaluate $\cos 120°$.

   **b** Using the cosine rule, show that $x^2 + 3x - 432 = 0$

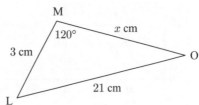

   **c** Hence, find $x$ correct to 3 significant figures.

   **d** Find the perimeter of triangle LMO.

**65** A circle has an area of 300 cm$^2$.

   **a** Find the radius of the circle correct to 3 decimal places.

   **b** Find the circumference of the circle correct to 2 significant figures.

**66** For two events $A$ and $B$, it is known that $P(A) = \frac{2}{5}$, $P(B) = \frac{3}{10}$, and $P(B \mid A) = \frac{1}{2}$.

  **a** Calculate $P(A \cap B)$.

  **b** Show that $A$ and $B$ are not independent.

  **c** Calculate $P(A \mid B)$.

**67** The weekly income $£I$ of an employee varies depending on their total weekly sales $£S$. The chart alongside shows the relationship between $I$ and $S$.

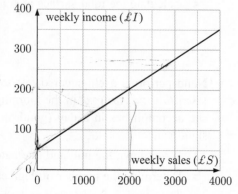

  **a** Use the graph to determine the employee's weekly income if:

    **i** no sales are made

    **ii** £2000 in sales are made.

  **b** In a given week an employee earns £275. Use the graph to estimate their total sales for that week.

  **c** The formula connecting $I$ and $S$ has the form $I = rS + t$, where $r$ and $t$ are both constants. Calculate the values of $r$ and $t$.

**68** A function $f$ is defined by $f : x \mapsto x^2 + \dfrac{2}{x}$ for $-4 \leqslant x \leqslant 4$.

  **a** Sketch $y = f(x)$ for the region $-4 \leqslant x \leqslant 4$.

  **b** Using technology, write down the coordinates of the local minimum.

  **c** Hence, find the intervals in the given domain where $f(x)$ is decreasing.

**69**

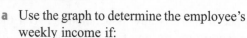

The examination marks for 200 students are displayed on the cumulative frequency graph shown. The pass mark for the examination was 30.

  **a** What percentage of the students passed?

  **b** A box and whisker plot for the examination data is:

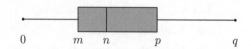

From the graph, estimate:

  **i** $m$   **ii** $n$   **iii** $p$   **iv** $q$

**70** A geometric sequence has its general term given by $u_n = 6(1.2)^{n-1}$.

  **a** Write down the first two terms of the sequence.

  **b** Find the first term of the sequence which is greater than 30.

  **c** Another geometric sequence has first term 2 and common ratio 1.35. Find the first term of this sequence which is greater than the equivalent term of the first sequence.

**71** Retro Bank offers the following interest rates and a choice of two investment options.

| Investment Term | $500 to $9999 | $10 000 to $39 999 | $40 000 plus |
|:---:|:---:|:---:|:---:|
| 3 months | 1.50% p.a. | 3.00% p.a. | 4.00% p.a. |
| 6 months | 1.50% p.a. | 3.15% p.a. | 3.65% p.a. |
| 9 months | 1.50% p.a. | 3.50% p.a. | 3.95% p.a. |
| 1 year | 2.00% p.a. | 4.65% p.a. | 4.95% p.a. |
| 2 years | 2.75% p.a. | 4.95% p.a. | 5.15% p.a. |
| 3 years | 2.75% p.a. | 5.05% p.a. | 5.35% p.a. |
| 4 years | 2.75% p.a. | 5.10% p.a. | 5.65% p.a. |
| 5 years | 2.75% p.a. | 5.15% p.a. | 6.00% p.a. |

*Option 1:* Interest compounded monthly.
*Option 2:* Interest compounded quarterly.

**a** Calculate the interest earned if $30 000 is invested for three years using:

   **i** *Option 1*          **ii** *Option 2*

**b** Calculate, in terms of *Option 2*, the percentage difference in the interests calculated in **a**.

**72** Use logic symbols to describe the shaded area on the following Venn diagrams:

**a**
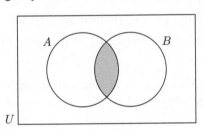

**b**
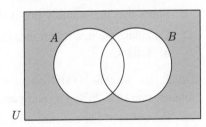

**c**
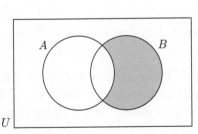

**d**
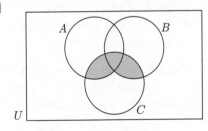

**73** The functions $f$ and $g$ are defined for $-5 \leqslant x \leqslant 5$ by

$$f : x \mapsto \frac{x}{x-2}, \quad x \neq 2 \quad \text{and} \quad g : x \mapsto x.$$

**a** Sketch the graphs of $y = f(x)$ and $y = g(x)$ on the same set of axes.

**b** Write down the equations of the horizontal and vertical asymptotes of the graph of $y = f(x)$.

**c** Find the solutions of $\dfrac{x}{x-2} = x$.

**74** For the solid shown, find:

    **a** the length of AE

    **b** the length of BE

    **c** the angle BE makes with the base ADEF.

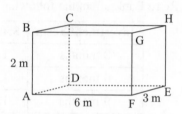

**75** Consider the following data regarding the time to complete a task compared with a person's age.

| Age ($x$ years) | 12 | 18 | 26 | 31 | 36 | 42 |
|---|---|---|---|---|---|---|
| Time ($y$ minutes) | 22 | 30 | 24 | 28 | 26 | 23 |

    **a** Use your graphics calculator to find the equation of the regression line for $y$ in terms of $x$.

    **b** Use your equation to estimate the time for a person aged 28 years to complete the task.

    **c** Use your graphics calculator to find the correlation coefficient $r$.

    **d** Comment on the reliability of your answer to **b**.

**76** The profit when $m$ machines are sold by a firm each month can be determined by the function $P(m) = 60m - 800 - m^2$ where $0 \leqslant m \leqslant 40$.

    **a** Write down a function for the rate of change in the profit for a given change in the number of machines sold by the firm.

    **b** Show that the monthly profit is maximised when 30 machines are sold.

    **c** Calculate the maximum monthly profit given that $P(m)$ is measured in thousands of dollars.

**77** Dong Hee invests 5000 Korean won (KRW) into an account which pays a nominal interest rate of 7.25% p.a. compounded monthly. Find:

    **a** the value of her account after 3 years

    **b** the total interest earned after 3 years

    **c** the difference in the amount of interest earned after 3 years if the interest was compounded quarterly.

**78** A student has access to two printers, A and B. The probability that printer A malfunctions is 1%, and the probability that printer B malfunctions is 2%. When attempting to print, the student always tries printer A first. Printer B is only used if printer A malfunctions.

    **a** Complete the tree diagram by filling in the missing values.

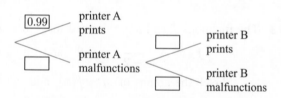

    **b** When the student tries to print a one page document, determine the probability that:

       **i** both printers malfunction       **ii** printer B prints the document

      **iii** printer A prints the document, given that the document is printed.

**79** The speed of sound can be found using the formula $S = 331.3 + 0.606T$ m s$^{-1}$, where $T$ is the temperature of the air in degrees Celsius.

   **a** Determine the speed of sound at 20°C. Do not round your answer.

   **b** Determine the distance sound travels in 10 minutes at 20°C. Write your answer in the form $a \times 10^k$, where $1 \leqslant a < 10$ and $k \in \mathbb{Z}$.

   **c** On a hot day, the temperature rises from 20°C to 45°C. Calculate the percentage increase in the speed of sound which results from this change in air temperature.

**80** The function $f : x \mapsto \sin 2x + 1$ has domain $-180° \leqslant x \leqslant 180°$.

   **a** For a graph of $y = f(x)$, write down the:

   **i** amplitude          **ii** period          **iii** $y$-intercept.

   **b** Sketch $y = f(x)$ on a set of axes, clearly showing all the features in **a**.

   **c** Hence, write down the range of $y = f(x)$.

**81** Line $A$ has equation $y = 2x + 5$ and line $B$ has equation $x - 4y = 8$. Point P is the $y$-intercept of line $A$ and point Q is the $x$-intercept of line $B$.

   **a** Write down the coordinates of:

   **i** P          **ii** Q.

   **b** Calculate the gradient of PQ.

   **c** Hence, or otherwise, calculate the *acute* angle PQ makes with the $x$-axis.

   **d** Line $A$ and line $B$ intersect at R. Find the coordinates of R.

**82** Consider the scatter diagrams shown below.

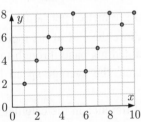

Scatter diagram I          Scatter diagram II          Scatter diagram III

   **a** For each of the cases shown above, is the association between $x$ and $y$ positive, negative, or zero?

   **b** Complete the table alongside by matching each description with scatter diagram I, II or III.

| Strength of correlation | Scatter diagram |
|---|---|
| Weak | |
| Moderate | |
| Strong | |

**83** Line $S$ has equation $2x + y = -2$.

   **a** Write down the gradient of $S$.

   **b** Line $T$ is parallel to line $S$ and passes through A(1, 4). Find the equation of line $T$.

   **c** A quadratic has equation $y = x^2 + bx + c$. Find $b$ and $c$ given that line $T$ is a tangent to this quadratic at A.

**84** Century Credit Union offers various loan repayment rates and terms. The table below shows monthly repayments per $10 000 borrowed.

| Table of monthly repayments per $10 000 | | | |
|---|---|---|---|
| Loan Term | Annual Interest Rate (% p.a.) | | |
| (years) | 6 | 7 | 8 |
| 5 | 193.3280 | 198.0112 | 202.7634 |
| 10 | 111.0205 | 116.1085 | 121.3276 |
| 15 | 84.3857 | 89.8828 | 95.5652 |
| 20 | 71.6431 | 77.5299 | 83.6440 |
| 25 | 64.4301 | 70.6779 | 77.1816 |

Andrew Lenselink borrows $30 000 to build an extra room onto his house. He organises a 10 year loan through Century Credit Union at 8% p.a.

**a**  **i**  Calculate his monthly loan repayment.

   **ii**  How much interest will Andrew pay over the entire term of the loan?

**b**  How much more interest would Andrew pay if the loan term was 20 years, assuming the interest rate remained the same?

**85** Usain Bolt set a world record at the Beijing Olympics by running the 100 m sprint in 9.69 seconds.

**a**  Calculate his average speed in metres per second during his world record race, giving your answer correct to 2 decimal places.

**b**  Convert this speed to kilometres per hour.

**c**  Bolt slowed down before the end of his race to celebrate. Scientists have estimated that if he had maintained his pace through to the finish, his time would have been 9.55 seconds. Calculate the average speed in $m s^{-1}$ to 2 decimal places for this estimated time.

**d**  Find the percentage difference in the calculated speeds, in terms of the faster speed.

**86** The Venn diagram shows the IASAS sports played by a group of students. The sets show how many play soccer ($S$), rugby ($R$), and do track ($T$). Find:

**a**  the total number of students in the group

**b**  the probability that a randomly chosen student plays only rugby

**c**  the probability that a randomly chosen student takes soccer and track only

**d**  the probability that a randomly chosen student plays soccer, given that he or she plays rugby.

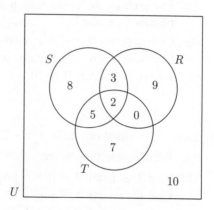

**87** The value of a car over time is calculated using the function $v = 24\,000r^t$, where $v$ is the value of the car in dollars, $t$ is the number of years after it was first purchased, and $r$ is a constant, $t \geqslant 0$ and $0 < r < 1$.

   **a** Write down the value of the car when it was first purchased.

   **b** If the value of the car after one year was $20\,400, find the value of $r$.

   **c** How long it will take for the value of the car to reduce to $8000? Give your answer to the nearest year.

**88** ABCD is a trapezium with BC parallel to AD. AD = 22 cm, BC = 12 cm, AB = 13 cm, and AE = 5 cm.

   **a** Calculate the height BE of the trapezium.

   **b** Calculate:

      **i** $B\widehat{A}E$         **ii** $A\widehat{B}C$

   **c** Calculate the length of the diagonal AC.

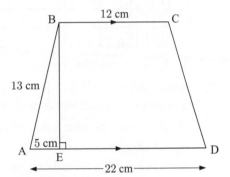

**89** Siddhanth is planning to buy a car when he finishes University in four years' time. The current price of the car is $15\,000.

   **a** Calculate the amount he needs to put in an account now, paying a nominal interest rate of 6.20% p.a. compounding monthly, to provide the money he wants in four years' time.

   **b** The price of the car is likely to increase in line with the rate of inflation, which is averaging 2.6% per annum. Estimate the price of the car in four years' time.

   **c** How much extra will he have to place in the account now to cover the effects of inflation?

**90** Ten students were given aptitude tests, one on language skills and one on mathematics. The table shows the results of these tests.

| Language $(x)$ | 12.5 | 15.0 | 10.5 | 12.0 | 9.5 | 10.5 | 15.5 | 10.0 | 14.0 | 12.0 |
|---|---|---|---|---|---|---|---|---|---|---|
| Mathematics $(y)$ | 32 | 45 | 27 | 38 | 18 | 25 | 35 | 22 | 40 | 40 |

   **a** Plot the data on a scatter diagram.

   **b** Given that the covariance $s_{xy}$ is 13.8, and the standard deviation of $x$ is 2.00, show that the correlation coefficient $r$ is 0.82, correct to two decimal places.

   **c** Use your results from **a** and **b** to comment on the statement:

        "Those who do well in language also do well in mathematics."

**91** Consider the function $f(x) = \dfrac{8}{x^2} + 2x - 3$.

   **a** Differentiate $f(x)$ with respect to $x$.

   **b** Find $f'(1)$ and explain what it represents.

   **c** Find the coordinates of the point where the gradient of the curve is zero.

**92**  **a**  Complete the truth table for the compound proposition $\neg b \wedge (c \Rightarrow (b \wedge a)) \Rightarrow \neg c$

| $a$ | $b$ | $c$ | $\neg b$ | $b \wedge a$ | $c \Rightarrow (b \wedge a)$ | $\neg b \wedge (c \Rightarrow (b \wedge a))$ | $\neg c$ | $\neg b \wedge (c \Rightarrow (b \wedge a)) \Rightarrow \neg c$ |
|---|---|---|---|---|---|---|---|---|
| T | T | T | | | | | | |
| T | T | F | | | | | | |
| T | F | T | | | | | | |
| T | F | F | | | | | | |
| F | T | T | | | | | | |
| F | T | F | | | | | | |
| F | F | T | | | | | | |
| F | F | F | | | | | | |

**b**  Is the proposition $\neg b \wedge (c \Rightarrow (b \wedge a)) \Rightarrow \neg c$ a tautology, a contradiction, or neither?

**93**  Melissa deposits €50 000 into a bank account which pays 6% p.a. simple interest. No extra money is deposited or withdrawn.

**a**  Determine the total value of the investment after:

  **i**  1 year                    **ii**  2 years.

**b**  Write down a formula for the total value of the investment after $n$ years.

**c**  Hence, calculate the number of years required for Melissa to double her original deposit.

**94**  Consider the function $f(x) = 12\cos 6x + 20$ on the restricted domain shown.

**a**  For this function, write down the:

  **i**  domain                    **ii**  range.

**b**  Determine the amplitude of $f(x)$.

**c**  A horizontal line $y = k$ is drawn such that it meets $y = f(x)$ exactly once. Determine the value of $k$.

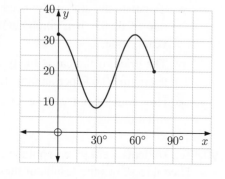

**95**  Consider A$(-4, 2)$ and B$(6, 6)$.

**a**  Write down the coordinates of M, the midpoint of the line segment AB.

**b**  Find the gradient of AB.

**c**  Line $L$ is perpendicular to AB and passes through M. Determine the equation of line $L$, giving your answer in the form $ax + by + d = 0$.

**d**  Hence, calculate the $x$-intercept of line $L$.

**96**  Greg needs to travel from Australia to Sweden for work. Prior to leaving, he converts Australian dollars (AUD) into Swedish kronor (SEK). The bank offers the rates in the table shown.

| 1 AUD | Buy | Sell |
|---|---|---|
| SEK | 6.36 | 6.39 |

**a**  If Greg exchanges 1000 Australian dollars into Swedish kronor, how much will he receive?

**b**  If Greg immediately exchanged his Swedish kronor back into Australian dollars, how much would he receive?

**c**  Calculate the resulting percentage loss if Greg converted his money from AUD into SEK and immediately back into AUD.

**97** The manager of a bank decides to investigate the time customers wait to be served. Most of the results are shown in the table below, and they are illustrated in the cumulative frequency graph alongside it.

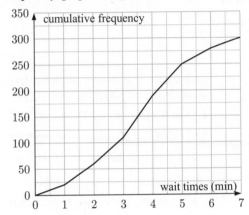

| Waiting time (t) in minutes | Number of customers |
|---|---|
| $0 \leqslant t < 1$ | $p$ |
| $1 \leqslant t < 2$ | 40 |
| $2 \leqslant t < 3$ | 50 |
| $3 \leqslant t < 4$ | 80 |
| $4 \leqslant t < 5$ | 60 |
| $5 \leqslant t < 6$ | $q$ |
| $6 \leqslant t < 7$ | 20 |

**a** Use the graph to estimate the median waiting time.

**b** Determine the values of $p$ and $q$.

**c** Hence, draw a frequency histogram for the data.

**98** The graph shows $y = \dfrac{4}{x}$ for $x > 0$.

Points $A(1, p)$ and $B(q, 1)$ lie on the curve.

**a** Determine the value of:

    **i** $p$         **ii** $q$

**b** Evaluate the gradient of line segment AB.

**c** Point C also lies on $y = \dfrac{4}{x}$. The tangent at C is parallel to AB.
Determine the coordinates of C.

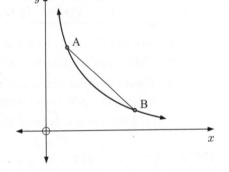

**99** A woman deposits $100 into her son's savings account on his first birthday. She deposits $125 on his second birthday, $150 on his third birthday, and so on.

**a** Calculate the amount of money she will deposit into her son's account on his 15th birthday.

**b** Find the total amount she will have deposited over the 15 years.

**100** The table shows the relative frequencies of the ages of the students at a school.

**a** If a student is randomly selected from this school, find the probability that the student is:

    **i** 13 or 14 years old

    **ii** 15 years of age or older.

**b** There are 900 students at the school.
Calculate the number of 17 year old students.

| Age (years) | Relative frequency |
|---|---|
| 13 | 0.16 |
| 14 | 0.25 |
| 15 | 0.28 |
| 16 | 0.20 |
| 17 | 0.11 |
| Total | 1 |

**101**  Consider the function  $f(x) = \sin(2x) - 2$  where  $0^\circ \leqslant x \leqslant 180^\circ$.

    **a**  Sketch this function for the given domain.

    **b**  Write down the period of the function.

    **c**  Find the minimum value of the function.

    **d**  Solve  $f(x) = -2.5$  for  $0^\circ \leqslant x \leqslant 180^\circ$.

**102**

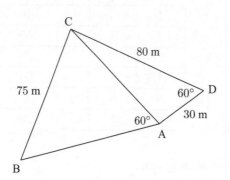

The figure shows two adjacent triangular fields ABC and ACD where  $AD = 30$  m,  $CD = 80$  m,  $BC = 75$  m,  $A\widehat{D}C = 60^\circ$, and  $B\widehat{A}C = 60^\circ$.

    **a**  Calculate the length of AC.

    **b**  Calculate the size of  $A\widehat{B}C$.

    **c**  Find the total area of the fields.

**103**  The following table gives the amount of petrol remaining in a motorbike's fuel tank and the number of kilometres travelled. The capacity of the tank is 10 litres.

| Remaining fuel ($x$ litres) | 10 | 8 | 6 | 4 | 2 | 1 |
|---|---|---|---|---|---|---|
| Distance ($y$ km) | 0 | 90 | 190 | 260 | 330 | 370 |

    **a**  Plot this data on a scatter diagram.

    **b**  Write down the equation of the straight line of regression for $y$ against $x$.

    **c**  The motorbike has travelled 220 km since its tank was refilled. Use your regression equation to estimate the amount of fuel left in the tank.

    **d**  Find the average distance travelled per litre over the 220 km.

**104**  \$10 000 is invested at 8.5% p.a. interest compounded monthly over 5 years. Find:

    **a**  the value of the investment after 5 years

    **b**  the amount of interest earned

    **c**  how much more interest would have been earned if the interest rate had been 9.5% p.a.

**105**  The diagram shows the graph of  $y = x^2 - ax$.

    **a**  Find the value of $a$.

    **b**  Find  $\dfrac{dy}{dx}$.

    **c**  Find the coordinates of the minimum point of the graph.

    **d**  Find the gradient of the tangent to the curve at  $x = 3$.

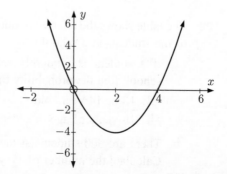

**106** Suppose $a = \frac{3}{7}$, $b = 8$, $c = \sqrt{2}$ and $d = 1 \times 10^{-2}$. Classify each of the following statements as true or false:

    **a** $7a \in \mathbb{N}$          **b** $c^2 - b \notin \mathbb{N}$          **c** $\frac{1}{d} \geqslant c^b$

    **d** $\frac{c}{b} \in \mathbb{Q}$          **e** $\sqrt{a - b} \in \mathbb{R}$

**107** For the two events $A$ and $B$, it is known that $P(A) = \frac{3}{7}$ and $P(B') = \frac{2}{3}$.

    **a** Determine $P(B)$.

    **b** Calculate $P(A \cup B)$ if $A$ and $B$ are:

        **i** mutually exclusive          **ii** independent.

**108** The graph shows the number of hours of daylight ($D$) experienced by a town, $t$ months after January 1st on any given year.

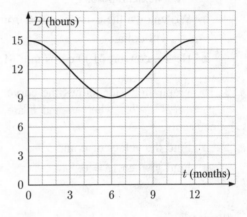

    **a** Find the minimum hours of daylight, and when this occurs.

    **b** Find the time since January 1st, for the number of hours of daylight to drop below 10.5.

    **c** For how many months of the year are there at least 13.5 hours of daylight?

    **d** The equation for the graph above has the form $D(t) = p\cos(qt)^\circ + r$. Find the values of $p$, $q$ and $r$.

**109** A $\chi^2$ test at a 5% significance level is used to determine whether *intelligence* is independent of *income level*. For this test, intelligence and income were each split into three classes. The resulting $\chi^2$ test statistic was 8.23.

    **a** State the null and alternative hypotheses.

    **b** Determine the number of degrees of freedom.

    **c** State the value of $\chi^2_{crit}$.

    **d** Based on these results, what conclusion can be drawn regarding *intelligence* and *income level*?

**110** Let $f(x) = \frac{1}{4}x^4 - 2x^2$.

    **a** Find $f'(x)$.

    **b** Evaluate $f'(-3)$, $f'(-2)$ and $f'(-1)$.

    **c** Hence, describe what happens to $f(x)$ at $x = -2$.

    **d** The graph of $y = f(x)$ has exactly 3 turning points. Given $(0, 0)$ is a local maximum and $(2, -4)$ is a local minimum, write down the values of $x$ for which $f(x)$ is increasing.

**111** P$(-3, 0)$, Q$(0, 4)$ and R$(8, 0)$ form the vertices of a triangle. The length of QR is $\sqrt{80}$ units.

    **a** Calculate the length of:    **i** PR    **ii** PQ.

    **b** Determine the size of angle QPR, giving your answer correct to 2 decimal places.

    **c** Calculate the area of triangle PQR.

**112** Consider the following currency conversions between US dollars (USD), Mexican pesos (MXN) and euros (EUR).

$$1 \text{ USD} = 13 \text{ MXN}$$
$$1 \text{ USD} = 0.65 \text{ EUR}$$

    **a** Convert 2750 US dollars into:

        **i** Mexican pesos               **ii** euros.

    **b** Write down the exchange rate from euros to:

        **i** US dollars                 **ii** Mexican pesos.

    **c** Hence, convert 5100 euros into Mexican pesos.

**113** The graph alongside shows the curve $y = a(2^x) + b$, where $a$ and $b$ are constants.

    **a** Find the values of $a$ and $b$.

    **b** Find $y$ when $x = 6$.

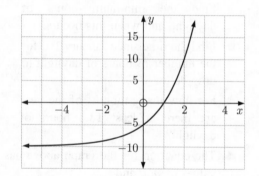

**114** The fourth term of an arithmetic sequence is 22 and the tenth term is 70. Suppose the first term is $u_1$ and the common difference is $d$.

    **a** Write down two equations in $u_1$ and $d$ that satisfy this information.

    **b** Solve the equations to find the values of $u_1$ and $d$.

    **c** Find the sum of the first 10 terms of the sequence.

**115** The table shows the number of left and right handed writers in a sample of 50 students.

|  | Left handed | Right handed | Total |
|---|---|---|---|
| Male | 4 | 26 | 30 |
| Female |  |  | 20 |
| Total | 7 |  | 50 |

    **a** Complete the table.

    **b** If a student was selected at random from the group, find the probability that the student is:

        **i** left handed              **ii** male and right handed

       **iii** right handed, given that the student is female.

**116** Find the value of $k$ if the lines $4x - 5y = 11$ and $2x + ky = -8$ are:

    **a** parallel             **b** perpendicular.

**117** The scatter diagram displays the amount James has spent on coffee in the cafeteria against the number of hours he was at work that week.

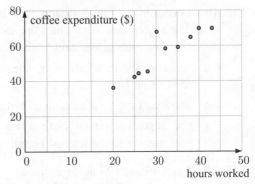

**a** James worked an average of 32 hours, and his average expenditure was $56 per week. Plot the mean point P(32, 56) on the graph.

**b** Draw the line of best fit passing through P.

**c** Use this line to predict the amount James will spend on coffee if he works a 35 hour week.

**d** Describe the nature and strength of the linear relationship between the length of time James works and the amount he spends on coffee. Comment on whether the predicted quantity found in **c** is a reliable estimate.

**118** A straight line $L$ has equation $54x - 2y = 17$.

**a** Find the gradient of the line.

**b** A curve has equation $y - x^3 = -12$, $0 \leqslant x \leqslant 5$. Find the gradient function for the curve.

**c** A tangent to the curve at point P is parallel to the straight line $L$. Find the coordinates of P.

**119** The rate of inflation since the beginning of 2002 has averaged $3\frac{1}{2}\%$ per year.

**a** A loaf of bread cost €1.40 on January 1, 2002. If the price increased at the same rate as inflation, find the cost of a loaf of bread on January 1, 2007.

**b** The value of a block of land was €260 000 on January 1, 2009. If the price had followed inflation, calculate its value on January 1, 2002.

**120** A group of 50 employees were surveyed regarding their interest in music, sport, and computers. The number of employees interested in each area is shown in the Venn diagram.

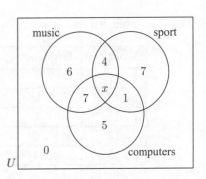

**a** Write down the value of $x$.

**b** If an employee is selected at random, determine the probability that they are:

  **i** interested in music

  **ii** interested in music, sport, and computers

  **iii** not interested in computers

  **iv** interested in sport, given that they are interested in music.

**121** The tangent to the curve $y = ax^2 - \dfrac{b}{x}$ at $x = -0.5$ is horizontal.

**a** Show that $a = 4b$.

**b** Given that the tangent at $x = -0.5$ has the equation $y = 3$, show that $a + 8b = 12$.

**c** Use the equations from **a** and **b** to determine the values of $a$ and $b$.

**122** Brian deposits £$x$ into his daughter's bank account on her 1st birthday. On her second birthday, he deposits £$1.5x$ into the account, and continues to add £$0.5x$ to the amount deposited for each subsequent birthday. The final deposit is made on her 20th birthday.

  **a** Write down, in terms of $x$, the amount Brian deposits into his daughter's bank account on her 3rd birthday.

  **b** Show that the total amount of birthday money Brian deposits is £$115x$.

  **c** For the total amount of birthday money to reach £20 000, find the value of $x$. Round your answer to the nearest pound.

**123** The depth of water $D$ at the entrance to a harbour $t$ hours after midnight on a particular day is given by $D(t) = 8 - 4\sin(15t)^\circ$ metres, $0 \leqslant t \leqslant 24$.

  **a** Determine the depth of water when:

  **i** $t = 0$ hours            **ii** $t = 14$ hours.

  **b** Write down the maximum depth of water.

  **c** At what time does the maximum depth of water occur?

  **d** Between what times is the water depth less than 6 metres?

**124** Line $L_1$ passes through $(0, 3)$ and $(6, 0)$.
Line $L_2$ has equation $y = -\frac{1}{2}x - 4$.

  **a** Show that $L_1$ is parallel to $L_2$.

  **b** Line $L_3$ is perpendicular to $L_1$ and meets $L_1$ at $(0, 3)$. Write down the equation of $L_3$, giving your answer in the form $y = ax + b$.

  **c** At what point does line $L_2$ meet $L_3$?

  **d** Calculate the perpendicular distance $d$ between $L_1$ and $L_2$.

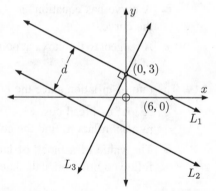

**125** The table and histogram below represent the same set of data.

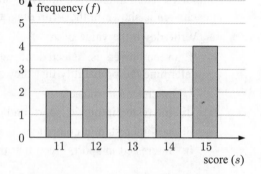

| Score ($s$) | Frequency ($f$) | $s \times f$ |
|:---:|:---:|:---:|
| 11 | 2 | 22 |
| 12 | $w$ | $x$ |
| 13 | 5 | 65 |
| 14 | 2 | 28 |
| 15 | 4 | 60 |
| Totals | $y$ | $z$ |

  **a** Determine the modal score.

  **b** Determine the value of:

  **i** $w$          **ii** $x$          **iii** $y$          **iv** $z$

  **c** Evaluate $\dfrac{z}{y}$ and interpret its meaning.

**126** ¥600 000 is to be invested for 6 years.

    **a** Simple Society Bank offers a return of 7% p.a. simple interest. Calculate the amount of interest this account will generate over the 6 year period.

    **b** Compound Credit Union offers a return of $r$% p.a. interest compounded monthly. What rate of $r$ is needed for Compound Credit Union to match the amount of interest offered by Simple Society Bank?

**127** The $n$th term of an arithmetic sequence is given by $u_n = 63 - 4n$.

    **a** Calculate the first two terms of this sequence.

    **b** Which term of the sequence is $-13$?

    **c** Two consecutive terms of this sequence, $u_k$ and $u_{k+1}$, have the sum 34. Find $k$.

**128** The box contains 8 red pens and 12 green pens. Juanita takes one pen from the box and notes its colour. She then takes a second pen from the box without replacing the first pen.

    **a** Complete the tree diagram alongside to show all probabilities.

    **b** Find the probability that she chooses two red pens.

    **c** Find the probability that she chooses at least one green pen.

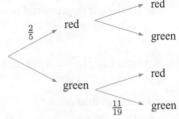

**129** A flu virus spreads in a school according to the exponential model   $N = 4 \times (1.775)^{0.5t}$. where $N$ is the number of people who have caught the virus, and $t$ is the number of days after the virus was first detected, $t \geqslant 0$.

    **a** Find the number of people who were initially infected.

    **b** Calculate the number of people who were infected after 16 days.

    **c** There are 1200 people in the school. Estimate the time it will take for everybody in the school to catch the flu.

**130** OABCD is a square based pyramid with base sides 4 cm, as shown in the diagram. Each slant edge of the pyramid is 7 cm long. DX is the perpendicular height of the pyramid.

    **a** Calculate the length of BX.

    **b** Calculate the angle between the line DB and the base OABC. Give your answer to the nearest degree.

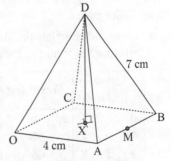

**131** A 60 cm length of wire is bent into a rectangle with length $x$ cm and width $y$ cm.

    **a** Use the given information to write an expression for $y$ in terms of $x$.

    **b** Write an expression for the area $A(x)$ of the rectangle enclosed by the wire.

    **c** Find $A'(x)$.

    **d** Use your answer to **c** to determine the value of $x$ which maximises the area. What are the dimensions of the rectangle in this case?

**132** The table below shows the sizes of drinks purchased from a store at different times of the day.

|          | Small | Medium | Large |
|----------|-------|--------|-------|
| Morning  | 15    | 23     | 4     |
| Afternoon| 24    | 24     | 11    |
| Evening  | 6     | 18     | 8     |

 a Write a suitable null hypothesis for a $\chi^2$ test on this data.

 b Write down the value of $\chi^2$.

 c Determine the number of degrees of freedom.

 d Given that the critical value at the 5% level of significance is 9.488, what conclusion can be drawn from this test? Justify your answer.

**133** The value of a car purchased 5 years ago for $21\,000$ depreciated in value by 15% in the first year, 12.5% in the second year, and 10% in the third year.

 a Find the average annual compounding rate of depreciation for the first 3 years. Give your answer correct to 3 decimal places.

 b If the car depreciated over the 5 years by the average rate found in a, find the current value of the car.

**134** A graph of $f(x) = a\sin bx + 4$ is defined for $0^o \leqslant x \leqslant 180^o$.

 a Find $a$ and $b$.

 b Using the graph of $y = f(x)$, solve $f'(x) = 0$.

 c Find the intervals where $f(x)$ is increasing.

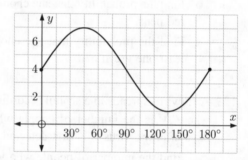

 d Find the equations of any horizontal tangents to $y = f(x)$.

**135** The given histogram shows the frequencies of a set of lengths.

 a Copy and complete the table below using information from the histogram.

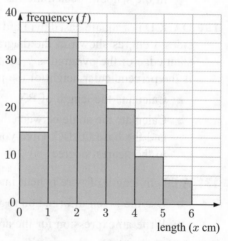

| Length ($x$ cm) | Frequency | Cumulative frequency |
|-----------------|-----------|----------------------|
| $0 \leqslant x < 1$ | 15 | 15 |
| $1 \leqslant x < 2$ | 35 | 50 |
| $2 \leqslant x < 3$ | 25 | 75 |
| $3 \leqslant x < 4$ | 20 | 95 |
| $4 \leqslant x < 5$ |    |    |
| $5 \leqslant x < 6$ |    |    |

 b Draw a cumulative frequency graph to represent this data.

 c Hence, estimate the 60th percentile.

**136** The statement *"If I watch a movie then I will relax"* consists of two propositions $p$ and $q$ such that $p \Rightarrow q$.

  **a** State $p$ and $q$ in words.

  **b** Under what conditions is the statement $p \Rightarrow q$ false?

  **c** In words, write down the contrapositive to $p \Rightarrow q$.

  **d** By completing the truth table below, show that the implication $p \Rightarrow q$ is logically equivalent to its contrapositive.

Contrapositive to $p \Rightarrow q$

| $p$ | $q$ | $\neg p$ | $\neg q$ | $p \Rightarrow q$ | |
|-----|-----|----------|----------|-------------------|---|
| T | T | | | | |
| T | F | | | | |
| F | T | | | | |
| F | F | | | | |

**137** Shane needs to borrow \$30 000 to be repaid over 5 years. He considers two financial institutions:

  • Classic Credit Union charge 6% p.a. simple interest over the loan term.

  • Superior Bank charge 8% p.a. compound interest according to the loan repayment schedule below.

| Total monthly repayment per \$10 000 borrowed | | | | | |
|---|---|---|---|---|---|
| Loan Term | Annual Interest Rate | | | | |
| (years) | 6 | 7 | 8 | 9 | 10 |
| 5 | 193.3280 | 198.0112 | 202.7634 | 207.5836 | 212.4704 |
| 10 | 111.0205 | 116.1085 | 121.3276 | 126.6758 | 132.1507 |
| 15 | 84.3857 | 89.8828 | 95.5652 | 101.4267 | 107.4605 |
| 20 | 71.6431 | 77.5299 | 83.6440 | 89.9726 | 96.5022 |

  **a** If Shane borrowed from Classic Credit Union, calculate the total amount of interest to be paid on the loan.

  **b** If Shane borrowed from Superior Bank, calculate the:

    **i** monthly repayment         **ii** total repayment.

  **c** Which financial institution charges the least interest overall? How much less do they charge?

**138** BCDE is the square base of the pyramid ABCDE. O is the centre of BCDE, and the vertex A sits directly above O. M is the midpont of CD.

  **a** If A sits 12 cm directly above O, and AM is 13 cm in length, calculate the length of OM.

  **b** Calculate the volume of the pyramid.

  **c** What angle do the triangular sides of the pyramid make with the square base?

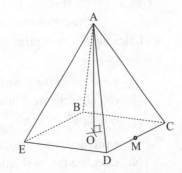

**139** An arithmetic sequence begins with the values 21, 29, 37, 45, ....

   **a** Write an expression for:

      **i** the $n$th term       **ii** the sum of the first $n$ terms.

   **b** Hence, determine the exact value of:

      **i** the 50th term       **ii** the sum of the first 50 terms.

**140** A tightrope connects two elevated platforms A and B. The curve of a tightrope between these platforms is given by the equation $y = 0.008x^2 - 0.8x + 50$. The units are metres.

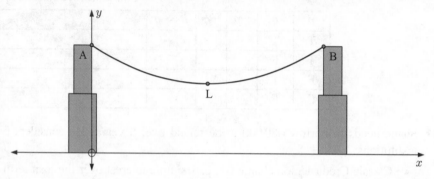

   **a** Find the height of the platform at A.

   **b** Given that platform B has the same height as platform A, determine:

      **i** the distance between the two platforms

      **ii** the domain for which $y = 0.008x^2 - 0.8x + 50$ represents the tightrope.

   **c** L is the lowest point along the tightrope. Determine the coordinates of L.

## B                LONG QUESTIONS

### EXERCISE 24B

**1** A competition offers three options for the first prize, each of which pays the winner a monthly sum for 24 months.

   *Option 1:* $8000 per month.

   *Option 2:* $1000 in the first month, then each successive month pays $600 more than the previous month.

   *Option 3:* $500 in the first month, then each successive month pays 20% more than the previous month.

   **a** Calculate the total prize value for *Option 1*.

   **b** For *Option 2*:

      **i** write down the amount won in each of the first three months

      **ii** calculate the total amount won over the 24 month period.

   **c** For *Option 3*:

      **i** write down the amount won in each of the first three months

      **ii** calculate the total amount won over the 24 month period.

**d** Which option is worth the greatest amount of money overall?

**e** The amount won in the first month under *Option 3* is to be altered so that the total prize over 24 months is worth $250 000. Calculate the new initial amount, writing your answer to the nearest cent.

**2** A jukebox contains 100 different songs, 60 of which are classified as rock songs. Songs from the jukebox are played at random and can be repeated.

**a** If two songs are played, what is the probability that:

**i** both are rock songs   **ii** one is a rock song   **iii** neither is a rock song?

**b** Explain why the sum of the results in **a** is 1.

**c** If three songs are played consecutively, determine the probability that they are all rock songs.

**d** The jukebox is altered so that once a song has been played, it cannot be repeated until all the songs are played. Complete a tree diagram showing the possible outcomes for the first three songs played.

Hence, or otherwise, determine the probability that:

**i** exactly one of the first three songs is a rock song

**ii** at least one of the first three songs is a rock song.

**3** Consider the function $f(x) = \dfrac{4}{x-1} + 2$.

**a** Find the axes intercepts for the graph $y = f(x)$.

**b** Determine the equations of the horizontal and vertical asymptotes of the function.

**c** Hence, write down the domain and range of the function.

**d** Draw the graph of $y = f(x)$ for the region $-6 \leqslant x \leqslant 6$, $-12 \leqslant y \leqslant 12$.

**e** Using an algebraic method, solve the equation $\dfrac{4}{x-1} + 2 = x + 1$.

**f** Hence, or otherwise, find the points where $y = f(x)$ intersects $y = x + 1$.

**g** Add the graph of $y = x + 1$ to the graph of $y = f(x)$ drawn in **d**.

**4** Line $S$ has equation $3x + 4y = 24$. It intersects the $x$-axis at A and the $y$-axis at B.

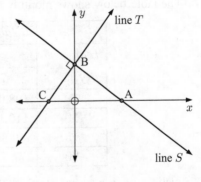

**a** Write down the coordinates of:

**i** A          **ii** B.

**b** Determine the:

**i** gradient of AB

**ii** distance between A and B.

**c** Line $T$ is drawn through point B perpendicular to line $S$. Determine the equation of line $T$.

**d** Line $T$ cuts the $x$-axis at C. Calculate the area of triangle ABC.

**e** Point D lies on the line segment AC such that the area of triangle ABD is 15 units$^2$. Determine the coordinates of D.

**5** To test the difficulty level of a new computer game, a company measures the time taken for a group of players to complete the game. Their results are displayed in the table opposite.

| Completion time (minutes) | Number of players |
|---|---|
| $0 \leqslant t < 30$ | 1 |
| $30 \leqslant t < 60$ | 4 |
| $60 \leqslant t < 90$ | 12 |
| $90 \leqslant t < 120$ | 18 |
| $120 \leqslant t < 150$ | 7 |
| $150 \leqslant t < 180$ | 2 |

  **a** How many players were surveyed?

  **b** Write down the modal class.

  **c** Using graph paper, draw a cumulative frequency graph for the data. Use 1 cm to represent 15 minutes on the horizontal axis, and 1 cm to represent 4 individuals on the vertical axis.

  **d** The game is considered too easy if either the mean or median completion time is below 90 minutes.

   **i** Estimate the median completion time using your cumulative frequency graph.

   **ii** Estimate the mean completion time using your calculator.

   **iii** Hence, comment on whether the game is too easy.

  **e** Complete the sentence below:

  The middle 50% of players completed the game in times between .... and .... minutes.

**6** Let $f(x) = x^3 - 6x^2 + px + q$, where $p$ and $q$ are real constants.

  **a** Find $f'(x)$.

  **b** The graph of $f(x)$ has a local maximum at $(1, 7)$. Find the values of $p$ and $q$.

  **c** By solving $f'(x) = 0$, determine the coordinates of a local minimum of the function.

  **d** Sketch $y = f(x)$ on the region $-1 \leqslant x \leqslant 5$, $-10 \leqslant y \leqslant 25$. Clearly show all turning points and axes intercepts.

  **e** Consider the tangent to $y = f(x)$ at $(1, 7)$.

   **i** Add this tangent to your sketch from **d**.

   **ii** Write down the equation of this tangent.

   **iii** At what other point does the tangent meet the curve?

**7** The table below shows monthly repayments per $10 000 borrowed.

| | Table of monthly repayments per $10 000 | | | |
|---|---|---|---|---|
| Loan term | Annual Interest Rate (% p.a.) | | | |
| (years) | 7 | 8 | 9 | 10 |
| 5 | 198.0112 | 202.7634 | 207.5836 | 212.4704 |
| 10 | 116.1085 | 121.3276 | 126.6758 | 132.1507 |
| 15 | 89.8828 | 95.5652 | 101.4267 | 107.4605 |
| 20 | 77.5299 | 83.6440 | 89.9726 | 96.5022 |

Justin buys a new car worth $60 000. He borrows the money at 8% p.a. over a loan term of 10 years.

  **a** Use the table of monthly repayments to determine the amount Justin will be required to repay each month.

**b** Determine the total amount Justin will repay over the 10 year loan term.

**c** How much interest will Justin pay in total?

**d** What rate of simple interest would be required to generate the same amount of interest on $60 000 over the same time period?

**e** The car Justin purchased depreciates at a rate of 20% p.a.

   **i** Calculate the value of the car at the end of 10 years.

   **ii** Calculate the fall in value of the car over 10 years.

**8** The racquet sports offered at a local club are tennis ($T$), badminton ($B$), and squash ($S$). The Venn diagram alongside shows the number of members involved in these activities.

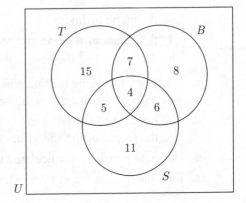

**a** Write down the number of members in the club.

**b** Write down the number of members who:

   **i** only play badminton

   **ii** do not play tennis

   **iii** play both tennis and squash, but not badminton.

**c** Is $\{\ \} \subset B$?

**d** Copy the diagram above, and shade the part that represents $S \cap (T \cup B)$.

**e** Write down the number of members in $S \cap (T \cup B)'$.

**9** A bag contains 5 red marbles and 3 green marbles.

**a** One marble is taken out of the bag. Find the probability that the marble is:

   **i** not red                                        **ii** red or green.

**b** One marble is taken out and its colour noted before it is returned to the bag. A second marble is then taken out of the bag. Find the probability that:

   **i** both marbles are red                           **ii** at least one marble is red.

**c** Two marbles are taken out of the bag at the same time. Find the probability that:

   **i** both marbles are green                         **ii** exactly one marble is green.

**d** Three marbles are taken out of the bag at the same time. Find the probability that exactly two of them are red.

**10** The vertices of a triangle are P(3, 5), Q(10, 6), and R($a$, 4). R is in the first quadrant.

**a** Calculate the distance PQ.

**b** If the distance PR is the same as PQ, find the value of $a$.

**c** Find the gradient of the line PQ.

**d** Find the equation of the line which passes through P and Q.

**e** The line through PQ meets the $x$-axis at S. Write down the coordinates of S.

**f** Find the angle between the $x$-axis and the line RS.

**11** The graph below shows the tide height in the local harbour $t$ hours after midnight.

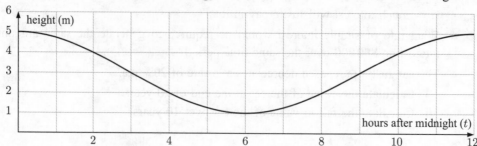

  **a** Use the graph to find:

    **i** the height of the tide at 2 am

    **ii** the time when the height of the tide is at a minimum.

  **b** Boats can access the harbour when the tide is *above* 3 metres. State the time interval when a boat can access the harbour.

  **c** The height $h$ of the tide can be modelled by the function $h(t) = a\cos(bt)° + c$. Use the graph to find the values of $a$, $b$ and $c$.

  **d** Use your equation to calculate the height of the tide at 2 pm.

  **e** Find the time in the evening when the tide will be at its lowest point.

**12** The lengths and weights of 10 melons are shown in the table below.

| Length, $x$ cm | 32 | 40 | 43 | 36 | 42 | 35 | 38 | 46 | 36 | 44 |
|---|---|---|---|---|---|---|---|---|---|---|
| Weight, $y$ kg | 1.9 | 2.8 | 2.8 | 2.4 | 2.5 | 2.3 | 2.6 | 2.8 | 2.0 | 2.5 |

  **a** Plot this information on a scatter diagram. Use a scale of 1 cm to represent 5 cm on the $x$-axis, and 1 cm to represent 0.25 kg on the $y$-axis.

  **b** Use your graphics calculator to calculate the linear correlation coefficient $r$. What does this value tell you about the relationship between the two variables?

  **c** Use your graphics calculator to determine the equation of the line of best fit. Draw this line on your graph.

  **d** Use the line on your graph to estimate:

    **i** the weight of a melon of length 35 cm

    **ii** the length of a melon of weight 2.5 kg.

  **e** The first melon was dropped and so could not be sold. Its data was therefore removed from the collection. Explain briefly what effect this will have on the line of best fit.

**13** Consider the function $f(x) = x^3 - 4x^2 + 3x - 4$.

  **a** Evaluate $f(0)$, $f(1)$ and $f(2)$.

  **b** Find $f'(x)$.

  **c** Write down the coordinates of the points where $f'(x) = 0$.

  **d** Describe the nature of each point found in **c**.

  **e** Sketch the graph of $y = f(x)$ for $-2 \leqslant x \leqslant 4$.

**14**  Billy and Bob each have 5000 US dollars to invest.

Billy invests his $5000 at 6.2% p.a. compounded annually.

Bob invests his $5000 at 5.8% p.a. compounded monthly.

a  Calculate how much money Billy and Bob have after 6 years.

b  Calculate how many years it will take for Billy to have $8500 in the bank.

c  At the beginning of year 7, Bob moves to France. He transfers his money into a bank in France at an exchange rate of 1 USD = 0.68 EUR. The bank charges 1.5% commission for this transaction.

  i  Calculate, in USD, the commission that the bank charges.

  ii  Calculate the amount of euros that Bob transfers to the bank in France. Give your answer correct to the nearest euro.

**15**  a  The 5th term of an arithmetic sequence is 50, and the sum of the first 15 terms is 1200.

  i  Determine two linear equations involving the first term $u_1$ and the common difference $d$.

  ii  Solve these equations simultaneously to find $u_1$ and $d$.

  iii  Write down the first 5 terms of the arithmetic sequence.

b  A geometric sequence begins at 100, and each term is half of the previous one.

  i  Write down the first 5 terms of the geometric sequence.

  ii  Find the sum of the first 10 terms of the sequence correct to 3 significant figures.

  iii  Find the sum of the first 15 terms of the sequence correct to 3 significant figures.

  iv  Explain the similarity in your answers to parts **ii** and **iii**.

c  Hence, or otherwise, determine the sum of the first 15 terms of the sequence $110 + 70 + 55 + 52.5 + ....$   Round your answer to the **nearest hundred**.

**16**  Consider the universal set  $U = \{x \mid 1 \leqslant x \leqslant 15, \ x \in \mathbb{Z}\}$

$P$, $Q$, and $R$ are subsets of $U$, where  $P = \{$factors of 12$\}$,  $Q = \{$multiples of 3$\}$,  and $R = \{$prime numbers$\}$

a  Construct a Venn diagram showing the relationship between $P$, $Q$, and $R$. Show each element of $U$ in an appropriate position.

b  Consider the following propositions:  $p$:  $x$ is a factor of 12.
$q$:  $x$ is a multiple of 3.
$r$:  $x$ is a prime number.

For what values of  $x \in U$  are the following statements true:

  i  $p \wedge q$        ii  $q \veebar r$        iii  $q \wedge \neg r$        iv  $\neg p \wedge \neg q \wedge \neg r$?

c  Consider the statement  $(p \wedge q) \wedge \neg r$.

  i  Write the statement in words.

  ii  Using an appropriate truth table, show that there is only one set of truth values for $p$, $q$ and $r$ which make this statement true. State the truth values of $p$, $q$ and $r$ in this case.

  iii  For what values of $x$ is  $(p \wedge q) \wedge \neg r$  true?

**17** A function $f$ is defined as $f : x \mapsto x^2 + x - 2$.

  **a** Factorise $f(x)$.

  **b** The graph of $y = f(x)$ has $x$-intercepts $\alpha$ and $\beta$, where $\alpha > \beta$. Find $\alpha$ and $\beta$.

  **c** Determine the coordinates of the vertex of $y = f(x)$.

  **d** Draw the graph $y = f(x)$ for $-5 \leqslant x \leqslant 5$.

  **e** On the same axes, draw the graph of $y = 6 - x$.

  **f** Use your graph to solve $x^2 + x - 2 = 6 - x$.

  **g** Check your answer to **f** using an algebraic method.

**18** Consider the figure shown.

  **a** Find the length of:

    **i** DB         **ii** BC

  **b** Find the measure of:

    **i** $A\hat{B}E$     **ii** $D\hat{B}C$

  **c** Find the area of triangle BCD.

  **d** Find the length of AE.

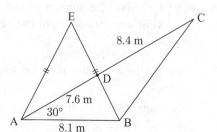

**19** A university lecturer is investigating the association between attendance at lectures and performance within first year mathematics examinations. The lecturer collects the following information:

| Mathematics exam result | Percentage attendance at lectures | | |
|---|---|---|---|
| | 0 - 39 | 40 - 79 | 80 - 100 |
| Pass | 12 | 50 | 78 |
| Fail | 18 | 20 | 22 |

  **a** What proportion of students:

    **i** attended less than 80% of lectures and failed the examination

    **ii** passed the examination after missing more than 60% of the lectures?

  **b** The university lecturer performs a $\chi^2$ test for independence using this data. Write down the:

    **i** null and alternative hypotheses     **ii** number of degrees of freedom

    **iii** value of $\chi^2_{crit}$ if the test is run at a 10% significance level.

  **c** To determine the value of $\chi^2_{calc}$, the university lecturer constructs a table of observed frequency values $f_o$ and expected frequency values $f_e$.

| $f_o$ | $f_e$ | $f_o - f_e$ | $(f_o - f_e)^2$ | $\dfrac{(f_o - f_e)^2}{f_e}$ |
|---|---|---|---|---|
| 12 | 21 | $-9$ | 81 | 3.857 143 |
| 50 | 49 | 1 | 1 | 0.020 408 |
| 78 | 70 | 8 | 64 | 0.914 286 |
| 18 | 9 | 9 | 81 | 9 |
| 20 | 21 | $-1$ | 1 | 0.047 619 |
| 22 | $a$ | $b$ | $c$ | $d$ |
| | | | Total | $\chi^2_{calc}$ |

    **i** Show that $a = 30$.

    **ii** Hence, determine the values of $b$, $c$, and $d$.

    **iii** Write down the value of $\chi^2_{calc}$.

  **d** What conclusion should the lecturer draw from these results? Explain your response.

**20** Consider the function $y = \dfrac{3}{2-x} + 1$.

   **a** Determine the axes intercepts of the graph of the function.

   **b** Sketch the graph of $y = \dfrac{3}{2-x} + 1$ for $-5 \leqslant x \leqslant 10$.

   **c** Write down the equation of the:

      **i** horizontal asymptote       **ii** vertical asymptote.

   **d** Points A$(3, -2)$ and B$(p, q)$ lie on $y = \dfrac{3}{2-x} + 1$ for some $p > 3$.

      Suppose the gradient of line segment AB is $m_{AB}$.

      **i** Explain why $m_{AB} > 0$.       **ii** Show that $m_{AB} = \dfrac{-3}{2-p}$ for $p > 3$.

      **iii** Calculate the missing values $a$ and $b$ in the table below.

| $p$ | 5 | 4 | 3.5 | 3.1 | 3.01 | 3.001 |
|---|---|---|---|---|---|---|
| $m_{AB}$ | 1.0000 | $a$ | 2.0000 | 2.7273 | 2.9703 | $b$ |

      **iv** Hence, or otherwise, comment on the likely value of $\dfrac{dy}{dx}$ at $x = 3$.

**21** The table opposite shows exchange rates between Japanese yen (JPY), Swiss francs (CHF), and British pounds (GBP). The shaded box shows 1 GBP $= 1.6000$ CHF.

| | GBP | CHF | JPY |
|---|---|---|---|
| 1 GBP $=$ | 1 | 1.6000 | $c$ |
| 1 CHF $=$ | $b$ | 1 | 80.000 |
| 1 JPY $=$ | $d$ | 0.0125 | $a$ |

   **a** Using this table, convert:

      **i** 10 000 GBP to CHF       **ii** 2500 CHF to JPY.

   **b** Determine the value of:

      **i** $a$       **ii** $b$

   **c** Write down the value of:

      **i** 1 CHF in JPY       **ii** 1 CHF in GBP.

   **d** Calculate the value of $c$.

   **e** Convert 9000 British pounds into Japanese yen assuming there is a charge of 1.5% commission on the transaction.

   **f** Find $d$ correct to 4 significant figures, giving your answer in the form $a \times 10^k$ where $1 \leqslant a < 10$ and $k \in \mathbb{Z}$.

**22**  **a** Consider $P = \{x \mid 3 \leqslant x < 10,\ x \in \mathbb{Z}\}$, $Q = \{2, 9, 15\}$, and $R = \{$multiples of 3 less than 12$\}$.

      **i** List the elements of $P$.

      **ii** Write down $n(P)$.

      **iii** State whether $P$ is finite or infinite.

      **iv** Explain why:       **(1)** $Q \not\subset P$   **(2)** $R \subset P$.

      **v** List the elements of:    **(1)** $P \cap Q$   **(2)** $R \cap Q$   **(3)** $R \cup Q$.

**b** On Venn diagrams like the one shown, shade the regions which are described by:

  **i** $(A \cup B)' \cap C$

  **ii** $C' \cap B$

  **iii** $B' \cap (A \cap C)$.

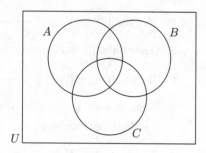

**23** Consider the following propositions:
  $p$: Pepin lives in Jakarta.
  $q$: Pepin rides a motorbike.
  $r$: Pepin plays the guitar.

**a** Write each of the following statements in symbols:

  **i** If Pepin does not ride a motorbike, then he does not live in Jakarta.

  **ii** If Pepin rides a motorbike, then he either lives in Jakarta or plays the guitar.

**b** Consider the compound proposition $\neg r \Rightarrow \neg(q \wedge p)$.

  **i** Write the compound proposition in words.

  **ii** Complete the following truth table for the compound proposition.

| $p$ | $q$ | $r$ | $\neg r$ | $(q \wedge p)$ | $\neg(q \wedge p)$ | $\neg r \Rightarrow \neg(q \wedge p)$ |
|-----|-----|-----|----------|----------------|--------------------|---------------------------------------|
| T | T | T | | | | |
| T | T | F | | | | |
| T | F | T | | | | |
| T | F | F | | | | |
| F | T | T | | | | |
| F | T | F | | | | |
| F | F | T | | | | |
| F | F | F | | | | |

  **iii** State whether the compound statement is a tautology.

  **iv** Describe in words, for the given propositions $p$, $q$ and $r$, the situation where the compound proposition is false.

**24** The daily profit made by a local baker selling $x$ homemade pies is given by
$$P = -0.05x^2 + 9x - 60 \text{ dollars.}$$

**a** Copy and complete the table alongside.

| $x$ | 0 | 20 | 40 | 60 | 80 | 100 |
|-----|---|-----|----|-----|----|-----|
| $P$ | | 100 | | 300 | | 340 |

**b** Plot the points in **a** with $x$ on the horizontal axis and $P$ on the vertical axis. Use these points to sketch the graph of $P$ against $x$.

**c** Find:

  **i** the number of pies that need to be sold to maximise the profit

  **ii** the maximum possible daily profit

  **iii** the number of pies that need to be sold to make a profit of $200

  **iv** the amount of money the baker loses if no pies are sold.

**25** In the diagram opposite, ABEF, ABCD and CDFE are all rectangles.
AD = 12 cm, DC = 20 cm, and DF = 5 cm.
M is the midpoint of EF, and N is the midpoint of CD.

**a** Calculate the length of AN.

**b** Calculate the length of AM.

**c** Calculate the size of the angle AM makes with the base ABCD.

**d** Calculate the area of triangle AMN.

**e** Find the surface area of the solid.

**f** Find the volume of the solid.

**26** The maximum daily temperature and the number of cups of coffee sold at a kiosk that day are given in the following table:

| Temperature ($T°C$) | 21 | 20.7 | 20 | 19 | 18 | 17.3 | 17 | 17.3 | 18 | 19 |
|---|---|---|---|---|---|---|---|---|---|---|
| Coffees sold ($n$) | 120 | 110 | 105 | 125 | 120 | 150 | 140 | 130 | 120 | 120 |

**a** Find:  **i** the mean temperature
  **ii** the standard deviation of the temperatures.

**b** Find the correlation coefficient $r$ and interpret this value.

**c**  **i** Find the equation of the least squares regression line.
  **ii** Estimate how many cups of coffee will be sold when the temperature is 19.6°C.

**d** On a day when the temperature is forecast to be 30°C, the owner estimates that only 40 cups of coffee will be sold. Discuss this estimate by comparison with the line of regression.

**27**  **a** The curve $y = x^3 + ax + b$ has a local minimum at the point $(2, -10)$.
Find the values of $a$ and $b$.

**b** The function $f$ is defined by $f : x \mapsto px^2 + qx + c$ where $p, q, c \in \mathbb{R}$.
$f(x)$ has a minimum value of $-6.8$ at the point A.
  **i** Given that $f'(x) = 10x - 4$, find the values of $p$ and $q$.
  **ii** Find the $x$-coordinate of A.  **iii** Find the value of $c$.

**28** Eddy decides to buy a boat with a price tag of €15 000. Eddy will make payments of €520 per month for three years.

**a** Determine the total amount Eddy will pay for the boat.

**b** Find the amount of interest he will have paid.

**c** Calculate the annual simple interest rate which has been charged.

**d** The local bank offers to lend him the full amount for the boat at a simple interest rate of 8% p.a., to be paid back over four years.
  **i** Calculate the amount Eddy would have to repay each month to the bank.
  **ii** Find the difference between the two monthly repayments.

**29** Let $U = \{\text{positive integers} \leqslant 20\}$,

$X = \{\text{factors of } 24 \text{ which are} \leqslant 20\}$, and $Y = \{\text{multiples of } 4 \text{ which are} \leqslant 20\}$

a List the elements of:

i $X$                    ii $Y$

b Complete the Venn diagram alongside by placing each element of $U$ in an appropriate position.

c Hence, write down the elements of:

i $X \cap Y$          ii $(X \cup Y)'$

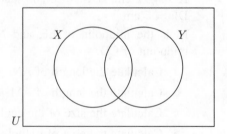

**30** A game is played where tickets are randomly selected from a bag. To begin with the bag contains five tickets, one of which is the winning ticket. Tickets are selected one at a time, without replacement, until the winning ticket is selected. At this point, the game ends.

a A tree diagram is used to illustrate the first two possible selections in the game. Copy and complete the tree diagram by filling in the probability values.

b Use the tree diagram to determine the probability that the game is won in two selections or less.

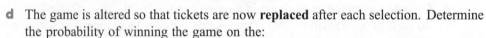

c Determine the probability of winning the game within:

i four selections          ii five selections.

d The game is altered so that tickets are now **replaced** after each selection. Determine the probability of winning the game on the:

i 1st selection          ii 2nd selection          iii 3rd selection.

e Using the results from **d**, determine the probability of winning the game if up to three selections are allowed.

f The values found in **d** form a geometric sequence. For this geometric sequence:

i write down the common ratio

ii show that the sum of the first $n$ terms is $1 - \left(\frac{4}{5}\right)^n$.

g Hence, determine the probability of winning the game if up to fifteen selections are allowed. Write your answer as a percentage, correct to 3 significant figures.

**31** Consider the function $y = 2\cos 3x$.

a For the graph of this function, determine the:

i $y$-intercept          ii period          iii amplitude.

b Draw the graph of $y = 2\cos 3x$ for $0° \leqslant x \leqslant 180°$.

c Which of the results from **a** would change if the original equation were replaced with $y = 2\sin 3x$?

d Sketch $y = 2\sin 3x$ on the same axes used in **b**.

e Use your graph to estimate the solutions to $\cos 3x = \sin 3x$ for $0° \leqslant x \leqslant 180°$.

**32** The points A$(0, 3)$ and B$(4, 0)$ form two vertices of triangle ABC.

**a** For the region $-2 \leqslant x \leqslant 12$, $-2 \leqslant y \leqslant 12$, plot points A and B.

**b** Calculate the distance between A and B.

**c** Find the gradient of the line segment AB.

**d** Given $A\widehat{B}C = 90°$, calculate:

    **i** the gradient of BC     **ii** the equation of the line BC.

**e** Point C has coordinates $(11.2, b)$.

    **i** Find $b$.     **ii** Add point C to your diagram from **a**.

**f** Calculate the area of triangle ABC.

**g** Determine the measure of angle ACB.

**33** A group of 250 IB students were given the option to participate in a survey. The table alongside shows participation levels according to gender.

| | Male | Female |
|---|---|---|
| Participated | 69 | 81 |
| Did not participate | 61 | 39 |

A $\chi^2$ test at a 5% significance level is performed to investigate the following hypotheses:

$H_0$: Participation in the survey was independent of gender.

$H_1$: Participation in the survey was not independent of gender.

**a** Show that the expected number of male students to participate in the survey is 78.

**b** Hence, complete the table of expected values below:

| | Male | Female | |
|---|---|---|---|
| Participated | 78 | | 150 |
| Did not participate | | | 100 |
| | 130 | 120 | |

**c** Write down the number of degrees of freedom.

**d** Determine the value of $\chi^2_{crit}$.

**e** Given $\chi^2_{calc} = 5.41$, discuss whether $H_0$ or $H_1$ is rejected.

**f** What conclusion can be drawn from this $\chi^2$ test?

The 150 completed surveys provided information on how far students travelled to get to school each day. This information is shown in the histogram alongside.

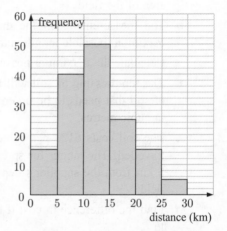

**g** Is the variable *distance* discrete or continuous?

**h** Using your calculator, estimate the:

    **i** mean

    **ii** standard deviation of the data.

**i** A student is selected at random. Given that this student completed a survey, determine the probability the student travels no more than 10 kilometres to school.

**34** A square based cuboid has an open top, as shown.
The cuboid has base width $x$ cm and height $h$ cm.

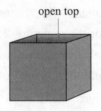

open top

  **a** Given that 4800 cm$^2$ of material was used
to construct this hollow cuboid, show that
$$h = \frac{4800 - x^2}{4x}.$$

  **b** Hence, show that the volume of the cuboid is given by $V = 1200x - \frac{1}{4}x^3$ cm$^3$.

  **c** Find $\dfrac{dV}{dx}$.

  **d** The table alongside shows values of $x$ and $V$.
Find the value of:

| $x$ | 10 | 30 | 60 |
|-----|----|----|-------|
| $V$ | $a$ | $b$ | 18 000 |

    **i** $a$                 **ii** $b$

  **e** Determine the dimensions required to maximise the volume of the cuboid.

  **f** Write down the maximum volume of the cuboid.

**35** Marinda invests €12 000 into a bank account offering 4.2% p.a. interest, compounded quarterly.

  **a** Calculate the interest earned after:

    **i** 1 year            **ii** 3 years.

  **b** Write down a formula for the value of Marinda's investment after $x$ years.

  **c** Determine how long it will take for Marinda's investment to reach €30 000. Give your answer to the nearest year.

  **d** What annual rate of simple interest would be needed for Marinda's investment to reach €30 000 in the same time as found in **c**?

**36** A rectangular field needs to be top-dressed. We need to know the area of the field so we can order the correct amount of soil. The tape measure used to measure the field has marks on it every 10 cm.

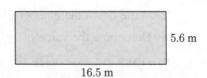

5.6 m

16.5 m

  **a** Use the measurements given to estimate the area of the field.

  **b** The measurements in the diagram involved some inaccuracy. Write down the maximum possible length and width of the field correct to 2 decimal places.

  **c** Calculate the maximum possible area of the field, correct to 3 significant figures.

  **d** The top-dressing of soil will be 2 cm thick across the field. Calculate the amount of soil that needs to be ordered to make sure there is sufficient. Give your answer in cubic metres.

  **e** The soil costs $120 per cubic metre, plus a delivery fee of $27.50 per kilometre travelled. The labour for spreading the soil costs $60 per cubic metre. The field is 5 km from the supplier's depot. Find the maximum total cost for top-dressing the field.

  **f** Find the difference in cost if the amount of soil ordered was based on your answer to **a**.

**37**  There are 60 senior students in a school.  Each of these students studies History, Geography or both of these subjects.  38 students study History, 31 study Geography and $n$ study both.

  **a**  Find the value of $n$.

  **b**  Draw a fully labelled Venn diagram to illustrate this information.

  **c**  Find the probability that a student selected at random studies only one of these subjects.

  **d**  28 of the 60 students are female.  17 females study History, and 15 females study Geography.  Find the probability that a student selected at random:

  **i**  is female and studies exactly one of these subjects

  **ii**  is male and studies both of these subjects.

  **e**  Of the History students, one is randomly selected.  Calculate the probability that this student:

  **i**  is female            **ii**  also studies Geography.

**38**  The intensity of light $L$ diminishes below the surface of the sea according to the formula $L = L_0 \times (0.95)^d$ units,  where $d$ is the depth in metres measured from the surface of the sea.

  **a**  If the intensity of light at the surface is 10 units, calculate the value of $L_0$.

  **b**  Find the intensity of light 25 m below the surface.

  **c**  A light intensity of 4 units is considered adequate for divers to be able to see clearly. Calculate the depth corresponding to this intensity of light.

  **d**  The table gives some values for the intensity of light at different depths.

| Depth ($d$ metres) | 10 | 20 | 30 | 50 |
|---|---|---|---|---|
| Intensity ($L$ units) | 5.99 | 3.58 | 2.15 | 0.769 |

  Using these values and your answers to **a**, **b** and **c**, graph the intensity of light against depth for $0 \leqslant d \leqslant 50$.

  **e**  Calculate the range of depths for which the light intensity is between 1 and 3 units.

**39**  The diagram shows a cuboid which measures 22.5 cm by 30 cm by 40 cm.

  **a**  Find the length of AC.

  **b**  Find the area of the plane ACGE.

  **c**  Find the volume of the triangular prism ACGEFB.

  **d**  Find the length of CE.

  **e**  Find $A\widehat{C}E$.

  **f**  Let M be the midpoint of CE. Find the area of triangle AMC.

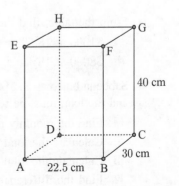

**40** The table shows the time taken for a group of runners to finish a cross country race.

| Time (min) | Number of students |
|---|---|
| $20 \leqslant t < 25$ | 5 |
| $25 \leqslant t < 30$ | 8 |
| $30 \leqslant t < 35$ | 15 |
| $35 \leqslant t < 40$ | 15 |
| $40 \leqslant t < 45$ | 5 |
| $45 \leqslant t < 50$ | 2 |

a Construct a cumulative frequency table for this data.

b Draw the corresponding cumulative frequency curve.

c Use the graph to estimate:
   i the median finishing time
   ii the interquartile range
   iii the number of runners who finished in under 38 minutes
   iv the time it took for the fastest 40% of the runners to complete the course.

d Runners whose times are in the top 30% will receive a certificate. Find the number of runners who will get a certificate.

e The first 3 runners will be awarded medals. Estimate the time that was needed to be awarded a medal.

**41** The cost of producing a pair of shoes is $15, and they are then sold for $x.

a Write an expression for the profit made on each pair sold.

b In a given period, a total of $(1500 - 9x)$ pairs are sold. Show that the profit made on all the shoes sold is $P = 1635x - 9x^2 - 22\,500$.

c Calculate the profit made when the shoes are sold for $100 per pair.

d Find $\dfrac{dP}{dx}$.

e Calculate to the nearest dollar the selling price that will maximise the profit, and find the maximum profit in this case.   '

**42** The table alongside shows the monthly repayments for a loan of 1000 New Zealand dollars, based on interest rates of 18% p.a. and 18.5% p.a.

| Number of years of the loan | Monthly repayments per $1000 | |
|---|---|---|
| | 18% p.a. | 18.5% p.a. |
| 1 | 94.75 | 95.07 |
| 2 | 51.45 | 51.72 |
| 3 | 37.15 | 37.43 |
| 4 | 30.11 | 30.39 |
| 5 | 26.14 | 26.26 |

a From the table, find the monthly repayment for a loan of:
   i $1000 at 18.5% p.a. taken over 1 year
   ii $8000 at 18% p.a. taken over 3 years.

b Sabeena borrows $12\,000$ to buy a motorbike. She must pay interest at 18.5% p.a. and the loan must be repaid over 4 years.
   i Find the monthly repayment.
   ii Calculate the total amount to be repaid on this loan over the 4 years.
   iii Calculate the total amount of interest paid on this loan.
   iv Find the difference in the total amount repaid if Sabeena had taken this loan over 3 years.

**43**  Consider the sum of the first $n$ positive integers $1 + 2 + 3 + .... + n$.

   **a**  Find the sum of the first 10 positive integers.

   **b**  Show that the sum of the first $n$ positive integers is given by the formula $\dfrac{n(n+1)}{2}$.

   **c**  Using this formula, calculate the sum of the first 1000 integers.

   **d**  Determine $n$ such that the sum of the first $n$ positive integers is 11 325.

   **e**  Consider the sequence  7, 14, 21, 28, ....

   **i**  Write an expression for the $n$th term.

   **ii**  Find the largest term which is no greater than 1000.

   **iii**  Determine a formula for the sum of the first $n$ terms.

   **f**  Calculate the sum of the positive integers which are no greater than 1000 and which are *not* divisible by 7.

**44**  A survey is conducted regarding the types of cardio equipment used by the 300 members of a fitness club.

   134 members use rowers $(R)$, 92 use treadmills $(T)$, and 144 use spin-bikes $(S)$.

   19 members use rowers, treadmills and spin-bikes.

   23 members use rowers and treadmills only.

   28 members use treadmills and spin-bikes only.

   41 members use spin-bikes and rowers only.

   **a**  Construct a Venn diagram to represent this information.

   **b**  Determine the number of fitness club members who do not use any type of cardio equipment.

   **c**  Find the proportion of the members that use:

   **i**  all three types of cardio equipment

   **ii**  exactly two of the three types of cardio equipment.

   **d**  Of the members who use at least one type of cardio equipment, what proportion use spin-bikes?

**45**  The data alongside concerns the height and weight of a set of objects. We wish to test the following hypotheses:

   $H_0$:  An object's weight is independent of its height.

   $H_1$:  An object's weight is dependent on its height.

|  | *Height* | | |
|---|---|---|---|
| | Tall | Short | Total |
| Heavy | 26 | 18 | 44 |
| *Weight*   Light | 14 | 30 | 44 |
| Total | 40 | 48 | 88 |

The table below sets out the elements required to calculate $\chi^2$ for this data.

| | $f_o$ | $f_e$ | $f_o - f_e$ | $(f_o - f_e)^2$ | $\dfrac{(f_o - f_e)^2}{f_e}$ |
|---|---|---|---|---|---|
| tall and heavy | 26 | 20 | 6 | 36 | 1.8 |
| short and heavy | 18 | 24 | −6 | 36 | 1.5 |
| tall and light | 14 | 20 | −6 | 36 | 1.8 |
| short and light | 30 | $a$ | $b$ | $c$ | $d$ |

**a** Complete the table by finding the values of $a$, $b$, $c$, and $d$.

**b** Find the value of $\chi^2_{calc}$ for this data.

**c** How many degrees of freedom are there?

**d** Write down the value of $\chi^2_{crit}$ for the 1% significance level.

**e** Should $H_0$ be rejected? Explain your answer and comment on the strength of your argument.

**46** Consider the functions $f(x) = -\cos 2x$ and $g(x) = \cos x + 1$, both defined on the domain $0^\circ \leqslant x \leqslant 360^\circ$.

**a** Write down the period of $f(x)$.

**b** Sketch $y = f(x)$ and $y = g(x)$ on the same set of axes.

**c** Use your graph to write down the *number* of solutions to the following equations for the interval $0^\circ \leqslant x \leqslant 360^\circ$:

  **i** $f(x) = 1$                  **ii** $f(x) = g(x)$

**d** Hence, or otherwise, solve $\cos 2x + \cos x + 1 = 0$ for $0^\circ \leqslant x \leqslant 360^\circ$.

**47** QS is a diagonal of quadrilateral PQRS where $PQ = 3$ cm, $RS = 6$ cm, $PS = 5$ cm, $\widehat{QSR} = 50^\circ$, and $\widehat{QPS} = 60^\circ$.

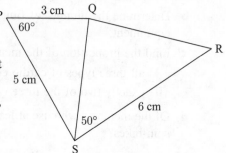

**a** Show that $QS = \sqrt{19}$ cm.

**b** Find the length of QR correct to 4 significant figures.

**c** Hence find, correct to 3 significant figures, the:

  **i** perimeter of PQRS

  **ii** area of PQRS.

**48** **a** Factorise $3x^2 - 8x + 4$.

**b** A function $f$ is defined by $f(x) = x(2 - x)^2$ for $0 \leqslant x \leqslant 2$. By fully expanding $f(x)$, find $f'(x)$.

**c** Hence, solve $f'(x) = 0$.

**d** A graph of $y = f(x)$ is shown alongside. Find the coordinates of the local maximum A.

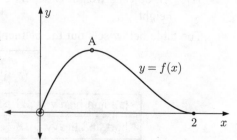

**e** State the range of $f(x)$.

**f** A tangent to $y = f(x)$ is drawn at $(1, 1)$. Determine the equation of this tangent.

**49** Aaron purchased a new car for \$40 000. The car depreciates at 25% p.a.

  **a** Let $V_n$ represent the value of the car after $n$ years.

   **i** Find $V_1$.

   **ii** Show that $V_3 = \$16\,875$.

   **iii** Deduce a formula for $V_n$ using the sequence of values $V_1$, $V_2$, $V_3$, ....

   **iv** Plot $V_n$ for $0 \leqslant n \leqslant 15$.

  **b** Aaron insured his car immediately after it was purchased. Initially, the annual cost of the insurance was \$1200. One year later, the annual insurance cost increased to \$1260.

   **i** Find the percentage increase in the annual insurance cost.

   **ii** Let $P_n$ represent the annual insurance cost after $n$ years, so $P_1 = \$1260$. Assuming the insurance cost increases by the same percentage each year, calculate $P_2$ and $P_3$.

   **iii** Write down a formula for $P_n$ in terms of $n$.

  **c** After how many whole years will the annual cost of car insurance be more than the depreciated value of the car?

**50** A group of students compare their average test results for Physics ($x$) and Chemistry ($y$).

| | Student | | | | | | | | | | | |
|---|---|---|---|---|---|---|---|---|---|---|---|---|
| | A | B | C | D | E | F | G | H | I | J | K | L |
| *Physics Test (x%)* | 43 | 45 | 50 | 51 | 55 | 56 | 59 | 63 | 65 | 72 | 77 | 93 |
| *Chemistry Test (y%)* | 52 | 53 | 57 | 57 | 58 | 62 | 63 | 70 | 72 | 87 | 88 | 100 |

  **a** Draw a scatter diagram for this data.

  **b** Find the mean point $(\overline{x}, \overline{y})$.

  **c** Add an approximate line of best fit to the scatter diagram drawn in **a**.

  **d** Using your graphics calculator, determine:

   **i** the product-moment correlation coefficient $r$

   **ii** the equation of the least squares regression line for $y$ on $x$.

  **e** Hence, predict to the nearest 1% the average test result in Chemistry for a student who achieved an average test result of 85% in Physics.

**51** The table alongside shows the number of balloons in a giant party pack.

| | Red | Yellow | Blue |
|---|---|---|---|
| *Large* | 12 | 5 | 9 |
| *Medium* | 15 | 8 | 10 |
| *Small* | 24 | 11 | 6 |

  **a** **i** Write down the total number of balloons in the pack.

   **ii** Write down the number of medium balloons in the pack.

  **b** One balloon is chosen at random from the pack. Find the probability that:

   **i** the balloon is not yellow       **ii** the balloon is either medium or small.

  **c** Two balloons are selected at random from the pack. Find the probability that:

   **i** both balloons are red         **ii** neither of the balloons are large

   **iii** exactly one of the balloons is blue     **iv** at least one of the balloons is blue.

    **d** Three balloons are selected at random from the pack. Find the probability that:

      **i** all three balloons are small and yellow

      **ii** exactly two balloons are medium and red.

**52**  **a** Sketch the graph of the function $f : x \mapsto 1 - 2\sin x$ where $-360° \leqslant x \leqslant 360°$.

    **b** Write down the range of $f(x)$ for the given domain.

    **c** Write down the amplitude of $f(x)$.

    **d** On the same diagram, sketch the graph of the function $g : x \mapsto \sin 0.5x$ where $-360° \leqslant x \leqslant 360°$.

    **e** Write down the period of $g(x)$.

    **f** Use the graphs to find the number of solutions to the equation $f(x) = g(x)$ in the given domain.

    **g** Solve the equation $1 - 2\sin x = \sin 0.5x$ for $-360° \leqslant x \leqslant 360°$.

**53** A yachting course is illustrated in the diagram alongside. The yachts start and finish at point O, and travel in the direction indicated.

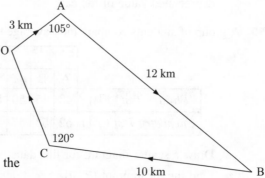

    **a** Find the distance from O to B.

    **b** Find $B\hat{O}C$.

    **c** Find the length of OC.

    **d** Calculate the area enclosed by the course OABC.

    **e** Due to a rounding error, the course designer stated the perimeter as 30 km. Calculate the percentage error in this approximation.

**54** Felicity is offered a new job and is given two salary options to choose from:

*Option A:*  $\$40\,000$ in the first year, and 5% extra each subsequent year.

*Option B:*  $\$60\,000$ in the first year, and $\$1000$ more each subsequent year.

    **a** Felicity believes that she will work for 3 years in this new job. Explain why *Option B* is best under this assumption.

    **b** Write down a formula for the amount of money earned in the $n$th year if she selects:

      **i** *Option A*          **ii** *Option B*

    **c** Determine the minimum length of time Felicity would need to work before the amount of money earned per year from *Option A* exceeds that of *Option B*.

    **d** Felicity decides that the best way to compare the two options is to consider the total income accumulated after the first $n$ years in each case. If $T_A$ and $T_B$ represent the total income earned over $n$ years for *Options A* and *B* respectively, show that:

      **i** $T_A = 800\,000(1.05^n - 1)$ dollars

      **ii** $T_B = 500n^2 + 59\,500n$ dollars

**e** The graph alongside shows $T_A$ and $T_B$ graphed against $n$.

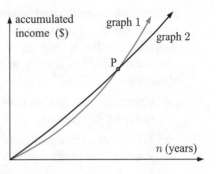

  **i** Write down which graph represents $T_A$ and which graph represents $T_B$.

  **ii** Find the coordinates of the point P, where $T_A$ meets $T_B$.

**f** Hence, write down a time interval, in whole years, for which *Option B* provides the greatest accumulated income.

**55** A club of beagle owners records the number of pups born per litter over a one year period. The results are shown in the frequency table opposite.

| Number of pups per litter (x) | Frequency (f) | x × f |
|---|---|---|
| 2 | 1 | 2 |
| 3 | 3 | 9 |
| 4 | 7 | 28 |
| 5 | 15 | s |
| 6 | 21 | 126 |
| 7 | 17 | t |
| 8 | 9 | 72 |
| 9 | 4 | 36 |
| 10 | 2 | 20 |

**a** Is this data discrete or continuous?

**b** Calculate the total number of litters for this one year period.

**c** Determine the value of:

  **i** $s$          **ii** $t$

**d** How many beagle pups were born over this one year period?

**e** Calculate the average number of pups per litter.

**f** Using your graphics calculator, draw a boxplot to represent this data.

**g** Hence, determine the:

  **i** range          **ii** interquartile range          **iii** median.

**56** PQRS is a square and forms the base of a pyramid. O is the centre of the base, and the vertex A is 30 cm directly above O. M is the midpoint of RS. The volume of the pyramid is 4000 cm³.

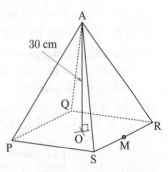

**a** Calculate the width of the square base.

**b** Calculate the distance OR.

**c** The triangular face ARS forms an angle $\theta$ with the square base.

  **i** Using a well labelled diagram, draw a triangle showing the correct position of angle $\theta$.

  **ii** Hence, calculate the measure of $\theta$.

**d** Calculate the total surface area of the pyramid.

**e** A wire frame is placed along the edges of the pyramid. If the wire costs $0.12 per cm, find the total cost of the frame.

**57** A furniture manufacturer constructs and sells wooden stools. The number $N$ of stools sold depends on the selling price per stool, €$x$. The relationship between $N$ and $x$ is illustrated alongside.

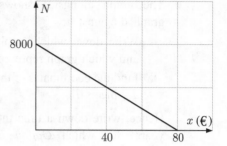

  **a** Calculate the gradient of this line and interpret its meaning.

  **b** Write down the equation of the line, giving your answer in the form $N = ax + b$.

  **c** If each wooden stool costs €50 to build, write an expression for the manufacturer's profit per stool.

  **d** Using the results of **b** and **c**, show that the total profit for the sale of $N$ chairs is given by $P = -100x^2 + 13\,000x - 400\,000$ euros.

  **e** Find $\dfrac{dP}{dx}$.

  **f** Calculate the value of $x$ required to produce the maximum profit, and the maximum profit in this case.

**58** Michael is saving to buy a house and needs $200\,000.

  **a** Three years ago, he invested a sum of money in an account paying 6.5% p.a. interest compounded half-yearly. This investment has just matured at $50\,000. How much did Michael invest three years ago?

  **b** Michael decides to reinvest his $50\,000 lump sum into an account for a period of $n$ years at 6.0% p.a. interest compounded annually.

  Copy and complete the table below showing the value of Michael's investment $V_n$ after $n$ years.

| $n$ (years) | 0 | 1 | 2 | 3 | 4 |
|---|---|---|---|---|---|
| $V_n$ ($) | 50 000 | 53 000 | 56 180 | | |

  **c** Write a formula for $V_n$ in terms of $n$.

  **d** Michael also decides to start an additional saving plan, whereby he deposits $3000 into a safe at the end of each year. Write down a formula for $S_n$, the amount of money in Michael's safe after $n$ years.

  **e** The total amount of money Michael has for his house after $n$ years is given by $T_n = V_n + S_n$. Calculate the missing values in the table below.

| $n$ (years) | 0 | 1 | 2 | 3 | 4 |
|---|---|---|---|---|---|
| $T_n$ ($) | 50 000 | 56 000 | 62 180 | | |

  **f** After how many whole years will Michael have the $200\,000 needed to buy his house?

**59** Mr Hilditch makes a cup of coffee in the staff room of his school, but accidentally leaves it behind. The approximate temperature of the coffee $t$ minutes after it is made is $A(t) = 95 - 3t$ °C.

  **a** Based on this model, estimate the temperature of Mr Hilditch's coffee:

    **i** initially                  **ii** after 30 minutes.

  **b** Sketch $A(t)$ for $0 \leqslant t \leqslant 30$. Clearly show the information obtained in **a**.

  **c** Discuss whether the use of $A(t)$ to represent the temperature of the coffee is valid in the long term. Give evidence to support your response.

  **d** The actual temperature of the coffee $t$ minutes after being made is
    $C(t) = 80 \times (0.8)^t + 15$ degrees, $t \geqslant 0$.
    Determine the actual temperature of the coffee:

    **i** initially                  **ii** after 30 minutes.

  **e** Add the graph of $C(t)$ to your graph from **b**.

  **f** Mr Hilditch will drink his coffee provided its temperature does not drop below 20°C. How long will it take for the coffee to become too cold to drink?

  **g** If left for a long time, the temperature of the coffee will eventually reach the temperature of the surrounding environment. Based on the model $C(t)$, find the temperature of the staff room where Mr Hilditch left his cup of coffee.

  **h** Consider the function $D(t) = A(t) - C(t)$.

    **i** Solve $D(t) = 0$, and give an interpretation of this result.

    **ii** Determine the maximum value of $D(t)$ for $0 \leqslant t \leqslant 30$.

    **iii** Interpret the value found in **ii**.

**60** Jose conducts a survey of 200 people to see which type of movie they prefer to watch. The results are shown in the table.

|  | Adventure | Comedy | Action | Drama |
|---|---|---|---|---|
| Men | 25 | 25 | 40 | 15 |
| Women | 18 | 34 | 12 | 31 |

Jose will conduct a $\chi^2$ test at the 5% level of significance to determine whether the preferred movie type is independent of gender.

  **a** State the null and alternative hypotheses.

  **b** Calculate the expected frequency for the number of females who prefer comedies. Give your answer to the nearest whole number.

  **c** Using your graphics calculator or otherwise, find the $\chi^2$ statistic for Jose's data.

  **d** Determine the number of degrees of freedom available for this calculation.

  **e** Write down the critical value for the test.

  **f** Give a conclusion for Jose's test, including reasons for your decision.

  **g** Jose realised after he had completed the test that he entered some information incorrectly. The adventure and drama numbers for males had been reversed. Perform the test again with the correct data, and state whether the conclusion drawn in **f** is still valid.

# ANSWERS

## EXERCISE 1A

**1 a** 23 **b** 18 **c** 78 **d** 168    **2 a** 503 **b** 3076
**3** €27 **4** Yes **5** $24 149 **6 a** 437 **b** 28 **c** 720
**7** 82 buckets **8** 38 400 apples **9** 25 laps
**10 a** 840 apartments **b** $2 856 000 **11** 63

## EXERCISE 1B.1

**1 a** 5, 25, 125, 625    **b** 6, 36, 216, 1296
**c** 7, 49, 343, 2401
**2 a** $2 \times 3^2$    **b** $3^2 \times 7^2$    **c** $2^2 \times 5^2 \times 7$
**d** $3 \times 5^3 \times 11$  **e** $2^2 \times 3^3$    **f** $3^2 \times 5 \times 7^3$
**3 a** 70 **b** 18 **c** 135 **d** 108 **e** 600 **f** 48 400
**4 a** 3888    **b** 590 625    **c** 104 544
**d** 41 544 503  **e** 36 450    **f** 857 500
**5** 8
**6 a** $2^1 = 2$             $2^2 - 2 = 2$
  $2^1 + 2^2 = 6$          $2^3 - 2 = 6$
  $2^1 + 2^2 + 2^3 = 14$      $2^4 - 2 = 14$
  $2^1 + 2^2 + 2^3 + 2^4 = 30$   $2^5 - 2 = 30$
**b** 254 $(= 2^8 - 2)$
**7 a** $2^{n-1}$, where $n$ is the number of the square
**b** $2^{39}$ grains    **c** $1 + 2^1 + 2^2 + .... + 2^{63} = 2^{64} - 1$
**8 a** 9 **b** 27 **c** 81 **d** combinations = $3^n$ **e** 6561

## EXERCISE 1B.2

**1 a** 1  **b** −1  **c** 1  **d** −1  **e** 1  **f** −1
**g** −1 **h** 9 **i** −64 **j** −64 **k** −49 **l** 27
**2 a** 512  **b** −243 **c** −3125 **d** 729 **e** 1296
**f** 6561 **g** −6561 **h** 5.117 264 691
**i** −0.764 479 956 4    **j** −20.361 584 96

## EXERCISE 1C.1

**1 a** 1, 3, 5, 15    **b** 1, 2, 4, 8, 16    **c** 21 = 3 × 7
**d** 1 and 21
**2 a** 1, 3, 9    **b** 1, 17    **c** 1, 2, 11, 22
**d** 1, 2, 3, 4, 6, 8, 12, 24   **e** 1, 2, 4, 7, 14, 28
**f** 1, 2, 3, 6, 7, 14, 21, 42
**g** 1, 2, 3, 4, 5, 6, 10, 12, 15, 20, 30, 60
**h** 1, 2, 3, 4, 6, 9, 12, 18, 27, 36, 54, 108
**3 a** 36 = 6 × 6    **b** 38 = 2 × 19    **c** 48 = 12 × 4
**d** 90 = 5 × 18    **e** 88 = 8 × 11    **f** 54 = 3 × 18
**g** 72 = 12 × 6    **h** 46 = 2 × 23    **i** 60 = 12 × 5
**4 a** 9    **b** 15    **c** 7    **d** 7
**e** 44    **f** 13    **g** 63    **h** 73
**5 a** 6, 8, 10    **b** 11, 13, 15, 17, 19
**6 a** 16, 18 **b** 1, 7 **c** 1 and 15, 3 and 13, 5 and 11
**7 a** even **b** even **c** even **d** odd **e** odd
**f** odd **g** even **h** odd **i** even

## EXERCISE 1C.2

**1 a** 2, 3, 5, 7, 11, 13, 17, 19, 23, 29, 31, 37, 41, 43, 47, 53, 59
**b** one, 2
**2** (other answers are possible)
  **a** 5    **b** 3    **c** 10    **d** 11
**3 a** $2 \times 7$ **b** $2^2 \times 5$ **c** $2^2 \times 7$ **d** $2^5$ **e** $2^3 \times 5$
**4 a** 3    **b** 15, 21, 25, 27    **c** 29

## EXERCISE 1C.3

**1 a** 4 **b** 3 **c** 7 **d** 9 **e** 13 **f** 6 **g** 3 **h** 4
**2** 8

## EXERCISE 1D

**1 a** 4, 8, 12, 16, 20, 24    **b** 5, 10, 15, 20, 25, 30
**c** 7, 14, 21, 28, 35, 42    **d** 11, 22, 33, 44, 55, 66
**2 a** 24    **b** 54
**3 a/b**  1  2  ③  4  ⑤  ⑥  7  8  ⑨  ⑩
  11 ⑫ 13 14 ⑮ 16 17 ⑱ 19 ⑳
  ㉑ 22 23 ㉔ ㉕ 26 ㉗ 28 29 ㉚
  31 32 ㉝ 34 ㉟ ㊱ 37 38 ㊴ ㊵
**c** 15, 30
**4 a** 36, 72, 108    **b** 60, 120
**c** none in the list (first one is 180)
**5 a** 10    **b** 21    **c** 20    **d** 24
**e** 18    **f** 60    **g** 140    **h** 36
**6 a** 105 **b** 198 **7** In 12 hours' time **8** 14.4 km

## EXERCISE 1E.1

**1 a** 7 **b** 14 **c** 13 **d** 5 **e** 8 **f** 5
**g** 7 **h** 5 **i** 2 **j** 4 **k** 1 **l** 8
**2 a** 15 **b** 3 **c** 3 **d** 16 **e** 32 **f** 2
**g** 17 **h** 4 **i** 8 **j** 8 **k** 6 **l** 36
**m** 4 **n** 2 **o** 14
**3 a** 12 **b** 7 **c** 14 **d** 6 **e** 5 **f** 64
**4 a** 8 **b** $\frac{1}{4}$ **c** 3 **d** 2
**5 a** 28 **b** 31 **c** 13 **d** 1 **e** 12 **f** 38
**6 a** 12 **b** −12 **c** 38 **d** 2 **e** −12 **f** −6
**g** 30 **h** 3 **i** −11 **j** 4 **k** −1 **l** −2

## EXERCISE 1E.2

**1 a** 45 **b** 6 **c** 14 **d** 10 **e** 10 **f** 1
**g** 4 **h** 25 **i** 1 **j** 18 **k** 2 **l** 1

## REVIEW SET 1A

**1 a** 46 **b** 25 **c** 165 **d** 348    **2** 111 situps
**3 a** $2^2 \times 5^3 \times 7$    **b** 3500
**4 a** 9    **b** 25    **c** −49    **d** −8
**5 a** 4 times    **b** 32 times
**6 a** 84, 91, 98    **b** 31, 37
**c** 2 and 20, 4 and 18, 6 and 16, 8 and 14, 10 and 12
**7 a** 1, 2, 4, 7, 14, 28    **b** 1, 31
**c** 1, 2, 3, 4, 6, 9, 12, 18, 36 **d** 1, 2, 4, 8, 16
**8 a** 4 **b** 18 **c** 14 **9 a** 30 **b** 56 **c** 60
**10 a** 21 **b** 9 **c** 42 **11 a** 12 **b** 29 **c** −15

## REVIEW SET 1B

**1** $271    **2** 4600 bars

**3** **a** 1    **b** −1    **c** 32    **d** −50.41    **4** 375

**5** Divisible by 3    **6** **a** $3 \times 11$    **b** $2^2 \times 3 \times 5$    **c** $2^3 \times 7$

**7** **a** 1 and 42, 2 and 21, 3 and 14, 6 and 7
   **b** 1, 2, 3, 6, 9, 18

**8** **a** 3    **b** 60    **9** the 12 000th

**10** **a** 15    **b** 3    **c** 22    **11** **a** −36    **b** −4    **c** 12

## EXERCISE 2A.1

**1** **a** 2700 s    **b** 4200 s    **c** 7528 s

**2** **a** 210 minutes    **b** 24 minutes    **c** 313 minutes
   **d** 4428 minutes

**3** **a** 4 hours 50 minutes    **b** 3 hours 37 minutes
   **c** 6 hours 14 minutes    **d** 14 hours 26 minutes

**4** **a** 53 minutes    **b** 9.03 am

**5** **a** 10.15 am    **b** 4.56 am    **c** 4.20 pm
   **d** 8.05 pm the previous day

**6** 6.50 am    **7** 3 hours 17 minutes

## EXERCISE 2A.2

**1** **a** 3.00 pm    **b** 9.00 pm    **c** 9.00 am    **d** 5.00 am

**2** **a** 8.00 am Wednesday    **b** 7.00 pm Tuesday
   **c** 12 noon Wednesday    **d** 4.00 pm Tuesday

**3** **a** 10.00 pm Friday    **b** 11 pm Friday
   **c** 2.30 am Saturday    **d** 3 pm Friday

**4** **a** 5 am Thursday    **b** midnight Thursday
   **c** 6 pm Wednesday    **d** 10 pm Wednesday

**5** 8.30 am    **6** 3.30 am the next day    **7** 5.25 pm Tuesday

## EXERCISE 2B

**1** **a** 16°C    **b** 82°C    **c** −12°C

**2** **a** 140°F    **b** 86°F    **c** 59°F

**3** **a** $-17\frac{7}{9}$°C    **b** $37\frac{7}{9}$°C    **c** $-6\frac{2}{3}$°C

**4** **a** 158°F    **b** 14°F    **c** 752°F

**6** **a** $-26\frac{2}{3}$°C    **b** 77°F    **7** −40°

## EXERCISE 2C

**1** **c** and **d**    **2** $1000 = 10^3$    $0.1 = 10^{-1}$
   $100 = 10^2$    $0.01 = 10^{-2}$
   $10 = 10^1$    $0.001 = 10^{-3}$
   $1 = 10^0$    $0.0001 = 10^{-4}$

**3** **a** 82 000    **b** 36    **c** 8.7    **d** 490
   **e** 0.0078    **f** 0.055    **g** 0.376    **h** 0.002 02

**4** **a** $3.9 \times 10^3$    **b** $1.7 \times 10^4$    **c** $4 \times 10^{-2}$
   **d** $7.1 \times 10^{-5}$    **e** $8.5 \times 10^1$    **f** $6.3 \times 10^0$
   **g** $2.48 \times 10^6$    **h** $1.08 \times 10^{-7}$

**5** **a** $4.5 \times 10^7$    **b** $3.8 \times 10^{-4}$    **c** $2.1 \times 10^5$
   **d** $4 \times 10^{-3}$    **e** $6.1 \times 10^3$    **f** $1.6 \times 10^{-6}$
   **g** $3.9 \times 10^4$    **h** $6.7 \times 10^{-2}$

**6** **a** 45 000 000    **b** 0.000 38    **c** 210 000    **d** 0.004
   **e** 6100    **f** 0.000 001 6    **g** 39 000    **h** 0.067

**7** **a** 6 800 000 000 people    **b** 0.000 000 1 Pa
   **c** 140 000 light years
   **d** 0.000 000 000 000 000 000 000 001 67 kg

**8** **a** $5.44 \times 10^7$ years    **b** $3 \times 10^{-3}$ m
   **c** $3.119 \times 10^8$ hands    **d** $4.7 \times 10^{-7}$ m

## EXERCISE 2D

**1** 1 000 000 mL    **2** **a** 1000    **b** 1 000 000 000    **3** $10^{12}$

**4** **a** 25 mL    **b** 26.58 $\mu$s    **c** 45 000 000 mm
   **d** 5.84 t    **e** 194.4 MJ    **f** $16\frac{2}{3}$ m s$^{-1}$
   **g** 140 000 mm$^2$    **h** 57.6 km h$^{-1}$    **i** 66.672 km h$^{-1}$

**5** 3.3 ha    **6** 216 000 000 J    **7** 1 kg m$^2$s$^{-2}$    **8** 8.64 knots

## EXERCISE 2E.1

**1** **a** 80    **b** 80    **c** 300    **d** 640
   **e** 3990    **f** 1650    **g** 9800    **h** 1020
   **i** 780    **j** 840    **k** 2120    **l** 2000

**2** **a** 100    **b** 500    **c** 900    **d** 1000
   **e** 5400    **f** 4800    **g** 13 100    **h** 44 000

**3** **a** 1000    **b** 6000    **c** 10 000    **d** 4000
   **e** 65 000    **f** 123 000    **g** 435 000    **h** 571 000

**4** **a** $15 000    **b** 470 kg    **c** €600    **d** 5700 km
   **e** 117 000 L    **f** £29 000    **g** $6 500 000    **h** 32 000 ha
   **i** 36 000 000 times    **j** $1 000 000 000

## EXERCISE 2E.2

**1** **a** 3.5    **b** 5.36    **c** 7.2    **d** 15.23    **e** 9.025
   **f** 12.6    **g** 0.44    **h** 9.28    **i** 0.01

**2** **a** 499.32    **b** 228.84    **c** 9.11    **d** 31.75    **e** 26.67
   **f** 0.88    **g** 7.41    **h** 5.93    **i** 0.48

## EXERCISE 2E.3

**1** **a** 570    **b** 16 000    **c** 71    **d** 3.0    **e** 0.72
   **f** 50    **g** 3.0    **h** 1800    **i** 0.041    **j** 46 000

**2** **a** 43 600    **b** 10 100    **c** 0.667    **d** 0.0368    **e** 0.319
   **f** 0.720    **g** 0.636    **h** 0.0637    **i** 19.0    **j** 257 000

**3** **a** 28.04    **b** 0.005 362    **c** 23 680    **d** 42 370 000
   **e** 0.038 79    **f** 0.006 378    **g** 0.000 8999    **h** 43.08

**4** **a** **i** 6000 people    **ii** 5800 people    **b** 6000

**5** **a** $4 \times 10^{-10}$    **b** $8.75 \times 10^{12}$    **c** $8.84 \times 10^{-3}$
   **d** $4.29 \times 10^{14}$    **e** $8.75 \times 10^{-16}$    **f** $7.18 \times 10^{10}$

**6** **a** $1.4 \times 10^5$ km    **b** $6.7 \times 10^5$ km    **c** $2.5 \times 10^8$ km

**7** **a** $6.78 \times 10^{16}$    **b** $1.22 \times 10^{20}$    **c** $1.82 \times 10^{-7}$
   **d** $7.59 \times 10^{-13}$    **e** $1.56 \times 10^{17}$    **f** $1.45 \times 10^{-14}$

**8** **a** $3.154 \times 10^7$ s    **b** $2.996 \times 10^8$ m

**9** **a** $4.00 \times 10^{13}$    **b** $2.59 \times 10^7$    **c** $7.08 \times 10^{-9}$
   **d** $4.87 \times 10^{-11}$    **e** $8.01 \times 10^6$    **f** $3.55 \times 10^{-9}$

**10** **a** **i** $2.88 \times 10^8$ km    **ii** $7.01 \times 10^{10}$ km
   **b** $2.5 \times 10^8$ km h$^{-1}$    **c** 0.9 s    **d** 3.94 times
   **e** Microbe C, 32.9 times

## EXERCISE 2F.1

**1** **a** 83.8 km h$^{-1}$    **b** 83.3 km h$^{-1}$    **2** 442 km h$^{-1}$

**3** 30 m s$^{-1}$ ($= 108$ km h$^{-1}$)    **4** **a** 321 km    **b** 32.7 km

**5** 7 hours 25 minutes 16 seconds

## EXERCISE 2F.2

**1** **a** $2.76 per kg    **b** 14.5 km per litre    **c** 27 L min$^{-1}$
   **d** $14.50 per hour    **e** 4° per h    **f** 5.5 kg m$^{-2}$
   **g** 10.45 cents per kWh    **h** 55 words/min

**2** **a** €586.80    **b** €16.77 per hour

**3** B, 11.65 bags per hectare    **4** Jo, 26.27 goals/match

**5** **a** 511 L per day    **b** **i** $29.90    **ii** 33.2 cents

**6 a** 10 minutes **b** 4 minutes 17 seconds

**7 a** $219.85 **b** 10.72 cents per kWh

**8 a** 13°C **b** 1.16°C per h

**9 a** 20 c per min **b** 4 kL per s **c** 108 L per h
**d** $2730 per kg **e** 52 596 deaths per year

**EXERCISE 2G**

**1 a** $\pm\frac{1}{2}$ cm **b** $\pm\frac{1}{2}$ mL **c** $\pm 50$ mL **d** $\pm 250$ g

**2** between 67.5 kg and 68.5 kg

**3 a** 26.5 mm - 27.5 mm **b** 38.25 cm - 38.35 cm
**c** 4.75 m - 4.85 m **d** 1.45 kg - 1.55 kg
**e** 24.5 g - 25.5 g **f** 3.745 kg - 3.755 kg

**4** between 36.35°C and 36.45°C

**5 a** 6.4 m **b** 6.05 m **c** 10 cm **6** 246 cm - 250 cm

**7** 788 cm and 792 cm **8 a** 55.25 cm² **b** 41.25 cm²

**9** Upper boundary = 1126.25 cm²
Lower boundary = 1058.25 cm²

**10** Upper: 40.375 cm² Lower: 31.875 cm²

**11** Upper: 248.625 cm³ Lower: 144.375 cm³

**12** Upper: 1545.7 cm³ Lower: 1502.1 cm³

**13** Upper: 1473.0 cm³ Lower: 922.5 cm³

**14** Upper: 347.69 cm³ Lower: 332.21 cm³

**EXERCISE 2H**

**1 a i** €2460 **ii** 0.180% **b i** −467 people **ii** −1.48%
**c i** $1890 **ii** 0.413% **d i** 189 cars **ii** 6.72%

**2 a i** −1.238 kg **ii** 19.8% **b i** 2.4 m **ii** 2.46%
**c i** −3.8 L **ii** 16.0% **d i** −22 hours **ii** 30.6%

**3 a** 100 m² **b** 99.91 m² **c** 0.09 m² **d** 0.090%

**4 a** 3254.224 cm³ **b** 3240 cm³ **c** −14.224 cm³
**d** −0.437%

**5 a** 65.25 km h⁻¹ **b** 4.75 km h⁻¹ **c** 7.28%

**REVIEW SET 2A**

**1** 6 hours 17 minutes

**2 a** 3.35 am the next day **b** 9.50 am **3** 440 000 g

**4** 95°F **5 a** 143 000 km **b** 0.000 004 5 m

**6 a** 1.96 × 10⁻⁵ s **b** 0.0110 s

**7 a i** 6.4 **ii** 6.38 **b i** 0.05 **ii** 0.047

**8 a** ±0.5 cm **b** between 35.5 cm and 36.5 cm
**c** Upper: 1332.25 cm² Lower: 1260.25 cm²

**9 a** 25.3 km h⁻¹ **b** 5 hours 35 minutes

**10 a i** −$590 **ii** −22.8%
**b i** −0.109 cm **ii** −0.417%

**11** Upper: 52 cm Lower: 48 cm **12** 5 pm

**REVIEW SET 2B**

**1** 165 minutes **2** 11 hours 4 minutes **3** $28\frac{8}{9}$°C

**4** 168 cm **5 a** 460 000 000 000 **b** 1.9 **c** 0.0032

**6 a** 1.276 × 10⁷ m **b** 4.2 × 10⁻⁷ cm **7** 313 sheets

**8 a i** 59.4 **ii** 59.40 **b i** 0.01 **ii** 0.0084

**9** $569.48 **10 a** −2.3 m **b** 6.71%

**11 a** £8.75 **b** Increases by £26.25

**12** 2.00 am the next day

**REVIEW SET 2C**

**1** 5 hours 52 minutes **2 a** 2.47 pm **b** 9.33 am **3** 10°C

**4** 24.1 km h⁻¹ **5 a** 0.005 73 **b** 3020 **c** 987.5

**6 a** 4.13 **b** 2.97

**7 a** 2 hours 9 minutes (2.15 hours) **b** 50 km h⁻¹

**8** Store B, 0.88 cents per g

**9** Upper: 27.625 cm² Lower: 20.625 cm²

**10 a** Actual area ≈ 6.16 m², Calculated area ≈ 7.07 m²
**b** 0.911 m² **c** 14.8%

**11 a i** 2 m **ii** 2.24 m **iii** 2.236 m
**b i** 1 **ii** 3 **iii** 4 **c** 2.24 m and 2.236 m

**12** 4.00 am

**EXERCISE 3A**

**1 a** $5 \in D$ **b** $6 \notin G$ **c** $d \notin \{a, e, i, o, u\}$
**d** $\{2, 5\} \subseteq \{1, 2, 3, 4, 5, 6\}$
**e** $\{3, 8, 6\} \nsubseteq \{1, 2, 3, 4, 5, 6\}$

**2 a i** $\{9\}$ **ii** $\{5, 6, 7, 8, 9, 10, 11, 12, 13\}$
**b i** $\varnothing$ **ii** $\{1, 2, 3, 4, 5, 6, 7, 8\}$
**c i** $\{1, 3, 5, 7\}$ **ii** $\{1, 2, 3, 4, 5, 6, 7, 8, 9\}$

**3 a** 5 **b** 6 **c** 2 **d** 9 **4 a** finite **b** infinite

**5 a** disjoint **b** not disjoint **6** True

**EXERCISE 3B.1**

**1** $8 = \frac{8}{1}$, $-11 = \frac{-11}{1}$

**2** It is written in the form $\frac{p}{q}$, but $q$ may not be 0, which it is in this case.

**3 a** True **b** True **c** False **d** True
**e** False **f** True **g** True **h** False

**4 a** $0.8 = \frac{8}{10}$ or $\frac{4}{5}$ **b** $0.71 = \frac{71}{100}$
**c** $0.45 = \frac{45}{100}$ or $\frac{9}{20}$ **d** $0.219 = \frac{219}{1000}$
**e** $0.864 = \frac{864}{1000}$ or $\frac{108}{125}$

**5 a** True **b** True **c** False **d** True

**6 a** infinite **b** infinite **7 a** $= \frac{4}{9}$ **b** $= \frac{7}{33}$ **c** $= \frac{325}{999}$

**EXERCISE 3B.2**

**1 a** rational **b** irrational **c** rational **d** rational

**2** $= \frac{3}{5}$ **3**

| | $\mathbb{Q}$ | $\mathbb{R}$ | $\mathbb{Z}$ | $\mathbb{Q}'$ | $\mathbb{N}$ |
|---|---|---|---|---|---|
| $\sqrt{2}$ | × | ✓ | × | ✓ | × |
| $5$ | ✓ | ✓ | ✓ | × | ✓ |
| $-\frac{1}{3}$ | ✓ | ✓ | × | × | × |
| $2.17$ | ✓ | ✓ | × | × | × |
| $-9$ | ✓ | ✓ | ✓ | × | × |

**EXERCISE 3C**

**1 a** finite **b** infinite **c** infinite **d** infinite

**2 a i** $A$ is the set of all $x$ such that $x$ is an integer between −1 and 7, including −1 and 7.
**ii** $\{-1, 0, 1, 2, 3, 4, 5, 6, 7\}$ **iii** 9
**b i** $A$ is the set of all $x$ such that $x$ is a natural number between −2 and 8.
**ii** $\{0, 1, 2, 3, 4, 5, 6, 7\}$ **iii** 8
**c i** $A$ is the set of all $x$ such that $x$ is a real number between 0 and 1, including 0 and 1.

**ii** not possible   **iii** infinite

**d**  **i** $A$ is the set of all $x$ such that $x$ is a rational number between 5 and 6, including 5 and 6.

  **ii** not possible   **iii** infinite

**3**  **a** $A = \{x \mid -100 < x < 100, \ x \in \mathbb{Z}\}$
  **b** $A = \{x \mid x > 1000, \ x \in \mathbb{R}\}$
  **c** $A = \{x \mid 2 \leqslant x \leqslant 3, \ x \in \mathbb{Q}\}$

**4**  **a**  **i** $\varnothing, \{a\}, \{b\}, \{c\}, \{a, b\}, \{a, c\}, \{b, c\}, \{a, b, c\}$, so 8 subsets

    **ii** $\varnothing, \{a\}, \{b\}, \{c\}, \{d\}, \{a, b\}, \{a, c\}, \{a, d\}, \{b, c\}, \{b, d\}, \{c, d\}, \{a, b, c\}, \{a, b, d\}, \{a, c, d\}, \{b, c, d\}, \{a, b, c, d\}$, so 16 subsets

  **b** $2^n$

**5**  **a** Yes  **b** No  **c** Yes  **d** Yes  **e** No  **f** No

## EXERCISE 3D

**1**  **a** $C' = \{\text{consonants}\}$  **b** $C' = \mathbb{N}$
  **c** $C' = \{x \mid x \geqslant -4, \ x \in \mathbb{Z}\}$
  **d** $C' = \{x \mid 2 < x < 8, \ x \in \mathbb{Q}\}$

**2**  **a** $\{2, 3, 4, 5, 6, 7\}$  **b** $\{0, 1, 8\}$  **c** $\{5, 6, 7, 8\}$
  **d** $\{0, 1, 2, 3, 4\}$  **e** $\{5, 6, 7\}$  **f** $\{2, 3, 4, 5, 6, 7, 8\}$
  **g** $\{2, 3, 4\}$

**3**  **a** 9  **b** 11  **4**  **a** False  **b** True

**5**  **a** $\{1, 2, 10, 11, 12\}$  **b** $\{1, 2, 3, 4, 12\}$
  **c** $\{1, 8, 9, 10, 11, 12\}$  **d** $\{3, 4, 5, 6, 7\}$
  **e** $\{1, 2, 8, 9, 10, 11, 12\}$  **f** $\{8, 9, 10, 11\}$
  **g** $\{1, 2, 5, 6, 7, 8, 9, 10, 11, 12\}$  **h** $\{2, 10, 11\}$

**6**  **a** $P = \{2, 3, 5, 7, 11, 13, 17, 19, 23\}$  **b** $\{2, 5, 11\}$
  **c** $\{2, 3, 4, 5, 7, 11, 12, 13, 15, 17, 19, 23\}$
  **d** $12 = 9 + 6 - 3$ ✓

**7**  **a** $P = \{1, 2, 3, 5, 6, 10, 15, 30\}$
    $Q = \{1, 2, 4, 5, 8, 10, 20, 40\}$
  **b** $\{1, 2, 5, 10\}$  **c** $\{1, 2, 3, 4, 5, 6, 8, 10, 15, 20, 30, 40\}$
  **d** $12 = 8 + 8 - 4$ ✓

**8**  **a** $M = \{32, 36, 40, 44, 48, 52, 56\}$, $N = \{36, 42, 48, 54\}$
  **b** $\{36, 48\}$  **c** $\{32, 36, 40, 42, 44, 48, 52, 54, 56\}$
  **d** $9 = 7 + 4 - 2$ ✓

**9**  **a** $R = \{-2, -1, 0, 1, 2, 3, 4\}$, $S = \{0, 1, 2, 3, 4, 5, 6\}$
  **b** $\{0, 1, 2, 3, 4\}$  **c** $\{-2, -1, 0, 1, 2, 3, 4, 5, 6\}$
  **d** $9 = 7 + 7 - 5$ ✓

**10**  **a** $C = \{-4, -3, -2, -1\}$
     $D = \{-7, -6, -5, -4, -3, -2, -1\}$
  **b** $\{-4, -3, -2, -1\}$  **c** $\{-7, -6, -5, -4, -3, -2, -1\}$
  **d** $7 = 4 + 7 - 4$ ✓

**11**  **a** $P = \{1, 2, 3, 4, 6, 12\}$, $Q = \{1, 2, 3, 6, 9, 18\}$,
     $R = \{1, 3, 9, 27\}$
  **b**  **i** $\{1, 2, 3, 6\}$  **ii** $\{1, 3\}$  **iii** $\{1, 3, 9\}$
     **iv** $\{1, 2, 3, 4, 6, 9, 12, 18\}$  **v** $\{1, 2, 3, 4, 6, 9, 12, 27\}$
     **vi** $\{1, 2, 3, 6, 9, 18, 27\}$
  **c**  **i** $\{1, 3\}$  **ii** $\{1, 2, 3, 4, 6, 9, 12, 18, 27\}$

**12**  **a** $A = \{4, 8, 12, 16, 20, 24, 28, 32, 36\}$
     $B = \{6, 12, 18, 24, 30, 36\}$, $C = \{12, 24, 36\}$
  **b**  **i** $\{12, 24, 36\}$  **ii** $\{12, 24, 36\}$
     **iii** $\{12, 24, 36\}$  **iv** $\{12, 24, 36\}$
  **c** $\{4, 6, 8, 12, 16, 18, 20, 24, 28, 30, 32, 36\}$
  **d** $12 = 9 + 6 + 3 - 3 - 3 - 3 + 3$ ✓

**13**  **a** $A = \{6, 12, 18, 24, 30\}$,  $B = \{1, 2, 3, 5, 6, 10, 15, 30\}$
     $C = \{2, 3, 5, 7, 11, 13, 17, 19, 23, 29\}$
  **b**  **i** $\{6, 30\}$  **ii** $\{2, 3, 5\}$  **iii** $\varnothing$  **iv** $\varnothing$
  **c** $\{1, 2, 3, 5, 6, 7, 10, 11, 12, 13, 15, 17, 18, 19, 23, 24, 29, 30\}$
  **d** $18 = 5 + 8 + 10 - 2 - 3 - 0 + 0$ ✓

## EXERCISE 3E

**1**  **a**                    **b**

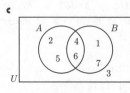

  **c**                    **d**

**2**  **a** $A = \{1, 3, 5, 7, 9\}$  **c**
     $B = \{2, 3, 5, 7\}$
  **b** $A \cap B = \{3, 5, 7\}$
     $A \cup B = \{1, 2, 3, 5, 7, 9\}$

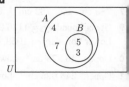

**3**  **a** $A = \{1, 2, 3, 6\}$  **c**
     $B = \{1, 3, 9\}$
  **b** $A \cap B = \{1, 3\}$
     $A \cup B = \{1, 2, 3, 6, 9\}$

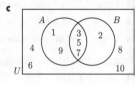

**4**  **a** $P = \{4, 8, 12, 16, 20, 24, 28\}$  **c**
     $Q = \{6, 12, 18, 24\}$
  **b** $P \cap Q = \{12, 24\}$
     $P \cup Q = \{4, 6, 8, 12, 16, 18, 20, 24, 28\}$

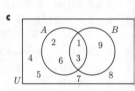

**5**  **a** $R = \{2, 3, 5, 7, 11, 13, 17, 19, 23, 29\}$
     $S = \{4, 6, 8, 9, 10, 12, 14, 15, 16, 18, 20, 21, 22, 24, 25, 26, 27, 28\}$
  **b** $R \cap S = \varnothing$
     $R \cup S = \{2, 3, 4, 5, 6, 7, 8, 9, 10, 11, 12, 13, 14, 15, 16, 17, 18, 19, 20, 21, 22, 23, 24, 25, 26, 27, 28, 29\}$
  **c**

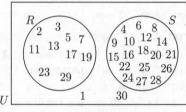

**6**  **a** $\{b, d, e, h\}$  **b** $\{e, f, h, i, j\}$  **c** $\{a, c, f, g, i, j, k\}$
  **d** $\{a, b, c, d, g, k\}$  **e** $\{e, h\}$  **f** $\{b, d, e, f, h, i, j\}$
  **g** $\{a, c, g, k\}$  **h** $\{a, b, c, d, f, g, i, j, k\}$

**7** **a**  **i** {a, b, c, d, h, j}     **ii** {a, c, d, e, f, g, k}
   **iii** {a, b, e, f, i, l}     **iv** {a, c, d}
   **v** {a, b, c, d, e, f, g, h, j, k}     **vi** {a, e, f}
   **vii** {a}     **viii** {a, b, c, d, e, f, g, h, i, j, k, l}
 **b**  **i** 12     **ii** 12

## EXERCISE 3F

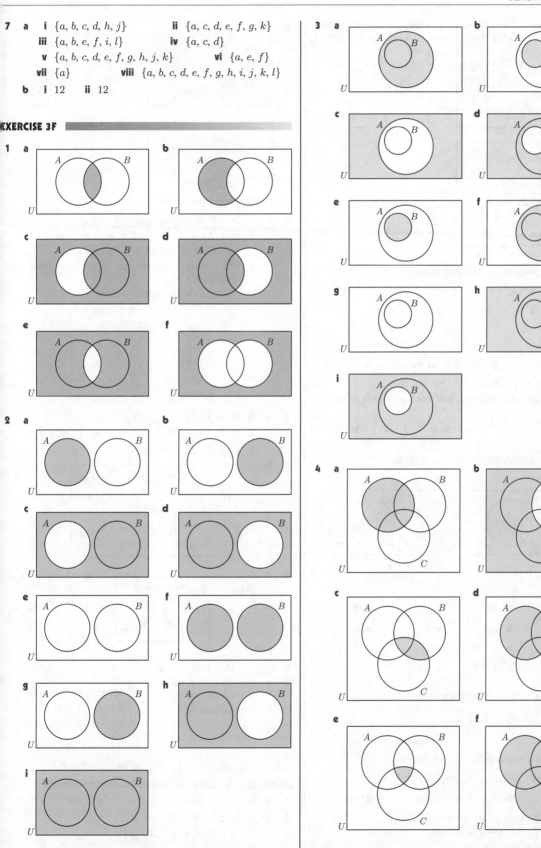

**g** 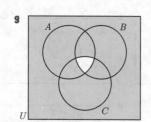   **h**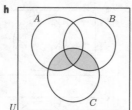

**i**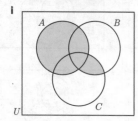

**5 a** 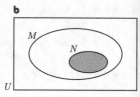   **b**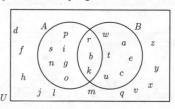

**c**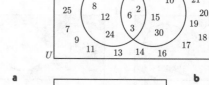

### EXERCISE 3G

**1 a** 7   **b** 14   **c** 14   **d** 7   **e** 5   **f** 9

**2 a** 5   **b** 6   **c** 17   **d** 8   **e** 3   **f** 2

**3 a** $b + c$   **b** $c + d$   **c** $b$
  **d** $a + b + c$   **e** $a + c + d$   **f** $d$

**4 a i** $2a + 4$   **ii** $4a + 4$   **iii** $3a - 5$   **iv** $5a - 1$
  **b i** $a = 6$   **ii** $a = \frac{32}{5}$ but $a \in \mathbb{N}$
so there cannot be 31 elements in $U$, but it is possible to have 29 elements.

**5 a** 15   **b** 4   **6 a** 18   **b** 6   **7 a** 7   **b** 23

### EXERCISE 3H

**1 a**   **2 a**

**b i** 9   **ii** 3   **iii** 3

**b i** 4   **ii** 2

**3** 13 players   **4** 20 people

**6 a** 16   **b** 33   **c** 14   **d** 7

**7 a** 29   **b** 6   **c** 1   **d** 11

**8 a** 3   **b** 5   **c** 5   **d** 21

**9 a** 3   **b** 4   **c** 9

### REVIEW SET 3A

**1 a** $\{3, 4, 5, 6, 7\}$   **b** 5

**2 a** rational   **b** rational, $= \frac{165}{1000}$
  **c** neither, it is undefined   **d** rational, $= \frac{56}{1}$
  **e** irrational   **f** rational, $= \frac{18}{99}$

**3 a** Yes   **b** Yes   **c** No   **d** Yes

**4 a** $X' = \{$orange, yellow, green, blue$\}$
  **b** $X' = \{-5, -3, -2, 0, 1, 2, 5\}$
  **c** $X' = \{x \mid x \geqslant -8, \ x \in \mathbb{Q}\}$

**6 a i** $\{s, p, r, i, n, g, b, o, k, w, a, t, e, u, c\}$
  **ii** $\{r, b, k\}$   **iii** $\{g, i, n, o, p, s\}$
  **b i** {the letters in 'springbok' or 'waterbuck'}
  **ii** {the letters common to both 'springbok' and 'waterbuck'}
  **iii** {the letters in 'springbok' but not 'waterbuck'}

**c**

| | | |
|---|---|---|
| $d$ | $A$   $p$   $r$   $w$   $B$ | |
| $f$ | $s$ $i$   $b$   $t$   $a$   $e$ | $z$ |
| $h$ | $n$ $g$   $o$   $k$   $u$ $c$ | $y$ |
| $U$ | $j$   $l$    $m$   $q$   $v$ | $x$ |

**7 a i** $\{1, 2, 3, 4, 6, 8, 12, 24\}$
  **ii** $\{1, 2, 3, 5, 6, 10, 15, 30\}$   **iii** $\{1, 2, 3, 6\}$
  **iv** $\{1, 2, 3, 4, 5, 6, 8, 10, 12, 15, 24, 30\}$

**b**

**8 a**   **b i** 72   **ii** 39   **iii** 268

**9** 6   **10 a** 9   **b** 7   **c** 17

**11 a** $P = \{1, 3, 5, 7, 9\}$   **c**
  $Q = \{2, 4, 6, 8, 10\}$
  **b** They are disjoint.

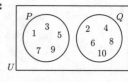

### REVIEW SET 3B

**1 a** True   **b** False   **c** True   **d** False   **e** False

**2 a i** $\{x \mid 5 < x < 12, \ x \in \mathbb{R}\}$
  **ii** $\{x \mid -4 \leqslant x < 7, \ x \in \mathbb{Z}\}$
  **iii** $\{x \mid x > 45, \ x \in \mathbb{N}\}$

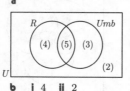

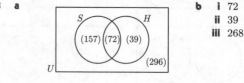

**b i** infinite  **ii** finite  **iii** infinite

**3** $\varnothing$, $\{1\}$, $\{3\}$, $\{5\}$, $\{1, 3\}$, $\{3, 5\}$, $\{1, 5\}$, $\{1, 3, 5\}$

**4 a i** $\{2, 4, 6, 8\}$  **b**

 **ii** $\{2, 4, 8\}$
 **iii** $\{3, 5, 7, 9\}$

**5 a** $\varnothing$  **b** $s+t$

**6 a** $C'$  **b** $(A \cap B) \cup (A \cap C)$  or  $A \cap (B \cup C)$

**7 a**

 **b i** 27
 **ii** 8
 **iii** 14

**8** 4

**9 a** $A = \{1, 2, 3, 4, 5, 6, 10, 12, 15, 20, 30, 60\}$
 $B = \{1, 2, 3, 5, 6, 10, 15, 30\}$
 **b** $B \subset A$
 **c**

**10 a** 1  **b** 7  **c** 15

## EXERCISE 4A.1

**1 a** $k^6$  **b** $5^8$  **c** $d^{10}$  **d** $11^{4+a}$
 **e** $p^7$  **f** $c^{8+m}$  **g** $x^{k+2}$  **h** $r^{11}$

**2 a** $7^5$  **b** $b^2$  **c** $5^3$  **d** $m^6$
 **e** $k^{12-a}$  **f** $y^5$  **g** $t^{m-4}$  **h** $x^{3a-2}$

**3 a** $5^6$  **b** $c^{12}$  **c** $3^{32}$  **d** $v^{25}$
 **e** $7^{6d}$  **f** $g^{8k}$  **g** $m^{3t}$  **h** $11^{2xy}$

**4 a** $b^{12}$  **b** $t^7$  **c** $p^{18}$  **d** $7^{6-n}$
 **e** $x^{6s}$  **f** $d^{k-3}$  **g** $3^{13}$  **h** $j^{12x}$
 **i** $11^7$  **j** $z^{7-4t}$  **k** $13^{5cd}$  **l** $w^{7p-1}$

**5 a** $2^2$  **b** $2^{-2}$  **c** $2^3$  **d** $2^{-3}$
 **e** $2^5$  **f** $2^{-5}$  **g** $2^1$  **h** $2^{-1}$
 **i** $2^6$  **j** $2^{-6}$  **k** $2^7$  **l** $2^{-7}$

**6 a** $3^2$  **b** $3^{-2}$  **c** $3^3$  **d** $3^{-3}$
 **e** $3^1$  **f** $3^{-1}$  **g** $3^4$  **h** $3^{-4}$
 **i** $3^0$  **j** $3^5$  **k** $3^{-5}$

**7 a** $2^{1+a}$  **b** $2^{2+b}$  **c** $2^{3+t}$  **d** $2^{2x}$
 **e** $2^n$  **f** $2^{c-2}$  **g** $2^{2m}$  **h** $2^{n+1}$
 **i** $2^1$  **j** $2^{3x-1}$

**8 a** $3^{2+p}$  **b** $3^{3a}$  **c** $3^{1+2n}$  **d** $3^{3+d}$
 **e** $3^{2+3t}$  **f** $3^{y-1}$  **g** $3^{1-y}$  **h** $3^{2-3t}$
 **i** $3^{3a-1}$  **j** $3^3$

**9 a** $2^5$  **b** $7^2$  **c** $5^6$  **d** $2^{10}$
 **e** $2^{4p}$  **f** $3^{3t}$  **g** $5^{a+2}$  **h** $2^{5n}$
 **i** $2^{3m-4n}$  **j** $5^{2p-4}$  **k** $2^3$  **l** $3^{2t+4}$
 **m** $2^{10-5r}$  **n** $3^{3-y}$  **o** $2^{2k}$  **p** $5^{4-3a}$

**10 a** $4a^2$  **b** $9n^2$  **c** $125m^3$  **d** $m^3n^3$
 **e** $\dfrac{a^3}{8}$  **f** $\dfrac{9}{m^2}$  **g** $\dfrac{p^4}{q^4}$  **h** $\dfrac{t^2}{25}$

**11 a** 1  **b** $\dfrac{1}{3}$  **c** $\dfrac{1}{49}$  **d** $\dfrac{1}{x^3}$
 **e** $\dfrac{6}{5}\left(1\tfrac{1}{5}\right)$  **f** 1  **g** $\dfrac{4}{7}$  **h** 6
 **i** $\dfrac{9}{16}$  **j** $\dfrac{5}{2}\left(2\tfrac{1}{2}\right)$  **k** $\dfrac{27}{125}$  **l** $\dfrac{151}{5}\left(30\tfrac{1}{5}\right)$

**12 a** $\dfrac{5}{n}$  **b** $\dfrac{1}{5n}$  **c** $\dfrac{n}{5}$  **d** $\dfrac{25}{n^2}$
 **e** $\dfrac{1}{mn}$  **f** $\dfrac{n}{m}$  **g** $\dfrac{m}{n}$  **h** $\dfrac{n}{m}$

## EXERCISE 4A.2

**1 a** $4a^2$  **b** $36b^4$  **c** $\dfrac{25k^2}{m^2}$
 **d** $\dfrac{t^3}{8s^3}$  **e** $8a^3$  **f** $27m^6n^6$
 **g** $\dfrac{y^6}{27z^3}$  **h** $1, c \neq 0, d \neq 0$  **i** $16a^4b^{16}$
 **j** $\dfrac{8a^6}{b^6}$  **k** $\dfrac{16a^6}{b^2}$  **l** $\dfrac{9p^4}{q^6}$

**2 a** $4b^3$  **b** $6w^5$  **c** $4p^2$  **d** $30c^{11}$  **e** $d^4$  **f** $3ab^2$
 **g** $4n^3$  **h** $t^7$  **i** $20s^2t^4$  **j** $k^{11}$  **k** $\dfrac{3xy^3}{2}$  **l** $b^9$

**3 a** $\dfrac{a}{b^2}$  **b** $\dfrac{1}{a^2b^2}$  **c** $\dfrac{4a^2}{b^2}$  **d** $\dfrac{1}{25m^4}$
 **e** $\dfrac{9b^2}{a^4}$  **f** $\dfrac{1}{27x^3y^{12}}$  **g** $\dfrac{a^2}{bc^2}$  **h** $\dfrac{a^2c^2}{b}$
 **i** $a^3$  **j** $\dfrac{b^3}{a^2}$  **k** $\dfrac{2}{ad^2}$  **l** $12am^3$

## EXERCISE 4A.3

**1 a** $a^{-n}$  **b** $b^n$  **c** $3^{n-2}$  **d** $a^nb^m$  **e** $a^{-2n-2}$

**2 a** $1 + 3x^{-1}$  **b** $3x^{-1} - 2$  **c** $5x^{-2} - x^{-1}$
 **d** $x^{-2} + 2x^{-3}$  **e** $x + 5x^{-1}$  **f** $x + 1 - 2x^{-1}$
 **g** $2x - 3 + 4x^{-1}$  **h** $x - 3x^{-1} + 5x^{-2}$
 **i** $5x^{-1} - 1 - x$  **j** $8x^{-1} + 5 - 2x^2$
 **k** $16x^{-2} - 3x^{-1} + x$  **l** $5x^2 - 3 + x^{-1} + 6x^{-2}$

**3 a** $4x + 2x^2$  **b** $5x^2 - 4x^3$  **c** $6x^3 + 3x^4$  **d** $x^3 + 3x$
 **e** $x^4 + x^3 - 4x^2$  **f** $x^6 - 3x^4 + 6x^3$  **g** $x^5 - 6x^3 + 10x^2$

## EXERCISE 4B

**1 a** Each row is made up of $(b + c)$ balls in total, and there are $a$ rows. $\therefore$ total number of balls is $a \times (b + c) = a(b + c)$
 **b i** $ab$  **ii** $ac$

**2 a** $4x + 12$  **b** $5x - 10$  **c** $24 - 8x$
 **d** $-2x - 5$  **e** $-3x + 21$  **f** $2x^2 + 12x$
 **g** $-6x^2 - 30x$  **h** $12x^2 - 20x$  **i** $-5x^2 + 10x$
 **j** $-18x + 15x^2$  **k** $7x^3 - 28x^2$  **l** $-36x^3 + 81x$

**3 a** $19x + 11$  **b** $22x - 15$  **c** $7x + 2$  **d** $7x - 30$
 **e** $5x^2 + 11x$  **f** $3x^2 - 2x + 10$  **g** $8x^2 - 23x - 7$
 **h** $22x^2 - 12x$  **i** $9x^2 - 22x$  **j** $-12x^2 + 30x - 20$

## EXERCISE 4C

**1 a** $x^2 + 9x + 14$  **b** $x^2 + 5x - 24$  **c** $x^2 - x - 20$
**d** $x^2 - 9x + 18$  **e** $2x^2 - 5x - 12$  **f** $6x^2 + 11x - 35$
**g** $20x^2 - 33x + 10$    **h** $4x^2 + 11x - 3$
**i** $-3x^2 - 7x + 20$    **j** $-18x^2 + 51x - 8$
**k** $-3x^2 + 23x + 36$    **l** $-35x^2 + 43x - 12$

**2 a** $x^2 - 16$  **b** $a^2 - 36$  **c** $49 - x^2$
**d** $9x^2 - 1$  **e** $16k^2 - 9$  **f** $25 - 36a^2$

**3 a** $x^2 + 14x + 49$  **b** $x^2 - 10x + 25$  **c** $4x^2 - 12x + 9$
**d** $25 + 30x + 9x^2$  **e** $49 - 28x + 4x^2$  **f** $16x^2 + 8xy + y^2$

## EXERCISE 4D

**1 a** $x^2 - 9$  **b** $x^2 - 1$  **c** $36 - x^2$
**d** $100 - x^2$  **e** $x^2 - 100$  **f** $a^2 - 49$
**g** $81 - y^2$  **h** $k^2 - 25$  **i** $x^2 - y^2$

**2 a** $4x^2 - 1$  **b** $25x^2 - 9$  **c** $16x^2 - 49$
**d** $36x^2 - 25$  **e** $64t^2 - 1$  **f** $25 - 81x^2$
**g** $49 - 16k^2$  **h** $100 - 9m^2$  **i** $1 - 144z^2$

**3 a** $9x^2 - y^2$  **b** $m^2 - 16n^2$  **c** $9p^2 - 49q^2$
**d** $64c^2 - 25d^2$  **e** $81x^2 - 4y^2$  **f** $36y^2 - 25x^2$

## EXERCISE 4E

**1 a** $x^2 + 6x + 9$  **b** $x^2 + 12x + 36$  **c** $x^2 + 4x + 4$
**d** $a^2 + 18a + 81$  **e** $25 + 10k + k^2$  **f** $49 + 14t + t^2$

**2 a** $x^2 - 6x + 9$  **b** $x^2 - 2x + 1$  **c** $x^2 - 16x + 64$
**d** $b^2 - 4b + 4$  **e** $16 - 8x + x^2$  **f** $49 - 14y + y^2$

**3 a** $9x^2 + 30x + 25$  **b** $16a^2 - 16a + 4$  **c** $4b^2 + 28b + 49$
**d** $9k^2 + 6k + 1$  **e** $25y^2 - 40y + 16$  **f** $9 - 12x + 4x^2$
**g** $16 + 24y + 9y^2$  **h** $1 + 10z + 25z^2$  **i** $4 - 12n + 9n^2$

**4 a** $x^4 + 6x^2 + 9$   **b** $y^4 - 14y^2 + 49$
**c** $25z^4 + 10z^2 + 1$   **d** $9 - 12a^2 + 4a^4$
**e** $m^4 + 2m^2n^2 + n^4$   **f** $x^4 - 2x^2y^2 + y^4$

**5 a** $-x^2 - 2x + 1$  **b** $x^2 - 5x + 5$  **c** $2x^2 + 4x - 5$
**d** $-8x - 65$  **e** $-11x + 31$  **f** $10x^2 - 15x$
**g** $10x^2 - 14x + 48$   **h** $x^2 + 3x - 16$
**i** $10x^2 - 28x + 20$   **j** $7 - 2x$

**6**

| $b$ | $(5+b)^2$ | $(5-b)^2$ | $(5+b)^2 - (5-b)^2$ |
|---|---|---|---|
| 0 | 25 | 25 | 0 |
| 1 | 36 | 16 | 20 |
| 2 | 49 | 9 | 40 |
| 3 | 64 | 4 | 60 |
| 4 | 81 | 1 | 80 |
| 5 | 100 | 0 | 100 |

Expand and simplify the algebraic expression $(5+b)^2 - (5-b)^2$.

## EXERCISE 4F

**1 a** $x^3 + 5x^2 + 11x + 10$   **b** $x^3 - x^2 - 10x + 6$
**c** $x^3 + 6x^2 + 7x + 10$   **d** $x^3 + x^2 - 10x + 8$
**e** $2x^3 - x^2 - 4x + 3$   **f** $4x^3 - 5x^2 - 3x + 1$
**g** $-x^3 - 5x^2 + 17x - 6$   **h** $6x^3 - 11x^2 - x + 6$

**2 a** $x^3 + 6x^2 + 12x + 8$   **b** $x^3 + 3x^2 + 3x + 1$
**c** $x^3 - 3x^2 + 3x - 1$   **d** $x^3 - 6x^2 + 12x - 8$
**e** $27x^3 + 27x^2 + 9x + 1$   **f** $8x^3 - 36x^2 + 54x - 27$

**3 a** $x^3 + 3x^2 + 2x$  **b** $x^3 + x^2 - 6x$  **c** $x^3 - 5x^2 + 4x$
**d** $2x^3 + 6x^2 + 4x$   **e** $2x^3 - 14x^2 + 24x$

**f** $-x^3 + x^2 + 6x$   **g** $-3x^3 + 3x^2 + 60x$
**h** $-3x^3 + 9x^2 - 6x$   **i** $x^3 + 5x^2 - 6x$

**4 a** $x^3 + 6x^2 + 11x + 6$   **b** $x^3 - 2x^2 - 5x + 6$
**c** $x^3 - 12x^2 + 44x - 48$   **d** $x^3 - 2x^2 - x + 2$
**e** $2x^3 - x^2 - 7x + 6$   **f** $4x^3 - 8x^2 - 9x + 18$
**g** $-4x^3 - 11x^2 + 43x - 10$   **h** $-3x^3 + 8x^2 + 33x + 10$

**5 a** 4  **b** 6  **c** 6  **d** 9  **e** 8  **f** 12  **g** 8  **h** 12

## REVIEW SET 4A

**1 a** $x^6$  **b** $2^{-7}$  **c** $a^6 b^{18}$    **2 a** $\frac{1}{27}$  **b** $\frac{y}{x}$  **c** $\frac{b}{a}$

**3 a** $3^3$  **b** $3^{2t}$  **c** $2^{3-m}$  **4 a** $\frac{5x}{y^2}$  **b** $\frac{1}{j^7}$  **c** $3g^3h^3$

**5 a** $\dfrac{t^3}{64s^3}$    **b** $1,\ m \neq 0,\ n \neq 0$    **c** $25p^6 q^2$

**6 a** $x + 8x^{-1}$    **b** $4x^2 + x^3 + x^5$  **c** $k^{-2x-6}$

**7 a** $7x^2 - 49x$    **b** $-8x^2 - 32x$

**8 a** $x^2 - 9$  **b** $2x^2 + 7x - 30$    **c** $49x^2 - 14xy + y^2$

**9 a** $2x^2 + 13x$  **b** $x^3 + 2x^2 - 37x + 10$  **10 a** 6  **b** 8

## REVIEW SET 4B

**1 a** $m^4$    **b** $1,\ y \neq 0$    **c** $\dfrac{w^2}{49z^2}$

**2 a** $k^{x-2}$    **b** $11^{r-4}$    **c** $3^{2+b}$

**3 a** $11^{-1}$    **b** $ab^{-2}$    **c** $jk^4 l^{-a}$

**4 a** $2^{-4}$    **b** $3^{k+4}$    **c** $5^{3a-b}$

**5 a** $\frac{1}{8}$    **b** 1    **c** $\frac{10}{3}$ $(3\frac{1}{3})$

**6 a** $\dfrac{a^{18}}{64b^6}$    **b** $\dfrac{25}{d^8}$    **c** $2z^4$

**7 a** $20x - 4x^2$    **b** $6x^2 + 13x + 6$

**8 a** $x^2 - 5x - 36$  **b** $x^2 + 14x + 49$  **c** $-x^2 - x + 6$

**9 a** $-x^2 - 8x - 9$  **b** $7x^2 + 27x + 9$

**10 a** $2x^3 + 13x^2 - 13x - 42$  **b** $x^3 - 3x^2 + 3x - 1$

## EXERCISE 5A

**1 a** 8  **b** 1  **c** 6  **d** 6  **e** 1  **f** $-18$  **g** $-4$  **h** $-8$

**2 a** $-\frac{3}{4}$    **b** $-2$    **c** $-1$    **d** $\frac{2}{7}$
**e** $-5$    **f** $-\frac{3}{2}$    **g** $-1$    **h** $-5$

**3 a** 1    **b** $-27$    **c** 25    **d** 1
**e** 63    **f** 27    **g** 36    **h** 18

**4 a** 1  **b** 4  **c** 3  **d** 5  **e** $\sqrt{53} \approx 7.28$
**f** $\sqrt{2} \approx 1.41$  **g** $\sqrt{42} \approx 6.48$  **h** 6

## EXERCISE 5B.1

**1 a** $x = -2$  **b** $x = 7$  **c** $x = 6$  **d** $x = -4$
**e** $x = \frac{11}{2}$  **f** $x = -3$  **g** $x = 7$  **h** $x = \frac{4}{3}$

**2 a** $x = 45$  **b** $x = 64$  **c** $x = -3$  **d** $x = 22$
**e** $x = 1$  **f** $x = 7$  **g** $x = \frac{23}{2}$  **h** $x = 17$

**EXERCISE 5B.2**

1   **a** $x = 1$   **b** $x = -4$   **c** $x = 9$   **d** $x = -2$
  **e** $x = \frac{1}{2}$   **f** $x = 6$

2   **a** $x = 6$   **b** $x = 3$   **c** $x = 2$   **d** $x = -4$
  **e** $x = \frac{1}{2}$   **f** $x = \frac{10}{3}$   **g** $x = 1$   **h** $x = 4$
  **i** $x = -2$   **j** $x = -\frac{7}{10}$

3   **a** $x \in \mathbb{R}$   **b** no solution
  **c** **a** has infinitely many solutions   **b** has no solutions

**EXERCISE 5B.3**

1   **a** $x = 1$   **b** $x = 2$   **c** $x = \frac{22}{9}$   **d** $x = -\frac{9}{5}$
  **e** $x = -\frac{2}{3}$   **f** $x = -\frac{19}{6}$   **g** $x = -9$   **h** $x = \frac{5}{4}$

**EXERCISE 5C**

1   **a** $x = \frac{10}{3}$   **b** $x = \frac{25}{6}$   **c** $x = \frac{17}{5}$
  **d** $x = -4$   **e** $x = \frac{10}{29}$   **f** $x = \frac{7}{29}$
  **g** $x = -\frac{5}{13}$   **h** $x = \frac{51}{23}$   **i** $x = -1$

2   **a** $x = \frac{15}{2}$   **b** $x = 6$   **c** $x = \frac{28}{3}$
  **d** $x = \frac{9}{20}$   **e** $x = \frac{5}{6}$   **f** $x = -\frac{3}{2}$
  **g** $x = \frac{7}{5}$   **h** $x = -\frac{13}{2}$   **i** $x = 6$

3   no solution $(x \neq 0)$

4   **a** $x = 1$   **b** $x = \frac{3}{5}$   **c** $x = -7$
  **d** $x = \frac{5}{7}$   **e** $x = 5$   **f** $x = \frac{16}{17}$
  **g** $x = -2$   **h** $x = -\frac{21}{38}$   **i** $x = -\frac{6}{41}$

**EXERCISE 5D**

1   **a** $x \approx 1.56$   **b** $x = 262$   **c** $x \approx 1.09$   **d** $x \approx -26.0$

2   **a** $x = -\frac{7}{3}$   **b** $x = -\frac{1}{13}$   **c** $x = \frac{17}{7}$

3   **a** $w = 55$   **b** $w = 92.5$

4   **a** $\approx 4.44^\circ C$   **b** $\approx -17.8^\circ C$   **c** $\approx 93.3^\circ C$

5   **a** 110 m   **b** 190 m

6   **a** $x = 9.5$   **b** $x \approx 6.56$   **c** $x \approx 10.5$   **d** $x \approx 37.3$

**EXERCISE 5E**

1   7    2   13    3   9    4   18 cm

5   **a** 85 cm   **b** 13 m by 6.5 m

6   11 years old    7   18 years old    8   6    9   10    10   10

**EXERCISE 5F**

1   **a** 35.8 cm   **b** 79.6 cm   **c** 15.9 m

2   **a** 44.1 m   **b** 129 m

3   **a** 80 km h$^{-1}$   **b** 260 km   **c** 7 h 52 min

4   **a** 98.5 cm$^2$   **b** 7.98 m   5   **a** 0.48 volts   **b** 60 ohms

6   **a** 7920 cm$^3$   **b** 1.59 cm   **c** 0.399 mm

7   **a** 11.3 km   **b** 71.0 m   8   **a** 598 cm$^2$   **b** 28.2 cm

**EXERCISE 5G.1**

1   **a** $y = \dfrac{4-x}{2}$   **b** $y = \dfrac{7-2x}{6}$   **c** $y = \dfrac{11-3x}{4}$
  **d** $y = \dfrac{8-5x}{4}$   **e** $y = \dfrac{20-7x}{2}$   **f** $y = \dfrac{38-11x}{15}$

2   **a** $y = \dfrac{x-4}{2}$   **b** $y = \dfrac{2x-7}{6}$   **c** $y = \dfrac{3x+12}{4}$
  **d** $y = \dfrac{4x-18}{5}$   **e** $y = \dfrac{7x-42}{6}$   **f** $y = \dfrac{12x+44}{13}$

3   **a** $x = b - a$   **b** $x = \dfrac{b}{a}$   **c** $x = \dfrac{d-a}{2}$
  **d** $x = t - c$   **e** $x = \dfrac{d-3y}{7}$   **f** $x = \dfrac{c-by}{a}$
  **g** $x = \dfrac{c+y}{m}$   **h** $x = \dfrac{c-p}{2}$   **i** $x = \dfrac{a-t}{3}$
  **j** $x = \dfrac{n-5}{k}$   **k** $x = \dfrac{a-n}{b}$   **l** $x = \dfrac{a-p}{n}$

4   **a** $x = ab$   **b** $x = \dfrac{a}{d}$   **c** $x = \dfrac{2}{p}$
  **d** $x = 2n$   **e** $x = \pm\sqrt{mn}$

**EXERCISE 5G.2**

1   $y = -\frac{5}{3}x + 6$;   $m = -\frac{5}{3}$;   $y$-intercept $= 6$

2   **a** $a = \dfrac{d}{2bK}$   **b** **i** $a = \frac{3}{56}$   **ii** $a = \frac{9}{40}$

3   **a** $d = st$ km
    **i** 180 km    **ii** 120 km    **iii** $126\frac{2}{3}$ km
  **b** $t = \dfrac{d}{s}$ h
    **i** 3 hours    **ii** 4 hours    **iii** 2 hours 12 minutes

4   **a** $n = \dfrac{100I}{Cr}$   **b** **i** 2.05 years   **ii** 10 years

**EXERCISE 5H.1**

1   **a** $x = 5$, $y = 2$   **b** $x = 3$, $y = 4$   **c** $x = -1$, $y = 5$
  **d** $x = 2$, $y = -4$   **e** $x = -3$, $y = 0$   **f** $x = \frac{1}{3}$, $y = \frac{2}{3}$

2   **a** $x = -5$, $y = 1$     **b** $x = \frac{1}{4}$, $y = \frac{15}{4}$
  **c** $x = 1$, $y = 3$     **d** $x = -2$, $y = -8$
  **e** $x = 4$, $y = -2$     **f** $x = \frac{1}{2}$, $y = \frac{5}{2}$

3   **a** $5 \neq 1$, so cannot solve    **b** no solution

4   **a** $x \in \mathbb{R}$    **b** infinitely many solutions

**EXERCISE 5H.2**

1   **a** $4x = 15$   **b** $2y = 12$   **c** $5x = 10$
  **d** $8x = 16$   **e** $-2y = 2$   **f** $3y = -3$

2   **a** $x = 2$, $y = 1$   **b** $x = 3$, $y = 2$   **c** $x = 3$, $y = 2$
  **d** $x = 2$, $y = -1$   **e** $x = \frac{1}{2}$, $y = 2$   **f** $x = \frac{4}{3}$, $y = -\frac{1}{3}$

3   **a** $3x - 3y = 6$    **b** $-2x - y = 1$
  **c** $-2x + 6y = 4$    **d** $9x - 6y = 12$

4   **a** $x = 2$, $y = 1$   **b** $x = -1$, $y = 3$   **c** $x = 2$, $y = 4$
  **d** $x = 3$, $y = -2$   **e** $x = -2$, $y = \frac{1}{2}$   **f** $x = 7$, $y = -3$
  **g** $x = \frac{2}{3}$, $y = 0$   **h** $x = \frac{3}{2}$, $y = -\frac{7}{2}$   **i** $x = 5$, $y = -7$

5   **a** $x \in \mathbb{R}$, there are infinitely many solutions
  **b** no solutions

**EXERCISE 5H.3**

1   **a** $x = 3$, $y = -2$    **b** $x = -4$, $y = \frac{1}{2}$
  **c** $x = 2.75$, $y = -3.5$   **d** $x = -3.5$, $y = 1.5$
  **e** $x = 4$, $y = 3$    **f** $x = -2.4$, $y = 3.9$

2   no solution

## EXERCISE 5I

**1** 40 and 18    **2** 27 and 55

**3** Small can = 240 mL, Large can = 420 mL

**4** Waltz = 3 minutes,  Sonatina = 7 minutes

**5** Short cable = 2.5 m,  Long cable = 4.2 m

**6** **a** 10 points    **b** 6 points

**7** 9 m  **8** 50 cm  **9** 12 of 3 L cans, 7 of 5 L cans  **10** 33 km

## EXERCISE 5J.1

**1** **a** $x = 3$    **b** $x = 2$    **c** $x = 4$    **d** $x = 0$
**e** $x = -1$  **f** $x = -2$  **g** $x = -3$  **h** $x = 2$

**2** **a** $x = -3$  **b** $x = 4$    **c** $x = 2$    **d** $x = 1$
**e** $x = \frac{4}{3}$  **f** $x = -\frac{3}{2}$  **g** $x = -\frac{1}{2}$  **h** $x = -\frac{3}{2}$
**i** $x = -\frac{2}{3}$  **j** $x = -\frac{5}{4}$  **k** $x = \frac{3}{2}$  **l** $x = \frac{5}{2}$
**m** $x = \frac{9}{2}$  **n** $x = \frac{1}{8}$  **o** $x = -3$  **p** $x = -1$
**q** $x = 0$  **r** $x = \frac{8}{3}$  **s** $x = 5$  **t** $x = -2$

**3** **a** $x = \frac{1}{7}$  **b** no solution  **c** $x = \frac{5}{2}$

**4** **a** $x = 2$  **b** $x = 3$  **c** $x = 1$  **d** $x = 2$
**e** $x = -2$  **f** $x = -2$

## EXERCISE 5J.2

**1** **a** $x \approx 4.32$  **b** $x \approx 6.64$  **c** $x \approx 12.3$  **d** $x \approx 16.3$
**e** $x \approx 3.10$  **f** $x \approx -0.353$ **g** $x \approx 4.04$  **h** $x \approx 36.8$
**i** $x \approx 4.95$  **j** $x \approx 6.39$  **k** $x \approx 2.46$  **l** $x \approx 9.88$

## REVIEW SET 5A

**1** **a** 100  **b** $\frac{1}{3}$  **c** 3    **2** **a** $x = -1$  **b** $x = 8$

**3** **a** $x = -4$  **b** $x = 4$    **4** **a** $x = -\frac{1}{4}$  **b** $x = 8$

**5** 11    **6** 11    **7** **a** $x = 4, \ y = 1$  **b** $x = -3, \ y = -\frac{1}{2}$

**8** **a** 224 000 J    **b** 1.19°C

**9** **a** $y = \dfrac{4x - 28}{3}$    **b** $y = \dfrac{k - d}{c}$    **c** $y = \dfrac{p}{q}$

**10** **a** $x = -2, \ y = 3$  **b** $x = 4, \ y = -1$    **11** 25 people

**12** **a** $x \approx 2.81$  **b** $x \approx 27.8$  **c** $x \approx 2.05$  **13** £10

## REVIEW SET 5B

**1** **a** $-33$    **b** $\frac{1}{5}$    **c** 4

**2** **a** $x = 20$    **b** $x = \frac{25}{4}$    **c** $x = -\frac{14}{3}$

**3** **a** $x = \frac{7}{4}$  **b** $x = -2$    **4** **a** $k = 4.7$  **b** $a = \frac{10}{11}$

**5** $1.98    **6** **a** 222 people per km$^2$  **b** 3 280 000 km$^2$

**7** **a** $n = \dfrac{P}{S - C}$    **b** 97 watches    **c** $S = \dfrac{P + Cn}{n}$
**d** €29.30

**8** **a** $x = \frac{5}{2}, \ y = \frac{13}{4}$  **b** $x = 5, \ y = -8$    **9** 3

**10** 24 m, 51 m    **11** **a** $x = -4$  **b** $x = \frac{3}{2}$  **c** $x = 6$

**12** 1620 adults, 1370 children

## EXERCISE 6A

**1** **a** $\sqrt{34}$ cm    **b** $\sqrt{20}$ cm    **c** $\sqrt{72}$ cm
**d** $\sqrt{233}$ km    **e** $\sqrt{392}$ m    **f** $\sqrt{250}$ km
**g** 1.12 cm    **h** 21.5 cm    **i** 8.38 cm

**2** **a** 8 cm    **b** $\sqrt{15}$ cm    **c** $\sqrt{24}$ km
**d** 2.53 km    **e** $\sqrt{3}$ m    **f** 8.98 cm

**3** **a** $x = \sqrt{7}$    **b** $x = \sqrt{2}$    **c** $x = \sqrt{7}$
**d** $x = \sqrt{5}$    **e** $x = \sqrt{5}$    **f** $x = \sqrt{8}$

**4** **a** $x = \sqrt{\frac{10}{9}}$    **b** $x = \sqrt{\frac{5}{4}}$    **c** $x = \sqrt{\frac{7}{4}}$
**d** $x = \sqrt{\frac{13}{16}}$    **e** $x = 1$    **f** $x = \frac{1}{2}$

**5** **a** $x = \sqrt{48}$    **b** $x = \sqrt{13}$    **c** $x = \sqrt{3}$
**d** $x = \sqrt{7}$    **e** $x = \sqrt{3}$    **f** $x = 1$

**6** **a** $x = \sqrt{5}, \ y = \sqrt{21}$    **b** $x = \sqrt{21}, \ y = \sqrt{22}$
**c** $x = \sqrt{3}, \ y = \sqrt{2}$

**7** **a** $x = \sqrt{14}$  **b** $x = -1 + \sqrt{7}$  **8** AC $\approx 4.92$ m $\left( \sqrt{\frac{97}{4}} \right)$

**9** **a** AB $= \sqrt{10}$ cm  **b** AB $= 2\sqrt{5}$ cm  **c** AB $= \sqrt{33}$ m

## EXERCISE 6B.1

**1** **a** 10 cm    **b** $\sqrt{18}$ m $\approx 4.24$ m    **2** 20 mm

**3** **a** $\sqrt{96}$ mm $\approx 9.80$ mm    **b** $5\sqrt{96}$ mm$^2 \approx 49.0$ mm$^2$

**4** 10 m $\times$ 30 m    **5** $\sqrt{5}$ cm    **6** $\sqrt{162}$ cm $\approx 12.7$ cm

**7** **a** $2\sqrt{39}$ m $\approx 12.5$ m    **b** $10\sqrt{39}$ m$^2 \approx 62.4$ m$^2$

**8** **a** $\sqrt{20}$ cm $\approx 4.47$ cm    **b** $2\sqrt{20}$ cm$^2 \approx 17.9$ cm$^2$

**9** 5 cm    **10** 12 mm

## EXERCISE 6B.2

**1** **a** 90°    **b** $a^2 + b^2 = c^2$

**2** **a** 4 cm    **b** 5 cm    **c** $\sqrt{208}$ cm $\approx 14.4$ cm

**3** 5 cm    **4** 29 mm

## EXERCISE 6C

**1** **a** not right angled  **b** right angled  **c** not right angled
**d** not right angled  **e** right angled  **f** right angled

**2** **a** right angle at A  **b** right angle at B    **c** right angle at C

**3** Measure the diagonal. If the diagonal, height and width of the frame satisfy Pythagoras' theorem, then there is a right angle opposite the diagonal.

## EXERCISE 6D

**1** **a** $x \approx 0.663$    **b** $x \approx 4.34$    **c** $x \approx 2.23$

**2** 46.28 m    **3** Yes    **4** 37.1 km    **5** 8.62 m

**6** **a** 92.4 cm  **b** 18 500 cm$^2$    **7** 5.97 m    **8** 0.697 m

**9** **a** 73.9 m  **b** 30.9 m    **10** 64 diagonal braces

**11** **a** 44.0 km to A and 61.6 km to B    **b** $248 000

**12** 72 m    **13** 55.0 cm

**14** **a** 100 cm    **b** 357 cm    **c** 457 cm

## EXERCISE 6E

**1 a**

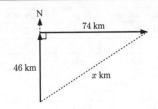

**b** 87.1 km

**2 a** 26.6 km        **b** 2 hours 40 minutes (2.66 hours)

**3 a** Jack 30 km, Will 38 km    **b** 48.4 km

**4 a** 2 hours 45 minutes (2.74 hours)

**b** 2 hours 31 minutes (2.52 hours)    **c** the train

**5** Francisca 2.68 km h$^{-1}$, Gisela 5.37 km h$^{-1}$

**6 a**                                    **b** 841 m

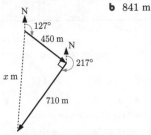

**7** 181 km

**8 a** 72 km        **c**

**b** 56 km

**d** 91.2 km

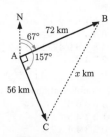

## EXERCISE 6F

**1** 6 cm      **2** 33.1 m      **3** 14.6 cm      **4** 3.46 cm

**5** 8.37 m    **6** 8.66 m      **7** 2.45 cm

**8 a** No      **b** Yes         **9** 3.5 m       **10** 1.92 m

## REVIEW SET 6A

**1** 1.8 m     **2** 453 m       **3** 7.79 m      **4** No, $4^2 + 5^2 \neq 8^2$

**5** 42 cm

**6 a** AR = 8.062 km, BR = 13.038 km    **b** €538 050

**7** 28.3 m    **8 a** Kate 2.5 km, Ric 3.25 km    **b** 4.10 km

**9** No, $8^2 + 5^2 + 3^2 < 10^2$    **10** 13 km    **11** 11.4 cm

## REVIEW SET 6B

**1** 3.53 m    **2** 1.79 m      **3** 1.98 m

**4** $2^2 + 5^2 = 29$, right angle at B.    **5** 42.4 m    **6** 41.2 m

**7 a** \$37 875 000    **b** \$34 000 000    **c** Option **b**

**8** 7.94 cm

**9 a**                                    **b** 599 km

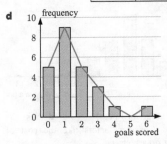

## REVIEW SET 6C

**1** 1950 mm    **2 a** 7.99 m    **b** 11.3 m    **3** 18.1 cm

**4 a** 11.3 m    **b** 45.3 m$^2$    **5** 35.2 m

**6** $3.2^2 + 2.1^2 = 3.83^2$ ✓ ∴ the concrete is rectangular.

**7** 17.3 m    **8** 8.60 m    **9** 1.73 cm

**10 a**                                    **b** 35.8 km

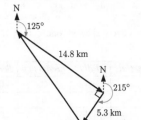

## REVIEW SET 6D

**1** 6 m    **2** $4^2 + (\sqrt{33})^2 = 7^2$, right angle at A

**4** 12.5 cm    **5** Yes    **6** 1.2 km

**7** $\sqrt{14}$ cm ≈ 3.74 cm    **8** 20.6 m    **9** 15.1 cm

## EXERCISE 7A

**1 a** quantitative discrete        **b** categorical
  **c** quantitative continuous      **d** quantitative continuous
  **e** categorical    **f** quantitative discrete    **g** categorical
  **h** quantitative discrete        **i** quantitative continuous
  **j** quantitative continuous      **k** quantitative continuous
  **l** categorical    **m** quantitative discrete

**2 a** 0, 1, 2, 3, ...., 15    **b** red, yellow, orange, green, ....
  **c** 0 - 15 minutes    **d** 0 - 25 m
  **e** Ford, BMW, Renault, ....    **f** 1, 2, 3, ...., 30
  **g** Australia, Hawaii, Dubai, ....    **h** 0.0 - 10.0
  **i** 0 - 4 L    **j** 0 - 60 hours    **k** $-20°C$ - $35°C$
  **l** cereal, toast, fruit, rice, eggs, ....    **m** 0, 1, 2, ...., 10

## EXERCISE 7B

**1 a** the number of goals scored in a game

**b** variable is counted, not measured

**c**

| Goals Scored | Tally | Frequency | Rel. Frequency |
|---|---|---|---|
| 0 | $\text{卌}$ | 5 | 0.208 |
| 1 | $\text{卌 IIII}$ | 9 | 0.375 |
| 2 | $\text{卌}$ | 5 | 0.208 |
| 3 | III | 3 | 0.125 |
| 4 | I | 1 | 0.042 |
| 5 | | 0 | 0 |
| 6 | I | 1 | 0.042 |
| | Total | 24 | |

**d**

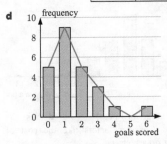

**e** 1 goal

**f** positively skewed, one outlier, (6 goals)

**g** 20.8%

**2  a**

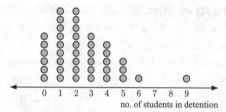

no. of students in detention

**b** 1 and 2   **c** positively skewed, one outlier, (9 detentions)
**d** $12\frac{1}{2}\%$

**3  a**

| No. of Commercials | Tally | Frequency | Rel. Freq. |
|---|---|---|---|
| 4 | \|\| | 2 | 0.059 |
| 5 | ＨＴ | 5 | 0.147 |
| 6 | ＨＴ ＨＴ | 10 | 0.294 |
| 7 | ＨＴ \|\|\|\| | 9 | 0.265 |
| 8 | ＨＴ | 5 | 0.147 |
| 9 | \|\|\| | 3 | 0.088 |
| | Total | 34 | |

**b**

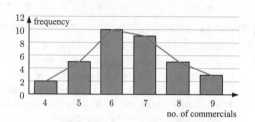

no. of commercials

**c** 6 commercials   **d** symmetrical, no outliers   **e** 79.4%

**4  a** 45   **b** 1 time   **c** 8   **d** 20%
**e** positively skewed, no outliers

**5  a**

| Peas in Pod | Tally | Freq. | Rel. Freq. |
|---|---|---|---|
| 3 | \|\|\|\| | 4 | 0.027 |
| 4 | ＨＴ ＨＴ \|\|\| | 13 | 0.087 |
| 5 | ＨＴ ＨＴ \| | 11 | 0.073 |
| 6 | ＨＴ ＨＴ ＨＴ ＨＴ ＨＴ \|\|\| | 28 | 0.187 |
| 7 | ＨＴ ＨＴ ＨＴ ＨＴ ＨＴ ＨＴ ＨＴ ＨＴ ＨＴ \|\| | 47 | 0.313 |
| 8 | ＨＴ ＨＴ ＨＴ ＨＴ ＨＴ \|\| | 27 | 0.180 |
| 9 | ＨＴ ＨＴ \|\|\|\| | 14 | 0.093 |
| 10 | \|\|\|\| | 4 | 0.027 |
| 11 | \| | 1 | 0.007 |
| 12 | | 0 | 0.000 |
| 13 | \| | 1 | 0.007 |
| | Total | 150 | |

**b**

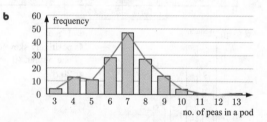

no. of peas in a pod

**c** Symmetrical, one outlier (13 peas)   **d** Yes
**e** Not necessarily.   (Consider factors like the cost of the fertiliser, changing prices, etc.)

---

**EXERCISE 7C**

**1  a**

| People waiting | Tally | Frequency | Rel. Freq. |
|---|---|---|---|
| 0 - 9 | \|\| | 2 | 0.067 |
| 10 - 19 | ＨＴ \| | 6 | 0.200 |
| 20 - 29 | ＨＴ ＨＴ \| | 11 | 0.367 |
| 30 - 39 | ＨＴ \|\| | 7 | 0.233 |
| 40 - 49 | \|\|\|\| | 4 | 0.133 |
| | Total | 30 | |

**b** 2 days   **c** 36.7%   **e** 20 - 29 people

**d**

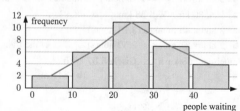

people waiting

**2  a** 37   **b** 40 - 49 employees   **c** negatively skewed
**d** 37.8%
**e** No, only that it was in the interval 50 - 59 employees.

**3  a  i** 38   **ii** 91   **iii** 18   **iv** 4   **v** 71.4%
**b** slightly negatively skewed, one outlier at 91

**4  a**

**Number of houses in a street**

```
0 | 6 8 5 6 6
1 | 5 9 1 8 4 2 2 7
2 | 0 3 4 4 2 5 8 7
3 | 4 8 5 6 9 4 5 2 6 4 0 2 7 2
4 | 2 7 4 0
5 | 6            5 | 6 = 56 houses
```

**b**

**Number of houses in a street**

```
0 | 5 6 6 6 8
1 | 1 2 2 4 5 7 8 9
2 | 0 2 3 4 4 5 7 8
3 | 0 2 2 2 4 4 4 5 5 6 6 7 8 9
4 | 0 2 4 7
5 | 6            5 | 6 = 56 houses
```

**c** It shows every value in the data set.
**d  i** 5   **ii** 56   **e** 52.5%   **f** 52.5%

**5  a**

**Bakery Sales**

```
    Pies        Pasties
              3 | 7 8 8 9
        9 8 7 | 4 | 1 3 4 5 6 7 8 9
      8 6 5 4 0 | 5 | 0 0 1 2 3 4 5 6 7 9
    9 7 5 3 3 2 1 0 | 6 | 0 1 3 7 8
  9 8 7 6 6 5 4 4 2 1 0 | 7 | 1 2 3 6
          5 2 2 1 | 8 |       6 | 0 = 60 items
```

**b** Pies 70 - 79,  Pasties 50 - 59   **c** Pies

**6  a**

**Passenger Numbers**

```
    Bus         Tram
  8 6 3 1 0 | 2 | 2 3 5
    8 5 3 0 | 3 | 0 5 8
8 8 3 3 1 1 0 | 4 | 3 5
      3 0 | 5 | 3 8
        3 | 6 | 0 3 8
        0 | 7 | 0 3 9        5 | 8 = 58 passengers
```

**b** Bus data is positively skewed, with modal class 40-49 passengers. The tram data is evenly distributed. In general, more people travel by tram than by bus.

## EXERCISE 7D

**1 a** Height is measured.

**b**

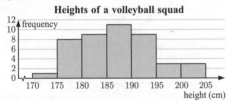

**Heights of a volleyball squad**

**c** $185 \leqslant H < 190$ cm. This is the class of values that appears most often.

**d** slightly positively skewed

**2 a** Continuous numerical

**b**

**Travel times to school**

| 0 | 3 6 8 8 8 8 |
|---|---|
| 1 | 0 0 0 0 0 2 2 2 4 4 4 4 5 5 5 5 6 6 6 6 7 8 8 8 8 9 |
| 2 | 0 0 0 1 2 4 5 5 5 6 7 7 8 |
| 3 | 1 2 2 2 3 4 5 7 8 |
| 4 | 0 2 5 5 5 6 |

$1 \mid 6 = 16$ minutes

**c** positively skewed   **d** 10 - 19 minutes

**3 a, b**

| Distance (m) | Tally | Frequency |
|---|---|---|
| 0.0 - 9.9 | \|\| | 2 |
| 10.0 - 19.9 | ЖII | 5 |
| 20.0 - 29.9 | ЖII \|\|\|\| | 9 |
| 30.0 - 39.9 | ЖII \| | 6 |
| 40.0 - 49.9 | \|\|\| | 3 |
|  | Total | 25 |

**c**

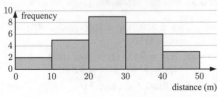

**Javelin Throwing Distances**

**d** 20.0 - 29.9 m   **e** 36%

**4 a** column graph   **b** frequency histogram

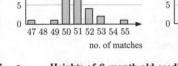

**5 a**

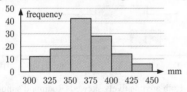

**Heights of 6-month old seedlings at a nursery**

**b** 20   **c** 58.3%   **d i** 1218   **ii** 512

**6 a, b**

| Weight (g) | Tally | Frequency |
|---|---|---|
| 100 - 124 | ЖII | 5 |
| 125 - 149 | ЖII | 5 |
| 150 - 174 | ЖII ЖII \| | 11 |
| 175 - 199 | \|\|\|\| | 4 |
| 200 - 224 | ЖII | 5 |
| 225 - 249 | ЖII \|\| | 7 |
| 250 - 274 | ЖII \|\|\|\| | 9 |
| 275 - 299 | \|\|\|\| | 4 |
|  | Total | 50 |

**c**

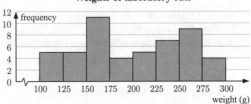

**Weights of laboratory rats**

**d** 50%

## EXERCISE 7E.1

**1 a i** 5.61 **ii** 6 **iii** 6   **b i** 16.3 **ii** 17 **iii** 18
  **c i** 24.8   **ii** 24.9   **iii** 23.5

**2 a** data set A: 6.46, data set B: 6.85
  **b** data set A: 7, data set B: 7
  **c** The data are the same except for the last value, which pushes the mean of Set B up.
  **d** 7 is the middle value in both data sets. It is not affected by extreme values.

**3** Ruth (164)   **4 a** 1 cup   **b** 1.8 cups   **c** 2 cups

**5 a** 44 points   **b** 44 points   **c** 40.2 points
  **d** increase, 40.3 points

**6** $185\,604$   **7** 3144 km   **8** 17.25 goals   **9** $x = 15$

**10** $a = 5$   **11** 37   **12** 14.8   **13** 6, 12   **14** 7, 9

## EXERCISE 7E.2

**1 a** Mean: $163\,770$, median: $147\,200$
    Mean has been affected by the extreme values (the two $> \$200$k)
  **b i** the mean   **ii** the median

**2 a** mean: $29\,300$, median: $23\,500$, mode: $23\,000$
  **b** It is the lowest value in the data set.
  **c** No, it is too close to the lower end of the distribution.

**3 a** mean: 3.19 mm, median: 0 mm, mode: 0 mm
  **b** The median is not in the centre as the data is positively skewed.
  **c** The mode is the lowest value.
  **d** Yes. 42 and 21.   **e** No.

## EXERCISE 7E.3

**1 a** 1 head   **b** 1 head   **c** 1.43 heads

**2 a i** 2.96 calls   **ii** 2 calls   **iii** 2 calls

**b**

**Phone calls made by teenagers**

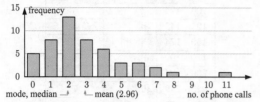

mode, median ⌐→ ⌐ mean (2.96)  no. of phone calls

**c** positively skewed  **d** There are extreme values present.
**e** mean

**3 a i** 49 matches  **ii** 49 matches  **iii** 49.0 matches
**b** No  **c** Need a larger sample.

**4 a i** 2.61 children  **ii** 2 children  **iii** 2 children
**b** This school has more children per family than average.
**c** positive  **d** mean is higher than the median, mode

**5 a i** 5.63 peas  **ii** 6 peas  **iii** 6 peas
**b i** 68.1 peas  **ii** 7 peas  **iii** 7 peas
**c** mean  **d** It has improved it.

## EXERCISE 7E.4

**1** 31.7  **2 a** 70  **b** $\approx 411\,000$ L  **c** $\approx 5870$ L
**3 a** 11.5 points  **b i** 11.3 points  **ii** 11.4 points
  **c ii** is closer to the actual mean than **i**. Smaller class intervals
  give better estimates.
**4** 90.1 km h$^{-1}$  **5** 768 m$^2$
**6 a** 125 people  **b** 119 marks  **c** $\frac{3}{25}$  **d** 137

## EXERCISE 7F

**1 a i** 6  **ii** $Q_1 = 4$, $Q_3 = 7$  **iii** 7  **iv** 3
  **b i** 17.5  **ii** $Q_1 = 15$, $Q_3 = 19$  **iii** 14  **iv** 4
  **c i** 24.9  **ii** $Q_1 = 23.5$, $Q_3 = 26.1$  **iii** 7.7  **iv** 2.6
**2 a** median = 2.45 min, $Q_1 = 1.45$ min, $Q_3 = 3.8$ min
  **b** range = 5.2 minutes, IQR = 2.35 minutes
  **c i** 2.45 min  **ii** 3.8 min  **iii** 0, 5.2, 5.2
**3 a** 3  **b** 42  **c** 20  **d** 13  **e** 29  **f** 39  **g** 16
**4 a i** 124 cm  **ii** $Q_1 = 116$ cm, $Q_3 = 130$ cm
  **b i** 124 cm  **ii** 130 cm  **c i** 29 cm  **ii** 14 cm
  **d** 14 cm
**5 a i** 7 peas  **ii** 6 peas  **iii** 5 peas  **iv** 7 peas  **v** 2 peas
  **b i** 10 peas  **ii** 7 peas  **iii** 6 peas  **iv** 8 peas
  **v** 2 peas
  **c** The fertiliser does improve the yield of peas.

## EXERCISE 7G.1

**1 a i** 35 points  **ii** 78 points  **iii** 13 points
  **iv** 53 points  **v** 26 points
  **b i** 65 points  **ii** 27 points
**2 a i** 98, 25 marks  **ii** 70 marks  **iii** 85 marks
  **iv** 55, 85 marks
  **b** 73 marks  **c** 30 marks
  **d** 67 marks
**3 a i** min = 3; $Q_1 = 5$; med = 6; $Q_3 = 8$; max = 10
  **ii**  **iii** 7
  **iv** 3

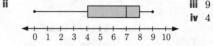

**b i** min = 0, $Q_1 = 4$; med = 7; $Q_3 = 8$, max = 9
  **ii**  **iii** 9
  **iv** 4

**c i** min = 117, $Q_1 = 127$, med = 132, $Q_3 = 145.5$,
  max = 151
  **ii**

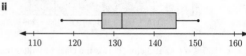

  **iii** 34  **iv** 18.5

**4 a** min = 33, $Q_1 = 35$, med = 36, $Q_3 = 37$, max = 40
  **b i** 7
  **ii** 2
  **c**

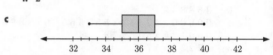

## EXERCISE 7G.2

**1 a** 12  **b** lower: 13.5, upper: 61.5  **c** 13.2 and 65
**2 a** median = 6, $Q_1 = 5$, $Q_3 = 8$  **b** 3
  **c** lower = 0.5, upper = 12.5  **d** Yes, 13.
  **e**

**EXERCISE 7G.3**

**1 a** Friday: min = \$20, $Q_1 = \$50$, med = \$70, $Q_3 = \$100$,
  max = \$180
  Saturday: min = \$40, $Q_1 = \$80$, med = \$100,
  $Q_3 = \$140$, max = \$200
  **b i** Friday: \$160 Saturday: \$160
  **ii** Friday: \$50 Saturday: \$60

**2 a i** Class 1 (96%)  **ii** Class 1 (37%)  **iii** Class 1
  **b i** 18  **ii** 55  **c i** 25%  **ii** 50%
  **d i** slightly positively skewed  **ii** negatively skewed
  **e** .... class 2, .... class 1

**3 a** Paul:  min = 0.8; $Q_1 = 1.3$; med = 2.3; $Q_3 = 3.3$;
  max = 6.9
  Redmond:  min = 0.2; $Q_1 = 2.2$; med = 3.7;
  $Q_3 = 5.7$; max = 11.5
  **b** Paul: 6.9, Redmond: 11.5
  **c**

**Mobile Phone call duration**

Redmond

Paul

**d** Both are positively skewed (Redmond's more so than Paul's).
  Redmond's phone calls were more varied in duration.

**EXERCISE 7H**

**1**

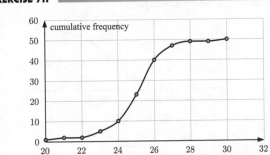

   **a** 25.2 cm    **b** **i** 40 people    **ii** 40 people

**2** **a**

| Length (cm) | Frequency | Cumulative frequency |
|---|---|---|
| $24 \leqslant x < 27$ | 1 | 1 |
| $27 \leqslant x < 30$ | 2 | 3 |
| $30 \leqslant x < 33$ | 5 | 8 |
| $33 \leqslant x < 36$ | 10 | 18 |
| $36 \leqslant x < 39$ | 9 | 27 |
| $39 \leqslant x < 42$ | 2 | 29 |
| $42 \leqslant x < 45$ | 1 | 30 |

**b**

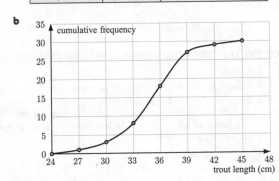

   **c** median $\approx 35$ cm
   **d** median = 34.5. Median from graph is a good approximation.

**3** **a** 9   **b** $\approx 28.3\%$  **c** 7 cm   **d** $\approx 2.4$ cm
   **e** 10 cm. 90% of the seedlings are 10 cm or less in height.

**4**

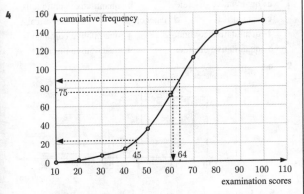

   **a** $\approx 61$ marks   **b** $\approx 87$ students   **c** $\approx 55$ students
   **d** $\approx 25$ students   **e** 75 marks

**5**

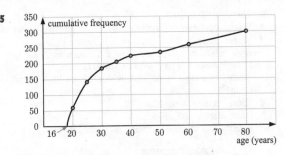

   **a** 26 years   **b** 36%   **c** **i** 0.527  **ii** 0.0267

**6** **a** 27 min    **b** 29 min    **c** 31.3 min
   **d** 4.3 min    **e** 28 min 12 sec

**7**

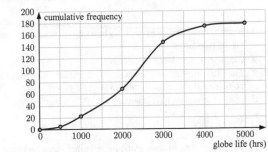

   **a** $\approx 2270$ hours   **b** $\approx 69\%$   **c** $\approx 63$

**EXERCISE 7I**

**1** **a** mean $\approx 4.87$, min = 1, $Q_1 = 3$, med = 5, $Q_3 = 7$,
    max = 9
   **b**

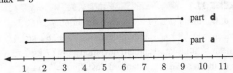

   **c**

   **d** mean $\approx 5.24$, min = 2, $Q_1 = 4$, med = 5, $Q_3 = 6.5$,
    max = 9

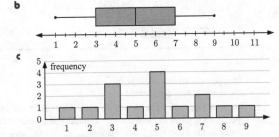

**2** **a** discrete
   **c**

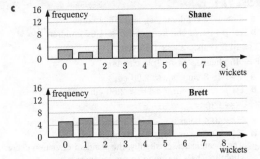

**d** There are no outliers.

**e** Shane: approximately symmetrical  Brett: positively skewed.

**f** Shane:  mean ≈ 2.89,  median = 3,  mode = 3
Brett:  mean ≈ 2.67,  median = 2.5,  mode = 2, 3
Shane's mean and median are slightly higher.
Shane has a clear mode of 3, whereas Brett has two modes (2 and 3)

**g** Shane:  Range = 6,  IQR = 2
Brett:  Range = 8,  IQR = 3
Shane's data set demonstrates less variability than Brett's.

**h**

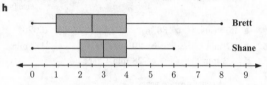

**i** Shane is more consistent with his bowling (in terms of wickets taken) than Brett.

**3  a** continuous (the data is measured)

**c** The '191' in the 'New' data set is an outlier. It should only be deleted if the measurement was done incorrectly.

**d** Old:    mean = 107,  median = 110.5,  range = 56,
IQR = 19
New:    mean = 134,  median = 132,  range = 84,
IQR = 18.5
The 'New' type of light globe has a higher mean and median than the 'old' type.
The IQR is relatively unchanged going from 'old' to 'new', however, the range of the 'new' type is greater, suggesting greater variability.

**e**

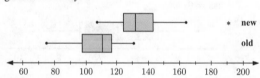

**f** Old type:  negatively skewed
New type:  positively skewed

**g** The 'new' type of light globes do last longer than the old type. Each number in the 5-number summary is at least 20% greater in the New type. The manufacturer's claim appears to be valid.

## EXERCISE 7J.1

**1  a, b**  mean = 55 L,  standard deviation ≈ 10.9 L

**2**  mean ≈ 1.69 kg,  standard deviation ≈ 0.182 kg

**3**  mean ≈ 93.8 kg,  standard deviation ≈ 6.77 kg

**4  a**  mean ≈ 78.1 g,  standard deviation ≈ 7.54 g
**b**  mean ≈ 78.1 g,  standard deviation ≈ 7.54 g

## EXERCISE 7J.2

**1  a** $\bar{x}$ ≈ 1.72 children,  $s_n$ ≈ 1.67 children
**b** est $\mu$ ≈ 1.72 children,  est $\sigma$ ≈ 1.67 children

**2** $\bar{x}$ ≈ 14.5 years,  $s_n$ ≈ 1.75 years

**3** $\bar{x}$ = 45 clients,  $s_n$ ≈ 3.28 clients

**4  a** $\bar{x}$ ≈ 48.3 cm,  $s_n$ ≈ 2.66 cm
**b** est $\mu$ ≈ 48.3 cm,  est $\sigma$ ≈ 2.66 cm

**5** $\bar{x}$ ≈ $390.30,  $s_n$ ≈ $15.87

**6  a** $\bar{x}$ ≈ 40.4 hours  $s_n$ ≈ 4.23 hours
**b** $\bar{x}$ ≈ 40.6 hours  $s_n$ ≈ 4.10 hours
The mean increases slightly, the standard deviation decreases slightly. These are good approximations.

**c**

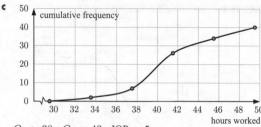

$Q_1$ ≈ 38,  $Q_3$ ≈ 43,  IQR ≈ 5

**d**

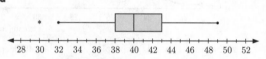

**7  a** $\bar{x}$ ≈ 17.5 cars,  $s_n$ ≈ 7.87 cars

**b**

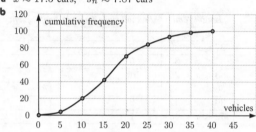

$Q_1$ ≈ 11,  $Q_3$ ≈ 22,  IQR ≈ 11

## EXERCISE 7J.3

**1  a** Sample A
**b** Sample A:  mean = 8,    Sample B:  mean = 8
**c** Sample A:  $s_n$ = 2,    Sample B:  $s_n$ ≈ 1.06
Sample B's standard deviation is smaller than Sample A's. The graph shows the data to be less 'spread out' in Sample B.

**2  a** Andrew: $\bar{x}$ = 25,  $s_n$ ≈ 4.97
Brad: $\bar{x}$ = 30.5,  $s_n$ ≈ 12.6
**b** Andrew

**3  a** No, because of random variation
**b  i** the sample mean    **ii** the sample standard deviation
**c** Less variability in the volume of soft drink per can.

## REVIEW SET 7A

**1  a** quantitative discrete      **b** quantitative continuous
**c** categorical      **d** categorical      **e** categorical
**f** quantitative continuous      **g** quantitative continuous
**h** quantitative discrete      **i** quantitative discrete

**2  a**

**b  i** median = 14.5 m      **ii** range = 17.3 m
**c** The data is positively skewed.

**3** $a$ = 2

**4**  **a**
```
0 | 7
1 | 8          Scale:  1 | 8  means  18 marks
2 | 7 9
3 | 2 2 5 6 8 9 9
4 | 0 3 4 4 5 6 6 7 8
```

**b** 45%   **c** 20%   **d** 90%

**e** negatively skewed, one outlier, 7 marks

**5**  **a**

| Distribution | Females | Males |
|---|---|---|
| shape | positively skewed | approx. symmetrical |
| median | 24.0 years | 26.7 years |
| range | 10 years | 6.4 years |

**b** In general, a female's first marriage will be at an earlier age, and the ages will have greater spread than a male's.

**6**

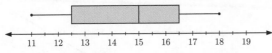

**7**  **a** 77 days        **b** 12 days

**8**  **a** $\bar{x} \approx 122$, $s_n \approx 7.94$    **b** $\bar{x} \approx 7.01$, $s_n \approx 0.984$

## REVIEW SET 7B

**1**  **a** quantitative continous    **b** categorical
**c** categorical               **d** quantitative continous
**e** quantitative continous    **f** quantitative discrete
**g** categorical

**2**  **a** minimum = 64.6 m,  maximum = 97.5 m

**b, c**

| Distance (m) | Tally | Frequency |
|---|---|---|
| $60 \leqslant d < 65$ | $\vert$ | 1 |
| $65 \leqslant d < 70$ | $\vert\vert\vert$ | 3 |
| $70 \leqslant d < 75$ | 卌 | 5 |
| $75 \leqslant d < 80$ | $\vert\vert$ | 2 |
| $80 \leqslant d < 85$ | 卌 $\vert\vert\vert$ | 8 |
| $85 \leqslant d < 90$ | 卌 $\vert$ | 6 |
| $90 \leqslant d < 95$ | $\vert\vert\vert$ | 3 |
| $95 \leqslant d < 100$ | $\vert\vert$ | 2 |
| | Total | 30 |

**d**

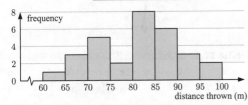

**e**  **i** mean $\approx 81.1$ m        **ii** median $\approx 83.1$ m

**3**  **a**

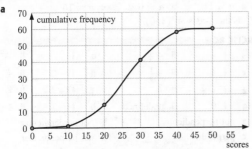

**b** median $\approx 26.0$    **c** IQR $\approx 12$
**d** $\bar{x} \approx 26.0$, $s_n \approx 8.31$

**4**  **a**  **i** £352.50        **ii** £336        **iii** £365.50
**b** £29.50        **c** $\bar{x} \approx$ £350, $s_n \approx$ £17.80

**5**  **a** 88    **b** $m = 24$

**6**  **a** $\bar{x} \approx 48.6$ min, $s_n \approx 7.63$ min
**b** est $\mu \approx 48.6$ min, est $\sigma \approx 7.63$ min

**7**  range = 19; $Q_1 = 119$; $Q_3 = 130$; $s_n \approx 6.38$

**8**  **a** $\bar{x} \approx 29.6$ allsorts; $s_n \approx 1.61$ allsorts
**b** More investigation is needed.

**9**  **a** min = 3; $Q_1 = 12$; med = 15; $Q_3 = 19$; max = 31
**b** range = 28; IQR = 7    **c** Yes: 31
**d**

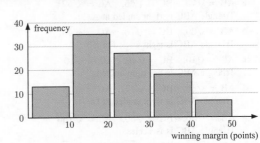

## REVIEW SET 7C

**1**

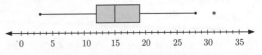

**2** 7, 9    **3** $\bar{x} \approx 414$ patrons

**4**  **a** A:  min = 11.0 s;  $Q_1 = 11.6$ s;  med = 12.0 s;
            $Q_3 = 12.6$ s;  max = 13.0 s
        B:  min = 11.2 s;  $Q_1 = 12.0$ s;  med = 12.6 s;
            $Q_3 = 13.2$ s;  max = 13.8 s
**b** A:  range = 2.0 s  IQR = 1.0 s
    B:  range = 2.6 s  IQR = 1.2 s
**c**  **i** A, the median time is lower.
    **ii** B, the range and IQR are higher.

**5**  **a** $\bar{x} \approx$ €104,  $s_n \approx$ €19.40
**b** est $\mu \approx$ €104,  est $\sigma \approx$ €19.40

**6**  **a** 120 students  **b** 65 marks  **c** 54 and 75
**d** 21 marks  **e** $\approx 73\%$  **f** 81 marks

**7**  **a**
```
        Brand X                Brand Y
          8 4 1 | 87 |
        9 8 6 5 5 2 | 88 |
  9 8 8 7 6 5 5 4 4 3 | 89 | 1 2 3 4 4 5 6 8
      8 7 5 4 4 3 1 1 | 90 | 0 1 1 1 3 3 3 4 4 6 7 7 9 9
              6 3 0 | 91 | 0 3 3 7
                    | 92 | 1 4 7 8    92 | 1 = 921 peanuts
```

**b**

| | Brand X | Brand Y |
|---|---|---|
| Outliers | None | None |
| Shape | Symmetrical | Positively skewed |
| Centre (median) | 896.5 peanuts | 903.5 peanuts |
| Spread (range) | 45 peanuts | 37 peanuts |

**c** Brand Y's data is clustered around the lower end of its range; whereas Brand X's data is approximately symmetrical. Brand Y's median is higher than Brand X's, and has less variability. In general, Brand Y has slightly more peanuts in their jars than Brand X.

## EXERCISE 8A.1

**1** **a** $\sqrt{13}$ units **b** $\sqrt{17}$ units **c** 3 units **d** 5 units
  **e** $\sqrt{53}$ units **f** 4 units **g** $\sqrt{37}$ units **h** $\sqrt{65}$ units
**2** Ling

## EXERCISE 8A.2

**1** **a** $\sqrt{10}$ units **b** $\sqrt{13}$ units **c** $\sqrt{58}$ units **d** $\sqrt{20}$ units
  **e** 2 units **f** $\sqrt{20}$ units **g** 5 units **h** $\sqrt{53}$ units
**2** **a** $\sqrt{45}$ km ($\approx 6.71$ km) **b** $\sqrt{97}$ km ($\approx 9.85$ km)
  **c** 5 km **d** 10 km
**3** **a** AB $= \sqrt{10}$, BC $= \sqrt{10}$, AC $= \sqrt{32}$
    Triangle ABC is isosceles.
  **b** AB $= \sqrt{73}$, BC $= \sqrt{50}$, AC $= \sqrt{17}$
    Triangle ABC is scalene.
  **c** AB $= 2$, BC $= 2$, AC $= 2$
    Triangle ABC is equilateral.
  **d** AB $= \sqrt{28}$, BC $= \sqrt{48}$, AC $= \sqrt{28}$
    Triangle ABC is isosceles.
**4** **a** AB $= \sqrt{13}$, BC $= \sqrt{65}$, AC $= \sqrt{52}$
    Triangle ABC is right angled at A.
  **b** AB $= \sqrt{20}$, BC $= \sqrt{20}$, AC $= \sqrt{40}$
    Triangle ABC is right angled at B.
  **c** AB $= \sqrt{10}$, BC $= \sqrt{40}$, AC $= \sqrt{10}$
    Triangle ABC is not right angled.
  **d** AB $= \sqrt{85}$, BC $= \sqrt{17}$, AC $= \sqrt{68}$
    Triangle ABC is right angled at C.
**5** **a** AB $= \sqrt{50}$, BC $= \sqrt{50}$, AC $= \sqrt{180}$
    Triangle ABC is isosceles.
  **b** AB $= \sqrt{65}$, BC $= \sqrt{13}$, AC $= \sqrt{52}$
    Triangle ABC is a scalene right angled triangle, with right angle at C.
  **c** AB $= \sqrt{10}$, BC $= \sqrt{20}$, AC $= \sqrt{10}$
    Triangle ABC is an isosceles right angled triangle, with right angle at A.
  **d** AB $= \sqrt{12}$, BC $= \sqrt{12}$, AC $= \sqrt{12}$
    Triangle ABC is equilateral.
**6** **a** $q = -1$ or 5 **b** $q = 0$ or $-4$ **c** $q = \pm 2$ **d** $q = 8$
**7** Triangle ABC is:
  • equilateral when $a = 1 \pm b\sqrt{3}$
  • isosceles otherwise.

## EXERCISE 8B

**2** **a** $(2, 3)$ **b** $(1, -3)$ **c** $(-2, 3)$ **d** $(1, 1)$
  **e** $(3, 1)$ **f** $(0, -1)$ **g** $(0, \frac{1}{2})$ **h** $(3, -1)$
**3** **a** $(3, 6)$ **b** $(\frac{5}{2}, 4)$ **c** $(1, 1\frac{1}{2})$ **d** $(3, 0)$
  **e** $(\frac{1}{2}, 3)$ **f** $(-1, 1)$ **g** $(-\frac{1}{2}, -1\frac{1}{2})$ **h** $(-2\frac{1}{2}, 4)$
**4** **a** $(3, -5)$ **b** $(-2, 3)$ **c** $(-1, 5)$ **d** $(4, -2)$
  **e** $(4, -1)$ **f** $(3, -\frac{1}{2})$
**6** **a** $(0, -9)$ **b** $(5, -5)$ **7** $(1, -5)$ **8** $(5, -2)$
**9** **a** $(-5, 4)$ **b** $\approx 3.16$ km **10** $(0, 1)$
**11** **a** $(1, 3\frac{1}{2})$ **b** 5.85 m
**12** **a** $(9, -2)$ **b** $(3, 7)$ **c** $(2, 5)$
**13** **a** **i** P$(2, 5)$ **ii** Q$(9, 4)$ **iii** R$(4, -1)$ **iv** S$(-3, 0)$
  **b** **i** $\sqrt{50}$ units **ii** $\sqrt{50}$ units
    **iii** $\sqrt{50}$ units **iv** $\sqrt{50}$ units
  **c** PQRS is a rhombus.

## EXERCISE 8C.1

**1** **a** $\frac{3}{2}$ **b** $-1$ **c** 0 **d** $\frac{2}{5}$
  **e** $-\frac{2}{3}$ **f** 3 **g** undefined **h** $-\frac{4}{3}$
**2** **a**  **b**
  **c**  **d**
  **e** **f**

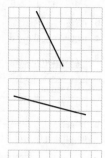

**3** **a** **A** and **D** **b** **B**
**4**

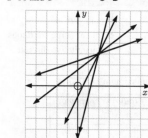

**5**

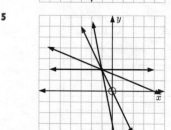

## EXERCISE 8C.2

**1** **a** 1 **b** $-\frac{1}{4}$ **c** $\frac{5}{3}$ **d** $-\frac{7}{3}$ **e** $-\frac{1}{3}$
  **f** 0 **g** $-\frac{2}{3}$ **h** undefined **i** $\frac{3}{2}$
**2** **a** 3 **b** 1 **c** $\frac{1}{4}$ **d** 0 **e** $-\frac{2}{3}$ **f** $-5$
**3** **a** $a = 11$ **b** $a = 6$ **c** $a = 15$
**4** Cuts the $x$-axis at $(4, 0)$.

## EXERCISE 8C.3

**1** **a** **i** $\frac{3}{4}$ **ii** $-\frac{4}{3}$ **b** **i** $\frac{1}{5}$ **ii** $-5$
  **c** **i** 4 **ii** $-\frac{1}{4}$ **d** **i** $-3$ **ii** $\frac{1}{3}$
  **e** **i** $-\frac{3}{7}$ **ii** $\frac{7}{3}$ **f** **i** $-4\frac{1}{2}$ **ii** $\frac{2}{9}$
  **g** **i** 0 **ii** undefined **h** **i** $-1$ **ii** 1
**2** **a** not perpendicular **b** not perpendicular
  **c** perpendicular **d** not perpendicular
  **e** perpendicular **f** not perpendicular

**3  a** **A** and **E**  **b** **C** and **F**, **B** and **D**

**4  a** $t = -3$  **b** $t = -10$

**5  a** $k = 2$  **b** $k = 1\frac{1}{2}$  **c** $k = 7$  **d** $k = -\frac{10}{3}$

**6  a** $AB = \sqrt{20}$,  $BC = \sqrt{5}$,  $AC = 5$
and $(\sqrt{20})^2 + (\sqrt{5})^2 = 25 = AC^2$

   **b** gradient of $AB = \frac{1}{2}$,  gradient of $BC = -2$
   $m_{AB} \times m_{BC} = -1$
   $\therefore$  AB is perpendicular to BC.

## EXERCISE 8C.4

**1  a** collinear  **b** not collinear  **c** collinear  **d** not collinear

**2  a** $n = 7$  **b** $n = 0$

## EXERCISE 8D

**1  a** $10\frac{1}{2}$  **b** The density of silver is $10\frac{1}{2}$ g per cm$^3$

   **c  i** 31.5 g  **ii** $\approx 9.52$ cm$^3$

**2  a** 82.2 kmh$^{-1}$  **b  i** 80 kmh$^{-1}$  **ii** 110 kmh$^{-1}$
   **c** Between the 5 and 6 hour mark.

**3  a** €3000
   **b** 0.18. This represents the cost (in euros per kilometre) of running the car for the first 500 km.
   **c** 0.23. This represents the average cost (in euros per km) of running the car.

**4  a** Biodiesel $= 33\frac{1}{3}$ MJ L$^{-1}$,  Ethanol $= 24$ MJ L$^{-1}$
   **b** the biodiesel

**5  a** No tax is paid on $6000 or less.
   **b** gradient of AB $\approx 0.33$,  gradient of BC $= 0.35$
   These represent the tax rates for the brackets $6k - $15k and $15k - $42k respectively.
   **c** The tax rate would increase again.

## EXERCISE 8E

**1  a** A: $y = -3$,  B: $y = -1$  **b** A: $x = -2$,  B: $x = 0$
   C: $y = 0$,  D: $y = 4$    C: $x = 1$,  D: $x = 4$

**2  a** vertical  **b** horizontal

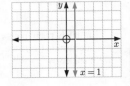

**c** vertical  **d** horizontal

**3  a** $y = -4$  **b** $x = 5$  **c** $x = -1$
   **d** $y = 2$  **e** $y = 0$  **f** $x = 0$

**4  a** $x = 2$  **b** $y = -2$

## EXERCISE 8F.1

**1  a** $y = x - 2$  **b** $y = -x + 4$  **c** $y = 2x$  **d** $y = -\frac{1}{2}x + 3$

**2  a** $y = 4x - 13$  **b** $y = -3x - 5$  **c** $y = -5x + 32$
   **d** $y = \frac{1}{2}x + \frac{7}{2}$  **e** $y = -\frac{1}{3}x + \frac{8}{3}$  **f** $y = 6$

**3  a** $2x - 3y + 11 = 0$  **b** $3x - 5y + 23 = 0$
   **c** $x + 3y - 5 = 0$  **d** $2x + 7y + 2 = 0$
   **e** $4x - y + 11 = 0$  **f** $2x + y - 7 = 0$
   **g** $7x + 2y - 18 = 0$  **h** $6x - y + 40 = 0$

**4  a** $y = \frac{5}{2}x - 2$  **b** $y = -2x + 3$  **c** $y = -2$
   **d** $y = -\frac{1}{5}x + \frac{2}{5}$  **e** $y = \frac{1}{6}x - \frac{11}{6}$  **f** $y = -\frac{2}{3}x - \frac{11}{3}$

**5  a** $x - 3y + 3 = 0$  **b** $5x - y - 1 = 0$
   **c** $x - y - 3 = 0$  **d** $4x - 5y - 10 = 0$
   **e** $x - 2y + 1 = 0$  **f** $2x + 3y + 5 = 0$

**6  a** $y = \frac{4}{3}x - 1$  **b** $y = \frac{2}{3}x + \frac{13}{3}$  **c** $y = x + 1$
   **d** $y = -2x - 2$  **e** $y = -\frac{2}{3}x + 2$  **f** $y = -\frac{3}{7}x - \frac{9}{7}$

**7  a** $M = \frac{1}{3}p + 2$  **b** $R = -\frac{5}{4}n + 2$  **c** $T = \frac{1}{2}x - 1$
   **d** $F = \frac{1}{10}x + 1$  **e** $H = -\frac{1}{2}z + 2$  **f** $W = -\frac{1}{6}t - 2$

## EXERCISE 8F.2

**1  a** 3  **b** $-2$  **c** 0  **d** undefined  **e** $\frac{2}{3}$  **f** $-\frac{4}{5}$

**2  a** $-3$  **b** $\frac{2}{7}$  **c** $-\frac{2}{7}$  **d** $\frac{3}{4}$  **e** $-\frac{4}{11}$  **f** $\frac{7}{9}$

**3  a** gradient $= -\dfrac{a}{b}$

   **b  i** $-\frac{2}{5}$  **ii** $\frac{3}{2}$  **iii** $-\frac{5}{4}$  **iv** $\frac{1}{3}$  **v** 2  **vi** $\frac{1}{4}$

## EXERCISE 8F.3

**1  a** Yes  **b** No  **c** Yes  **d** Yes

**2  a** $k = -5$  **b** $k = -6$  **c** $k = 41$  **d** $k = 1$

**3  a** $a = 2$  **b** $a = 7$  **c** $a = \frac{1}{3}$

**4  a  i** $(3, 5\frac{1}{2})$  **ii** $(4\frac{1}{5}, 4)$
   **b** $\{(x, y) \mid 5x + 4y = 37,\ 1 \leqslant x \leqslant 5\}$  **c** No

## EXERCISE 8G.1

**1  a** $y = \frac{1}{2}x + 2$  **b** $y = 2x + 1$

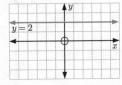
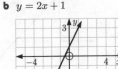

**c** $y = -x + 3$  **d** $y = -3x + 2$

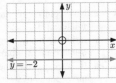
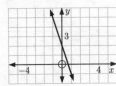

**e** $y = -\frac{1}{2}x$  **f** $y = -2x - 2$

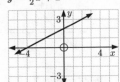
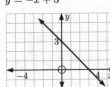

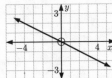
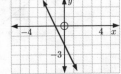

**g** $y = \frac{3}{2}x$

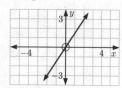

**h** $y = \frac{2}{3}x + 2$

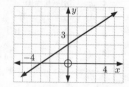

**i** $y = -\frac{3}{4}x - 1$

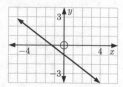

**2 a** $x + 2y = 8$

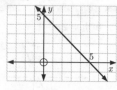

**b** $4x + 3y - 12 = 0$

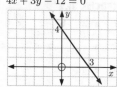

**c** $2x - 3y = 6$

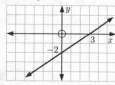

**d** $3x - y = 6$

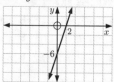

**e** $x + y = 5$

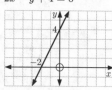

**f** $x - y = -5$

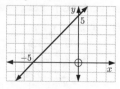

**g** $2x - y + 4 = 0$

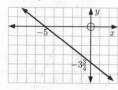

**h** $9x - 2y = 9$

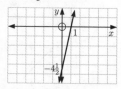

**i** $3x + 4y = -15$

---

### EXERCISE 8G.2

**1 a**

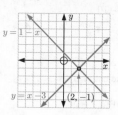

$y = 1 - x$
$y = x - 3$
$(2, -1)$

**b**

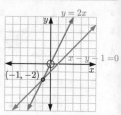

$y = 2x$
$x - y - 1 = 0$
$(-1, -2)$

**c**

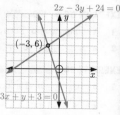

$(-3, 0)$
$x - 2y + 3 = 0$
$4x + 3y + 12 = 0$

**d**

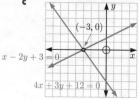

$2x - 3y + 24 = 0$
$(-3, 6)$
$3x + y + 3 = 0$

**e**

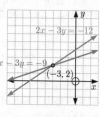

$(\frac{2}{3}, 7)$
$3x - 2y = -12$
$3x + y = 9$

**f**

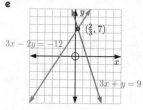

$2x - 3y = -12$
$x - 3y = -9$
$(-3, 2)$

**g**

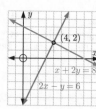

$(4, 2)$
$x + 2y = 8$
$2x - y = 6$

**h**

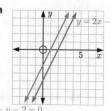

$y = 2x - 4$
$2x - y - 2 = 0$

Lines are parallel,
∴ do not intersect.

**i**

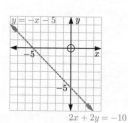

$y = -x - 5$
$2x + 2y = -10$

Infinitely many points of intersection (lines are coincident).

**2 a** No points of intersection (same gradient, different $y$-intercept).
 **b** Infinitely many points of intersection (same gradient, same $y$-intercept, ∴ same line).
 **c** If $k = 5$, the lines are coincident, and ∴ have infinitely many points of intersection.
 If $k \neq 5$, the lines are parallel, and there are no points of intersection.

### EXERCISE 8G.3

**1 a** $(-3, 2)$  **b** $(1, 4)$  **c** $(2.3, 1.4)$  **d** $(0.9, -3.1)$
**2 a** No points of intersection (lines are parallel).
 **b** Infinitely many points of intersection (lines are coincident).
**3 a** $(15, 260)$
 **b** The potter must make 15 pots to break even.

## EXERCISE 8H

1  **a** $y = x - 4$  **b** $y = 2x + 6$  **c** $y = \frac{6}{5}x + \frac{7}{2}$  **d** $y = 1$

2  $y = \frac{2}{3}x + \frac{5}{3}$

3  **a** Hospital S  **b** $(-1, -2)$  **c** $y = x - 1$

4  **a** Perpendicular bisector of PQ: $y = \frac{1}{3}x + 2$
   Perpendicular bisector of QR: $y = 2x - 3$
   **b** Centre of circle $= (3, 3)$

5  **a** P(5, 3),  Q(4, 0),  R(2, 2)
   **b**  **i** $y = x - 2$  **ii** $y = -3x + 12$  **iii** $y = -\frac{1}{3}x + \frac{8}{3}$
   **c** X$(3\frac{1}{2}, 1\frac{1}{2})$  **d** Yes
   **e** They will meet at a single point.
   **f** It is the point equidistant from all three vertices.

## REVIEW SET 8A

1  **a** 5 units  **b** $-\frac{4}{3}$  **c** $(1, 4)$

2  $x$-intercept is $-2$, $y$-intercept is 5, gradient is $\frac{5}{2}$

3  $y = -2x + 6$  4  $a = 7\frac{1}{5}$  5  $c = 2$

6  **a** $y = -3x + 4$  **b** $x + 2y - 5 = 0$

7
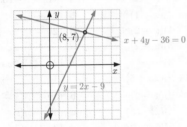

8  5 units  9  **a** $-4$  **b** $\frac{1}{4}$  **c** $x - 4y + 6 = 0$

10  C(3, 0)  11  $k = 4 \pm \sqrt{24}$

## REVIEW SET 8B

1  $(5, 1\frac{1}{2})$  2  **a** $\frac{2}{3}$  **b** 4  **c** $-\frac{3}{2}$  **d** undefined

3  **a** $y = -3x + 5$  **b** $y = -\frac{3}{2}x + \frac{5}{2}$

4  **a** $x$-intercept $\frac{14}{3}$, $y$-intercept 7
   **b** $x$-intercept $\frac{12}{5}$, $y$-intercept $-4$

5  Yes  6  **a** $k = \frac{3}{4}$  **b** $k = -12$

7
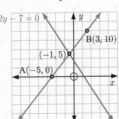

8  **a** $y = 3$  **b** $x = -6$  9  $5x - 3y - 4 = 0$

10  **a** (7, 0)  **b** $x + 2y - 7 = 0$  **c** $3 + 2(2) - 7 = 0$ ✓
   **d** The perpendicular bisector of a circle's chord passes through
   the centre of the circle.

11  **a** AC has gradient 0,  MN has gradient 0
   $\therefore$  AC and MN are parallel.
   **b** AC has length 6,  MN has length 3
   $\therefore$  MN $= \frac{1}{2}$AC

## REVIEW SET 8C

1  **a** $2x - 3y - 17 = 0$  **b** $x - 3y - 11 = 0$

2  **a** $k = -\frac{21}{5}$  **b** $k = \frac{15}{7}$

3  **a** T$(0, 2 + \sqrt{8})$  or  T$(0, 2 - \sqrt{8})$
   **b** $y = \sqrt{8}x + (2 + \sqrt{8})$

4  **a** 50  **b** 82
   **c** The gradient of AB is the average speed of the truck
   between A and B, in km h$^{-1}$.
   The gradient of OC is the average speed of the truck
   over the whole day, in km h$^{-1}$.

5  Triangle KLM is a right angled isosceles triangle.

6  Z(2, −2)

7  **a** $y = -\frac{1}{3}x + 4$  **b** $5x - 2y + 1 = 0$

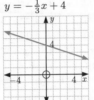 

8  $x - 2y + 9 = 0$

9  **a**  **i** gradient of AB $= -\frac{1}{4}$,  gradient of DC $= -\frac{1}{4}$
   The gradients are equal, $\therefore$ AB $\parallel$ DC.
   **ii** gradient of BC $= \frac{3}{5}$,  gradient of AD $= \frac{3}{5}$
   The gradients are equal, $\therefore$ BC $\parallel$ AD.
   **b** parallelogram
   **c** AB $=$ DC $= \sqrt{68}$,  BC $=$ AD $= \sqrt{306}$
   **d**  **i** $(2\frac{1}{2}, 2\frac{1}{2})$  **ii** $(2\frac{1}{2}, 2\frac{1}{2})$
   **e** The diagonals of a parallelogram bisect each other.

10

| | Equation of line | Gradient | $x$-intercept | $y$-intercept |
|---|---|---|---|---|
| **a** | $5x - 2y - 10 = 0$ | $\frac{5}{2}$ | 2 | $-5$ |
| **b** | $4x + 5y = 20$ | $-\frac{4}{5}$ | 5 | 4 |
| **c** | $y = -2x + 5$ | $-2$ | $\frac{5}{2}$ | 5 |
| **d** | $x = 8$ | undefined | 8 | none |
| **e** | $y = 5$ | 0 | none | 5 |
| **f** | $x + y = 11$ | $-1$ | 11 | 11 |

11  **a** AB $=$ BC $=$ CD $=$ DA $= 5$ units  **b** $(2, 1)$ for both
   **c** $m_{AC} = -2$,  $m_{BD} = \frac{1}{2}$

## REVIEW SET 8D

1  **a** $\sqrt{34}$ units  **b** $-\frac{3}{5}$  **c** $3x + 5y + 12 = 0$

2  scalene  3  $k = -5$  4  K(10, 15)

5  **a** 330 L  **b** from B to C
   **c** 18 L per minute  **d** 20.5 L per minute

6  $c = \frac{11}{2}$

7  **a** $-\frac{3}{2}$  **b** $-\frac{5}{3}$

8  **a** $r = \frac{5}{7}a + 2$  **b** $K = \frac{3}{5}s + 3$

9  **a** $t = -32$  **b** $t = -\frac{13}{5}$

10  **a** PQ $=$ PR $= \sqrt{20}$ units  **b** M(4, 4)
   **c** gradient of PM $= -\frac{1}{3}$, gradient of QR $= 3$

**d**

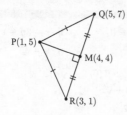

P(1, 5), Q(5, 7), M(4, 4), R(3, 1)

**11 a i** $y = 2$ **ii** $x = 0$ **iii** $4x - 3y + 18 = 0$
 **b i** $(-3, 2)$ **ii** $(0, 6)$

## EXERCISE 9A

**1 a** $x$ **b** $2x$ **c** $x + 1$ **d** $x - 1$
 **e** $-3x$ (or $3x$) **f** $x - 1$ (or $1 - x$)

**2 a** $x(2x + 3)$ **b** $x(4x - 7)$ **c** $-3x(x - 5)$
 **d** $5x(x + 5)$ **e** $2x(1 - 4x)$ **f** $2(x^2 - 6)$
 **g** $3x(1 - 2x)$ **h** $2x(2x + 5)$ **i** $3x(4 - 7x)$

**3 a** $(x + 3)(x + 2)$ **b** $(x - 1)(x - 1)$ **c** $-(x + 2)$
 **d** $-(x + 4)(x + 11)$ **e** $(x - 2)(11 - x)$ **f** $5x$
 **g** $2(x - 1)(x - 5)$ **h** $2x(7x - 9)$ **i** $-(x - 2)(x + 2)$

## EXERCISE 9B

**1 a** $(x + 5)(x - 5)$ **b** $(3 + x)(3 - x)$
 **c** $(a + 8)(a - 8)$ **d** $(10 + x)(10 - x)$
 **e** $(2x + 7)(2x - 7)$ **f** $(1 + 4x)(1 - 4x)$
 **g** $(5t + 9)(5t - 9)$ **h** $(7 + 6x)(7 - 6x)$

**2 a** $5(x + 2)(x - 2)$ **b** $2(1 + 7x)(1 - 7x)$
 **c** $-7(x + 3)(x - 3)$ **d** $4(5 + a)(5 - a)$
 **e** $3(3x + 4)(3x - 4)$ **f** $2(5 + 2k)(5 - 2k)$
 **g** $4(3x + 1)(3x - 1)$ **h** $-2(x + 6)(x - 6)$

**3 a** $(x + \sqrt{5})(x - \sqrt{5})$ **b** $(\sqrt{14} + x)(\sqrt{14} - x)$
 **c** cannot be factorised **d** $(x + 2 + \sqrt{6})(x + 2 - \sqrt{6})$
 **e** cannot be factorised **f** $(x + 4 + \sqrt{10})(x + 4 - \sqrt{10})$

**4 a** $2(x + 5)(x - 5)$ **b** $(9 + x)(9 - x)$
 **c** $(x + \sqrt{3})(x - \sqrt{3})$ **d** $16(2 + t)(2 - t)$
 **e** $(x + 5 + \sqrt{7})(x + 5 - \sqrt{7})$ **f** $(7x + 3)(7x - 3)$
 **g** $(\sqrt{21} + x)(\sqrt{21} - x)$ **h** $(x - 1 + \sqrt{5})(x - 1 - \sqrt{5})$
 **i** $4(5 + 3a)(5 - 3a)$

**5 a** $(2x + 7)(2x - 1)$ **b** $(x - 11)(x + 1)$
 **c** $3(x + 3)(1 - 3x)$ **d** $3(x + 2)(6 - x)$
 **e** $(4x + 7)(2x + 3)$ **f** $(5x - 8)(3x + 2)$

## EXERCISE 9C

**1 a** $(x + 5)^2$ **b** $(x - 7)^2$ **c** $(t - 10)^2$
 **d** $(x + 2)^2$ **e** $(b - 1)^2$ **f** $(x + 8)^2$
 **g** $(k - 3)^2$ **h** $(x - 4)^2$ **i** $(z + 9)^2$

**2 a** $(2x - 5)^2$ **b** $(3x + 2)^2$ **c** $(4x - 1)^2$
 **d** $(3n - 5)^2$ **e** $(6x - 1)^2$ **f** $2(x + 6)^2$
 **g** $-3(x + 1)^2$ **h** $2(4x - 3)^2$ **i** $-4(5x - 1)^2$

## EXERCISE 9D

**1 a** $(x + 4)(x + 1)$ **b** $(x + 5)(x - 3)$ **c** $(x - 4)(x + 3)$
 **d** $(x - 7)(x - 3)$ **e** $(x + 6)(x - 3)$ **f** $(a + 2)(a + 9)$
 **g** $(x - 7)(x + 9)$ **h** $(x + 3)(x + 11)$ **i** $(x + 1)(x - 20)$
 **j** $(x - 8)^2$ **k** $(x + 7)(x - 7)$ **l** $(x - 4)(x + 12)$

**2 a** $2(x + 2)(x - 5)$ **b** $3(x + 2)(x + 6)$
 **c** $5(x + 4)(x - 5)$ **d** $-(x - 2)(x - 7)$
 **e** $4(x + 2)(x - 6)$ **f** $-2(x + 4)(x - 6)$
 **g** $7(x + 2)(x - 3)$ **h** $-3(x + 1)(x + 9)$
 **i** $-5(x - 4)^2$

## EXERCISE 9E.1

**1 a** $4x(x + 2)$ **b** $x(5 - x)$ **c** $2x(3x - 2)$
 **d** $3(x^2 + 5)$ **e** $-2x(x - 5)$ **f** $6x(3 - 2x)$

**2 a** $(x + 9)(x - 9)$ **b** $(x + 1)^2$ **c** $(x + 3)(x + 9)$
 **d** $(x - 18)(x - 2)$ **e** $(x + \sqrt{22})(x - \sqrt{22})$ **f** $(t - 5)^2$
 **g** $(x + 12)(x - 5)$ **h** $(x + 12)^2$ **i** $(k + 6)(k - 8)$

**3 a** $5(x + 2)(x + 4)$ **b** $3(x + 2)(x - 2)$ **c** $6(x - 3)^2$
 **d** $-2(x - 2)(x - 8)$ **e** $(7x - 2)^2$ **f** $-3(x - 4)(x - 6)$
 **g** $5(4 + x)(4 - x)$ **h** $4(x - 12)(x + 1)$ **i** $-2(4x - 1)^2$

## EXERCISE 9E.2

**1 a** $7x = x + 6x$ **b** $5x = 6x - x$
 **c** $11x = 8x + 3x$ **d** $-6x = 2x - 8x$
 **e** $14x = 16x - 2x$ **f** $-19x = -25x + 6x$

**2 a** $(2x + 3)(x + 1)$ **b** $(3x + 2)(x + 3)$
 **c** $(3x + 1)(x + 2)$ **d** $(2x + 1)(3x + 2)$
 **e** $(5x + 3)(x + 2)$ **f** $(3x + 1)(2x + 3)$
 **g** $(2x + 3)^2$ **h** $(3x + 1)(3x + 2)$
 **i** $(5x + 2)(2x + 5)$

**3 a** $(2x + 3)(x - 2)$ **b** $(3x + 2)(x - 4)$
 **c** $(2x - 1)(2x - 3)$ **d** $(5x - 2)(x - 3)$
 **e** $(2x + 5)(2x - 3)$ **f** $(2x + 1)(3x - 5)$
 **g** $(5x + 4)(2x - 1)$ **h** $(3x - 4)(3x + 2)$
 **i** $(2x - 3)(4x - 1)$ **j** $(3x - 2)(5x + 3)$
 **k** $(3x - 2)(4x - 3)$ **l** $(7x + 5)(x - 2)$

**4 a** $-(3x + 2)(x + 1)$ **b** $-(2x + 5)(2x + 3)$
 **c** $-(5x + 3)(x - 2)$ **d** $-(3x + 7)(2x - 1)$
 **e** $-(3x + 2)(3x - 5)$ **f** $-(2x - 3)(5x - 6)$

## EXERCISE 9F

**1 a** $x = \pm 2$ **b** $x = \pm 4$ **c** $x = \pm 1$
 **d** $x = \pm\sqrt{7}$ **e** no real solutions **f** $x = 0$
 **g** $x = \pm 3$ **h** $x = \pm\sqrt{5}$ **i** no real solutions

**2 a** $x = 7$ or $-1$ **b** $x = 2$ or $-4$ **c** no real solutions
 **d** $x = 2 \pm\sqrt{10}$ **e** $x = -4 \pm\sqrt{13}$ **f** no real solutions
 **g** $x = 7$ **h** $x = 4$ or $-1$ **i** $x = \dfrac{-1 \pm \sqrt{14}}{3}$

## EXERCISE 9G.1

**1 a** $x = 0$ **b** $a = 0$ **c** $y = 0$
 **d** $a = 0$ or $b = 0$ **e** $x = 0$ or $y = 0$
 **f** $a = 0$ or $b = 0$ or $c = 0$ **g** $a = 0$
 **h** $p = 0$ or $q = 0$ or $r = 0$ or $s = 0$
 **i** $a = 0$ or $b = 0$

**2 a** $x = 0$ or $5$ **b** $x = 0$ or $-3$ **c** $x = -1$ or $3$
 **d** $x = 0$ or $7$ **e** $x = 0$ or $-1$ **f** $x = -6$ or $\frac{3}{2}$
 **g** $x = -\frac{1}{2}$ or $\frac{1}{2}$ **h** $x = -2$ or $7$ **i** $x = 5$ or $-\frac{2}{3}$
 **j** $x = 0$ **k** $x = 5$ **l** $x = \frac{1}{3}$

## EXERCISE 9G.2

1 a $x = 0$ or $-2$  b $x = 0$ or $-\frac{5}{2}$  c $x = 0$ or $\frac{3}{4}$
  d $x = 0$ or $\frac{5}{4}$  e $x = 0$ or $3$  f $x = \frac{1}{2}$ or $0$

2 a $x = -2$ or $-7$  b $x = -5$ or $-6$  c $x = 3$ or $-5$
  d $x = 3$ or $-4$  e $x = 3$ or $2$  f $x = 2$
  g $x = 3$ or $-2$  h $x = 12$ or $-5$  i $x = 10$ or $-7$
  j $x = 2$ or $-5$  k $x = 4$ or $3$  l $x = 12$ or $-3$

3 a $x = 2$ or $\frac{1}{2}$  b $x = \frac{1}{3}$ or $-3$  c $x = -\frac{5}{3}$ or $-4$
  d $x = \frac{1}{2}$ or $-3$  e $x = 5$ or $\frac{1}{2}$  f $x = -1$ or $-\frac{5}{2}$
  g $x = -\frac{1}{3}$ or $-4$  h $x = 3$ or $-\frac{2}{5}$  i $x = \frac{1}{2}$ or $-9$
  j $x = 1$ or $-\frac{5}{2}$  k $x = \frac{4}{3}$ or $-2$  l $x = \frac{3}{2}$ or $-6$

4 a $x = \frac{1}{3}$ or $-\frac{5}{2}$  b $x = \frac{2}{3}$ or $-\frac{1}{2}$  c $x = -\frac{1}{3}$ or $-\frac{1}{2}$
  d $x = 3$ or $-\frac{1}{21}$  e $x = \frac{2}{5}$ or $-\frac{1}{2}$  f $x = 1$ or $-\frac{3}{10}$

5 a $x = -3$ or $-4$  b $x = 1$ or $-3$  c $x = 3$ or $-3$
  d $x = \frac{2}{3}$ or $-1$  e $x = -\frac{1}{2}$  f $x = 4$ or $\frac{5}{2}$

6 a $x = \sqrt{6}$ or $-\sqrt{6}$  b $x = \sqrt{8}$ or $-\sqrt{8}$
  c $x = \sqrt{10}$ or $-\sqrt{10}$  d $x = 4$ or $-3$
  e $x = -1$ or $-5$  f $x = 2$ or $-1$  g $x = \frac{1}{2}$ or $-1$
  h $x = 1$ or $-\frac{1}{3}$  i $x = 4$ or $-1$

## EXERCISE 9H

1 a $x = 2 \pm \sqrt{7}$  b $x = -3 \pm \sqrt{2}$  c $x = 2 \pm \sqrt{3}$
  d $x = -2 \pm \sqrt{5}$  e $x = 2 \pm \sqrt{2}$  f $x = \frac{1 \pm \sqrt{7}}{2}$
  g $x = \frac{-4 \pm \sqrt{7}}{9}$  h $x = \frac{-7 \pm \sqrt{97}}{4}$

2 a $x = -2 \pm 2\sqrt{2}$  b $x = \frac{-5 \pm \sqrt{57}}{8}$  c $x = \frac{5 \pm \sqrt{13}}{2}$
  d $x = \frac{1 \pm \sqrt{7}}{2}$  e $x = \frac{1 \pm \sqrt{5}}{2}$  f $x = \frac{3 \pm \sqrt{17}}{4}$

## EXERCISE 9I

1 a $x \approx -0.697$ or $-4.30$  b $x \approx 1.54$ or $-0.869$
  c $x \approx -1.89$ or $2.39$  d $x \approx 1.40$ or $-0.896$
  e $x \approx 0.836$ or $-1.44$  f $x \approx 0.896$ or $-1.40$

## EXERCISE 9J

1 $-5$ and $7$, or $-7$ and $5$  2 $5$ (or $\frac{1}{5}$)  3 $14$
4 $18$ and $20$, or $-18$ and $-20$
5 $15$ and $17$, or $-15$ and $-17$  6 $15$  7 $3.48$ cm
8 $7$ m by $10$ m, or $5$ m by $14$ m  9 a $x = 5$  b $x = 6$
10 No.  11 b $6$ cm $\times$ $6$ cm $\times$ $7$ cm
12 $11.2$ cm $\times$ $11.2$ cm  13 $221$ ha  14 $2.03$ m

15 a If speed $= \dfrac{\text{distance}}{\text{time}}$, then time $= \dfrac{\text{distance}}{\text{speed}}$.

  b $\dfrac{1000}{v}$ is the time (in hours) the plane takes to travel $1000$ km
    at $v$ km h$^{-1}$.

    $\dfrac{1000}{v - 120}$ is the time (in hours) the plane would take if it
    were travelling $120$ km h$^{-1}$ slower. There is a difference of
    $\frac{1}{2}$ hour between the two times.

  d $554$ km h$^{-1}$

16 $61.8$ km h$^{-1}$  17 c $1.5$ m
18 a AB $= \sqrt{x^2 + 625}$  b BC $= \sqrt{x^2 - 160x + 7025}$
  c $x \approx 8.78$

## REVIEW SET 9A

1 a $(x + 3)(x - 7)$  b $(2t + 5)(2t - 5)$
  c $3(x + 4)(x - 6)$  d $(2x - 1)(3x + 2)$

2 a $x = 8$ or $3$  b $x = \frac{3}{2}$ or $-\frac{2}{5}$

3 a $x = 7$ or $-3$  b $x = 3$ or $2$

4 a $x = \pm\sqrt{28}$  b $x = 1$ or $-2$

5 $20$ cm by $13$ cm  6 $x = 2$  7 $x = -3 \pm 2\sqrt{5}$

## REVIEW SET 9B

1 a $(x - 11)(x + 3)$  b $(y - 4)(y + 8)$  c $(x - 5)^2$

2 a $x = 3$ or $-8$  b $x = 3$ or $-3$  c $x = \frac{1}{2}$ or $-\frac{3}{4}$

3 a $x = 4$ or $-5$  b $x = 9$ or $-6$

4 a $x \approx 0.317$ or $-6.32$  b $x \approx -1.48$ or $3.15$

5 BC $= 5$ cm or $16$ cm  6 $5$ or $2$  7 $x = 1 \pm \sqrt{101}$

## REVIEW SET 9C

1 a $(\sqrt{13} + x)(\sqrt{13} - x)$  b $(x - 1)(8 - x)$

2 a $(x - 9)(x + 2)$  b $(2x + 7)(2x - 7)$
  c $2(k - 10)(k + 3)$  d $(5x + 2)(x + 2)$

3 a $x = 3$ or $2$  b $x = 4$  c $x = 3$ or $-\frac{7}{3}$

4 a $x \approx 18.6$ or $2.11$  b $x \approx 1.24$ or $-3.24$

5 $8$ cm, $15$ cm, $17$ cm  6 $28.4$ km h$^{-1}$  7 $x = 7 \pm \sqrt{42}$

## REVIEW SET 9D

1 a $4(x + 3)(x - 3)$  b $(a - 10)(a + 3)$  c $(2x - 3)(3x + 4)$

2 a $x = 0$ or $\frac{5}{2}$  b $x = 6$ or $-2$  c $x = 2$ or $-\frac{3}{4}$

3 a $x = 3$ or $-9$  b $x = -1$ or $-5$  c $x = \frac{1}{3}$ or $-2$

4 Richard is $7$ years old.  5 $1.17$ seconds

6 $1.5$ km by $1.5$ km  7 $x = \frac{5 \pm \sqrt{17}}{4}$

## EXERCISE 10A

1 a function - $x$-coordinates are all different
  b not a function - two points with the same $x$-coordinate
  c not a function - all points have the same $x$-coordinate
  d function - $x$-coordinates are all different
  e fucntion - $x$-coordinates are all different
  f not a function - the points all have the same $x$-coordinate

2 a function  b function  c function
  d not a function  e function  f not a function
  g function  h not a function

3 No - vertical lines are not functions  4 $y = \pm\sqrt{9 - x^2}$

## EXERCISE 10B

1 a $2$  b $8$  c $-1$  d $-13$  e $1$

2 a $2$  b $2$  c $-16$  d $-68$  e $\frac{17}{4}$

3 a $-3$  b $3$  c $3$  d $-3$  e $\frac{15}{2}$

4 a $7 - 3a$  b $7 + 3a$  c $-3a - 2$
  d $10 - 3b$  e $1 - 3x$  f $7 - 3x - 3h$

5 a $2x^2 + 19x + 43$  b $2x^2 - 11x + 13$
  c $2x^2 - 3x - 1$  d $2x^4 + 3x^2 - 1$
  e $2x^4 - x^2 - 2$  f $2x^2 + 4hx + 2h^2 + 3x + 3h - 1$

6 a i $-\frac{7}{2}$  ii $-\frac{3}{4}$  iii $-\frac{4}{9}$  b $x = 4$
  c $G(x + 2) = \dfrac{2x + 7}{x - 2}$  d $x = \frac{9}{5}$

**7** $f$ is the function; $f(x)$ is the value of $y$ for a given value of $x$

**8** **a** $V(4) =$ €6210. This is the photocopier's value 4 years after purchase.
  **b** $t = 4.5$. This is the length of time it takes for the value of the photocopier to reach €5780.
  **c** €9650

**9**

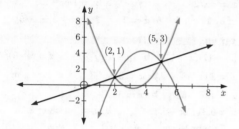

**10** $f(x) = -2x + 5$  **11** $a = 3,\ b = -2$

**12** $a = 3,\ b = -1,\ c = -4$

## EXERCISE 10C

**1** **a** Domain: $\{x \mid x \geqslant -1\}$, Range: $\{y \mid y \leqslant 3\}$
  **b** Domain: $\{x \mid -1 < x \leqslant 5\}$, Range: $\{y \mid 1 < y \leqslant 3\}$
  **c** Domain: $\{x \mid x \neq 2\}$, Range: $\{y \mid y \neq -1\}$
  **d** Domain: $\{x \mid x \in \mathbb{R}\}$, Range: $\{y \mid 0 < y \leqslant 2\}$
  **e** Domain: $\{x \mid x \in \mathbb{R}\}$, Range: $\{y \mid y \geqslant -1\}$
  **f** Domain: $\{x \mid x \in \mathbb{R}\}$, Range: $\{y \mid y \leqslant 6\frac{1}{4}\}$
  **g** Domain: $\{x \mid x \geqslant -4\}$, Range: $\{y \mid y \geqslant -3\}$
  **h** Domain: $\{x \mid x \in \mathbb{R}\}$, Range: $\{y \mid y > -2\}$
  **i** Domain: $\{x \mid x \neq -2,\ x \neq 2\}$,
    Range: $\{y \mid y \leqslant -1 \text{ or } y > 0\}$

**2** **a** $x < -6$  **b** $x = 0$  **c** $x \geqslant \frac{3}{2}$

**3** **a** Domain: $\{x \mid x \geqslant 0\}$, Range: $\{y \mid y \geqslant 0\}$
  **b** Domain: $\{x \mid x \neq 0\}$, Range: $\{y \mid y > 0\}$
  **c** Domain: $\{x \mid x \leqslant 4\}$, Range: $\{y \mid y \geqslant 0\}$
  **d** Domain: $\{x \mid x \in \mathbb{R}\}$, Range: $\{y \mid y \geqslant -\frac{9}{4}\}$
  **e** Domain: $\{x \mid x \in \mathbb{R}\}$, Range: $\{y \mid y \leqslant \frac{25}{12}\}$
  **f** Domain: $\{x \mid x \neq 0\}$, Range: $\{y \mid y \geqslant 2 \text{ or } y \leqslant -2\}$
  **g** Domain: $\{x \mid x \neq 2\}$, Range: $\{y \mid y \neq 1\}$
  **h** Domain: $\{x \mid x \in \mathbb{R}\}$, Range: $\{y \mid y \in \mathbb{R}\}$
  **i** Domain: $\{x \mid x \neq 2,\ x \neq -1\}$,
    Range: $\{y \mid y \leqslant \frac{1}{3} \text{ or } y \geqslant 3\}$
  **j** Domain: $\{x \mid x \neq 0\}$, Range: $\{y \mid y \geqslant 2\}$
  **k** Domain: $\{x \mid x \neq 0\}$, Range: $\{y \mid y \geqslant 2 \text{ or } y \leqslant -2\}$
  **l** Domain: $\{x \mid x \in \mathbb{R}\}$, Range: $\{y \mid y \geqslant -8\}$

## EXERCISE 10D

**1** **a** **i**

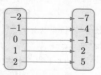

  **iv**

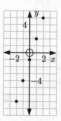

  **ii** $\{-7, -4, -1, 2, 5\}$
  **iii** is a function

**b** **i**

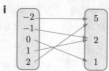

  **iv**

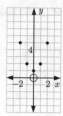

  **ii** $\{1, 2, 5\}$
  **iii** is a function

**c** **i**

  **iv**

  **ii** $\{-5, -1, 3, 7, 11\}$
  **iii** is a function

**d** **i**

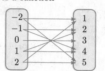

  **iv**

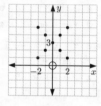

  **ii** $\{1, 2, 3, 4, 5\}$
  **iii** is not a function

**e** **i**

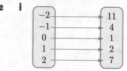

  **iv**

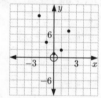

  **ii** $\{1, 2, 4, 7, 11\}$
  **iii** is a function

**f** **i**

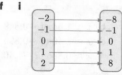

  **iv**

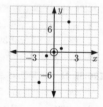

  **ii** $\{-8, -1, 0, 1, 8\}$
  **iii** is a function

**g** **i**

  **iv**

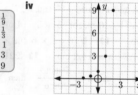

  **ii** $\{\frac{1}{9}, \frac{1}{3}, 1, 3, 9\}$
  **iii** is a function

**h** **i**

  **iv**

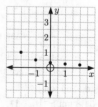

  **ii** $\{\frac{1}{5}, \frac{1}{4}, \frac{1}{3}, \frac{1}{2}, 1\}$
  **iii** is a function

**i i**

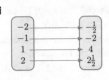

**iv**

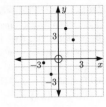

**ii** $\{-2, -\frac{1}{2}, 2\frac{1}{2}, 4\}$

**iii** is a function

**2 a i** $\{-2, -1, 0, 1, 2\}$    **ii** $\{1, 3, 5, 7, 9\}$
    **iii** $f : x \mapsto 2x + 5$

**b i** $\{0, 1, 2, 3, 4\}$    **ii** $\{1, 2, 3, 4, 5\}$
    **iii** $f : x \mapsto -x + 5$

**c i** $\{-3, 0, 3, 6, 9\}$    **ii** $\{-23, -11, 1, 13, 25\}$
    **iii** $f : x \mapsto 4x - 11$

**d i** $\{-3, 3, 6, 9, 15\}$    **ii** $\{-23, -11, -5, 1, 13\}$
    **iii** $f : x \mapsto -2x + 7$

**3 a i**        **b i**

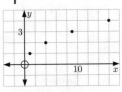

**ii** $f : x \mapsto \sqrt{x}$     **ii** $f : x \mapsto x^2$

**c i**        **d i**

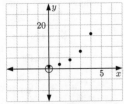

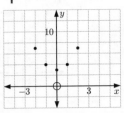

**ii** $f : x \mapsto 2^x$     **ii** $f : x \mapsto x^2 + 3$

## EXERCISE 10E

**1 a** €170    **b** €320    **c** €720

**2 a** 100°C    **b** 0°C    **c** 40°C    **d** 190°C

**3 a** $V(0) = 25\,000$ pounds.
    This is the purchase price of the car.
**b** $V(3) = 16\,000$ pounds
    This is the value of the car 3 years after purchase.
**c** $t = 5$
    It will take 5 years for the value of the car to decrease to
    £10 000.

**4** $f(x) = 4x - 1$

**5 a**

| $t$ | 0 | 1 | 2 | 3 | 4 | 5 |
|---|---|---|---|---|---|---|
| $C$ | 60 | 105 | 150 | 195 | 240 | 285 |

**b** $C = 60 + 45t$    **c** $352.50

**6 a**

| $t$ | 0 | 1 | 2 | 3 | 4 | 5 |
|---|---|---|---|---|---|---|
| $V$ | 265 | 254 | 243 | 232 | 221 | 210 |

**b**

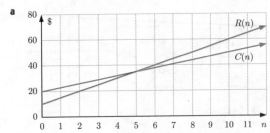

**c** $V(t) = 265 - 11t$    **d i** 100 L    **ii** 24.1 minutes

**7 a** $C = 158 + 365n$    **b** €1526.75    **c** $\approx 13\,300$ km

**8 a** $W = 50s + 250$    **b** $1925    **c** $11\,600

**9 a**

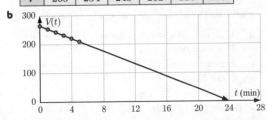

**b** 5 packs    **c** $n > 5$    **d** 55 packs

**10 a** $R(n) = 7n$,    **b**
      $C(n) = 2.5n + 300$
**c** 67 adaptors
**d** 289 adaptors

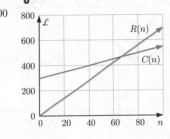

**11 a** $C(n) = 6000 + 3.25n$
    $R(n) = 9.5n$
**b**            **c** 960 books
                  **d** 2560 books

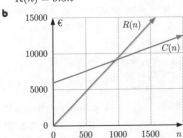

**12 a** $C(n) = 2100 + 28n$,   $R(n) = 70n$
**b**            **c** $P(n) = 42n - 2100$
                  **d i** $3150
                    **ii** 81 carburettors

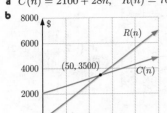

## REVIEW SET 10A

**1 a** 0   **b** $-15$   **c** $-\frac{5}{4}$   **2** $a = -6$, $b = 13$

**3 a** $g(x+1) = x^2 - x - 2$   **b** $g(x^2 - 2) = x^4 - 7x^2 + 10$

**4 a  i** Domain: $\{x \mid x \in \mathbb{R}\}$,  Range: $\{y \mid y \geqslant -5\}$
**ii** is a function
**b  i** Domain: $\{x \mid x \in \mathbb{R}\}$,  Range: $\{y \mid y = -3 \text{ or } y = 1\}$
**ii** is a function

**5 a** $x = 0$   **b**
**c** Domain: $\{x \mid x \neq 0\}$,
Range: $\{y \mid y > 0\}$

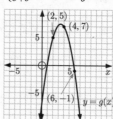

$f(x) = \frac{2}{x^2}$

**6 a**

**d**

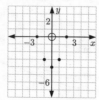

**b** $\{-4, -3, 0\}$
**c** is a function

**7 a**

| $d$ | 0 | 1 | 2 | 3 | 4 |
|-----|---|---|---|---|---|
| $C$ | 130 | 210 | 290 | 370 | 450 |

**b**

**c** $C = 130 + 80d$
**d** £40

## REVIEW SET 10B

**1 a** is a function   **b** is not a function   **c** is a function

**2 a** 1   **b** $-5$   **c** $3x - 2$   **d** $3x^2 - 3x - 5$

**3** $a = 3$, $b = -1$

**4 a** Domain: $\{x \mid x \in \mathbb{R}\}$,  Range: $\{y \mid y \geqslant -4\}$
**b** Domain: $\{x \mid x \neq 0, \ x \neq 2\}$,
Range: $\{y \mid y > 0 \text{ or } y \leqslant -1\}$

**5 a** $x = 0$   **b** $x < 2$   **c** defined for all $x \in \mathbb{R}$

**6 a  i**

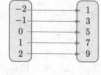

**ii** $\{-2, -1, 0, 1, 2\}$
**iii** $\{1, 3, 5, 7, 9\}$

**b  i**

**ii** $\{-2, -1, 0, 1, 2\}$
**iii** $\{2, 4, 8\}$

**7 a** $O = 160 - 5t$   **b** 85 L
**c  i** 22 minutes   **ii** 32 minutes

## REVIEW SET 10C

**1 a** function ($x$-coordinates are all different)
**b** not a function (two points have the same $x$-coordinate)
**c** not a function ($x$-coordinates are the same)

**2 a** Domain: $\{x \mid x \geqslant -2\}$,  Range: $\{y \mid 1 \leqslant y < 3\}$
**b** Domain: $\{x \mid x \in \mathbb{R}\}$
Range: $\{y \mid y = -1 \text{ or } y = 1 \text{ or } y = 2\}$

**3**

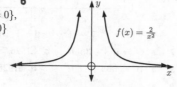

(There are other answers.)

**4** $a = 1$, $b = -6$, $c = 5$

**5 a  i** Domain: $\{x \mid x \neq 1\}$,  Range: $\{y \mid y > -1\}$
**ii** is a function
**b  i** Domain: $\{x \mid -2 \leqslant x \leqslant 2\}$,
Range: $\{y \mid -2 \leqslant y \leqslant 2\}$
**ii** is not a function

**6 a  i** Domain:
$\{0, 1, 2, 3, 4\}$
Range:
$\{-1, 2, 5, 8, 11\}$
**b  i** Domain:
$\{-2, 1, 0, 1, 2\}$
Range:  $\{3\}$

**ii**

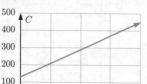

**ii**

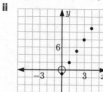

**iii** $f: x \mapsto 3x - 1$    **iii** $f: x \mapsto 3$

**7 a** $C(n) = 2.4n + 1750$,  $R(n) = \frac{11}{3}n$
**b**

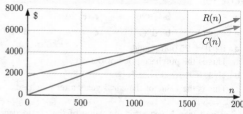

**c** 1383 tennis balls (461 complete packs)   **d** 566 packs

## EXERCISE 11A.1

**1 a** 82.5 m   **b** 29.5 cm   **c** 6.25 km
**d** 7380 cm   **e** 0.2463 m   **f** 0.009 761 km

**2 a** 4130 mm   **b** 3 754 000 m   **c** 482 900 cm
**d** 26 900 mm   **e** 47 000 cm   **f** 3 880 000 mm

**3** 7.26 km   **4** 18 000 candles

## EXERCISE 11A.2

**1 a** 5900 g   **b** 2.6 kg   **c** 0.003 75 t
**d** 15 000 000 mg   **e** 4 800 000 g   **f** 0.0016 kg
**g** 1738.5 mg   **h** 0.046 218 t   **i** 36 100 mg

**2** 20 000 nails   **3 a** 6.21 t   **b** 9

## EXERCISE 11B

**1 a** 11.7 m  **b** 35 mm  **c** 6.2 km
  **d** 172 cm  **e** $(4x - 4)$ cm  **f** $(4x + 2)$ m
  **g** $(13x + 2)$ km  **h** $(6y - 8)$ cm  **i** $8x$ km

**2 a**

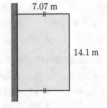

220 m, 300 m

  **b** 1040 m

**3** 17.5 km

**4 a** 132 m  **b** 660 m  **c** 66 posts  **d** $445.50

**5 a** 20.2 m  **b** $22.32

**6 a** 7.97 cm  **b** 44.3 m  **c** 410 mm  **7** 240 m

**8 a** 48.6 m  **b** 225 bricks  **c** $1057.50

**9 a** 91.5 m  **b** 156 m

**10 a** 11.9 m  **b** 5.20 m

**11** 1.27 m

## EXERCISE 11C.1

**1 a** 0.056 m²  **b** 480 ha  **c** 0.55 cm²
  **d** 130 000 m²  **e** 0.046 17 m²  **f** 0.0721 km²
  **g** 0.000 008 43 km²  **h** 59 m²  **i** 0.000 989 km²

**2 a** 845 m²  **b** 180 panels

## EXERCISE 11C.2

**1 a** 280 km²  **b** 910 m²  **c** 66.7 m²  **d** 1780 m²

**2 a** $(2x^2 + 9x + 4)$ cm²  **b** $(\pi y^2)$ mm²
  **c** $\left(\dfrac{5x^2 + 3x}{2}\right)$ m²  **d** $\left(\dfrac{3x^2 + 3x}{2}\right)$ cm²
  **e** $(y^2 + 2y)$ cm²  **f** $(2\pi x^2)$ cm²

**3 a** $\left(\dfrac{x^2 - x}{2}\right)$ m²  **b** $(3y^2 + 4y - 4)$ cm²

**4 a** 83 cm²  **b** 506 cm²  **c** 143 cm²

**5 a** 125 cm²  **b** 76.0 cm²  **c** 90 cm²

**6 a** $A = 2k^2$  **b** $A = \dfrac{\pi(z^2 - y^2)}{2}$  **c** $A = (\pi - 2)x^2$

## EXERCISE 11C.3

**1 a** 43.2 m²
  **b**

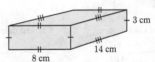

  **c** 118  **d** 2.6 t  **e** $835.20

**2** 99.5 m²  **3** medium size

**4 a** 4 m  **b** 50.3 m²  **c** $160.85
  **d** When opened out, the curved wall is a rectangle. The width is $h$ (the height of the cylinder), and the length is $2\pi r$ (the circumference of the end). The area is therefore $2\pi r \times h$.
  **e** 151 m²  **f** $678.58  **g** $840

**5 a** $BC = \dfrac{100}{x}$ m  **b** Length of netting = AB + BC + CD
  **c** $x \approx 7.07$  $\therefore \ L = x + \dfrac{100}{x} + x$
  **d**

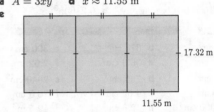

7.07 m, 14.1 m

$= 2x + \dfrac{100}{x}$ m

**6 a** $A = 3xy$  **d** $x \approx 11.55$ m
  **e**

17.32 m, 11.55 m

## EXERCISE 11C.4

**1 a** 413 cm²  **b** 5.78 m²  **c** $78x^2$ mm²

**2 a** 84 cm²  **b** 392 m²

**3 a**

2.5 cm

surface area $= 37.5$ cm²

  **b**

3 cm, 8 cm, 14 cm

surface area $= 356$ cm²

  **c**

5 cm, 3 cm, 4 cm, 8 cm

surface area $= 108$ cm²

**4 a** 11 900 cm²
  **b**

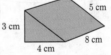

34 cm, 81 cm

area $\approx 2750$ cm²

34 cm, 219 cm

area $\approx 7450$ cm²

34 cm, 75 cm

area $= 2550$ cm²

34 cm, $\sqrt{27297}$ cm

area $\approx 5620$ cm²

  **c** $539.92

**5** $239.10  **6** 2310 cm²

## EXERCISE 11C.5

**1 a** 1005.3 cm²  **b** 145.3 cm²  **c** 188.5 cm²
  **d** 549.8 m²  **e** 1068.1 cm²  **f** 63.6 km²

**2** 84.8 cm²

**3  a** $8\pi x^2$ cm$^2$    **b** $16\pi x^2$ cm$^2$    **c** $12\pi x^2$ cm$^2$
**d** $24\pi x^2$ cm$^2$

**4  a** 19.4 m$^2$    **b** £883.38    **c** £21 201.23

**5  a** 5.39 m    **b** 46.4 m$^2$    **c** $835.24

**6  a** 12.6 m$^2$    **b** €508.94    **7  a** $4\pi r^2$    **b** 5.40 m

**8  a** $3\pi r^2$    **b** 4.50 cm    **c** 4.24 cm

### EXERCISE 11D.1

**2  a** 39.1 m$^3$    **b** 510 mm$^3$    **c** 0.469 m$^3$
**d** 3 820 000 cm$^3$    **e** 0.005 27 cm$^3$    **f** 17 900 cm$^3$
**g** 692 cm$^3$    **h** 0.183 46 m$^3$    **i** 5100 cm$^3$

**3  a** 5 000 000 ball bearings    **b** 0.216 m$^3$

### EXERCISE 11D.2

**1  a** 5.54 m$^3$    **b** 373 cm$^3$    **c** 390 cm$^3$
**d** 1180 cm$^3$    **e** 36.9 cm$^3$    **f** 2.62 m$^3$

**2  a** 25.1 cm$^3$    **b** 765 cm$^3$    **c** 2940 cm$^3$
**d** 463 cm$^3$    **e** 4.60 cm$^3$    **f** 26.5 cm$^3$
**g** 648 000 cm$^3$    **h** 72.6 cm$^3$    **i** 19.5 m$^3$
**j** 1870 m$^3$    **k** 11.6 cm$^3$    **l** 156 cm$^3$

**3  a** $V = \frac{32}{3}\pi x^3$    **b** $V = abc$    **c** $V = 3\pi y^2(y - 4)$

**4  a** 1.36 cm    **b** 6 cm

**5  a**

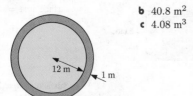

**b** 40.8 m$^2$
**c** 4.08 m$^3$

**6  a**

Uncooked cake        Cooked cake

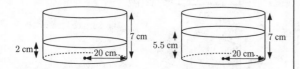

**b** 2510 cm$^3$    **c** 6910 cm$^3$    **d** 175%

**7  a** 0.5 m    **b** 0.45 m    **c** 0.373 m$^3$

**8  a** 7.18 m$^3$    **b** €972    **9  a** 8.58 m$^3$    **c** 32.6%

**10  a** 2    **b** $54.60    **c** 2
**d** $35.90    **e** $90.50

**11**  217 tonnes

**12  a** 2.67 cm    **b** 3.24 cm    **c** 4.46 cm
**d** 2.60 m    **e** 1.74 cm    **f** 5.60 m

### EXERCISE 11E

**1  a** 4210 mL    **b** 8630 L    **c** 4.6 L
**d** 56.9 kL    **e** 0.003 97 kL    **f** 12 000 mL

**2  a** 40.8 kL    **b** 1860 bottles

**3  a** 83 m$^3$    **b** 3200 cm$^3$    **c** 2.3 L
**d** 7 154 000 L    **e** 0.46 m$^3$    **f** 4 600 000 cm$^3$

**4  a** 12.9 kL    **b** 61.2 kL    **c** 68.0 kL

**5**  12.2 L    **6**  594 000 kL

**7  a** 1.32 m$^3$    **b** 1.32 kL    **c** 10.5 cm

**8  a** 189 mL    **b** 3.25 mL

**9  a** 954 mL    **b** 4.92 kL    **c** 5155    **d** €10 567.75

**10**  7.8 cm    **11**  35 truckloads

### EXERCISE 11F

**1  a** 5 g cm$^{-3}$    **b** 1.33 g cm$^{-3}$    **2**  569 g    **3**  312 cm$^3$

**4  a** 2.25 g cm$^{-3}$    **b** 20 g cm$^{-3}$    **5**  19.3 g cm$^{-3}$

**6**  4.90 cm    **7**  472 000 beads    **8**  4 240 000 t

### EXERCISE 11G

**1  a** 30 bricks per layer, 8 layers (assuming no cuts)
**b**

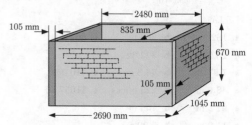

**c**  More than 240 (say, about 275) to allow for breakages.
**d**  1.39 m$^3$.  1.5 m$^3$ should be ordered to allow for spillage.
**e**  70.7 L

**2  a**  Slant height ≈ 1.06 m
**b**  Hemisphere surface area ≈ 4.02 m$^2$        **d**  3890 kg
    Cylinder surface area ≈ 9.05 m$^2$
    Cone surface area ≈ 2.67 m$^2$

**3  a** 16.8 m    **b** 2.16 m$^3$    **c** 8.04 m$^2$

**4  a** 11.9 m$^3$    **b** 5.8 m    **c** 1.36 m$^3$ more

### REVIEW SET 11A

**1  a** 0.0305 t    **b** 93 000 mL    **c** 8.033 cm$^3$

**2**  379 tiles    **3**  51.52 m    **4**  38.8 m

**5  a** 7.14 km$^2$    **b** 50.0 m$^2$    **6  a** 26 643 m$^2$    **b** 2.66 ha

**7  a** 67.45 m$^2$    **b** $222.75    **8**  2670 m$^2$

**9  a** 4.99 m$^3$    **b** 853 cm$^3$    **c** 0.452 m$^3$    **10**  3.22 m$^3$

**11**  1.03 m    **12**  0.52 m$^3$    **13  a** 2.71 g cm$^{-3}$    **b** 1.62 m$^3$

### REVIEW SET 11B

**1  a** 0.023 m$^3$    **b** 50.62 km$^2$    **c** 534 mg

**2**  13.6 m    **3  a** 24.2 m    **b** 11 posts

**4  a** 17.3 m$^2$    **b** Style 1: 900 cm$^2$,  Style 2: 800 cm$^2$
    **c** Style 1: 192 tiles,  Style 2: 216 tiles    **d** Style 2

**5  a** $A = 3xy$    **b** $A = \frac{\pi r^2}{2} - r^2$    **c** $A = \frac{\pi a^2}{4} + 2a^2$

**6  a** 377.0 cm$^2$    **b** 339.8 cm$^2$    **c** 201.1 cm$^2$

**7**  8000 rectangles    **8**  13.6 m$^2$    **9**  16 300 spikes

**10**  82 400 cm$^3$    **11**  74 cones    **12**  68.4 mm    **13  a** 4.10 kg

### REVIEW SET 11C

**1  a** 0.0243 m    **b** 32 000 cm$^3$    **c** 0.000 845 kg

**2**  25 000 erasers    **3**  1120 m

**4  a** $(8x - 8)$ km    **b** $(3y + 1)$ mm    **c** $(7x + 8)$ cm

**5  a** 3.77 cm    **b** The circle, 3.09 cm

**6  a** 164 cm$^3$    **b** 120 m$^3$    **c** 10 300 mm$^3$    **7**  4.64 m$^2$

**8**  5.03 m$^3$    **9**  5680 L    **10**  434 cm$^2$    **11**  5 tanks

**12  a** 11 cm    **b** 5.59 m    **c** 11.0 cm    **13**  0.936 g cm$^{-3}$

## EXERCISE 12A

**1 a** Yes **b** No **c** Yes **d** Yes **e** Yes **f** No

**2 a** $y = 0$ **b** $y = 5$ **c** $y = -15$ **d** $y = 12$

**3 a** $f(2) = 3$, $f(-1) = -9$ **b** $f(0) = 1$, $f(-3) = 22$
**c** $g(3) = -29$, $g(-2) = -4$

**4 a** No **b** Yes **c** Yes **d** No **e** No **f** No

**5 a** $x = -3$ **b** $x = -2$ or $-3$ **c** $x = 1$ or $4$
**d** no real solutions

**6 a** $x = 1$ or $0$ **b** $x = 3$ or $-1$ **c** $x = -7$ or $\frac{1}{2}$
**d** $x = 3$ or $2$

**7 a** **i** 75 m **ii** 195 m **iii** 275 m
**b** **i** $t = 2$ s or $t = 14$ s **ii** $t = 0$ s or $t = 16$ s
**c** These height levels are each obtained twice, once on the way up, and once on the way down.

**8 a** **i** $-\$40$ **ii** $\$480$ **b** 10 cakes or 62 cakes

## EXERCISE 12B.1

**1 a**

| $x$ | $-3$ | $-2$ | $-1$ | $0$ | $1$ | $2$ | $3$ |
|---|---|---|---|---|---|---|---|
| $y$ | $1$ | $-2$ | $-3$ | $-2$ | $1$ | $6$ | $13$ |

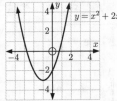

$y = x^2 + 2x - 2$

**b**

| $x$ | $-3$ | $-2$ | $-1$ | $0$ | $1$ | $2$ | $3$ |
|---|---|---|---|---|---|---|---|
| $y$ | $6$ | $1$ | $-2$ | $-3$ | $-2$ | $1$ | $6$ |

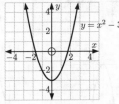

$y = x^2 - 3$

**c**

| $x$ | $-3$ | $-2$ | $-1$ | $0$ | $1$ | $2$ | $3$ |
|---|---|---|---|---|---|---|---|
| $y$ | $15$ | $8$ | $3$ | $0$ | $-1$ | $0$ | $3$ |

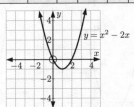

$y = x^2 - 2x$

**d**

| $x$ | $-3$ | $-2$ | $-1$ | $0$ | $1$ | $2$ | $3$ |
|---|---|---|---|---|---|---|---|
| $y$ | $-10$ | $-4$ | $0$ | $2$ | $2$ | $0$ | $-4$ |

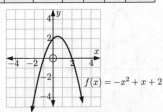

$f(x) = -x^2 + x + 2$

**e**

| $x$ | $-3$ | $-2$ | $-1$ | $0$ | $1$ | $2$ | $3$ |
|---|---|---|---|---|---|---|---|
| $y$ | $25$ | $16$ | $9$ | $4$ | $1$ | $0$ | $1$ |

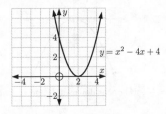

$y = x^2 - 4x + 4$

**f**

| $x$ | $-3$ | $-2$ | $-1$ | $0$ | $1$ | $2$ | $3$ |
|---|---|---|---|---|---|---|---|
| $y$ | $-17$ | $-4$ | $5$ | $10$ | $11$ | $8$ | $1$ |

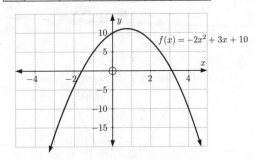

$f(x) = -2x^2 + 3x + 10$

## EXERCISE 12B.2

**1 a**

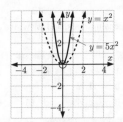

$y = 5x^2$ opens upwards and is 'thinner'.

**b**

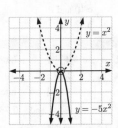

$y = -5x^2$ opens downwards and is 'thinner'.

**c**

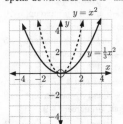

$y = \frac{1}{3}x^2$ opens upwards and is 'wider'.

**d**

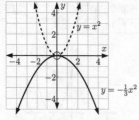

$y = -\frac{1}{3}x^2$   opens downwards and is 'wider'.

**e**

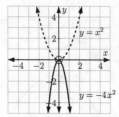

$y = -4x^2$   opens downwards and is 'thinner'.

**f**

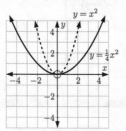

$y = \frac{1}{4}x^2$   opens upwards, and is 'wider'.

## EXERCISE 12C.1

**1  a** 3    **b** $-1$    **c** $-4$    **d** 1    **e** 5    **f** 0
   **g** 8    **h** $-5$    **i** 2

**2  a** 3    **b** $-6$    **c** 49    **d** 15    **e** 0    **f** 20

## EXERCISE 12C.2

**1  a** 2 and 5    **b** 3 and $-4$    **c** $-6$ and $-3$
   **d** 7 and $-1$    **e** 0 and 8    **f** $-5$ and 5
   **g** $-4$    **h** 2    **i** $-1$

## EXERCISE 12C.3

**1  a** $-2$ and 3    **b** 4 and $-4$    **c** no $x$-intercepts
   **d** 0 and 3    **e** 6    **f** 2.19 and $-3.19$    **g** $-7$ and 3
   **h** 5    **i** 5 and $-1\frac{1}{2}$    **j** no $x$-intercepts
   **k** 1 and $-\frac{5}{6}$    **l** 0.434 and $-0.768$

**2  a** $x$-intercepts 1 and $-2$,  $y$-intercept $-2$
   **b** $x$-intercept $-3$,  $y$-intercept 9
   **c** $x$-intercepts $-5$ and 2,  $y$-intercept $-10$
   **d** no $x$-intercepts,  $y$-intercept 4
   **e** $x$-intercepts 4 and $-3$,  $y$-intercept $-36$
   **f** $x$-intercept $-4$,  $y$-intercept $-16$
   **g** $x$-intercepts 0 and 7,  $y$-intercept 0
   **h** $x$-intercepts $-1.27$ and 2.77,  $y$-intercept 7
   **i** $x$-intercepts $-3$ and 3,  $y$-intercept $-18$
   **j** no $x$-intercepts,  $y$-intercept $-9$
   **k** $x$-intercepts $-\frac{1}{2}$ and $\frac{3}{2}$,  $y$-intercept $-3$
   **l** $x$-intercepts $-\frac{2}{3}$ and $\frac{5}{2}$,  $y$-intercept $-10$

## EXERCISE 12C.4

**1  a**

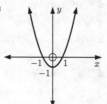

**b**

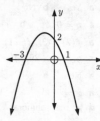

**c**

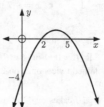

**d**

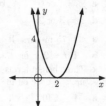

**2  a**

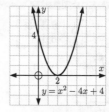

$y = x^2 - 4x + 4$

**b**

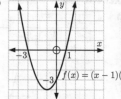

$f(x) = (x - 1)($

**c**

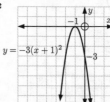

$y = 2(x + 2)^2$

**d**

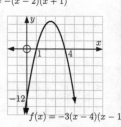

$y = -(x - 2)(x + 1)$

**e**

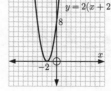

$y = -3(x + 1)^2$

**f**

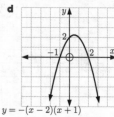

$f(x) = -3(x - 4)(x - 1)$

**g**

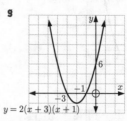

$y = 2(x + 3)(x + 1)$

**h**

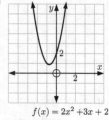

$f(x) = 2x^2 + 3x + 2$

**i**

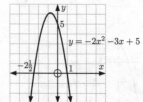

$y = -2x^2 - 3x + 5$

**EXERCISE 12D.1**

**1** **a** $x = 3$  **b** $x = -\frac{5}{2}$  **c** $x = 1$
 **d** $x = -4$  **e** $x = 3$  **f** $x = -4$

**2** **a** $x = 4$  **b** $x = -2$  **c** $x = 1$
 **d** $x = \frac{11}{2}$  **e** $x = 5$  **f** $x = -2$

**EXERCISE 12D.2**

**1** **a** $x = -3$  **b** $x = 4$  **c** $x = -\frac{5}{4}$
 **d** $x = \frac{3}{2}$  **e** $x = 0$  **f** $x = \frac{7}{10}$
 **g** $x = 3$  **h** $x = \frac{5}{3}$  **i** $x = -4$

**EXERCISE 12E**

**1** **a** $(2, 3)$  **b** $(-1, 4)$  **c** $(3, 8)$
 **d** $(0, 3)$  **e** $(-3, -18)$  **f** $(1, -1)$
 **g** $(\frac{1}{2}, -\frac{5}{4})$  **h** $(\frac{3}{4}, -\frac{7}{8})$  **i** $(6, 7)$

**2** **a** minimum  **b** minimum  **c** maximum
 **d** minimum  **e** minimum  **f** maximum
 **g** minimum  **h** maximum  **i** maximum

**3** **a** **i** $x$-intercepts:  **iv**
   1 and 3
   $y$-intercept: 3
  **ii** $x = 2$
  **iii** $(2, -1)$

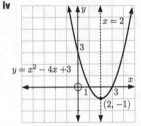

**b** **i** $x$-intercepts:  **iv**
   $-2$ and 6
   $y$-intercept: 12
  **ii** $x = 2$
  **iii** $(2, 16)$

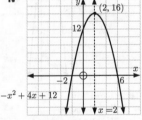

**c** **i** $x$-intercepts:  **iv**
   $-2$ and 0
   $y$-intercept: 0
  **ii** $x = -1$
  **iii** $(-1, -1)$

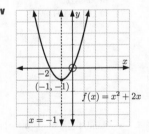

**d** **i** $x$-intercepts:  **iv**
   $-5$ and 3
   $y$-intercept: $-15$
  **ii** $x = -1$
  **iii** $(-1, -16)$

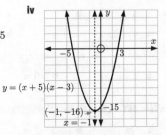

**e** **i** $x$-intercept: 5  **iv**
   $y$-intercept: 25
  **ii** $x = 5$
  **iii** $(5, 0)$

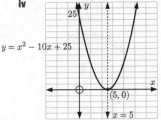

**f** **i** $x$-intercepts:  **iv**
   $-\frac{3}{2}$ and $-\frac{1}{2}$,
   $y$-intercept: $-3$
  **ii** $x = -1$
  **iii** $(-1, 1)$

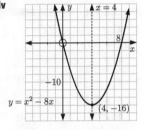

**g** **i** $x$-intercepts:  **iv**
   0 and 8
   $y$-intercept: 0
  **ii** $x = 4$
  **iii** $(4, -16)$

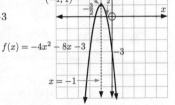

**h** **i** $x$-intercepts:  **iv**
   $-2$ and 3
   $y$-intercept: $-12$
  **ii** $x = \frac{1}{2}$
  **iii** $(\frac{1}{2}, -12\frac{1}{2})$

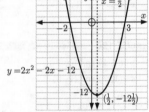

**i** **i** $x$-intercept: $-4$,  **iv**
   $y$-intercept: $-16$
  **ii** $x = -4$
  **iii** $(-4, 0)$

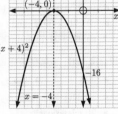

**j** **i** $x$-intercepts:  **iv**
   $-\frac{1}{3}$ and $\frac{1}{3}$
   $y$-intercept: $-1$
  **ii** $x = 0$
  **iii** $(0, -1)$

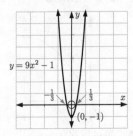

**k** **i** $x$-intercepts:
$\frac{1}{3}$ and 1

$y$-intercept: 1

**ii** $x = \frac{2}{3}$

**iii** $(\frac{2}{3}, -\frac{1}{3})$

**iv**

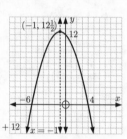

$y = 3x^2 - 4x + 1$

**l** **i** $x$-intercepts:
4 and $-6$

$y$-intercept: 12

**ii** $x = -1$

**iii** $(-1, 12\frac{1}{2})$

**iv**

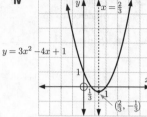

$f(x) = -\frac{1}{2}x^2 - x + 12$

## EXERCISE 12F

**1** **a** $y = 2(x-1)(x-2)$
**b** $y = 2(x-2)^2$
**c** $y = (x-1)(x-3)$
**d** $y = -(x-3)(x+1)$
**e** $y = -3(x-1)^2$
**f** $y = -2(x+2)(x-3)$

**2** **a** $y = \frac{3}{2}(x-2)(x-4)$
**b** $y = -\frac{1}{2}(x+4)(x-2)$
**c** $y = -\frac{4}{3}(x+3)^2$
**d** $y = \frac{1}{4}(x+3)(x-5)$
**e** $y = -(x+3)(x-3)$
**f** $y = 4(x-1)(x-3)$

**3** **a** $y = 3x^2 - 18x + 15$
**b** $y = -4x^2 + 6x + 4$
**c** $y = -x^2 + 6x - 9$
**d** $y = 4x^2 + 16x + 16$
**e** $y = \frac{3}{2}x^2 - 6x + \frac{9}{2}$
**f** $y = -\frac{1}{3}x^2 + \frac{2}{3}x + 5$

## EXERCISE 12G

**1** **a** $(1, 1)$ and $(0, -1)$
**b** $(-2, -5)$ and $(2, 3)$
**c** $(1, 7)$ and $(2, 8)$
**d** $(-3, -9)$ and $(4, 5)$
**e** $(3, 0)$
**f** graphs do not intersect

**2** **a** $(0.586, 5.59)$ and $(3.41, 8.41)$    **b** $(3, -4)$
**c** graphs do not intersect
**d** $(-2.56, -18.8)$ and $(1.56, 1.81)$
**e** $(0.176, -3.09)$ and $(-5.68, -0.162)$
**f** $(9.90, -27.7)$ and $(0.101, 1.70)$    **g** $(0.5, -1.75)$

## EXERCISE 12H

**1** **a** 3 m    **b** 0.5 s    **c** 4 m    **d** 1.5 s

**2** **a** 10 necklaces    **b** \$100

**3** **a** 20 televisions    **b** \$100    **c** 10 or 30

**4** **a**

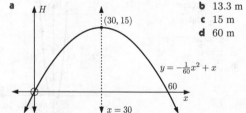

$y = -\frac{1}{60}x^2 + x$

**b** 13.3 m
**c** 15 m
**d** 60 m

**6** 250 m by 500 m

**7** **a** **Hint:** Consider the total length of all the fencing.
**c** 100 m by 112.5 m

**8** **a** 41.7 m by 41.7 m    **b** 50 m by 31.25 m

**9** 40 toasters    **10** 157 barbecues

## REVIEW SET 12A

**1** **a** $-15$    **b** $-17$    **c** $x = -3$ or 6

**2** **a**

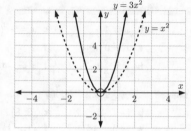

**b**

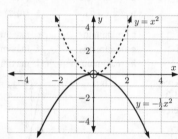

**3** **a** **i** downwards    **ii** 6    **iii** $-3$ and 1    **iv** $x = -1$

**b**

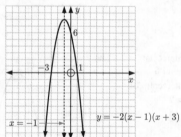

$y = -2(x-1)(x+3)$

**4** **a** **i** $-15$
**ii** $-3$ and 5
**iii** $x = 1$
**iv** $(1, -16)$

**b**

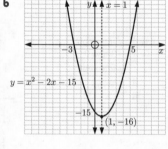

$y = x^2 - 2x - 15$

**5** **a** 0 and 4    **b** $-1\frac{2}{3}$ and 2    **c** $-4$ and 15

**6** **a** B    **b** C    **c** A    **d** D

**7** **a** $y = 3x^2 - 24x + 48$    **b** $y = -\frac{1}{2}x^2 + \frac{1}{2}x + 3$

**8** Maximum value is 5, when $x = 1$.

**9** **a** 2 seconds    **b** 80 m    **c** 6 seconds

## REVIEW SET 12B

**1** **a** No    **b** $x = -2$ or 7

**2 a i** upwards
**ii** 12
**iii** 2 (touches)
**iv** $x = 2$

**b**
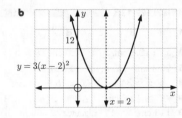
$y = 3(x - 2)^2$
$x = 2$

**3 a i** $-10$
**ii** 2 and 5
**iii** $x = 3\frac{1}{2}$
**iv** $\left(3\frac{1}{2}, 2\frac{1}{4}\right)$

**b**
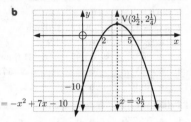
$V(3\frac{1}{2}, 2\frac{1}{4})$
$y = -x^2 + 7x - 10$
$x = 3\frac{1}{2}$

**4** axis of symmetry is $x = \frac{4}{3}$, vertex is $\left(\frac{4}{3}, \frac{37}{3}\right)$

**5 a** $y = \frac{20}{9}(x - 5)(x + 1)$    **b** $y = -\frac{2}{7}(x - 7)(x - 1)$
**c** $y = \frac{2}{9}(x + 3)^2$

**6** $(-9, -21)$ and $(-2, -7)$    **7** $a = 5$, $b = 6$

**8 a** $\left(1000x - \frac{3}{2}x^2\right)$ m$^2$    **b** $\approx 16.7$ ha
**c** Per field: 333 m by 250 m

REVIEW SET 12C

**1 a** $-6$    **b** 34    **c** $x = -4$ or $-1$
**2 a** $\left(-\frac{3}{2}, -\frac{15}{2}\right)$    **b** $-3$
**c**
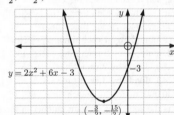

$y = 2x^2 + 6x - 3$
$-3$
$\left(-\frac{3}{2}, -\frac{15}{2}\right)$

**3**
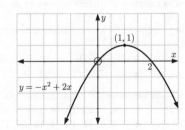
$(1, 1)$
$2$
$y = -x^2 + 2x$

**4 a** $y = 3(x + 3)(x - 3)$
**b** $y = -2(x + 1)(x - 6)$

**5** $(0.219, -8.56)$ and $(2.28, -4.44)$    **6** $(1.5, -1.5)$

**7 b** \$20    **c** \$800    **8** $y = -4x^2 + 4x + 24$

**9 a** $x = -5$    **b** $-1$

**EXERCISE 13A**

**1 a i** BC **ii** AC **iii** AB    **b i** QR **ii** PQ **iii** PR
**c i** JL **ii** JK **iii** KL

**2 a** $z$ cm **b** $x$ cm **c** $y$ cm **d** $y$ cm **e** $x$ cm

**EXERCISE 13B.1**

**1 a i** $\frac{q}{r}$ **ii** $\frac{p}{r}$ **iii** $\frac{q}{p}$    **b i** $\frac{l}{j}$ **ii** $\frac{k}{j}$ **iii** $\frac{l}{k}$
**c i** $\frac{3}{5}$ **ii** $\frac{4}{5}$ **iii** $\frac{3}{4}$

**2 a i** $\frac{p}{r}$ **ii** $\frac{q}{r}$ **iii** $\frac{p}{q}$ **iv** $\frac{q}{r}$ **v** $\frac{p}{r}$ **vi** $\frac{q}{p}$
**b i** $\frac{y}{x}$ **ii** $\frac{z}{x}$ **iii** $\frac{y}{z}$ **iv** $\frac{z}{x}$ **v** $\frac{y}{x}$ **vi** $\frac{z}{y}$
**c i** $\frac{12}{13}$ **ii** $\frac{5}{13}$ **iii** $\frac{12}{5}$ **iv** $\frac{5}{13}$ **v** $\frac{12}{13}$ **vi** $\frac{5}{12}$
**d i** $\frac{8}{17}$ **ii** $\frac{15}{17}$ **iii** $\frac{8}{15}$ **iv** $\frac{15}{17}$ **v** $\frac{8}{17}$ **vi** $\frac{15}{8}$
**e i** $\frac{4}{7}$ **ii** $\frac{\sqrt{33}}{7}$ **iii** $\frac{4}{\sqrt{33}}$ **iv** $\frac{\sqrt{33}}{7}$ **v** $\frac{4}{7}$ **vi** $\frac{\sqrt{33}}{4}$
**f i** $\frac{5}{\sqrt{34}}$ **ii** $\frac{3}{\sqrt{34}}$ **iii** $\frac{5}{3}$ **iv** $\frac{3}{\sqrt{34}}$ **v** $\frac{5}{\sqrt{34}}$ **vi** $\frac{3}{5}$

**EXERCISE 13B.2**

**1 a** $\sin 21^o = \frac{x}{k}$    **b** $\cos 50^o = \frac{x}{m}$    **c** $\tan 38^o = \frac{x}{t}$
**d** $\cos 56^o = \frac{a}{x}$    **e** $\tan 41^o = \frac{p}{x}$    **f** $\sin 36^o = \frac{x}{n}$
**g** $\tan 73^o = \frac{x}{l}$    **h** $\sin 21^o = \frac{b}{x}$    **i** $\tan 46^o = \frac{r}{x}$

**2 a** 7.00 cm **b** 7.50 m **c** 7.82 cm **d** 4.82 cm
**e** 5.55 m **f** 21.5 cm **g** 18.8 cm **h** 5.17 m
**i** 6.38 m **j** 4.82 cm **k** 7.22 cm **l** 43.3 m

**3 a** $x \approx 3.98$    **b i** $y \approx 4.98$ **ii** $y \approx 4.98$

**4 a** $x \approx 2.87$, $y \approx 4.10$    **b** $x \approx 16.40$, $y \approx 18.25$
**c** $x \approx 10.77$, $y \approx 14.50$

**EXERCISE 13B.3**

**1 a** $\theta \approx 36.9^o$    **b** $\theta \approx 48.6^o$    **c** $\theta \approx 40.6^o$
**d** $\theta \approx 42.6^o$    **e** $\theta \approx 13.7^o$    **f** $\theta \approx 52.4^o$
**g** $\theta \approx 76.1^o$    **h** $\theta = 60^o$    **i** $\theta \approx 36.0^o$

**2 a** $\theta \approx 56.3^o$    **b i** $\phi \approx 33.7^o$    **ii** $\phi \approx 33.7^o$

**3 a** $\theta \approx 39.7^o$, $\phi \approx 50.3^o$    **b** $\alpha \approx 38.9^o$, $\beta \approx 51.1^o$
**c** $\theta \approx 61.5^o$, $\phi \approx 28.5^o$

**4 a** The triangle cannot be drawn with the given dimensions.
**b** The triangle cannot be drawn with the given dimensions.
**c** The result is not a triangle, but a straight line of length 9.3 m.

**EXERCISE 13C.1**

**1 a** $x \approx 4.125$    **b** $\alpha \approx 75.52^o$    **c** $\beta \approx 40.99^o$
**d** $x \approx 6.293$    **e** $\theta \approx 51.89^o$    **f** $x \approx 12.56$

**EXERCISE 13C.2**

**1 a** $\theta \approx 36.9^o$    **b** $r \approx 11.3$    **c** $\alpha \approx 61.9^o$
**2** 7.99 cm    **3** $89.2^o$    **4** $47.2^o$    **5** 13.9 cm

**EXERCISE 13C.3**

**1** $22.4^o$    **2** 11.8 cm    **3** $119^o$    **4** 36.5 cm
**5** 46.7 m    **6 a** $x \approx 3.44$ **b** $\alpha \approx 51.5^o$    **7** $\beta \approx 129^o$

**EXERCISE 13D**

**1** 18.3 m    **2 a** 371 m **b** 1.62 km    **3** 159 m    **4** 1.58$^o$
**5** $26.4^o$    **6** 418 m    **7** 72.0 m    **8** $\theta \approx 12.6^o$
**9** 9.56 m    **10 a** 82.4 cm **b** 77.7 L    **11** 10.9 m
**12** 786 m    **13** 962 m

## EXERCISE 13E.1

1  a  18.4 cm     b  35.3°
2  a  10.8 cm     b  36.5°     c  9.49 cm     d  40.1°
3  a  10.2 m      b  No
4  a  DC ≈ 2.01 m, CE = 2 m     b  6.84°     5  a  45°

## EXERCISE 13E.2

1  a  i  GF        ii  HG        iii  HF        iv  GM
   b  i  MC        ii  MN
   c  i  XW        ii  WZ        iii  XZ        iv  XM
2  a  i  DÊH       ii  CÊG       iii  AĜE       iv  BX̂F
   b  i  PŶS       ii  QŴR       iii  QX̂R       iv  QŶR
   c  i  AQ̂X       ii  AŶX
3  a  i  45°       ii  35.3°     iii  63.4°     iv  41.8°
   b  i  21.8°     ii  18.9°     iii  21.0°
   c  i  36.9°     ii  33.9°     iii  33.9°
   d  i  58.6°     ii  64.9°
4  a  109 m       b  17.3°

## EXERCISE 13F

1  a  28.9 cm$^2$     b  384 km$^2$     c  26.7 cm$^2$     2  $x \approx 19.0$
3  18.9 cm$^2$     4  137 cm$^2$     5  a  71.616 m$^2$     b  8.43 m

## EXERCISE 13G

1  a  28.8 cm     b  3.38 km     c  14.2 m
2  CÂB ≈ 52.0°, CB̂A ≈ 59.3°, AĈB ≈ 68.7°     3  112°
4  a  40.3°  b  107°     5  a  $\cos\theta = \frac{13}{20}$  b  $x \approx 3.81$

## EXERCISE 13H.1

1  a  $x \approx 28.4$     b  $x \approx 13.4$     c  $x \approx 3.79$
   d  $x \approx 4.19$     e  $x \approx 8.81$     f  $x \approx 4.43$
2  a  $a \approx 21.3$ cm     b  $b \approx 76.9$ cm     c  $c \approx 5.09$ cm

## EXERCISE 13H.2

1  a  $x \approx 9.85°$     b  $x \approx 41.3°$     c  $x \approx 32.7°$
2  a  30.9°     b  28.7°     c  30.1°
3  b  The triangle cannot be drawn with the given dimensions.

## EXERCISE 13I

1  17.7 m     2  207 m     3  23.9°     4  44.3°     5  9.38°
6  69.1 m     7  a  38.0 m     b  94.0 m     8  55.1°
9  a  29.5°     b  £9047.96
10  CA ≈ 11.7 km, CB ≈ 8.49 km
11  a  74.9 km$^2$  b  7490 ha     12  9.12 km     13  85.0 mm

## EXERCISE 13J

1  $C \approx 62.1°$ or 117.9°     2  $P \approx 23.0°$
3  a  $A \approx 34.8°$     b  $B \approx 53.5°$ or 126°
   c  $C \approx 84.1°$ or 95.9°
4  No. The ratios in the sine rule are not equal.

## EXERCISE 13K

1  7.55 km     2  136 km     3  12.6 km h$^{-1}$     4  323°T
5  a  072°     b  342°     c  252°     d  293°
6  a  8.76 km     b  104°     7  a  296°     b  561 km
8  distance ≈ 14.1 km, bearing 109°     9  2 hours 17 minutes
10  a  i  5.63 km     ii  115°
    b  i  Esko        ii  3 min 41 s     c  295°
11  a  46.9 ha     b  2.64 km

## REVIEW SET 13A

1  a  $c$  b  $b$  c  $\dfrac{b}{c}$  d  $\dfrac{a}{b}$     2  a  $x \approx 14.0$  b  $x \approx 35$
3  $x \approx 12.4$ cm,  $y \approx 21.0$ cm,  $\theta = 36°$     4  8.19°
5  22.4 km     6  8.74°     7  14 km$^2$
8  a  $x \approx 34.1$     b  $x \approx 18.9$
9  AC ≈ 12.6 cm     CÂB ≈ 48.6°     AĈB ≈ 57.4°
10  113 cm$^2$     11  distance ≈ 560 m,  bearing ≈ 079.7°

## REVIEW SET 13B

1  $\sin\theta = \frac{5}{13}$,  $\cos\theta = \frac{12}{13}$,  $\tan\theta = \frac{5}{12}$
2  AC ≈ 111 mm,  AB ≈ 120 mm
3  a  $x \approx 2.8$     b  $x \approx 4.2$     c  $x \approx 5.2$     4  80.9 m
5  a  90°     b  33.9°     6  31.6 mm     7  125°
8  a  275 m     b  2.86 ha     9  17.7 m     10  7.32 m
11  a  49.9°     b  56.8° or 123.2°

## REVIEW SET 13C

1  a  0.2756     b  0.7431     c  −8.1443
2  a  $x \approx 38.7$  b  $x \approx 37.1$     3  $x \approx 25.7$, $\theta \approx 53.6°$, $\alpha \approx$
4  131.4 mm (13.1 cm)     5  a  SV     b  XŜT     c  WÛS
6  a  58.4°     b  68.3°     7  a  10 600 m$^2$     b  1.06 ha
8  204 m     9  74.4°     10  distance ≈ 179 km, bearing ≈ 352°
11  a  There are two possible values for AB̂C, which means two
       possible areas for △ABC.
    b  2.23 m$^3$

## EXERCISE 14A

1  a  4, 13, 22, 31          b  45, 39, 33, 27
   c  2, 6, 18, 54           d  96, 48, 24, 12
2  a  Start with 8, add 8 each time. 40, 48
   b  Start with 2, add 3 each time. 14, 17
   c  Start with 36, subtract 5 each time. 16, 11
   d  Start with 96, subtract 7 each time. 68, 61
   e  Start with 1, multiply by 4 each time. 256, 1024
   f  Start with 2, multiply by 3 each time. 162, 486
   g  Start with 480, divide by 2 each time. 30, 15
   h  Start with 243, divide by 3 each time. 3, 1
   i  Start with 50 000, divide by 5 each time. 80, 16
3  a  Each term is the square of its term number in the sequence.
      25, 36, 49
   b  Each term is the cube of its term number in the sequence.
      125, 216, 343
   c  Each term is  $n(n + 1)$, where $n$ is the term number.  30,
      42, 56
4  a  79, 75          b  1280, 5120          c  625, 1296
   d  1, $\frac{1}{2}$          e  13, 17          f  16, 22

## EXERCISE 14B

1  a  2, 4, 6, 8, 10     b  4, 6, 8, 10, 12     c  1, 3, 5, 7, 9
   d  −1, 1, 3, 5, 7     e  5, 7, 9, 11, 13     f  13, 15, 17, 19, 21
   g  4, 7, 10, 13, 16     h  1, 5, 9, 13, 17
2  a  2, 4, 8, 16, 32          b  6, 12, 24, 48, 96
   c  3, $\frac{3}{2}$, $\frac{3}{4}$, $\frac{3}{8}$, $\frac{3}{16}$          d  −2, 4, −8, 16, −32
3  17, 11, 23, −1, 47
4  a  5, 8, 11, 14, 17, ....     b  5, 8, 11, 14, 17, ....
   c  100, 93, 86, 79, 72, ....     d  100, 93, 86, 79, 72, ....
   e  5, 10, 20, 40, 80, ....     f  5, 10, 20, 40, 80, ....
   g  48, 24, 12, 6, 3, ....     h  48, 24, 12, 6, 3, ....
Each pair describes the same sequence. (a and b, c and d, ....)

## EXERCISE 14C

**1 a** 73 **b** 65 **c** 21.5

**2 a** 101 **b** $-107$ **c** $a + 14d$

**3 b** $u_n = 11n - 5$ **c** 545 **d** Yes **e** No

**4 b** $u_n = 91 - 4n$ **c** $-69$ **d** the 97th term

**5 b** $u_1 = 1$, $d = 3$ **c** 169 **d** $u_{151} = 451$

**6 b** $u_1 = 32$, $d = -\frac{7}{2}$ **c** $-227$ **d** $n \geqslant 68$

**7 a** $k = 17\frac{1}{2}$ **b** $k = 4$ **c** $k = 4$ **d** $k = 0$
**e** $k = 7$ **f** $k = -4$

**8 a** $k = 3$ or $-2$ **b** $k = 1$ or $-3$ **c** $k = 3$ or $-1$

**9 a** $u_n = 6n - 1$ **b** $u_n = -\frac{3}{2}n + \frac{11}{2}$
**c** $u_n = -5n + 36$ **d** $u_n = -\frac{3}{2}n + \frac{1}{2}$

**10 a** 6.25, 7.5, 8.75 **b** $3\frac{5}{7}$, $8\frac{3}{7}$, $13\frac{1}{7}$, $17\frac{6}{7}$, $22\frac{4}{7}$, $27\frac{2}{7}$

**11 a** $u_1 = 36$, $d = -\frac{2}{3}$ **b** 100 **12** $u_{7692} = 100\,006$

## EXERCISE 14D

**1 a** $b = 18$, $c = 54$ **b** $b = \frac{5}{2}$, $c = \frac{5}{4}$
**c** $b = 3$, $c = -\frac{3}{2}$

**2 a** 96 **b** 6250 **c** 16

**3 a** 6561 **b** $\dfrac{19\,683}{64}$ $(307\frac{35}{64})$ **c** 16 **d** $ar^8$

**4 b** $u_n = 5 \times 2^{n-1}$, $u_{15} = 81\,920$

**5 b** $u_n = 12 \times (-\frac{1}{2})^{n-1}$, $u_{13} = \frac{3}{1024}$

**6** $u_{10} \approx -0.601$ **7** $u_n = 8\sqrt{2} \times \left(\dfrac{1}{\sqrt{2}}\right)^n$

**8 a** $k = \pm 14$ **b** $k = 2$ **c** $k = -2$ or $4$

**9 a** $u_n = 3 \times 2^{n-1}$ **b** $u_n = 32 \times (-\frac{1}{2})^{n-1}$
**c** $u_n = 3 \times (\sqrt{2})^{n-1}$ or $u_n = 3 \times (-\sqrt{2})^{n-1}$
**d** $u_n = 10 \times \left(\dfrac{1}{\sqrt{2}}\right)^{n-1}$ or $u_n = 10\left(-\dfrac{1}{\sqrt{2}}\right)^{n-1}$

**10 a** $u_9 = 13\,122$ **b** $u_{14} = 2916\sqrt{3}$ **c** $u_{18} \approx 0.000\,091\,6$

## EXERCISE 14E.1

**1 a** \$2800 **b** \$6500 **c** £5705 **d** €6672

**2 a** \$4500 **b** £17\,040 **c** €32\,250 **d** £1160

## EXERCISE 14E.2

**1 a** £3993 **b** £993 **2** €11\,470.39

**3 a** ¥40\,815 **b** ¥10\,815

**4** \$23\,602.32 **5** €47\,240.61

## EXERCISE 14E.3

**1 a** Month 1 = 5 cars    Month 4 = 44 cars
Month 2 = 18 cars    Month 5 = 57 cars
Month 3 = 31 cars    Month 6 = 70 cars
**b** The constant difference $d = 13$. **c** 148 cars
**d** 20 months

**2 b** 111 online friends **c** 18 weeks

**3 a** Day 1 = 97.3 tonnes
Day 2 = 94.6 tonnes
Day 3 = 91.9 tonnes
**b** $d = -2.7$, the cattle eat 2.7 tonnes of hay each day.
**c** $u_{25} = 32.5$. After 25 days (i.e., July 25th) there will be 32.5 tonnes of hay left.
**d** 16.3 tonnes

## EXERCISE 14E.4

**1 a i** $\approx 1550$ ants **ii** $\approx 4820$ ants **b** $\approx 12.2$ weeks

**2 a** $\approx 278$ **b** Year 2047

**3 a i** $\approx 73$ **ii** $\approx 167$ **b** 30.5 years

**4 a** $\approx 949\,000$ **b** 18.1 months

**5 a i** $\approx 2860$ **ii** $\approx 184\,000$ **b** 14.5 years

## EXERCISE 14F.1

**1 a i** $S_n = 3 + 11 + 19 + 27 + .... + (8n - 5)$ **ii** 95
**b i** $S_n = 42 + 37 + 32 + 27 + .... + (47 - 5n)$ **ii** 160
**c i** $S_n = 12 + 6 + 3 + 1\frac{1}{2} + .... + 12 \times (\frac{1}{2})^{n-1}$ **ii** $23\frac{1}{4}$
**d i** $S_n = 2 + 3 + 4\frac{1}{2} + 6\frac{3}{4} + ...... + 2 \times (1.5)^{n-1}$ **ii** $26\frac{3}{8}$
**e i** $S_n = 1 + \frac{1}{2} + \frac{1}{4} + \frac{1}{8} + ...... + \dfrac{1}{2^{n-1}}$ **ii** $1\frac{15}{16}$
**f i** $S_n = 1 + 8 + 27 + 64 + ...... + n^3$ **ii** 225

**2 a** 20 **b** 20 **c** 30 **d** 10
**e** 25 **f** 10 **g** 168 **h** 310

**3** $\displaystyle\sum_{k=1}^{20}(3k - 1)$, $S_{20} = 610$

## EXERCISE 14F.2

**1 a** 91 **b** 91 **c** 91

**2 a** 820 **b** $3087\frac{1}{2}$ **c** $-1460$ **d** $-740$

**3 a** 1749 **b** 2115 **c** $1410\frac{1}{2}$

**4 a** 160 **b** $-630$ **c** 135 **5** 203 **6** $-115\frac{1}{2}$

**7** 18 **8 a** 65 **b** 1914 **c** 47\,850

**9 a** 14\,025 **b** 71\,071 **c** 3367

**10** $u_1 = 56$, $u_2 = 49$ **11** $-2, 4, 10$ or $10, 4, -2$

**12** $2, 5, 8, 11, 14$ or $14, 11, 8, 5, 2$

## EXERCISE 14F.3

**1 a** 93 **b** 93

**2 a** $23\frac{125}{128}$ **b** $\approx 189\,134$ **c** $\approx 4.00$ **d** $\approx 0.585$

**3 a** $S_n = \dfrac{\sqrt{3}\left((\sqrt{3})^n - 1\right)}{\sqrt{3} - 1}$ **b** $S_n = 24\left(1 - (\frac{1}{2})^n\right)$
**c** $S_n = 1 - (0.1)^n$ **d** $S_n = \frac{40}{3}\left(1 - (-\frac{1}{2})^n\right)$

**4 a** 124 **b** $\approx 79.98$ **c** $-134\,217\,732$

**5 c** \$26\,361.59

**6 a** $S_1 = \frac{1}{2}$, $S_2 = \frac{3}{4}$, $S_3 = \frac{7}{8}$, $S_4 = \frac{15}{16}$, $S_5 = \frac{31}{32}$
**b** $S_n = \dfrac{2^n - 1}{2^n}$ **c** $S_n = 1 - \left(\frac{1}{2}\right)^n = \dfrac{2^n - 1}{2^n}$
**d** as $n \to \infty$, $S_n \to 1$

## REVIEW SET 14A

**1 a** arithmetic **b** arithmetic and geometric
**c** neither **d** neither **e** arithmetic

**2** $k = -\frac{11}{2}$ **3** $u_n = 33 - 5n$, $S_n = \dfrac{n}{2}(61 - 5n)$

**4** $k = \dfrac{2}{\sqrt{3}}$ or $-\dfrac{2}{\sqrt{3}}$

**5** $u_n = \frac{1}{6} \times 2^{n-1}$ or $u_n = -\frac{1}{6} \times (-2)^{n-1}$

**6** 21, 19, 17, 15, 13, 11

**7 a** $u_8 = \dfrac{1}{15\,625}$ **b** $u_8 = 6\frac{1}{2}$ **c** $u_8 = a - 7d$

**8 a** Week 1: 2817 L    Week 3: 2451 L
Week 2: 2634 L    Week 4: 2268 L

**c** after 16.4 weeks

**9 a** $1^2 + 2^2 + 3^2 + 4^2 + 5^2 + 6^2 + 7^2$

**b** $\frac{4}{3} + \frac{5}{4} + \frac{6}{5} + \frac{7}{6} + \frac{8}{7} + \frac{9}{8} + \frac{10}{9} + \frac{11}{10}$

**10 a** $-492$ **b** $7\,324\,218$

## REVIEW SET 14B

**1 b** $u_1 = 6$, $r = \frac{1}{2}$ **c** $0.000\,183$

**2 a** $81$ **b** $u_{35} = -1\frac{1}{2}$ **c** $-486$ **3 a** $1587$ **b** $47\frac{253}{256}$

**4 a** $\frac{1}{3}, \frac{1}{9}, \frac{1}{27}, \frac{1}{81}, \frac{1}{243}$ **b** $17, 22, 27, 32, 37$

**c** $\frac{4}{3}, 1, \frac{4}{5}, \frac{2}{3}, \frac{4}{7}$

**5 a** €8415.31 **b** €2415.31

**6 a** $33$ **b** $4(n+1) - 7 - (4n - 7) = 4$

**c** The difference between terms is always the same.

**d** $1328$

**7** $u_n = (\frac{3}{4})2^{n-1}$ **a** $49\,152$ **b** $24\,575\frac{1}{4}$

**8** $u_{11} \approx 0.000\,406$ **9 a** $17$ **b** $255\frac{511}{512}$

**10 a** $163$ s (2 min 43 s) **b** in 49 days

## REVIEW SET 14C

**1 b** $u_1 = 63$, $d = -5$ **c** $u_{37} = -117$ **d** $u_{54} = -202$

**2 b** $u_n = 3 \times 4^{n-1}$, $u_9 = 196\,608$

**3** $u_n = 73 - 6n$, $u_{34} = -131$ **4** $7953.20

**5 a** $70$ **b** $\approx 241.2$ **6 a** $\approx 3470$ **b** $2016$

**7 a** $u_n = 89 - 3n$ **b** $u_n = \dfrac{2n+1}{n+3}$

**c** $u_n = 100 \times (0.9)^{n-1}$

**8** $u_{12} = 10\,240$ **9** $k = -2$ or $4$

**10 a** 2001: $630\,000$, 2002: $567\,000$ **b** $\approx 4\,560\,000$ sheets

## EXERCISE 15A.1

**1 a i** 16 200 ZAR **ii** 2430 ZAR

**b i** 3888.89 SGD **ii** 0.25 SGD

**2 a i** 6392.64 TWD **ii** 1176.36 NOK **iii** 1365.36 CNY

**b i** 850.08 USD **ii** 5803.33 CNY

**c i** 3.13 USD **ii** 21.36 CNY

**3 a i** 2319.98 CNY **ii** 10 322.55 RUB

**b i** 1 CNY = 6.7889 INR **ii** 1 RUB = 0.2247 CNY

**c** 6742.45 CNY

**4 a i** 1253 ZAR **ii** 2153.50 MXN **b** 46 440 RUB

**c i** $p \approx 1.718$ **ii** $q \approx 3.990$ **iii** $r = 1$ **d** 1 peso

**5 a i** 310 AUD **ii** 575 AUD

**b i** 165 GBP **ii** 235 GBP

## EXERCISE 15A.2

**1 a** 196.41 EUR **b** 174.63 GBP **c** 404.55 SGD

**d** 318.03 AUD

**2 a** 390.13 USD **b** 739.69 USD **c** 142.28 USD

**d** 969.75 USD

**3 a** 929.52 USD **b** 26.72 USD **c** 267.70 USD

**4 a** 3666.23 USD **b** 7743.72 USD **c** 272.10 USD

**d** 2685.72 USD

**5 a** 992.28 baht **b** 384.01 pesos **c** 15.99 pesos

**6 a** 2789.74 rupees **b** 409.74 yuan **c** 15.26 yuan

**7 a** 41 817.60 kwanza **b** 3091.42 pula **c** 108.58 pula

## EXERCISE 15A.3

**1 a i** £7.50 UK **ii** 922.65 USD

**b i** £5.25 UK **ii** €519.57

**c i** £18 UK **ii** $3359.72 NZ

**2 a i** 4.50 SGD **ii** £105.54 UK

**b i** 12.60 SGD **ii** 532.39 AUD

**c i** 27 SGD **ii** €711.87

## EXERCISE 15A.4

**1 a** 1511.07 USD **b** 1552.05 CAD

**c** 10 117.61 SAR **d** 679.43 GBP

## EXERCISE 15B.1

**1 a** £630 **b** $449.88 **c** ¥238 333 **d** €4402.46

**2 A** **3** $2600 **4** £14 400 **5** €20 219.78

**6 a** $6\frac{2}{3}\%$ p.a. **b** 9.41% p.a. **7** $11\frac{2}{3}\%$ p.a.

**8** 15.4% p.a. **9 a** 4 years **b** 7 years

**10** 3 years

## EXERCISE 15B.2

**1** $274.83 **2** 787.50 baht **3** €1418.75

**4** £1660 **5** Lesley's

## EXERCISE 15C.1

**1 a** €5512.69 **b** $7293.04 **c** £8938.83

**2 a** €111.39 **b** £763.30 **c** ¥77 157

**3 a** $17 496 **b** $2496

**4 a** ¥1 072 659 **b** ¥184 659

## EXERCISE 15C.2

**1** $9021.58 **2** €301.26

**3 a** $7650 **b** $8151.65 **c** $8243.81

## EXERCISE 15C.3

**1** £13 373.53 **2** $546.01

**3 a** 4725 yuan **b** 4940.81 yuan **c** 4998.89 yuan

**d** 5028.61 yuan **e** 5048.67 yuan

**4** Bank A **5** the compound interest account; €800.78

## EXERCISE 15C.4

**1** £6630.98 **2** $4079.77 **3** €4159.08 **4** ¥199 713

**5** $20 836.86 **6** €80 000 **7** €1564.95

**8** 2 years 5 months **9** 2 years 9 months

**10** 13 years 3 months **11** 6 years 353 days **12** 14.5% p.a.

**13** 6.00% p.a. **14** 5.25% p.a. **15** the shares

## EXERCISE 15C.5

**1 a** $1676.03 **b** $1669.09

**2 a** monthly: $863.16 ($\approx 3.20\%$ p.a.)

half-yearly: $859.58 ($\approx 3.18\%$ p.a.)

**b** monthly: $1148.08 ($\approx 4.25\%$ p.a.)

half-yearly: $1143.33 ($\approx 4.23\%$ p.a.)

**3 a** 6.40% p.a. paid at maturity **b** $3200

**c** $1776

## EXERCISE 15C.6

**1** 5.4% p.a. compounded half-yearly

**2** 7.75% p.a. compounded half-yearly

**3 a i** 4.95% p.a. **ii** 5.01% p.a. **b** option **ii**

**4 a i** 8.06% p.a. **ii** 8.11% p.a. **b** option **ii**

**5** 12 times

**6 a i** 6.379% p.a. **ii** 6.398% p.a. **iii** 6.399% p.a.
**iv** 6.40% p.a.
**b** 6.40% p.a. paid at maturity, $2560

## EXERCISE 15D

**1 a**

| Age (years) | Depreciation | Book Value |
|---|---|---|
| 0 | | €2500 |
| 1 | 15% of €2500 = €375 | €2125 |
| 2 | 15% of €2125 = €318.75 | €1806.25 |
| 3 | 15% of €1806.25 = €270.94 | €1535.31 |

**b i** €375 **ii** €318.75 **iii** €270.94

**2 a** €26 103.52 **b** €83 896.48

**3 a** ¥30 013 **b** ¥57 487

**4** 24.8% **5** 18.4% **6 a** $175 702.59 **b** $64 297.41

## EXERCISE 15E

**1 a** $24.40 **b** $1464 **c** $264

**2 a** $361.90 **b** $17 371.20 **c** $3371.20

**3 a** £2025.60 **b** £5160

**4** Option **A**: €3185.60; Option **B**: €2669
Carla would pay less interest under Option **B**.

## EXERCISE 15F.1

**1 a** £1343.92 **b** £1806.11 **c** £2427.26

**2 a** 66 354.49 Swiss francs **b** 56020.65 Swiss francs
**c** 10 333.84 Swiss francs **d** 3.44%

**3 a** €22 444.54 **b** €22 110.15 **c** €334.39 **d** 0.502%

**4** Decreased

## EXERCISE 15F.2

**1** 402 594.60 francs

**2 a** $18 013.95 **b** $15 876.55

**3 a** €12 916.22
**b i** €10 090.13 **ii** €9156.55 **iii** €8317.11

**4 a** £7812.50 **b i** £27 627.24 **ii** £25 105.97

**5 a** €3060.45 **b** €2596.06 **c** greater than 4.20% p.a.

## REVIEW SET 15A

**1 a i** 444.30 CAD **ii** 1808.70 TJS
**b** 7242.82 TJS **c** 4880.99 TJS

**2 a** 3191.68 krone **b** 613.55 Swiss francs
**c** 26.45 Swiss francs

**3** 6 years **4** 5.77% p.a. **5** $657.26

**6** Bank A: $185 250, Bank B: $231 995.25, Bank C: $220 787.17
Val should deposit her money in Bank B.

**7 a** $59 900.22 **b** $75 099.78 **8** in 3 years

**9 a** $29 364.66 **b** $26 608.31 **c** $2756.35 **d** 3.34%

## REVIEW SET 15B

**1 a** 99 yuan **b** ¥71 265 **2** $395 151.52

**3** £31 772.58 **4** €970.26 **5 a** 4.80% p.a. **b** £236.22

**6 a** €378.20 **b** €22 692 **c** €5692

**7 a** Option 1: $26 373.20, Option 2: $26 706.00
**b** Option 1: $7873.20, Option 2: $8206.00
**c** Option 1, will result in less interest charged.

**8 a** $507 **b** $5420

**9 a** £12 116.18 **b** £11 055.79

## EXERCISE 16A.1

**1 a** 0.78 **b** 0.22 **2 a** 0.487 **b** 0.051 **c** 0.731

**3 a** 43 days **b i** 0.0465 **ii** 0.186 **iii** 0.465

**4 a** 0.0895 **b** 0.126

## EXERCISE 16A.2

**1 a** 0.265 **b** 0.861 **c** 0.222

**2 a** 0.146 **b** 0.435 **c** 0.565

**3 a i** 0.189 **ii** 0.55 **b** 0.381 **c** 0.545

## EXERCISE 16B

**1 a** {A, B, C, D} **b** {BB, BG, GB, GG}
**c** {ABCD, ABDC, ACBD, ACDB, ADBC, ADCB, BACD,
BADC, BCAD, BCDA, BDAC, BDCA, CABD, CADB,
CBAD, CBDA, CDAB, CDBA, DABC, DACB, DBAC,
DBCA, DCAB, DCBA}
**d** {BBB, BBG, BGB, GBB, BGG, GBG, GGB, GGG}

**2 a** 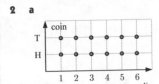 **b**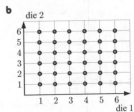

**c** 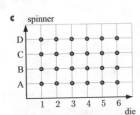 **d**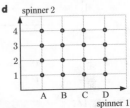

**3 a** 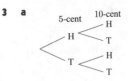 **b**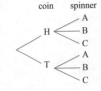

**c** 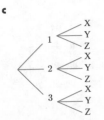 **d**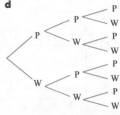

## EXERCISE 16C

**1** **a** $\frac{3}{15} = \frac{1}{5}$ **b** $\frac{5}{15} = \frac{1}{3}$ **c** $\frac{7}{15}$ **d** $\frac{12}{15} = \frac{4}{5}$
  **e** $\frac{3}{15} = \frac{1}{5}$ **f** $\frac{8}{15}$

**2** **a** 4 **b** **i** $\frac{4}{12} = \frac{1}{3}$ **ii** $\frac{8}{12} = \frac{2}{3}$

**3** **a** $\frac{9}{36} = \frac{1}{4}$ **b** $\frac{4}{36} = \frac{1}{9}$ **c** $\frac{16}{36} = \frac{4}{9}$ **d** $\frac{1}{36}$
  **e** $\frac{2}{36} = \frac{1}{18}$ **f** $\frac{6}{36} = \frac{1}{6}$ **g** $\frac{3}{36} = \frac{1}{12}$ **h** $\frac{24}{36} = \frac{2}{3}$

**4** **a** $\frac{1}{7}$ **b** $\frac{2}{7}$ **c** $\frac{124}{1461}$
  **d** $\frac{237}{1461}$ {remember leap years}

**5** **a** AKN, ANK, KAN, KNA, NAK, NKA
  **b** **i** $\frac{2}{6} = \frac{1}{3}$ **ii** $\frac{2}{6} = \frac{1}{3}$ **iii** $\frac{4}{6} = \frac{2}{3}$ **iv** $\frac{4}{6} = \frac{2}{3}$

**6** **a** BBB, BBG, BGB, GBB, BGG, GBG, GGB, GGG
  **b** **i** $\frac{1}{8}$ **ii** $\frac{1}{8}$ **iii** $\frac{1}{8}$ **iv** $\frac{3}{8}$ **v** $\frac{4}{8} = \frac{1}{2}$ **vi** $\frac{7}{8}$

**7** **a** ABCD, ABDC, ACBD, ACDB, ADBC, ADCB, BACD, BADC, BCAD, BCDA, BDAC, BDCA, CABD, CADB, CBAD, CBDA, CDAB, CDBA, DABC, DACB, DBAC, DBCA, DCAB, DCBA.
  **b** **i** $\frac{12}{24} = \frac{1}{2}$ **ii** $\frac{12}{24} = \frac{1}{2}$ **iii** $\frac{12}{24} = \frac{1}{2}$
  **iv** $\frac{12}{24} = \frac{1}{2}$ **v** $\frac{12}{24} = \frac{1}{2}$

**8** HHHH, HHHT, HHTH, HTHH, THHH, HHTT, HTHT, THHT, HTTH, THTH, TTHH, HTTT, THTT, TTHT, TTTH, TTTT
  **a** $\frac{1}{16}$ **b** $\frac{6}{16} = \frac{3}{8}$ **c** $\frac{5}{16}$ **d** $\frac{15}{16}$ **e** $\frac{4}{16} = \frac{1}{4}$

## EXERCISE 16D.1

**1**
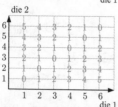
  **a** $\frac{1}{4}$ **b** $\frac{1}{4}$ **c** $\frac{2}{4} = \frac{1}{2}$ **d** $\frac{3}{4}$

**2** **a**
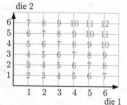
  **b** 10 **c** **i** $\frac{1}{10}$
  **ii** $\frac{2}{10} = \frac{1}{5}$
  **iii** $\frac{6}{10} = \frac{3}{5}$
  **iv** $\frac{6}{10} = \frac{3}{5}$

**3** **a** $\frac{1}{36}$ **b** $\frac{2}{36} = \frac{1}{18}$ **c** $\frac{20}{36} = \frac{5}{9}$ **d** $\frac{11}{36}$
  **e** $\frac{10}{36} = \frac{5}{18}$ **f** $\frac{25}{36}$

## EXERCISE 16D.2

**1** **a**

  **b** **i** $\frac{2}{36} = \frac{1}{18}$
  **ii** $\frac{9}{36} = \frac{1}{4}$
  **iii** $\frac{10}{36} = \frac{5}{18}$

**2** **a** die 2

| | | | | | | |
|---|---|---|---|---|---|---|
| 6 | 5 | 4 | 3 | 2 | 1 | 0 |
| 5 | 4 | 3 | 2 | 1 | 0 | 1 |
| 4 | 3 | 2 | 1 | 0 | 1 | 2 |
| 3 | 2 | 1 | 0 | 1 | 2 | 3 |
| 2 | 1 | 0 | 1 | 2 | 3 | 4 |
| 1 | 0 | 1 | 2 | 3 | 4 | 5 |
|   | 1 | 2 | 3 | 4 | 5 | 6 |

die 1
  **b** **i** $\frac{6}{36} = \frac{1}{6}$
  **ii** $\frac{8}{36} = \frac{2}{9}$
  **iii** $\frac{6}{36} = \frac{1}{6}$

**3** **a**
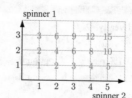
  **b** **i** $\frac{2}{15}$
  **ii** $\frac{7}{15}$
  **iii** $\frac{6}{15} = \frac{2}{5}$

## EXERCISE 16E.1

**1** **a** $\frac{1}{36}$ **b** $\frac{1}{6}$ **c** $\frac{25}{36}$ **2** **a** $\frac{1}{8}$ **b** $\frac{1}{8}$

**3** **a** $\frac{6}{625}$ **b** $\frac{506}{625}$ **4** **a** $\frac{1}{16}$ **b** $\frac{15}{16}$

**5** **a** 0.56 **b** 0.06 **c** 0.14 **d** 0.24

**6** **a** $\frac{8}{125}$ **b** $\frac{12}{125}$ **c** $\frac{27}{125}$

## EXERCISE 16E.2

**1** **a** $\frac{14}{55}$ **b** $\frac{1}{55}$ **2** **a** $\frac{7}{15}$ **b** $\frac{7}{30}$ **c** $\frac{7}{15}$

**3** **a** $\frac{3}{100}$ **b** $\frac{1}{1650}$ **c** $\frac{1}{161\,700}$ **d** $\frac{7372}{8085}$

**4** **a** $\frac{4}{7}$ **b** $\frac{2}{7}$

## EXERCISE 16F

**1** **a**
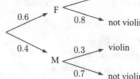
  **b** **i** 0.28
  **ii** 0.24

**2** **a**
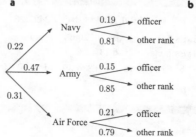
  **b** **i** 0.177
  **ii** 0.958
  **iii** 0.864

**3** **a**
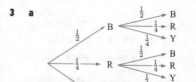
  **b** $\frac{1}{4}$
  **c** $\frac{1}{16}$
  **d** $\frac{5}{8}$
  **e** $\frac{3}{4}$

**4**

$$P(\text{win}) = \frac{7}{50}$$

**5**

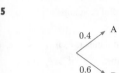

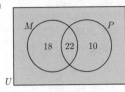

$P(\text{spoiled}) = 0.032$

**6** $\frac{17}{40}$   **7** $\frac{9}{38}$   **8 a** $\frac{11}{30}$   **b** $\frac{19}{30}$

## EXERCISE 16G

**1 a** $\frac{20}{49}$  **b** $\frac{10}{21}$  **2 a** $\frac{3}{10}$  **b** $\frac{1}{10}$  **c** $\frac{3}{5}$

**3 a** $\frac{27}{100}$  **b** $\frac{23}{50}$  **4 a** $\frac{1}{3}$  **b** $\frac{2}{15}$  **c** $\frac{4}{15}$  **d** $\frac{4}{15}$

**5 a** $\frac{1}{5}$  **b** $\frac{3}{5}$  **c** $\frac{4}{5}$  **6** $\frac{19}{45}$

**7 a** $\frac{1}{4950}$  **b** $\frac{4753}{4950}$  **c** $\frac{197}{4950}$  **8** $\frac{7}{36}$

## EXERCISE 16H

**1 a** $\frac{3}{17}$  **b** $\frac{14}{17}$  **2 a** $\frac{17}{29}$  **b** $\frac{26}{29}$  **c** $\frac{5}{29}$

**3 a** $\frac{9}{65}$  **b** $\frac{4}{65}$  **c** $\frac{52}{65} = \frac{4}{5}$

**4 a** $\frac{19}{40}$  **b** $\frac{20}{40} = \frac{1}{2}$  **c** $\frac{32}{40} = \frac{4}{5}$  **d** $\frac{25}{40} = \frac{5}{8}$

   **e** $\frac{13}{40}$  **f** $\frac{7}{20}$

**5 a** $\frac{38}{50} = \frac{19}{25}$  **b** $\frac{26}{50} = \frac{13}{25}$  **c** $\frac{12}{50} = \frac{6}{25}$  **d** $\frac{7}{19}$

**6 a** $\frac{14}{30} = \frac{7}{15}$  **b** $\frac{2}{30} = \frac{1}{15}$  **c** $\frac{4}{30} = \frac{2}{15}$

**7 a** **i** $\dfrac{b+c}{a+b+c+d}$  **ii** $\dfrac{b}{a+b+c+d}$

   **iii** $\dfrac{a+b+c}{a+b+c+d}$  **iv** $\dfrac{a+b+c}{a+b+c+d}$

  **b** $P(A \text{ or } B) = P(A) + P(B) - P(A \text{ and } B)$

**8 a** $k = 5$

  **b** **i** $\frac{14}{60} = \frac{7}{30}$  **ii** $\frac{11}{60}$  **iii** $\frac{7}{60}$  **iv** $\frac{53}{60}$

   **v** $\frac{7}{60}$  **vi** $\frac{8}{60} = \frac{2}{15}$  **vii** $\frac{41}{60}$  **viii** $\frac{31}{60}$

**9 a**

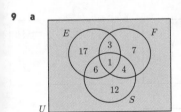

  **b** **i** $\frac{27}{50}$

   **ii** $\frac{15}{50} = \frac{3}{10}$

   **iii** $\frac{16}{50} = \frac{8}{25}$

   **iv** $\frac{10}{50} = \frac{1}{5}$

   **v** $\frac{4}{50} = \frac{2}{25}$

**10 a** $a = 3$, $b = 3$

  **b** **i** $\frac{12}{40} = \frac{3}{10}$  **ii** $\frac{4}{40} = \frac{1}{10}$  **iii** $\frac{7}{40}$

   **iv** $\frac{15}{40} = \frac{3}{8}$  **v** $\frac{25}{40} = \frac{5}{8}$

## EXERCISE 16I.1

**1** 0.6   **2** 0.2   **3** 0.35

**4 a** Yes  **b** **i** $\frac{4}{15}$  **ii** $\frac{7}{15}$  **iii** $\frac{11}{15}$

**5 a** $\frac{11}{25}$  **b** $\frac{12}{25}$  **c** $\frac{8}{25}$  **d** $\frac{7}{25}$  **e** $\frac{4}{25}$  **f** $\frac{23}{25}$

  **g** not possible  **h** $\frac{11}{25}$  **i** not possible  **j** $\frac{12}{25}$

## EXERCISE 16I.2

**1 a**

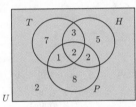

   $\therefore$ 22 students study both subjects.

  **b** **i** $\frac{18}{50} = \frac{9}{25}$

   **ii** $\frac{22}{40} = \frac{11}{20}$

**2 a** $\frac{15}{40} = \frac{3}{8}$  **b** $\frac{14}{40} = \frac{7}{20}$  **c** $\frac{8}{40} = \frac{1}{5}$  **d** $\frac{15}{23}$

**3 a** $\frac{28}{50} = \frac{14}{25}$  **b** $\frac{40}{50} = \frac{4}{5}$  **c** $\frac{10}{50} = \frac{1}{5}$  **d** $\frac{5}{23}$

  **e** $\frac{18}{28} = \frac{9}{14}$

**4** $\frac{5}{6}$

**5 a** $\frac{13}{20}$  **b** $\frac{7}{20}$  **c** $\frac{11}{50}$  **d** $\frac{7}{25}$  **e** $\frac{4}{7}$  **f** $\frac{1}{4}$

**6 a** $\frac{3}{5}$  **b** $\frac{2}{3}$  **7 a** 0.46  **b** $\frac{14}{23}$  **8** 0.429

**9 a** 0.45  **b** 0.75  **c** 0.65  **10 a** 0.0484  **b** 0.393

**11 a** $\frac{20}{95} = \frac{4}{19}$  **b** $\frac{22}{95}$  **c** $\frac{83}{95}$

  **d** $\frac{22}{34} = \frac{11}{17}$  **e** $\frac{14}{34} = \frac{7}{17}$  **f** $\frac{12}{39} = \frac{4}{13}$

**12 a**

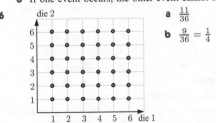

  **b** **i** $\frac{5}{30} = \frac{1}{6}$  **ii** $\frac{13}{30}$  **iii** $\frac{4}{13}$

   **iv** $\frac{23}{30}$  **v** $\frac{8}{18} = \frac{4}{9}$  **vi** $\frac{2}{12} = \frac{1}{6}$

## EXERCISE 16J

**1** Yes

**2 a** $\frac{7}{30}$  **b** $\frac{7}{12}$  **c** $\frac{7}{10}$

  $A$ and $B$ are **not** independent events.

**3 a** 0.35  **b** 0.85  **c** 0.15  **d** 0.15  **e** 0.5

**4** $\frac{14}{15}$  **6** 0.9

## REVIEW SET 16A

**1 a** ABCD, ABDC, ACBD, ACDB, ADBC, ADCB, BACD, BADC, BCAD, BCDA, BDAC, BDCA, CABD, CADB, CBAD, CBDA, CDAB, CDBA, DABC, DACB, DBAC, DBCA, DCAB, DCBA

  **b** **i** $\frac{12}{24} = \frac{1}{2}$  **ii** $\frac{8}{24} = \frac{1}{3}$

**2 a** $\frac{3}{8}$  **b** $\frac{1}{8}$  **c** $\frac{5}{8}$  **3 a** $\frac{2}{5}$  **b** $\frac{13}{15}$  **c** $\frac{4}{15}$

**4 a** 0  **b** 0.45  **c** 0.8

**5 a** The occurrence of one event does not affect the probability of the other event occurring.

  **b** If one event occurs, the other event cannot occur.

**6**

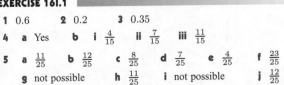

  **a** $\frac{11}{36}$

  **b** $\frac{9}{36} = \frac{1}{4}$

**7 a** $\frac{10}{40} = \frac{1}{4}$   **b** $\frac{37}{40}$   **c** $\frac{10}{25} = \frac{2}{5}$   **8** $\frac{5}{9}$

## REVIEW SET 16B

**1 a** $\frac{7}{39}$   **b** $\frac{21}{74}$   **c** $\frac{108}{402} = \frac{18}{67}$

**2 a**

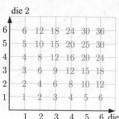

die 2

|   | 1 | 2 | 3 | 4 | 5 | 6 |
|---|---|---|---|---|---|---|
| 6 | 6 | 12 | 18 | 24 | 30 | 36 |
| 5 | 5 | 10 | 15 | 20 | 25 | 30 |
| 4 | 4 | 8 | 12 | 16 | 20 | 24 |
| 3 | 3 | 6 | 9 | 12 | 15 | 18 |
| 2 | 2 | 4 | 6 | 8 | 10 | 12 |
| 1 | 1 | 2 | 3 | 4 | 5 | 6 |

die 1

**b** **i** $\frac{4}{36} = \frac{1}{9}$
   **ii** $\frac{10}{36} = \frac{5}{18}$
   **iii** $\frac{8}{36} = \frac{2}{9}$

**3**

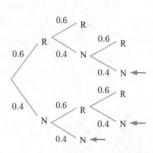

P(N wins) = 0.352

**4 a** $\frac{1}{5\,177\,125}$   **b** $\approx 0.0239$   **5 a** 0.259   **b** 0.703

**6**

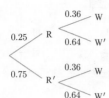

   **a** 0.09
   **b** 0.52

**7** 0.496

**8 a** $\frac{20}{42} = \frac{10}{21}$   **b** $\frac{5}{42}$   **c** $\frac{30}{42} = \frac{5}{7}$   **d** $\frac{29}{42}$
   **e** $\frac{9}{42} = \frac{3}{14}$   **f** $\frac{12}{24} = \frac{2}{7}$   **g** $\frac{5}{20} = \frac{1}{4}$   **h** $\frac{3}{15} = \frac{1}{5}$

## REVIEW SET 16C

**1** BBBB, BBBG, BBGB, BGBB, GBBB, BBGG, BGBG, GBBG,
BGGB, GBGB, GGBB, BGGG, GBGG, GGBG, GGGB, GGGG
   ∴ P(2 boys, 2 girls) $= \frac{6}{16} = \frac{3}{8}$

**2 a** $\frac{5}{33}$   **b** $\frac{19}{66}$   **c** $\frac{5}{11}$   **d** $\frac{16}{33}$

**3 a** $\frac{12}{25}$   **b** $\frac{12}{25}$   **c** $\frac{7}{8}$   **4 a** $\frac{5}{8}$   **b** $\frac{1}{4}$

**5** 0.9975   **6 a** $\frac{31}{70}$   **b** $\frac{21}{31}$   **7** Yes

**8 a** $\frac{5}{50} = \frac{1}{10}$   **b** $\frac{14}{50} = \frac{7}{25}$   **c** $\frac{13}{50}$

## EXERCISE 17A.1

**1 a** proposition, false
   **c** proposition, true
   **e** proposition, true
   **g** not a proposition
   **i** not a proposition
   **k** proposition, indeterminate
   **m** not a proposition
   **o** proposition, true

   **b** proposition, false
   **d** proposition, false
   **f** proposition, true
   **h** proposition, true
   **j** proposition, false
   **l** not a proposition
   **n** proposition, indeterminate
   **p** proposition, false

**2 a** **i** ¬p: not all rectangles are parallelograms
       **ii** p is true.
   **b** **i** ¬m: $\sqrt{5}$ is not an irrational number.   **ii** m is true.
   **c** **i** ¬r: 7 is not a rational number.   **ii** r is true.
   **d** **i** ¬q: $23 - 14 \neq 12$   **ii** ¬q is true.
   **e** **i** ¬r: $52 \div 4 \neq 13$   **ii** r is true.
   **f** **i** ¬s: The difference between two odd numbers is not always even.
       **ii** s is true.
   **g** **i** ¬t: The product of consecutive integers is not always even.
       **ii** t is true.
   **h** **i** ¬u: Not all obtuse angles are equal.   **ii** ¬u is true.
   **i** **i** ¬p: Not all trapeziums are parallelograms.
       **ii** ¬p is true.
   **j** **i** ¬q: Not all triangles with two equal angles are isosceles.
       **ii** q is true.

**3 a** $x \geqslant 5$   **b** $x < 3$   **c** $y \geqslant 8$   **d** $y > 10$

**4 a** **i** No   **ii** ¬r: Kania scored 60% or less.   **b** **i** Yes
   **c** **i** No   **ii** ¬r: Fari is not at soccer practice.
   **d** **i** Yes   **e** **i** No   **ii** I did not drink black tea today.

**5 a** $x \in \{1, 2, 3, 4\}$   **b** $x \in \{\text{horses, sheep, goats, deer}\}$
   **c** $x < 0,\ x \in \mathbb{Z}$   **d** $x$ is a female student
   **e** $x$ is a female non-student

## EXERCISE 17A.2

**1 a** **i** $P = \{21, 24, 27\}$   **ii** $P = \{2, 4, 6, 8, 10\}$
       **iii** $P = \{1, 2, 3, 6, 7, 14, 21, 42\}$
   **b** **i**                                    **ii**

**2 a**

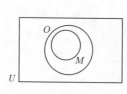

   **b**

   **c**

**3 a** **i**

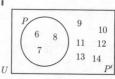

       **ii** $P' = \{9, 10, 11, 12, 13, 14\}$

**b** **i**

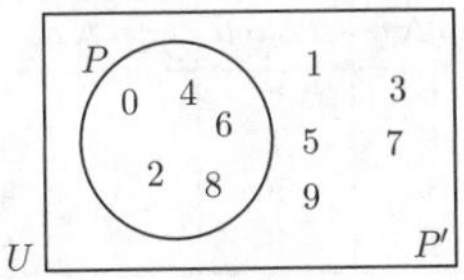


**ii** $P' = \{1, 3, 5, 7, 9\}$

## EXERCISE 17B.1

**1** **a** $p \wedge q$: Ted is a doctor and Shelly is a dentist.
**b** $p \wedge q$: $x$ is greater than 15 and less than 30.
**c** $p \wedge q$: It is windy and it is raining.
**d** $p \wedge q$: Kim has brown hair and blue eyes.

**2** **a** True **b** False **c** False **d** True **e** False

**3** **a**

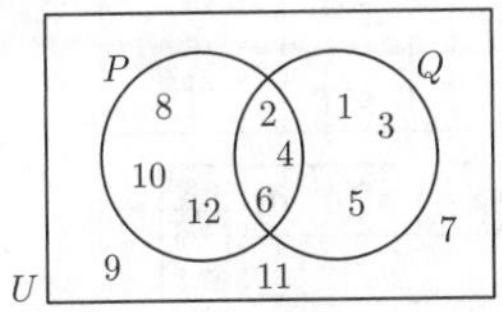


**b** $\{2, 4, 6\}$

## EXERCISE 17B.2

**1** **a** $p \vee q$: Tim owns a bicycle or a scooter.
**b** $p \vee q$: $x$ is a multiple of 2 or a multiple of 5.
**c** $p \vee q$: Dana studies Physics or Chemistry

**2** **a** True **b** True **c** False **d** True

**3** **a** $p \veebar q$: Meryn will visit Japan or Singapore, but not both, next year.
**b** $p \veebar q$: Ann will invite Kate or Tracy, but not both, to her party.
**c** $p \veebar q$: $x$ is a factor of 56 or 40, but not both.

**4** **a** False **b** True **c** False **d** True

**5** **a** $\neg r$ **b** $r \wedge s$ **c** $\neg s \wedge \neg r$ **d** $r \vee s$

**6** **a** $\neg x$ **b** $x \wedge y$ **c** $x \vee y$ **d** $\neg(x \wedge y)$ **e** $x \veebar y$

**7** **a** $p$: Phillip likes icecream. $q$: Phillip likes jelly.
$p \wedge q$: Phillip likes icecream and jelly
**b** $p$: Phillip likes icecream. $q$: Phillip likes jelly.
$p \vee \neg q$: Phillip likes icecream or Phillip does not like jelly.
**c** $p$: $x$ is greater than 10. $q$: $x$ is a prime number.
$p \wedge q$: $x$ is both greater than 10 and a prime number.
**d** $p$: Tuan can go to the mountains.
$q$: Tuan can go to the beach.
$p \veebar q$: Tuan can go to the mountains or to the beach, but not both.
**e** $p$: The computer is on. $\neg p$: The computer is not on.
**f** $p$: Angela has a watch. $q$: Angela has a mobile phone.
$\neg p \wedge q$: Angela does not have a watch but does have a mobile phone.
**g** $p$: Maya studied Spanish. $q$: Maya studied French.
$p \veebar q$: Maya studied one of Spanish or French.
**h** $p$: I can hear thunder. $q$: I can hear an aeroplane.
$p \vee q$: I can hear thunder or an aeroplane.

**8** **a** True **b** True

**9** **a**

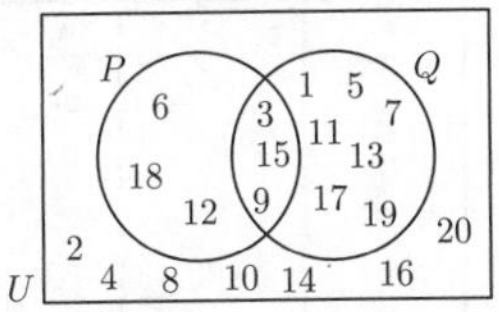


**b** **i** $\{2, 4, 6, 8, 10, 12, 14, 16, 18, 20\}$
**ii** $\{1, 3, 5, 6, 7, 9, 11, 12, 13, 15, 17, 18, 19\}$
**iii** $\{3, 9, 15\}$ **iv** $\{1, 5, 6, 7, 11, 12, 13, 17, 18, 19\}$

**10** **a**

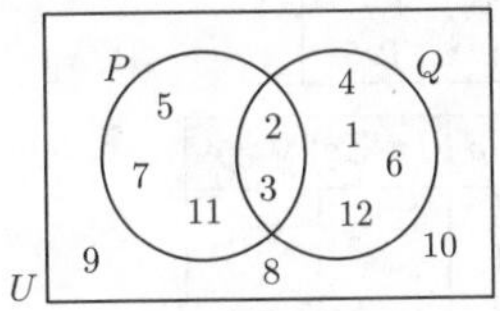


**b** **i** $x$ is both prime and a factor of 12.
**ii** $x$ is prime or a factor of 12.
**iii** $x$ is prime or factor of 12, but not both.

**c** **i** $\{2, 3\}$ **ii** $\{1, 2, 3, 4, 5, 6, 7, 11, 12\}$
**iii** $\{1, 4, 5, 6, 7, 11, 12\}$

**11** **a** False **b** True **c** True **d** True
**e** True **f** False **g** True **h** False

**12** **a** $p \wedge q$ **b** $p \veebar q$ **c** $\neg p$

**13** **a** **i** $P \cup Q$ **ii**

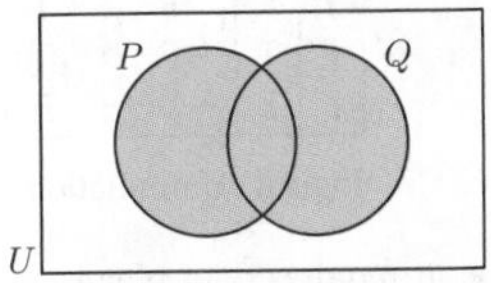


**b** **i** $P' \cup Q$ **ii**

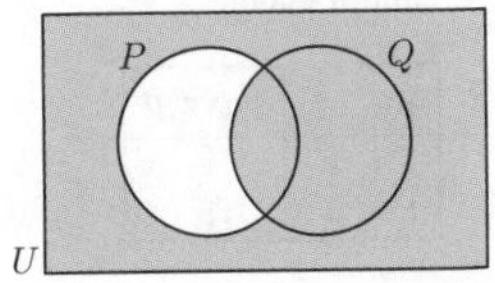


**c** **i** $(P \cap Q') \cup (Q \cap P')$
**ii**

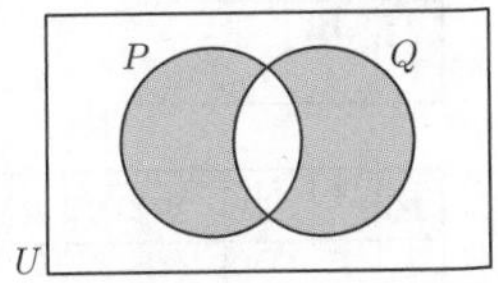


**d** **i** $P' \cap Q'$ **ii**

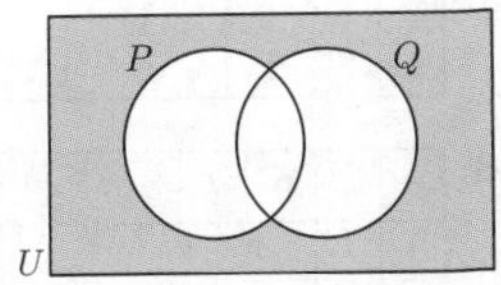


**14** **a** The captain is old, but not male.
**b** The captain is old or male. **c** The captain is old.

## EXERCISE 17C.1

**1** **a**

| $p$ | $q$ | $\neg p$ | $\neg p \wedge q$ |
|---|---|---|---|
| T | T | F | F |
| T | F | F | F |
| F | T | T | T |
| F | F | T | F |

**b**

| $p$ | $q$ | $p \veebar q$ | $\neg(p \veebar q)$ |
|---|---|---|---|
| T | T | F | T |
| T | F | T | F |
| F | T | T | F |
| F | F | F | T |

**c**

| $p$ | $q$ | $\neg p$ | $\neg q$ | $\neg p \vee \neg q$ |
|---|---|---|---|---|
| T | T | F | F | F |
| T | F | F | T | T |
| F | T | T | F | T |
| F | F | T | T | T |

**d**

| $p$ | $p \vee p$ |
|---|---|
| T | T |
| F | F |

**2 a i**

| p | q | ¬p | ¬q | ¬p ∧ ¬q |
|---|---|---|---|---|
| T | T | F | F | F |
| T | F | F | T | F |
| F | T | T | F | F |
| F | F | T | T | T |

**ii** neither

**b i**

| p | q | p ∨ q | ¬p | (p ∨ q) ∨ ¬p |
|---|---|---|---|---|
| T | T | T | F | T |
| T | F | T | F | T |
| F | T | T | T | T |
| F | F | F | T | T |

**ii** tautology

**c i**

| p | q | p ⊻ q | p ∧ (p ⊻ q) |
|---|---|---|---|
| T | T | F | F |
| T | F | T | T |
| F | T | T | F |
| F | F | F | F |

**ii** neither

**d i**

| p | q | p ∧ q | p ⊻ q | (p ∧ q) ∧ (p ⊻ q) |
|---|---|---|---|---|
| T | T | T | F | F |
| T | F | F | T | F |
| F | T | F | T | F |
| F | F | F | F | F |

**ii** logical contradiction

**3 a** It requires both $p$ and $¬p$ to be true at the same time, which cannot occur.

**b**

| p | ¬p | p ∧ ¬p |
|---|---|---|
| T | F | F |
| F | T | F |

**4 a**

| p | ¬p | ¬(¬p) |
|---|---|---|
| T | F | T |
| F | T | F |

**b**

| p | p ∧ p |
|---|---|
| T | T |
| F | F |

**c**

| p | q | ¬p | ¬p ∧ q | p ∨ (¬p ∧ q) | p ∨ q |
|---|---|---|---|---|---|
| T | T | F | F | T | T |
| T | F | F | F | T | T |
| F | T | T | T | T | T |
| F | F | T | F | F | F |

**d**

| p | q | p ⊻ q | ¬(p ⊻ q) | ¬q | p ⊻ ¬q |
|---|---|---|---|---|---|
| T | T | F | T | F | T |
| T | F | T | F | T | F |
| F | T | T | F | F | F |
| F | F | F | T | T | T |

**e**

| p | q | ¬p | q ∨ ¬p | ¬(q ∨ ¬p) | ¬q | p ∨ q | ¬q ∧ (p ∨ q) |
|---|---|---|---|---|---|---|---|
| T | T | F | T | F | F | T | F |
| T | F | F | F | T | T | T | T |
| F | T | T | T | F | F | T | F |
| F | F | T | T | F | T | F | F |

**f**

| p | q | ¬p | p ∨ q | ¬p ⊻ (p ∨ q) | ¬q | p ∨ ¬q |
|---|---|---|---|---|---|---|
| T | T | F | T | T | F | T |
| T | F | F | T | T | T | T |
| F | T | T | T | F | F | F |
| F | F | T | F | T | T | T |

**5 a**

| p | q | ¬p | ¬q | ¬p ∧ q | p ∧ ¬q | (¬p ∧ q) ∨ (p ∧ ¬q) |
|---|---|---|---|---|---|---|
| T | T | F | F | F | F | F |
| T | F | F | T | F | T | T |
| F | T | T | F | T | F | T |
| F | F | T | T | F | F | F |

**b** $p \veebar q$

**6 a i** I like apples or bananas.
**ii** I do not like apples or bananas.
**iii** I do not like apples.
**iv** I do not like apples and I do not like bananas.

**b**

| p | q | p ∨ q | ¬(p ∨ q) | ¬p | ¬q | ¬p ∧ ¬q |
|---|---|---|---|---|---|---|
| T | T | T | F | F | F | F |
| T | F | T | F | F | T | F |
| F | T | T | F | T | F | F |
| F | F | F | T | T | T | T |

**7 a**

| p | q | p ⊻ q | q ∧ (p ⊻ q) | (p ⊻ q) ∨ p |
|---|---|---|---|---|
| T | T | F | F | T |
| T | F | T | F | T |
| F | T | T | T | T |
| F | F | F | F | F |

**b i** $-3 \leqslant x < 2$ or $x > 7$   **ii** $x > 7$   **iii** $x \geqslant -3$

**8 a** Any tautology has all the values in their truth table column as true.
**b** Any logical contradiction has all the values in their truth table column as false.

**9 a** It is a tautology.   **b** It is a logical contradiction.
**c** It is a tautology.

## EXERCISE 17C.2

**1 a**

| p | q | r | ¬p | q ∧ r | ¬p ∨ (q ∧ r) |
|---|---|---|---|---|---|
| T | T | T | F | T | T |
| T | T | F | F | F | F |
| T | F | T | F | F | F |
| T | F | F | F | F | F |
| F | T | T | T | T | T |
| F | T | F | T | F | T |
| F | F | T | T | F | T |
| F | F | F | T | F | T |

**b**

| p | q | r | ¬q | p ∨ ¬q | (p ∨ ¬q) ∧ r |
|---|---|---|---|---|---|
| T | T | T | F | T | T |
| T | T | F | F | T | F |
| T | F | T | T | T | T |
| T | F | F | T | T | F |
| F | T | T | F | F | F |
| F | T | F | F | F | F |
| F | F | T | T | T | T |
| F | F | F | T | T | F |

**c**

| p | q | r | p ∨ q | ¬r | p ∧ ¬r | (p ∨ q) ∨ (p ∧ ¬r) |
|---|---|---|---|---|---|---|
| T | T | T | T | F | F | T |
| T | T | F | T | T | T | T |
| T | F | T | T | F | F | T |
| T | F | F | T | T | T | T |
| F | T | T | T | F | F | T |
| F | T | F | T | T | F | T |
| F | F | T | F | F | F | F |
| F | F | F | F | T | F | F |

**2 a**

| $p$ | $q$ | $r$ | $p \vee q$ | $r \wedge p$ | $\neg(r \wedge p)$ | $(p \vee q) \vee \neg(r \wedge p)$ |
|---|---|---|---|---|---|---|
| T | T | T | T | T | F | T |
| T | T | F | T | F | T | T |
| T | F | T | T | T | F | T |
| T | F | F | T | F | T | T |
| F | T | T | T | F | T | T |
| F | T | F | T | F | T | T |
| F | F | T | F | F | T | T |
| F | F | F | F | F | T | T |

∴ tautology

**b**

| $p$ | $q$ | $r$ | $p \veebar r$ | $\neg q$ | $(p \veebar r) \wedge \neg q$ |
|---|---|---|---|---|---|
| T | T | T | F | F | F |
| T | T | F | T | F | F |
| T | F | T | F | T | F |
| T | F | F | T | T | T |
| F | T | T | T | F | F |
| F | T | F | F | F | F |
| F | F | T | T | T | T |
| F | F | F | F | T | F |

∴ neither

**c**

| $p$ | $q$ | $r$ | $q \wedge r$ | $p \vee q$ | $\neg(p \vee q)$ | $(q \wedge r) \wedge \neg(p \vee q)$ |
|---|---|---|---|---|---|---|
| T | T | T | T | T | F | F |
| T | T | F | F | T | F | F |
| T | F | T | F | T | F | F |
| T | F | F | F | T | F | F |
| F | T | T | T | T | F | F |
| F | T | F | F | T | F | F |
| F | F | T | F | F | T | F |
| F | F | F | F | F | T | F |

∴ logical contradiction

**3 a i** Jake owns a phone and a TV.
**ii** Jake owns a phone, a TV and a laptop.
**iii** Jake owns a TV and a laptop.
**iv** Jake owns a phone, a TV and a laptop.

**b**

| $p$ | $q$ | $r$ | $p \wedge q$ | $(p \wedge q) \wedge r$ | $q \wedge r$ | $p \wedge (q \wedge r)$ |
|---|---|---|---|---|---|---|
| T | T | T | T | T | T | T |
| T | T | F | T | F | F | F |
| T | F | T | F | F | F | F |
| T | F | F | F | F | F | F |
| F | T | T | F | F | T | F |
| F | T | F | F | F | F | F |
| F | F | T | F | F | F | F |
| F | F | F | F | F | F | F |

**4**

| $p$ | $q$ | $r$ | $p \vee q$ | $(p \vee q) \vee r$ | $q \vee r$ | $p \vee (q \vee r)$ |
|---|---|---|---|---|---|---|
| T | T | T | T | T | T | T |
| T | T | F | T | T | T | T |
| T | F | T | T | T | T | T |
| T | F | F | T | T | F | T |
| F | T | T | T | T | T | T |
| F | T | F | T | T | T | T |
| F | F | T | F | T | T | T |
| F | F | F | F | F | F | F |

**5 a i** Mary will study French or German next year.
**ii** Mary will study Mathematics, and French or German next year.
**iii** Mary will study Mathematics and French next year.
**iv** Mary will study Mathematics and German next year.
**v** Mary will study Mathematics and French, or Mathematics and German, next year.

**b**

| $p$ | $q$ | $r$ | $q \vee r$ | $p \wedge (q \vee r)$ | $p \wedge q$ | $p \wedge r$ | $(p \wedge q) \vee (p \wedge r)$ |
|---|---|---|---|---|---|---|---|
| T | T | T | T | T | T | T | T |
| T | T | F | T | T | T | F | T |
| T | F | T | T | T | F | T | T |
| T | F | F | F | F | F | F | F |
| F | T | T | T | F | F | F | F |
| F | T | F | T | F | F | F | F |
| F | F | T | T | F | F | F | F |
| F | F | F | F | F | F | F | F |

**6 a**

| $p$ | $q$ | $r$ | $q \wedge r$ | $p \vee (q \wedge r)$ | $p \vee q$ | $p \vee r$ | $(p \vee q) \wedge (p \vee r)$ |
|---|---|---|---|---|---|---|---|
| T | T | T | T | T | T | T | T |
| T | T | F | F | T | T | T | T |
| T | F | T | F | T | T | T | T |
| T | F | F | F | T | T | T | T |
| F | T | T | T | T | T | T | T |
| F | T | F | F | F | T | F | F |
| F | F | T | F | F | F | T | F |
| F | F | F | F | F | F | F | F |

**b i** 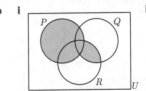 **ii**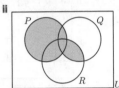

They are equivalent statements.

## EXERCISE 17D

**1 a** antecedent: I miss the bus.
consequent: I will walk to school.
**b** antecedent: The temperature is low enough.
consequent: The lake will freeze.
**c** antecedent: $x > 20$. consequent: $x > 10$.
**d** antecedent: You jump all 8 hurdles.
consequent: You may win the race.

**2 a** If the sun is shining, then I will go swimming.
**b** If $x$ is a multiple of 6, then $x$ is even.
**c** If there are eggs in the fridge, then Jan will bake a cake.

**3 a i** Rome is the capital of Italy if and only if Paris is the capital of France.
**ii** True
**b i** $2x + 3 = 10$ is an expression if and only if $2x + 3$ is an expression.
**ii** False.
**c i** Cows have nine legs if and only if horses have five heads.
**ii** True.

**4 a** $p \Rightarrow q$   **b** $q \Rightarrow p$   **c** $\neg q$   **d** $\neg p$
**e** $\neg p \Rightarrow \neg q$   **f** $p \Rightarrow \neg q$   **g** $\neg q \Rightarrow p$   **h** $p \Leftrightarrow q$

**5 a**

| $p$ | $q$ | $\neg q$ | $p \Rightarrow \neg q$ |
|---|---|---|---|
| T | T | F | F |
| T | F | T | T |
| F | T | F | T |
| F | F | T | T |

**b**

| $p$ | $q$ | $\neg q$ | $\neg p$ | $\neg q \Rightarrow \neg p$ |
|---|---|---|---|---|
| T | T | F | F | T |
| T | F | T | F | F |
| F | T | F | T | T |
| F | F | T | T | T |

**c**

| $p$ | $q$ | $p \wedge q$ | $(p \wedge q) \Rightarrow p$ |
|---|---|---|---|
| T | T | T | T |
| T | F | F | T |
| F | T | F | T |
| F | F | F | T |

**d**

| $p$ | $q$ | $p \Rightarrow q$ | $q \land (p \Rightarrow q)$ |
|---|---|---|---|
| T | T | T | T |
| T | F | F | F |
| F | T | T | T |
| F | F | T | F |

**e**

| $p$ | $q$ | $\neg q$ | $p \Leftrightarrow \neg q$ |
|---|---|---|---|
| T | T | F | F |
| T | F | T | T |
| F | T | F | T |
| F | F | T | F |

**f**

| $p$ | $q$ | $p \Leftrightarrow q$ | $\neg p$ | $(p \Leftrightarrow q) \land \neg p$ |
|---|---|---|---|---|
| T | T | T | F | F |
| T | F | F | F | F |
| F | T | F | T | F |
| F | F | T | T | T |

**g**

| $p$ | $q$ | $\neg q$ | $p \land \neg q$ | $p \Rightarrow (p \land \neg q)$ |
|---|---|---|---|---|
| T | T | F | F | F |
| T | F | T | T | T |
| F | T | F | F | T |
| F | F | T | F | T |

**h**

| $p$ | $q$ | $p \Rightarrow q$ | $\neg p$ | $(p \Rightarrow q) \Rightarrow \neg p$ |
|---|---|---|---|---|
| T | T | T | F | F |
| T | F | F | F | T |
| F | T | T | T | T |
| F | F | T | T | T |

**6 a**

| $p$ | $q$ | $p \veebar q$ | $p \Leftrightarrow q$ | $\neg(p \Leftrightarrow q)$ |
|---|---|---|---|---|
| T | T | F | T | F |
| T | F | T | F | T |
| F | T | T | F | T |
| F | F | F | T | F |

**b**

| $p$ | $q$ | $\neg p$ | $\neg p \Rightarrow q$ | $p \lor q$ |
|---|---|---|---|---|
| T | T | F | T | T |
| T | F | F | T | T |
| F | T | T | T | T |
| F | F | T | F | F |

**c**

| $p$ | $q$ | $p \veebar q$ | $q \Rightarrow (p \veebar q)$ | $p \land q$ | $\neg(p \land q)$ |
|---|---|---|---|---|---|
| T | T | F | F | T | F |
| T | F | T | T | F | T |
| F | T | T | T | F | T |
| F | F | F | T | F | T |

**d**

| $p$ | $q$ | $p \Leftrightarrow q$ | $p \land q$ | $\neg p$ | $\neg q$ | $\neg p \land \neg q$ | $(p \land q) \lor (\neg p \land \neg q)$ |
|---|---|---|---|---|---|---|---|
| T | T | T | T | F | F | F | T |
| T | F | F | F | F | T | F | F |
| F | T | F | F | T | F | F | F |
| F | F | T | F | T | T | T | T |

**7 D**

**8 a**

| $p$ | $q$ | $\neg p$ | $\neg p \land q$ | $p \Rightarrow (\neg p \land q)$ |
|---|---|---|---|---|
| T | T | F | F | F |
| T | F | F | F | F |
| F | T | T | T | T |
| F | F | T | F | T |

∴ neither

**b**

| $p$ | $q$ | $p \land q$ | $p \lor q$ | $(p \land q) \Rightarrow (p \lor q)$ |
|---|---|---|---|---|
| T | T | T | T | T |
| T | F | F | T | T |
| F | T | F | T | T |
| F | F | F | F | T |

∴ tautology

**c**

| $p$ | $q$ | $\neg q$ | $p \Rightarrow \neg q$ | $\neg p$ | $\neg p \Rightarrow q$ | $(p \Rightarrow \neg q) \lor (\neg p \Rightarrow q)$ |
|---|---|---|---|---|---|---|
| T | T | F | F | F | T | T |
| T | F | T | T | F | T | T |
| F | T | F | T | T | T | T |
| F | F | T | T | T | F | T |

∴ tautology

**EXERCISE 17E**

**1 a** Converse: If Nicole is warm, then she is wearing a jumper.
　　Inverse: If Nicole is not wearing a jumper, then she is not warm.

　**b** Converse: If two triangles are equiangular, then they are similar.
　　Inverse: If two triangles are not similar, then they are not equiangular.

　**c** Converse: If $x = \pm\sqrt{6}$, then $2x^2 = 12$.
　　Inverse: If $2x^2 \neq 12$, then $x \neq \pm\sqrt{6}$.

　**d** Converse: If Alex is having fun, he is in the playground.
　　Inverse: If Alex is not in the playground, then he is not having fun.

　**e** Converse: If a triangle has its three sides equal in length, then it is equilateral.
　　Inverse: If a triangle is not equilateral, then its three sides are not equal in length.

**2 a** If a bush does not have thorns, then it is not a rose bush.

　**b** If a person does not make correct decisions all the time, then he or she is not an umpire.

　**c** If a person does not have good kicking skills, then he or she is not a good soccer player.

　**d** If a substance does not take the shape of the container in which it is placed, then it is not a liquid.

　**e** If a person is not a doctor, then the person is not fair and clever.

**3 a** If a person does not study Mathematics, then he or she is not a high school student.

　**b** **i** Keong studies Mathematics.
　　**ii** Tamara is not a high school student.
　　**iii** Nothing can be deduced.

**4 a** If $x^2$ is not divisible by 9 then $x$ is not divisible by 3.

　**b** If $x$ is not even, then $x$ is not a number ending in 2.

　**c** If PQ $\nparallel$ SR or PS $\nparallel$ QR then PQRS is not a rectangle.

　**d** If $\widehat{KML}$ does not measure $60^{\circ}$, then KLM is not an equilateral triangle.

**5 a** **i** If a house has a chimney then it has at least 3 windows.
　　**ii** If a house does not have at least 3 windows, then it does not have a chimney.
　　**iii** If a house does not have a chimney then it does not have at least 3 windows.

　**b** **i** Implication: True　　Converse: False
　　　Inverse: False　　Contrapositive: True
　　**ii** Implication: True　　Converse: True
　　　Inverse: True　　Contrapositive: True
　　**iii** Implication: False　　Converse: True
　　　Inverse: True　　Contrapositive: False

**6 a** **i** No weak students are in Year 11.
　　**ii** No Year 11 students are weak.

　**b** **i** If $x \in W$ then $x \notin E$.　**ii** If $x \in E$ then $x \notin W$.

　**c** They are contrapositives.

## EXERCISE 17F.1

**1  a**  $p \Leftrightarrow q$

$\dfrac{\neg q}{\neg p}$

**b**  $(p \Leftrightarrow q) \wedge \neg q \Rightarrow \neg p$

**c**

| $p$ | $q$ | $p \Leftrightarrow q$ | $\neg q$ | $(p \Leftrightarrow q) \wedge \neg q$ | $\neg p$ | $(p \Leftrightarrow q) \wedge \neg q \Rightarrow \neg p$ |
|---|---|---|---|---|---|---|
| T | T | T | F | F | F | T |
| T | F | F | T | F | F | T |
| F | T | F | F | F | T | T |
| F | F | T | T | T | T | T |

We have a tautology, $\therefore$ argument is valid.

**2  a**  **i**  $(p \Rightarrow q) \wedge \neg q \Rightarrow \neg p$    **ii**  $(p \vee q) \wedge \neg p \Rightarrow q$

**iii**  $(p \vee q) \Rightarrow p$    **iv**  $(p \Rightarrow q) \wedge \neg p \Rightarrow \neg q$

**v**  $(p \Rightarrow q) \wedge (q \Rightarrow p) \Rightarrow p$

**b**  **i**

| $p$ | $q$ | $p \Rightarrow q$ | $\neg q$ | $(p \Rightarrow q) \wedge \neg q$ | $\neg p$ | $(p \Rightarrow q) \wedge \neg q \Rightarrow \neg p$ |
|---|---|---|---|---|---|---|
| T | T | T | F | F | F | T |
| T | F | F | T | F | F | T |
| F | T | T | F | F | T | T |
| F | F | T | T | T | T | T |

$\therefore$ argument is valid.

**ii**

| $p$ | $q$ | $p \vee q$ | $\neg p$ | $(p \vee q) \wedge \neg p$ | $(p \vee q) \wedge \neg p \Rightarrow q$ |
|---|---|---|---|---|---|
| T | T | T | F | F | T |
| T | F | T | F | F | T |
| F | T | T | T | T | T |
| F | F | F | T | F | T |

$\therefore$ argument is valid.

**iii**

| $p$ | $q$ | $p \vee q$ | $(p \vee q) \Rightarrow p$ |
|---|---|---|---|
| T | T | T | T |
| T | F | T | T |
| F | T | T | F |
| F | F | F | T |

$\therefore$ argument is not valid.

**iv**

| $p$ | $q$ | $p \Rightarrow q$ | $\neg p$ | $(p \Rightarrow q) \wedge \neg p$ | $\neg q$ | $(p \Rightarrow q) \wedge \neg p \Rightarrow \neg q$ |
|---|---|---|---|---|---|---|
| T | T | T | F | F | F | T |
| T | F | F | F | F | T | T |
| F | T | T | T | T | F | F |
| F | F | T | T | T | T | T |

$\therefore$ argument is not valid.

**v**

| $p$ | $q$ | $p \Rightarrow q$ | $q \Rightarrow p$ | $(p \Rightarrow q) \wedge (q \Rightarrow p)$ | $(p \Rightarrow q) \wedge (q \Rightarrow p) \Rightarrow p$ |
|---|---|---|---|---|---|
| T | T | T | T | T | T |
| T | F | F | T | F | T |
| F | T | T | F | F | T |
| F | F | T | T | T | F |

$\therefore$ argument is not valid.

**3  a**  valid    **b**  not valid    **c**  valid    **d**  not valid

**5  b**  Don has visited Australia and New Zealand.

**6  a**  valid    **b**  not valid    **c**  valid

**d**  not valid    **e**  valid    **f**  not valid

## EXERCISE 17F.2

**1  a**  It is sunny and I am warm. Hence, I feel happy.

**b**  It is sunny and I am not warm. Hence, I do not feel happy.

**c**  I am warm and I feel happy. Hence, it is sunny.

**2  B**    **3  b**  $p, q, r$ are all true.

**4  a**  $p$: I do not like the subject.    $q$: I do not work hard.

$r$: I fail.

**b**  $(p \Rightarrow q) \wedge (q \Rightarrow r) \wedge \neg r \Rightarrow \neg p$

**c**  Argument is valid, $\therefore$ conclusion is a result of valid reasoning.

**5**  not valid

## REVIEW SET 17A

**1  a**  proposition, true    **b**  not a proposition

**c**  not a proposition    **d**  proposition, indeterminate

**e**  not a proposition    **f**  proposition, true

**g**  not a proposition    **h**  proposition, false

**i**  proposition, indeterminate    **j**  proposition, true

**2  a**  $x$ is not an even number.

**b**  $x$ is an even number or is divisible by 3.

**c**  $x$ is an even number or is divisible by 3, but not both.

**d**  If $x$ is an even number, then $x$ is divisible by 3.

**e**  $x$ is not an even number and is divisible by 3.

**f**  $x$ is not an even number or $x$ is divisible by 3, but not both.

**g**  If $x$ is an even number then $x$ is not divisible by 3.

**h**  If $x$ is not an even number then $x$ is not divisible by 3.

**3  a**  $p \Rightarrow q$, 7    **b**  $\neg p$, 4    **c**  $q \wedge \neg p$, 14

**d**  $p \veebar q$, 2    **e**  $\neg p \wedge \neg q$, 6

**Note:**  There are other numbers that satisfy these statements.

**4  a**  Implication:  If I love swimming, then I live near the sea.

$p \Rightarrow q$

Inverse:  If I do not love swimming, then I do not

$\neg p \Rightarrow \neg q$  live near the sea.

Converse:  If I live near the sea, then I love swimming.

$q \Rightarrow p$

Contrapositive:  If I do not live near the sea, then I do not

$\neg q \Rightarrow \neg p$  love swimming.

**b**  Implication:  If I like food, I eat a lot.

$p \Rightarrow q$

Inverse:  If I do not like food, I do not eat a lot.

$\neg p \Rightarrow \neg q$

Converse:  If I eat a lot, then I like food.

$q \Rightarrow p$

Contrapositive:  If I do not eat a lot, then I do not like food.

$\neg q \Rightarrow \neg p$

**5  a**

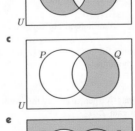

**b**

**c**

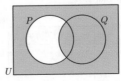

**d**

**e**

**f**

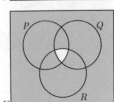

**6** **a** {1, 2, 3, 4, 6, 12}    **b** {1, 3, 5, 7, 9}    **c** {1, 3}
   **d** {1, 2, 3, 4, 5, 6, 7, 9, 12}

**7** **a** invalid    **b** invalid    **c** invalid

## REVIEW SET 17B

**1** **a** $P = \{20, 24, 28\}$,  $Q = \{1, 2, 3, 4, 6, 8, 12, 24\}$
   $R = \{20, 22, 24, 26, 28\}$,  $P \cap Q \cap R = \{24\}$

   **b** **i** {24}   **ii** {24}   **iii** {20, 24, 28}

**2** **a** Eddy is not good at football.
   **b** The maths class does not include more than 10 boys.
   **c** The writing is not illegible.
   **d** Ali does not own a new car.

**3** **a** If an animal is a bird then it has two legs.
   **b** If an animal is a snake, then it is not a mammal.
   **c** If a polygon is a rectangle, then it does not have five sides.
   **d** If this equation has a solution, then the solution is not a real solution.

**4** **a** It is neither.   **b** $x$ is zero or positive.

**5** **a** $\neg(p \vee q)$   **b** $p \wedge \neg q$   **c** $p \wedge q \wedge r$

**6** **a** logically equivalent   **b** logically equivalent
   **c** not logically equivalent   **d** logically equivalent

**7** **a** $p$: The sun is shining.   $q$: I wear my shorts.
   $(p \Rightarrow q) \wedge p \Rightarrow q$
   The argument is valid.

   **b** $p$: Marty is a teacher.   $q$: Marty works hard.
   $(p \Rightarrow q) \wedge \neg p \Rightarrow \neg q$
   The argument is not valid.

## REVIEW SET 17C

**1** **a** $x > 3$ for $x \in \mathbb{Z}$   **b** $x \in$ {brush, hairclip, bobby pin}
   **c** $x$ is a woman, but is not tall.

**2** **a**

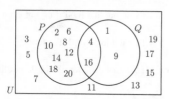

   **b** **i** {4, 16}   **ii** {1, 3, 4, 5, 7, 9, 11, 13, 15, 16, 17, 19}
   **iii** {3, 4, 5, 7, 11, 13, 15, 16, 17, 19}

**3** Inverse:  If a quadrilateral is not a rhombus, then its diagonals are not equal.
   Converse:  If the diagonals of a quadrilateral are equal then the quadrilateral is a rhombus.
   Contrapositive:  If the diagonals of a quadrilateral are not equal then the quadrilateral is not a rhombus.

**4** **a** $\neg p \Rightarrow \neg q$   **b** $\neg p \Rightarrow q$   **c** $q \wedge \neg p$   **d** $\neg p \vee q$

**5** **a** If the plane leaves from gate 5, then it leaves this morning and it does not leave from gate 2.
   **b** $\neg r \Leftrightarrow q \vee p$

**6** **a**

| $p$ | $q$ | $p \Rightarrow q$ | $(p \Rightarrow q) \wedge q$ | $(p \Rightarrow q) \wedge q \Rightarrow p$ |
|---|---|---|---|---|
| T | T | T | T | T |
| T | F | F | F | T |
| F | T | T | T | F |
| F | F | T | F | T |

$\therefore$ it is neither

**b**

| $p$ | $q$ | $p \wedge q$ | $p \vee q$ | $\neg(p \vee q)$ | $(p \wedge q) \wedge \neg(p \vee q)$ |
|---|---|---|---|---|---|
| T | T | T | T | F | F |
| T | F | F | T | F | F |
| F | T | F | T | F | F |
| F | F | F | F | T | F |

$\therefore$ logical contradiction

**c**

| $p$ | $q$ | $\neg p$ | $\neg p \Leftrightarrow q$ |
|---|---|---|---|
| T | T | F | F |
| T | F | F | T |
| F | T | T | T |
| F | F | T | F |

$\therefore$ it is neither

**d**

| $p$ | $q$ | $\neg q$ | $p \vee \neg q$ | $(p \vee \neg q) \Rightarrow q$ |
|---|---|---|---|---|
| T | T | F | T | T |
| T | F | T | T | F |
| F | T | F | F | T |
| F | F | T | T | F |

$\therefore$ it is neither

**e**

| $p$ | $q$ | $r$ | $\neg p$ | $\neg p \vee q$ | $(\neg p \vee q) \Rightarrow r$ |
|---|---|---|---|---|---|
| T | T | T | F | T | T |
| T | T | F | F | T | F |
| T | F | T | F | F | T |
| T | F | F | F | F | T |
| F | T | T | T | T | T |
| F | T | F | T | T | F |
| F | F | T | T | T | T |
| F | F | F | T | T | F |

$\therefore$ it is neither

**f**

| $p$ | $q$ | $p \wedge q$ | $(p \wedge q) \Rightarrow q$ |
|---|---|---|---|
| T | T | T | T |
| T | F | F | T |
| F | T | F | T |
| F | F | F | T |

$\therefore$ tautology

**7** **a** $p$: Fred is a dog.   $q$: Fred has fur.
   $r$: Fred has a cold nose.
   $(p \Rightarrow q) \wedge (q \Rightarrow r) \wedge p \Rightarrow r$
   The argument is valid.

   **b** $p$: Viv is a judge.   $q$: Viv wears a robe.
   $r$: Viv wears a wig.
   $(p \Rightarrow q \vee r) \wedge (\neg r \wedge \neg p) \Rightarrow \neg q$
   Argument is not valid.

## EXERCISE 18A

**1** **a**

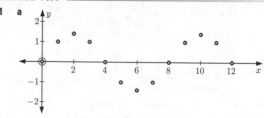

Exhibits approximately periodic behaviour.

**b**

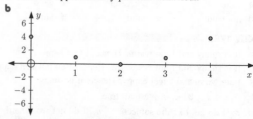

Does not exhibit periodic behaviour.

**c**

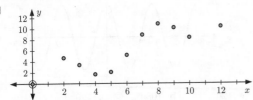

Does not exhibit periodic behaviour.

**d**

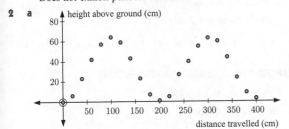

Does not exhibit periodic behaviour.

**2  a**

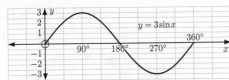

**b** Data is periodic.

  **i** $y = 32$   **ii** 64 cm   **iii** 200 cm   **iv** 32 cm

  **c** It is reasonable to fit a curve to this data.

**3  a** periodic       **b** periodic        **c** periodic
   **d** not periodic     **e** periodic        **f** periodic

**4  a** 2   **b** 8   **c** (2, 1)   **d** 8 units
   **e** $y = -1$

**EXERCISE 18B.1**

**1  a**

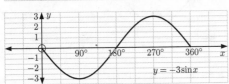

**b**

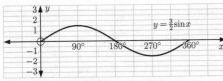

**c**

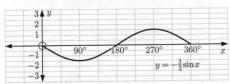

**d**

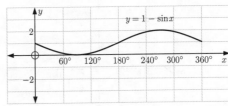

**2  a**

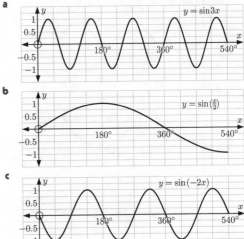

**b**

**c**

**3  a** $90°$   **b** $90°$   **c** $1080°$   **d** $600°$

**4  a** $b = \frac{2}{5}$   **b** $b = 3$   **c** $b = \frac{1}{6}$

**EXERCISE 18B.2**

**1  a** $y = 3\sin x$   **b** $y = \sin x - 2$   **c** $y = -2\sin x - 1$
   **d** $y = \sin 2x$   **e** $y = -4\sin(\frac{x}{2})$   **f** $y = \sin(\frac{x}{2})$
   **g** $y = 2\sin 3x$   **h** $y = 2\sin 2x - 3$

**2  a**

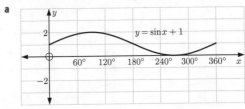

**b**

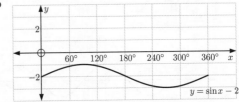

**c**

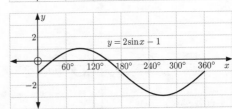

**d**

**e**

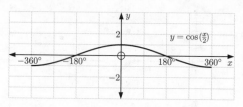

$y = \sin 3x + 1$

**f**

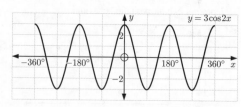

$y = 1 - \sin 2x$

## EXERCISE 18C

**1  a**

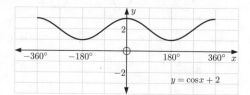

$y = \cos x + 2$

**b**

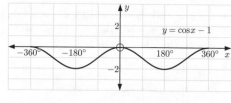

$y = \cos x - 1$

**c**

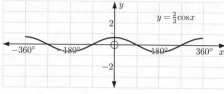

$y = \frac{2}{3}\cos x$

**d**

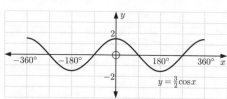

$y = \frac{3}{2}\cos x$

**e**

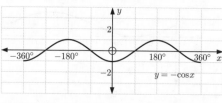

$y = -\cos x$

**f**

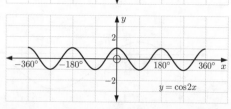

$y = \cos 2x$

**g**

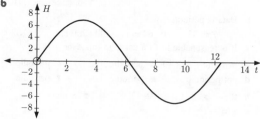

$y = \cos\left(\frac{x}{2}\right)$

**h**

$y = 3\cos 2x$

**2  a** $120^o$     **b** $1080^o$     **c** $720^o$

**3  a** affects the amplitude,  $b$ affects the period  (period $= \frac{360}{|b|}$)
   $c$ affects the principal axis

**4  a** $y = 2\cos 2x$   **b** $y = \cos\left(\frac{x}{2}\right) + 2$   **c** $y = -5\cos 2x$

## EXERCISE 18D

**1** $T = 9.5\cos(30t) - 9.5$

**2  a** $H \approx 7\sin(29.0t)$

**b**

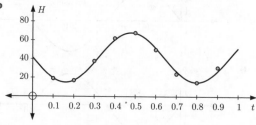

**3** $H = -10\cos(3.6t) + 12$

**4  a** $H \approx -26.5\sin(562.5t) + 41.5$  {period $\approx 0.64$ s}

**b**

**c** 83 cm     **d** 4.07 m s$^{-1}$

## EXERCISE 18E.1

**1  a** $x \approx 15^o, 165^o, 375^o, 525^o$     **b** $x \approx 205^o, 335^o$

**2  a** $x \approx 55^o, 305^o, 415^o, 665^o$     **b** $x \approx 255^o, 465^o$

**3  a** $x \approx 20^o, 70^o, 200^o, 250^o, 380^o, 430^o$
   **b** $x \approx 100^o, 170^o, 280^o, 350^o, 460^o, 530^o$

## EXERCISE 18E.2

**1  a** $x \approx 24.5^o, 156^o$     **b** $x \approx 222^o, 318^o$
   **c** no solutions     **d** $x \approx 4.66^o, 85.3^o, 185^o, 265^o$
   **e** $x \approx 105^o$     **f** $x \approx 104^o, 166^o$

## EXERCISE 18F

**1** **a** **i** 7500 grasshoppers     **ii** 10 500 grasshoppers
   **b** 10 500 grasshoppers at $t = 1, 5, 9$ weeks
   **c** **i** $t = \frac{1}{3}, 1\frac{2}{3}, 4\frac{1}{3}, 5\frac{2}{3}, 8\frac{1}{3}, 9\frac{2}{3}$
     **ii** $t = 2\frac{1}{3}, 3\frac{2}{3}, 6\frac{1}{3}, 7\frac{2}{3}, 10\frac{1}{3}, 11\frac{2}{3}$
   **d** $0.627 \leqslant t \leqslant 1.37, \ 4.63 \leqslant t \leqslant 5.37, \ 8.63 \leqslant t \leqslant 9.37$

**2** **a** $H = 20$ m    **b** $t = \frac{3}{4}$     **c** 3 minutes
   **d**

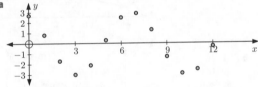

**3** **a** 400 buffalo    **b** **i** $\approx 577$ buffalo    **ii** 400 buffalo
   **c** $P(1) = 650$ buffalo
    This is the maximum population size.
   **d** 150 buffalo, after 3 years
   **e** $t \approx 0.262$ years (about 3 months)

**4** **a** **i** True    **ii** True    **b** 105.8 cents L$^{-1}$
   **c** $\approx$ days 3, 11, 17, 25    **d** 98.6 cents on days 7 and 21

## REVIEW SET 18A

**1** **a**

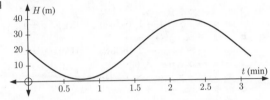

   approximately periodic
   **b**

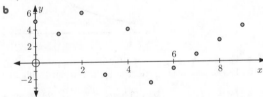

   not periodic

**2**

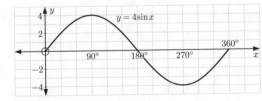

**3** **a** maximum = 2, minimum = 0
   **b** maximum = 2, minimum = $-2$
   **c** maximum = 2, minimum = $-8$
   **d** maximum = $1\frac{1}{3}$, minimum = $\frac{2}{3}$

**4** **a** $x \approx 115^{\circ}, 245^{\circ}, 475^{\circ}, 605^{\circ}$    **b** $x \approx 25^{\circ}, 335^{\circ}, 385^{\circ}$

**5** **a** $x \approx 72.5^{\circ}, 287^{\circ}$
   **b** $x = 15^{\circ}, 45^{\circ}, 135^{\circ}, 165^{\circ}, 255^{\circ}, 285^{\circ}$
   **c** $x \approx 62.6^{\circ}, 117^{\circ}$

**6** **a** 5000 beetles
   **b** Smallest: 3000 beetles, Largest: 7000 beetles
   **c** $0.5 < t < 2.5, \ 6.5 < t \leqslant 8$

## REVIEW SET 18B

**1** **a** not periodic      **b** periodic

**2**

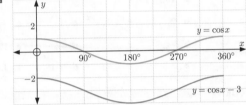

**3** **a** $1800^{\circ}$    **b** $90^{\circ}$    **c** $720^{\circ}$    **d** $120^{\circ}$

**4** **a** $x \approx -350^{\circ}, -190^{\circ}$    **b** $x \approx 45^{\circ}$

**5** **a**

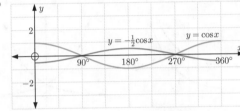

   **b**

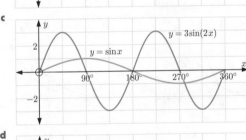

   **c**

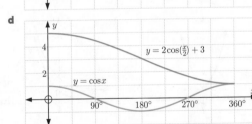

   **d**

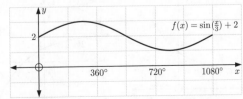

**6** **a** maximum: $-5^{\circ}$C, minimum: $-79^{\circ}$C
   **b** $T \approx 37 \sin(0.514d) - 42$    **c** $\approx 700$ Mars days

## REVIEW SET 18C

**1** **a** **i** 2 **ii** 1    **b** **i** 3 **ii** $\frac{1}{2}$    **c** **i** 1 **ii** $-5$

**2** **a**

   **b** $1 \leqslant k \leqslant 3$

**3**  **a** $y = -4\cos(2x)$    **b** $y = \cos(4x) + 2$

**4**  **a** $x \approx 22.5°, 158°, 382°, 518°, 742°, 878°$
    **b** $x \approx 235°, 485°, 955°$

**5**  **a**  **i** $y = -1$    **ii** 1    **iii** $360°$
    **b**  **i** $y = 2$    **ii** 3    **iii** $90°$

**6**  **a** 28 mg per m$^3$    **b** 6 pm Monday

## EXERCISE 19A

**1**  **a** 1    **b** $-1$    **c** $-2$    **d** $-2\frac{1}{2}$    **e** $-2\frac{3}{4}$

**2**  **a** 15    **b** 135    **c** 5    **d** $\frac{5}{81}$    **e** $1\frac{2}{3}$

**3**  **a** 32    **b** 2    **c** 4    **d** 1    **e** $\frac{1}{16}$

**4**  **a** $\frac{1}{5}$    **b** $\frac{1}{125}$    **c** 1    **d** 25    **e** 125

**5**  **a** 3    **b** 3.3    **c** 4.83    **d** 2.48    **e** 4.31

## EXERCISE 19B

**1**  **a** 1.4    **b** 1.7    **c** 2.8    **d** 0.3    **e** 2.7    **f** 0.4

**2**  **a**
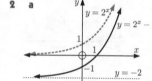
**b**
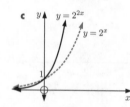

**c**
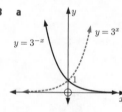
**d**
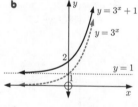

**3**  **a**
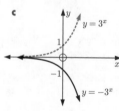
**b**

**c**
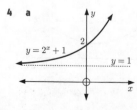
**d**

**4**  **a**
**b**

**c**
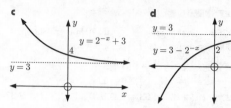
**d**
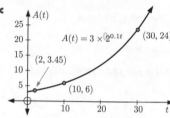

**5**  **a** $y \approx 3.67$   **b** $y \approx -0.665$   **c** $y \approx 3.38$   **d** $y \approx 2.62$

**6**  **a** as $x \to \infty$, $y \to \infty$
      as $x \to -\infty$, $y \to 1$ (above)    HA is $y = 1$
    **b** as $x \to \infty$, $y \to -\infty$
      as $x \to -\infty$, $y \to 2$ (below)    HA is $y = 2$
    **c** as $x \to \infty$, $y \to 3$ (above)
      as $x \to -\infty$, $y \to \infty$    HA is $y = 3$
    **d** as $x \to \infty$, $y \to 3$ (below)
      as $x \to -\infty$, $y \to -\infty$    HA is $y = 3$

## EXERCISE 19C.1

**1**  **a** 3 m$^2$
    **b**  **i** 3.45 m$^2$
       **ii** 6 m$^2$
       **iii** 24 m$^2$
    **c**
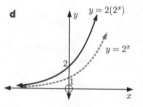

**2**  **a** 50
    **b**  **i** 76
       **ii** 141
       **iii** 396
    **c**
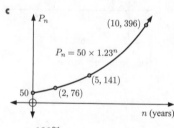

**3**  **a** $V_0$    **b** $2V_0$    **c** 100%
    **d** 183%, percentage increase at 50°C compared with 20°C

**4**  **a** $B_0 = 12$    **b** 146 bears    **c** 248% increase

## EXERCISE 19C.2

**1**  **a** 250 g   **b**  **i** 112 g   **ii** 50.4 g   **iii** 22.6 g
    **c**                                        **d** $\approx$ 346 years
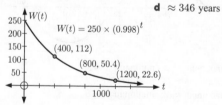

**2**  **a** 100°C    **c**
    **b**  **i** 81.2°C
       **ii** 75.8°C
       **iii** 33.9°C
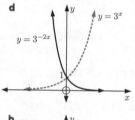
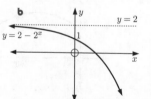

**3  a** 0.6 amps

**b  i** 0.424 amps

**ii** 0.106 amps

**iii** 0.0188 amps

**c**

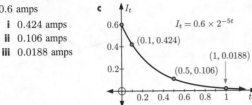

$I_t = 0.6 \times 2^{-5t}$

(0.1, 0.424)

(0.5, 0.106)

(1, 0.0188)

**4  a** $L_0$ candelas

**b** 99.0% decrease

**5  a**

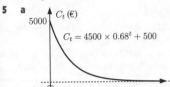

$C_t = 4500 \times 0.68^t + 500$

**b** €5000

**c** €1293.42

**d** $C = 500$, the value of the car approaches €500.

**6  a** $T = 340 \times 0.93^n$

**c** 237 turtles

**d** In 2053

**b**

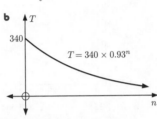

$T = 340 \times 0.93^n$

## REVIEW SET 19A

**1  a** 3     **b** 24     **c** $\frac{3}{4}$

**2  a**

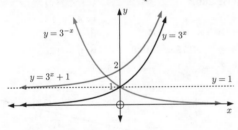

$y = 3^{-x}$

$y = 3^x$

$y = 3^x + 1$

$y = 1$

**b**  $y = 3^x$:    as $x \to \infty$, $y \to \infty$
                     as $x \to -\infty$, $y \to 0$

$y = 3^{-x}$:    as $x \to \infty$, $y \to 0$
                     as $x \to -\infty$, $y \to \infty$

$y = 3^x + 1$:    as $x \to \infty$, $y \to \infty$
                     as $x \to -\infty$, $y \to 1$

**3  a** $20

**b  i** $62.12

**ii** $599.20

**iii** $5780.04

**d** during 1994

**c**

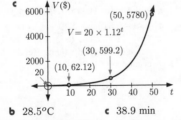

$V(\$)$

(50, 5780)

$V = 20 \times 1.12^t$

(30, 599.2)

(10, 62.12)

**4  a** $T_0 = 180$     **b** 28.5°C     **c** 38.9 min

## REVIEW SET 19B

**1  a** 125     **b** 5     **c** $\frac{1}{125}$

**2**

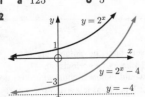

$y = 2^x$

$y = 2^x - 4$

$y = -4$

**a** $y = 2^x$ has $y$-intercept 1 and horizontal asymptote $y = 0$

**b** $y = 2^x - 4$ has $y$-intercept $-3$ and horizontal asymptote $y = -4$

---

**3  a** $W_0$ grams     **b  i** 61.6%     **ii** 8.84%

**c** after 94.9 years

**4  a** $P_0 = 16$     **b** 34 rhinoceroses     **c** after 54.4 years

## EXERCISE 20A

**1  a** weak positive correlation, linear, no outliers

**b** strong negative correlation, linear, one outlier

**c** no correlation

**d** strong negative correlation, not linear, one outlier

**e** moderate positive correlation, linear, no outliers

**f** weak positive correlation, not linear, no outliers

**2  a**

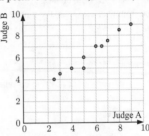

**b** There appears to be **strong**, **positive** correlation between Judge A's scores and Judge B's scores. This means that as Judge A's scores increase, Judge B's scores **increase**.

**3  a**

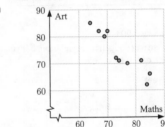

**b** There is a strong negative correlation between Mathematics and Art marks.

**4  a** D     **b** A     **c** B     **d** C

**5  a** There is a moderate positive correlation between *hours of study* and *marks obtained*.

**b** The number of marks is greater than 50, so the outlier appears to be an error. It should be discarded.

## EXERCISE 20B.1

**1** weak positive correlation

**2  a** $r = 1$, the data is perfectly positively correlated.

**b** $r = -1$, the data is perfectly negatively correlated.

**c** $r = 0$, there is no correlation.

**3  a** B     **b** A     **c** D     **d** C     **e** E

**4  a** $r \approx 0.485$     **b** $r \approx -0.0804$

**5  a**

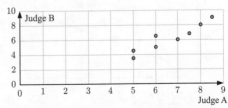

Judge B

Judge A

**b** There appears to be a **strong**, **positive** correlation between Judge A's scores and Judge B's scores. This means that as Judge A's scores increase, Judge B's scores **increase**.

**c** $r \approx 0.943$, indicating a strong linear relationship between Judge A's scores and Judge B's scores.

**6**  **a**

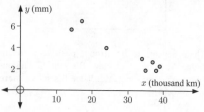

**b** negative      **c** $r \approx -0.911$

**d** As the distance from goal increases, the number of successful shots generally **decreases**.

## EXERCISE 20B.2

**1**  **a** $r^2 \approx 0.244$      **b** very weak positive correlation

**2**  **a**

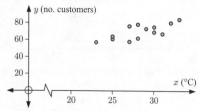

**b** $r \approx -0.951$, $r^2 \approx 0.904$

**c** There is a very strong, negative correlation between tread depth and number of km travelled.

**3**  **a**

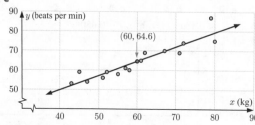

**b** $r \approx 0.743$, $r^2 \approx 0.552$

**c** There is a moderate, positive linear association between the number of customers and the noon temperature.

**4** $r \approx 0.917$, $r^2 \approx 0.841$.  There is a strong, positive association between *age* and *distance thrown*.

## EXERCISE 20C

**1**  **a, e**

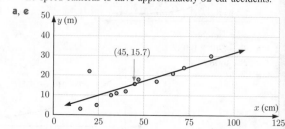

**b** $r \approx 0.929$, $r^2 \approx 0.863$

**c** There is a strong, positive correlation between *weight* and *pulse rate*.

**d** (60, 64.6)

**f** 68 beats per minute. This is an interpolation, so the estimate is reliable.

**2**  **a, d**

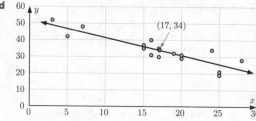

**b** $r \approx -0.878$, $r^2 \approx 0.771$

**c** There is a strong, negative correlation between *number of speed cameras* and *number of car accidents*.

**e** At $y \approx 52$. This means that we would expect a city with no speed cameras to have approximately 52 car accidents.

**3**  **a, e**

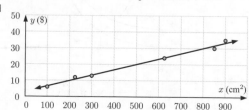

**b** (20, 22)      **c** tall and thin      **d** (45, 15.7)

**f** $\approx 37$ m. This is an extrapolation, so the prediction may not be reliable.

## EXERCISE 20D.1

**1**  **a** $\overline{x} = 5$, $\overline{y} = 8$      **b** $s_x = 2$

  **c** $y = -1.6x + 16$      **d** yes

**2**  **a** $y \approx -0.795x + 10.8$      **b** $y \approx 0.160x + 42.5$

**3**  **a, d**

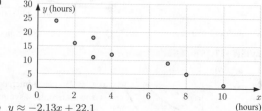

**b** There is a very strong, positive correlation between *area* and *price*.

**c** $y \approx 0.0335x + 3.27$

**e** $43.42, this is an extrapolation, so it may be unreliable.

**4**  **a** $y \approx -0.513x + 27.9$      **b** $y \approx 22.2$

  **c** $x = 11$ is close to $\overline{x}$, so $x = 11$ is likely to be in the range of supplied values. Hence, the estimate is likely to be accurate.

**5**  **a**

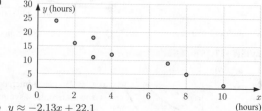

**b** $y \approx -2.13x + 22.1$

**c** gradient $\approx -2.13$, for every hour the children spend exercising, they watch 2.13 hours less television.

  $y$-intercept $\approx 22.1$, we would expect a child who does not exercise at all to watch 22.1 hours of television per week.

**d** 11.5 hours

**EXERCISE 20D.2**

**1 a**

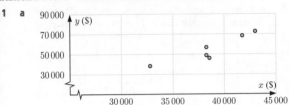

**b** $r \approx 0.921$, $r^2 \approx 0.848$

**c** There is a strong positive association between the starting salaries for Bachelor degrees and the starting salaries for PhDs.

**d** $y \approx 3.44x - 78\,300$

**e** gradient $\approx 3.44$, for every \$1 increase in the Bachelor degree salary, there is a \$3.44 increase in the PhD salary.

**f i** \$59 400

**ii** This is an interpolation, so the prediction is likely to be reliable.

**2 a**

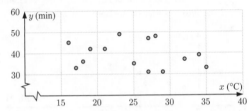

**b** $r \approx -0.219$, $r^2 \approx 0.0481$

**c** There is no correlation between *temperature* and *time*.

**d** no

**3 a** $r \approx -0.924$, $r^2 \approx 0.853$

**b** There is a strong, negative correlation between the *petrol price* and the *number of customers*.

**c** $y \approx -4.27x + 489$

**d** gradient $\approx -4.27$, for every 1 cent per litre increase in the price of petrol, a service station will lose 4.27 customers.

**e** $-5.10$ customers

**f** It is impossible to have a negative number of customers. This extrapolation is not valid.

**4 a**

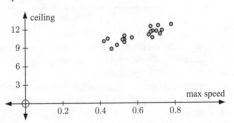

**b** $r \approx 0.840$, $r^2 \approx 0.706$    **c** moderate positive correlation

**d** $y \approx 8.12x + 6.09$    **e** 11.0 km

**5 a**

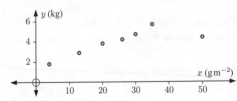

(50, 4.4) is the outlier.

**b i** $r \approx 0.798$    **ii** $r \approx 0.993$

**c i** $y \approx 0.0672x + 2.22$    **ii** $y \approx 0.119x + 1.32$

**d** The one which excludes the outlier.

**e** Too much fertiliser often kills the plants, or makes them sick.

**EXERCISE 20E.1**

**1 a** $\chi^2_{calc} \approx 13.5$    **b** $\chi^2_{calc} \approx 2.53$    **c** $\chi^2_{calc} \approx 0.495$

**d** $\chi^2_{calc} \approx 0.0722$    **e** $\chi^2_{calc} \approx 4.30$    **f** $\chi^2_{calc} \approx 0.731$

**EXERCISE 20E.2**

**1** $\chi^2_{calc} \approx 16.8$, df $= 1$, $p \approx 0.000\,041\,6$

As $\chi^2_{calc} > 3.84$, we reject $H_0$. So, the variables are not independent.

**2 a** $\chi^2_{calc} \approx 5.20$, df $= 3$, $p \approx 0.158$

**i** As $\chi^2_{calc} < 7.81$, we do not reject $H_0$. So, at a 5% level, the variables $P$ and $Q$ are independent.

**ii** As $\chi^2_{calc} < 6.25$, we do not reject $H_0$. So, at a 10% level, $P$ and $Q$ are independent.

**b** $\chi^2_{calc} \approx 11.3$, df $= 6$, $p \approx 0.0809$

**i** As $\chi^2_{calc} < 12.59$, we do not reject $H_0$. So, at a 5% level, the variables are independent.

**ii** As $\chi^2_{calc} > 10.64$, we reject $H_0$. So, at a 10% level, the variables are not independent.

**3** $\chi^2_{calc} \approx 8.58$, df $= 2$, $p \approx 0.0137$

As $\chi^2_{calc} > 5.99$, we reject $H_0$. So, at a 5% level, there is an association between *age* and *the party to vote for*.

**4** $\chi^2_{calc} \approx 22.6$, df $= 3$, $p \approx 0.000\,048\,4$

As $\chi^2_{calc} > 6.25$, we reject $H_0$, suggesting that low income people are more likely to smoke cigarettes.

**5** $\chi^2_{calc} \approx 22.6$, df $= 3$, $p \approx 0.000\,048\,8$

As $\chi^2_{calc} > 11.34$, we reject $H_0$, suggesting that heavier people are more likely to develop diabetes.

**EXERCISE 20E.3**

**1 a**

|  | $P_1$ | $P_2$ | $P_3$ | $P_4$ |
|---|---|---|---|---|
| $Q_1$ | 4.88 | 10.3 | 13.6 | 16.3 |
| $Q_2$ | 4.12 | 8.70 | 11.4 | 13.7 |

**b** 25%

**c** Combine columns $P_1$ and $P_2$:

|  | $P_1$ & $P_2$ | $P_3$ | $P_4$ |
|---|---|---|---|
| $Q_1$ | 11 | 15 | 19 |
| $Q_2$ | 17 | 10 | 11 |

Expected values:

|  | $P_1$ & $P_2$ | $P_3$ | $P_4$ |
|---|---|---|---|
| $Q_1$ | 15.2 | 13.6 | 16.3 |
| $Q_2$ | 12.8 | 11.4 | 13.7 |

**2 a** $\chi^2_{calc} \approx 16.9$, df $= 6$, $p \approx 0.009\,59$

As $\chi^2_{calc} > 16.81$, we reject $H_0$. So, at a 1% level, *intelligence level* and *cigarette smoking* are not independent.

**b** Combine the *high* and *very high* data columns.

**c** $\chi^2_{calc} \approx 13.2$, df $= 4$, $p \approx 0.0104$

As $\chi^2_{calc} < 13.28$, we do not reject $H_0$. So, at a 1% level, *intelligence level* and *cigarette smoking* are independent. This is a different conclusion from the one in **a**.

**REVIEW SET 20A**

**1 a**

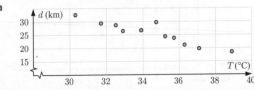

**b** $r \approx -0.928$, a strong negative linear relationship exists between the variables.

**c** $d = -1.64T + 82.3$, $50.0°C$

**2** $\chi^2_{calc} \approx 7.37$, df $= 2$, $p \approx 0.0251$

As $\chi^2_{calc} > 5.99$ we reject $H_0$. So, at a 5% level, *wearing a seat belt* and *severity of injury* are not independent.

**3 a, c**

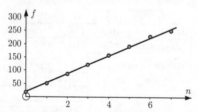

**b** $(13.3, 57.1)$

**d** There is a moderate positive correlation between *time in the store* and *money spent*.

**4 a**

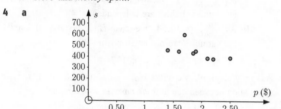

**b** Yes, the point $(1.7, 597)$ is an outlier. It should not be deleted as there is no evidence that it is a mistake.

**c** $s \approx -116p + 665$

**d** No, the prediction would not be accurate, as that much extrapolation is unreliable.

**5 a** number of waterings, $n$    **b** $f \approx 34.0n + 19.3$

**c**

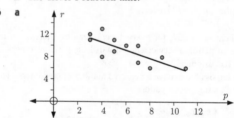

**d i** $104$ $(n = 2.5)$,    $359$ $(n = 10)$

   **ii** $n = 10$ is unreliable as it is outside the poles and over watering could be a problem. $n = 2.5$ is reliable.

**6** $\chi^2_{calc} \approx 13.0$, df $= 6$, $p \approx 0.0433$

**a** As $\chi^2_{calc} > 12.59$, we reject $H_0$. So, at a 5% level, $P$ and $Q$ are not independent.

**b** As $\chi^2_{calc} < 16.81$, we do not reject $H_0$. So, at a 1% level, $P$ and $Q$ are independent.

## REVIEW SET 20B

**1 a**

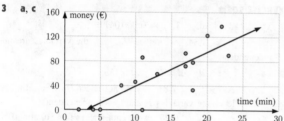

**b** $r \approx -0.819$, $r^2 \approx 0.671$

**c** There is a moderate, negative correlation between a flat's distance from the centre of Bristol, and its price.

**2 a**

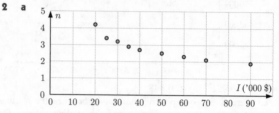

**b** $r \approx -0.908$, $r^2 \approx 0.825$    **c** $n \approx -0.0284I + 4.12$

**d** Vera is right, the data is non-linear.

**3** $\chi^2_{calc} \approx 42.1$, df $= 2$, $p \approx 7.37 \times 10^{-10}$

$\chi^2_{calc} > 5.99$, so we reject $H_0$. So, at a 5% level, *age of driver* and *increasing the speed limit* are not independent.

**4** $\chi^2_{calc} \approx 25.6$, df $= 9$, $p \approx 0.00241$

$\chi^2_{calc} > 21.67$, so we reject $H_0$. So, at a 1% level, *intelligence level* and *business success* are not independent.

**5 a**

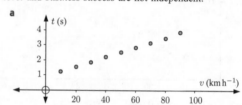

A linear model seems appropriate.

**b** $t \approx 0.0322v + 0.906$

**c i** $2.68$ seconds    **ii** $4.44$ seconds

**d** The driver's reaction time.

**6 a**

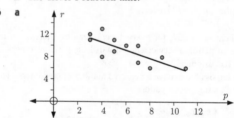

**b** $r \approx -0.706p + 13.5$ dozen maidens

**c** $r \approx -0.763$, $r^2 \approx 0.582$. There is a moderate negative relationship. This supports Superman's suspicions.

**d** $9.25$ dozen ($111$ maidens)

**e** This would predict that Silent Predator would abduct a negative number of maidens, which is unrealistic.

**f** $r$-int $\approx 13.5$, $p$-int $\approx 19.1$ These represent how many dozen maidens we would expect one villain to abduct if the other villain did not abduct any.

**g** Silent Predator

## EXERCISE 21A.1

**1 a** In one minute, Karsten's heart is expected to beat $67$ times.

   **b** $4020$

**2 a** $\approx 0.00150$ errors per word

   **b** $\approx 0.150$ errors per 100 words

**3** Niko

**4 a** $0.000177$ mm per km    **b** $1.77$ mm per $10\,000$ km

**5 a** $89.0$ km h$^{-1}$    **b** $24.7$ m s$^{-1}$

**EXERCISE 21A.2**

1  a  $0.1 \text{ ms}^{-1}$     b  $0.9 \text{ ms}^{-1}$     c  $0.5 \text{ ms}^{-1}$

2  a  i  3.1 beetles per g     ii  4.5 beetles per g
   b  The decrease is slow at first, then becomes more rapid from
      2 g until 8 g, when the decrease slows down.

**EXERCISE 21A.3**

1  a  $1 \text{ ms}^{-1}$       b  $3 \text{ kmh}^{-1}$
   c  \$48 per item sold         d  $-4.3$ bats per week

2  a  8000 L                   b  3000 L
   c  10 667 L per hour        d  3000 L per hour

**EXERCISE 21B**

1  a  7          b  7          c  11          d  16
   e  0          f  $\frac{3}{2}$          g  5          h  $-2$

2  a  $-3$         b  6          c  $-8$

**EXERCISE 21C**

1  a  $f'(x) = 1$              b  $f'(x) = 0$
   c  $f'(x) = 3x^2$           d  $f'(x) = 4x^3$

2  a  $f'(x) = 2$              b  $f'(x) = -1$
   c  $f'(x) = 2x - 3$         d  $f'(x) = 4x + 1$

**EXERCISE 21D**

1  a  $f'(x) = 3x^2$            b  $f'(x) = 6x^2$
   c  $f'(x) = 14x$            d  $f'(x) = 2x + 1$
   e  $f'(x) = -4x$            f  $f'(x) = 2x + 3$
   g  $f'(x) = 3x^2 + 6x + 4$  h  $f'(x) = 20x^3 - 12x$
   i  $f'(x) = 6x^{-2}$         j  $f'(x) = -2x^{-2} + 6x^{-3}$
   k  $f'(x) = 2x - 5x^{-2}$    l  $f'(x) = 2x + 3x^{-2}$

2  a  $f'(x) = 12x^2 - 1$      b  47          c  $-1$

3  a  $g'(x) = 1 - x^{-2}$      b  $\frac{8}{9}$          c  $\frac{3}{4}$

4  a  4          b  $-\frac{16}{729}$          c  $-7$     d  $\frac{13}{4}$     e  $\frac{1}{8}$
   f  $-11$

5  $\dfrac{dy}{dx} = 18x + 6$

6  a  $\dfrac{dy}{dx} = 4 + \dfrac{3}{x^2}$   This is the instantaneous rate of
                                           change in $y$ as $x$ changes.
   b  $\dfrac{dS}{dt} = 4t + 4$   This gives the speed of the car
                                at time $t$, in metres per second.
   c  $\dfrac{dC}{dx} = 3 + 0.004x$   This is the instantaneous rate of
                                     change in production cost as the
                                     number of toasters changes.

**EXERCISE 21E**

1  a  $y = 8x - 16$      b  $y = 12x + 16$      c  $y = -3x - 6$
   d  $y = -\frac{3}{4}x + 2$      e  $y = 7x - 5$      f  $y = -3x - 5$
   g  $y = 2x$          h  no tangent exists at $x = 0$
   i  $y = \frac{1}{2}x + 2$      j  $y = -3x - 8$

2  a  $\left(-\frac{3}{2}, \frac{11}{4}\right)$      b  $\left(\frac{1}{3}, -\frac{23}{27}\right)$ and $(-1, -1)$

   c  $(-2, -1)$ and $(2, 3)$      d  $\left(\dfrac{-b}{2a}, \dfrac{-b^2 + 4ac}{4a}\right)$

**EXERCISE 21F**

1  a  $f''(x) = 6$                 b  $f''(x) = 12x - 6$
   c  $f''(x) = 12x^{-4} - 6x^{-3}$   d  $f''(x) = 4x^{-3}$

2  a  $\dfrac{d^2y}{dx^2} = -6x$   b  $\dfrac{d^2y}{dx^2} = 2 - 30x^{-4}$   c  $\dfrac{d^2y}{dx^2} = 8x^{-3}$

3  a  i  375 m                ii  1500 m
   b  i  100 m per min        ii  30 m per minute per minute

4  a  $t = 0$, $t \approx 2.76$ and $t \approx 7.24$ minutes
   b  $t \approx 5.44$ min.  She is 261 m from home.

   c  i  $-160$ m              ii  $-120$ m per minute

      iii  40 m per minute per minute
      Kelly is 160 m from home, travelling away from her home
      at 120 m per minute, and slowing down.

**REVIEW SET 21A**

1  a  33 televisions per month      b  140 televisions per month
   c  250 televisions per month

2  a  $f'(x) = 21x^2$               b  $f'(x) = 6x - 3x^2$
   c  $f'(x) = 8x - 12$             d  $f'(x) = 7 + 4x$

3  a  $f'(x) = 4x^3 - 3$  b  29   c  $-3$      4  $y = 4x + 2$

5  a  $f''(x) = 6 - 2x^{-3}$  b  $f''(x) = 2$      6  $f'(x) = 3$

**REVIEW SET 21B**

1  a  i  5                ii  $4\frac{1}{2}$          iii  4.1
   b  $f'(x) = 2x + 2$      c  gradient $= 4$

2  a  $\dfrac{dy}{dx} = 6x - 4x^3$      b  $\dfrac{dy}{dx} = 1 + x^{-2}$

   c  $\dfrac{dy}{dx} = 2 - x^{-2} + 6x^{-3}$

3  $y = 9x - 11$      4  $\left(-\frac{1}{\sqrt{2}}, -2\sqrt{2}\right)$ and $\left(\frac{1}{\sqrt{2}}, 2\sqrt{2}\right)$

5  a  $-17$      b  $-17$      c  $-6$      6  $f'(x) = 3x^2 - 2$

**REVIEW SET 21C**

1  a  $f'(x) = 4x^3 + 6x^2 + 6x$   b  $f'(x) = -6x^{-4} - 4x^{-5}$
   c  $f'(x) = -x^{-2} + 8x^{-3}$

2  a  $-5$  b  $-12$  c  $\frac{7}{9}$  d  $-1$      3  $y = -24x + 36$

4  $S'(t) = 0.9t^2 - 36t + 550$
   This gives the instantaneous rate of change in weight, in grams
   per second, for a given value of $t$.

5  a  $\dfrac{d^2y}{dx^2} = 42x$      b  $\dfrac{d^2y}{dx^2} = 4 + 10x^{-3}$

6  a  4      b  $-\frac{7}{4}$      c  $-3$      7  $f'(x) = 2x + 2$

**EXERCISE 22A.1**

1  a  i  $x > 0$  ii  never    b  i  never  ii  $-2 \leqslant x \leqslant 3$
   c  i  $-2 < x \leqslant 0$          ii  $0 \leqslant x < 2$
   d  i  $x \leqslant 2$               ii  $x \geqslant 2$
   e  i  never  ii  $x \in \mathbb{R}$   f  i  $x \in \mathbb{R}$  ii  never
   g  i  $1 \leqslant x \leqslant 5$         ii  $x \leqslant 1$, $x \geqslant 5$
   h  i  $2 \leqslant x < 4$, $x > 4$    ii  $x < 0$, $0 < x \leqslant 2$
   i  i  $x \leqslant 0$, $2 \leqslant x \leqslant 6$   ii  $0 \leqslant x \leqslant 2$, $x \geqslant 6$

2  a  increasing for all $x \in \mathbb{R}$    b  decreasing for all $x \in \mathbb{R}$
   c  increasing: $x \geqslant 0$, decreasing: $x \leqslant 0$
   d  decreasing for all $x \in \mathbb{R}$
   e  increasing: $x \geqslant -\frac{3}{4}$, decreasing: $x \leqslant -\frac{3}{4}$

**f** increasing: $x \leqslant 0$, $x \geqslant 4$, decreasing: $0 \leqslant x \leqslant 4$

**g** increasing: $-\frac{\sqrt{2}}{\sqrt{3}} \leqslant x \leqslant \frac{\sqrt{2}}{\sqrt{3}}$,

decreasing: $x \leqslant -\frac{\sqrt{2}}{\sqrt{3}}$, $x \geqslant \frac{\sqrt{2}}{\sqrt{3}}$

**h** increasing: $-\frac{1}{2} \leqslant x \leqslant 3$, decreasing: $x \leqslant -\frac{1}{2}$, $x \geqslant 3$

**i** increasing: $x \leqslant -2.618$, $x \geqslant -0.382$
decreasing: $-2.618 \leqslant x \leqslant -0.382$

**j** increasing: $x \leqslant 0.268$, $x \geqslant 3.732$
decreasing: $0.268 \leqslant x \leqslant 3.732$

### EXERCISE 22A.2

**1  a** A is a local maximum.    B is a horizontal inflection.
C is a local minimum.

**b**

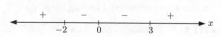

**c  i** $x \leqslant -2$, $x \geqslant 3$          **ii** $-2 \leqslant x \leqslant 3$
**d**

**e** For **b** we have intervals where the function is increasing
(+) or decreasing (−). For **d** we have intervals where the
function is above (+) or below (−) the $x$-axis.

**2  a** $x = \frac{5}{4}$

**b** $f'(x) = 4x - 5$.  $f'(x) = 0$ when $x = \frac{5}{4}$
The vertex of the quadratic (a local minimum here) is always
on the axis of symmetry.

**3  a** local minimum at $(0, -2)$

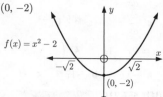

**b** stationary inflection at $(0, 1)$

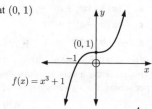

**c** local maximum at $(-1, 4)$,
local minimum at $(1, 0)$

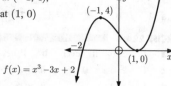

**d** local maximum at $(0, 0)$,
local minima at $(-1, -1)$
and $(1, -1)$

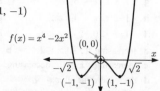

**e** stationary inflection at $(2, 9)$

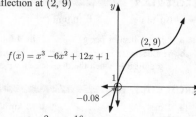

**f** local minimum at $(-\frac{2}{\sqrt{3}}, -\frac{16}{3\sqrt{3}})$,
local maximum at $(\frac{2}{\sqrt{3}}, \frac{16}{3\sqrt{3}})$

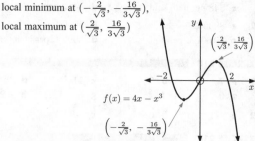

**4** $f(x)$ has a stationary point when $x = -\frac{b}{2a}$.
local maximum if $a < 0$, local minimum if $a > 0$

**5** $a = 9$

**6  a** $a = -12$, $b = -13$
**b** local maximum at $(-2, 3)$, local minimum at $(2, -29)$

**7  a** greatest value $= 63$, least value $= -18$
**b** greatest value $= 4$, least value $= -16$

**8** Minimum hourly cost: \$529.80 when 104 hinges are made.
Maximum hourly cost: \$680.95 when 150 hinges are made.

### EXERCISE 22B.1

**1  a** $\dfrac{dM}{dt} = 3t^2 - 6t$          **b** $\dfrac{dR}{dt} = 8t + 4$

**2  a** $cm^2\,s^{-1}$    **b** $m^3$ per minute

**3  a** $B'(t) = 0.6t + 30$  thousand per day
$B'(t)$ is the instantaneous rate of growth of the bacteria.
**b** $B'(3) = 31.8$
After 3 days, the bacteria are increasing at a rate of
31.8 thousand per day.
**c** $B'(t)$ is always positive for $0 \leqslant t \leqslant 10$,
∴ $B(t)$ is increasing for $0 \leqslant t \leqslant 10$.

**4  a** \$118 000    **b** $\dfrac{dP}{dt} = 4t - 12$  thousand dollars per year.
**c** It gives the instantaneous rate of change in profits.
**d  i** $0 \leqslant t \leqslant 3$      **ii** $t \geqslant 3$
**e** \$100 000, when $t = 3$ years.
**f** $t = 4$, $\dfrac{dP}{dt} = 4$;  $t = 10$, $\dfrac{dP}{dt} = 28$;  $t = 25$, $\dfrac{dP}{dt} = 88$
These figures represent the rate at which profits are increasing
(in \$1000 per year) in 4 years, 10 years and 25 years
respectively.

**5  a** 19 000 $m^3$ per minute    **b** 18 000 $m^3$ per minute
**6  a** 1.2 m
**b** $s'(t) = 28.1 - 9.8t$  This is the speed of the ball (in $m\,s^{-1}$).
**c** $t \approx 2.87$s.  The ball has reached its maximum height.
**d** 41.5 m
**e  i** $28.1\ m\,s^{-1}$    **ii** $8.5\ m\,s^{-1}$    **iii** $-20.9\ m\ s^{-1}$
The sign tells us whether the ball is travelling upwards (+)
or downwards (−).
**f** 5.78 s

**7**  **a**  2 m

**b**  $t = 2$, $H = 11$ m;  $t = 3$, $H = 14$ m;
$t = 5$, $H = 16.4$ m;  $t = 10$, $H = 18.2$ m;
$t = 50$, $H = 19.64$ m

**c**  $\dfrac{dH}{dt} = \dfrac{18}{t^2}$ m per year

**d**  $t = 1$, $\dfrac{dH}{dt} = 18$ m per year

$t = 3$, $\dfrac{dH}{dt} = 2$ m per year

$t = 10$, $\dfrac{dH}{dt} = 0.18$ m per year

**e**  $\dfrac{18}{t^2}$ can never be negative, as $t^2 \geqslant 0$ for all real $t$.
The tree is always growing.

## EXERCISE 22B.2

**1**  **a**  $\dfrac{dT}{dr} = 2r + \dfrac{100}{r^2}$    **b**  $\dfrac{dA}{dh} = 2\pi + \tfrac{1}{2}h$

**2**  pounds per item produced

**3**  **a**  **i**  €4500    **ii**  €4000

  **b**  **i**  decrease of €210.22 per km h$^{-1}$

    **ii**  increase of €11.31 per km h$^{-1}$

**4**  **a**  $C'(x) = 0.000\,216x^2 - 0.001\,22x + 0.19$ dollars per item.
This is the rate at which costs are increasing with respect to the production level $x$.

  **b**  $C'(300) \approx \$19.26$
It estimates the cost of producing the 301st item.

  **c**  $\$19.33$

**5**  **a**  $C'(x) = 0.0009x^2 + 0.04x + 4$ dollars per pair.

  **b**  $C'(220) = \$56.36$
This estimates the cost of making the 221st pair of jeans.

  **c**  $C(221) - C(220) \approx \$56.58$
This is the actual cost of making the 221st pair of jeans.

  **d**  $C''(x) = 0.0018x + 0.04$
$C''(x) = 0$ when $x \approx -22.2$
It is the point at which the cost per pair of jeans starts increasing, however, it is out of the bounds of the model.

**6**  **a**  Near part is 2 km from the shore line, far part is 3 km away.

  **b**  $\dfrac{dy}{dx} = \tfrac{3}{10}x^2 - x + \tfrac{3}{5}$

At $x = \tfrac{1}{2}$, $\dfrac{dy}{dx} = 0.175$
The gradient of the hill at a point 500 m from the shoreline is 0.175 (going uphill).

At $x = 1\tfrac{1}{2}$, $\dfrac{dy}{dx} = -0.225$
The gradient of the hill at a point 1.5 km from the shoreline is 0.225 (going down).

  **c**  2.55 km from the sea. The depth is 0.0631 km (63.1 m)

**7**  **a**  $T = 0^\circ$C, $R = 20$ ohms;  $T = 20^\circ$C, $R = 20$ ohms;
$T = 40^\circ$C, $R = 16$ ohms

  **b**  $\dfrac{dR}{dt} = \tfrac{1}{10} - \tfrac{1}{100}T$ ohms per $^\circ$C    **c**  $T \leqslant 10$

**8**  **a**

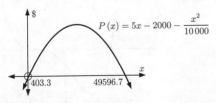

$$P(x) = 5x - 2000 - \dfrac{x^2}{10\,000}$$

$404 \leqslant x \leqslant 49\,596$

**b**  $P'(x) = 5 - \dfrac{x}{5000}$,    $0 \leqslant x \leqslant 25\,000$

**9**  **a**  $R(x) = 30x$

  **b**  $P(x) = -0.002x^3 - 0.04x^2 + 20x - 3000$

  **c**  $P'(x) = -0.006x^2 - 0.08x + 20$

  **d**  $P'(50) = 1$    This means that producing 51 items instead of 50 increases profit by about \$1.

## EXERCISE 22C

**1**  10 racquets    **2**  61.25 m    **3**  10 workers    **4**  50 fittings

**5**  $x = 250$ items    **6**  10 blankets    **7**  25 km h$^{-1}$

**8**  **c**  $C = 27x - \dfrac{x^3}{4}$

  **d**  $\dfrac{dC}{dx} = 27 - \tfrac{3}{4}x^2$;  $\dfrac{dC}{dx} = 0$ when $x = 6$

  **e**  6 cm by 6 cm

**9**  **a**  $2x$ cm    **b**  $V = 200 = 2x \times x \times h$

  **c**  **Hint**:  Show $h = \dfrac{100}{x^2}$ and substitute into the surface area equation.

  **d**
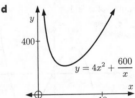

$$y = 4x^2 + \dfrac{600}{x}$$

  **e**  $SA_{\min} \approx 213$ cm$^2$,
$x \approx 4.22$

  **f**
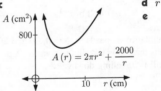

5.62 cm, 8.43 cm, 4.22 cm

**10**  **a**  recall that $V_{\text{cylinder}} = \pi r^2 h$ and that $1$ L $= 1000$ cm$^3$

  **b**  recall that $SA_{\text{cylinder}} = 2\pi r^2 + 2\pi rh$

  **c**
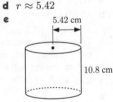

$$A(r) = 2\pi r^2 + \dfrac{2000}{r}$$

  **d**  $r \approx 5.42$

  **e**  5.42 cm, 10.8 cm

**11**  **b**  6 cm by 6 cm

**12**  **a**  $0 \leqslant x \leqslant \dfrac{200}{\pi}$

  **c**  $x = \dfrac{200}{\pi}$ m, $l = 0$  (a circular track)

**13**  **a**  2.225 m    **b**  Yes

  **c**  $h'(x) = 0.56x^3 - 0.588x^2 + 2.078x - 2.471$
$h'(0) \approx -2.47$,  $h'(7) \approx 2.47$

**14**  **b**  $\dfrac{1}{\sqrt{3}}$ m by $\dfrac{\sqrt{2}}{\sqrt{3}}$ m

**15**  **b**  $y = \dfrac{100}{x^2}$    **e**

  **d**  $x \approx 5.11$

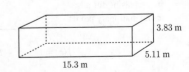

3.83 m, 5.11 m, 15.3 m

## REVIEW SET 22A

**1**  **a**  increasing: $x \leqslant -1$, $x \geqslant 4$, decreasing: $-1 \leqslant x \leqslant 4$

  **b**  increasing: $x > -3$, decreasing: $x < -3$

  **c**  increasing: $x \leqslant 6$, decreasing: never

**2  a** $y$-intercept is 0
   **b** local maximum
      at $(-1, 2)$
      local minimum
      at $(1, -2)$

   **c**

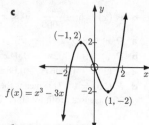

$f(x) = x^3 - 3x$

**3  a** $x$-intercepts:
      $0, 2$ (touch)
      $y$-intercept: 0
   **b** local maximum
      at $\left(\frac{2}{3}, \frac{32}{27}\right)$
      local minimum
      at $(2, 0)$

   **c**

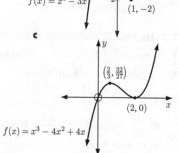

$f(x) = x^3 - 4x^2 + 4x$

**4** 4 cm by 4 cm

**5** Maximum daily profit is \$285.60 when $x = 33$
   (which is 33 000 chopsticks)

## REVIEW SET 22B

**1** maximum value is 21,  minimum value is 1

**2  a** local maximum
      at $(-2, 51)$,
      local minimum
      at $(3, -74)$
   **b** increasing for
      $x \leqslant -2$ and $x \geqslant 3$
      decreasing for
      $-2 \leqslant x \leqslant 3$

   **c**

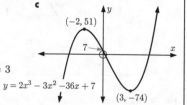

$y = 2x^3 - 3x^2 - 36x + 7$

**3  a** $H'(t) = 19 - 1.6t$ m s$^{-1}$
   **b** $H'(0) = 19$ m s$^{-1}$,  $H'(10) = 3$ m s$^{-1}$,
      $H'(20) = -13$ m s$^{-1}$
      These are the instantaneous speeds at $t = 0$, 10 and 20 s. A
      positive sign means the ball is travelling upwards. A negative
      sign means the ball is travelling downwards.
   **c** 23.8 s

**4  a**

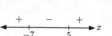

   **b**

**5** 6 cm from each end

**6  a** $P = \pi r + 2x + 2r$ m     **b** $x = 100 - r - \frac{\pi}{2}r$ m
   **d** $x \approx 28.0$ m,  $r \approx 28.0$ m

## REVIEW SET 22C

**1  a** $A = -3$,  $B = 7$
   **b** local maximum at $(-1, 9)$,  local minimum at $(1, 5)$

**2  a** $y$-intercept is $-4$     **d**
   **b** increasing for all $x$
   **c** no stationary points

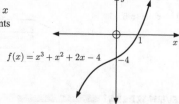

$f(x) = x^3 + x^2 + 2x - 4$

**3  a  i** €312          **ii** €1218.75
   **b  i** 9.1 euros per km h$^{-1}$     **ii** 7.5 euros per km h$^{-1}$
   **c** 3 km h$^{-1}$

**4  a** $y = \dfrac{1}{x^2}$ m     **c** 1.26 m by 1.26 m by 0.630 m

**5  b** 42 days

**6** maximum value is $25\frac{1}{3}$,  minimum value is $-1\frac{2}{3}$

## EXERCISE 23A

**1  a  i, iv**

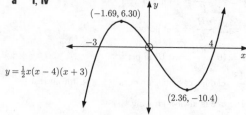

$y = \frac{1}{2}x(x - 4)(x + 3)$

   **ii** $x$-intercepts are $-3$, 0, and 4,  $y$-intercept is 0
   **iii** local max $(-1.69, 6.30)$,  local min $(2.36, -10.4)$

   **b  i, iv**

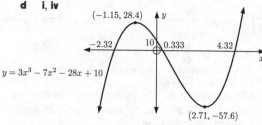

$y = -3x^3 - 24x^2 - 48x$

   **ii** $x$-intercepts are $-4$ and 0,  $y$-intercept is 0
   **iii** local min $(-4, 0)$,  local max $(-1.33, 28.4)$

   **c  i, iv**

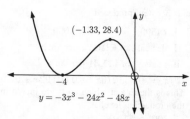

$y = \frac{4}{5}x^4 + 5x^3 + 5x^2 + 2$

   **ii** $x$-intercepts are $-4.97$ and $-1.55$,  $y$-intercept is 2
   **iii** local min $(-3.88, -33.5)$ and $(0, 2)$,
      local max $(-0.805, 2.97)$

   **d  i, iv**

$y = 3x^3 - 7x^2 - 28x + 10$

   **ii** $x$-intercepts $-2.32$, 0.333, 4.32,  $y$-intercept 10
   **iii** local max $(-1.15, 28.4)$, local min $(2.71, -57.6)$

   **e  i, iv**

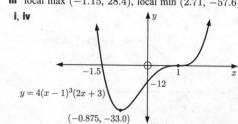

$y = 4(x - 1)^3(2x + 3)$

**ii** $x$-intercepts are $-1.5$ and $1$, $y$-intercept is $-12$
**iii** local min $(-0.875, -33.0)$

**f** **i, iv**

$y = -x(x+2)(x-1)(x-4)$

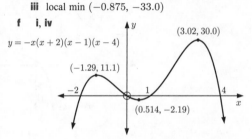

**ii** $x$-intercepts are $-2$, $0$, $1$, and $4$, $y$-intercept is $0$
**iii** local max $(-1.29, 11.1)$ and $(3.02, 30.0)$,
local min $(0.514, -2.19)$

**2 a** **i, v**

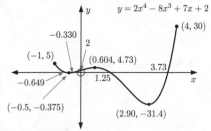

**ii** $x$-intercepts $-0.649$, $-0.330$, $1.25$, $3.73$,
$y$-intercept is $2$
**iii** local min $(-0.5, -0.375)$ and $(2.90, -31.4)$,
local max $(0.604, 4.73)$
**iv** global maximum $(4, 30)$,
global minimum $(2.90, -31.4)$

**b** **i, v**

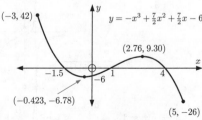

**ii** $x$-intercepts are $-1.5$, $1$, and $4$, $y$-intercept is $-6$
**iii** local min $(-0.423, -6.78)$, local max $(2.76, 9.30)$
**iv** global maximum $(-3, 42)$, global minimum $(5, -26)$

**c** **i, v**

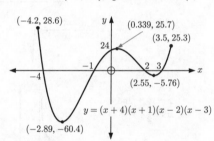

**ii** $x$-intercepts are $-4$, $-1$, $2$, and $3$, $y$-intercept is $24$
**iii** local min $(-2.89, -60.4)$ and $(2.55, -5.76)$,
local max $(0.339, 25.7)$
**iv** global maximum $(-4.2, 28.6)$,
global minimum $(-2.89, -60.4)$

**d** **i, v**

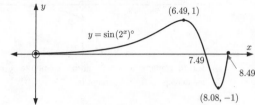

**ii** $x$-intercept is $0$, $y$-intercept is $0$
**iii** local max $(0, 0)$, local min $(2, -8)$
**iv** global maximum $(0, 0)$,
global minimum $(-1, -8)$ or $(2, -8)$

**3 a** $28.0$ **b** **i** $6.27$ **ii** $4.03$ **iii** $6.27$ **4** $-2.03$
**5 a** local max $(6.49, 1)$, local min $(8.08, -1)$ **b** $7.49$, $8.49$
**c** $-1 \leqslant y \leqslant 1$ **d** $y = \sin(2^x)^o$ is not periodic
**e**

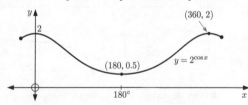

**6 a** local max $(0, 2)$ and $(360, 2)$, local min $(180, 0.5)$
**b** $2$ **c** $0.5 \leqslant y \leqslant 2$ **d** period $360^o$, amplitude $0.75$
**e**

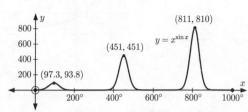

**7 a** $(97.3, 93.8)$, $(451, 451)$, $(811, 810)$
**b** **i** The graph approaches $1$ close to the $y$-axis.
**ii** $f(0) = 0^0$, which is undefined.
**c** no
**d**

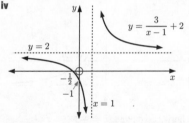

**EXERCISE 23B**

**1 a** **i, iv**

$y = \dfrac{3}{x-1} + 2$

$y = 2$

$x = 1$

**ii** vert. asymptote $x = 1$, horiz. asymptote $y = 2$
**iii** $x$-intercept is $-\frac{1}{2}$, $y$-intercept is $-1$

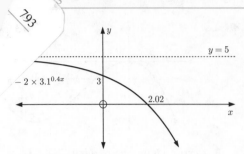

$y = 5$

$-2 \times 3.1^{0.4x}$   3

2.02

**ii** horiz. asymptote $y = 5$
**iii** $x$-intercept is 2.02, $y$-intercept is 3

**c** **i, iv**

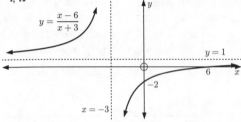

$y = \dfrac{x-6}{x+3}$

$y = 1$

6

$-2$

$x = -3$

**ii** vert. asymptote $x = -3$, horiz. asymptote $y = 1$
**iii** $x$-intercept is 6, $y$-intercept is $-2$

**d** **i, iv**

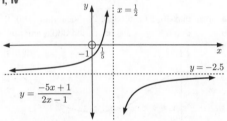

$x = \frac{1}{2}$

$-1$   $\frac{1}{5}$

$y = -2.5$

$y = \dfrac{-5x+1}{2x-1}$

**ii** vert. asymptote $x = \frac{1}{2}$, horiz. asymptote $y = -2.5$
**iii** $x$-intercept is $\frac{1}{5}$, $y$-intercept is $-1$

**e** **i, iv**

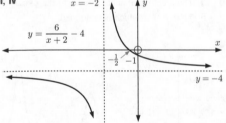

$x = -2$

$y = \dfrac{6}{x+2} - 4$

$-\frac{1}{2}$   $-1$

$y = -4$

**ii** vert. asymptote $x = -2$, horiz. asymptote $y = -4$
**iii** $x$-intercept is $-\frac{1}{2}$, $y$-intercept is $-1$

**f** **i, iv**

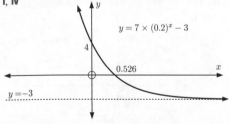

$y = 7 \times (0.2)^x - 3$

4

0.526

$y = -3$

**ii** horiz. asymptote $y = -3$
**iii** $x$-intercept is 0.526, $y$-intercept is 4

**2** **a** **i** V.A. $x = -2$   **ii**

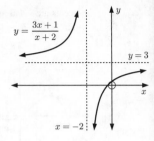

$y = \dfrac{3x+1}{x+2}$

$y = 3$

$x = -2$

**b** **i** V.A. $x = -\frac{4}{3}$   **ii**

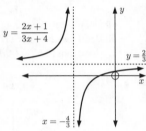

$y = \dfrac{2x+1}{3x+4}$

$y = \frac{2}{3}$

$x = -\frac{4}{3}$

**c** **i** V.A.s $x = -4$ and $x = 1$   **ii**

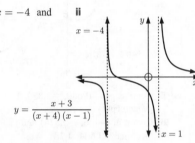

$x = -4$

$y = \dfrac{x+3}{(x+4)(x-1)}$

$x = 1$

**d** **i** V.A.s $x = -\frac{5}{2}$ and $x = 3$   **ii**

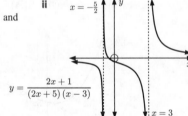

$x = -\frac{5}{2}$

$y = \dfrac{2x+1}{(2x+5)(x-3)}$

$x = 3$

**e** **i** V.A.s $x = -6$ and $x = 2$   **ii**

$x = -6$   $x = 2$

$y = \dfrac{-7}{x^2 + 4x - 12}$

**f** **i** V.A.s $x = -3$ and $x = \frac{7}{2}$   **ii**

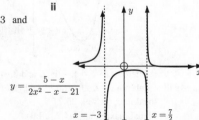

$y = \dfrac{5-x}{2x^2 - x - 21}$

$x = -3$   $x = \frac{7}{2}$

**3 a**

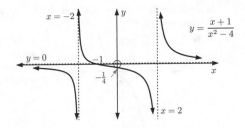

$y = \dfrac{x+1}{x^2-4}$

**b**

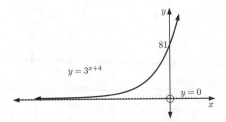

$y = 3^{x+4}$

**c**

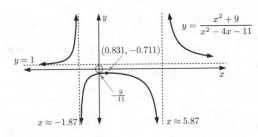

$y = \dfrac{x^2+9}{x^2-4x-11}$

**d**

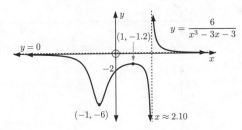

$y = \dfrac{6}{x^3-3x-3}$

**e**

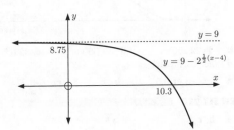

$y = 9 - 2^{\frac{1}{2}(x-4)}$

**f**

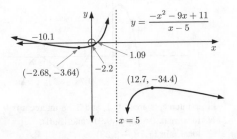

$y = \dfrac{-x^2-9x+11}{x-5}$

**4**

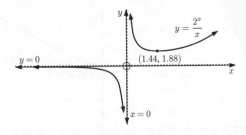

$y = \dfrac{2^x}{x}$

**5 a  i** 0    **ii** $f(-6) \approx -0.281$, $f(1) = 6$
    **iii** $-1.59$    **iv** $y = 0$

**b**

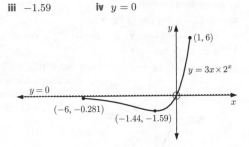

$y = 3x \times 2^x$

## EXERCISE 23C

**1 c**

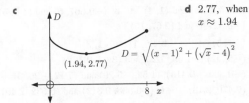

$D = \sqrt{(x-1)^2 + \left(\sqrt{x}-4\right)^2}$

**d** 2.77, when $x \approx 1.94$

**e** The shortest distance from A(1, 4) to the graph of $y = \sqrt{x}$ is 2.77 units. The closest point on the graph to A is the point with $x \approx 1.94$.

**2 a** $AP = (8-x)$ m,  $BP = \sqrt{x^2+16}$ m,  $CP = \sqrt{x^2+25}$ m
   **b** $D = 8 - x + \sqrt{x^2+16} + \sqrt{x^2+25}$
   **c**

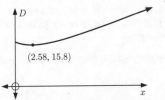

   **d** 2.58 metres from N

**3 a** $(32-x)$ cm by $(40-2x)$ cm
   **b** $V = x(32-x)(40-2x)$ cm$^3$    **c** 4608 cm$^3$
   **d** 8 cm × 24 cm × 24 cm

**4 a** $PA = \sqrt{(x-1)^2+36}$,  $PB = \sqrt{(x-7)^2+25}$
   **b** $S = \sqrt{(x-1)^2+36} + \sqrt{(x-7)^2+25}$
          $+ \sqrt{(x-3)^2+9}$
   **c**

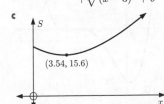

   **d** at (3.54, 8)

**d**

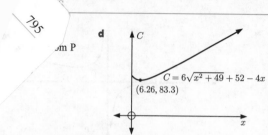

$$C = 6\sqrt{x^2 + 49} + 52 - 4x$$
(6.26, 83.3)

## EXERCISE 23D

**1** **a** $(-0.851, -4.70)$ and $(2.35, 1.70)$
**b** the graphs do not meet
**c** $(-1.12, -5.36)$ and $(1.79, 3.36)$
**d** $(-3, -4)$ and $(1.33, 9)$   **e** $(-1.67, -3)$ and $(5, 1)$
**f** the graphs do not meet

**2** **a**

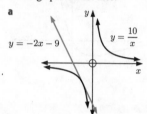

$y = -2x - 9$
$y = \dfrac{10}{x}$

**b** No, there are two intersection points.
**c** The graphs intersect at $(-2.5, -4)$ and $(-2, -5)$.

**3** **a** $(-1.5, 0.25)$ and $(1, 4)$   **b** $(-0.667, 5)$ and $(1.5, 5)$
**c** $(-0.5, -4)$ and $(2.67, 15)$

**4** **a** $(-1, 5)$   **b** $(0, 1)$ and $(1, 3)$
**c** $(-5, 32)$ $(-1.69, 3.22)$ and $(3.03, 0.122)$
**d** $(-0.802, -0.414)$, $(1.52, -5.29)$ and $(7.17, -2650)$
**e** $(0.470, 2.13)$   **f** $(-0.838, 0.313)$ and $(0.632, 2.40)$

**5** **a** $x \approx 1.19$   **b** $(-1.19, -1.68)$ and $(1.19, 1.68)$
**c** It is easier to determine how many solutions an equation has using 'graph' mode.

**6** **a** $(18.9, 0.946)$
**b** $(-194, -0.970)$, $(-131, -0.654)$ and $(69.6, 0.348)$

**7** **a** $(0, 0)$   **b** $(-90, -1)$, $(0, 0)$ and $(90, 1)$

**8** **a** $x \approx -1.81$ or $1.42$   **b** $x \approx 0.293$ or $1.51$
**c** $x \approx -1.88$ or $1.23$   **d** $x \approx -2.86$ or $2.44$
**e** $x = 30°$, $150°$ or $270°$

## REVIEW SET 23A

**1** **a**

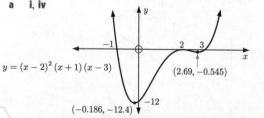

$y = x^3 + 3$

**b**

$y = -2x^2(x + 4)$
(0, 0)

**2** **a** **i, iv**

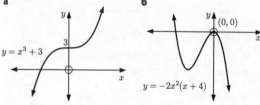

$y = (x - 2)^2 (x + 1)(x - 3)$
$(2.69, -0.545)$
$-12$
$(-0.186, -12.4)$

**ii** $x$-intercepts are $-1$, $2$, and $3$, $y$-intercept is $-12$

---

**iii** local min $(-0.186, -12.4)$ and $(2.69, -0.545)$, local max $(2, 0)$

**b** **i, iv**

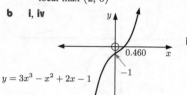

$y = 3x^3 - x^2 + 2x - 1$
0.460
$-1$

**ii** $x$-intercept 0.460, $y$-intercept $-1$
**iii** no local maxima or minima

**3** **a** $-1.62$   **b** $0$   **c** $-1.62$

**4** **a, e**

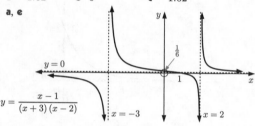

$y = 0$
$\frac{1}{6}$
1
$y = \dfrac{x - 1}{(x + 3)(x - 2)}$
$x = -3$   $x = 2$

**b** vertical asymptotes are $x = -3$ and $x = 2$, horizontal asymptote is $y = 0$
**c** $x$-intercept is $1$, $y$-intercept is $\frac{1}{6}$   **d** no turning points

**5** **a**

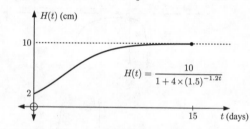

$H(t)$ (cm)
10
$H(t) = \dfrac{10}{1 + 4 \times (1.5)^{-1.2t}}$
2
15   $t$ (days)

**b** 2 cm   **c** 8.83 cm   **d** 2.85 days   **e** yes, 10 cm

**6** **a**

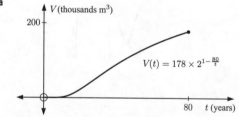

$V$ (thousands m$^3$)
200
$V(t) = 178 \times 2^{1 - \frac{80}{t}}$
80   $t$ (years)

**b** **i** 22 250 m$^3$   **ii** 89 000 m$^3$   **c** 32.0%
**d** after 43.7 years

**7** **a** $x = -3$ or $0.5$   **b** $x \approx -8.00$ or $-0.221$

## REVIEW SET 23B

**1** **a** **ii, v**

$(-0.281, 9.91)$
9
$y = -(x - 1)(x + 1)(x - 3)^2$
$-1$   1   3
$(1.78, -3.23)$

**iii** $x$-intercepts are $-1$, $1$, and $3$, $y$-intercept is $9$
**iv** local max $(-0.281, 9.91)$ and $(3, 0)$, local min $(1.78, -3.23)$

**b  ii, v**

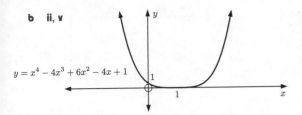

$y = x^4 - 4x^3 + 6x^2 - 4x + 1$

**iii** $x$-intercept is 1,  $y$-intercept is 1     **iv** local min $(1, 0)$

**2** $-1.82$       **3** $(1.21, 1.42)$ and $(5.79, 10.6)$

**4  a** $x = -1$   **b** $y = -3$   **c** $-\frac{1}{3}$   **d** $-1$
  **e**

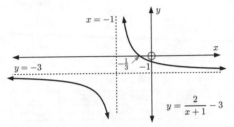

$y = \dfrac{2}{x + 1} - 3$

**5  a  i** $0$       **ii** $y = 0$     **iii** $-0.531$
  **iv** $f(-4) = -0.25$,  $f(1) = 2$
  **b**

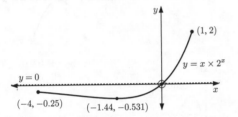

$y = x \times 2^x$

$(-4, -0.25)$    $(-1.44, -0.531)$    $(1, 2)$

**6  a**

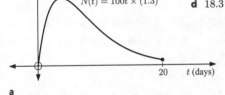

$N(t) = 100t \times (1.3)^{-t}$

  **b** 77 people
  **c** $t \approx 3.81$ days, 140 people
  **d** 18.3 days

**7  a**

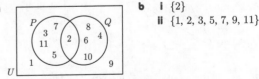

$R(t) = \dfrac{100 \times 3^{0.03t}}{25 + 3^{0.05t - 10}}$

  **b** 2800 million tonnes per year
  **c** 10 300 million tonnes per year, when $t \approx 266$
  **d** when $t \approx 227$ or $311$

**8  a** 49.8 m       **b** 36.0 m

## EXERCISE 24A

**1  a** 0.31       **b** 0.305       **c** $3.050\,85 \times 10^{-1}$

**2  a  i** If Farouk studies for the test, Farouk scores a good mark.
   **ii** If Farouk does not study for the test, Farouk does not score a good mark.

**b  i** $q \Rightarrow p$
   **ii** $\neg q \Rightarrow \neg p$

**c**

| $p$ | $q$ | $p \Rightarrow q$ | $\neg p$ | $\neg q$ | $\neg q \Rightarrow \neg p$ |
|---|---|---|---|---|---|
| T | T | T | F | F | T |
| T | F | F | F | T | F |
| F | T | T | T | F | T |
| F | F | T | T | T | T |

**3  a** $a \approx 0.866$,  $b = 0.5$,  $c = -0.5$
  **b** $\{-0.5, 0, 0.5, 0.866, 1\}$

**4  a** A$(0, 9)$,  B$(6, 0)$    **b** M$(3, 4.5)$    **c** $-\frac{3}{2}$
  **d** $2x - 3y = -7.5$

**5  a** $\approx 26$ cm    **b**
  **c** 26 cm

| Length (cm) | Frequency |
|---|---|
| $0 < x \leqslant 10$ | 15 |
| $10 < x \leqslant 20$ | 40 |
| $20 < x \leqslant 30$ | 75 |
| $30 < x \leqslant 40$ | 50 |
| $40 < x \leqslant 50$ | 20 |

**6  a** $f'(x) = 10x^4 - 10x$    **b** $f''(x) = 40x^3 - 10$
  **c** $y = -2$

**7  a** Option A: \$15 124.98,  Option B: \$15 024
  **b** Option A, by \$100.98

**8  a** $9.46 \times 10^{12}$ km    **b** $2.08 \times 10^{18}$ km

**9  a  i** $x = 3, 4, 5, 10$    **b**
   **ii** $x = 3, 5$
   **iii** $x = 1, 3, 5, 7, 8, 9$

| $p$ | $q$ | $\neg p$ | $\neg p \wedge q$ | $p \veebar q$ |
|---|---|---|---|---|
| T | T | F | F | F |
| T | F | F | F | T |
| F | T | T | T | T |
| F | F | T | F | F |

**10  a  i** $a = 0$    **ii** $b = -2$
   **b  i** $\{-2, -1, 0, 2\}$    **ii** $\{0, 4, 6, 8\}$

**11  a** $x = 5$    **b** C$(-5, 2)$
   **c** $5x + 2y + 21 = 0$    **d** D$(5, -23)$

**12  a  i** $H_0$: *time spent on co-curricular activities* and *grade average* are independent.
   **ii** df $= (3 - 1) \times (3 - 1) = 4$    **iii** $\chi^2_{calc} \approx 5.31$
  **b** $H_0$ is not rejected
  **c** The test does not support the principal's belief.

**13  a** $y = f(c)$    **b** $x = b, c, d$    **c** $x \leqslant b, x \geqslant d$
   **d** negative    **e** The tangent lines are parallel.

**14  a** €108 640    **b** £2 066 091.16    **c** no

**15  a** 6260.9 m²    **b** 6300 m²    **c** 0.625%

**16  a**
   **b  i** $\{2\}$
     **ii** $\{1, 2, 3, 5, 7, 9, 11\}$

**17  a** $x^2 - 3x - 18 = (x + 3)(x - 6)$
   **b  i** A$(-3, 0)$ **ii** B$(\frac{3}{2}, -\frac{81}{4})$ **c** $(-2, -8)$ and $(5, -8)$

**18  a**
   **b** $x \approx 663$
   **c** 689 m

**19  a**

| Time (t min) | Frequency |
|---|---|
| $0 < x \leqslant 10$ | 5 |
| $10 < x \leqslant 20$ | 4 |
| $20 < x \leqslant 30$ | 10 |
| $30 < x \leqslant 40$ | 17 |
| $40 < x \leqslant 50$ | 14 |
| $50 < x \leqslant 60$ | 3 |
| $60 < x \leqslant 70$ | 5 |

**b** $\bar{x} \approx 35.3$, $s \approx 15.6$
**c** 37.9%

**20  a** $2x^2 + 8x - 10$    **b** $f'(x) = 4x + 8$
**c  i** $a = -\frac{13}{4}$    **ii** $\left(-\frac{13}{4}, -\frac{119}{8}\right)$

**21  a** 1955.3 yuan    **b** 1926 yuan    **c** €486.76

**22  a  i** 3.2 m  **ii** 2.56 m  **b** $4 \times (0.8)^n$ m  **c** 4.6 cm

**23  a** $P(A') = 1 - a$  **b  i** $2a(1-a)$  **ii** $a^2$  **c** $a \approx 0.755$

**24  a  i** 1    **c**
    **ii** 4
**b** $y = 6$

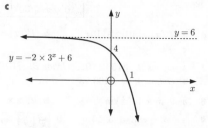

**25  a** 56.5 cm³    **b** 3 cm    **c** 96.5 cm²

**26  a** strong positive correlation    **b** $y \approx 0.779x + 3.48$
**c** $s_y \approx 3.30$, this is the standard deviation of $y$, a measure of how spread the $y$ values are.

**27  a** $C(1500) = 2$, when 1500 bars are produced each day, the cost per bar is $2.
**b** $C'(x) = 0.000\,008x - 0.008$    **c** $x = 1000$    **d** $1

**28  a  i** $3.10    **ii** $3.60    **b** $2.00

**29  a** 1 200 000 m    **b** $1.2348 \times 10^6$ m

**30  a  i** Antonio plays football, and is not good at kicking a ball.
    **ii** If Antonio is not good at kicking a ball, then he plays football.
**b  i** $p \veebar q$    **c**
**ii** $\neg p \Rightarrow \neg q$

| $p$ | $q$ | $\neg q$ | $\neg q \Rightarrow p$ |
|---|---|---|---|
| T | T | F | T |
| T | F | T | T |
| F | T | F | T |
| F | F | T | F |

**31  a** $p = 2$, $q = 3$, $r = 5$    **b** $x \approx 65°$

**32  a**    **b  i** 9.33 m
    **ii** 71.3°

13 m

8 m

**33  a  i** 198 months    **ii** 9 months    **b** yes
**c**

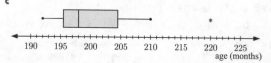

190   195   200   205   210   215   220   225
age (months)

**34  a** $f'(x) = 6x^2 + 6x^{-3} - 24$    **b** $f'(2) = \frac{3}{4}$
**c** $3x - 4y = 134$

**a** $\approx 1.8739$    **b** 3748 yen    **c** 8004.70 rupees

**36**

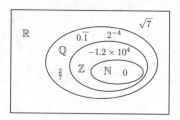

**37  a  i** 0.05  **ii** 0.55  **iii** 0.45  **b** no, $P(A \cap B) \neq 0$

**38  a**

14 cm    17 cm
35°
C    B    A

**b** $A\widehat{B}C \approx 28.19°$
**c** 106 cm²

**39  a  i** 48  **ii** 100.25  **iii** 15.0  **b** 8.33%

**40  a**

| Constant | $a$ | $b$ | $c$ |
|---|---|---|---|
| Value | positive | negative | positive |

**b** none    **c**

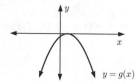

$y = g(x)$

**41  a**    **b  i** $0.910 \leqslant t \leqslant 8$
    **ii** $0.379 < t < 1.79$

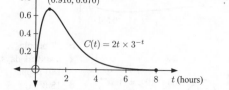

(0.910, 0.670)
0.8
0.6
0.4
0.2
$C(t) = 2t \times 3^{-t}$
2   4   6   8   $t$ (hours)

**42  a  i** £24 310.13  **ii** £24 427.72  **b** 0.484%

**43  a  i** d, s  **ii** h, k  **iii** a, b, d, h, k, r, s  **iv** f, g
**b  i** 7    **ii** 3

**44  a** $\frac{1}{6}$    **b** $\frac{1}{9}$    **c** $\frac{5}{18}$

**45  a** $y = 3x^2 - 3x - 18$    **b** $-18$    **c** $\left(\frac{1}{2}, -\frac{75}{4}\right)$

**46  a** 89.7 m    **b** 1220 m²    **c** 609 m³

**47  a**

| Score (%) | Frequency | Cum. Freq. |
|---|---|---|
| $50 \leqslant S < 60$ | 6 | 6 |
| $60 \leqslant S < 70$ | 15 | 21 |
| $70 \leqslant S < 80$ | 20 | 41 |
| $80 \leqslant S < 90$ | 10 | 51 |
| $90 \leqslant S < 100$ | 4 | 55 |

**b**

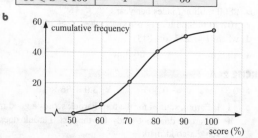

cumulative frequency
60
40
20
50   60   70   80   90   100
score (%)

**c** **i** 11     **ii** $\approx 83\%$

**58**  **a** 0    **b** $f'(x) = 6x^2 - 10x - 4$     **c** $-\frac{1}{3}$ and 2

**59**  **a** \$787.50    **b** 9.52\%    **c** $\approx 23$ months

**50**  **a** 191 m    **b** 6.04 m s$^{-1}$

**51**  **a** $p = 20$, $q = 30$, $r = 45$

   **b** **i** 0.36    **ii** 0.34    **iii** 0.654

**52**  **a**

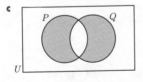

**53**  **a** **i** 27.6 cm    **ii** 23.3 cm    **b** 6010 cm$^3$

**54**  **a** $\dfrac{dy}{dx} = 3x^2 - 8x + 3$    **b** $y = 6x - 17$

**55**  **a** **i** €12    **ii** \$41.50    **b** 1 AUD = 0.6 EUR    **c** €44 100

**56**  **a** 137.5    **b** 27

   **c**

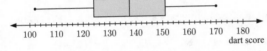

**57**  **a** $-5, 2, 9$  **b** arithmetic sequence  **c** 688  **d** 34 150

**58**  **a**

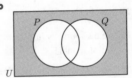

   **c**

**59**  **a** **i** 3  **ii** 720$^o$  **b** **i** $x \approx 219^o$  **ii** $x = 0^o$

**60**  **a** 89.8 cm$^3$    **b** 120 cm$^3$     **c** 187 cm$^2$

**61**  **a** $H_0$: *travel time* and *quality of work* are independent.
     $H_1$: *travel time* and *quality of work* are not independent.

   **b** 1

   **c** Since $p > 0.05$, we do not reject $H_0$. At a 5% level of significance, *travel time* and *quality of work* are independent.

**62**  **a** $f''(x) = 6x - \dfrac{6}{x^3}$    **b** $x = 1$

   **c** $(1, -2)$       **d** $0 < x \leqslant 3$

**63**  **a** €5620.50    **b** €156.13     **c** €373.50

**64**  **a** $-\frac{1}{2}$      **c** $x \approx 19.3$     **d** 43.3 cm

**65**  **a** 9.772 cm    **b** 61 cm

**66**  **a** $\frac{1}{5}$    **b** $P(B \mid A) \neq P(B)$    **c** $\frac{2}{3}$

**67**  **a** **i** £50  **ii** £200  **b** £3000  **c** $r = 0.075$, $t = 50$

**68**  **a**

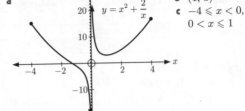

   **b** $(1, 3)$

   **c** $-4 \leqslant x < 0$,   $0 < x \leqslant 1$

**69**  **a** 70\%

   **b** **i** $m \approx 28$  **ii** $n \approx 35$  **iii** $p \approx 42$  **iv** $q = 100$

**70**  **a** 6, 7.2    **b** $u_{10} \approx 31.0$

   **c** 40.2 (the 11th term, and $u_{11} \approx 37.2$)

**71**  **a** **i** \$4896.25    **ii** \$4874.26

   **b** *Option 1* is 0.451\% better than *Option 2*.

**72**  **a** $a \wedge b$   **b** $\neg(a \vee b)$   **c** $b \wedge \neg a$   **d** $(a \vee b) \wedge c$

**73**  **a**

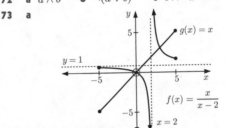

   **b** horiz. asymptote $y = 1$, vert. asymptote $x = 2$

   **c** $x = 0$ or 3

**74**  **a** $\sqrt{45}$ m    **b** 7 m     **c** 16.6$^o$

**75**  **a** $y \approx -0.0151x + 25.9$   **b** 25.5 min   **c** $r \approx -0.0550$

   **d** Unreliable, as there is virtually no correlation between the variables.

**76**  **a** $P'(m) = 60 - 2m$, $0 \leqslant m \leqslant 40$

   **c** \$100 000

**77**  **a** 6210.76 KRW    **b** 1210.76 KRW    **c** 8.03 KRW

**78**  **a**

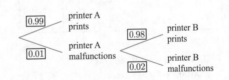

   **b** **i** 0.0002      **ii** 0.0098     **iii** 0.990

**79**  **a** 343.42 m s$^{-1}$   **b** $2.06 \times 10^5$ m   **c** 4.41\%

**80**  **a** **i** 1       **ii** 180$^o$     **iii** 1

   **b**

   **c** $\{y \mid 0 \leqslant y \leqslant 2\}$

**81**  **a** **i** P(0, 5)      **ii** Q(8, 0)

   **b** $-\frac{5}{8}$     **c** 32.0$^o$    **d** $(-4, -3)$

**82 a** positive for each case  **b**

| Strength of correlation | Scatter diagram |
|---|---|
| Weak | II |
| Moderate | I |
| Strong | III |

**83 a** $-2$  **b** $y = -2x + 6$  **c** $b = -4$, $c = 7$

**84 a i** $364  **ii** $13680  **b** $16560

**85 a** $10.32 \text{ m s}^{-1}$  **b** $37.2 \text{ km h}^{-1}$  **c** $10.47 \text{ m s}^{-1}$
**d** $1.44\%$

**86 a** 44 students  **b** $\frac{9}{44}$  **c** $\frac{5}{44}$  **d** $\frac{5}{14}$

**87 a** $24000  **b** $r = 0.85$  **c** 7 years

**88 a** 12 cm  **b i** $67.4°$  **ii** $113°$  **c** 20.8 cm

**89 a** $11712.88  **b** $16621.90  **c** $1266.47

**90 a**

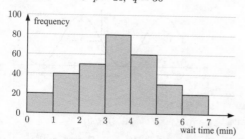

**c** The statement is true in general.

**91 a** $f'(x) = -\dfrac{16}{x^3} + 2$

**b** $f'(1) = -14$, the gradient of the tangent to $f(x)$ at the point where $x = 1$.

**c** $(2, 3)$

**92 a**

| a | b | c | ¬b | $b \wedge a$ | $c \Rightarrow (b \wedge a)$ | $\neg b \wedge (c \Rightarrow (b \wedge a))$ | ¬c | $\neg b \wedge (c \Rightarrow (b \wedge a)) \Rightarrow \neg c$ |
|---|---|---|---|---|---|---|---|---|
| T | T | T | F | T | T | F | F | T |
| T | T | F | F | T | T | F | T | T |
| T | F | T | T | F | F | F | F | T |
| T | F | F | T | F | T | T | T | T |
| F | T | T | F | F | F | F | F | T |
| F | T | F | F | F | T | F | T | T |
| F | F | T | T | F | F | F | F | T |
| F | F | F | T | F | T | T | T | T |

**b** tautology

**93 a i** €53000  **ii** €56000
**b** $V_n = 50000 + 3000n$ euros  **c** 17 years

**94 a i** $\{x \mid 0° \leqslant x \leqslant 75°\}$  **ii** $\{y \mid 8 \leqslant y \leqslant 32\}$
**b** 12  **c** $k = 8$

**95 a** M(1, 4)  **b** $\frac{2}{5}$  **c** $5x + 2y - 13 = 0$  **d** $\frac{13}{5}$

**96 a** 6360 SEK  **b** 995.31 AUD  **c** $0.469\%$

**97 a** 3.5 minutes  **b** $p = 20$, $q = 30$
**c**

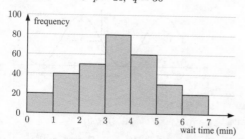

**98 a i** $p = 4$  **ii** $q = 4$  **b** $-1$  **c** C(2, 2)

**99 a** $450  **b** $4125  **100 a i** 0.41  **ii** 0.59  **b** 99

**101 a**

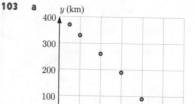

$f(x) = \sin(2x) - 2$

**b** $180°$
**c** $-3$
**d** $x = 105°, 165°$

**102 a** 70 m  **b** $53.9°$  **c** 3440 m²

**103 a**

**b** $y \approx -40.7x + 417$
**c** 4.84 litres
**d** 42.6 km per litre

**104 a** $15273.01  **b** $5273.01  **c** $777.08

**105 a** $a = 4$  **b** $\dfrac{dy}{dx} = 2x - 4$  **c** $(2, -4)$  **d** 2

**106 a** true  **b** true  **c** true  **d** false  **e** false

**107 a** $P(B) = \frac{1}{3}$  **b i** $\frac{16}{21}$  **ii** $\frac{13}{21}$

**108 a** 9 hours on July 1st  **b** 4 months
**c** 4 months  **d** $p = 3$, $q = 30$, $r = 12$

**109 a** $H_0$: *intelligence* and *income level* are independent.
$H_1$: *intelligence* and *income level* are not independent.
**b** 4  **c** 9.49
**d** At a 5% significance level, *intelligence* and *income level* are independent.

**110 a** $f'(x) = x^3 - 4x$
**b** $f'(-3) = -15$, $f'(-2) = 0$, $f'(-1) = 3$
**c** local minimum  **d** $-2 \leqslant x \leqslant 0$, $x \geqslant 2$

**111 a i** 11 units  **ii** 5 units  **b** $53.13°$  **c** 22 units²

**112 a i** 35750 MXN  **ii** 1787.50 EUR
**b i** 1 EUR = 1.54 USD  **ii** 1 EUR = 20 MXN
**c** 102000 MXN

**113 a** $a = 5$, $b = -10$  **b** $y = 310$

**114 a** $u_1 + 3d = 22$, $u_1 + 9d = 70$
**b** $u_1 = -2$, $d = 8$  **c** 340

**115 a**

|  | Left handed | Right handed | Total |
|---|---|---|---|
| Male | 4 | 26 | 30 |
| Female | 3 | 17 | 20 |
| Total | 7 | 43 | 50 |

**b i** 0.14  **ii** 0.52  **iii** 0.85

**116 a** $k = -\frac{5}{2}$  **b** $k = \frac{8}{5}$

**117** **a, b**

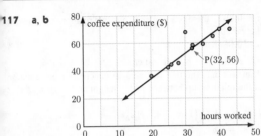

  **c** $61
  **d** strong positive relationship, the prediction in **c** is reliable

**118** **a** 27    **b** $\dfrac{dy}{dx} = 3x^2$    **c** P(3, 15)

**119** **a** €1.66    **b** €204 357.65

**120** **a** $x = 20$   **b**   **i** $\frac{37}{50}$   **ii** $\frac{2}{5}$   **iii** $\frac{17}{50}$   **iv** $\frac{24}{37}$

**121** **c** $a = 4,\ b = 1$    **122** **a** £2x    **c** $x = 174$

**123** **a**   **i** 8 m    **ii** 10 m
  **b** 12 m    **c** 6 pm    **d** between 2 am and 10 am

**124** **b** $y = 2x + 3$    **c** $(-2.8, -2.6)$    **d** 6.26 units

**125** **a** 13
  **b**   **i** $w = 3$   **ii** $x = 36$   **iii** $y = 16$   **iv** $z = 211$
  **c** $\dfrac{z}{y} \approx 13.2$, the mean of the data set

**126** **a** ¥252 000    **b** $r \approx 5.86$

**127** **a** $u_1 = 59,\ u_2 = 55$    **b** 19th term    **c** $k = 11$

**128** **a**

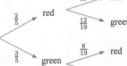

  **b** $\frac{14}{95}$    **c** $\frac{81}{95}$

**129** **a** 4 people    **b** 394 people    **c** $19.9 \approx 20$ days

**130** **a** 2.83 cm    **b** $66^o$

**131** **a** $y = 30 - x$    **b** $A(x) = x(30 - x)$ cm$^2$
  **c** $A'(x) = 30 - 2x$    **d** $x = 15$, 15 cm × 15 cm

**132** **a** $H_0$: *drink size* and *time of day* are independent.
  **b** $\chi^2 \approx 7.11$    **c** 4
  **d** $\chi^2 < 9.488$, so at a 5% significance level *drink size* and *time of day* are independent.

**133** **a** 12.524%    **b** $10 756.44

**134** **a** $a = 3,\ b = 2$    **b** $x = 45^o,\ 135^o$
  **c** $0^o \leqslant x \leqslant 45^o,\ 135^o \leqslant x \leqslant 180^o$    **d** $y = 7,\ y = 1$

**135** **a**

| Length (x cm) | Frequency | Cumulative frequency |
|---|---|---|
| $0 \leqslant x < 1$ | 15 | 15 |
| $1 \leqslant x < 2$ | 35 | 50 |
| $2 \leqslant x < 3$ | 25 | 75 |
| $3 \leqslant x < 4$ | 20 | 95 |
| $4 \leqslant x < 5$ | 10 | 105 |
| $5 \leqslant x < 6$ | 5 | 110 |

**b**

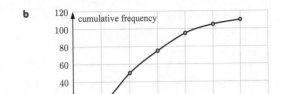

  **c** $\approx 2.6$ cm

**136** **a** $p$: I watch a movie,   $q$: I will relax.
  **b** $p$ true but $q$ false (I watch a movie, but do not relax.)
  **c** If I have not relaxed, then I did not watch a movie.
  **d**

| $p$ | $q$ | $\neg p$ | $\neg q$ | $p \Rightarrow q$ | Contrapositive $\neg q \Rightarrow \neg p$ |
|---|---|---|---|---|---|
| T | T | F | F | T | T |
| T | F | F | T | F | F |
| F | T | T | F | T | T |
| F | F | T | T | T | T |

**137** **a** $9000    **b**   **i** $608.30    **ii** $36 498
  **c** Superior Bank, by $2502

**138** **a** OM = 5 cm    **b** 400 cm$^3$    **c** $67.4^o$

**139** **a**   **i** $u_n = 13 + 8n$    **ii** $S_n = 4n^2 + 17n$
  **b**   **i** $u_{50} = 413$    **ii** $S_{50} = 10 850$

**140** **a** 50 m   **b**   **i** 100 m   **ii** $0 \leqslant x \leqslant 100$   **c** L(50, 30)

## EXERCISE 24B

**1** **a** $192 000
  **b**   **i** $1000, $1600, $2200    **ii** $189 600
  **c**   **i** $500, $600, $720    **ii** $196 242.12
  **d** *Option 3*    **e** $636.97

**2** **a**   **i** 0.36    **ii** 0.48    **iii** 0.16
  **b** All the possible outcomes are covered in **a**.    **c** 0.216
  **d**   **i** 0.289    **ii** 0.939

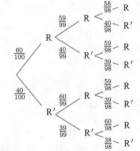

**3** **a** $x$-intercept is $-1$
  $y$-intercept is $-2$
  **b** horizontal asymptote $y = 2$,
  vertical asymptote $x = 1$
  **c** Domain $\{x \mid x \neq 1\}$,
  Range $\{y \mid y \neq 2\}$
  **e** $x = -1$ or 3
  **f** $(-1, 0)$ and $(3, 4)$
  **d, g**

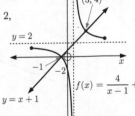

$f(x) = \dfrac{4}{x - 1} + 2$

**4 a i** $A(8, 0)$ **ii** $B(0, 6)$ **b i** $-\frac{3}{4}$ **ii** 10 units
**c** $y = \frac{4}{3}x + 6$ **d** 37.5 units$^2$ **e** $D(3, 0)$

**5 a** 44 players **b** $90 \leqslant t < 120$
**c**

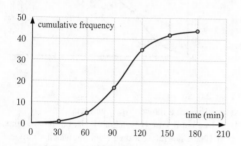

**d i** $\approx 100$ min **ii** 96.8 min **iii** no
**e** ".... between 75 and 115 minutes."

**6 a** $f'(x) = 3x^2 - 12x + p$ **b** $p = 9, \ q = 3$ **c** $(3, 3)$
**d, e i**

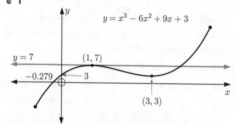

**e ii** $y = 7$ **iii** $(4, 7)$

**7 a** \$728 **b** \$87 360 **c** \$27 360
**d** 4.56% p.a. **e i** \$6442.45 **ii** \$53 557.55

**8 a** 56 members **b i** 8 **ii** 25 **iii** 5 **c** yes
**d** **e** 11

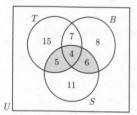

**9 a i** $\frac{3}{8}$ **ii** 1 **b i** $\frac{25}{64}$ **ii** $\frac{55}{64}$
**c i** $\frac{3}{28}$ **ii** $\frac{15}{28}$ **d** $\frac{15}{28}$

**10 a** $PQ = \sqrt{50}$ units **b** $a = 10$ **c** $\frac{1}{7}$
**d** $x - 7y + 32 = 0$ **e** $S(-32, 0)$ **f** $5.44°$

**11 a i** 4 m **ii** 6 am **b** midnight to 3 am, 9 am to noon
**c** $a = 2, \ b = 30, \ c = 3$ **d** 4 m **e** 6 pm

**12 a**

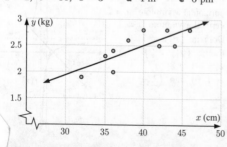

**b** $r \approx 0.797$, there is a moderate positive relationship between the variables.
**c** $y \approx 0.0565x + 0.244$
**d i** 2.2 kg **ii** 40 cm
**e** With less data the line will be a less accurate representation of the relationship between melon length and weight.

**13 a** $f(0) = -4, \ f(1) = -4, \ f(2) = -6$
**b** $f'(x) = 3x^2 - 8x + 3$
**c** $(0.451, -3.37)$ and $(2.22, -6.11)$
**d** $(0.451, -3.37)$ is a local maximum
$(2.22, -6.11)$ is a local minimum
**e**

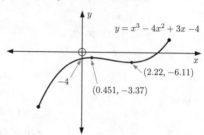

**14 a** Billy: \$7173.27, Bob: \$7075.23
**b** 9 years **c i** 106.13 USD **ii** €4739

**15 a i** $u_1 + 4d = 50, \ u_1 + 7d = 80$
**ii** $u_1 = 10, \ d = 10$ **iii** 10, 20, 30, 40, 50
**b i** 100, 50, 25, 12.5, 6.25 **ii** 200 **iii** 200
**iv** The terms get successively smaller, and adding the extra terms does not alter the overall sum when rounded to 3 significant figures.
**c** 1400

**16 a**

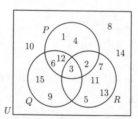

**b i** $x = 3, 6, 12$ **ii** $x = 2, 5, 6, 7, 9, 11, 12, 13, 15$
**iii** $x = 6, 9, 12, 15$ **iv** $x = 8, 10, 14$
**c i** $x$ is a factor of 12, and a multiple of 3, but is not prime.
**ii**

| $p$ | $q$ | $r$ | $p \wedge q$ | $\neg r$ | $(p \wedge q) \wedge \neg r$ |
|---|---|---|---|---|---|
| T | T | T | T | F | F |
| T | T | F | T | T | T |
| T | F | T | F | F | F |
| T | F | F | F | T | F |
| F | T | T | F | F | F |
| F | T | F | F | T | F |
| F | F | T | F | F | F |
| F | F | F | F | T | F |

$p$ is true, $q$ is true, $r$ is false.
**iii** $x = 6, 12$

**17 a** $f(x) = (x + 2)(x - 1)$ **b** $\alpha = 1, \ \beta = -2$
**c** $\left(-\frac{1}{2}, -\frac{9}{4}\right)$

**d, e**

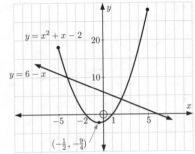

$y = x^2 + x - 2$

$y = 6 - x$

$(-\frac{1}{2}, -\frac{9}{4})$

**f** $x = -4$ or $2$

**18 a i** DB $\approx 4.09$ m          **ii** BC $\approx 9.86$ m
   **b i** $\widehat{ABE} \approx 68.2°$          **ii** $\widehat{DBC} \approx 57.5°$
   **c** $17.0$ m$^2$      **d** AE $\approx 10.9$ m

**19 a i** $0.19$          **ii** $0.06$
   **b i** $H_0$: *attendance* and *performance* are independent.
       $H_1$: *attendance* and *performance* are not independent.
   **ii** $2$     **iii** $4.61$
   **c ii** $b = -8$, $c = 64$, $d \approx 2.13$
   **iii** $\chi^2_{calc} \approx 16.0$
   **d** $\chi^2_{calc} > \chi^2_{crit}$, so at a 10% significance level *attendance* and *performance* are not independent.

**20 a** $x$-intercept is $5$, $y$-intercept is $\frac{5}{2}$
   **b**

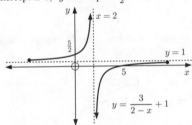

$y = \dfrac{3}{2-x} + 1$

   **c ii** $y = 1$          **iii** $x = 2$
   **d i** The graph is increasing for $x \geqslant 3$.
   **iii** $a = 1.5$, $b \approx 2.9970$     **iv** $\dfrac{dy}{dx} = 3$

**21 a i** $16\,000$ CHF          **ii** $200\,000$ JPY
   **b i** $a = 1$          **ii** $b = 0.625$
   **c i** $1$ CHF $= 80$ JPY     **ii** $1$ CHF $= 0.625$ GBP
   **d** $c = 128$    **e** $1\,134\,720$ JPY     **f** $\approx 7.813 \times 10^{-3}$

**22 a i** $P = \{3, 4, 5, 6, 7, 8, 9\}$     **ii** $n(P) = 7$     **iii** finite
   **iv (1)** $2$ and $15$ are in $Q$, but not $P$
       **(2)** $R = \{3, 6, 9\}$, all these elements are in $P$
   **v (1)** $\{9\}$     **(2)** $\{9\}$     **(3)** $\{2, 3, 6, 9, 15\}$
   **b i**          **ii**

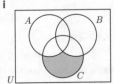 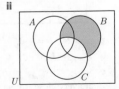

**iii**

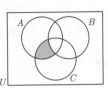

**23 a i** $\neg q \Rightarrow \neg p$          **ii** $q \Rightarrow p \vee r$
   **b i** If Pepin does not play the guitar, then he does not both ride a motorbike *and* live in Jakarta.
   **ii**

| $p$ | $q$ | $r$ | $\neg r$ | $q \wedge p$ | $\neg(q \wedge p)$ | $\neg r \Rightarrow \neg(q \wedge p)$ |
|---|---|---|---|---|---|---|
| T | T | T | F | T | F | T |
| T | T | F | T | T | F | F |
| T | F | T | F | F | T | T |
| T | F | F | T | F | T | T |
| F | T | T | F | F | T | T |
| F | T | F | T | F | T | T |
| F | F | T | F | F | T | T |
| F | F | F | T | F | T | T |

   **iii** not a tautology
   **iv** Pepin does not play the guitar, but he does ride a motorbike and he does live in Jakarta.

**24 a**

| $x$ | 0 | 20 | 40 | 60 | 80 | 100 |
|---|---|---|---|---|---|---|
| $P$ | $-60$ | 100 | 220 | 300 | 340 | 340 |

   **b**

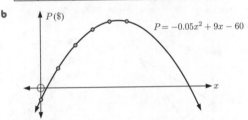

$P = -0.05x^2 + 9x - 60$

   **c i** $90$ pies     **ii** $\$345$     **iii** $37$ or $143$     **iv** $\$60$

**25 a** AN $= \sqrt{244} \approx 15.6$ cm     **b** AM $= \sqrt{269} \approx 16.4$ cm
   **c** $17.7°$     **d** $39.1$ cm$^2$     **e** $660$ cm$^2$     **f** $600$ cm$^3$

**26 a i** $18.7°C$          **ii** $1.38°C$
   **b** $r \approx -0.744$, there is a moderate negative correlation between $n$ and $T$.
   **c i** $n = -6.82T + 252$     **ii** $118$ cups of coffee
   **d** Using the regression line, 47 should be sold, so the owner may be underestimating. However, this is an extrapolation, so the regression line estimate may be unreliable.

**27 a** $a = -12$, $b = 6$
   **b i** $p = 5$, $q = -4$     **ii** $\frac{2}{5}$     **iii** $c = -6$

**28 a** €$18\,720$     **b** €$3720$     **c** $8.27\%$
   **d i** €$412.50$     **ii** €$107.50$

**29 a i** $X = \{1, 2, 3, 4, 6, 8, 12\}$
       **ii** $Y = \{4, 8, 12, 16, 20\}$
   **b**

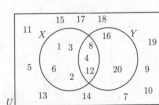

**c** **i** $X \cap Y = \{4, 8, 12\}$
　　**ii** $(X \cup Y)' = \{5, 7, 9, 10, 11, 13, 14, 15, 17, 18, 19\}$

**30** **a**

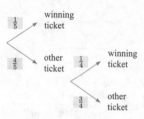

**b** $\frac{2}{5}$　**c** **i** $\frac{4}{5}$　**ii** 1　**d** **i** $\frac{1}{5}$　**ii** $\frac{4}{25}$　**iii** $\frac{16}{125}$
**e** $\frac{61}{125}$　**f** **i** $\frac{4}{5}$　**g** 96.5%

**31** **a** **i** 2　　**ii** $120°$　　**iii** 2
**b, d**

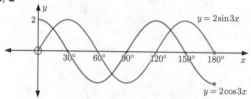

$y = 2\sin 3x$
$y = 2\cos 3x$

**c** $y$-intercept　　**e** $x = 15°, 75°, 135°$

**32** **a**

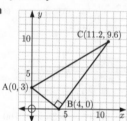

**b** 5 units
**c** $-\frac{3}{4}$
**d** **i** $\frac{4}{3}$
　　**ii** $y = \frac{4}{3}x - \frac{16}{3}$
**e** **i** $b = 9.6$
**f** 30 units$^2$
**g** $22.6°$

**33** **b**

| | Male | Female | Total |
|---|---|---|---|
| Participated | 78 | 72 | 150 |
| Did not participate | 52 | 48 | 100 |
| Total | 130 | 120 | 250 |

**c** 1　**d** $\chi^2_{crit} = 3.84$　**e** $H_0$ is rejected
**f** Participation in the survey was not independent of gender.
**g** continuous　**h** **i** 12.5　**ii** 6.19　**i** 0.367

**34** **c** $\frac{dV}{dx} = 1200 - \frac{3}{4}x^2$
**d** **i** $a = 11\,750$　**ii** $b = 29\,250$
**e** base width 40 cm, height 20 cm　**f** 32 000 cm$^3$

**35** **a** **i** €511.99　　**ii** €1602.45
**b** $V = 12\,000(1.0105)^{4x}$ euros　**c** 22 years　**d** 6.82%

**36** **a** 92.4 m$^2$
**b** maximum length 16.55 m, maximum width 5.65 m
**c** 93.5 m$^2$　**d** 1.87 m$^3$　**e** $474.13　**f** $3.99

**37** **a** $n = 9$　　**b**
**c** $\frac{17}{20}$

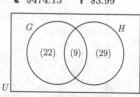

**d** **i** $\frac{2}{5}$　**ii** $\frac{1}{12}$
**e** **i** $\frac{17}{38}$　**ii** $\frac{9}{38}$

$o = 10$　**b** 2.77 units　**c** 17.9 m

**d**

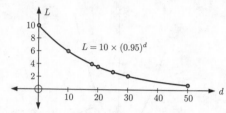

$L = 10 \times (0.95)^d$

**e** Between 23.5 m and 44.9 m.

**39** **a** 37.5 cm　**b** 1500 cm$^2$　**c** 13 500 cm$^3$
**d** 54.8 cm　**e** $46.8°$　**f** 375 cm$^2$

**40** **a**

| Time (min) | Frequency | Cumulative frequency |
|---|---|---|
| $20 \leqslant t < 25$ | 5 | 5 |
| $25 \leqslant t < 30$ | 8 | 13 |
| $30 \leqslant t < 35$ | 15 | 28 |
| $35 \leqslant t < 40$ | 15 | 43 |
| $40 \leqslant t < 45$ | 5 | 48 |
| $45 \leqslant t < 50$ | 2 | 50 |

**b**

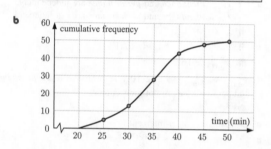

**c** **i** 34 min　**ii** 8 min　**iii** 37 runners　**iv** 32 min
**d** 15　　**e** 23 min

**41** **a** $(x - 15)　**c** $51\,000　**d** $\frac{dP}{dx} = 1635 - 18x$
**e** $91 per pair, $51\,756 profit

**42** **a** **i** $95.07　　**ii** $297.20
**b** **i** $364.68　　**ii** $17\,504.64　**iii** $5504.64
　　**iv** $1334.88

**43** **a** 55　　**c** 500 500　**d** $n = 150$
**e** **i** $u_n = 7n$　**ii** $u_{142} = 994$　**iii** $S_n = \frac{7n(n+1)}{2}$
**f** 429 429

**44** **a**

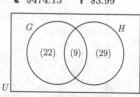

**b** 60
**c** **i** 6.33%
　　**ii** 30.7%
**d** 60%

**45** **a** $a = 24$, $b = -6$, $c = 36$, $d = 1.5$
**b** $\chi^2_{calc} = 6.6$　**c** 1　　**d** $\chi^2_{crit} = 6.63$
**e** $\chi^2_{calc} < \chi^2_{crit}$, so $H_0$ not be rejected. However, the values
are very close, so our argument is not very strong.

**46 a** $180°$

**b**

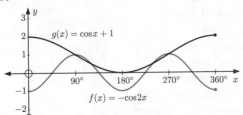

**c i** 2    **ii** 4    **d** $x = 90°, 120°, 240°, 270°$

**47 b** QR $\approx 4.624$ cm    **c i** 18.6 cm    **ii** 16.5 cm$^2$

**48 a** $3x^2 - 8x + 4 = (3x - 2)(x - 2)$

**b** $f'(x) = 3x^2 - 8x + 4$    **c** $x = \frac{2}{3}$ or 2

**d** $A\left(\frac{2}{3}, \frac{32}{27}\right)$    **e** $\{y \mid 0 \leqslant y \leqslant \frac{32}{27}\}$    **f** $y = -x + 2$

**49 a i** $V_1 = \$30\,000$    **iii** $V_n = 40\,000(0.75)^n$

**iv**

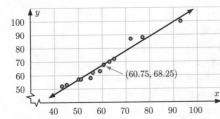

**b i** 5%    **ii** $P_2 = \$1323$, $P_3 = \$1389.15$

**iii** $P_n = 1200(1.05)^n$

**c** 11 years

**50 a, c**

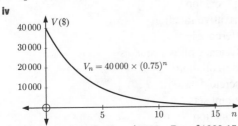

**b** (60.75, 68.25)

**d i** $r \approx 0.981$    **ii** $y \approx 1.06x + 3.61$    **e** 94%

**51 a i** 100    **ii** 33    **b i** 0.76    **ii** 0.74

**c i** 0.258    **ii** 0.546    **iii** 0.379    **iv** 0.439

**d i** 0.001 02    **ii** 0.0552

**52 a, d**

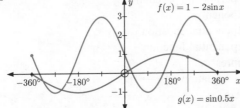

**b** $\{y \mid -1 \leqslant y \leqslant 3\}$    **c** 2    **e** 720°    **f** 4

**g** $x \approx -317°, -247°, 23.5°, 180°$

**53 a** 13.1 km    **b** 41.4°    **c** 4.83 km    **d** 38.3 km$^2$

**e** 0.569%

**54 a** In 3 years she will earn $183 000 under *Option B*, compared with $126 100 under *Option A*.

**b i** $A_n = 40\,000 \times (1.05)^{n-1}$    **ii** $B_n = 59\,000 + 1000n$

**c** 14 years

**e i** graph 1 represents $T_A$, graph 2 represents $T_B$

**ii** P(22.3, 1 580 000)

**f** $0 \leqslant n \leqslant 22$

**55 a** discrete    **b** 79    **c i** $s = 75$    **ii** $t = 119$

**d** 487    **e** 6.16

**f**

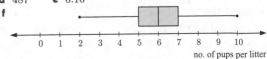

no. of pups per litter

**g i** 8    **ii** 2    **iii** 6

**56 a** 20 cm    **b** OR $= 10\sqrt{2}$ cm

**c i**

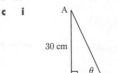

**ii** $\theta \approx 71.6°$

**d** 1660 cm$^2$    **e** $25.52

**57 a** $-100$, for every €1 increase in the selling price, the number of stools sold decreases by 100.

**b** $N = -100x + 8000$    **c** $€(x - 50)$

**e** $\dfrac{dP}{dx} = -200x + 13\,000$    **f** $x = 65$, €22 500 profit

**58 a** $41 269.54

**b**

| $n$ (years) | 0 | 1 | 2 | 3 | 4 |
|---|---|---|---|---|---|
| $V_n(\$)$ | 50 000 | 53 000 | 56 180 | 59 550.80 | 63 123.85 |

**c** $V_n = 50\,000 \times (1.06)^n$ dollars    **d** $S_n = 3000n$ dollars

**e**

| $n$ (years) | 0 | 1 | 2 | 3 | 4 |
|---|---|---|---|---|---|
| $T_n(\$)$ | 50 000 | 56 000 | 62 180 | 68 550.80 | 75 123.85 |

**f** 19 years

**59 a i** 95°C    **ii** 5°C

**b, e**

temperature (°C)

$A(t) = 95 - 3t$

$C(t) = 80 \times (0.8)^t + 15$

(30, 5)    $t$ (min)

**c** No, we would not expect the temperature to drop at a constant rate in the long term. The coffee's temperature should approach that of its surroundings.

**d i** 95°C    **ii** 15.1°C

**f** 12.4 min    **g** 15°C

**h i** $t = 0$ or 26.6, at these times the approximate temperature $A(t)$ is equal to the actual temperature $C(t)$.

**ii** 42.6°C

**iii** This is the maximum amount by which $A(t)$ overestimates the actual temperature.

**60 a** $H_0$: *movie type* and *gender* are independent.

$H_1$: *movie type* and *gender* are not independent.

**b** 28    **c** $\chi^2 \approx 22.7$    **d** 3    **e** 7.81

**f** $\chi^2 > 7.81$, so we reject $H_0$, and conclude that *movie type* and *gender* are not independent.

**g** $\chi^2 \approx 16.9$, which is still $> 7.81$, so the conclusion is valid.

# INDEX